CHRISTIAN IV ÅRET 1988

*Christian IV by Karel van Mander c. 1643. Frederiksborg A2741*

# Christian IV and Europe

*The 19th Art Exhibition of the Council of Europe*

*Denmark 1988*

*Christian IV. Engraving by Simon de Passe 1629 (cat. 28). Frederiksberg.*

## *Patron*

HER MAJESTY QUEEN MARGRETHE II

---

# THE FOUNDATION FOR CHRISTIAN IV YEAR 1988

## *Board*

Rigsantikvar dr. Olaf Olsen
Chairman

Direktør Peter Augustinus
Vice-Chairman

Generalsekretær Charlotte Christensen · Museumsinspektør Steffen Heiberg
Landsretssagfører Kristian Mogensen · Departementschef Jørgen Harder Rasmussen
Bankdirektør Arthur Schmiegelow

## *Præsidium*

Borgmester Per Bødker Andersen · Bankdirektør Tage Andersen
Direktør Niels Arnth-Jensen · Direktør Peter Augustinus
Borgmester Knud Axelsen · Højesteretssagfører Jon Palle Buhl
Generalsekretær Charlotte Christensen · Direktør Erik Haunstrup Clemmensen
Direktør dr. Torben Holck Colding · Vicedirektør Niels Dittmer
Landsretssagfører Esben Dragsted · Professor dr. Svend Ellehøj †
Direktør Bjarne Fogh † · Professor dr. Henrik Glahn
Professor dr. Kristof Glamann · Bankdirektør Bendt Hansen
Ambassadør Preben Hansen · Museumsinspektør Steffen Heiberg
Nationalbankdirektør dr. Erik Hoffmeyer · Kabinetssekretær dr. Niels Eilschou Holm
Borgmester Jens S. Jensen · Mag. art. Bente Kjølbye
Landsretssagfører Kristian Mogensen · Direktør Erik Mollerup
Rigsantikvar dr. Olaf Olsen · Departementschef Jørgen Harder Rasmussen
Bankdirektør Arthur Schmiegelow · Direktør Hugo Schrøder
Forfatteren Peter Seeberg · Borgmester Thorkild Simonsen
Direktør Poul J. Svanholm · Kabinetssekretær Mogens Wahl †
Overborgmester Egon Weidekamp · Industriminister Nils Wilhjelm
Direktør Mads Øvlisen

## COUNCIL OF EUROPE

Marcelino Oreja
Secretary General

José Vidal-Beneyto
Director of Education, Culture and Sport

David Mardell
Head of Division. Directorate of Education, Culture and Sport

Irene Herrenschmidt
Administrative Assistant, Directorate of Education, Culture and Sport

### *European Organizing Committee*

Sjefantikvar Sigrid Christie, Riksantikvaren, Oslo

Överintendent Per Bjurström, Statens Konstmuseer, Stockholm

Director, Dr. Rüdiger Klessmann, Herzog Anton Ulrich-Museum, Braunschweig

Curator Peter Thornton, Sir John Soane's Museum, London

Director General, Dr. Simon H. Levie, Rijksmuseum, Amsterdam

### *Organizing Secretary of the 19th Art Exhibition of the Council of Europe*

Charlotte Christensen

## DANISH ORGANIZING COMMITTEE

Museumsdirektør dr. phil. Povl Eller
Det Nationalhistoriske Museum på Frederiksborg

Museumsinspektør mag. art. Steffen Heiberg
Det Nationalhistoriske Museum på Frederiksborg

Generalsekretær mag. art. Charlotte Christensen
Christian IV året 1988

Museumsdirektør mag. art. Lisbet Grandjean
Teatermuseet

Museumsinspektør mag. art. Vibeke Woldbye
Kunstindustrimuseet,
Direktør for Boligministeriets Samlinger på Kronborg

Museumsdirektør cand. mag. Mette Müller
Musikhistorisk Museum og Carl Claudius' Samling

Museumsinspektør cand. phil. Ole Kongsted
Musikhistorisk Museum og Carl Claudius' Samling

Museumsdirektør mag. art. Villads Villadsen
Statens Museum for Kunst

Museumsinspektør mag. art. Olaf Koester
Statens Museum for Kunst

Overinspektør mag. art. Erik Fischer
Den Kongelige Kobberstiksamling

Museumsimspektør mag. art. Jan Garff
Den Kongelige Kobberstiksamling

Museumsdirektør mag. art. Mogens Bencard
De Danske Kongers Kronologiske Samling på Rosenborg

Museumsinspektør cand. mag. Jørgen Hein
De Danske Kongers Kronologiske Samling på Rosenborg

Rigsantikvar dr. phil. Olaf Olsen
Nationalmuseet

Overinspektør cand. art. Niels-Knud Liebgott
Nationalmuseets 2. afd.

Cand. mag. Henrik Larsen
Nationalmuseets 2. afd.

Museumsdirektør cand. mag. Finn Askgaard
Tøjhusmuseet

Overbibliotekar
cand. phil. Erland Kolding Nielsen
Det Kongelige Bibliotek

Førstebibliotekar cand. phil.
Jesper Düring Jørgensen
Det Kongelige Bibliotek

Museumsinspektør
cand. mag. Poul Dedenroth-Schou
Museet på Koldinghus

Museumsdirektør mag. art. Jens Erik Sørensen
Aarhus Kunstmuseum

Museumsinspektør mag. art. Nina Damsgaard
Aarhus Kunstmuseum

Cand. jur. Aase Hofmann
juridisk konsulent

Oberst Jørgen Schousboe
PR-medarbejder

*Secretariat*

Sekretær Ella Kjærulff

Mag. art. Jens Peter Munk

*Committee of Music*

Lektor cand. mag. Niels Krabbe
Musikvidenskabeligt Institut

Cand. mag. Knud Ketting
Dansk Musik Informations Center

Lektor cand. mag. Niels Martin Jensen
Musikvidenskabeligt Institut

Programredaktør cand. phil. Bent Erik Rasmussen
DR, Musikafdelingen

Generalsekretær mag. art. Charlotte Christensen
Christian IV året 1988

## SPONSORS OF CHRISTIAN IV YEAR 1988

Kong Frederik og Dronning Ingrids Fond
Dronning Margrethe og Prins Henriks Fond
Kultur- og Kommunikationsministeriet
Europarådet
Andelsbanken
Augustinus Fonden
Baltica A/S
Bang & Olufsen A/S
Sophus Berendsen A/S
Bikubenfonden
Bing og Grøndahl
Olga og Esper Boels Fond
Byggeriets Realkreditfond
C. A. C. Fonden
Carlsberg A/S
Carlsbergfondet
Aktieselskabet Danisco
De Danske Spritfabrikkers Gavefond
De Danske Sukkerfabrikkers Gave- og Støttefond
Den Danske Bank
Den Danske Frimurerorden
Margot og Thorvald Dreyers Fond
Finansieringsinstituttet for Industri og Håndværk A/S
Fonden til Fædrelandets Vel
Hafnia-Haand i Haand Fondet
Brødrene Hartmann's Fond
Knud Højgaards Fond
Illum Fondet
Kjøbenhavns Handelsbank A/S
Konsul George Jorck og Hustru Emma Jorck's Fond
Vilhelm Kiers Fond
Kreditforeningen Danmark
Københavns Kommune
Landsbankernes Reallånefond
LK-NES Fondet
Magasin du Nord's Fond
A. P. Møller og Hustru Chastine McKinney Møllers Fond til almene Formaal
Otto Mønsteds Fond
Novo's Fond
Ny Carlsbergfondet
Nykredit

Egmont H. Petersens Fond
Privatbanken A/S
Den Danske Provinsbank
Carl Roos' Legat
Royal Copenhagen
Skandinavisk Tobakskompagni's Gavefond
F. L. Smidth & Co. A/S's Gavefond
Sonning-Fonden
Sparekassen SDS
Det Store Nordiske Telegraf-Selskab A/S
Superfos a/s
Topsikring A/S
Tuborgfondet
Overretssagfører L. Zeuthens Mindelegat

## LENDERS

*Denmark*

Det Nationalhistoriske Museum på Frederiksborg, Hillerød
Den kgl. Maleri og Skulptursamling, Statens Museum for Kunst, København
Den Kongelige Kobberstiksamling, Statens Museum for Kunst, København
De Danske Kongers Kronologiske Samling på Rosenborg, København
Nationalmuseet 1. afd.: Danmarks Oldtid, København
Nationalmuseet 2. afd.: Historisk tid til 1660, København
Nationalmuseet 3. afd.: Dansk Folkemuseum, Brede
Nationalmuseet 4. afd.: Etnografisk Samling, København
Den kgl. Mønt- og Medaillesamling, København
Tøjhusmuseet, København
Det kongelige Bibliotek, København
Museet på Koldinghus
Handels- og Søfartsmuseet på Kronborg
Helsingør Bymuseum
Skt. Mariæ Kirke, Helsingør Domkirke
Skt. Olai Kirke, Helsingør
Kunstmuseet »Lunden«, Horsens
Boligministeriet, Ejendomsdirektoratet, København
Botanisk Museum, København
Davids Samling, København
Geologisk Museum, København
Den Hirschsprungske Samling, København
Det Kongelige Garnisonsbibliotek, København
Det kongelige kjøbenhavnske Skydeselskab og Danske Broderskab
Kunstakademiets Bibliotek, København
Det danske Kunstindustrimuseum, København
Københavns Bymuseum
Landsarkivet for Sjælland
Marinens Bibliotek, København
Musikhistorisk Museum og Carl Claudius' Samling, København
Ny Carlsberg Glyptotek, København
Ordrupgaardsamlingen, Charlottenlund
Orlogsmuseet, København
Rigsarkivet, København
Søofficersforeningen, København
Teatermuseet, København
Thorvaldsens Museum, København
Universitetsbiblioteket 2. afd., København
Zoologisk Museum, København
Lolland-Falsters Stiftsmuseum, Maribo
Nivaagaards Malerisamling, Nivaa
Landsarkivet for Fyn, Odense
Møntergaarden, Odense
Randers Kulturhistoriske Museum
Skt. Mortens Kirke, Randers
Den antikvariske Samling i Ribe
Roskilde Domkirke
Roskilde Museum
Sorø Kunstmuseum
Landsarkivet for Nørrejylland
Aalborg Historiske Museum
Statsbiblioteket, Aarhus
Gammel Estrup, Jyllands Herregårdsmuseum, Auning
Gavnøfonden
Valdemar Slots Herregårdsmuseum
Kunsthallens Auktioner, København
Thorvaldsen Samlingen, Nysø
Hærens Officerskole, Frederiksberg Slot
Forsvarets Bygningstjeneste, København

*Sweden*

Statens Konstmuseer, Nationalmuseum, Stockholm
Statens Konstmuseer, Slottssamlingarna, Stockholm
Kungliga Husgerådskammaren, Stockholm
Livrustkammaren, Stockholm
Drottningholms Teatermuseum, Stockholm
Krigsarkivet, Stockholm
Kungliga Biblioteket, Stockholm
Kungliga Vitterhets-, Historie och Antikvitetsakademien, Stockholm
Stockholms Universitets Konstsamling
Statens Sjöhistoriska Museum, Stockholm
Malmö Museer

Skoklosters Slott, Bålsta
Thomasgymnasiet, Strängnäs
Uppsala Universitetsbibliotek
Österåkers och Östra Ryds Kyrkoråd, Åkersberga
Per Brahegymnasiet, Jönköping

*Norway*
Bergverksmuseet, Kongsberg
Kongsberg Kirke
Kunstindustrimuseet, Oslo
Nasjonalgalleriet, Oslo
Riksarkivet, Oslo
Universitetsbiblioteket, Oslo
Universitetets Etnografiske Museum, Oslo
Tromsø Museum

*German Federal Republic*
Städtische Kunstsammlungen Augsburg
Staatliche Museen Preussischer Kulturbesitz, Berlin
Staatliches Institut für Musikforschung Preussischer Kulturbesitz, Berlin
Staatsbibliothek Preussischer Kulturbesitz, Musikabteilung, Berlin
Herzog Anton Ulrich-Museum, Braunschweig
Braunschweigisches Landesmuseum, Braunschweig
Kunstsammlungen der Veste Coburg
Museum für Hamburgische Geschichte, Hamburg
Staats- und Universitätsbibliotek Hamburg
Niedersächsisches Landesmuseum, Hannover
Herzoglich Oldenburgische Verwaltung, Harmsdorf
Bayerisches Armeemuseum, Ingolstadt
Gesamthochschul-Bibliothek, Landesbibliothek und Murhardsche Bibliotek, Kassel
Staatliche Kunstsammlungen, Kassel
Schleswig-Holsteinische Landesbibliothek, Kiel
Ratsbücherei Lüneburg
Bayerische Staatsgemäldesammlungen, München
Germanisches Nationalmuseum, Nürnberg
Staatsgalerie Stuttgart
Württembergisches Landesmuseum, Stuttgart
Herzog August Bibliothek, Wolfenbüttel

*Great Britain*
Her Majesty Queen Elisabeth II
His Grace of Duke of Buccleuch and Queensberry, K.T., Drumlanrig Castle
His Grace The Duke of Norfolk, Arundel Castle
The British Library, London
The British Museum, London
Dulwich Picture Gallery, London
The Marquess of Tavistock, Woburn Abbey
National Maritime Museum, Greenwich
Victoria & Albert Museum, Department of Prints, Drawings & Photographs, and Paint, London
Victoria & Albert Museum, Department of Furniture, London
Victoria & Albert Museum, Department of Sculpture, London
Victoria & Albert Museum, Theatre Museum, London
The Trustees of the Chatsworth Settlement
S. Frances Ltd., London

*The Netherlands*
Rijksmuseum, Amsterdam
Amsterdams Historisch Museum
Stedelijk Museum »Het Prinsenhof«, Delft
Rijksdienst Beeldende Kunst, Haag
Stedelijk Museum »De Lakenhal«, Leiden
Prentenkabinet der Rijksuniversiteit, Leiden
Museum Boymanns-van-Beuningen, Rotterdam
Rijksmuseum »Het Catharijneconvent«, Utrecht
Centraal Museum, Utrecht

*Belgium*
Kunsthistorische Musea, Antwerpen

*France*
Musée des Beaux-Arts et d'Archeologie de Rennes

*Italy*
Galleria Palatina, Firenze
Accademia Filarmonica di Verona

*Austria*
Kunsthistorisches Museum, Wien

*Switzerland*
Sotheby's Zürich AG

*Ireland*
National Museum of Ireland, Dublin

*German Democratic Republic*
Staatliche Kunstsammlungen Dresden
Museum der Stadt Gotha
Ratschulbibliothek, Zwickau

*Soviet Union*
Rustkammeret, Kreml, Moskva

*India*
Ny Jerusalems Kirken, Trankebar

*United States of America*
The Art Museum, Princeton N.J.

*And a number of private lenders*

*Front cover: Christian IV. Bronze bust by François Dieussart (cat. 1022). Rosenborg. Photo: Bent Næsby.*

*Back cover: Coat of arms, probably from Christian IV's crown. At the top, the three Danish lions. Forming the ring, the Danish provincial coats of arms (cat. 622). Photo: Lennart Larsen.*

# CHRISTIAN IV AND EUROPE

*Catalogue published by the Foundation for Christian IV Year 1988*

Editor: Steffen Heiberg. 
Layout: Steffen Heiberg and Poul Kristensen
Linotype Baskerville from Text Fotosats I/S · Jørgen Kristensen
Reproduction: Bernh. Middelboes Reproduktionsanstalt (colour),
BJ-Offset Repro and Poul Kristensen
Printed on Uno-Cote from A/S De forenede Papirfabrikker at
Poul Kristensen Grafisk Virksomhed, Herning
Printer to the Royal Danish Court

ISBN 87-982843-2-0

# Contents

Preface 12

Frederiksborg 15
*Christian IV – the Fortunes and Fate of af King*

Kronborg 73
*Christian IV – Patron of the Arts*
The Visual and Performing Arts at the Danish Court 1588-1648 73
Tapestries 115
Christian IV and Music 119
Christian IV and Drama 142

Rosenborg 153
*Treasures of Christian IV*

Nationalmuseet 221
*Christian IV – The enterprising King*

Den kgl. Kobberstiksamling 291
*Rubens' cantoor · Selected Drawings by Willem Panneels*

Statens Museum for Kunst 301
*The Age of Christian IV · Art Centres and Artists in Northern Europe*

Tøjhusmuseet 351
*Christian IV – Defender of Crown and Faith*

Rundetårn / Trinitatis kirke 397
*"Things in Heaven and Earth" · Science and Learning during the Reign of Christian IV*

Koldinghus 463
*Christian IV and his Architecture*

Aarhus Kunstmuseum 507
*Christian IV · The Image of Posterity*

Colour-plates 545

Literature 590

Corrigenda 605

Contributors to the catalogue and exhibitions organizers 606

# Preface

King Christian IV appears in a special light in the memory of the Danish people. All Danes know who he was and what he looked like, and most of them even recall the dates of his reign – 1588 to 1648.

Why should this be so? One reason may be that we are constantly reminded of him by the sight of the many splendid buildings erected on his initiative which form his legacy to us. Those we love. The wonderful Round Tower which presents the King's crowned monogram high above the roofs of the King's town of residence; the fairy-tale palace of Rosenborg in Kongens Have; the Exchange with its elegant dragon spire and its many gables; the Nyboder quarter's yellow buildings; the long vaulted halls of the Royal Danish Arsenal; festive Frederiksborg with its cluster of unusually concordant buildings; Kronborg, which Christian IV rebuilt and improved; the soaring spires of Roskilde Cathedral; in Jutland, the gigantic tower of the royal castle of Koldinghus.

Through his incredible energy and ingenuity Christian IV exercised influence in many other areas besides architecture. He concerned himself with all public matters, and in political and military contexts he repeatedly made appearances on the European scene fired with ambitions which tended to prove too great for his capacities. He was an impatient soul and wanted to take part in everything. His royal will-power and urge for action manifested themselves in a never-ending flood of orders, commands, regulations and directions, more than enough to cause his officials to run out of breath and to make the members of his council object.

By then it was usually too late. Many things went wrong during the reign of Christian IV. So many, in fact, that one may well wonder why the King became so popular. In the later years of Christian IV Denmark had lost its age-old standing as the unquestioned leader among the Northern nations, and the strong economic growth and social stability which had lasted for decades had deteriorated into crisis and decline.

It would be unfair to blame all this adversity on Christian IV. The foreign political situation was often unfavourable seen from a Danish point of view. New and strong centres of power were springing up in Europe, and the economic difficulties originated in an international crisis in marketing possibilities. But the country's situation was made worse because of the King's ill-starred warfare and unsuccessful diplomatic tactics. Many of the costly initiatives he took in order to strengthen and modernize trade in his Danish-Norwegian realm were ahead of or quite outside the limits of what the community of that day could be expected to cope with.

Even so, most of the many reigning years of Christian IV were bright years for Denmark; especially remarkable is the fact that his epoch blossomed into the unequalled heyday of Danish art, music and science. Christian IV's Denmark looked toward Europe, adopting new trends and fresh impulses in the cultural sphere, and becoming capable of artistic achievement and creativity in her own right.

In this development the King's own hand can be felt everywhere, directing and experimenting. He was a decidedly artistic person himself, with a feeling for the beautiful and the noble. He possessed considerable artistic talent and liked to have artists and musicians attached to his court. Even if Christian IV did not attain his political ambitions, he did secure a fine position for Denmark in Europe's cultural life.

There is every reason to celebrate this. In the 4th centenary of Christian IV's accession to the throne we are taking stock of the King's activities and showing their significance for Denmark viewed in a European perspective. Books will be published, sheet music and records brought out, and recitals given with music from the age of Christian IV. But the most important feature will be the chain of exhibitions, held at a selection of museums in Denmark, of which this book is the joint catalogue. For these exhibitions works of art and historical relics have been borrowed from the greater part of Europe, and the European perspective is stressed by the fact that the Council of Europe has made this the 19th Council of Europe Exhibition.

Her Majesty Queen Margrethe II has accorded

the initiative great honour in consenting to place *Christian IV Year 1988* under her patronage, and Her Majesty has not only followed the preparations with inspiring expert knowledge, but has also lent works of art from the royal collections to the exhibitions.

The Christian IV Year-Foundation, which has been set up for this specific purpose, is responsible for carrying the many events into effect. The Foundation's executive committee is assisted by a presiding committee which consists of representatives of Danish cultural life, economic life, and public administration.

The day-to-day management and co-ordination of the extensive preparations has been in the hands of Mrs. Charlotte Christensen, M.A. in Art History. It was she who first came up with the idea and who took the initiative to celebrate the 4th centenary in this manner; throughout the preparation period she has been the central figure in this work. She is General Secretary of the 19th Council of Europe Exhibition.

Christian IV Year 1988 is without comparison the largest cultural campaign ever undertaken in Denmark. It has been a costly project but is has met with very great interest and generosity on the part of public authorities, non-profit-making trusts and private firms, to whom we have turned for financial support. On the occasion of the publication of this large catalogue the executive committee wishes to address their warmest thanks to all contributors as well as to the members of the Christian IV Year's presiding committee who have actively helped give the collection great support from many quarters.

The planning of the ten exhibitions which combine to form the 19th Council of Europe Exhibition has meant a great load of work for the institutions and professionals involved. It has given great encouragement in this work that the many lenders have willingly made their works of art and treasures available although the loan period exceeds by far what is usual with regard to large international exhibitions. We are grateful for every single loan. It has been a special honour to have been promised a loan from Her Majesty Queen Elizabeth II of England's collections. These loans are of great value to the exhibition since the relations between the English and the Danish royal houses were so close in the age of Christian IV.

Our colleagues at the Swedish royal collections have taken a particularly difficult task upon themselves, as the larger part of the sculptures by Adrian de Vries from the Frederiksborg fountain now in the park of Drottningholm have had to be taken down and undergo thorough restoration work before being displayed at Statens Museum for Kunst in Copenhagen.

In addition to the loans from member countries of the Council of Europe, the exhibitions also contain paintings and works of art brought here from more distant countries such as the United States of America and India. We are also grateful to have been able to procure important loans from DDR with the help of their Ministry of Culture, and no less to be able to borrow the magnificent Christian IV pieces of silver from the Kremlin treasury, this loan having been secured by means of the agreement on cultural co-operation between Denmark and the Soviet Union.

Experiences of earlier Council of Europe exhibitions have been imparted to us by Mr. David Mardell who has committed himself with enthusiasm to *Christian IV and Europe* and has facilitated the organizers' way through the many international formalities to be complied with. However, the greatest – and most important – assistance has been given us by the foreign commissioners appointed for us through the Council of Europe. They have all of them in their individual home countries organized the loans for the exhibitions and transportation to Denmark as well. Furthermore, through their insight and learning, they have helped us choose the works of art which can best depict Christian IV and Europe, and thanks to their authority secured us permission to borrow them. By this assistance from colleagues, which we will always remember with gratitude, they have also contributed to the scholarly research which has been a major incentive for the organizers in the preparation of the exhibitions.

Now the 19th Council of Europe Exhibition has come into being, consisting of ten exhibitions in different parts of Denmark. Hundreds of people – museum staff, librarians, advisers from other areas of scholarship, students, craftsmen, technicians and many others – have worked hard to make the rich diversity of these exhibitions into an event of international standard. May their efforts be crowned with success.

When the exhibitions close and are taken down, they will live on in this catalogue. That, too, has been a great and demanding task, for which there is every reason to thank its editor, Mr. Steffen Heiberg, museum curator, as well as its many contributors.

*Olaf Olsen*

185

# Frederiksborg

## *Christian IV: The fortunes and fate of a King*

The exhibition attempts to draw a picture of Christian IV's personality, his family situation, and the outer context of his life together with his political aims and ambitions. It gives an impression, at the same time, of Denmark's role as a European political power.

On his accession to the throne, Christian IV took over a well-run kingdom which held a position of significance in Europe. When he died in 1648 Denmark was a kingdom in total political and economic chaos. He was the first Danish king to leave the kingdom smaller than it had been when he acceded to it, and under his rule Denmark lost for ever its position as one of the powerful nations of Europe. It is therefore paradoxical that in popular legend he is seen as the nation's great king. There are several reasons for this. In order to justify the introduction of absolute monarchy through Frederik III's coup d'etat in 1660, twelve years after Christian IV's death, contemporary historians represented Christian IV as an outstanding statesman and military commander whose good intentions were thwarted by a nobility which set the narrow, selfish interests of their class above the welfare of the nation. Contributing to the persitence of this image, without doubt, were the many buildings the King had constructed – Frederiksborg, Rosenborg, the Exchange, the Armoury, the Round Tower – which gave an impression of true might. The Christian IV myth was cemented once and for all by the Romantic artists and poets. Later historians' criticisms of his policies have never been able to shift the popular image. To a growing extent in recent years historical research has explained the decline during his rule as the consequence of long-term economic and social trends. The key factor is what historians call "the crisis of the 17th century". Many European countries in the 1600s experienced periods of violent internal unrest and external menace. For Spain, the German Empire, Poland, and Denmark the crisis resulted in a lasting decline, but France and England, in spite of civil war, strengthened their positions. For Sweden, Denmark's rival for influence in the Baltic, the 17th century became "the time of power".

This "evolution" cannot however be seen as an inescapable natural process. It was of course constantly influenced by the decisions taken by political and military leaders. The exhibition in Frederiksborg Museum therefore sets out to show how Christian IV, from the background of his own political ideas, reacted to the challenges of the surrounding world. It is first and foremost based on contemporary pictures. Each exhibition room has its particular theme, which is presented in a brief introduction.

*Steffen Heiberg*

### The official Portrait

The exhibition shows a comprehensive series of portraits of Christian IV and his family as well as political protagonists –and antagonists – within the country and abroad. Even though the portraits are arranged according to historical rather than artistic context, the exhibition gives an idea of the changing conventions in Danish portrait-painting from the middle of the 16th century to the middle of the 17th.

The object of portrait-painting was not merely to produce a naturalistic likeness of the model. The pictures were obviously expected to bear a resemblance to their subjects, but it was equally important that the subjects should be represented with the highest possible status. The concept of official portrait-painting is most clearly formulated in 1584 by Giovani Paolo Lomazzo, who in *Trattato dell'arte* stresses that emperors, kings and dukes should be depicted with the dignity, majesty and distinction appropriate to their rank, even when the models did not possess such qualities in reality.

The oldest portraits in the exhibition are the pictures of Christian III and Queen Dorothea (cat. 8,9), which were painted around 1550, probably by Jacob Binck. With their calm poses and strong background colours – particularly the portrait of the Queen – they show

3

knowledge of the two Lucas Cranachs; the pictures are an expression of the close political and cultural relations between Denmark and Saxony after the marriage between Christian III's daughter Anna (die gute Mutter Anna) and the Elector August.

Quite different conventions are to be seen in Hans Knieper's full-length portrait of Frederik II from 1581 (cat. 10). The King's dignity and rank are emphasized by symbols of power such as the helmet, baton, and coat of arms, and by the way he is placed in front of silk drapery and on a marble floor. The artist's task has been just as much to depict the monarchy as to portray the person of Frederik II. The red and yellow colours which dominate the picture's diagonals (sash, plume, coat of arms) symbolize the dynasty – the royal house of Oldenborg. Hans Knieper, who was Flemish, was evidently familiar with the new international court style which had been created at the Habsburg courts by painters such as Titian and Jacob Seissenegger, and which had spread from there over the whole of Europe.

The many Danish portraits of the nobility from the end of the 16th century show that already then a specifically Danish tradition of portrait-painting was establishing itself. Some of the pictures are ascribed to the Dutchman Gerrit Cornelisz., who worked for the Danish court from 1584 to 1601, but no piece is definitively attributable to him. The Danish portraits all have a rigidly formal arrangement and dark colours. The men are nearly always turned to the right with the left hand on the sword and the right hand on the hip, while the women have the hands clasped in front of the body. Originally this was a variant of the Flemish court portrait, as we know it from the portraits of Antonis van Moor, but this arrangement was used in portraits of nobility long after new ideas had won their way into artistic practice at the court as a characteristic expression of the Danish nobility's self-image and conservative standards.

The influence of van Moor is much more directly visible in a series of portraits of Christian IV and his family executed by Jacob van Doordt of Hamburg, who occasionally worked for the Danish court between 1607 and 1626. In one large full-length picture of Christian IV as military commander, from 1611, (cat. 151) van Doordt simply takes over a pose which van Moor used for a portrait of Philip II of Spain (Escorial).

Jacob van Doordt's brother Abraham was the surveyor of the art collections of James I, and in 1624 he himself went to England with introductions from Christian IV. There he painted a full-length portrait of Christian IV's nephew, Charles I, in the same composition as Christian IV, although in civil dress. Van Doordt was also the first miniature-painter of significance in Denmark. A pair of miniatures which he made of Christian IV clearly show familiarity with the English miniatures of the time.

Jacob van Doordt is an example of how connections between the royal houses fostered artistic contacts. Apart from the Danish and English courts he worked for Duke Heinrich Julius of Braunschweig-Wolfenbüttel, who was married to Christian IV's sister Elizabeth. He also carried out work for Christian IV's two other sisters, Duchess Augusta of Holstein-Gottorp and Electress Hedevig of Saxony.

Christian IV visited his sister and brother-in-law, Queen Anne and King James, in England, in 1606 and again in 1614. His portrait was painted on each occasion (cat. 94 and 3). The later picture was painted by the English court painter Marcus Geraerts. (I am indebted to Mrs. Chatlotte Christensen who traced this interesting painting.) The close family interrelations led to an extensive exchange of portraits, which explains the comparatively large number of Danish portraits of that period in England; there are also a good many English portraits of the English royal house in Denmark, in spite of some of them having been lost in the Frederiksborg fire of 1859. Among those destroyed were two full-figure representations of Queen Anne and King James; the picture of Anne was signed Marcus Geraerts, 1609.

A portrait of Christian IV's son, Duke Frederik, (cat. 95) painted by Pieter Isaacsz., was acquired for Frederiksborg from England a few years ago. This picture and two other portraits of Princes on Gaunø (cat. 99-100), also by Isaacsz., are the first secular portraits in Denmark in which the subjects are shown against an open landscape.

Pieter Isaacsz. was Dutch, but had special links with Denmark. He was born and brought up in Elsinore, where his parents had taken refuge following the disturbances in the Netherlands. As an artist he was a pupil of Cornelius Ketel and Hans van Aachen. He worked for a number of years in Amsterdam, but maintained his associations with Denmark and returned c. 1608. His pictures are much more colorful than those of Jacob van Doordt, although he used background landscape only in portraits of children. His ceremonial pictures of Christian IV are more traditional in composition, with drapery and symbols of power. In the large double portrait of Christian IV and Queen Anna Cathrine at Rosenborg he placed the figures on a Persian carpet instead of on the traditional tiled floor – a feature which was typical of contemporary English portraits and which he may have known from Christian IV's portraits of his relatives. His chief work as Danish court painter was the three-quarter-length portrait of Christian IV (cat. 185), which must be described as the most outstanding mannerist portrait in Denmark, and which must internationally be regarded as one of the epoch's master-pieces.

The "Emperor's War" in 1625-29 was accompanied by a temporary lessening of artistic activity in Denmark, which can also be detected in the portrait-painting. Additional contributing factors were that Pieter Isaacsz. died in 1625 and that van Doordt's last visit to Denmark was in 1626. A third painter of stature, Francis Cleyn, who probably produced the full-length portrait of Prince Christian at Fredensborg (cat. 98), likewise abandoned Denmark and settled in England, where he became involved in tapestry-making at Mortlake.

The main reviver of Danish portrait-painting in Christian IV's later years was Karel van Mander (III). His grandfather was the Dutch painter of the same name who is known in particular for his book on Dutch artists, »Het Schielder-Boeck«. The father, carpet-weaver Karel van Mander (II), made a series of tapestries for Christian IV (p. 56), circa 1620. After the father's death his mother moved to Copenhagen in 1623. When he was about twenty years old, in 1630, Karel van Mander was given his first commissions by the King. In the 1630s he worked together with the King's favourite painter, the Dane, Morten Steenwinckel. There are no pictures which can with certainty be ascribed to Steenwinckel, but a large double equestrian portrait of Christian IV and Christian, the Prince-Elect, at Valdemars Slot, from around 1634, is attributed to him. Nor of van Mander's work can any pieces be identified with certainty before his travels abroad from 1635-38, but the documented prices he obtained for his work show that his rank was still secondary. After his travels in 1635-38, which took him to the Netherlands and Italy, he became the unchallenged master of portrait-painting in Denmark. He introduced the new conventions for official portrait-painting which had been developed by Rubens and his pupils and their successors, van Dyck, Honthorst, Sustermans, David Beck and others. As regards composition van Mander maintained several traditional features, such as drapery and tiled floors, but used them more freely and combined them with new elements. His portrait of Christian IV in civil dress from about 1642 (cat. 5) preserves the old-fashioned drapery, but drawn to one side reto reveal a view of an Arcadian landscape. In a double portrait of the Prince Elect and Magdalene Sibylla (Frederiksborg A 2740) the upswept drapery provides a view of idealized classical architecture. The portrait of Leonora Christine (cat. 140) has no drapery whatsoever; she is standing framed by an arch consisting of trees and foliage. The idealized landscapes and classical architecture, it must be supposed, were completely at variance with the subject's everyday surroundings, and were intended, like the drapery and the tiled floors, to emphasize their special position in society. A more traditionally decorated piece with all the symbols of power can be seen in van Mander's military portrait of Christian IV from 1643 (cat. 193). Here it is not idealized architecture that is shown behind the drapery, but Frederiksborg, which was meant to be interpreted as the seat of power. Van Mander's chef d'oeuvre is a large equestrian portrait in the Great Hall (Riddersal) at Frederiksborg (Frederiksborg A 2741) with the turmoil of battle in the background and the King partly framed by an arch of foliage. Many more of this format were forthcoming from other painters in Denmark. But van Mander maintained more freedom in relation to the conventions, and it is through his talent for varying and combining these that he came to be the great reviver of Danish portrait-painting.

His only rival was Abraham Wuchters, who was born in Antwerp around 1608 and came to Denmark in 1638. The portraits by Wuchters contain more variety, from one to the next, than can be found in van Mander's relatively homogeneous work. This was not because his style was more varied than van Mander's, but because he kept closer to his models. He used many different models however which testifies to an extensive knowledge of contemporary European art. For instance, on several occasions he used some of van Dyck's compositions virtually without alteration (e.g. the equestrian portrait of Christian V, Frederiksborg A 2892). This has made it difficult to pinpoint his artistic identity. The characteristically bluff faces of Wuchters's subjects, often painted with a "provocatively broad brush" have been suggested as a distinctive feature of his work. This is particularly typical of the part of his work produced after Christian IV's death. A good example is the portrait of Christian IV's son-in-law Hans Lindenov from about 1658 (cat. 144). It is also true of the first picture he painted in Denmark, a portrait of Christian IV from 1638 (cat. 191), with the King standing in the foreground of a landscape which is placed at a strangely low level.

On the other hand, the portraits he painted of Christian IV's sons, Frederik and Ulrik Christian Gyldenløve, in 1645-46 (cat. 130, 146), show the same fashionable elegance as van Mander's portraits. This may be the result of direct influence from van Mander, but may also well be at the request of the client, who was Christian IV himself.

Karel van Mander and Abraham Wuchters were the outstanding personalities in Danish portrait-painting in the 1640s, partly by virtue of their artistic mastery and partly because they represent to us the renewal of the official portrait which stemmed from Rubens and his pupils. But they were not the only painters in Denmark. The nobility also had its painters, only one of whom shall be mentioned here – the Dane, Johan Timm, who very probably painted the portraits of Holger Rosenkrantz (cat. 177) and Christen Thomesen Sehested (cat. 197). Timm is representative of the tradition of Danish portraits of nobility which persisted with enormous tenacity until about 1650. In the 1650s this tradition weakened and the aristocracy, to a greater extent than previously, followed the artistic conventions prevalent at the court. This can be taken as an expression of the general disintegration of the cultural and political values of the "old Danish nobility", and thus as an admission of reality on their part. Absolutism was just round the corner.

*Steffen Heiberg*

# Christian IV and Frederiksborg

Christian IV, the eldest son of Frederik II and Sophie of Mecklenburg, was born in Frederiksborg Castle on 12th April 1577. Both parents, each in their own way, were strong and individualistic personalities. Frederik II has often been depicted as a rough soldier type without intellectual interests, for whom war and hunting were the only content of life; a man whose stupidity and immature rashness brought his kingdom to the edge of the abyss, but who luckily was kept in his proper place by wise and sober-minded advisers, who managed to extricate Denmark from the futile Seven Years' War with Sweden. The traditional image of Frederik II has been drastically revised in recent historical writing, in which he appears as a man who by the strength of principle and will-power carried Denmark intact through the Seven Years' War and thereby saved the country's existence. In a relatively conflict-free cooperation with the Council of the Realm, and with a never-faltering sense of his own and the realm's prestige, he exploited the favourable political and economic circumstances after the Treaty of Stettin in 1570 to make Denmark the strongest power in the Baltic. With its prominent position on Øresund, Kronborg, which Frederik II built between 1575 and 1585, became a symbol of Danish mastery of the Baltic Sea: *Dominium maris Baltici.*

So far we have sketched out the political inheritance which Frederik II handed over on his premature death in 1588. Internally also the barometer was set for peace and stability. The structure of the Danish state had been determined after Christian III's defeat of the citizen and peasant uprising against the political and social system. After the capture of Copenhagen in 1536 Christian III imprisoned the Catholic bishops and at a meeting of the Estates (Herredag) in Copenhagen that same autumn the Lutheran reformation was effected. At the same time a new political system was created, based on a division of power between the nobles and the Council of the Realm, which after the imprisonment of the bishops consisted exclusively of secular noblemen. The principles that were established in 1536 for the new order, both in secular life and in the Church, also formed the basis of the Danish state in the time of Christian IV. They characterized Denmark as a Protestant country and its society as class-based in which only the aristocracy had political rights. In this it reflected economic and social reality. Christian III appeared to posterity as the ideal of a Protestant prince, and Arild Huitfeldt (cat. 45) in his history of Denmark represented Christian III as the great model for the young Christian IV.

The most grandiose expression of the Danish monarchy's ambitions was Frederiksborg Castle, which Chri-

*4*

stian IV, after pulling down his father's previous construction (cat. 1), built in 1600-1620. The architect is not known, even though we have the names of several master-builders involved in the work. The rectilineal ground-plan with several courtyards owes its origins to French chateau-architecture. Both the outer and inner decoration is an expression of the idea of monarchy. Characteristic features of the external decoration are the many triumphal arches, and gates in the form of triumphal arches, through which the route to the castle's various departments passes. The triumph *motif* had been taken over from antiquity by the Renaissance, but whereas the triumphal arch in prehistory had been raised to the memory of distinct events, in the Renaissance it was used to glorify the virtues and ideals of the king and of royal power through extravagant use of allegorical figures. Triumphal arches tended to be erected on a Prince's entry to a larger town, but such festivities were very rare in Denmark quite simply because Danish towns with the exception of Copenhagen were too small to provide a reasonable framework. The route under the arches at Frederiksborg can, however, be seen as an entry. It passes Adrian de Friis's Fountain of Neptune, which personified Christian IV symbolically as the master of the sea – i.e. the Baltic and the North Sea (c.f. p. 343). The last triumphal arch is the portal of the Castle Chapel. On the arch is a representation of the first Christian Danish king and his son. This is to symbolise that the Danish monarchy is Christian and hereditary. This latter point was a spurious claim, since Denmark's was an elective monarchy. Frederiksborg Castle Chapel is one of the largest Lutheran royal chapels in Europe. The interior of the Chapel is richly decorated. The modern observer may only see a confusing number of figures and emblems, but all have their own distinct positions and symbolise the virtues a Christian king should possess. The decoration of the Chapel is a *speculum regale* or visual allegory, which in pictorial form expresses the concept of the Christian monarchy. The king's virtues and duties are described largely with the help of figures from classical a mythology one might well otherwise consider to be alien in a Christian church.

The Chapel still has a considerable proportion of its original fittings – first and foremost the altar-piece and pulpit, both made of silver and ebony by the Hamburg silversmith Jacob Mores. From Christian IV's time there is also an organ made by Esaias Compenius, which was installed in the south end of the gallery in 1617. This was a present from Christian IV's sister, the dowager Duchess Elizabeth of Braunschweig-Wolfenbüttel.

Christian IV fitted out Frederiksborg with great splendour. Two major national disasters have deprived us of all the interiors from the time of Christian IV with the exception of the Chapel. In 1658-60 the Castle was occupied by Swedish troops, who removed most of the Castle's great collection of paintings and also took away Adrian de Friis's fountain figures. In 1859 large parts of the Castle's interior were destroyed by a fire. The fire razed Christian IV's Oratory at the north end of the Chapel and the Riddersal above the Chapel. Also destroyed in the Oratory was a series of paintings of scenes from the life of Christ, which Christian IV had commissioned in Holland from inter alia Adrian van Niewland, Jan Pinjnas and Pieter Lastman. Further victims were the tapestries with representations of Christian IV's achievements made by Karel van Mander (II) in Delft. Finally, about two-thirds of the royal portrait collection, which had been installed in the Castle at the beginning of the century, were lost.

The restoration of the Castle was brought about with the aid of sums procured by a national appeal. Among the largest contributers was the founder of the Carlsberg Brewery, brewer J. C. Jacobsen. On the initiative of the brewery the Castle was established as a "national historical" museum, economically supported by the Carlsberg Foundation, the intention being to create a Danish parallel to Versailles, where the work of Danish artists would be used to present the history of the Danish nation. The main function of the museum today is that of a national portrait gallery.

*1*

1

## Frederiksborg Castle before 1602, seen from the south-east

Probably by Hans Knieper (born in Antwerp – Elsinore 1587) – c. 1580-84
Oil on canvas. 83×185 cm
Gripsholm 85
Painting of the first Frederiksborg Castle, demolished in 1599-1602 and replaced by the new palace of Christian IV. The stable wings and the two round towers on the southernmost island from 1562 escaped demolition, however, and were allowed to remain standing. On the right is the original main building erected by Herluf Trolle a few years before Frederik II acquired the manor of Hillerødsholm in 1560 and changed its name to Frederiksborg. This picture corresponds in outline with the depiction of the first Frederiksborg on the Elsinore tapestry by Hans Knieper (cat. 758) and may well be the prototype. The rider in the foreground is Frederik II and not, as often stated, Christian IV.
*Provenance:* First recorded at Gripsholm 1699. Probably war booty from Frederiksborg 1658-60. According to the Frederiksborg inventory of 1650 (R.A.) the Summer-Parlour contained among other pictures "one piece, showing the shape and buildings of the old Frederiksborg".
*Literature:* Mackeprang & Flamand Christensen 1950 33-38. Lichtenberg 1983 37-53. Heiberg 1984 194ff.

2

## Tyge (Tycho) Brahe (1546-1601), astronomer

Oil on canvas. 106×92 cm
Frederiksborg A 8191
When Christian IV was born, Tyge Brahe was commissioned to cast and read the prince's horoscope. The calculations made by Tyge Brahe indicated a brilliant future and a long life if Christian survived the dangers which would threaten him in the 56th and 57th year of his life. Born under the planet Venus, he would be certain of a good appearance, generosity, and integrity of mind, although with a predisposition to sensual indulgence. Mars promised gallantry and a passion for games and hunting. Mercury promised intelligence and an inclination towards the arts and sciences. Finally, the position of Jupiter indicated great honour and fame especially in the early years of manhood.
*Provenance:* Purchased 1982. Formerly at Hvedholm.
*Literature:* Heiberg 1982 96-102.

3

## Christian IV

Marcus Gheeradts the Younger (Bruges 1561 – London 1639). Inscribed "Anno 1614"
Oil on canvas. 226×140 cm
The Art Museum, Princeton University. Inv. 83-31
Painted during Christian IV's visit to England in July 1614. The King is depicted as a Knight of the Garter. On 25th July Christian IV noted in his calendar "on St James' Day we went to receive the collar that belongs to the Order of the Garter".
*Provenance:* Gift from Mr. and Mrs. Stuart P. Feld. Sold at Hirsch and Adler, New York 1974. Cfr. kat. 303.
*Literature:* Acquisitions of The Art Museum 1983 11. Heiberg 1986 92-98.

4

## Frederiksborg Castle with Sparepenge seen from the south-east. In the foreground Frederik III mounted.

Laurens Baratta (born in Rome, active in Utrecht 1628, in Denmark c. 1652-54). Inscribed "L. Baratta 1652"
Oil on canvas. 206×206 cm
Gripsholm 1143
Baretta's painting from 1652, though executed four years after the death of Christian IV, is undoubtedly the picture that gives the best impression of Christian IV's Frederiksborg.
*Provenance:* Probably Swedish war booty 1658-60. Gripsholm inventory 1699.

5

## Christian IV

Karel van Mander (Delft c. 1609 – Copenhagen 1670)
Oil on canvas. 242×146 cm
Statens Museum for Kunst inv. 709
Deposited at Amalienborg Palace
Christian IV, painted c. 1642, as most people know him. The reason his appearance is familar to so many Danes today is to be found in Karel van Mander's many portraits from the 1640s. These also inspired the character of the King in J. L. Heiberg's ever popular play, 'Elverhøi'. Similarly, the portrait of the King at the Battle of Kolberger Heide in the King's mortuary in Roskilde Cathedral, painted by Wilhelm Marstrand in 1863-66, is also based on portraits by van Mander as are many other historical paintings of the 19th century.
*Provenance:* Kunstkammeret 1670. Inventory 1737, 875/44. 1788 to Christiansborg Palace. Amalienborg Palace 1817, 1852 to Det kgl. Billedgalleri. 1870 to Amalienborg.
*Literature:* Eller 1971 142ff.

6

## Ulrik III (1528-1603), Duke of Mecklenburg, maternal grandfather of Christian IV

Artist unknown c. 1585
Inscribed "V.G.G. VLRICH HERZOG ZV MECKELNBVRG"
Oil on canvas. 232×144 cm
Frederiksborg A 4073
*Provenance:* Acquired from the former Royal Saxon Collections in Dresden 1926.

7

## Probably Elizabeth of Denmark (1524-86), married Ulrik III of Mecklenburg 1556, maternal grandmother of Christian IV

Artist unknown c. 1585. Inscribed "HETZOG.ADOLPH VON SCHLESWIG.HOLSTEIN.GEMALIN".
Oil on canvas. 206×116 cm
Gripsholm 1310
The incorrect inscription was probably added in the 18th century. The painting is the companion to a portrait of Ulrik III of Mecklenburg (Gripsholm 1331) of a type similar to Frederiksborg A 1473 (cat. 6). Consequently, it either represents the Duke's first wife, Elizabeth of Denmark, or his second wife Anna of Pomerania-Wolgast (1554-1626). On the basis of the costume the picture can be dated to the 1580s and, as the woman portrayed is elderly, it is most likely Elizabeth of Denmark, daughter of Frederik I and half sister of Christian III.
*Provenance:* Gripsholm inventory 1699.

8

## Christian III, born 1504, King of Denmark and Norway 1534-59, Christian IV's paternal grandfather

Possibly Jacob Binck (Cologne c. 1500 – Königsberg (?) 1569)
Oil on canvas. 70×52 cm
Frederiksborg A 2509
Without sufficient documentation, this picture has been ascribed to Jost Verheiden, who worked for the Danish Court 1554-61. The similarity between this picture and the type and manner of Jacob Binck's portraits is so striking, however, that it is most likely that Binck was the artist.
*Provenance:* Acquired 1918 from Historisches Museum Johanneum, Dresden. The painting may have come to Saxony with Christian III's daughter, who in 1548 married the Elector August of Saxony.
*Literature:* Beckett 1897 94f. Beckett 1932 11f. Andrup 1925 no. 3.

9

## Dorothea, (1511-71) Queen of Denmark, paternal grandmother of Christian IV

Probably by Jacob Binck c. 1550
Oil on canvas. 56×51 cm
Frederiksborg R 215
The painting is an original from c. 1550. A contemporary replica on canvas inscribed "Alles von Gott" and the date 1550 is now at Koldinghus. This portrait is probably by Jacob Binck, who worked for Christian III about 1550.
*Provenance:* Høyens Frederiksborgrevision 1831 no. 187

(?). Acquired by The Frederiksborg Museum after 1878. *Literature:* DBL 3rd ed. (Dorothea). Weilbach (Jacob Binck).

10

## Frederik II, born 1534, King of Denmark and Norway 1559-88, father of Christian IV

By Hans Knieper. Inscribed "FRIDERICVS SECVNDVS REX DANORVM ET NORWEGIA.ETZ. ÆTATIS SVÆ: 47. Anno. 1581"
Oil on canvas. 220×111 cm
Frederiksborg A 2171
*Provenance:* Acquired from Landesmuseum in Kassel 1914. Ordered by Landgrave Wilhelm IV of Hesse-Cassel for the Castle of Cassel 12th April 1581. Payment to Hans Knieper 14th August 1581. Forwarded 20th August 1581. Received in Cassel 4th September 1581. (Correspondance: Rigsarkivet Copenhagen, TKUA Hessen A I and Ausländisch Registrant 1581. Payment to Hans Knieper: Sound Toll Registers 1581 925).
*Literature:* Andrup 1925 no. 10. Beckett 1937 19f. Heiberg 1982 96-102. Heiberg 1984 183-204. DBL 3rd ed. (Knieper, Melchior Lorck).

11

## Same

Johan Gregor van der Schardt (Nijmwegen c. 1529 – Nuremberg 1581). Worked for Frederik II 1577-79
Painted terra-cotta bust. H. 35 cm. W. 27 cm. D. 24 cm.
Colour plate II
Frederiksborg A 2783
A study for the bronze bust Rosenborg 7.134 (cat. 12)
*Provenance:* Acquired in 1919 from Kaiser Friedrich Museum, Berlin. Formerly in Praun Collection, Nuremberg, which possessed several of the studies by van der Schardt for his cast work.
*Literature:* Liisberg 1921-23 121-38. Andrup 1925 no. 9. Heiberg 1984 183-204. Lichtenberg 1985 147-64.

12

## Same

Johan Gregor van der Schardt, 1578-79
Bronze bust, H. 43 cm. W. 36 cm. D. 40 cm.
Rosenborg 7.134
This bust and its counterpart representing Queen Sophie (cat. 15) were acquired by Frederik VI in Vienna 1815 from Wilhelm von Schønfeld, who had bought it in 1782 at a sale of the effects from the former Kunstkammer of Rudolf II in Prague. It is likely that the busts first came to Prague as presents from Frederik II to Rudolf II. The bust of Frederik II corresponds so closely to the terra-cotta bust by the same artist (cat. 11) that it is taken to be a study for the bronze bust. This bust and its counterpart, therefore, must be considered identical with the metal busts (alternately referred to as being of brass and copper) for which v.d. Schardt received payment from Frederik II in 1577-79. Presumably another pair of busts of the King and Queen had been cast, since two brass busts were destroyed by fire at Kronborg in 1629.
*Provenance:* Kancelliets brevbøger 1578 19/4, 16/11, 1579 16/4. Sound Toll Register 1578 fol. 1093. Rentemesterregnskab 1579/80 fol. 237. Entered into the Kunstkammer 1815. In the 1820s transferred to the Art Museum in Dronningens Tværgade (inv. CAc 118). To Rosenborg 1867.
*Literature:* Liisberg 1921-23 121-38. Heiberg 1984 183-204. Lichtenberg 1985 147-64.

13

## Same

Melchior Lorck (Flensborg c. 1527 – after 1583).
Inscribed "Melchior Lorichs ad vivum delineabat A° 1580 Et in ære skulpebat A° 1582"
Woodcut. 44.5×31.7 cm
Frederiksborg
*Literature:* DBL (Lorck). Fischer 1964 33-72. Heiberg 1984.

14

## Sophie of Mecklenburg (1557-1631), Queen of Denmark, married Frederik II in 1572, mother of Christian IV

Possibly by Antonius Sandfeldt (German? in Denmark – 1567-1581 –)
Oil on canvas. 72×54.4 cm
Rosenborg 1.1
On the basis of the costume the picture is dated to the middle of the 1570s and is therefore a portrait of Queen Sophie from about the time when her son Christian IV was born. It has been attributed to Hans Knieper, but the technique used differs considerably from any of Knieper's documented pictures. Another possibility is Antonius Sandfeldt, a painter who worked at the Danish Court from 1567 to 1581.
Kunstkammeret 1737 875/43. To Frederiksborg 1814. Høyens Frederiksborgrevision 1831 no. 959. Transferred to Rosenborg 1858.
*Literature:* DMP II 35. Andrup 1933 98f. Malmö Museum 1977 cat. 16.

15

## Same

Johan Gregor van der Schardt
Bronze bust. 46.5×36.7×34.8
Rosenborg 7.135
Counterpart to cat. 12

*14*

## Engraved portraits of Christian IV

The art of printing and the graphic visual arts (woodcuts, engraving, etching, etc.) were of course used in propagandist publications for Christian IV and the monarchy both domestically and abroad. Books and printed material of many kinds: political pamphlets, accounts of court festivities, translations of the Bible, historical works, etc., were often adorned with an engraving of the King. Many of the portraits were also sent out as single printed copies. Well over 100 contemporary graphic portraits of Christian IV are known, the oldest from childhood, the latest from 1648. A series of engravings which give an impression of the changes in his appearance are exhibited here.

16

Lambert Cornelisz (working in Amsterdam 1594-1621). Probably later than 1594. From a model c. 1582-84
Engraving. 9.8×7.5 cm (pl.)
Frederiksborg
The face mask seems cognate with Hans Knieper's portrait from c. 1582-84 (cat. 36).
*Literature:* Strunk 225. Faaborg 1105. Hollstein V 39 no. 5.

17

Crispin de Passe the Elder (Arnemuiden 1564 – Utrecht 1637) 1595
Engraving. 14.8×11.7 cm
Frederiksborg
*Literature:* Strunk 220. Faaborg 1101. Hollstein XV 226 no. 669

18

Crispin de Passe the Elder(?) c. 1596
Engraving. 15.2×11.6 cm (pl.)
Frederiksborg
*Literature:* Faaborg 1102.

19

Dominicus Custos (Antwerp after 1550 – Augsburg 1612) c. 1595
Engraving. 17.3×11.9 cm (pl.)
Frederiksborg
Probably the model for a wax relief of Christian IV dated 1595 (cat. 594).
*Literature:* Strunk 233. Faaborg 1140.

20

Jan Muller (Amsterdam 1571 – Amsterdam 1628). Earlier than 1628. Portrait type from c. 1605
Engraving. 18.6×12.4 cm
Frederiksborg
Many versions are known. This engraving is based on a model by the Danish painter Remmert Petersen. An oil painting with a similar face mask is now in a Norwegian private collection.
*Literature:* Strunk 228. Faaborg 1149.

21

Later than c. 1605
Engraving. 46.5×33.5 cm
Frederiksborg
*Literature:* Strunk 259. Faaborg 1152.

22

Nicolaus Andrea (born in Flensborg, active 1573-1606) 1606
Engraving. 30×20 cm. Reduced
Frederiksborg
Executed for Salvator Fabris: "De lo schermo overo scienza d'arme." Copenhagen 1606. The model is a portrait of a type identical with Frederiksborg A 2771 dated 1604 (cat. 1243).
*Literature:* Strunk 240. Faaborg 1148. Hollstein, German Engravings II 60 no. 4.

23

Renold Elstrack (London 1570-after 1625)
Engraving. 18.5×11.3 (pl.)
Frederiksborg
The model is a canvas in the tradition of Frederiksborg A 8706, which was painted in England 1606 (cat. 94).
*Literature:* Strunk 252. Faaborg 1207. Hind II 169-70. Heiberg 1986 92ff.

24

With Christian the Prince Elect (1603-47)
Willem de Passe (Cologne 1598-London c. 1637)
Executed c. 1614
Engraving. 30×20.2 cm (reduced)
Frederiksborg
Probably engraved in the 1620s with Elstrack's print (cat. 23) as model for the portrait of the King. The model for the Prince Elect is unknown.
*Literature:* Strunk 249. Faaborg 1203. Hind II 288 no. 4. Hollstein XVI no. 37.

*22*

25

Jan Muller 1625, from the model by Pieter Isaacsz c. 1612
Engraving printed in red. 42.2×29.9 cm (pl.)
Frederiksborg
The model is Frederiksborg A 1893 (cat. 185).
*Literature:* Strunk 253. Faaborg 1190. Hollstein XIV 111 no. 81 (cf. IX 231 no. 5).

26

Dated 1621
Engraving. 19.6×12.8 cm (reduced)
The face mask is cognate with the miniature by Jacob van Doordt, Rosenborg 3.78 from 1616 (cat. 64).
*Literature:* Strunk 244. Faaborg 1211.

27

Engraving. 32.4×27.3 cm (pl.)
Frederiksborg
*Literature:* Strunk 245. Faaborg 1214.

28

Simon de Passe (Cologne c. 1595 – Copenhagen 1647)
1629 from a model c. 1623
Engraving. 41×29.2 cm (pl.)
Frederiksborg
The model is a portrait of the same type as Jacob van Doordt's miniature, Rosenborg 1.127 (cat. 65).
*Literature:* Strunk 264. Faaborg 1222. Hollstein XVI 163 no. 43. Schepelern 1951 13f.

29

Claes Jansz Visscher (Amsterdam 1586 – Amsterdam 1652)
Engraving. 48.1×37 cm. Reduced
Frederiksborg
*Literature:* Strunk 270b. Faaborg 1230.

30

Simon de Passe 1633
Engraving. 31.4×20 cm (pl.)
Frederiksborg
Executed for the 1633 edition of the Bible.
*Literature:* Strunk 272. Faaborg 1242. Hollstein XVI 163 no. 44. Schepelern 1951 16ff. Eller 1971 16f.

31

Theodor Matham (Haarlem c. 1605/06 – Amsterdam 1676)
Engraving. 42.8×30.9 (pl.)
Frederiksborg
The prototype is the portrait by Abraham Wuchters (?), Frederiksborg A 2642, from c. 1638-39 (cat. 192).

*33*

*Literature:* Strunk 275b. Faaborg 1251. Eller 1971 202f. Sass 1973 582. Elllehøj 1973 603f.

32

Albert Haelwegh (Amsterdam c. 1600 – Copenhagen 1673)
Engraving. 61.8×39.2 (reduced)
Frederiksborg
After Karel van Mander (cf. cat. 5).
*Literature:* Strunk 297. Sthyr 1. Faaborg 1264. Hollstein VIII 199 no. 27.

33

Albert Haelwegh c. 1644
Engraving. 54.9×40.1 cm (pl.)
Frederiksborg
After Karel van Mander. Cat. 67 is probably Haelwegh's preliminary study for the engraving.
*Literature:* Faaborg 1393. Strunk 307. Sthyr 6. Eller 1971 144f.

34

Albert Haelwegh c. 1644
Engraving. 58.9×44.2
Frederiksborg
The model is an equestrian portrait in civil dress by Karel van Mander, of which only copies are known today (cf. cat. 194).
*Literature:* Strunk 287. Faaborg 1350. Sthyr 3. Hollstein VIII 199 no. 26. Eller 1971 154ff.

35

## Christian IV

Probably by Hans Steenwinckel (Copenhagen 1587 – Copenhagen 1639). Ca. 1614
Alabaster head. 26×24×29 cm
Nationalmuseets 2. afdeling. Inv. D 532
The head probably originates from a sepulchral monument commissioned by Christian IV for himself in 1614. The monument, which was executed by Hans Steenwinckel the Younger, was stored at the Arsenal in Copenhagen where it was destroyed by fire in 1647.
*Provenance:* Presented to Museet for Nordiske Oldsager by Videnskabernes Seslskab in 1869
*Literature:* H. Petersen 1890 96-102. Eller 1973 129f.

# Christian IV's upbringing

Frederik II attached great importance to procuring a good education for his son. In 1583 the Castle Chaplain at Frederiksborg, Hans Mikkelsen, was entrusted with the academic education of Christian IV, while the education of the future king in courtly skills such as horsemanship, dancing and courtly manners was assigned to an immigrant Pomeranian nobleman, Henrik Ramel.

Christian IV's upbringing was based on a pedagogic system created by the distinguished German humanist Johann Sturm. Great stress was laid on teaching the Prince to express himself in writing. The letters in Christian IV's handwriting which are still preserved – more than 3000 of them – reveal his considerable skill in formulating light and straightforward phrases in contrast to the very involved constructions which were the normal written style of the time.

Technical and practical subjects were also included in the syllabus, which at that time was rare. In 1587 Frederik II had a warship rigged out on Skanderborg Lake and there Christian IV became acquainted with navigation and practical seamanship. As an adult he was to reveal a knowledge of engineering beyond an elementary level, and he often gave evidence of insight into disciplines such as building and ship-construction.

The purpose of this education was not just to acquire

35

particular skills. It was equally essential to influence the Prince's attitudes and world picture. Through daily Bible-reading he was instructed in the Lutheran faith, through copying out sections of Erasmus of Rotterdam's treatise Institutio Principis Christiani (Concerning the upbringing of a Christian prince) Christian was indoctrinated into his princely duties. As God's intermediary on earth he had to ensure the happiness and welfare of his subjects, and it was his duty to protect the country and the true faith. In order to be equal to these great tasks the Prince had to possess qualities such as wisdom, charity, honesty and constancy.

## The Regency

When Frederik II died in 1588 Christian IV was only 11 years old. A regency government was therefore appointed, consisting of four noble councillors with an experienced Chancellor, Niels Kaas, at its head.

With great skill the Regency guided Dano-Norwegian realm through the dangerous period without a ruling king. Strong elements within the aristocracy wanted to use the opportunity to weaken the power of the monarchy, but the Regency refused absolutely to further aristocratic class interests, knowing full well that in the last analysis the monarchy was the only safeguard of the nobility's privileges.

The Regency also defended their Royal ward's interests where they conflicted with those of the Dowager Queen Sophie. Sophie worked to obtain a new partitioning of Slesvig and Holstein so that the King's younger brothers could gain the status of ruling dukes. The Rigsråd and the knights of the Duchies under the leadership of Henrik Rantzau obstructed these plans, which led, in 1593 to a rupture between Christian IV and his mother. Later a reconciliation took place between the young King and the Dowager Queen, but when Christian IV took over government he categorically refused to consider a new partitioning.

## Christian IV's coronation

As a condition for being crowned and thereby taking over the rule of the kingdom, Christian IV had to sign a coronation charter. This was a kind of constitution which laid down the judicial basis for the exercise of royal power, assured the Council of the Realm of a share in government, and guaranteed the privileges of the nobility.

The coronation itself took place in Vor Frue Church in Copenhagen on 29th August 1596; it was a religious ceremony in which the king was sworn to office. It was accompanied by great festivities: tilting at the ring, tournaments, fencing displays, theatre performances, fireworks, and so on, all to spread splendour throughout the Kingdom of Denmark and give it added prestige. An official account of the coronation was issued in Danish, German and Latin. It is worth noting that the official coronation account omitted the speech in Latin with which the Bishop of Zealand, Peder Winstrup, introduced the church ceremony, stressing the divine nature of the monarchy and referring to the kings as gods. It is possible that his choice of words was too much at variance with the principles of the Danish elective monarchy, by which the king was supposed to rule in accordance with God's laws, but he himself was a mere human being, who could be deposed if he developed into a tyrant.

*Literature:* Molbech 1849-50 245-306. Liisberg 1890-91 29-114. Troels Lund 1893. Holck 1943 485ff. Bøggild-Andersen 1944 260-92. Cedergreen Bech 1963 510-25.

36

## Christian IV as a child

Hans Knieper c. 1582-84
Oil on canvas. 82.5×61 cm. Colour plate I
Rosenborg 1.137
The only known painting of Christian IV as a child. It was probably the prototype for the rendering of Christian IV on Hans Knieper's tapestry (cat. 758), executed c. 1584. This painting may be the "Portrait after the young master and prince", for which, along with other works, Knieper was paid 200 Rix dollars from the Sound Toll in 1582.
*Provenance:* Sound Toll Register 1582 Expenditure f. 1046? Kunstkammeret 1737 875-42. To Frederiksborg 1814. The Frederiksborg Revision by Høyen 1831 no. 259. Rescued from the Frederiksborg fire of 1859. Salvage list no. 18. To Rosenborg 1860.
*Literature:* Beckett 1892-94 197-204.
DMP II 68. Mackeprang and Flamand Christensen 1950 8 95.

37

## Frederik II's funeral in Roskilde on June 5th 1588

Engraving, 20 prints, each of which c. 20×35 cm. From *Typus pompæ funebris 5. Junij 1588 habitæt Rodtschildij in exiqvijs D. Friderici II. Daniæ etc. regis, opera et concilio HENRICI RANZOWIJ efformatus et D. Christiano IIII. dedicatus a FRANC. HOGENBERGIO et SIM. NOVELLANO.*
Frederiksborg
The 20 prints showing the procession at Frederik II's funeral in Roskilde were executed by Frans Hogenberg and Simon Novellanus in Cologne. They were published in a book on the initiative of Henrik Rantzau (cat. 40). Henrik Rantzau probably took the idea from England where, in 1587, Theodor de Bry had done a similar series of 30 prints showing the procession at Sir Philip Sidney's funeral (A.M. Hind: Engraving in England I 1952 132ff, Plate 60-67).

38

## Copenhagen Castle c. 1690

Artist unknown
Oil on canvas. 20×30 cm
Københavns Bymuseum. Inv.no. 1919.274
The first Copenhagen Castle c. 100 years after the Coronation of Christian IV. The castle had however hardly changed in appearance. It was still dominated by the massive Blue Tower, the spire of which had been erected by Christian IV on the occasion his Coronation in 1596. The bell shaped construction of the spire was repeated later on in the big Barbican of the Frederiksborg Palace. At the top of its spire the Blue Tower had three crowns, which symbolized a dream of Christian IV's to subdue Sweden and restore the Kalmar Union. In the background the Stock Exchange, built by Christian IV 1619-40, can be seen.
*Provenance:* Acquired from S.L. Tuxen 1919.
*Literature:* Gamrath 1975 97ff.

38a

## Hans the Younger (1545-1622), Duke of Schleswig-Holstein-Sonderburg, paternal uncle of Christian IV

Artist unknown c. 1600. Inscribed "VON GOTTES GENADEN IOHANNES ERBE ZV NORWEGEN HERTZOG ZV SCHLESWIG HOLSTEIN STORMARN VNND DER DITMARSH GRAFF ZV OLDENBVRGK VNND DELLMENHORST. G:G:G:M:F:"
Oil on canvas. 198×116 cm
Frederiksborg R 223
As the younger brother of Frederik II, Hans inherited parts of Schleswig and Holstein. The Estates of the Duchies, however, refused to recognize him as reigning Sovereign on a par with the King and the Duke of Gottorp.
*Provenance:* Probably identical with the "Portrait of Hans, Duke of Sonderburg, in full length with a frame", which in 1636 was hanging in "the small Winter Parlour" at Frederiksborg. The Frederiksborg revision by Høyen 1831 no. 199 or no. 200. After the fire at Frederiksborg it was transferred to Rosenborg. Returned to Frederiksborg in 1881.
*Literature:* J.S. Jensen 1971. Eller 1971 34 38 428.

39

## Henrik Ramel (1550-1610), Lord Steward, Councillor of the Realm

Artist unknown c. 1605-10
Oil on canvas. 110×85 cm
Private collection, Sweden
Henrik Ramel was born in Pomerania. He was widely travelled and had served under several princes before coming to Denmark in 1581, where he soon gained the confidence of Frederik II. By virtue of his knowledge of European political and constitutional law he was appointed leader of the German Chancellery in 1583 and was thus a kind of Foreign Minister. In 1584, Frederik II bestowed Bækkeskov Abbey (now Bäckaskog) in Scania on him, and at the same time, he became a naturalized member of the Danish nobility. In 1585 he became Lord Steward to Prince Christian (IV) and consequently became responsible for the education of the Prince. After the death of Frederik II, the Regency, for national reasons, was forced to dismiss him from his office as

*40*

Lord Steward. When in 1596 Christian IV acceeded to the Throne, Ramel was compensated and became a Counsellor of the Realm.

40

## Henrik Rantzau (1526-98), Governor of the Duchies of Schleswig-Holstein

Artist unknown. Inscribed "Der Ges. E:E:H: Hinrich Rantzow weil: Kon: holls Stadthal. Raht: vn: amb: vf: Segeb: zu Breiteb: Rantz: In Gott endtschlaff im 73 Jahre Seines alters A° 1598" and "Des Zeitlichen Lebens Ausgangck Ist Des Ewigen Ein Anfanggk"
Oil on wood. 26×19 cm
Frederiksborg A 808
Among the noblemen of his time Henrik Rantzau was without doubt the one most anxious to master European Renaissance culture, which he had got to know in his youth at the Court of Emperor Karl V. Breitenburg, his Holstein residence, was the most sumptuously furnished manor in Northern Europe, but it was destroyed during the Thirty Years War. Rantzau was Royal Governor of Schleswig and Holstein and was one of the closest coadjutors of Frederik II. He honoured the memory of Frederik II by erecting memorials to him at Segeberg and on his estates. He also published two books of engravings, the first of which depicted major events in the King's reign, while the second showed the processions at Frederik II's funeral in Roskilde June 5th 1588 (cat. 37).
*Provenance:* Klevenfeldt's sale 1777 no. 104. The Hielmstierne Catalogue 1786 371 no. 65. To Frederiksborg 1812. The Frederiksborg Revision by Høyen 1831 no. 203. Salvage list no. 83.
*Literature:* DBL 3rd ed. Troels-Lund 1893. Lorenzen 1912. Brandt 1927.

41

## Niels Kaas of Taarupgaard (1534-94), Councillor of the Realm, the King's Chancellor

Unknown artist from the 1580s. 18th century inscription "Niels Kaas til Taarupgaard Danemarcks Riges Canceller"
Oil on canvas. 77×62 cm
Rosenborg 1.138
In 1571 Niels Kaas became the King's Chancellor and the head of the central administration. On the death of Frederik II in 1588, he became a member of the Regency for the minor Christian IV. By virtue of his wide experience of politics and administration he became the virtual head of the Regency. He was favourably disposed towards monarchism and refuted all attempts on the part of the nobility to take advantage of the King's minority to weaken the monarchy. He was an eminent example of the humanistically cultured nobleman, and he had an extensive knowledge of history, constitutional law and theology. The Regency's wide support of scientific studies, from which Tyge Brahe and others benefited, was largely due to Niels Kaas.
*Provenance:* Klevenfeldt's sale 1777 no. 215. The Hielmstierne Collection 1786, 361 no. 45. To Frederiksborg 1812. The Frederiksborg Revision by Høyen 1831 no. 205. Salvage list no. 137.
*Literature:* DBL 3rd ed. Troels-Lund 1893. DMP III 87.

42

## Jørgen Rosenkrantz of Rosenholm, (1523-96). Councillor of the Realm

Artist unknown 1589
Oil on canvas. 59×45 cm
Rosenborg 1.2
Jørgen Rosenkrantz had a very close association with Frederik II. In 1563 he became a Councillor of the Realm, and in 1588 a member of the Regency for the minor Christian IV. He took a vivid interest in cultural matters, and he was the builder of Rosenholm and Skaføgaard, two manors which rank among the most outstanding Renaissance monuments in Denmark. This portrait is a replica after Frederiksborg A 7421 (permanent loan to Rosenholm), which is dated 1589. Accord-

ing to the Frederiksborg revision by Høyen, the picture had an inscription, now lost, "HR. JØRGEN ROSENKRANTZ TIL ROSENHOLM 1589".
*Provenance:* Hielmstierne 1786 375 no. 72. To Frederiksborg 1812. The Frederiksborg Revision by Høyen 1831 no. 202. After the fire at Frederiksborg it was transferred to Rosenborg. Salvage list no. 57.
*Literature:* DBL 3rd ed. DMP III 87.

43

## Steen Brahe of Knudstrup (1547-1620), Councillor of the Realm

Artist unknown 1594. In the top left-hand corner is the Brahe coat of arms and a comtemporary inscription "1594". The top right-hand corner has an inscription from c. 1615-20 "STEEN BRADE TILL KNVDSTRVP: BRENTWED. HVEDHOLM ENGELSTHOLM. OC TÆRSLØS.ÆT:SVÆ:47"
Oil on canvas. 101.5×78.5 cm
Frederiksborg A 2732
Steen Brahe was the brother of the famous astromoner Tyge Brahe. Like most of his contemporaries, but unlike his brother, he chose the traditional departmental career. In 1578, at the age of 31, he was appointed Councillor of the Realm, and for the next 42 years he remained an influential member of the Council. For a short while he deputized in the Regency for the minor Christian IV.
*Provenance:* Acquired 1923 from Hvedholm, a manor, which came into the possession of Steen Brahe 1611 and which remained in the Brahe family until 1788.
*Literature:* DBL 3rd ed. Andrup 1925 no. 46.

44

## Christoffer Valkendorf of Glorup (1525-1601), Lord High Steward, member of the Regency 1588-90

Copy from 1899 by Knud Larsen (1865 Vinderød-1922 Frederiksberg) of a painting in Svinninge Kirke, executed in 1768 by N.P. Dahlin after a lost painting
Oil on canvas. 114×79 cm
Frederiksborg A 1202
Valkendorf was a competent administrator. As Frederik II rarely visited Copenhagen, Valkendorf was appointed Lord Lieutenant of Copenhagen Castle in the King's absence. This position made him virtually head of the Exchequer and of Bremerholm, the naval base of the country. In 1588 he became a member of the Regency for the minor Christian IV. Valkendorf had to resign however, after an internal confrontation in 1590. In 1596 he was rehabilitated and appointed Lord High Steward, the highest office of state, by Christian IV as his first act on coming to the throne.

In the period between Absalon and Christian IV, no other person has done so much for Copenhagen as Valkendorf, and the endeavours by Christian IV to make Copenhagen the financial centre of Northern Europe were no doubt inspired by Valkendorf. The tower of St. Nikolaj, which was erected by Valkendorf, is still there as a sign of Valkendorf's achievements. He also supported education and science, and the still existing Valkendorf Kollegium was founded by him.
*Literature:* DBL 3rd edn. Troels-Lund 1877. Same 1893 I. Hassø 1933. Venge 1975.

45

## Arild Huitfeldt (1546-1609), Councillor of the Realm, historian

Albert Haelvegh 1652, after a lost painting
Engraving. 25×15.8
Frederiksborg
Arild Huitfeldt was a Councillor of the Realm and for some time a member of the Regency. He is chiefly remembered for his important survey of the History of Denmark, 1596-1604, which provides an historical justification of the "dyarchy", i.e. the Danish political system, in which the power is divided between the noble Council and the King.
*Literature:* Westergaard 5454. Sthyr 144.

46

## Sophie of Mecklenburg, Queen of Denmark, mother of Christian IV

Jacob van Doordt (died in Stockholm in 1629). Inscribed "SOPHIA VON GOTTES GNADEN ZU DENNEMARCKEN NORWEGEN DER WENDEN UND GOTTEN KONIGIN GEBORNE ZU MECKELBURG HERTZOG ZU SCHLESWIG HOLSTEIN STORMARN UND DER DITMARSCHEN GRAFIN ZU OLDENBURG UND DELMENHORST WITTWE. AN: 1626."
Oil on canvas. 115×102 cm
Frederiksborg A 2784
*Provenance:* Acquired from Mauritshuis, the Hague in 1922. The picture probably came to the Netherlands with Christian IV's niece Sophie Hedevig of Braunschweig-Wolfenbüttel (1592-1642), when in 1607 she married Ernst Casimir of Nassau-Diek. A similar picture was destroyed by fire at Frederiksborg in 1859 (the Revision by Høyen 1831 no. 100). This picture originally hung at Husum Castle, where it probably came as a present for Sophie's daughter Augusta, who lived there as a widow. This picture was likewise dated 1626. These were probably the two paintings for which van Doordt was paid on 24th August 1626. (Rigsarkivet. Dronning Sophies regnskaber).
*Literature:* Andrup 1925 no. 26. Friis 1890-1901 149f. Beckett 1937 33-40. Eller 1970.

47

## Christian IV's Entry into Berlin on 6th October 1595

Signed "CK 1595"
Engraving. 19.5×29 cm
Frederiksborg
In the autumn of 1595, Christian IV went on a tour of a number of Protestant Courts. In Berlin he was received by the Elector of Brandenburg, Johan Georg, with great festivity, and it was probably during this visit that a marriage was arranged between Christian IV and the Elector's grandchild Princess Anna Cathrine. It is not known to whom the signature "CK2" refers.

48

## Procession at the Coronation of Christian IV on 29th August 1596

Engraving, executed by Philip Uffenbach for "Dennemärckische Krönung, D.i., Kurtze doch gründliche bescreibung, mit was ceremonien Solennitet, die Krönung Christiani des IV., d. 29. Aug. dieses Jars, verrichtet und volnzogen worden." (Frankfurt a.d. Oder 1597). 21.1×27.1 cm
Frederiksborg
The top right-hand corner depicts the ceremony in Vor Frue Cathedral. To the left, the Coronation procession can be seen leaving the cathedral. In the middle of the picture, the King is passing the triumphal arch at Amagertorv. In the corner of the arch are four classical giants, Hector, Alexander, Hannibal, and Scipio. On the left hand a tap, set up at Amagertorv, through the spout of which red and white wine was flowing by turns for public enjoyment. At the same spot, a huge ox, stuffed with game and poultry, was roasted on a spit for the citizens.
*Literature:* Krogh 1938 187-98.

49

## Inventions and Tilting at the Ring at the Coronation of Christian IV in 1596

Engraving by Philip Uffenbach, 1597. 28.5×36 cm. From the same book as the above
Frederiksborg
One of the major attractions of the Coronation festivities was the tilting at the ring, which took place at Amagertorv on 3rd-4th September. A traditional part of the tilting game was a procession of so-called inventions, where the participants would imitate various allegorical figures, which were often performed with great imagination. Christian, Margrave of Brandenburg, allegorized "the Mountain of Virtues". His invention was created by the Italian sculptor Giovani Maria Nosseni, and was awarded the prize for the best invention.
*Literature:* Krogh 1938 187-98.

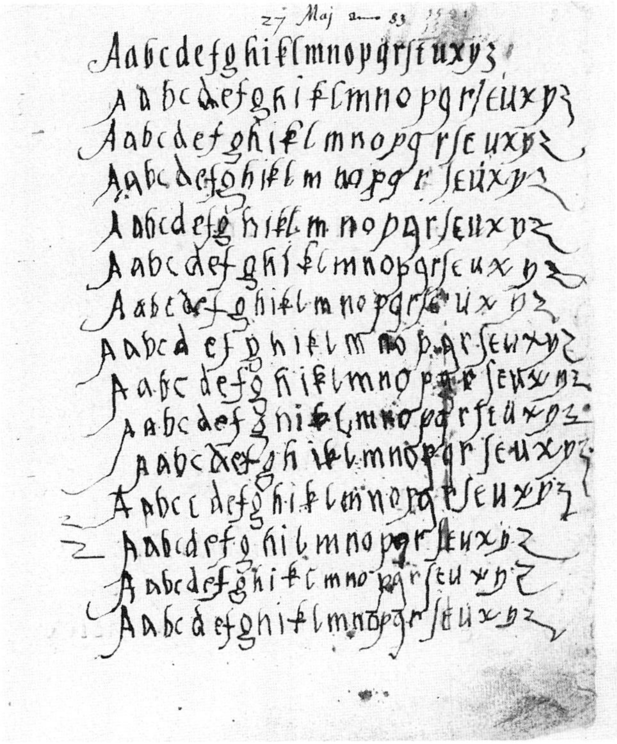

*52*

50

## Detail from the Procession at the Coronation of Christian IV

Frederik Christian Lund (Copenhagen 1826 – Copenhagen 1901). Inscribed "F. C. Lund, 8. juli 58 Frederiksborg"
Indian ink on pasteboard. 25.5×35.5 cm
Frederiksborg A 5082
Drawing after a tapestry executed by Karel van Mander II for the Great Hall at Frederiksborg c. 1616-20. The tapestry was destroyed in the fire at Frederiksborg in 1859 (c.f. cat. 56).
*Literature:* Bredius 1885 1-22. Beckett 1914 164f. Andrup 1932 108-40. Andrup 1933-34 141. Gerson 1942 148, 150, 168-82. Eller 1973 165f. Heiberg 1984 9f.

51

## Ladies of the Nobility watching the Coronation of Christian IV in 1596

F. C. Lund. Inscribed "F. Lund d: 15 Juli 1858. Frbr."
Water-colour. 25.6×40.4 cm
Frederiksborg A 5018
Cf. above

*53*

52

## Christian IV's Exercise Book, 1583-91

Rigsarkivet
The book is held open at a page with letters, copied by Christian IV on his first day at school on 27th May 1583, from his teacher's instruction.

53

## Danish and Spanish Warships

Drawing executed by Christian IV as a child
Pen and ink. 10.1×16.1 cm (size of paper)
Rigsarkivet
This drawing was enclosed in Christian IV's exercise book, and is therefore assumed to have been done by him. It shows a combat between Danish and Spanish warships and reflects the standards laid down in the educational programme for the young King. Spain was the leading Catholic power and was regarded as the principal enemy, for political as well as ideological reasons.

54

## Letter from Christian IV in his own Hand to his Grandmother, Duchess Elisabeth. Dated 15th May 1584

Rigsarkivet
The oldest example known of a letter in Christian IV's own hand. More than 3000 of such letters have been preserved.
*Literature:* EB VIII no. 1.

55

## Christian IV's Latin Exercise Book, 1591-93

Rigsarkivet
The King's Latin exercises also included writing imaginary letters, in which the young King would report on everyday occurrences. The page exhibited shows his description of a visit he paid Tycho Brahe on the island of Hven on 3rd July 1592.
*Literature:* Troels-Lund 1876 307-59.

57

## The Calendar of Christian IV, 1621

Rigsarkivet
Christian IV did not keep a diary, but throughout his life he made entries of the daily events in his calendars. The entries could concern matters such as travels, receptions of envoys, financial transactions, loss and profit at games etc.
*Literature:* Schlegel 1774 26-71.

58

## Christian IV

Nicolaus Schwabe (Dresden c. 1570 – Copenhagen 1629). Signed
Gold medal. 3.9 cm in diameter
L. E. Bruun 15240
*Literature:* Galster 33.

59

## Christian IV

Nicolaus Schwabe c. 1600. Signed "SF" (Schwabe fecit)
Gold medal c. 1600. 4.1 cm in diameter
L. E. Bruun 15244

60

## Christian IV

Jacob van Doordt (?) c. 1616
Pencil drawing. 29.7×14.7 cm
Department of Prints and Drawings. The British Museum inv. Fawkener 5213-32
The drawing has been attributed to Pieter Isaacsz, but the facemask is of a type close to that of Jacob van Doordt's miniature (cat. 64).
*Provenance:* Formerly in the William Fawkener Collection.
*Literature:* Beckett 1932 28. Heiberg 1986 94-96.

*60*

61

## Christian IV

Artist unknown c. 1606
Oval miniature. 5.7×4.6 cm
The Duke of Buccleuch's Collections 21/7
On the basis of the costume the miniature is dated to about 1606. It was either executed in England during Christian IV's visit to his brother-in-law, James I and his sister, Queen Anne in 1606, or he could have taken it with him as a present.
*Literature:* Heiberg 1986 96.

62

## Christian IV

Jacob van Doordt c. 1610
Oil on copper. 13.5×9.5 cm
Rosenborg 1.98
Facemask and costume correspond to a three-quarter-length in life size at Rosenborg (inv. 3.164), inscribed with the signature, no longer legible, X/D 1610 designating Jacob van Doordt.
*Provenance:* First mentioned in the Rosenborg inventory of 1696, 123 no. 7.
*Literature:* DMP IV 1. Beckett 1932 26. Beckett 1937 34. Rosenborg 1948 no. 4. Eller 1973 146.

63

## Christian IV

Jacob van Doordt. Inscribed in gilt letters "A° 1611"
Miniature inserted in an oval gold locket. On the reverse is the King's crowned monogram. 4.5×3.3 cm
Rosenborg 3.84
The miniature is unsigned, but the same technique has been used as with other known miniatures by van Doordt (cat. 80). It has been attributed to Isaac Oliver. Oliver and Christian IV, however, had no contact with each other in 1611. On 17th January 1612, on the other hand, van Doordt received 50 Rix dollars for "two portraits of His Majesty, which he has executed and made into two small patterns".
*Provenance:* Rentemesterregnskab (accounts) 1611/12 f. 546 (?). Rosenborg inv. 1696 62 D3.
*Literature:* DMP IV 3. Williamson 1904 90. Steneberg 1934 249 260. Danish Art Treasures, Victoria & Albert 1948 cat. 231. Holck Colding 1953 117. Eller 1973 146. DBL 3rd ed. (van Doordt).

64

## Christian IV

Jacob van Doordt. Inscribed "1616"
Oval miniature, inserted in a gold locket. On the reverse a crowned C4 and a botanical design. 4.9×4.0 cm
Rosenborg 3.78
*Provenance:* Rosenborg inv. 1696 62 D4.
*Literature:* DMP IV 6f.

65

## Christian IV

Signed and dated "X/D 1623" indicating Jacob van Doordt
Octagonal miniature on parchment. 11.7×9.8
Rosenborg 1.127
*Provenance:* Rosenborg inv. 1696, 64E-19
*Literature:* DMP IV 7. Beckett 1932 27. Steneberg 1934 219. Beckett 1937 36.

*65*

*66*

66

## Kirsten Munk

Signed and dated "1623 X/D" indicating Jacob van Doordt
Octagonal miniature on parchment. 11.7×9.7 cm
Rosenborg 1.128
Portrait type is similar to cat. 113 and Frederiksborg A 7299.
*Provenance:* Rosenborg inv. 1696 64 E19.
*Literature:* See above.

67

## Christian IV

Albert Haelwegh, c. 1644
Drawing
Victoria and Albert Museum, London
Inscribed "Christianus quartus D.g. Daniæ norvegiæ vandalorum Gothorum. Rex Dux Slesvici Holsatiae Storm Dethm Vc. Carel van Mander pinx. A Haelvech del". The drawing is a preliminary sketch for the engraving by Haelwegh (cat. 33).

68

## Christian IV

Karel van Mander, c. 1645
Oval miniature on silver. 3.1×2.5 cm
Frederiksborg A 4432
*Provenance:* Purchased from an art dealer in 1930.
*Literature:* Eller 1971 157.

69

## Christian IV

Karel van Mander c. 1645
Oval miniature inserted in a silver locket with a crowned C4 and a botanical design on the reverse. 2.0×1.4 cm.
Colour Plate XLI
Rosenborg 3.82
Painted later than 1644, when Christian IV was injured on the right side of his face. After this he would only be painted in left profile.
*Provenance:* Rosenborg inv. 1696 62 D12.
*Literature:* Eller 1971 158.

70

## August, Elector of Saxony (1526-86). Married Anna, daughter of Christian III

Round miniature on cardboard. Diam. 3.2 cm
Frederiksborg A 2563
The portrait type is identical with the full length paintings by Lucas Cranach in the Historisches Museum in Dresden and the Kunsthistorisches Museum in Vienna.
*Provenance:* Purchased in Dresden 1920.
*Literature:* Andrup 1925 no. 7.

71

## Anna (1532-85), daughter of Christian III

Round miniature on cardboard. Diam. 3.4 cm
Frederiksborg A 2564
Counterpart of the above
*Provenance:* Purchased in Dresden 1920.
*Literature:* Andrup 1925 no. 6.

72

## Johan Sigismund (1572-1619), Elector of Brandenburg, brother-in-law of Christian IV

Oil on metal. 3.9×3.2 cm
Frederiksborg A 6870
One side shows the Elector, head and shoulders, and the inscription "A° 1612"; the other side depicts Anna, his consort (died 1625).
*Provenance:* Purchased from an art dealer in London 1948/49.

*67*

73

## Philip Sigismund (1568-1623), Duke of Braunschweig-Wolfenbüttel

Gold pendant. 6.7×5.1 cm
Frederiksborg A 4336
Philip Sigismund was the brother of the reigning Duke of Braunschweig-Wolfenbüttel, Heinrich Julius, who married Elisabeth, sister of Christian IV. Philip Sigismund was an important stalwart for Christian IV in his endeavours to get control of the secularized dioceses in North Germany.
*Provenance:* Purchased from an art dealer in Denmark 1929.

74

## Elisabeth (1573-1626), sister of Christian IV, married Heinrich Julius, Duke of Braunschweig-Wolfenbüttel

Jacob van Doordt
Miniature. 5×3.7 cm, 21.3×16.8 cm in frame
The Duke of Buccleuch's collections inv. 21/4. Oval miniature, set in a frame of filigree work with pearls and stones.

75

## Same

Probably by Jacob van Doordt c. 1607
Heart-shaped miniature on parchment. 5×5 cm
Frederiksborg A 2540
*Provenance:* Purchased in Gotha 1918.
*Literature:* Andrup 1920 106. Andrup 1925 no. 27. Rosenborg 1948 cat. 1.

76

## Anne of Denmark (1574-1619), sister of Christian IV, married James I (VI) of England and Scotland

Isaac Oliver (born in Rouen, died 1617 in London). Inscribed with the monogram "IO"
Miniature. 5.8×4.3 cm
Frederiksborg A 4877
Miniature inserted in a gold case, with an enamelled reverse. Below a baroque pearl. The box was probably executed by the goldsmith George Heriot (1563-1624). Among the hair jewels is a crowned C IV, and on the starched collar is a crowned S (which refers to her mother, Queen Sophie).
*Provenance:* Purchased at the sales of Pierpont Morgan's Collection of Miniatures 1935.

77

## Anne of Denmark, James I (1566-1625) and Charles I (1600-1649)

Simon de Passe 1616
Two engraved silver plates in a gold frame with diamonds. Oval. 6.3×5 cm
Frederiksborg A 4878
*Provenance:* Purchased at the sales of the Pierpont Morgan Collection of Miniatures in 1935.

78

## Christian II (1583-1611), Elector of Saxony, married Hedevig, sister of Christian IV

Oil on metal. 3.9×3.2 cm
Frederiksborg A 6869
Set in a silver gilt locket.
*Provenance:* Purchased from an art dealer in London 1948/49.

79

## Hedevig (1581-1641), sister of Christian IV, married Christian II, Elector of Saxony

C. 1620. The name has been inscribed later
Oval miniature on parchment. 7.3×6.0 cm
Frederiksborg A 2539
*Provenance:* Acquired from Gotha 1918
*Literature:* Andrup 1920 106. Andrup 1925 no. 29.

80

## Gustavus II Adolphus (1594-1632), king of Sweden

Jacob van Doordt
Inscribed: "1629"
Miniature on vellum set in a silver gilt locket.
Frederiksborg A 2685
*Provenance:* Acquired in 1923 from Etatsråd Glückstadt, by whom it had been purchased in 1921 in Dresden.
*Literature:* Andrup 1925 no. 38. Steneberg 1934 260f.

81

## Christen Friis of Kragerup (1581-1639), the King's Chancellor

Executed c. 1635
Miniature on copper. 2.1×1.8 cm
Frederiksborg A 7061
Same facemask as the portrait of Christen Friis at Börringe Kloster dated 1635 and as Frederiksborg A 2809 (cat. 75).
*Provenance:* Acquired in 1951 from Ørumgaard.

82

## Christian, the Prince Elect 1603-47

The 1630s
Oval miniature on paper. 4.2×3.6 cm
Frederiksborg A 2541
*Provenance:* Acquired in Gotha, 1918
*Literature:* Andrup 1925 no. 31. Eller 1971 122.

83

## Same

Two miniatures on either side of an oval silver plate executed in 1647 by Valentin Wagner (Dresden 1616 – Dresden 1655). 3.3×3.0 cm
a. A head and shoulders of the Prince after a prototype by Karel van Mander.
b. A head and shoulders of the Prince as a corpse.
Frederiksborg A 2542
The miniatures were probably in the possession of Princess Magdalena Sibylla, the Prince's consort, into whose Saxon family they have passed by descent.
*Provenance:* Acquired from Gotha in 1918.
*Literature:* Andrup 1925 no. 34. Eller 1971 136f, 167.

84

## Sophie Elisabeth (1619-1657), daughter of Christian IV and Vibeke Kruse

Oval gold medal. 3.3×2.7 cm
Frederiksborg A 5572
*Provenance:* Purchased in Rostock in 1937.

85

## The Order of the Mailed Sword-Arm

Executed in 1617 probably by Corvianus Saur (Bauerkirchen, Bavaria c. 1555/60 – Copenhagen 1635)
9×6.4 cm
Frederiksborg B 2424
An mailed arm with a sword hanging in two chains fastened to a piece of jewellery. On the arm is the crowned monogram of Christian IV and "1617". Executed in gold and enamel in blue, white, red, and green. Set with table-cut stones. (Cf. cat. 179, 563).
*Provenance:* Acquired from the entailed estate of movables of the Bille-Scheel family in 1924. The provenance makes it likely that the specimen in question is identical with the one acquired by Jørgen Skeel, later Marshall of the Realm, in 1617.
*Literature:* Schepelern 1980 12-16

86

## The Mailed Sword-Arm

Probably Nicolaus Schwabe c. 1616
Silver medal. Diam. 5.7 cm
L. E. Bruun 15260
*Literature:* Galster 44.

87

## The Coronation of Christian IV in 1596

Nicolaus Schwabe, 1596. Signed and dated
Silver Medal. Diam. 5.7 cm
L. E. Bruun 15242
*Literature:* Galster 34.

90

## Prince Christian's Marriage to Magdalene Sibylla of Saxony on 5th Oktober, 1634

Paul Walther, 1635 (working in Dresden from 1633 until the 1640s). Signed and dated
Gold medal. Diam. 4.8 cm
L. E. Bruun 15263

91

## The Peace of Brømsebro, 1645

Johan Blum (– 1599-1668 – working in Bremen and Copenhagen). Signed and dated
Silver medal. 5.2 cm
L. E. Bruun 15266
*Literature:* Galster 76.

# Queen Anna Cathrine and her children

In the autumn of 1595 Christian IV visited Berlin where the marriage was arranged between the Danish King and Anna Cathrine, daughter of Margrave Joachim Frederik, who became Elector of Brandenburg in 1598. Christian IV's marriage to Anna Cathrine took place at Haderslevhus on 27th November 1597, and on 11th June 1598 the Queen was crowned in Copenhagen.

Anna Cathrine is one of the most nondescript queens in the history of Denmark. She had no political influence and made no impression whatsoever on court life. As regards the relationship between the spouses little is known. Anna Cathrine accompanied the King on his journeys round the country, but she did not visit England with him in 1606. While she was still alive Christian IV began a relationship with one of her chambermaids, Kirsten Madsdatter.

Anna Cathrine became the mother of six children, of and three lived, i.e. Prince Christian, born in 1603, and in 1608 elected successor to the throne, Prince Frederik, born in 1609, who in fact succeeded Christian IV on the throne in 1648, since the "Prince-Elect" died the year before, and finally Duke Ulrik, born in 1611.

The day after Queen Anna Cathrine gave birth to Duke Ulrik, Kirsten Madsdatter, piquantly enough, was delivered of a son, who was named Christian Ulrik Gyldenløve (died 1633). Christian IV was the first Danish king to give his "natural" children the name Gyldenløve.

Kirsten Madsdatter's father was the Lord Mayor of Copenhagen, Matthias Hansen, who built the still-existing house at Amagertorv where the Kongelige Porcelainsfabrik (Royal Copenhagen) now has its shop. There is no known portrait of Christian Ulrik Gyldenløve or of Kirsten Madsdatter.

91a

## Cupboard. Originally in the possession of Queen Anna Cathrine

Glass cupboard made of oak with intarsia decorations in maple, dark oak, and nutmeg (?). On the lower section black stencil paintings. The cupboard has carvings and painted hermae. On the cornice gilt ornamentations with a crowned CA (Anna Cathrine)
H. 245 cm. W. 230. D. 71 cm. About 1600
Statsinventariekommissionen. Deposited at Frederiksborg Castle Chapel
The intarsia on this cupboard resembles the inlaid decorations in the Chapel of Frederiksborg Castle and is probably from c. 1600. First recorded in the Frederiksborg Castle inventory of 1650, where it was mentioned under "the bedroom of Her Late Majesty" with a note to the effect that it was supposed to have belonged to Queen Anna Cathrine. The cupboard can be seen in F. C. Lund's painting from 1858 (Frederiksborg A 8689) of a room in the Castle called "the Rose". The cupboard is now in the Chapel.
*Literature:* DK III 1849.

92

## Christian, the Prince Elect

Adriaen Matham after a lost painting by Pieter Isaacsz. from 1615
Engraving. 21.4×14.1 cm
Frederiksborg
*Literature:* Faaborg 759. Liisberg 1926 206.

93

## Frederic III (1609-70), King of Denmark and Norway 1648, and Ulrik (1611-33), Bishop of Schwerin, sons of Christian IV

Adriaen Matham after lost paintings by Pieter Isaacsz. from 1615
Engraving. 25.2×31.3 cm
Frederiksborg
*Literature:* Faaborg 2802. Liisberg 1926 206f.

91a

*96*

94

## Christian IV

Unknown English artist, 1606
Oil on canvas. 112×88 cm. Colour plate IX
Frederiksborg A 8706
The King is wearing the badge of the Order of the Garter on a string round his neck. The picture was painted in 1606 during the King's visit to his sister, Queen Anne, and his brother-in-law, James I of England, where more versions of the same portrait-type are to be found (Knole, Badminton). On the basis of this a number of engravings of Christian IV have been executed in England (cf. cat. 23-24).
*Provenance:* Donated by Dame Anne Warburton in 1986. During the 20th century this picture has passed through different private English collections. Sold at Christie's in 1965.
*Literature:* Heiberg 1986 92-98.

95

## Frederik III as a child

Pieter Isaacsz. (Elsinore 1569 – Elsinore 1625). Inscribed "ANO 1615"
Oil on canvas. 139×108 cm. Colour plate XII
Frederiksborg A 7395
The six-year-old Prince is depicted in musketeer's costume. The disposition and pose of the figure correspond almost exactly to an illustration in the Dutch engraver Jacob de Gheyns' "Waffen handlung von der Rüren, Musquetten und Spiessen" from 1608. At the same time, it happens to be the oldest Danish portrait with a landscape background. The castle behind the figure is Frederiksborg (cf. cat. 96).
*Provenance:* Acquired from an English private collection 1959. Formerly at Rushbroke Hall, Suffolk.
*Literature:* Paulsen 1974/75 78ff. Heiberg 1983 12.

96

## Frederiksborg Castle from the southeast

Pieter Isaacsz. c. 1614
Indian ink and wash. 17.9×32.1 cm
Frederiksborg A 7322
This drawing is the earliest known depiction of Christian IV's Frederiksborg. It is a preliminary study for the landscape background in the painting of Prince Frederik (III) as a child by Pieter Isaacsz., dated 1615. It is sketched before the erection of the Chancellery on the middle island. On the left are the buildings by Frederik II with the two round towers from the 1560s, the Castellan's House from about 1610, and the main castle built between 1604-09. On the right is the Sparepenge, built c. 1600 in the style of an Italian villa (demolished c. 1720). The houses visible in the foreground are placed where today the Helsingørgade runs through Hillerød.
*Provenance:* Acquired in 1957 by exchange from St. Annen Museum in Lübeck, to which it came in the 1890s from a private collection.
*Literature:* Paulsen 1974/75 78ff.

97

97

## Christian IV and Queen Anna Cathrine

Jacob van Doordt. Inscribed "Anno 1611"
Oil on canvas. 55×54 cm
Gripsholm 2019
The picture is a counterpart to another double portrait of Frederik II and Queen Sophie, likewise dated 1611 (Gripsholm 2005). The portrait type of Christian IV and that of his Queen have been repeated in a number of other paintings by van Doordt. (cf. cat.)
*Provenance:* Karlberg's inventory, 1719 no. 93. To Gripsholm after 1794. The picture is probably Swedish war-booty.
*Literature:* Beckett 1932 26-28. Steneberg 1934 249. Beckett 1937 33-40. Rosenborg 1948 no. 9.

98

## Christian, the Prince Elect

C. 1620
Oil on canvas. 225×143 cm
Rosenborg 3.174. On permanent loan to Fredensborg
Francis Beckett attributes the painting to Franz Cleyn, who in 1619 was paid for a portrait of the Prince Elect.
*Provenance:* In Kunstkammeret without number, transferred to Amalienborg in 1827. At Frederiksborg as inv. 712. In Det kgl. Billedgalleri 1852-53. To Rosenborg 1870.
*Literature:* Beckett 1937.

98

99

## Frederik III as a Child

Pieter Isaacsz. c. 1616-20
Oil on canvas. 170×110 cm
Gavnøfonden no. 117

The picture is a counterpart to the portrait of Duke Ulrik (cat. 100), and like it was for many years listed as unidentified at Gavnø Castle. On the basis of an engraving by Adrian Matham (cat. 93), Otto Andrup identified the child as Duke Frederik, second son of Christian IV. The identification is confirmed by the fact that the boy is obviously identical with the child on Pieter Isaacsz.'s portrait of Frederik III with Frederiksborg Castle in the background (cat. 95), with which Andrup was not familiar. Andrup suggested that the master of the two paintings of the princes might be a certain Cornelis Sueris, who in 1618 was paid for some portraits of the King's sons. Another possibility, put forward by Andrup, was the tapestry weaver Karel van Mander (II), who from 1616-1620 executed a number of tapestries illustrating the achievements of Christian IV for the Great Hall of Frederiksborg. The greenish colour of the flesh and the gay colours used, however, point to Pieter Isaacsz. as the artist. In 1615, Isaacsz. had painted Prince Frederik in a similar military pose (cat. 95).

*Provenance:* In the collection of Otto Thott of Gavnø, statesman and collector. Thott may have acquired it, when in the 1730s, a number of older paintings were discarded from the royal palaces.

*Literature:* Andrup 1917 67ff. Andrup 1932 139f.

100

## Duke Ulrik, (1611-33), as child

Probably by Pieter Isaacsz. c. 1618-20
Oil on canvas. 170×110 cm
Gavnøfonden no. 116

Originally at Gavnø, this painting was for many years listed as unidentified. On the basis of an engraving by Adriaen Matham (cat. 93) Otto Andrup made the suggestion that the boy in the picture could be Duke Ulrik, the youngest son of Christian IV by his Queen Anna Cathrine. Yet another argument can be added in favour of this theory. At Ibstrup (the present Jægersborg), built by Christian IV immediately after 1609, there was a portrait of Duke Ulrik which, in an inventory of 1732, was recorded as follows: "Same (Duke Ulrik) with a "Fyhrmysser" (mortar) in front of him, a musket in his left and a hat in his right hand". This description is so clear that the two paintings must be identical. Late in the year 1732, the paintings at Ibstrup were placed in the charge of Jægermester C. C. Gram. Since then it has not been possible to trace them. Like many other old paintings in the Royal palaces they may have been discarded in the years that followed. Otto Thott of Gavnø, statesman and collector, acquired a number of paintings formerly in the Royal collections, and the portrait of Ulrik at Gavnø may well be the one recorded at Ibstrup in 1732. It is significant, however, that the counterpart showing Duke Frederik (cat. 99) is not mentioned in the Ibstrup-inventory.

*Literature:* Andrup 1917 67ff. Andrup 1932 139f.

# Dynastic connections

After 1536 Denmark was the most important Lutheran state outside Germany. Political and religious conditions therefore made it natural that the Danish kings should cooperate with the Lutheran princes in Germany. An expression of this was the number of dynastic connections which secured for Denmark a significant influence in the Lutheran part of Germany, which came to function as a buffer-zone separating Denmark from Catholic Europe and the Counter-Reformation. It thus became a natural goal of Danish foreign policy to ensure the Lutheran princes' independence of the German Emperor and their religious freedom. Christian IV became much more directly involved than his predecessors in German affairs. The Danish King, who before the Thir-

*99*

*100*

ty Years' War had been one of Europe's wealthiest rulers, tried through lending money to economically weak princes and through military pressure to build up a true political dominion in Northern Germany.

## Kirsten Munk

After the death of Queen Anna Cathrine in 1612 Christian IV had several mistresses. First there was Kirsten Madsdatter, who died in the same year as the Queen, and later there was Karen Andersdatter, who bore him a son, Hans Ulrik Gyldenløve (Cat. 146). The King's relatives pressed him to enter into a new princely marriage. This however was not to be. Instead, in 1615, the 38-year-old King embarked on a relationship with a 17-year-old girl of noble family, Kirsten Munk. The King only just managed to have his way. Kirsten's mother, Ellen Marsvin (Cat. 137), in fact obstructed his purpose for some time. She saw quite clearly that if the womanizing King were to discard her daughter at a later date Kirsten would be in an unfortunate situation. A former royal mistress did not have the best prospects in the nobility's marriage market. She therefore sought economic insurance for her daughter (and for herself), together with actual marriage. Christian thus had to provide comprehensive guarantees before he could write in his diary on 31 December 1615 that "... Kirsten Munk came to me in marriage." There was never any question of a church wedding, but in fact such a ceremony was not necessary to make the marriage legally valid, and the King himself saw it as a reality. The truth was that the girl was virtually sold to a man twenty years her senior, and rumour also had it that Kirsten was against the match but was forced into it by Ellen Marsvin. About the warmth of the King's feelings there was, however, no doubt, and in the 13 years that followed, Kirsten bore 12 children. Her growing repugnance for a union which had perhaps always been against her will was probably the source of her severing their cohabitation in 1628. Before then she had already had a relationship with a German nobleman, Rhinegrave Otto Ludwig of Salm, of which the King in all probability was not aware at the time. An intrigue of Ellen Marsvin's, in 1630, led to the beginning of an affair between the King and Kirsten's chambermaid, Vibeke Kruse, who became his permanent mistress. Ellen Marsvin and Kirsten Munk later asserted that it was the King's relationship with Vibeke Kruse which caused the end of the union. For Christian IV the break with Kirsten Munk was a particularly hard blow, because it came at the same time as his defeat in the German War. In the King's letters from the following years we can trace how his thoughts revolved around Kirsten Munk, and he wrote numerous accounts of the course of events which laid all the blame on Kirsten Munk. He constantly exerted pressure to make her and her mother acknowledge that the fault was Kirsten's, but this was never conceded. In retaliation Kirsten Munk was kept in virtual imprisonment in the Manor of Boller near Horsens.

*Literature:* Birket-Smith I-II, 1879-81. EB II-VIII, 1889-1948.

101

## Augusta (1580-1639), sister of Christian IV, married Johan Adolf, Duke of Schleswig-Holstein-Gottorp, in 1596

Artist unknown. Inscribed "AUGUSTA GEBORNE AVS KONIGLICHEM STAMMEN ZV DENMARCKEN. HERTZOGIN ZV SCHLESWIG. HOLLSTEIN. e. AN° DN. 1601."
Oil on canvas. 211×129 cm
Gripsholm 1306

*Provenance:* Recorded at Gripsholm, 1699. This painting of Augusta and a counterpart of her consort, Duke Johan Adolf, may originally have come to Sweden as presents for Johan Adolf's sister, Queen Christine, who had married the Swedish King, Carl IX.

*Literature:* DBL 3rd ed.

102

## Johan Adolf (1575-1616), Duke of Schleswig-Holstein-Gottorp

Artist unknown, c. 1600
Oil on canvas. 109×99 cm
Frederiksborg A 4074

Johan Adolf ruled the Gottorp part of Southern Jutland and Holstein i.e. the part which had been allotted to his father, Duke Adolf, in 1544, when the Duchies were divided between Christian III and his brothers. Johan Adolf's chief political ambition was to set his part of Schleswig free of the Danish King's sovereignty.

*Provenance:* Acquired in 1926 from the former Royal Saxon Collections in Dresden.

*Literature:* DBL 3rd ed.

103

## Christian II, Elector of Saxony (1583-1611) and his consort, Hedevig of Denmark (1581-1641), brother-in-law and sister of Christian IV

Artist unknown, the 1630s. Inscribed "Von gottes Gnaden Christian der ander Herzog zu Sachsen/ Jülich Cleve und Berg Churfürst" and "Von gottes Gnaden Hedwig Geboren aus Königlichem Stamm zu Dennemarchen Churfürstin und Hertzogin zu Sachsen, Jülich Cleve und Berg. Wittwe"
Oil on canvas. 35×28 cm
Frederiksborg A 4389

Since the Reformation, one of the primary ambitions of Danish foreign policy had been to maintain the closest possible connections with Saxony, politically as well as dynastically, Saxony being the most important Lutheran state of Germany. The numerous Danish-Saxon marriages may be seen as a manifestation of this. Anna, paternal aunt of Christian IV, (cat. 71) had been married to August I, Elector of Saxony (cat. 70) and Christian IV's sister, Hedevig married Christian II, Elector of Saxony (cat. 103). In 1634, Magdalena Sibylla, niece of Hedevig and Christian, married the Danish Prince Elect, Christian.

*Provenance:* Acquired on the Cologne art market, 1930. The inscription corresponds with other inscriptions on portraits in the former Royal Saxon Collections. This painting was probably sold after the abdication of the King of Saxony in 1918.

104

## Hedevig of Denmark

Inscribed "Von Gottes Gnaden Hedwig Geborne aus Königlichem Stam Dennemarck Churfurstin und Herzogin zu Sachsen. Wittwe Anno 1630"
Oil on copper. 25×20 cm
Frederiksborg A 2504

*Provenance:* Acquired in 1918 from the Duke of Saxony-Coburg-Gotha.

*Literature:* Andrup 1925 no. 30.

105

## One of the daughters of Christian I, Elector of Saxony, either Sophie (1587-1635) or Dorothea (1591-1617)

C. 1600. Inscribed at the bottom left-hand side "I Z" (signature?)
Oil on canvas. 113×84.5 cm
Frederiksborg R 218

Francis Beckett believed the portrait to be by Hans Knieper (cf. cat. 1 and 10) and a representation of one of Frederik II's daughters. On the basis of the big embroidered lace collar, however, it is possible to date the portrait about 1600. Being the portrait of a child, it cannot possibly represent one of Frederik II's daughters as they were born between 1573 and 1581. *Vide* also the portrait of Augusta (1580-1639) from 1601 (cat. 101)

The picture is identical with the one recorded by Høyen (Frederiksborg no. 913). Høyen presumed that it was a picture of a daughter of the Elector, Christian I. It was hung together with a number of portraits of members of the Saxon Electoral House which were destroyed by fire in 1859. The Saxon portraits seem already to have been at Frederiksborg in 1650. In "Krydshuset", by the passage leading from the Ship's Room were "Two sisters of the Elector Hans Georg of Saxony with hands set in a gilt frame". The Saxon portraits were still in the same place in 1677 and in 1741. The present picture seems always to have been at Frederiksborg.

*Provenance:* To Denmark probably as a present from the Electoral family of Saxony. Hedevig, sister of Christian IV, married the Elector, Christian II, who was the brother of Sophie and Dorothea (cf. cat. 103).

Frederiksborg inv. of 1650. Frederiksborg inv. 1741, 258/118. The Frederiksborg revision by Høyen 1831/913. Rescued in the fire at Frederiksborg. Transferred to the Frederiksborg Museum after 1878.

*Literature:* Beckett 1897 204.

106

## Duke Hans (1583-1602), brother of Christian IV

Constantin Hansen (Rome 1804 – Frederiksberg 1880)
Drawing.
Det kongelige Bibliotek

This drawing is sketched after the only known contemporary portrait of Duke Hans, which was destroyed by fire in 1859.

In 1602, a marriage was arranged between Hans and Xenia, daughter of the Russian Tzar Boris Godunov. Hans, however, died in Russia before the wedding took place.

*Provenance:* Acquired with the Winding Collection from Kunstindustrimuseet in 1911.

107

## Elisabeth (1573-1626), sister of Christian IV, married Heinrich Julius, Duke of Braunschweig-Wolfenbüttel in 1590

Probably a contempory copy after van Doordt (died in Stockholm in 1629)
Inscribed "Von GOTTES gnaden Elizabeth geboren aus Køniglichem Stammen zu Dennemarcken/ Herzogin zu Braunschweig und Lüneburghen Anno 1609"
Oil on canvas. 126×99 cm
Frederiksborg A 4078

The marriage between Elisabeth and Heinrich Julius inaugurated an era of close political relations between Denmark and Braunschweig-Wolfenbüttel. Christian IV aided his brother-in-law and later on the Duke's and Elisabeth's sons, Friedrich Ulrik and Christian with handsome loans, which in reality made Braunschweig-Wolfenbüttel politically and financially a vassal state of Christian IV's. Yet another manifestation of the close relations between Christian and Elisabeth is the Compenius Organ in the Chapel of Frederiksborg, which in 1617 came to Denmark as a present from Elisabeth.

*Provenance:* Acquired from the former Royal Saxon Collections, 1926.

108

## Ulrik (1578-1624), Prince of Denmark, Bishop of Schwerin, brother of Christian IV

Artist unknown c. 1620. Inscribed "Von Gottes Gnaden Ulrich: Erbe zu Norwegen. Administrator des Stiffts Schwerin"
Oil on canvas. 209×129.5 cm
Frederiksborg A 4076

Providing for the younger sons was frequently a problem for the Royal Houses. Christian IV's mother, the Queen Dowager Sophie, demanded a new partition of the Royal parts of Schleswig and Holstein. This demand was firmly rejected by the Regency and Christian IV, resulting in a downright break of the relations between the King and his mother in 1596. Later, however, a solution was found. Instead of getting a part of the Duchies, Ulrik received 200.000 Rix dollars plus the revenues of the former church estates in the diocese of Schleswig. Futhermore, he took over the administration of the diocese of Schwerin in Mecklenburg from his paternal grandfather, Duke Ulrich. Ulrich was not a prominent personage, but he was a useful pawn in Christian IV's North German policy.

*Provenance:* Acquired on the Dresden art market in 1926. The inscription indicates that the picture was formerly in the Royal Saxon Collections.

*Literature:* DBL 3rd ed.

109

## Anne of Denmark (1574-1619), sister of Christian IV, married James I (VI) of England and Scotland

Oil on panel. 96.5×110 cm
Frederiksborg R 210

This picture is one of a series of family portraits, three of which are described by N. L. Høyen in 1831: a portrait of Christian III (Høyen no. 1172), "Head and shoulders framed in a grey cartouche", which still exists (Frederiksborg R 211). Another portrait representing Elizabeth, sister of Christian IV (Høyen no. 174), was destroyed in the fire at Frederiksborg 1859. The third picture is this portrait of Anne (Høyen 173). According to Høyen, all

*109*

three pictures were painted by "the same master". The unnamed master probably used another painting, viz. Høyen no. 962, as prototype for his portrait of Anne. From the detailed description, it appears that "her hair is dressed in a darker manner and embellished with a row of pearls at the top. Her black dress is adorned with pearl embroidery on seams and braidings with red embroidery in between. Besides the pearls, she is also wearing a black string round her neck with a seal ring". The picture, which was destroyed by fire in 1859, was inscribed "Marco Gerardi Brüggience fecit. 1609". Just at that time, Marcus Geraerts the Younger was attached to the English Court (cf. cat. 3). Geraerts' portrait is probably a present from Anne to Christian IV.
*Provenance:* To Frederiksborg 1825. The Frederiksborg revision by Høyen 1831 no. 173.

110

## James I (1566-1625), King of Scotland 1567, King of England 1603, brother-in-law of Christian IV

Attributed to Johan de Critz (Antwerp c. 1555 – London 1641)
Oil on canvas. 200.5×129.5 cm
Alleyn's College of God's Gift. Dulwich Picture Gallery (London) inv. 548

The marriage between his sister and King James was an event of great importance to Christian IV. After James' accession to the English Throne in 1603, the alliance with Great Britain became the cornerstone of Danish foreign policy. The close relations between the two Royal Houses were emphasized still further by Christian IV's two visits to England in 1606 and 1614. In 1624-25, James was the prime mover behind the formation of the Evangelical Alliance, on the basis of which Christian IV could involve himself in the German War in 1625.
*Provenance:* Possibly at Holland House. From there to the Duchess of Warrick's in the early 18th. century. The picture hung at Bilton Hall, her manor house, and was then sold at Christie's in 1898. Purchased by H. Yates Thompson, who donated it to Alleyn's College.
*Literature:* Tudor and Jacobean Portraits I 1969 179. Strong 1969 259 264.

111

## James I

By F. C. Lund. Inscribed "Jacob 1ste af England. F. Lund – d.22 Juli 1858."
Pen and Indian ink. 23.7×19.3 cm (size of the sketch)
Frederiksborg A 5034
Sketched after a portrait which was destroyed in the fire at Frederiksborg, 1859. The drawing and a description

*112*

from 1831 indicate that the portrait in question must have been of a type similar to cat. 110, apart from the fact that the lost painting was a three-quarter length portrait painted on panel. There was another portrait of James I at Frederiksborg, a full-length, which was likewise destroyed in the fire. The portrait type is not known.
*Literature:* Høyens Frederiksborg Revision. 1831 no. 696.

112

## Kirsten Munk (1598-1658), married Christian IV in 1615

Artist unknown, c. 1615
Oil on canvas. 66.5×55 cm. Frame in tortoiseshell
Kunstindustrimuseet, Oslo inv. OK 9586
According to tradition, this has been listed as a portrait of Queen Anna Cathrine, but has also been identified as Elisabeth, Duchess of Braunschweig-Wolfenbüttel, sister of Christian IV. Both identifications must be rejected. The badge in the necklace, with the monogram of Christian IV, indicate that the model must have been closely related to the King. The dress dates the picture to about 1615. As the model is a very young girl, the possibility of her being Elisabeth is ruled out as she was 42 years old in 1615. Nor could it be Anna Cathrine, who died in 1612 at the age of 37. Kirsten Munk seems to be the only girl who was so closely connected with the King that it would be natural for her to wear his monogram in her necklace. Christian IV married Kirsten Munk on 31st December 1615, when she was 17 years old.
*Provenance:* Purchased from a private collection in London, whereupon it was sold to the Kunstindustrimuseum in 1923. The picture probably came to England as a present from Christian IV to his sister, Queen Anne.
*Literature:* Wiese Rygge 1968-69 52-65 (calls it Elisabeth of Denmark).

113

## Kirsten Munk (1598-1658) and her children, Valdemar Christian (1622-56), Anna Cathrine (1618-33), Sophie Elisabeth (1619-57), and Leonora Christina (1621-98)

Jacob van Doordt, c. 1623
Oil on canvas. 186×199 cm. Colour plate XXXIII
Private collection
A portrait of Kirsten Munk, quite identical with this one, is at the Frederiksborg Museum (A 7290). The Frederiksborg painting, however, is a three-quarter length and leaves out the children. It is signed by Jacob van Doordt and dated 1623.
*Provenance:* Probably in the possession of Christiane, a daughter of Christian IV, who married Hannibal Sehested.
*Literature:* DMP I 24. Beckett 1937 33-40. Eller 1973 144f.

114

## Kirsten Munk

Inscribed "Cirstine Munk" and "F. C. Lund. Frederiksborg i Juni 1858."
Watercolour. 33.5×24.4 cm
Frederiksborg A 5027
Watercolour executed after a painting from 1624 by Jacob van Doordt which was destroyed in the Frederiksborg fire, 1859. The roses on the table symbolize Love. It was precisely in 1624 that Rosenborg, which was the setting of the King's life with Kirsten Munk, acquired its name.
*Literature:* Eller 1971 83.

116

## Count Valdemar Christian (1622-56), son of Christian IV and Kirsten Munk

Attributed to Reinholdt Timm. Possibly painted in 1634
Oil on canvas. 111×78 cm
Valdemars Slot, Tåsinge
This painting may be identical with "a portrait of the honourable Count Valdemar" for which Reinholdt Timm received payment on 17th January, 1635 (Registers of the Rentemester 1634/35, Expenditure). It may always have been at Valdemars Slot, a manor built by Christian IV for his son Valdemar Christian, 1635-43. Valdemar Christian, however, never stayed there.

*Literature:* DMP X 11. Beckett 1937 73ff. Kunst- og Industriudstillingen i København 1879 no. 117.

117

### Valdemar Christian

Justus Sustermans (Antwerp 1597 – Florence 1681), 1638-39
Oil on canvas. 71×54.5 cm
Galleria Palatina, Palazzo Pitti, Florence. Inv. Palatina N. 190
Painted during Valdemar Christian's stay in Italy, 1638-39. Valdemar Christian had a changeable life. As a part of his father's endeavours to find allies against Sweden, a marriage was negotiated between Valdemar Christian and Irene, daughter of the Russian Tzar Michael Feodorovitsj. Valdemar Christian arrived in Russia in 1644 with a Danish legation bringing numerous presents for the Tsar. The negotiations broke down, however, possibly on account of Sweden's defeat of Denmark in 1644. In addition to this, Valdemar Christian and his escort were detained in Russia for more than a year. On his return, he enlisted in the Emperial army at his father's request. In the discord between Christian IV and Kirsten Munk, he, like his sisters and brothers, sided against his father. He was killed in action in 1656 while serving in the Swedish army.
*Provenance:* Collezioni medico-lorensi.
*Literature:* Bautier 1912 41f. Cipriani 1966 24. Rusconi 1937 286. Chiarini and others 1983 109.

## Christian, the Prince Elect

In 1608 Christian, eldest son of Christian IV and Queen Anna Cathrine, was elected successor to the Throne by the Council of the Realm, and in 1610 he was acclaimed by the Estates of the Realm in the four major regions (Zealand, Scania, Funen and Jutland). The up-bringing and education of the Prince was first entrusted to Christen Friis of Kragerup (cat. 176) and later to Christen Thomesen Sehested (cat. 197), following guiding principles which the King himself had formulated.

During Christian IV's German campaign in 1626 Prince Christian in his father's absence took over government. Christian IV however rapidly became displeased with his son's conduct of affairs, and overrode several of his decisions. The King was especially infuriated by the Prince's relationship with a widow of noble rank, Anne Lykke, who followed the Prince Elect on his travels around the country. The end of the story was that Christian IV arrested Anne Lykke and held her in Bohus Castle, from where she was only released after strong protests from the Council of the Realm. From 1628 to 1632 the Prince's residence was Malmøhus, and from 1632 it was Nykøbing Castle on Falster. In 1634 Prince Christian's marriage to Princess Magdalena Sibylla of Saxony took place in Copenhagen with great festivities. The lavish scale of the celebrations was to demonstrate that Denmark had surmounted the consequences of the defeat in the German War and that Christian IV was still one of Europe's leading monarchs.

Prince Christian has often been depicted as a drunken nonentity. His conduct of life, especially before his marriage, was certainly dissolute but he himself was the hardest hit by it, since his health was not strong enough to weather his excesses. But there is no reason to underestimate him. The fact that Christian IV was not satisfied with his conduct of the realm during the German War and later kept him in the background does not mean that he was at fault. Christian IV wanted to decide everything himself down to the most minute detail and regularly disparaged decisions taken by officials on every level.

To a greater extent than his father, Prince Christian was interested in art and learning. Art to Christian IV was principally a means of stressing the prestige of the monarchy. The Prince, on the other hand, seems also to have been a collector. Through connections abroad he received offers of works of art, and we know that he purchased etchings by Rembrandt. He was also responsible for preventing the melting down of the first of the Gold Horns from Gallehus. His enjoyment of music was shared with his father, and it was probably owing to his efforts that Heinrich Schütz came to Denmark in 1633.

In his later years he was often ill; he died in 1647 while on a visit to Saxony for reasons of health.
*Literature:* Prince Christian's Letters I-II, 1952-56. DBL 3rd ed. Memoirer og Breve XX 1914. Andrup 1920 96-110. Hermansen 1960, 16-44. Eller 1971. Schepelern 1971. Askgaard 1978, 109-26.

118

### Christian, the Prince Elect

Probably by Albert Freyse, who died in Wolfenbüttel, 1652. (Formerly inscribed (?) "A. Freit depinxit ad vivum 1641")
Oil on canvas. 204×118 cm
Private collection, Germany
The castle in the background is Nykøbing Castle on Falster, which from 1634 was the residence of the Prince Elect.
*Literature:* Eller 1971 162 166. Rudloff 1957 172.

119

### Princess Magdalena Sibylla of Saxony (1617-68). Married Christian, the Prince Elect in 1634

Probably by Albert Freyse
Oil on canvas. 204×116 cm
Private collection, Germany
Counterpart to cat. 118.

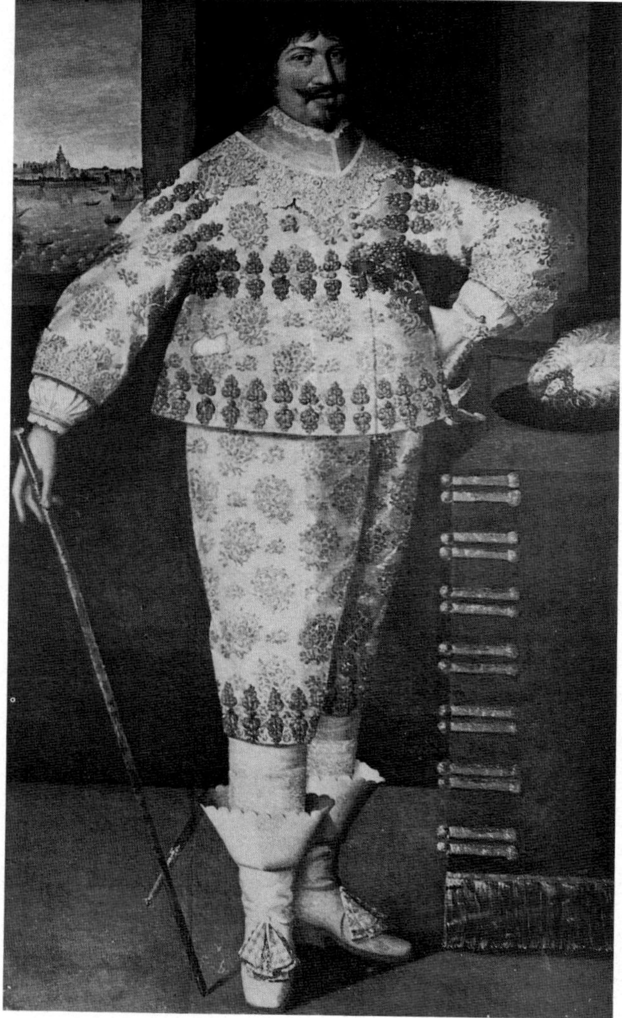

*118*

120

## Christian IV on horseback. In the background Christian, the Prince Elect, and the Sound with Elsinore and Kronborg Castle

C. 1635-39, by Adriaen Muiltjes (c. 1600 – Haarlem 1647/48)
Oil on copper. 40.1×31.2 cm
Rosenborg 1.130
This picture is cognate with cat. 121, where the Prince is depicted in the foreground and the King in the background. The pictures are unsigned, but a small painting representing the Prince Elect hunting near Nykøbing Castle and a larger one representing Christian IV at Rosenborg Castle are by the same artist. Both pictures are signed "AM" indicating Adriaen Muiltje, who was employed by the Prince Elect at Nykøbing Castle, 1635-39. Muiltjes made copies of pictures by Morten Steenwinckel and others, which may well be the reason why this picture was recorded as a painting by Steenwinckel in the Rosenborg inventory of 1696.
*Provenance:* The Rosenborg inv. 1696 118 no. 5.
*Literature:* DMP II 148. Andrup 1936 108f (attributed to Morten Steenwinckel). Eller 1971 118f.

121

## Christian, the Prince Elect on horseback. In the background Christian IV and Nykøbing Castle

C. 1635-39, by Adriaen Muiltjes
Oil on copper. 40.4×31.2 cm
Rosenborg 1.133
Counterpart to cat. 120.
*Provenance:* The Rosenborg inv. 1696 118 no. 6.
*Literature:* DMP II 179 Rosenborg 1948 no. 22.

122

## Christian, the Prince Elect on horseback

C. 1635
Oil on canvas. 55×75.5 cm
Rosenborg
*Provenance:* Purchased from the painter C. T. Melchior in 1866.
*Literature:* DMP II 180. Rosenborg 1948 no. 18. Frederiksborgmuseet 1981 no. 180.

123

## Christian, the Prince Elect, and Princess Magdalena Sibylla

C. 1638-40. Karel van Mander
Oil on canvas. 86×102 cm
Private collection
Karel van Mander repeated the same portrait type in several representations of Prince Christian and Princess Magdalena Sibylla, including the large double portrait Frederiksborg A 2740. The identity of the person in the background is not known.
*Provenance:* The picture derives from Orebygaard, which was formerly a part of the barony Guldborgland. (Inventory of the portraits on Orebygaard, 1863 p. 62 in the archives of the Statens Museum for Kunst.
*Literature:* Lolland-Falsters Stiftsmuseum Maribo 1940 no. 1. Eller 1971 170f.

123a

## Christian, the Prince Elect

Artist unknown
Marble bust. 77.2×79.5×34.0 cm
Museen der Stadt Gotha, Schlossmuseum.
Inv. 1761/P 71

124

## Procession at the marriage between Christian, the Prince Elect and Magdalena Sibylla, Princess of Saxony in Copenhagen, 1634 (known as The Grand Wedding)

Engraving by Crispin de Pas II from Triumphus Nuptialis Danicus (Copenhagen 1648). 38.9×47.7 cm. Inscribed "Christophorus Swenckius inventor. Crispin de Pas delin."
Frederiksborg
One of the biggest events at Prince Christian's wedding was the tilting at the ring at Amagertorv. The engraving depicts the procession which marched Christian IV and the Prince to the tilting course. The long procession with its many characters and scenes from classical history and mythology should be interpreted as a complex allegorical representation of the monarchy as the basis of all earthly harmony.
*Literature:* EB III 235. Regiæ Nuptiæ, Copenhagen 1637. Triumphus Nuptialis Danicus, Copenhagen 1648. Caroli Ogerii Ephemerides sive iter Danicum, Svecicum, Polonicum, Paris 1656. Memoirer og Breve XX 1914. Schepelern 1951 20.

125

## Fireworks at "The Grand Wedding", 1634

Engraving from Triumphus Nuptialus Danicus. Inscribed "Christophorus Swenckius junior inventor". 14.5×13.4 cm
Frederiksborg

126

## Fireworks at "The Grand Wedding", 1634

Engraving from Triumphus Nuptialis Danicus. Inscribed "Christophorus Swenckius junior inventor". 14.5×13.4 cm
Frederiksborg

127

## Christian IV and the Prince Elect

Inscribed "HC" and "1644"
Engraving. 16×23.7 cm
Frederiksborg
It is not known to whom the signature HC refers.
*Literature:* Strunk 313b. Faaborg 1367.

*119*

128

## The City of Malmø swearing allegiance to Prince Christian on 15th April, 1610

Parchment with 22 seals in silver lockets
Rigsarkivet
Although Denmark was an elective monarchy, it had been a constitutional practice since the Reformation that the Council of the Realm elected the King's eldest son successor to the Throne while the King was still alive. In 1608, the five-year-old Prince Christian was elected successor to the Throne, and in 1610, he received the oath of allegiance from the estates of the four principal provinces (Scania, Zealand, Funen, and Jutland).

*130*

## Duke Frederik and Duke Ulrik

While they were still young boys, the two youngest sons of Christian IV and Anna Cathrine became pawns in Christian IV's foreign policy game. With a judicious blend of military threats and bribery Christian IV had his sons appointed as prince-bishops in a series of North German dioceses. The purpose was to build up a Danish political and military power base in Northern Germany. By these means Christian IV by 1624 had control of Bremen, Verden, Schwerin and Halberstadt, and Osnabrück diocese was added to these in 1626.

All this was lost, however, in the German War, and at the peace table in Lübeck in 1629 Christian IV undertook not to intervene any further in the internal affairs of the German realm. In spite of this the choice of Frederik as Archbishop of Bremen was successfully brought off in 1634.

In 1643 Frederik was married to Sophie Amalie of Braunschweig-Lüneburg. When Denmark and Sweden went to war in the same year Frederik had to leave his diocese, which was occupied by Swedish troops. The defeat of Denmark meant that Frederik had to abandon hope of regaining the Bremen diocese. In 1648, however, he was chosen as King of Denmark and Norway after Christian IV, following the death of his older brother Christian, the Prince Elect, in 1647. In order to become king he had to sign a coronation charter which was more rigid than any signed by previous kings; this was a consequence of the conflict between his father and the Concil of the Realm. His attempt to restore the prestige of the monarchy in a new war with Sweden ended in the catastrophic peace treaty of Roskilde in 1658, whereby Denmark relinquished Scania and was reduced for ever to the rank of a secondary power. In contrast to this his personal involvement during the siege of Copenhagen from 1658 to 1660 won new esteem for the monarchy, which helped to enable him to introduce absolute monarchy in 1660.

The youngest son, Duke Ulrik, became an officer and served in Sweden, Holland and Saxony. During the fighting in 1632 in Silesia he took Tycho Brahe's celestial globe from a Jesuit monastery in Neisse as war-booty, and sent it to Copenhagen. Ulrik, like many of Christian IV's other children, had artistic and musical gifts. He wrote poems in Latin and painted. Wallenstein was among the subjects of his portraits. He was also the author of a Latin treatise in which he criticized the vices of the times, such as drunkenness. In 1633, during a visit to the Emperor's headquarters, he was murdered by a German soldier.

*Literature:* DBL 3rd ed. Schäfer 1902. Lorenz 1969. Tandrup 1979.

129

### Christian IV and his family, c. 1635

Frans v. Beusecom
Engraving. 36.2×49.2 cm
Frederiksborg
Christian IV is sitting in the middle. On his right are the Prince Elect and Magdalena Sibylla standing. On the King's left is his second son, Duke Frederik (III), carrying a stick.

130

### Frederik III

Abraham Wuchters (Antwerp c. 1610 – Copenhagen 1682)
Oil on canvas. 237×144 cm
Rosenborg 5.355. At Amalienborg on permanent loan.
On 16 October 1645, Abraham Wuchters was commissioned by Christian IV to paint his son, Duke Frederik, and his son's consort, Sophie Amalie. In 1646, Wuchters was granted permission to have the portraits engraved

on copper. They were printed in honour of Frederik III's coronation in 1648 (Sthyr 130 and 131).
*Provenance:* Frederiksborg inv. 1705 253. To Christiansborg, 1788. Presumably rescued in the fire at Christiansborg, 1794. To Amalienborg from Det kongelige Kunstkammer, 1827. To Det kongelige Billedgalleri 1832/53 (inv. 710). To Christiansborg, 1868. To Rosenborg, 1870. To Kronborg, 1884. To Amalienborg, 1885 (Christian VII's Wing).
*Literature:* Karl Madsen 1915 172. Charlottenborg 1961 no. 26. Eller 1971 204-08. Eller 1973 227ff.

131

## Sophie Amalie (1628-85), Princess of Braunschweig-Lüneburg, married Frederik III in 1643

Johan Vilhelm Gertner (Copenhagen, 1818 – Copenhagen, 1871). Inscribed "Frederiksborg Slot 1857"
Pencil. 17.2×9.1 cm
Det kongelige Bibliotek
Sketched after a painting destroyed in the fire at Frederiksborg, 1859. The lost painting was the counterpart to cat. 130 and was probably identical with no. 667 in the Frederiksborg Revision by Høyen, 1831.
*Provenance:* Acquired from the Winding Collection in the Kunstindustrimuseet, 1911.
*Literature:* Eller 1971 208f. Eller 1973 227ff.

132

## Frederik III

David Beck (Delft, 1621 – probably The Hague, 1650)
Indian ink and black chalk. 26.2×21.9 cm
Prentenkabinet der Rijksuniversiteit, Leiden inv. AW 1208
Probably sketched during David Beck's visit to Copenhagen, January-April 1652. Exhibited here for the first time in Denmark.
*Provenance:* The Adama van Scheltema Collection. The A. Welcker Collection (1955).
*Literature:* Steneberg 1955 154f. Steneberg 1956 57ff 62. Eller 1971 237.

133

## Sophie Amalie

David Beck
Indian ink and black chalk. 26.1×21.7 cm
Prentenkabinet der Rijksuniversiteit, Leiden inv. AW 1209
Counterpart to cat. 132.

134

## Fireworks in honour of the marriage between Frederik III and Sophie Amalie of Braunschweig-Lüneburg, Glückstadt 18th October 1643

Engraving. 30×36.8 cm
Frederiksborg

135

## Duke Ulrik

Artist unknown, c. 1630
Oil on canvas. 197×116 cm
Gavnøfonden no. 227
A portrait similar to this was destroyed in the fire at Frederiksborg, 1859. A smaller version of the painting is at Rosenborg.
*Literature:* Andrup 1914 227.

136

## Hercules and the Oxen of Geryon

Albert Haelwegh
Engraving. 34.2×26.3 cm
Frederiksborg
The prototype for the engraving is not known, but it may have been a painting, since lost, of Hercules and the Oxen of Geryon, which in 1650 hung at Frederiksborg in "the bedchamber next to the small Winter Parlour". This painting was part of a series of paintings by Jacob Rappost, 1608-10. In the text, written on the engraving, Duke Ulrik is likened to Hercules in to virtues and qualities.
*Literature:* Sthyr 5.

# Christian IV's other children and sons-in-law

Several of Christian IV and Kirsten Munk's children had dramatic fates. Two of the daughters, Leonora Christine (cat. 140) and Hedevig (cat. 141) followed their husbands Corfitz Ulfeldt (cat. 139) and Ebbe Ulfeldt (cat. 141) into exile, and both were later imprisoned in Denmark. During her 22-year detention in Blåtårn Leonora Christine wrote her memoirs – "Jammersminde" (memory of woe) – which became the chief example of the genre in Danish literature, and which was a brilliant statement in her own and Corfitz Ulfeldt's defence. There has always been debate as to how much she knew about or had a part in her husband's treason. In any event she followed him loyally through all life's vicissitudes. A third son-in-law, Hannibal Sehested, also had to leave the country for political reasons. His relationship with his wife Christiane was bad, and she refused to accompany him.

Christian IV wanted his and Kirsten Munk's daughters to marry into the richest aristocracy in order to secure their economic future. But he also used the sons-in-law politically. By placing them in the Council of the Realm he hoped to end the Council's opposition to his policies. The two most significant sons-in-law were Corfitz Ulfeldt and Hannibal Sehested. Both loyally supported their royal father-in-law initially. In 1642 Hannibal Sehested became vicegerent in Norway, where with great talent he carried out a modernization of the administration which increased the Norwegian state revenues. Corfitz Ulfeldt was appointed Rigshofmester (Lord High Stewart of the Realm), the highest official in the state, in 1643. From then on Ulfeldt changed attitude and emerged as leader of the opposition to Christian IV's policies. This change of position was without doubt opportunistic. As a consequence of the weakening of the monarchy the very ambitious Ulfeldt saw the best opportunity to play a central role in liaison with the opposition in the Council of the Realm.

As Rigshofmester, Ulfeldt had charge of the Navy and the Royal Dockyard in Copenhagen, which was the State's naval station, as a special area of responsibility. Ulfeldt misused his position of power, and in league with Copenhagen merchants who supplied the fleet with timber, heavy goods and provisions, carried out wholesale fraud which in less than ten years made a fortune for him equal to the monarchy's entire income for a year. Christian IV was perfectly aware of what was happening, but the old King had no strength for a battle with Ulfeldt; out of consideration for his favourite daughter Leonora Christine he allowed Ulfeldt full licence in the carrying out of his office. The situation changed with the King's death in 1648. Frederik III was hostile, not least because the Ulfeldt couple probably grossly offended the young Queen Sophie Amalie's dignity. Ulfeldt did not have support in the Council either. During long sojourns abroad in his youth he had acquired elements of Italian and French Renaissance culture to a higher degree than could be claimed by any other Danish nobles; with his provocative demeanour and cynical opinions he offended his peers, who were, to a greater extent than he was, rooted in the humanist cultural tradition and the old Lutheran ideals of the Danish nobility. Ulfeldt did not dare to stay for the investigation of his administration which Frederik III initiated in 1651, but fled to Sweden to await an opportunity for revenge. The chance came with Karl X Gustav's war against Denmark in 1657-58. At the hardest peace-settlement ever inflicted on Denmark, the Treaty of Roskilde, 1658, by which the whole of East Denmark was lost, Ulfeldt was the chief Swedish negotiator. But Ulfeldt's triumph was short-lived. He lost his position with Karl Gustav and was accused of treason. Later he and Leonora Christine fled to Denmark, where he should have been rehabilitated by the terms of the Roskilde treaty. Both were arrested and after brutal imprisonment in Hammershus Ulfeldt had to throw himself on Frederik III's mercy. In 1663 he was permitted to travel abroad for reasons of health, but conspired against the Danish King during the journey. In 1664 he died on the Rhine near Basel, hunted down by Danish agents. By that time Leonora Christine had already been put in prison in England, after she had rashly requested Charles II to pay back a loan which Ulfeldt had made him.

Hannibal Sehested also lost his position in 1651 because of an enquiry into his administration. Sehested had become extremely rich in the course of his years as Norwegian Vicegerent. The real motive however was political. Frederik III was afraid that Sehested's strong centralisation of the Norwegian administration under the office of vicegerent might result in loosening of the ties between Norway and Denmark. Sehested did not sever all connections with Denmark as Ulfeldt had done, but repeatedly asked for the King's mercy. The opportunity came in 1660, when Frederik III could use Sehested's political talent in the peace negotiations with Sweden. In the autumn of 1660 Sehested was the political architect of the coup d'etat which paved the way for absolute monarchy, and in the following years he organised the monarchy's new administrative system, which was to last with some modifications until 1848. Sehested's political and administrative talents were without doubt among the most outstanding ever produced in Denmark.

*Literature:* Molbech 1842 and 1852. Birket-Smith 1879-81. Fredericia 1894. Lind 1894-95. Bøggild-Andersen 1946-70. Ellehøj 1964.

137

## Ellen Marsvin (1572-1649), mother of Kirsten Munk

Artist unknown. Inscribed "F.E.M.F.M." (The coats of arms of E.M.'s father and mother) and "1648". Doubled arms of the Marsvin and Gyldenstierne families
Oil on canvas. 84×69 cm
Frederiksborg A 5666
The picture was painted in 1648. Ellen Marsvin is in mourning honouring the death of Christian IV. Strangely enough, there is only one portrait of Ellen Marsvin besides this one and a replica of it. The other existing portrait was painted as early as 1589 (Frederiksborg A 5669).
*Provenance:* Acquired from Rosenholm, 1937.
*Literature:* DBL 3rd ed. Eller 1971 186.

138

## Probably Kirsten Munk

Oil on canvas. 58×45.5 cm
Frederiksborg A 4097
In the Saxon inventories, this portrait is listed as a pic-

*139*

ture of the consort of Christian IV. The woman portrayed bears a considerable resemblance to Kirsten Munk. Neither the painter's technique nor the dress is Danish, however.
*Provenance:* Acquired from the former Royal Saxon Collections in Dresden, 1926.

139

## Corfitz Ulfeldt (1606-64), Lord High Steward, married Leonora Christina, daughter of Christian IV and Kirsten Munk, 1636

Engel Jansz. Rooswijk (Haarlem, 1584 – Delft, 1651 (?)).
Inscribed "1638" and "ætatis 33". The Ulfeldt arms
Oil on canvas. 193×264 cm
Frederiksborg A 833
Painted shortly after 1637, when Ulfeldt was appointed Governor of Copenhagen Castle by his royal father-in-law. According to Høyen, it was signed "Roswyck fecit". Engel Rooswijk was the brother of Karel van Mander's mother, Cornelia, and he lived in Copenhagen c. 1638-40. He also painted Christian IV.
*Provenance:* To Kunstkammeret 1698. Kunstkammeret, 1737, 880/136. To Frederiksborg, 1814. The Frederiksborg Revision by Høyen, 1831 no. 296 (here called Laurids Ulfeldt). Salvage List no. 79. To Rosenborg, 1860. To Frederiksborg, 1894.
*Literature:* Eller 1971 128-31 178. DBL 3rd ed.

140

## Leonora Christina (1621-98), daughter of Christian IV and Kirsten Munk, married Corfitz Ulfeldt, 1636

Karel van Mander, c. 1643-44
Oil on canvas. 223×124 cm. Colour plate XXXVII
Frederiksborg A 7435
The little dog at the bottom of the picture symbolizes fidelity. The tame wolf at her left hand is an allusion to her husband's family, the Ulfeldts. A similar portrait, though this time a double portrait with her brother Valdemar Christian, is in a Danish private collection.
*Provenance:* Acquired from Rosenholm, 1937.
*Literature:* Paulsen 1958 10-14. DBL 3rd ed. Eller 1971 173 175 178 182ff.

141

## Ebbe Ulfeldt (1616-82), married Hedevig, daughter of Christian IV and Kirsten Munk, 1642

Artist unknown. Inscribed "Aetatis: 23, Anno 1639-24... Amsterdam. P. Ramstorp". Later inscription "Grefve Cor: Ulfeldt"
Oil on canvas. 128×92 cm
Gripsholm 496
This picture does not resemble any known portraits of Corfitz Ulfeldt. The age on the inscription, however, fits another of Christian IV's sons-in-law, namely Ebbe Ulfeldt, who in 1651 went to Sweden. Ulfeldt had left Denmark on account of an inquiry which had then been

142

instituted into his administration as provincial Governor of Bornholm.
*Provenance:* Donated by Count G. L. Cederhielm, Bjärke Säby.
*Literature:* DBL 3rd ed.

142
## Hannibal Sehested (1609-66), Councillor of the Realm, Governor of Norway, married Christiane, daughter of Christian IV and Kirsten Munk, 1642

Karel van Mander, about 1650
Oil on canvas. 74.5×55 cm
Frederiksborg A 822
*Provenance:* To Kunstkammeret 1705. The Kunstkammer inventory of 1737, 879/107. To Frederiksborg, 1814. The Frederiksborg Revision by Høyen, 1931 no. 251. To Rosenborg after the fire at Frederiksborg, 1859. Salvage List no. 255. To Frederiksborg, 1894.
*Literature:* Eller 1971 229 246f. DBL 3rd ed.

143
## Christiane (1626-70), daughter of Christian IV and Kirsten Munk, married Hannibal Sehested, 1642

Abraham Wuchters
Oval. Oil on copper. 48×36 cm
Frederiksborg A 2012
*Provenance:* Acquired from Rønninge Søgaard in 1911.
*Literature:* Eller 1971 391. DBL 3rd ed.

144
## Hans Lindenov (1616-59), Councillor of the Realm, married Augusta, daughter of Christian IV and Kirsten Munk, 1639

Abraham Wuchters
Oil on paper. 26×19.5 cm
Gavnøfonden no. 470
Hans Lindenov was one of the richest men in Denmark, but contrary to the the King's other sons-in-law, he never played a political role.
*Provenance:* Klevenfeldt's Sale, 1777 no. 117.
*Literature:* Andrup 1914 no. 470. DBL 3rd ed. Eller 1971 275f.

145
## Possibly Dorothea Elizabeth (1629-87), Vice-Prioress of St Reinold's Augustinian Convent in Cologne, daughter of Kirsten Munk. Known as "the Degraded Lady"

Oil on canvas. 91×75 cm
Private collection
Dorothea Elizabeth was born on 1st September 1629. After the break between Christian IV and Kirsten Munk, which occured on Martinmas eve (on 10th November, 1628), Christian IV refused to acknowledge the child as his own. Otto Ludvig, Rhine-grave of Salm, with whom Kirsten Munk had an affair, cannot have fathered the child, however, as he is kown to have left Denmark in October of 1628.
*Literature:* Birket-Smith I-II 1879-81. DBL 3rd ed.

146
## Hans Ulrik Gyldenløve (1615-45), son of Christian IV and Karen Andersdatter

Copy, c. 1645. Inscribed "Hans Ulrich Gyldenlöv Commandant paa Cronborg Søn ved Fr: Karen Anders Datter"
Oil on canvas. 133×109.5 cm
Rosenborg 7.8
In the background Kronborg Castle, where Hans Ulrik was Lord Lieutenant. The picture is a contemporary

copy after the original by Abraham Wuchters, which was destroyed in the fire at Frederiksborg, 1859. The original was dated 1645.
*Provenance:* Klevenfeldt's Sale, 1777 no. 152b. The Hjelmstierne Collection p. 354 no. 28. To Frederiksborg, 1812. The Frederiksborg Revision by Høyen, 1831 no. 965. To Rosenborg 1858.
*Literature:* DMP II 217. Eller 1971 209. DBL 3rd ed.

147

## Probably Ulrik Christian Gyldenløve (1630-58), son of Christian IV and Vibeke Kruse

Inscribed "A. Wuchters f. A° 164-"/ the last figure is illegible
Oil on canvas. 208.6×123.5 cm
Statens Museum for Kunst, inv. 617
The portrait was probably painted in 1645, when Christian IV commissioned Wuchters to paint his other sons, Duke Frederik (III), and Hans Gyldenløve.
Purchased from the heirs of Captain Schaper. Klevenfeldt's Sale, 1777 no. 137 (called Valdemar Christian).
*Literature:* K. Madsen 1915 166-70. Eller 1971 209f. Eller 1973 228f. DBL 3rd ed.

148

## Elisabeth Sophie Gyldenløve (1633-53), daughter of Christian IV and Vibeke Kruse, married Claus Ahlefeldt 1648

Inscribed "Abr. Wuchters fecit 1649"
Oil on canvas. 201×111.5 cm
Frederiksborg A 7304
Formerly, the painting had an inscription from the 18th century "Frk. Anna Cathrine, Frantz Rantzaus Forlofvede, C4ti og Kirsten Munks datter. Or: af Ab. Wuchters." The inscription is probably by the collector, Terkel Klevenfeldt. A replica in an Austrian collection which is the counterpart to a portrait of Claus Ahlefeldt proves the painting to be a representation of Elisabeth Sophie Gyldenløve.
*Provenance:* Klevenfeldt's Sale, 1777 no. 138, where it was purchased by Corfitz Ulfeldt's descendants in Bohemia. Acquired by Frederiksborg from the State of Czechoslovakia in 1955.
*Literature:* Frederiksborgmuseets erhvervelser 1954-64 no. 12. Eller 1971 214f. Sass 1973 584f.

149

## Christian IV

Silk embroidery on canvas. 50.5×43.5 cm
Frederiksborg A 2663
Attributed to Leonora Christina according to a doubtful tradition which rests on little else than the geographical proximity of Maribo Kloster, the Abbey in which Leonora Christina spent her last years, to Orebygaard, which belonged to her sister-in-law, Anna Elisabeth von Gröben and Sophie Ulfeldt, daughter of the latter.
*Provenance:* Presented by Baron F. M. Rosenørn-Lehn of Orebygaard, 1922.
*Literature:* Bøe 1950-58 196-219. Andrup 1925 no. 21.

*143*

# "Dominium Maris Baltici" The Struggle for the Baltic

Christian IV's foreign and military policy was based on the plain fact that one of the world's most important trade routes went through the Danish straits. From the ports in the eastern Baltic – Danzig (Gdansk), Riga and Konigsberg – the English and particularly the Dutch ships brought to Western Europe not only grain but also heavy goods such as tar, flax, hemp, wax, tallow and timber, which was needed for ship-building and other purposes. This gave the Danish straits great strategic significance. A strong fleet was therefore the necessary basis for defence of the area crucial to Denmark around Øresund and for the country's independence. This was the background to Christian IV's claim to possess mastery of the Baltic – "DOMINIUM MARIS BALTICI" – which was thus a policy of security and not just the expression of the King's ambitions for political and military expansion. Without a strong navy the country would risk being dragged into the war between Spain, the "superpower" of the time, and the Netherlands. There were actually Spanish plans to settle in the Øresund area to block the Baltic trade which formed a vital part of the economy of the Netherlands.

Of the Baltic states, however, only Sweden could threaten Denmark. In the Seven Year's War, 1563-70, Sweden had successfully challenged Denmark on all sides of the Baltic. Immediately after his accession to the throne in 1596, Christian IV had started a vast rearmament of the navy, which Sweden as a result of internal political unrest could not match.

In 1598-99 the Swedish King Sigismund, who was also king of Poland, was driven out by his brother Karl IX (cat. 156). Sigismund's desire to recapture Sweden resulted in a Swedish-Polish conflict, which continued sporadically through decades. This naturally weakened Sweden in relation to Denmark, but the conflict was also a danger to Christian IV. He would be faced, if Sigismund were to win Sweden back, with a united Swedish-Polish force which would control almost all the Baltic coastline and the Baltic ports. What was more, Sigismund was Catholic and probably would have tried to reinstate Catholicism in Sweden, which could thus have become a spring-board for a Catholic offensive against Denmark. It did not improve the situation that Sigismund was brother-in-law to the Spanish king Philip III. Danish support for Sigismund was thus out of the question.

Karl IX resumed the Vasa Kings' traditional anti-Danish policies. Recognizing the Danish fleet's superiority in the Baltic, Karl concentrated on securing control of the Scandinavian Arctic coast and the Kola Peninsula. There were no firm borders in this area, which from ages back had been fought over by Denmark(-Norway), Sweden and Russia. Karl IX's purpose was to control the West-European trade with Russia by the route north of Norway. By putting obstacles in the way of Baltic trade he aimed to make the Arctic route an alternative for the West European ships, which would thus avoid the Øresund toll that was crucial to the finances of the Danish state.

Whether Karl IX or Sigismund emerged victorious, Denmark would be in a dangerous situation. Christian IV therefore sought to secure his kingdom by thoroughly defeating Sweden in a preventive war. A decisive victory over Sweden could at the same time bring about the dream of reviving the Nordic union under Danish leadership.

The Council of the Realm was against Christian's warplans, partly because its members did not believe in the possibility of a decisive victory on account of Sweden's special natural conditions and partly because they in fact had particular authority over policies in relation to Sweden. Following the Treaty of Stettin in 1570, in the event of conflict between the Kings, the Councils of the two countries should meet at the border and negotiate a settlement. A war culminating in clear victory would therefore certainly cause the abolition of the Council of the Realm's special influence on policies towards Sweden.

Nevertheless, when a series of border-meetings had ended without result, as a consequence of ever-strengthening Swedish provocation in North Scandinavia and in the Baltic, Christian IV succeeded in imposing war in 1611 – the so-called Kalmar War.

As the Council had predicted, it was not possible to bring Sweden to its knees. On the other hand, as a result of almost total Danish superiority at sea, Sweden was not in a position to threaten the Danish mainland. The peace which was negotiated with English mediation in Knærod in 1613 was therefore advantageous to Christian IV. Sweden gave up all demands in Northern Scandinavia and had to pay a large war-indemnity. Until the indemnity was paid Denmark as security would hold Alvsborg, which had been captured during the war together with the area around the town of Gothenborg. Kalmar, which had given the war its name, was however given back to Sweden.

Even though he had not achieved his goal, Christian IV celebrated the peace as a major triumph, and as a memento of it he asked the tapestry-maker Karel van Mander in Delft to produce a series of tapestries for the Knights' Hall in Frederiksborg, showing Christian IV's victories. The tapestries were destroyed in the Frederiksborg fire of 1859. We know about the appearance of some of the tapestries from drawings by F. C. Lund and Heinrich Hansen from 1858 (cat. 50, 51, 160-63). On the basis of these drawings the Frederiksborg Museum has had the tapestries for the Knigths' Hall recreated.

*Literature:* Schäfer 1913. Palme 1942. Ellehøj 1964. Altman 1973. Tandrup 1979. Parker 1979. Roberts 1953-58.

151

## Christian IV

Jacob van Doordt. Inscribed "1611"
Oil on canvas. 240×143.7 cm
Rosenborg. 3.172. At Amalienborg on permanent loan
Christian IV is depicted as a commander with a baton in his hand. Executed in 1611, the year of the Kalmar War. This is probably the only one of the original three full-lengths, for which Jacob van Doordt was paid by the "Rentekammer" on 17. January, 1612, which exists today.

*Provenance:* Rentemesterregnskab (accounts), 1611-12 f. 546 (?). To Amalienborg, 1817. To Det kongelige Billedgalleri 1852/53 (inv. 711). To Rosenborg, 1870.

*Literature:* Madsen 1901-07 70. The Rådhus Exhibition 1901 no. 336. Steneberg 1934 245-66. Beckett 1937 33ff. Rosenborg 1948 no. 6. Eller 1973 143ff. Heiberg 1986 97f.

152

## Jonas Charisius (1571-1619), secretary at the German Chancellery

Hendrik Hondius (Duffel, 1573 – The Hague, after 1649)
Engraving. 19×12 cm
Frederiksborg
Although he was a commoner, Jonas Charisius nevertheless became one of the most influential of the King's advisers in matters of foreign policy and financial affairs. His actual influence is difficult to assess, but it is obvious that after his death in 1619 the King's policies became much more unstable and haphazard lacking their former consistency and determination.
*Literature:* Strunk 542. Westergaard 2075. DBL 3rd ed.

153

## Jacob Ulfeldt (1567-1630), Councillor, Chancellor of the Realm

Oil on canvas. 40.5×29.5 cm
Frederiksborg A 2630
For many years Jacob Ulfeldt was one of Christian IV's supporters in the Council of the Realm, and he was often employed on diplomatic missions. Like most of the councillors, however, he was strongly opposed to the King's intervention in Germany in 1625.
*Provenance:* Acquired from Count Kalnocky in Bratislava, 1920.
*Literature:* Tandrup 1979. DBL 3rd ed.

154

## Eske Brock of Estrup Manor (1560-1625), Councillor of the Realm

Artist unknown, c. 1615
Oil on canvas. 187.5×112.3 cm
Gl. Estrup. Jyllands Herregårdsmuseum, inv. 2
At the time of his death, Eske Brock was without doubt the biggest landowner in Denmark. He also built Gl. Estrup, which is now the home of the Country House Museum of Jutland. As a councillor he tried to mediate between Christian IV and those opposed to the King's expansive foreign politics. Posterity knows Eske Brock mostly from his diaries, where the results of a cheerful evening were marked by one or more crosses.
*Provenance:* Derived from Gl. Estrup. Acquired by Frederiksborg, 1937/38 and the sold to Jyllands Herregårdsmuseum on Gl. Estrup.
*Literature:* DBL 3rd ed. Ladewig Petersen 1974.

155

## Christen Holck (1558-1641), Councillor of the Realm

Inscribed "ANNO 1626/ÆTATIS 69". The arms of the Holck's and Reventlow's (paternal and maternal arms)
Oil on copper. 34×29 cm
Private collection
For many years Christen Holck was the advocate of the fraction of the Council which was opposed to Christian IV's active foreign policies. Christian Holck found these policies unrealistic and dangerous. He is probably the author of a very sharply phrased Council report from 1604, in which the Council, on political and military grounds, refuses to give its consent to the preventive war against Sweden which Christian IV found was essential for the future security of Denmark.
*Literature:* DMP VIII 211. Tandrup 1979. DBL 3rd ed.

156

## Karl IX (1550-1611), King of Sweden, 1604-11

C. 1605. Copy. Inscribed "Carl 9de utförde djerft med djup Statskonst Stora och tvetydige värf"
Oil on canvas. 118×90 cm
Gripsholm 456
*Provenance:* Gripsholm inv. 1745.

157

## Gustavus II Adolphus (1594-1632), King of Sweden, 1611-32

Attributed to Matthäus Merian (Basel, 1593 – Schwalbach, 1650) C. 1631
Oil on canvas. 107×94 cm
Skoklosters slott, Sweden. Inv. 132
Gustavus Adolphus is the great heroic figure in Swedish history. He became King at the age of 16 in 1611, during the Kalmar War. To avoid throwing Sweden into a fight for her very existence, he had to make peace with Denmark in Knærød 1613 on terms which were very harsh for Sweden. Through a series of administrative and military reforms, he and Axel Oxenstierna transformed the very old-fashioned Sweden into one of the best organized states of Europe. This modernization was the background for the victories over Russia and Poland and later on for the successful intervention in Germany, 1630-32, which gained Sweden the advantage in the struggle for power in the North. From a European point of view, the significance of Gustavus Adolphus' victory was that he forestalled the creation of a Catholic and absolutist Germany under the Emperor in Vienna and thereby saved German Protestantism.
*Provenance:* First recorded in the Skokloster inventory, 1728. Possibly identical with a portrait of Gustavus Adolphus listed in the estate register of Carl Gustav Wrangel, 1676.

*Literature:* Nordiska Museet 1932 no. 66. Strömbom 1932 no. 132. Malmborg 1944 13f. Weibull 1932 1-22. Roberts I-II 1953-58. Gustav II Adolf – 350 år efter Lützen. Livrustkammaren 1932. Barudio 1982. Ladewig Petersen 1983 195-206.

158

## Axel Oxenstierna (1583-1654), Swedish Chancellor of the Realm

Jacob Henrik Elbfas (1664 Stockholm). Inscribed: "ÆTATIS SVÆ 43 ANNO 1626"
Oil on canvas. 135×126 cm
Gripsholm 229
In 1612, at the age of 29, Oxenstierna was appointed Chancellor of the Realm. In close collaboration with King Gustavus Adolphus he transformed the old-fashioned, almost mediaeval Sweden into a modern state superior to almost any European country as regards to efficient development of resources.
*Provenance:* Formerly at Tyresjö Manor which was built by Axel Oxenstierna's brother, Gabriel. In 1826 the manor was purchased by Count Carl Adolf Ludvig Stackelberg, who presented the picture to Gripsholm. First recorded in the 1831 inventory.
*Literature:* Ahnlund 1932. Ahnlund 1940. Roberts I-II 1953-58. The Nationalmuseum Stockholm 1966 no. 67.

159

## Johan Skytte (1577-1645), Swedish Councillor of the Realm, Diplomat

Artist unknown. Inscribed "ÆTATIS SVÆ 57" and "ANNO 1634". The arms of the Skytte family
Oil on canvas. 104×77 cm
Private collection, Sweden
Johan Skytte was tutor to the later King Gustavus Adolphus. In 1617 he became a Councillor of the Realm and in the same year Chancellor of the University of Uppsala. Later on, he was appointed Governor of Livonia and in 1634 he became President of Göta Hovrät. He visited Copenhagen on several occasions between 1615-17, partly to try to postpone the payment of "The Release of Älvsborg", the war indemnity that Sweden was to pay after the Kalmar War, and partly to negotiate a Swedish-Danish alliance against Poland.
*Literature:* The Nationalmuseum Stockholm, 1966 no. 173. M. Roberts 1953-78.

160

## The Battle of Øland

F. C. Lund. Inscribed "Öland 31. Mai 1612." and "F. C. Lund 1858"
Indian ink and watercolour. 25.6×35.7
Frederiksborg A 5015
The prototype of the sketch is a woven tapestry by Karel van Mander II for the Great Hall of Frederiksborg Castle, executed c. 1616-20. The tapestry was destroyed in the fire at Frederiksborg, 1859.
*Literature:* Bredius 1885 1-22. Beckett 1914 164f. Andrup 1932 108-40. Andrup 1933-34 141. Gerson 1942 148, 150, 168-82. Eller 1973 165f. Heiberg 1984 9f.

161

## The Surrender of Kalmar, 1611

Heinrich Hansen (Haderslev, 1821 – Frederiksborg, 1890). Inscribed "Calmars overgivelse". Executed in 1858
Pencil and watercolour. 18.7×10.8 cm
Frederiksborg A 504
Cf. cat. 160

162

## Christian IV Besieging Kalmar on 3rd May 1611

F. C. Lund. Inscribed "Calmars Erobring 3. Mai 1611" (!) and "F C Lund d 6te Juli 1858"
Pen and pencil. 25.6×22.6 cm
Frederiksborg A 5013
Cf. cat. 160

163

## Christian IV at Älvsborg, 24th May 1612

Heinrich Hansen. Inscribed "Elsborg 24 Mai 1612"
Pencil and watercolour. 18.2×9.4
Frederiksborg A 503
Cf. cat. 160

*162*

164

### Christian IV's Proposal to the Council of the Realm of 30th January 1611 (Copenhagen)

Written in the King's own hand
Rigsarkivet
For as long as possible the Council tried to thwart Christian IV's plans for a war against Sweden. According to his coronation charter, the King was not permitted to make war without the consent of the Council, but at the meeting of the Council in January-February of 1611, the King declared in his proposal (memorandum) to the Council that in case it were to refuse to give its assent, he would make war in his capacity of formal Duke of Holstein and not as King of Denmark.
*Literature:* EB 1887-89 I no. 33.

165

### Report by the Council of the Realm concerning the relations with Sweden of 9th February 1611

Written in Christen Holck's hand
Rigsarkivet
Faced with the King's threat to open war on Sweden as Duke of Holstein, the Council gave up all resistance and consented to the declaration of war, but at the same time protested against the King's attempts to circumvent the coronation charter.
*Literature:* Erslev I 1883-85 no. 40.

## Christian IV and Europe

Even after the Treaty of Knærød relations with Sweden remained the main problem in Denmark's foreign policy. The Nordic power struggle changed character, however. In recognition that it was not possible to alter the balance of power through military clashes on the Scandinavian peninsula, Denmark and Sweden each tried to strengthen their position relative to the other by expansion, respectively in Northern Germany and in the Baltic.

The most important link in the chain of Christian IV's German expansion policy was the gaining of control of the former church property in Northern Germany which had been transformed into secular bishoprics at the time of the Reformation, and which was administered by "prince-bishops" chosen by the chapters of the cathedrals. By means of a mixture of military pressure and bribery Christian IV tried to force through the choice of his younger sons as bishops in a number of German dioceses.

Christian IV's policy of expansion met resistance from many sides, partly from the lesser German princes, who felt under threat, and partly from the Dutch, who reluctantly watched Denmark gain control of regions very near their own borders.

A serious hindrance to Christian IV's plans was an anti-Danish pact between Sweden and the Netherlands, entered into in 1614. After 1621, however, this pact disintegrated as a result of major political developments in Europe. In 1618 the Protestant Electoral Prince, Friedrich V of Pfalz, was chosen King of Bohemia. The choice set off open war between Catholics and Protestants in Germany. In 1621 Friedrich was driven out of Bohemia by the German Emperor, and the Catholic army under Tilly threatened the Lutheran states in Northern Germany. In the same year, war broke out between Spain and the Netherlands. The Netherlands, under threat both from the Spanish army in Flanders and from Tilly's army in Germany, worked to set up an anti-Hapsburg alliance (both the Emperor and the Spanish King were Hapsburgs) consisting of Denmark, the Netherlands and England.

Even though Friedrich of Pfalz was his son-in-law, James I did not wish to engage in the continental war because he was working for a marriage between the heir to the English throne, Prince Charles, and a Spanish Princess. In these circumstances Christian IV also held back, but favoured giving very comprehensive economic support to Friedrich of Pfalz and the Protestant army in Germany under Count Ernst of Mansfeld and Christian IV's own nephew, Duke Christian of Braunschweig-Wolfenbüttel.

The menace to the Netherlands meanwhile gave Christian IV the chance to split up the Swedish-Dutch pact by creating a Danish-Dutch alliance. At the same time the Netherlands tacitly accepted Danish expansion in Northern Germany. Between 1621 and 1624 Christian IV gained control of the dioceses of Bremen, Verden, Schwerin and Halberstadt. Also during this time the Duke of Braunschweig-Wolfenbüttel, who was heavily in debt, became totally dependent on Christian IV and had to mortgage his territory to the Danish King. Denmark thus became the absolute power in the region.

In 1624 there arose a new attempt to create a Protestant alliance. This time the initiative came from England. James I had given up the Spanish marriage negotiations and instead had arranged a marriage between Prince Charles and the French Princess, Henrietta Maria; this paved the way for a political understanding between England and France. The new master of France's foreign policy, Cardinal Richelieu, supported the plans for an anti-Hapsburg alliance in order to prevent France being surrounded by a Hapsburg super-power. For religious reasons Richelieu, who was one of the Catholic Church's highest-ranking prelates, could not openly engage Catholic France on the Protestant side, but behind the scenes French diplomacy supported King James's alliance plans.

The goal of the Western powers' diplomacy was to press Christian IV into intervening in Germany. In order to exert pressure on him the Western powers also set up negotiations with Sweden on the possibility of Swedish intervention. This Christian IV would do anything in the world to prevent. It would mean that Denmark would be isolated, and that Sweden would gain a military footing in Northern Germany and could thus surround Denmark. The pressure worked. Despite violent opposition from the Council of the Realm, which accorded no credibility to the Western powers' pledges of help, Christian IV decided to attack Tilly in 1625.

The Council's mistrust of England and France proved well-founded. The promised help failed to materialize or was only produced on an inadequate scale. Christian IV found himself standing alone in the battle with the Emperor and the league of Catholic Princes. By virtue of his strong financial position Christian IV could of course raise a considerable army, which in terms of size was the equal of Tilly's. The Bohemian nobleman Albrecht von Wallenstein meanwhile assembled still another army on behalf of the Emperor. Christian then found himself in a militarily untenable position. In August 1626 his army was beaten by Tilly at Lutter am Barenberge, near Wolfenbüttel. In 1627 Wallenstein occupied Jutland. Danish naval superiority however made it impossible for Wallenstein to land troops on the islands or in Scania to finish the war. Wallenstein actually had plans to establish an imperial Baltic fleet, but these were wholly unrealistic. At the same time negotiations were in process for an alliance between Denmark and Sweden against the Emperor; Sweden felt threatened by the imperial advance to the Baltic. On the Danish side these negotiations were probably not seriously intended, but they achieved a certain effect. In order to avoid Swedish involvement Wallenstein offered Christian IV peace without cession of territory, on condition that in future he would not meddle in internal German concerns. On this basis the Treaty of Lübeck was concluded in 1629.

*Literature:* Fridericia I-II 1876-81. Opel 1878. Schäfer 1913. Wedgewood 1957. Ellehøj 1964. Polisensky 1970. Tandrup 1979. Parker 1979.

167

## The Revells of Christendome

1609 by Thomas Cockson (working in London 1591-1636)
Engraving. 29.2×37.2 cm
The British Museum. Department of Prints and Drawings. Inv. 1849-3-15-10
Satire on the political conditions in Europe following the Twelve Years Truce between the Dutch Republic and Spain, which had been a serious retreat for the Pope and the Counter Reformation. The Pope's enemies, James I of England, Henri IV of France, and Christian IV of Denmark are depicted playing against the Pope and his representatives (the monks). To the left James is trying to deprive the Pope of his tiara. To the right Prince Maurits, Governor of the Dutch Republic, is watching the game attentively.
*Literature:* Hind I 1952 254.

168

## Friedrich V (1596-1632), Elector of Pfalz, King of Bohemia, 1619-20

Michiel v. Mierveld (Delft, 1567 – Delft, 1641). Studio work
Oil on panel. 65×53 cm
Frederiksborg A 25
The picture was painted in the middle of the 1620s when Friedrich was living in exile in the Netherlands after his lands had been occupied by Spain and the Catholic League.
*Provenance:* Presented by Assistant Curator J. Leemejer before 1885.

169

## Maximilian I (1573-1651), Duke of Bavaria in 1598, Elector in 1623

C. 1623-30. Inscribed "MAX. CO.P.R.V.BA.D.S.R.T.ARCHD. ET.EL."
Oil on canvas. 114×88 cm
Bayerisches Armeemuseum, Ingolstadt. Inv. A 1283
In 1609 Maximilian became the leader of the Catholic League. After the outbreak of the Thirty Years War he supported the Emperor, Ferdinand II, with an army directed by Tilly which crushed the Bohemian rebellion and defeated Christian IV at Lutter am Barenberg in 1626. He fought against Wallenstein's plans for an absolutist Empire.
*Provenance:* Acquired from the Bayrische Staatsgemälde Sammlung (inv. 4463).
*Literature:* Wittelsbach und Bayern 1980 II/1 and II/2 Barudio 1985.

170

## Christian the Younger (1599-1626), Duke of Braunschweig-Wolfenbüttel

Paulus Moreelse (Utrecht, 1597 – Utrecht, 1638). Inscribed "Moreelse fe: 1619"
Oil on canvas. 126.3×87.7 cm
Herzog Anton-Ulrich Museum, Brunswick no. 649
Christian was a younger son of Heinrich Julius, Duke of Brunswick-Wolfenbüttel, and Elisabeth, sister of Christian IV. As part of his endeavours to build a Danish Dominium in Northern Germany, Christian IV had his nephew elected administrator of the diocese of Halberstadt. From the outbreak of the Thirty Years' War, he officiated as a mercenary leader, partly on funds provided by Christian IV, and he supported Friedrich of Pfalz. By and large, his army was destroyed by the army

of the Catholic League under Tilly in 1623. In 1625 he went into the service of Christian IV, but died in the following year.
*Provenance:* Possibly a gift from Duke Christian the Younger to the owner of Schloss Gemen near Münster where the picture hung until 1820. In 1892 it was acquired by the Herzog Anton Ulrich Museum in Brunswick.
*Literature:* Herzog Anton Ulrich Museum, Braunschweig. Verzeichnis der Gemälde 1969 no. 649. Wittelsbach und Bayern 1980 II/2 no. 568. De Jonge 1938 no. 52. Gerson 1942 255. Tandrup 1979. Klessman 1983 144f.

171

## Albrecht Wenzel Eusebius Wallenstein (1583-1634), Duke of Friedland, Imperial Commander

Pieter de Jode
Engraving. 24.3×17.3 cm
Frederiksborg
In Danish history Wallenstein is remembered first and foremost as the commander who occupied Jutland, 1627-29. He is one of the most disputable figures of the Thirty Years' War. He has been considered an unprincipled adventurer but has also been regarded as a German patriot whose struggle for a united Germany was destroyed by the egoism of the individual states and the French diplomacy.
*Literature:* Barudio 1985.

ALBERT. DVX .FRITLAND. COM. WALLEST. ETC.
Ant. van Dyck pinxit


*171*

173

## Johannes T'Serclaes, Count of Tilly (1559-1632), Commander of the army of the Catholic League

Pieter de Jode
Engraving. 23.9×18.1 cm
Frederiksborg
Tilly was in command of the army of the Catholic League. He crushed the Bohemian Rebellion in 1618, beat Duke Christian of Brunswick-Wolfenbüttel at Stadtlohn in 1623, and defeated Christian IV at Lutter am Barenberg. In 1631 he himself was defeated by Gustavus Adolphus at Breitenfeld. He represented the traditional Dutch military School.
*Literature:* Hollstein IX 208 no. 264.

174

## Charles I (1600-49), King of England and Scotland, nephew of Christian IV

Probably by Jacob van Doordt, 1625
Oil on canvas. 219×137 cm
H. M. Queen Elizabeth II, inv. Windsor Castle 3076
On entering into the Danish-English Alliance in the Hague in 1625, Charles I had promised to support Christian IV's German campaign with a considerable amount of money. Difficulties at home and abroad, however, made it impossible for Charles to keep his promises. His fight for Absolutism and his support of the High Church started the English Civil War, which ended with his defeat by the Parliament army under Cromwell and his execution in 1649. Oliver Millar has attributed this painting to Jacob van Doordt, who in 1624 received a letter of recommendation from Christian IV adressed to James I and Charles I. The composition and the technique used resemble van Doordt and it may well be identical with a picture recorded in the inventory at York House 1635 of pictures in the possession of the Duchess of Buckingham: "Abra: Dorts Bro: A Picture of King Charles at length".
*Provenance:* York House, 1635 (?). From there to Collam Hall. Sold at Christie's on 1 May 1925 and at Sotheby's on 23rd July 1957 (368) where it was acquired for Her Majesty the Queen of England's Collection.
*Literature:* Millar 1962 925-26. Millar 1963 no. 113. Heiberg 1986 97f.

*174*

175

## Friedrich III (1597-1659), Duke of Schleswig-Holstein-Gottorp

Artist unknown. Inscribed "F.E:Z.N.H.Z.S.H, 1639" (Friedrich Erbe zu Norwegen. Herzog zu Schleswig Holstein)
Oil on canvas. 202×135 cm
Frederiksborg A 2887
Despite the close family ties, Christian IV and his nephew, Duke Friedrich III of Gottorp were on bad terms. The Danish expansion in Northern Germany before 1625 had been effected partly at the cost of Gottorp interests, and the Duke held Christian IV responsible for the disasters of the German War which had also reached the Duke's lands, while on his part Christian IV found that the Duke had betrayed him. Concurrently with the Swedish military success in Germany after 1630, Friedrich III increasingly looked to Sweden for protection.
*Provenance:* Acquired at the Sale of paintings formerly at Søby Søgaard in 1924.
*Literature:* Andrup 1925 no. 35.

176

## Christen Friis of Kragerup (1581-1639), the King's Chancellor

Artist unknown. 28.5×20.5 cm
Frederiksborg A 2809
A portrait corresponding with this one in full-length at Börringe Kloster is dated 1635. In 1616 Christen Friis became a Councillor of the Realm and at the same time Chancellor. He was an outstanding administrator and modernized the legislative system which in many respects was out of date. Like the other Councillors of the Realm, Christen Friis was decidedly against the idea of meddling with the internal affairs of Germany. After the German War, the King increasingly ignored him and favoured his German advisors in matters of foreign politics. Christen Friis is a fine representative of the cultural traditions of the Danish nobility with its deep affection for the Danish language, history and literature. As a patron of poetry and learning he is outstanding in Danish history. When the age of Christian IV is generally regarded as the heyday of Learning this is to a large extent Christen Friis's merit.
*Provenance:* Acquired from Frijsenborg Manor, 1923.
*Literature:* Andrup 1925 no. 58. Fridericia 1876-81. Arup I-II 1932-55. Ellehøj 1964. Schepelern 1971. Tandrup 1979. DBL 3rd ed.

177

## Holger Rosenkrantz "the erudite" (1574-1642), Councillor of the Realm, theological writer

Probably by Johan Timm. Inscribed "ÆTATIS SVÆ 61. Anno 1636". The Rosenkrantz arms. Another inscription from the 18th century "H. Holger Rosenkrantz"
Oil on canvas. 112×86 cm
Frederiksborg A 7771
Holger Rosenkrantz was one of the central figures of the Council, where he tried to mediate between Christian IV and a group of Councillors who tended to be more and more sceptical of the King's abilities as a political leader. Holger Rosenkrantz is not remembered for his political achievements, however. As a young man he had dedicated himself to the study of divinity and philosophy. As Councillor he had to put aside these studies, but he was one of the founders of Sorø Academy in 1621 whose aim was to limit the travels abroad of young Danish noblemen who, according to the erudite Holger Rosenkrantz, were exposed to a theological and moral influence of a dangerous kind on their travels. He was also a member of the commission which in 1621 introduced reforms in tuition at the University of Copenhagen. Tormented by remorse at having deserted his proper vocation, Holger Rosenkrantz took the unheard of step and resigned from the Council of the Realm in 1627. Rosenkrantz, however, saw Danish politics sub specie æternitatis and

was convinced that by deserting his theological studies he had contributed to the disasters of his country.
*Provenance:* Acquired from Ryegaard, 1970, to which it probably came in 1802 from Rosenholm. All known portraits of Holger Rosenkrantz are replicas or copies of this painting.
*Literature:* Eller 1971 93ff. J. O. Andersen 1896. Rosenkrantz 1924. Kornerup I-II 1928-68. Glebe Møller 1966 and 1980. Ladewig Petersen 1974. Tandrup 1979. DBL 3rd ed.

178

## Anders Bille of Rosendal (1580-1633), Councillor of the Realm, Lord Lieutenant of Helsingborg Castle

Artist unknown 1615 or 1616. Inscribed: "ÆTATIS SVÆ 36". The arms of the Bille family
Oil on canvas. 105×82.5 cm
Private collection, Sweden
Like most of his colleagues in the Council, Anders Bille strongly supported a defensive foreign policy. The Danish diplomatic defeat at the border-conference at Knærød 1624, which was partly due to the Danish lack of armaments, seemed however to have made him the "hawk" in the relations with Sweden.
*Literature:* Tandrup 1979. DBL 3rd ed.

179

## Albret Skeel of Fussingø (1572-1639), Admiral of the Realm, Lord Lieutenant of Riberhus Castle

Artist unknown, c. 1616-20
Oil on canvas. 68×53 cm
Frederiksborg A 2424
Albret Skeel is depicted as a knight of the Mailed Sword-Arm, an order of chivalry which Christian IV in 1616 bestowed on a number of Danish and Holstein noblemen, who from a military point of view had distinguished themselves during the Kalmar War. Albret Skeel was appointed Councillor of the Realm and Admiral of the Realm on the same occasion. As Councillor, he soon turned into a sharp critic of Christian IV's foreign policies and was especially opposed to any action in Germany. In 1623 he retired from office as Admiral of the Realm in the middle of a Council meeting, but continued as a private member of the Council. According to an unproven tradition his resignation as Admiral was the result of his drawing his sword on the King in the heat of the moment during Council negotiations.
*Provenance:* Acquired from England in 1917.
*Literature:* Andrup 1925 no. 57. Tandrup 1979. DBL 3rd ed.

180

## Memorandum by the Council of the Realm on Foreign Relations of 11th February 1625

Written in Jacob Ulfeldt's hand
Rigsarkivet
In the beginning of 1625, when it was quite obvious that Christian IV intended to intervene in Germany on behalf of Friedrich of Pfalz, the Council in a state-paper on 11th February which warned the King against the intervention. According to the Council there were no immediate threats from the Emperor that could warrant Denmark's interference. The Council warned the King of the uncertain diplomatic basis on which the war would be declared and of the danger that England and France might suddenly withdraw. It also pointed out that if the war went badly, Sweden could be relied upon to make use of the situation. Therefore the Council proposed that the King should go no further than the financial support of James I as hitherto.
*Literature:* Erslev I 1883-85 no. 88.

# "The meek King"

The clergyman and poet Claus Christoffersen Lyschander in 1611 published a poem which he called "The Triumph of Calmar", in which Christian IV is portrayed as conqueror standing in "the chariot of triumph and victory". The triumph motif is also used by the painter Pieter Isaacsz. in a portrait of the King from about 1612 (cat. 185). The picture shows Christian IV with baton, the emblem of his authority as commander. To the right, in front of the King, are his crown, sceptre and helmet placed on a column-base; on the base itself can be seen a relief with another portrait of Christian IV, where he is standing in a Roman triumphal chariot while being crowned with laurels by the Goddess of Victory.

The antithesis of the portrait of the victorious King is the picture, painted by an unknown artist, of the suffering Christ (cat. 186). This was painted at the request of Christian IV and shows a vision he had at the Castle of Rothenburg in Niedersachsen on the morning of 8th December, when he was praying for the troubled evangelical church. In the frame of the picture is a slip of paper with an explanation written by the King himself.

In December 1625 Christian IV found himself in a politically and militarily critical situation. The expected support from France and England, which Christian IV had made the basis for his decision to intervene in Germany, was not forthcoming, and the peace negotiations being conducted with the Emperor held little hope of a settlement which would allow the King to emerge from the War with honour intact. Christian IV faced crippling defeat, which would probably bring with it great suffering for him as King, for his people and for the protestant church. Peder Winstrup, in his coronation address in 1596, had said that the King should be like "a living, inspired picture of Christ". So far Christian IV's life had been all greatness and triumph. Now came the time for suffering. Christian IV took his strange experience as a sign that just as Christ suffered for mankind's sake, so he would suffer for his people and the evangelical church. He would have to accept the burden of martyrdom. There is a representation of this idea in the altarpiece in Elmelunde Church on the island of Møen, where the King's monogram is flanked by the instruments of Christ's suffering (photograph).

The suffering and humble King was also the theme of a picture which hung in the Oratory of the Chapel at Frederiksborg, but which was lost in the Frederiksborg fire of 1859. Its appearance is, however, known from a picture of an interior painted by Heinrich Hansen in 1858 (cat. 187). This showed Christian IV in penitential apparel, sunk deep in prayer, in front of Christ and the Cross. We know, however, that the King in the picture originally was attired in "a royal garment with his sceptre and crown in front of him". An alteration of this kind can only have been made on the King's orders and could really only make sense in the context of the defeat in the Thirty Years' War.

*186*

A third picture, popularly called "Christian IV in the steam-bath" shows a dream-vision Christian IV had the night before the battle of Lister Dyb, in 1644, when he commanded the Danish navy against a combined Swedish-Dutch fleet (cat. 188). The picture shows Christian IV's honourable resurrection. The dream and the picture are images of the King who offers his life for his people, the King as martyr. The three pictures are thus symbolic representations of the duties of a Christian king.

*Literature:* Rasmussen 1957-59, 60-75. Johannsen 1974, 67-139. Johannsen 1984, 127-54.

185

## Christian IV

Pieter Isaacsz.
Oil on panel. 130×108 cm. Frontispiece p. 14
Frederiksborg A 1893
Executed during the Kalmar War or immediately afterwards. On the stone pedestal to the right is a representation of Christian IV in relief riding in a Roman triumphal chariot. Undoubtedly, this relief refers to the military triumphs of the Kalmar War, possibly the conquest of Kalmar in 1611. Original for cat. 25.
*Provenance:* Acquired in 1909/10 from the Kaiser Friedrich Museum in Berlin, where it may have come as a present for Johan Sigismund, Elector of Brandenburg, who was the brother-in-law of Christian IV.
*Literature:* Liisberg 1924-25 195-218. Beckett 1937 87. Eller 1973 87. Heiberg 1983 12f.

186

## Ecce Homo. Christian IV's Vision at Rothenburg Castle on 8th December 1625

Reinholdt Timm?
Oil on canvas. 63×52.5 cm
Rosenborg 1.144
A note, inserted in the frame, has the King's own description of his vision. "Dijser gestalt ist miir den 8. Decem: auff dem hausse Rodenburg Morgens Friie gezeiiget der hon vnd Spott, So vnser Erlösses vnd Seelichmacher Christus Jesus vnserendthalben gelitten, beii wierendem gebet zu Godt führ die nodt der gansen Euangeliske kirschen Anno 1625. Christianus IIII D. G. Rex Daniæ et Norvegiæ etc. Ma: pro: Sc."
*Provenance:* In Kunstkammeret 1737, 858/36. To Rosenborg, 1824. A number of versions are known.
*Literature:* Rasbech 1832 136-42. Høyen 1871 204-07. Rasmussen 1957-59 60-75. Johannsen 1984 127-54.

187

## The Oratory of Christian IV in the Chapel of Frederiksborg Castle before the fire in 1859

Heinrich Hansen
Oil on canvas. 40.5×56 cm
Frederiksborg A 962

Together with other depictions of the Oratory by Heinrich Hansen, this painting laid the groundwork for the reconstruction of the Oratory after the fire in 1859. Originally, the room was adorned with paintings of scenes from the life of Christ which had been executed in the Netherlands for Christian IV by Pieter Lastman, Adrian van Nieulandt, Jan Penay, Werner v. Valkert, and the signature "P.H." (Pieter van Harlingen?). Pieter Isaacsz. had also contributed to the series with a painting. The Oratory also contained a representation of Christian IV wearing penance clothes in front of Christ Crucified. This picture is visible on the right-hand side of Heinrich Hansen's painting.

*Provenance:* Purchased at the Sale of Haagen Hagen in 1898.

*Detail of 187*

*187*

*Literature:* Charlottenborg 1860 no. 49. For further details of the Oratory see: Beckett 1914 159ff. DK Frederiksborg Amt 1973 1878-88. Johannsen 1984 126-53.

188

## Christian IV's Dream on the night before the Battle of Lister Dyb

Artist unknown, c. 1644
Oval. Oil on canvas. 181×157 cm
Rosenborg inv. 2.79
*Provenance:* Kunstkammeret, 1690 96/144; 1737 858/35. To Rosenborg [1824].
*Literature:* DMP II 157-58. Johannsen 1984 136ff.

189

## Christian IV

Artist unknown, c. 1629. Inscribed "REX CHRISTIANUS IIII 1620"
Oil on canvas. 65×55 cm
Frederiksborg A 449
A representation of Christian IV from the time of the Peace of Lübeck and the break between the King and Kirsten Munk. The year on the inscription has been corrupted. A picture corresponding to this one was sold at Winkel and Magnussen, Sale 123 no. 69, 1932.
*Provenance:* Acquired on the art market, 1885.

190

## The Ratification by the Emperor Ferdinand II of the Peace of Lübeck of 3rd/13th June 1629

On parchment with the Emperor's appended seal
Rigsarkivet
*Literature:* DNT IV, 77.

*188*

# Brømsebro

Although Christian IV settled the Treaty of Lübeck in 1629 without loss of land, the Thirty Years' War carried with it an almost irreparable loss of prestige. The situation became still more dangerous when the Swedish King, Gustavus Adolphus carried through what Christian IV had failed to do. Swedish victory in Germany gave Sweden the unchallenged lead among the Nordic powers, and, even worse, left Sweden with the possibility of attacking Denmark from the south. On account of this it became necessary to maintain much larger military forces than had been needed in peacetime before.

The armament policy made heavy economic demands, but an antiquated administrative system and mutual suspicion between Christian IV and the Council of the Realm made it impossible to mobilize the kingdom's resources in proportion to these demands. Out of fear of strengthening the monarchy the Council refused the necessary reforms. On the contrary, the Council increasingly tended to attach political conditions to the granting of tax-levies. Influential members of the Council, doubting Christian IV's abilities as a political leader because of the outcome of the Thirty Years' War, tried in this way to make him answerable to the administration. In order to avoid economic dependence on the grants of the Council Christian IV resorted to drastic rises in the Øresund toll, which hit the Dutch trade hard. From the point of view of foreign policy this was particularly rash and it provoked new Swedish-Dutch cooperation directed against Denmark.

The goal of Christian IV's foreign policy was to prevent Sweden from making political gains out of her military victories. The outlook in this direction improved when his mediation efforts achieved the convening of a European peace congress in the Westphalian towns of Münster and Osnabrück. The master of Sweden's foreign policy, Axel Oxenstierna, then decided to rule Christian IV completely out of the game. With support from the Netherlands, Sweden shattered Danish domination of the Baltic in the Torstenson War of 1643-45. But the Netherlands did not want merely to replace Danish hegemony in the North and the Baltic with Swedish power. With Dutch and French conciliation a treaty was arranged at a border meeting in Brømsebro in August 1645. As at the peace negotiations in Knærød in

1613 it was the Western powers' aim to prevent the strong Nordic party, now Sweden, from completely beating down the weak. The treaty was hard enough on Denmark, however; she had to relinquish the Norwegian territories of Jämtland and Härjedalen together with the Baltic islands Gotland and Oesel. None of these areas was part of the true core of Denmark. What was worse, Sweden as a guarantee of the maintenance of peace was to hold the old Danish province of Halland as security for thirty years; in fact Halland was lost for good.

After the Treaty of Brømsebro Christian IV was a broken man and his last years were bitter. Denmark's dominance of the Baltic collapsed and its now qualified independence was subject to the actions of other powers. The Council blamed the King for all misfortunes and the opposition between the King and Council resulted in almost total political deadlock. The King even had to endure the humiliation of seeing his son-in-law Corfitz Ulfeldt, in whom he had invested such great expectations, emerging as leader of the opposition, while in the quarrels between the King and Kirsten Munk all their common children and their spouses supported Kirsten Munk. Everywhere he met opposition and sabotage. That this to a great extent was rooted in suspicion of his personality and his qualities of leadership he probably never grasped. He himself experienced his fate as martyrdom inflicted by God. In 1647 Christian, the Prince Elect, died, and there was now no chosen successor to the throne. When Christian IV himself died on 28th February 1648 it seemed as if the future of the monarchy itself was threatened.

But Christian IV had himself, with his heroism at the sea-battle of Kolberger Heide, where a splinter of granite destroyed one of his eyes, strengthened the image of monarchy. In many circles within Danish society it was the Council and the nobility who were blamed for the misfortunes. This was related to the fact that the aristocratic form of government no longer corresponded to economic and social reality. There was no longer any foundation for the nobility's political and social privileges.

From the 1630s onwards the Danish state in reality was financed by the rich Copenhagen citizens, and without their trade- and monetary-credit it would not have been possible to wage the war of 1643-45. Against this background the citizens experienced the political monopoly of the nobility as intolerable. Anger with the nobles made the citizenry take the side of the monarchy. A bourgeois point-of-view arose which saw in Christian IV a king who fought for the nation's interests but who was sabotaged by incompetent nobles who clung on to anachronistic political privileges.

The interpretation of Christian IV as a political martyr laid the basis for the Christian IV myth which helped his son, Frederik III, to eliminate aristocratic government with the help of the citizens in 1660; it was then used to justify the absolute monarchy.

*Literature:* Fridericia I-II 1876-81. Idem 1894. J.Jørgensen 1957. Ellehøj 1964. Lorenz 1969. Heiberg 1976. Parker 1979. Gamrath og Ladewig Petersen 1980. Ladewig Petersen 1980.

*189*

191

## Christian IV

Inscribed: "Abraham Wuchters fecit Anno 163(?)"
Oil on canvas. 204×110 cm. Colour plate XXXVI
Frederiksborg A 2501
Formerly, the date of the painting was recorded to be "1638". It is the earliest work by Wuchters in Denmark.
*Provenance:* Acquired from Veste Coburg 1918.
*Literature:* Andrup 1925 no. 20. Eller 1971 197f. 201f, 418.

192

## Same

Executed about 1638. Signed "AW fc." (monogram) indicating Abraham Wuchters (?)
Oil on panel. 71×53 cm
Frederiksborg A 2642
*Provenance:* Acquired from the Kunsthistorisches Museum in Vienna, 1921. The picture probably came to Vienna as a gift from Christian IV to the Emperor Ferdinand III.
*Literature:* Rostrup Bøyesen 1941 119. Eller 1971 202f, 270f. Saas 1973 582. Ellehøj 1973 603f.

193

## Same

Karel van Mander. Inscribed "1645"
Oil on canvas. 208×135 cm
Frederiksborg A 7298
*Provenance:* Acquired from the State of Czechoslovakia in 1955. The picture was formerly inscribed "C 4tus Rex Daniæ", which inscription resembles the ones the collector Terkel Klevenfeldt inserted in the pictures of his private collection. This portrait may therefore well be identical with no. 132 of Klevenfeldt's Sale, 1777 (Paintings in full-length. King Christian IV in a frame) which were acquired by the Bohemian descendants of Corfitz Ulfeldt. Numerous variants are known of this portrait-type.
*Literature:* Eller 1971 146f.

194

## Same on Horseback

Artist unknown, the 1640s
Oil on canvas. 71×57 cm
H. M. Queen Elisabeth II. Inv. Hampton Court no. 504
In about 1642-44, Karel van Mander painted an equestrian portrait of Christian IV in a military and a civil version. The military version is known from two large paintings at Frederiksborg (A 2741 in the Great Hall) and at Schloss Eutin, and also from a sketch. The civil version is known from small-sized pictures only (Rosenborg, which is a copy after an engraving by Albert Haelwegh, Frederiksborg A 505, Hampton Court, and Musei Iskusstw, Kirchinjow, USSR). None of these paintings, however, seem to be by Karel van Mander. For reasons unknown, the picture at Hampton Court has been attributed to Andreas Quant, a painter who is otherwise unknown.
*Provenance:* Purchased by King George V of Great Britain when he was Prince of Wales. Carlton House inv. 1816 no. 464 (called Gustavus Adolphus of Sweden).
*Literature:* Collins-Baker 1929 120. Andrup 1936 111-14. Eller 1971 157.

195

## Tage Thott of Eriksholm (1580-1658), Councillor of the Realm

Unknown Danish artist, c. 1648. Inscribed "HER TAGE THOT OTTESØN TIL ERIKSHOLM:RIDER DANMARKES RIGES RAAD". Thott-våben. Oil on canvas 111×84 cm
Gavnøfonden no. 687
Tage Thott was one of the richest landowners in Denmark. He owned about a dozen manor houses in Scania, and the nickname "The King of Scania" indicate his local position. In 1624 he became a Councillor of the Realm and for many years he was spokesman of the fraction within the Council which was opposed to the King's foreign policies, which Thott considered to be unrealistic and dangerous. He is wearing a dark costume, rather old-fashioned for its time, but which reflects his conservative outlook rather well.
*Literature:* DBL 3rd ed. Fridericia 1876-81. Tandrup 1979.

196

## Jørgen Skeel of Odden (1578-1631), Commander-in-Chief

Old copy. The arms of the Skeel and Brahe families
Oil on canvas
Gl. Estrup. Jyllands Herregårdsmuseum no. 6
Jørgen Skeel is wearing "the Mailed Sword-Arm" (Cf. cat. 85) which he received in 1616. Later on, the relations between Jørgen Skeel and the King became less friendly. In 1627, when he was elected Commander-in-Chief by the nobility and the Council of the Realm, the King refused to sanction the choice at first, but finally had to submit.
*Provenance:* The picture seems always to have been at Gl. Estrup, a manor house, which belonged to Jørgen Skeel.
*Literature:* DBL 3rd ed.

197

## Christen Thomesen (Sehested) (1590-1657), Councillor of the Realm, the King's Chancellor

Johan Timm (Copenhagen c. 1615 – Copenhagen 1674). Inscribed: "Ætatis suæ 45. Anno 1635". The Sehested arms. The name is inscribed later
Oil on canvas. 108.8×85.5 cm
Frederiksborg A 7773
Christen Thomesen was thoroughly conversant with constitutional law and modern languages and was often employed as a diplomat. In 1625 he became a Councillor of the Realm, and in 1639 he was appointed Chancellor to the King. Politically, he was a conservative who fought all attempts at reforms for fear that the nobility should lose its position. However, he was possessed of a high degree of moral integrity and Christian humility, qualities which characterized the best members of the old nobility.
*Provenance:* Acquired from Ryegaard in 1970.
*Literature:* Eller 1971 91-102, 277.

199

## Christian IV as Mediator, c. 1643

Adrian van de Venne (Delft 1589 – The Hague, 1662). Inscribed "Adrian v. Venne"
Oil on panel. 120×165 cm. Colour plate XLI
Rosenborg 7.12
This picture is an allegory representing Christian IV as mediator. The King is seated under a canopy. On a table next to the King are the regalia, on the floor a helmet.

*197*

Piety (Pietas) is leading Peace (Pax) up to the King, who receives good advice from Wisdom (Prudentia) and Justice (Justitia). Behind the King a family group which includes Prince Christian, Princess Magdalena Sibylla, Prince Frederik, and Princess Sophie Amalie. Behind Pax the Countries of Europe symbolized by their Kings as standard-bearers. Before the standards Helvetia (Switzerland) with the liberty cap on a pole. The Swiss liberty cap was commonly used as a symbol of freedom. Officially, the object of the King's mediation was to restore the freedom of Germany. The real objective was to check the Swedish increase of power.
*Provenance:* The Frederiksborg inv. 1677. Kunstkammeret, 1705 inv. 1737, 891/85. To Frederiksborg, 1827. The Frederiksborg Revision by Høyen, 1831 no. 672. To Rosenborg, 1836.
*Literature:* DMP II 7f. Eller 1973 212f. Heiberg 1984 21f.

200

## Christian IV sketched in small letters

Hans Wechter of Erfurt, c. 1640
Sketched on parchment mounted on wood. 18×22.5 cm
Rosenborg 1.69
This sketch is executed in letters of the alphabet written in gold. The hair, however, is done in black. Altogether, the letters compose the twelve chapters of The Ecclesiastes, The Proverbs of Solomon, Chapter 25, The Ecclesiasticus Chapter 5, and The First Book of Kings, Chapter 3. This is probably a reference to Christian IV's role as mediator.
*Provenance:* In Kunstkammeret, 1690 68/149. Inv. 1737 797/777. After the dissolution to Kunstmuseet in Dronningens Tværgade as no. CBd 3. To Rosenborg, 1858.

201

## Axel Oxenstierna (1583-1654), Swedish Chancellor of the Realm

David Beck (Delft, 1621 – probably The Hague, 1650)
Oil on canvas. 98×77 cm
Private collection, Sweden
After the death of Gustavus II Adolphus in 1632, Oxenstierna was in supreme control of the Regency during the minority of Queen Christina. In order to prevent the mediation of Christian IV intefering with Sweden's plans for making the most of her military triumphs in Germany, Oxenstierna initiated an attack on Denmark in 1643-45. As things were, it was possible for Sweden to attack Scania as well as Jutland. Even if Sweden failed to achieve all her ends, Christian IV was ruled out, and most important of all, the Danish dominion of the Baltic had been destroyed for good, and Sweden was now undeniably the most powerful state in Northern Europe.
*Literature:* Steneberg 1955 152-54. Cf. cat. 157, 158.

202

## Christian IV and Axel Oxenstierna (?) throwing dice for the Sound toll

C. 1644
Engraving. 26.9×35.5 cm
Frederiksborg
Dutch satire on the political conditions in the North and the Sound Toll policy of Christian IV, which badly affected the Dutch trade. The persons depicted are Christian IV and probably Axel Oxenstierna, who are playing for the toll with "alea belli" the dice of war. The war referred to in the picture is the Torstenson War, 1643-45.
*Literature:* Faaborg 1385.

203

## Lennart Torstensson (1603-51), Swedish Field Marshal and Councillor of the Realm

Inscribed: "Lenhard Torstenson Grefwe til Ortalia Friherre til Wiresta Ano 1648"
Oil on canvas. 208×122 cm
Gripsholm 1949
Torstensson was the leading Swedish commander during the last phase of the Thirty Years' War. In 1643-44, he removed his army from Germany and occupied the Duchies and Jutland. The Torstensson War, 1643-46, is named after him.

202

204

## Christian IV

Copy after Karel van Mander, c. 1645
Oil on canvas. 86.5×63 cm
Frederiksborg A 2545
At the Battle of Kolberger Heide on 1st July 1644, Christian IV was injured in the right side of his face and lost the sight of his right eye. After this event he preferred to be painted in profile.
*Provenance:* Acquired from Brussels 1919. Claimed by the vendor to have belonged to a family who were closely connected with the Ulfeldts.
*Literature:* Andrup 1925 no. 24. Heiberg 1984 22f.

205

## Christian IV lying in state

Inscribed: "Regna Firmat Pietas C4/fecit Hafnia I. G. Reinold Argentoratensis. 1648"
Watercolour on parchment. 18.5×23.4 cm
Rosenborg 1.68
The picture is probably a preliminary sketch for the two oil paintings of Christian IV lying in state (Wedellsborg and Rosenborg). The artist is unknown though the surname "Argentoratensis" indicates that he came from Strasbourg.
*Provenance:* Kunstkammeret 1775 248/c599. To Rosenborg 1785. Inv. 1797, 185 no. 17.
*Literature:* DMP II 160. Rosenborg 1948 no. 23.

206

## Letter from Christian IV to Corfitz Ulfeldt of 17th May 1642, written in the King's own hand

Frederiksborg B 3300
A considerable number of letters from Christian IV's last years are orders to Corfitz Ulfeldt to take care of various matters. This letter of 17th May 1642 is characteristic of the King's habit of mingling big and small matters. The letter concerns matters as different as the manning of the Navy, the supply of artillery for the frontier fortresses, the paying of Danish agents (envoys) abroad, the measuring of a piece of oak, and the ordering of juniper lathes.
*Literature:* EB VIII 1948 no. 132.

207

## Letter from Christian IV to Corfitz Ulfeldt of 25th February 1648 (Frederiksborg)

Rigsarkivet
This letter was written three days before the death of Christian IV and it may well be the last letter he ever wrote. Compared to the letter of 17th May 1642, this letter was obviously written by a much aged man.
*Literature:* EB VIII 1948 no. 376.

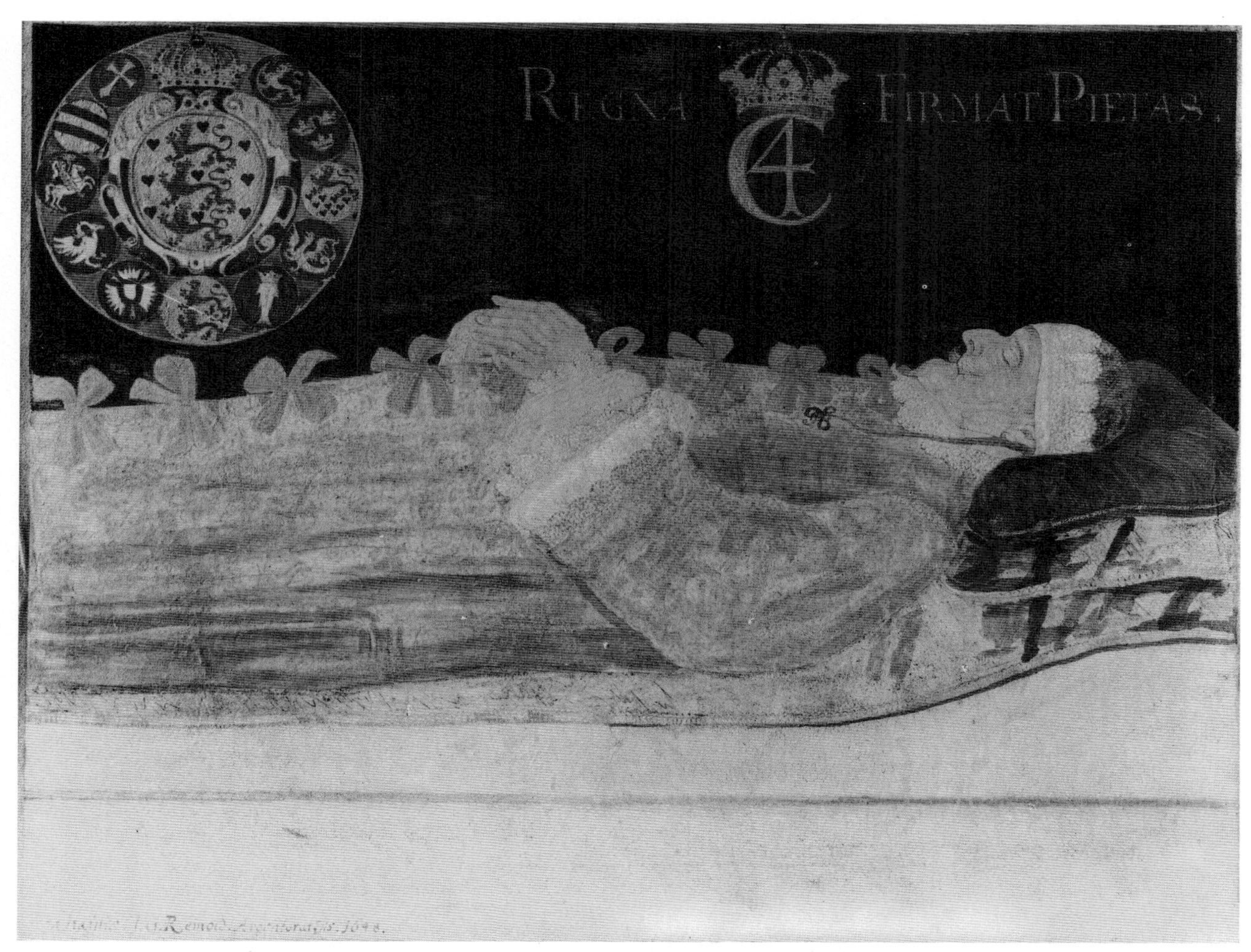


205

*~~233~~ 223*

# Kronborg

## *Christian IV – Patron of the Arts*

### The Visual and Performing Arts at the Danish Court 1588-1648

Some excellent artists had worked at the court of Frederik II, Christian IV's father; the painter and engraver Melchior Lorck, the sculptor Johann Gregor van der Schardt, and Hans Knieper, who executed portraits of the Royal Familiy and the cartoons for the great series of tapestries designed for Kronborg Castle, which was completed with the portraits of the young Prince Christian and his father. At Tycho Brahe's mansion Uranienborg, on the island of Hven, out in the Sound, a mini-court existed where the Arts also flourished, with Hans Knieper, van der Schardt, and the architect Hans van Steenwinckel as its star members.

When Christian IV ascended the throne in 1588, none of these artists were active at the Danish Court. It is difficult to gain an impression of the visual arts in the early years of his reign, since most of the evidence concerning the artists then at work comes from documentary sources. We know of Jan van Wijk only from the engraving made of his view of Copenhagen (cat. 853) and the records tell us that Didrik Moll was commissioned to execute a series of illuminated depictions of the coronation in 1596. Poul Rumler is presumably responsible for some early decorations at Rosenborg.

The first artists of a European stature whose works for Christian IV are still preserved were the portrait painter Jacob van Doordt and the painters Franz Cleyn and Pieter Isaacsz., both of whom had visited Italy. Pieter Isaacsz. was a pupil of Hans van Aachen, who later became court painter to Rudolf II at Prague. Isaacsz. subsequently worked in Amsterdam, where he became acquainted with the famous architect and sculptor Hendrick de Keyser who figures in Danish art history as the creator of sculpture for Frederiksborg Castle. In 1607, a Dane (probably Søren Kjær), was apprenticed to Isaacsz. and in the same year the Danish King acquired a painting from his master listed as "David with a perspective".

Through his dynastic connections, Christian IV came to be influenced by some of the most important centres of art in Germany such as Dresden and Wolfenbüttel and after 1600, important artistic connections were forged with the glamorous Rudolfine court at Prague. Moreover, once James I had become king of England as well as Scotland, Christian IV could also exchange works of art with the court in London and could furthermore check for himself what was happening in the artistic field in England, during his two visits in 1606 and 1614.

It is not easy for us to gain any very clear idea of the artistic activity that evolved under Christian IV, since so few works have survived. A great number of the pictures, sculptures and tapestries which were in Kronborg and Frederiksborg were removed by the victorious Swedes in the war of 1658-1660. The Swedish king had the right to dispose of such loot and a certain amount was distributed among his generals. The Danish origin of these works of art was soon forgotten. Things did not go much better in Denmark, however. Those pictures which remained in the Danish royal castles were in some cases sold in the 18th century while others were given to high-ranking officials; the remainder for the most part perished in the several disastrous fires which swept through the Danish royal castles in the 18th and 19th centuries. The registration of works surviving from the reign of Christian IV in Danish and Swedish collections is a research project that has yet to be initiated.

Information about the collections formed by Christian IV comes principally from two sources: the list of works of art bought for the King by the Danish diplomat Jonas Charisius in the Netherlands in 1607 and 1608, and the inventories of the collection at Frederiksborg Castle recording its state in 1636 and 1650. Mention is made in the latter to some 450 paintings or more, but only very rarely is an artist's name given. A comparison with the inventory taken in 1661, after the war, shows how great were the losses and is an indication of what must have been removed to Sweden.

After the earlier war with the Swedes, the Kalmar War

*Søren Kiær: Ceres, Bacchus and Venus. 166×242 cm. Statens Konstsamlingar NM384*

of 1611-1613, Christian IV had seen himself as a triumphant victor, and a whole series of commissions reflect the King's joyous state of mind. The most important was the challenging task, allocated to Adrian de Vries in Prague, to produce suitable sculptures for the Neptune Fountain which was to be set up at Frederiksborg Castle, an apotheosis of the King's and indeed of Denmark's position as ruler of the Baltic and the North Seas. These sculptures were the most valuable of the Swedish war spoils of 1659.

Much energy was also devoted to the embellishment of the principal rooms at Rosenborg and Frederiksborg castles with paintings, ceiling decorations of carved wood and plasterwork, marble chimneypieces, splendid chandeliers and woven tapestries.

A set of tapestries with scenes of the Triumph of Scipio after Giulio Romano was already at Frederiksborg, and a new series was ordered from Karel van Mander II showing episodes from the life of Christian IV. The artist was expected to visit the scenes of the most notable events of the recent war to make sketches of the localities on the spot, by way of preparation for his task (cf. cat. 50, 51, 160-163). These tapestries were destroyed in the Frederiksborg fire of 1859.

The decoration of three important rooms was begun after the Kalmar War, but only one scheme – the Winter Room in Rosenborg – survives in something like its original guise to give us an impression of the artistic intention. Recent examinations of the panel makers' marks have shown that the paintings were executed at the same time as the decorative elements of the room and that, together, they form a significant ensemble, created shortly after 1617.

At this time Pieter Isaacsz. acted as the artistic entrepreneur in the decoration of the Oratory at Frederiksborg Castle which was lost in the fire of 1859. He placed orders with Pieter Lastman, Werner van den Valckert and Adriaen van Nieulandt among others, while he himself painted an Annuciation for this splendid room.

Today we can only obtain a hazy notion of its appearance from the interiors depicted by Heinrich Hansen (see cat. 187) and from Niels Laurits Høyen's description of its enrichment with the use of costly types of wood, ivory, silver and glass painted with miniature-like delicacy.

The third substantial commission made in those years differed from the two others in that extensive use was made of artists who were either Danish or had settled in Denmark. This was the decoration of the long gallery on the top storey at Rosenborg Castle. A carefully considered iconographic programme was drawn up for the artists to follow, the painters involved being Franz Cleyn, Reinhold Timm and Søren Kiær while Pieter Isaacsz. and his son Isaac Isaacsz. supplied paintings which were to hang in the room. All the paintings decorating the ceiling were removed when Frederik IV totally altered the room around the turn of the 17th century, and it is now difficult to determine the positions or sequence of the paintings that survive. Without further research in the archives and technical examination of the surviving works, it is impossible to solve all the riddles connected to the "Ages of Man" series. Nor is it clear which pictures were on the ceiling and which on the walls in the long gallery.

Fragments of a number of the other decorative schemes in Christian IV's castles have survived, one of which included three works by Søren Kiær, described in the Frederiksborg inventory of 1636 as being "In the Dowager Queen's small chamber". They belong to what was once a set of seven mythological scenes, including a Danaë, a Bacchus, Ceres, and Venus, a Judgement of Paris, a Venus and Cupid, a Pyramis and Thisbe, and a Satyr "who has a woman in his arms, and a naked child creeping on all fours below".

Søren Kiær's three paintings are in the Nationalmuseum in Stockholm, where they where formerly ascribed to other more famous artists like Miereveld and Gillis Cogniet, and they are indeed paraphrases of works by these painters. Unfortunately, it has not been possible to exhibit these works at Kronborg, as they are painted on very large panels. The same is the case with a most interesting painting, by Franz Cleyn, showing Christ with the little children, which today hangs in the church for Mariefred, Sweden (Statens Konstmuseer). Like the three paintings by Søren Kiær, the painting by Franz Cleyn must also have been among the Swedish trophies acquired the during the war of 1658-60.

The portraits of Christian IV are dealt with elsewhere in this catalogue, but mention should be made of the interesting artistic links between the Danish and English courts (a subject as yet by no means thorougly explored), which are represented in the Kronborg exhibition by the portrait of Christian IV lent from a private collection in Great Britain, the Woburn Abbey portrait of Anne of Denmark and the Pieter Isaacsz. portrait from Northwick Park, here identified as being of Kirsten Munk, the wife of Christian IV. Isaacsz. was a pupil of the painter Cornelis Ketel, who worked in England for a number of years.

In the 1620s, when the extensive decoration of Frederiksborg and Rosenborg had been completed and Denmark became involved in the Thirty Years' War, Christian IV purchased and commissioned fewer works of art. At the beginning of the 1630s, Karel van Mander III received a payment from the King, but little is known about the early career of this artist. The wedding of the heir to the throne, Prince Christian, and Princess Magdalena Sibylla of Saxony gave rise to a costly demonstration of Denmark's aspirations to become a major European power. Composers, choreographers and painters were involved in the preparations for the celebration of the magnificent nuptials which took place in 1634. Christian IV commissioned Gerrit van Honthorst to execute the scenes from "Aethiopica", and the painting of cupids carrying the monograms of the Danish Royal Family was probably also made for this wedding. Hont-

*Franz Cleyn(?): Christ and the children. Mariefreds kirke. Gripsholm 2096*

horst was likewise employed in a second series of paintings for Kronborg, the great cycle representing the History of Denmark, based partly on drawings by Crispin de Passe the Younger.

The artists represented by the surviving paintings are Honthorst, Claes Moeyaert, Adrian van Nieulandt, Salomon Koninck and Isaac Isaacsz. As for the related drawings in the Department of Prints and Drawings in Copenhagen, these include works by Abraham Bloemaert, Adam Willaertz, Jan Bijlert, Nicolaus Knüpfer, Simon Peter Tilemann and Palamedesz., most of them painters of the Utrecht school. "The Finding of Prince Sven's Body", by Karel van Mander III, after a scene bearing on Danish history from Torquato Tasso's "Gerusalemme liberata", has the same antiquarian character as the Kronborg series. The original setting of Karel van Mander's "Aethiopica" series, now in Kassel, has still not been established. The paintings came to Germany as a donation from the Swedish Royal Family but were probably part of the booty of the Danish-Swedish war of the mid 17th century.

The original setting for the van Mander paintings now at Gavnø and in the Nasjonalgalleri in Oslo (cat. 316, 317, 318) is equally uncertain. The paintings, here ascribed to Franz Cleyn and Reinhold Timm, must have formed part of an unknown scheme for interior decoration, executed probably shortly after 1620 (cat. 295, 296, 323). Tradition has it that they were among a number of paintings which were restored and hung in Frederiksberg Castle in 1701 and which are said to have come from Glückstadt Castle.

It is important when we look at works like these to imagine the rich settings in which they were originally placed. Information about the decoration of each room can be gathered from contemporary inventories. Colour was used profusely and the rooms were furnished with a wealth of materials of different kinds. The walls were covered with textiles or wall-hangings of rich gilded leather, the floors were patterned and the ceilings ornamented with stucco or wood, occasionally embellished with silver. The chairs were covered with woven or embroidered tablecarpets. Cabinets and chests were embellished with woods of different colours and everything was commonly seen by flickering firelight – and, on gala occasions, by a thousand candles. In one room was a polarbear skin, and in another a complete stuffed leopard. Even the bedding in the Royal bedchamber was brilliant in colour: the King had a bedspread of red silk damask, three green satin featherbeds and two matching "head quilts", an eiderdown described a being "flame yellow", and a pillow of blue taffeta as well as a blue featherbed. Removed from this riot of colours and rich materials, from the settings for which they were designed, these paintings must inevitably be less effective and it is hard for us to judge how they looked when seen in their original surroundings.

One room of the Kronborg exhibition contains a small selection of paintings from Rosenborg, nearly all by unknown artists. They have been included to give some idea of the pictures which filled the more modest rooms in the royal castles. It is belived that most of them were originally hung in the castles of Christian IV.

The final flourish of artistic talent produced the portraits by Karel van Mander III and Abraham Wuchters, which have for generations stood as the accepted image of the King and of his family – the corpulent Crown Prince, his favourite daughter the worldly Leonora Christina, and the ambitious sons-in-law.

We know little or nothing of the King's personal views on aesthetics and philosophy. Although we have many letters from his hand, he made no explicit statements on such matters. Which of his advisers could have stimulated his artistic ambitions is also a matter for conjecture. It is quite evident, however, that the abundance of sculpture and painting acquired or commissioned during his reign served "the greater glory of God", of the Kingdom of Denmark, and of the Ruler himself.

*Charlotte Christensen*

# The Rosenborg Series

When Rosenborg was rebuilt after 1615, the Great Hall on the castle's top floor was created and its ceiling was decorated with a series of paintings on the life of man, executed by artists born in Denmark or with close ties to this country. The exact number of paintings which formed the original decoration cannot be established, but is is known that the joiner Hans Jørgen Dill received payment for "29 large frames, which went under the ceiling in the Great Hall" and this odd number is found in other records connected with the ceiling decoration. The inventory of Rosenborg from 1696, shortly before the reconstruction of the hall in 1705-07, gives the number of paintings in the ceiling as 30, and mentions two paintings at one of the big marble chimneypieces in the room. The pictures originally hung at the walls had, however, already been removed and were replaced by the woven tapestries by Berent van der Eichen depicting scenes from the Scanian War. During the reign of Christian IV, a trumpeter's chair was set up in the Great Hall, probably in connection with the Great Nuptials in 1634.

Contemporary descriptions of the Great Hall are to be found in the diary of Christian the Younger of Anhalt from 1623 and in the account of Prince Christian's wedding in 1634 left by Charles Ogier, secretary to the French envoy, Count d'Avaux.

"Afterwards, we went up to a big room, which is at the top of the house and is furnished with beautiful paintings, representing the entire life of man, and statues made of stucco; this room is arched and without pillars and it has two chimneypieces of marble" (Christian of Anhalt); and "Here is a large arched hall (aula fornicata), in which there are many beautiful paintings, which represent the occupations and pleasures of man at all ages; most of them are excellently executed" (Ogier).

The Danish art historian Philip Weilbach gives the first list of paintings presumably connected with the decoration of the Great Hall, in "Konst og Æsthetik", 1870. Included here are a number of pictures, which N. L. Høyen (Skrifter I, 1871), considered might belong to the Rosenborg series. Høyen's list of the relevant paintings, destroyed in the Frederiksborg fire of 1859, is as follows: Isaac Isaacsz.: Caesar receiving envoys from Asia, and Death surprises the rich old man as he proposes to a young beauty, by Reinhold Timm. Furthermore some paintings which with less certainty can be related to the series: Franz Cleyn: Chess players in a princely tent outside a besieged city and by Pieter Isaacsz.: Wine, song and music and A master builder showing his sketches to a Sultan. No drawings after these paintings have survived.

Weilbach states that he gives 25 paintings from the series, but only lists 24 titles. Discounting those which were destroyed by fire, only two of these have not been included in this exhibition – "A Carnival" by Morten Steenwinckel, which cannot be identified and "Esther kneeling before Ahasverus" (KMS inv. 1177) by "Lantzon", which has no connection with the series. Weilbach's attributions are given in the bibliography for each painting listed in his present catalogue. A considerable number of these paintings were correctly identified as part of the decoration of the Great Hall, whereas others cannot with certainty be identified as part of the series on the age of man. The paintings in question are Franz Cleyn's Baptism, the Allegory on the Sound by Isaac Isaacsz. and the Banquet scene besides Pieter Isaacsz.'s Bathing at an Oriental harbour and the Cadmus painting. A particular difficulty arises from the fact that the documents have not recently been carefully reexamined, since some of the payments to the artists (e.g. Beckett 1937) do not always refer unambiguously to the Great Hall. A distinction must also be made between the paintings originally placed in the ceiling and the pictures which were hung on the walls.

The restoration of the paintings which has been carried out since 1985 has provided information on the canvas of the paintings. It can be seen that the Cadmus painting, the Banquet and Bathing at an Oriental harbour are on fine Netherlandish canvas, whereas the Boys' School, the Fireworks scene and Tilting at the Ring were painted on rough canvas, probably made in Denmark. Analysis of canvas types will be continued as restoration and conservation of the paintings proceeds.

The main theme of the iconological programme is the life of man, presumably divided into the Seven Ages of Man, with a further division according to the Seven Planets (the "Planetenkinder"-motif; see Stein 1987). It is impossible today to reconstruct the entire programme, due to the fragmentary survival of the series. It may have contained other features, such as the Four Elements, the Cardinal Humours, and an allusion to the Reign of Peace under Christian IV. Important is, however, that the series form the first major secular decoration in Denmark, for which a specific iconological programme must be presupposed. *Charlotte Christensen*

*212*

*208*

## Franz Cleyn

Rostock 1582 – London 1658
208
*The Presentation in the Temple*
Oil on canvas. 182×307.5 cm
Statens Museum for Kunst Sp. 793/inv. 1168
A copy of the painting by Tintoretto in the Accademia, Venice (1554). A Baptism of Christ has been added on the right. In the foreground of this group a nude male figure copied from "Il Giorno" of the sepulchral monument of Giuliano di Medici in the Sagrestia Nuova, S. Lorenzo, Florence. Assuming that the painting was actually painted as part of the decorative scheme for Rosenborg, it may be an allegory of "Infans", the first of the Seven Ages of Man.
*Provenance:* To The Royal Danish Kunstkammer from Frederiksborg 1827, here invented as 1827, 7/a983. In the same year transferred to The Royal Picture Gallery.
*Literature:* Weilbach 1870 161. Friis 1872-78 38. Wanscher 1930 47. Beckett 1937 50. The Royal Museum of Fine Arts cat. 1946 no. 120. Stein 1983 117 and 1987 38f.

## Attributed to Søren Kiær

209
*A Nursery*
Oil on canvas. 180×233 cm
Frederiksborg G 11 (A 4040)
An allegory of the first of the Seven Ages of Man "Infans". For the attribution to Søren Kiær see Beckett, 1937.
Until recently no documented works by Kiær were known, but the discovery of three paintings in the Nationalmuseum, Stockholm, provide us with an opportunity of further attributions to Kiær.
*Provenance:* The Great Hall, Rosenborg. The Royal Picture Gallery inv. 1164. To Frederiksborg 1881.
*Literature:* Weilbach 1870 161. Friis 1872-78 38 (as Cleyn?). Wanscher 1930 46f. Beckett 1937 61f (as Søren Kjær?). Eller 1973 156 (as Timm). Stein 1983 117 (as workshop of Timm). Ibid 1987 36ff.

## Francis Cleyn

210
*Children on their way to School (also called "The Path to Wisdom")*
Signed lower left "F. Cleyn"
Oil on canvas. 254×320 cm. Colour-plate XXIII
Frederiksborg G 23 (A 4043)
An allegory of the second of the Seven Ages of Man, "Puer". The painting may be identified as the "Børnelegh" (Children at Play), for which a payment to Cleyn is documented in 1619. A previous identification of the "Børnelegh" with a small painting at Rosenborg is doubtful, as the considerable sum of 200 dollars would indicate a painting of a much larger size.
*Provenance:* The Great Hall, Rosenborg. The Royal Picture Gallery inv. 1174. To Frederiksborg 1881.
*Literature:* Weilbach 1870 161. Friis 1872-78 36. Wanscher 1930 48. Beckett 1937 46. Eller 1973 155. Stein 1983 117. Ibid 1984 375 and 1987 38 42.

211
*A Boys' School*
Oil on canvas. 236×311.5 cm
Statens Museum for Kunst inv. 1172
Presumbly and allegory of "Puer" and a depiction of Grammar, the first subject in the Trivium, according to the Scholastic system of the Artes Liberales.
*Provenance:* The Great Hall, Rosenborg. Recorded as 1882/83.
*Literature:* Weilbach 1870 164 (as Thim). Friis 1872-78 38. Wanscher 1930 48 (as Thim). Beckett 1936 12. Ibid 1937 52. Eller 1973 156. Stein 1983 114. Ibid 1987 27 29. Sorø 28 May – 18 June 1936, no. 2 (as Timm).

## Attributed to Reinhold Timm

died in Sorø 1639
212
*A Lecture in an Academy for the Nobility*
Oil on canvas. 245×315 cm
Frederiksborg G 19 (A 4042)
Probably a representation of "Puer" and an allegory of Rhetoric, one of the Seven Liberal Arts.
*Provenance:* The Great Hall, Rosenborg. To Frederiksborg 1881 from The Royal Picture Gallery.
*Literature:* Weilbach 1870 162. Friis 1872-78 39. Liisberg 1924-25 211 218. Wanscher 1930 48. Beckett 1937 69 (as Timm). Stein 1970 7 (as P. Isaacsz. or Timm). Ibid 1983 114 (as P. Isaacsz. or Timm). Ibid 1987 27 30 (as Timm).

## Reinhold Timm

213
*A Sculptor's Studio*
Oil on canvas. 241.3×288.5 cm
Statens Museum for Kunst inv. 1175
A representation of the third of the Seven Ages of Man "Adolescens". According to M. Stein, the picture is an allegory of "The Children of Mercury".

*214*

215

*Provenance:* Executed for the ceiling of the Great Hall, Rosenborg.
*Literature:* Weilbach 1870 164. Friis 1872-78 38. Wanscher 1930 48. Beckett 1937 65f. Eller 1973 157. Stein 1983 113. Ibid 1984 375ff and 1987 23f.

214
*Wrestling on a Bridge.* 1622
Signed lower left, beneath the foot of the sitting youth "RT" (composite monogram)
Oil on canvas. 247×312.5 cm
Statens Museum for Kunst inv. 1171
An allegory of the Children of the Sun cf. the engraving by Maerten van Heemskerk from his series of the Seven Planets. In addition it is an allegory of one of the Seven Ages of Man, either "Adolescens" or "Juventus". The composition may have been inspired by Cornelis Cornelisz. van Haarlem's picture "The Massacre of the Innocents" from 1591 (Frans Hals Museum, Haarlem).
*Provenance:* The Great Hall, Rosenborg. To the Royal Danish Kunstkammer 1827 from Frederiksborg. Here recorded as 1827, 7/a973. In the same year transferred to The Royal Picture Gallery.
*Literature:* Weilbach 1870 164. Friis 1872-78 38. Wanscher 1930 48. Beckett 1937 63f. Rostrup Bøyesen 1943 140. Stein 1970 7. Ibid 1983 113 and 1987 22f.

## Attributed to Reinhold Timm

215
*Feminine Pursuits*
Oil on canvas. 179×337 cm
Frederiksborg G 13 (A 4044)
Probably an allegory of the fourth of the Seven Ages of Man, Juventus, or perhaps of Adolescens? The naked child resting on the back of the lace-maker, is copied after "The Upbringing of Cupid" by Titian c. 1565 (Rome, Galleria Borghese). The painting differs stylistically from the documented works by Timm.
*Provenance:* The Great Hall, Rosenborg. Frederiksborg 1881, from The Royal Picture Gallery.
*Literature:* Weilbach 1870 164. Friis 1872-78 38. Wanscher 1930 47. Beckett 1937 68f. Eller 1973 158. Stein 1983 118. Ibid 1987 38 f 41 47.

## Reinhold Timm

216
*The Tilt*
Oil on canvas. 185×315 cm. Colour-plate XXIII
Frederiksborg G 16 (A 4041)
Presumably an allegory of the fourth of the Seven Ages of Man, Juventus (or, according to Stein, Adolescens).
*Provenance:* The Great Hall, Rosenborg. Frederiksborg 1881, from The Royal Picture Gallery.
*Literature:* Weilbach 1870 164. Friis 1872-78 38.

Wanscher 1930 47ff. Beckett 1937 67f. Tidens Konsthistoria 9 1950 204. Eller 1973 158f. Stein 1983 117. Ibid 1987 38 44; Sorø 28 May – 18 June 1936 no. 3.

## Franz Cleyn

217
*A Bethrothal*
Signed lower right "F Cle ..."
Oil on canvas. 183×308 cm
Statens Museum for Kunst Sp. 794/inv. 1167
An allegory of Juventus (the fourth of the Seven Ages of Man), in the context of other pictures in the Rosenborg series.
*Provenance:* The Great Hall, Rosenborg (?). To the Royal Danish Kunstkammer from Frederiksborg in 1827, recorded as 1827, 7/a984. In the same year transferred to The Royal Picture Gallery as Sp. 794.
*Literature:* Weilbach 1870 161. Friis 1872-78 38. Wanscher 1930 47f. Beckett 1937 49f. The Royal Museum of Fine Arts cat. 1946. no. 119. Eller 1973 156. Stein 1983 117. Ibid 1987 48 46.

218
*Fireworks at Castel Sant'Angelo in Rome.* C. 1619.
Oil on canvas. 173×299 cm. Colour-plate XXIV
Frederiksborg G 12 (A 4039)
Since the beginning of the 16th century, the famous fireworks "La Girandola" was displayed every year on 29 June on occasion of the feast-day of St. Peter and St. Paul. Similar fireworks displays could be seen over the Castel Sant'Angelo as part of the coronation festivities for a new pope. It cannot be determined to which of the Seven Ages of Man this picture should be assigned; but it may represent Virilitas, Manhood.
*Provenance:* Executed for the ceiling of the Great Hall at Rosenborg. On 15 May 1619 Cleyn received payment for two paintings one of which is described as depicting a fireworks. The Royal Picture Gallery inv. 1169. To Frederiksborg 1881.
*Literature:* Weilbach 1870 161. Friis 1872-78 36ff. Wanscher 1930 46ff. Beckett 1937 44ff. Eller 1973 155. Stein 1983 122. Ibid 1987 47ff.

## Isaac Isaacsz.

Amsterdam 1599 – Amsterdam after 1665
219
*A Banquet.* 1622
Signed on the pedestal of the pillar on the left "Isaac Isacs fecit ANTWARP A° 1622"
Oil on canvas. 253×315.5 cm. Colour-plate XXII
Statens Museum for Kunst Sp. 228
Isaacsz's painting is evidently influenced by compositions by Paolo Veronese (c. 1528-1588) such as "The Feast at the House of Levi", 1573 (Venice, Accademia). This painting cannot have been part of the ceiling decoration of the Great Hall at Rosenborg intact until the turn of the 17th century, as it is recorded in the inventory of the Royal Danish Kunstkammer in 1673. If it was

*217*

ever hung in the Great Hall it could have been placed on one of the walls. Similar banqueting scenes can be found in illustrations of Baltazzar's Feast (see i.e. the engraving by Jan Muller, 1590 and the painting by Frans II Francken, Stockholms universitets Samling) and the story of Esther. According to M. Stein, the subject of the painting is the wedding of Aeneas and Lavinia.
*Provenance:* Forwarded from Antwerp exempt of duty according to a passport issued by Christian IV on 25 February 1622. To The Royal Danish Kunstkammer 1775 as 274/7. 1827 to the Royal Picture Gallery.
*Literature:* Ramdohr 1792 110. Weilbach 1870 162. Friis 1872-78 39. Hertz 1921-23 373. Ibid 1924-25 331. Wanscher 1930 49. Beckett 1937 97f. Royal Museum of Fine Arts cat. 1946 no. 342. Eller 1973 154. Stein 1983 122. Ibid 1987 47ff 52.

## Pieter Isaacsz.

Elsinore 1569 – Elsinore 1625
220
*A Bathhouse*
Oil on canvas 245×304 cm
Statens Museum for Kunst inv. 1178
Probably a representation of Virilitas and an allegory of The Children of Venus.
*Provenance:* The Great Hall, Rosenborg. Recorded 1882-83.
*Literature:* Weilbach 1870 162f. Friis 1872-78 39. Liisberg 1924-25 211 218. Wanscher 1930 48. Beckett 1937 90. Tidens Konsthistoria 9 1950 205. Stein 1970 7. Eller 1973 152. Stein 1983 113. Ibid 1987 23 25f.

221
*Bathing at an Oriental Harbour*
Oil on canvas. 241×289.5 cm. Colour-plate XXII
Statens Museum for Kunst inv. 1176/1378
Probably a representation of Virilitas and perhaps an allegory of the Children of Luna traditionally connected with humidity. According to Stein the subject is found in the De Antiquitatibus Judaicis XV, Chapter 3 by Flavius Josephus: Herod the Great persuades his young brother-in-law, the high priest Aristobulos, to swim. Later he is killed by drowning.
*Provenance:* The Great Hall, Rosenborg (?). Recorded 1882/83.
*Literature:* Weilbach 1870 163. Friis 1872-78 39. Liisberg 1924-254 211 218. Beckett 1937 92f. Stein 1970. Eller 1973 152f. Stein 1983 122f. Ibid 1984 375ff and 1987 47ff 56-72.

222
*Saturn and the Scholar* (also called *"Death and Old Age"*)
Oil on canvas. 227×343 cm
Statens Museum for Kunst inv. 1170
An allegory of the last of the Seven Ages of Man, Decrepitas, and of the Children of Saturn. The Fates, or Parcae, spin the thread of life and cut it at their pleasure. The winged figure with the scythe and the hourglass is Time. The scholar indicates the "vita contemplativa". Saturn in connected with cold weather and accompanied by beggars.
*Provenance:* The Great Hall, Rosenborg. Recorded 1882/83.
*Literature:* Weilbach 1870 163. Friis 1872-78 39. Liisberg 1924-25 211 218. Wanscher 1930 49. Beckett 1937 91. Eller 1973 152f. Stein 1983 113. Ibid 1987 25ff.

## Isaac Isaacsz.

223
*Allegory of the Sound.* 1622
Signed bottom left "Isaac Isacs fecit IN ANTWARP A° 1622"
Frontispiece p. 72
Oil on canvas. 259×307 cm
Statens Museum for Kunst Sp. 801
The allegorical figures are copied from Rubens' painting of "Earth and the Sea" (c. 1618, The Hermitage, Leningrad); the lion recurs in Rubens' "Poseidon and Amphitrite" (c. 1614, formerly in the Kaiser Friederich-Museum, Berlin, destroyed in 1945). The painting has been considered to be part of the series of paintings from the Great Hall at Rosenborg. It has no connection with the allegorical system of the Seven Ages of Man, but it may have hung on one of the walls of the Hall. However this may be, the intention was to symbolize Danish Naval supremacy.
*Provenance:* Rosenborg. 1705 to the Royal Danish Kunstkammer. Recorded 1737, 892/86. In 1827 transferred to The Royal Picture Gallery.
*Literature:* Hauber 1777 96. Weilbach 1870 162. Friis 1872-78 39. Wanscher 1930 49. Beckett 1937 98. Gerson 1942 456. Rostrup Boyesen 1943 140. Royal Museum of Fine Arts cat. 1946 no. 343. Eller 1973 154f. Stein 1983 122. Langberg 1985 93f. Stein 1987 51.

## Attributed to Hendrick Goltzius

Venlo 1558 – Haarlem 1617
224
*Cadmus slaying the Dragon*
Oil on canvas. 189×248 cm. Colour-plate XXIV
Statens Museum for Kunst inv. 1183. On permanent loan to the Museum at Koldinghus.
The painting represents a scene in Ovid, Metamorphoses, III, 26-94: In connection with the offering to Jove, Cadmus has sent his companions to fetch water from a well guarded by a dragon. When Cadmus sets out in search of his companions he finds them killed. Cadmus kills the dragon, transfixing it to an oak tree with his spear. The painting was previously considered to be part of the Rosenborg series, but is recorded as early as 1689 in the inventory of the Royal Danish Kunstkammer. The accounts for the payments for the pictures commissioned for Rosenborg make no reference to one of the Cadmus story, and the documentary evidence would

226

seem to exclude the posibility that a large painting, not specifically ordered for the Great Hall, was included in the Rosenborg decoration.
Stein (1987) suggests that the painting is an allegory of Youth coming to grips with the Trivium, the lower division of the Seven Liberal Arts: Grammar, Rhetoric and Dialectics. He compares it with an engraving of Cadmus from Wendel Dietterlin "Architectura", 1598. For the attribution to Goltzius, see: C. Christensen and L. W. Nichols (1986).
*Provenance:* The Royal Danish Kunstkammer 1689, 136. Recorded 1737, 890/75. To Frederiksborg 1827. To the Royal Picture Gallery after 1859.
*Literature:* Hauber 1777 96 (as Honthorst). Weilbach 1870 164. Friis 1872-78 39. Beckett 1937 76f (as Rappost, confused with the Hercules series). Eller 1973 158. Stein 1983 114f and 1987 35 (Reinhold Timm?). C. Christensen and Nichols 1986 3ff.

# The Decoration of the King's Chamber at Kronborg Castle

Aethiopica, a romance by the Greek author Heliodor, was printed for the first time in 1534, after which it appeared in many editions in various European languages until about 1600. It was the source for a scene in Torquato Tasso's Gerusalemme Liberato and Shakespeare alluded to it in Twelfth Night. Christian IV probably knew of the book, since it provided the theme for one of the decorations at Kronborg Castle. Theagenes was a descendant of Thetis and Achilles, Chariclea the white daughter of the black Egyptian king and queen Hydaspes and Persina. A romance about a happy love affair between two young people which ends in the preparations for a wedding feast was presumably chosen for the decoration of Kronborg along with the celebrations in music, song and dance at The Great Nuptials in 1634 when the Heir Apparent and Magdalena Sibylla of Saxony were married. The scenes from the love story Aethiopica are surrounded by small canvases with winged cupids carrying the monograms of Frederik II and Queen Sophie, Christian IV and Queen Anna Cathrine and the heir to the throne, Prince Christian and Princess Magdalena Sybilla. The paintings arrived in Denmark in 1635.

*Charlotte Christensen*

## Gerrit van Honthorst

Utrecht 1590-Utrecht 1656

225
*Flying cupids with the monograms of Frederik II and Queen Sophie.* 1635
Signed and dated 1635 in the scroll on the far left
Oil on canvas
Kronborg Castle
In a letter from Christian IV dated 11.10.1635, orders are given for the monograms in the pictures, which have come from Holland, to be changed. No technical examination of the paintings has been made to determine how the monograms were originally painted.
*Provenance:* Commissioned for Kronborg, delivered to Denmark before 11.10.1635 (EB III no. 511).
*Literature:* Beckett 1916 25f and 1937 104. Hoogewerff 1924 13. Judson 117f Cat. Rais 117. Braun 1966 286 Cat. W9 (as Willem van Honthorst).

226
*Flying cupids with Christian IV's monogram.* 1635
Signed on the banner in the right hand corner "G. Honthorst fe. 1635"
Oil on canvas
Kronborg Castle
*Literature:* Beckett 1917 26f and 1937 104. Hoogewerff 1924 13. Judson 1959 117f. Cat. Rais 118. Braun 1966 287 Cat. W10

*232*

227
*Cupids with Queen Anna Cathrine's monogram.* 1635
Oil on canvas
Kronborg Castle
*Literature:* Beckett 1917 26 35. Hoogewerff 1924 13. Beckett 1937 104. Judson 1959 117f. Cat.Rais 119. Braun 1966 287 Cat. W11.

228
*Cupids with the Heir Apparent and Magdalena Sibylla's monograms.* 1635
Oil on canvas
Kronborg Castle
*Literature:* Beckett 1917 26 and 1937 104. Hoogewerff 1924 13. Judson 1959 117f. Cat.Rais 119a. Braun 1966 288 Cat. W12.

229
*Theagenes and Chariclea on the beach.* 1635
Oil on canvas
Kronborg Castle
The literary source is Heliodor's romance Aethiopica I 2.
*Literature:* Beckett 1917 28 and 1937 104. Hoogewerff 1924 9 13. (NB: Hoogewerff lists that the commission was from "King Frederick of Denmark"). Stechow 1953 145. Judson 1959 117f. Cat.Rais 131. Braun 1966 283ff Cat. W5.

230
*Theagenes meets Chariclea.* 1635
Oil on canvas
Kronborg Castle
The literary source is Heliodor's romance Aethiopica III 5.
*Literature:* Beckett 1917 28ff. and 1937 104. Hoogewerff 1924 9 13. Stechow 1953 151. Judson 1959 117f. Cat. Rais 130. Braun 1966 285 Cat. W6.

231
*The Coronation of Theagenes.* 1635
Oil on canvas
Kronborg Castle

232
*Chariclea is recognised by her parents.* 1635
Oil on canvas
Kronborg Castle
The scene is taken from Heliodor's romance Aethiopica X 14.
*Literature:* Beckett 1917 28ff and 1937 104. Hoogewerff 1924 9 13. Stechow 1953 150f. Judson 1959 117f Cat. Rais 126. Braun 1966 286 Cat. W8

# The Kronborg series. An illustrated History of Denmark

In the mid 19th century, the 44 drawings were transferred to Den kgl. Kobberstiksamling from Det kgl. Bibliotek where they had been since the beginning of the 18th century. In the 1780s, they had been parted into a folio and catalogued, the themes being interpreted with the help of the works on Danish history by Holberg and Suhm. Only a few have texts and names inscribed on them. An old numbering system ("Old no.") seems to be quite fortuitous. Nor is the original order reconstructed in the new listing which F. R. Friis had printed 100 years later, after he had demonstrated the connection between the drawings and the planned redecoration of Kronborg after the fire of 1629. In 1637, Christian IV had directed his engraver, Simon de Pas of Utrecht, to procure 80 drawings of heroic events in Danish history, to be executed by "the best Dutch artists", so that large paintings could be made from them afterwards for the Great Hall at Kronborg. Copperplate engravings were to be made of the 80 drawings and they were to be printed with historical explanations. The choice of themes lay with Ole Worm (1588-1654), antiquarian, physician and collector. He must have been assisted by several scholars, notably Peder Spormand, professor of history and geography at Copenhagen since 1635. The main sources were:

1. Danorum regum heroumque Historiæ ... a Saxone Grammatico, ed. Christiern Pedersen, Paris 1514, fol. (from heathen times to c. 1200). Quoted from the edition of J. Olrik and H. Ræder, Copenhagen 1931.
2. Den Danske Krønicke som Saxo Grammaticus screff ... af Latinen udsæt ... Aff Anders Søffrinsøn Vedel, [Cop.] 1575 fol.
3. Arild Huitfeld: Danmarckis Rigis Krønicke 1-X, Kbh. 1595-1604, 4 (from heathen times to 1559, quotations from 2nd ed. I-II, Cop. 1652, fol.).
4. Danske Kongers Slectebog aff Claudio Christophoro Lyschandro, Cop. 1622, fol. (from heathen times to Christian I).
5. Joannis Meursii Historiæ Danicæ Libri III, Hafniæ 1630, 4 (1448-1523).
6. Joannis Isaaci Pontani Rerum Danicarum Historia, Amstelodami 1631, fol. (from heathen times to 1448).
7. Snorre Sturlesøns Norske Kongers Chronica Udsat paa Danske aff H. Peder Claussøn, Cop. 1633, 4° (published on Worm's initiative).

The main source may have been Pontanus 1631 (6), who gives copious quotations from Saxo and many other printed works. He is the only source for drawings nos. 1-10, but Saxo and Huitfeldt were probably the basis for the lost original chronology of the pictures. The series of engravings was never completed. When Simon de Pas died in 1647 his completed copperplates, which could well have comprised the themes which are now missing, were confiscated. The 44 still extant drawings probably represent those not yet engraved by Simon de Pas when he died. 27 of the drawings are signed. Nos. 42 and 43 belong to a different series, no. 44 is a later addition.

The paintings have suffered many vicissitudes of fortune. 15 are preserved, 3 in Denmark, 12 in Sweden, where they were taken after Karl Gustaf Wrangel's occupation of Kronborg in 1658. Some of them are shown at this exhibition. Titles of 4 more are known, but these have now disappeared. Most of the artists belonged to the circle known to Simon de Pas in his hometown of Utrecht. These were:

1. Gerard van Honthorst (1590-1656): 10 drawings, 9 paintings.
2. Crispin de Pas II (1597/98-c 1670): 12 signed, 16 attributed drawings.
3. Nicolaus Knüpfer (c 1603-1655): 1 drawing, 1 lost painting.
4. Jan van Bijlert (1598-1666): 1 drawing, 1 lost painting.
5. Abraham Bloemaert (1564-1651): 1 drawing.
6. Simon Peter Tilemann (1601-c 1670): 1 drawing.
7. Adriaen van Nieulandt (1587-1658): 1 painting.
8. Adam Willaerts (1577-1664): 1 drawing.
9. Palamades Palamadesz. (1607-1638): 1 drawing.
10. Claes Moeyaert (1600-1655): 1 signed and 1 attributed painting.
11. Isaac Isaacsz. (1599-1649): 1 signed, 1 attributed painting.
12. Salomon Koninck (1609-1656): 1 signed painting.

4 paintings exist for which there are no corresponding drawings, and changes in style and composition between the drawings and the paintings are often considerable. Although the paintings give the series its artistic quality, the drawings are of interest because they represent an early phase in a complex production process. This pretentious project contributes to our understanding of Christian IV, his time and personality by showing his desire to appear as a patron of the arts on an international scale, despite adversity. The redecorated castle of Kronborg was to be the renown and ornament of the Kingdom. The Danes' glorious past was depicted here for the first time in a series of such canonical episodes as were later to form the basis of popular national history.

A full survey of the Kronborg series, containing a complete catalogue of all the drawings and paintings and comprising a detailed historical and art historcial commentary will be published by Den kgl. Kobberstiksamling.

*H. D. Schepelern and Ulla Houkjær*

## *Drawings*

### Crispin de Passe II

Cologne c 1597-Antwerp c 1670

233
*A heathen procession leading human sacrifices out of a town*
Inscribed "crispin de pas". After 1637
Pencil, pen, brown ink, brush, brown and black ink wash. 25.3×37.7 cm
Den kgl. Kobberstiksamling Tu 121-1. Old no. 37
Pontanus p. 1. on the sacrificial rites of the Cimbrians: "there is a place here called Lejre, the headquarters of the kingdom in this area which is called Sjælland, where everyone gathers every ninth year in January after the time in which we celebrate Epiphany. There they sacrifice to their gods 99 humans and an equivalent number of horses, dogs and cocks" (quoted from Strabo VII, 2, 1-3 and Thietmar of Merseburg).

234
*Sacrificing humans and animals before the idols*
Inscribed "crispin de pas fecit". After 1637
Pen, brown ink, brush, brown and black ink wash. 25.2×37.5 cm
Den kgl. Kobberstiksamling Tu 121-2. Old no. 41.
Pontanus p. 1.: "It is said that the Cimbrians observed the following custom: their wives accompany them to war with some old, greyhaired prophetesses dressed in white with linen shifts fastened with clasps, with bronze belts and bare feet. With swords drawn, they met the prisoners in the camp, cut them down and took them to a copper cauldron which could hold about 20 amphora. Over this was a scaffold on to which a high priestess climbed and cut the throat of each one over the cauldron. They read omens from the blood that flowed into the cauldron. Others slit open the remaining bodies, gazed at the entrails and foretold the victory of their people". (From Strabo VII, 2, 1-3).

235
*Priestesses take omens from the entrails of human sacrifices*
Inscribed "crispin de pas f. 1639".
Pencil, pen, brown ink, brush, brown and black ink wash. 23.8×37.8 cm
Den kgl. Kobberstiksamling Tu 121-3. Old no. 29
Cf. no. 234.

236
*Animal sacrifice before the idol of Thor*
Inscribed "crispin de pas invent. 1639".
Pen, brown ink, brush, brown and black ink wash. 23.8×37.8 cm
Den kgl. Kobberstiksamling Tu 121-4. Old no. 26
Cf. no. 233.

237
*The Cimbrians defeat the Romans*
Not inscribed. After 1637
Pencil, pen, brown ink, brush, brown and black ink wash. 25.7×37.9 cm
Den kgl. Kobberstiksamling Tu 121-5. Old no. 38
Pontanus p. 2-3 tells of the Romans' defeat at the hands of the Cimbrians between 113 and 109 BC. (Livy: Periochae books 63 and 65).

238
*Battle at a bridge. The Cimbrians plundering fallen Romans*
Inscribed "Cris. de pas 111 1639".
Pencil, pen, brown ink, brush, brown and black ink wash, white colour. 28.3×33.8 cm
Den kgl. Kobberstiksamling Tu 121-6 Old no. 15
The drawing is a study of preparatory sketch for a signed painting by Gerrit van Honthorst (1590-1656). The painting is now in Vittskövle Castle, Sweden. Cf. cat. 237.

239
*Cimbrian horsemen crossing the Adige*
Inscribed "crispin de pas 1639".
Pencil, pen, brown ink, brush, brown and black ink wash. 25.4×37.6 cm
Den kgl. Kobberstiksamling Tu 121-7. Old no. 48
Pontanus p. 6-7 gives the following account (from Livy: Periochae, book 68, 98 BC): Catulus had fortified the Roman camp at Adige, the Cimbrians attacked and conquered it; since the Romans had fought bravely, they were released after swearing on a copper ox.

240
*Captured Romans are set free having sworn an oath on a copper ox*
Not inscribed. After 1637
Pencil, pen, brown ink, brown and black ink wash. 24.0×38.0 cm
Den kgl. Kobberstiksamling Tu 121-8. Old no. 36.
Cf. no. 239.

241
*In the Cimbrian camp Scaurus, the captured Roman legate, is slain by Bolus, the Cimbrian leader*
Inscribed "Crispin de pas in Copen: (= Copenhagen) fecit 1639"
Pen, brown ink, brush, brown and black ink wash. 23.8×38.1 cm
Den kgl. Kobberstiksamling Tu 121-9. Old no. 28
Pontanus p. 3 tells the story (from Livy: Periochae, book 67, 106 BC) of Scaurus, who led the Roman army against the Cimbrians. The army was defeated and he himself taken captive. When he warned the Cimbrians against crossing the Alps, the Cimbrians' chief killed him with his own hand.

243

242
*In Rome, Cimbrian emissaries present Emperor Augustus (63 BC-14 AD) with a copper vessel*
Augustus (63 BC-14 AD)
Not inscribed. After 1637
Pen, brown ink, brush, brown and black ink wash. 23.9×27.9 cm
Den kgl. Kobberstiksamling Tu 121-10. Old no. 27
Pontanus p. 10 gives the following account: that the Cimbrians had created a state between their peninsula and the Elbe when Augustus was emperor is substantiated by Strabo's story that they sent emissaries to the Emperor with a copper cauldron to make him forget old enmity and make a new friendship pact. (Strabo VII, 2). Pontanus p. 22 places the event in the time of Frode Fredegod.

## Nicolaus Knüpfer

Leipzig? c 1603-Utrecht 1655

243
*King Skjold's single combat with Skate*
Inscribed "N. Knüpfer fec.". After 1637
Pencil, pen, brown ink, brush, brown ink wash, white colour. 25.7×40.5 cm
Den kgl. Kobberstiksamling Tu 121-11. Old no. 36
Saxo III, 3,1-3: King Skjold became famous in his youth for meeting a bear when he was out hunting and tying it up with his belt, then leaving it for his companions to kill (see the subsidiary theme in the background of the drawing). When he had grown up and was wooing the beautiful Alvilda, he killed his rival, the Teuton Skate, within sight of both armies.

## Gerrit van Honthorst

1590-1656

244
*Uffe, son of King Vermund, slays two Saxons on an islet in the Eider*
Inscribed "G. Honthorst fecit". Two inscriptions below "kn.p." and "Uffo"
Pencil, pen, brown ink, brush, brown and black ink wash, white colour. 28.0×40.1 cm
Den kgl. Kobberstiksamling Tu 121-12. Old no. 5
Saxo IV, 4,5-11: King Vermund's son Uffe "the meek", who is considered to have been dumb, kills two Saxons on an island in the Eider and asserts his right to succeed his father in Denmark.

245
*The election of a king at a thingstead in a forest*
Inscribed "G. Honthorst fec.". After 1637
Pencil, pen, brown ink, brush, brown ink wash, white colour. 27.6×39.9 cm
Den kgl. Kobberstiksamling Tu 121-13. Old no. 11
Friis gives the drawing the title "Dan Mikillati, king of Scania and the Gothic island, is elected also as king of Jutland and Angul in the year 280". The old number 11 is also found on no. 18 and it is possible that this drawing, like nos. 42 and 43, belongs to quite a different series, perhaps on the history of the Batavians.

246
*Frode Fredegod is hailed by many kings*
Inscribed "G. Honthorst fecit". After 1637
Pencil, pen, brown ink, brush, brown and black ink wash, white colour. 28.0×40.5 cm
Den kgl. Kobberstiksamling Tu 121-14

The scene fits best with Saxo V,15,1, where we learn that after Frode Fredegod's many victories, "The Danish name was glorious in nearly every country from the praise of Danish bravery". Pontanus adds (p. 23) that he made 220 kings tributary. The drawing is study for at painting by Gerrit van Honthorst which is presumed to have been removed by the Swedes in the war of 1658-1660 (cat. 281).

247
*King Ingild Vendemod kills his father's assassins at a banquet*
Inscribed "G. Honthorst fecit". After 1637
Pencil, pen, brown and black ink, brush, brown and black ink wash, white colour. 28.1×40.5 cm
Den kgl. Kobberstiksamling Tu 121-15. Old No. 7
Saxo IV,9,8-18 tells of Frode IV's son, Ingild Vendemod, who gave himself up to gluttony and lust. He married a daughter of his father's murderer, the Saxon king Snerting and was on friendly terms with her brothers. In a long poem, the warrior Stærkodder first enjoins the queen to relinquish her crown and shame the king, after which he (the king) kills his brothers-in-law at a banquet. Pontanus (p. 26) records a shorter version.

248
*King Jarmeric puts captured Wends to the torture*
Inscribed "G. Honthorst faciebat". After 1637
Pencil, pen, brown ink, brush, brown ink wash, white colour. 27.4×39.9 cm
Den kgl. Kobberstiksamling Tu 121-16. Old no. 10
Saxo VIII, 10,5: After conquering Sweden, King Jarmeric fought against the Wends, with whom he had been a captive. He hung 40 captives on a rope together with the same number of wolves.

## Jan van Bijlert

Utrecht 1603-Utrecht 1671

249
*The endurance of King Hrolf Kraki*
Inscribed "J. Bylaer pinxit". After 1637
Oil on paper. Brunaille: brush, white and brown colour. 25.7×40.2 cm
Den kgl. Kobberstiksamling Tu 121-17. Old no. 8
Saxo II, 6, 4-5: Hrolf Kraki visits the Swedish king Adils who puts his guests' endurance to test by exposing them to violent heat from the fireplace. Finally, they throw their shields down on to the fire and jump over it. In the whole series, only this sheet and cat. 273 are done with a brush in thick colours, all the other numbers are pen and wash drawings.

## Gerrit van Honthorst

250
*Lamentation at the death of Hrolf Kraki*
Inscribed "Gerh. Honthorst fecit" and "Leyr". After 1637
Pencil, pen, brown ink, brush, brown ink wash, white colour. 27.9×40.5 cm
Den kgl. Kobberstiksamling Tu 121-18. Old no. 11
Saxo II, 8, 2: King Hrolf's brother-in-law Hjortvarth visits him at Lejre and kills him and his warriors in a treacherous attack. Beneath the drawing, there is a description of the contents, which supports the identification of the motif.

## Crispin de Passe II

251
*Harold Klak received by Emperor Ludwig (778-840) in the year 826*
Not inscribed. After 1637
Pencil, pen, brown and black ink, brush, brown and black ink wash. 26.6×39.0 cm
Den kgl. Kobberstiksamling Tu 121-19. Old no. 20
Saxo IX,4,36-37 in the story of Ragnar Lodbrok, tells of the pretender to the throne Harold Klak, who seeks support from Emperor Louis the Pious in Mainz and allows himself and his family to be baptised. Ragnar soon returns home from war and frustrates the attempt to introduce Christianity to Denmark. The subject is dealt with in detail by Adam of Bremen and others. The drawing is a study for the painting cat. 283.

## Gerrit van Honthorst

252
*Harold Klak and his family are baptised in Mainz*
Inscribed "G. Honthorst fecit". After 1637
Pencil, pen, brown ink, brush, black ink wash, white colour. 27.6×40.0 cm
Den kgl. Kobberstiksamling Tu 121-20. Old no. 12
The drawing is a study for the painting cat. 282.

## Crispin de Passe II

253
*The Danes in Nottingham make peace with King Burhedus of Mercia*
Inscribed "Crispin de pas inve". After 1637
Pencil, pen, brown and black ink, brush, brown and black ink wash 23.7×38.0 cm
Den kgl. Kobberstiksamling Tu 121-21. Old no. 31
The source for this scene is Huitfeldt (p. 60), who includes it in the story of Ragnar Lodbrok by utilising Polydorus Virgilius: Historia Anglica, book 4, on the Danish occupation of the castle in Nottingham, which the Mercian king Burhedus cannot capture, even with help from the king of Wessex, Æthelwulf and his brother, Arthur; therefore peace is concluded.

254
*King Athelstane of England sends a sword to the king of Norway, Harold the Fair-haired*
Not inscribed. After 1637

Pencil, pen, brown ink, brush, brown and black ink wash, white colour. 23.9×38.1 cm
Den kgl. Kobberstiksamling Tu 121-22. Old no. 33
The source is Snorri's Edda in Peder Claussøn Friis' translation, Norske Kongers Chronica, printed in Copenhagen 1633 on Worm's initiative. Friis relates correctly from the 1757 edition of Heimskringla, 61: King Athelstane of England sendt King Harold the Fairhaired of Norway a valuable sword. When the king takes hold of the hilt, the envoy says that King Harold is now King Athelstane's sword bearer or man.

## Artist unknown

255
*Duke Rollo is enfeoffed with Normandy in the year 911*
Not inscribed. Previously attributed to Crispin de Pas II. After 1637
Pencil, pen, brown ink, brush, brown, black and blue ink wash. 29.7×39.8 cm
Den kgl. Kobberstiksamling Tu 121-23. Old no. 9
The Danish defeat in England 895 and Rollo's subsequent expedition to Normandy and agreement with Charles the Simple is dealt with in detail by Pontanus (p. 116-117) and Lyschander in the Slectebog p. 352. Rollo's acceptance of the fiefdom is dated to 911. Three inscriptions on the drawing itself specify the person on the left as the French king "Carolus crassus", on the right "Duke Rollo" and the city in the background as "Paris".

## Abraham Bloemaert

Gorkum 1564-Utrecht 1651

256
*Poppo's ordeal by fire*
Inscribed "Abr. Bloemaert delineavit". After 1637
Pencil, pen, brown ink, brush, brown ink wash, white colour. 24.2×36,9 cm
Den kgl. Kobberstiksamling Tu 121-24. Old no. 39
Sources for the legend on Bishop Poppo's ordeal by fire are uncertain. Poppo's name appears in Widukind of Corvey's Saxon Chronicle. Saxo, X, 11, 3-4 tells the story under Sweyn Forkbeard.

## Artist unknown

257
*Tymme Sjællandsfar in England*
Not inscribed. Previously attributed to Crispin de Pas II. After 1637
Pencil, pen, brown and black ink, brush, brown, black and blue ink wash. 27.9×40.1 cm
Den kgl. Kobberstiksamling Tu 121-25. Old no. 6
This incident is only found in Saxo X, 14,3 where there is a description of how a soldier named Tymme Sjællandsfar roused the retreating Danish army during Canute's (c 1000-1035) struggle in England. Tymme took a big branch to use as a banner and headed the troops who then regained their fighting spirit.

258
*The death of bishop William*
Not inscribed. After 1637
Pencil, pen, brown ink, brush, brown and black ink wash. 27.0×39.2 cm
Den kgl. Kobberstiksamling Tu 121-26. Old no. 24
There is an account in Saxo, XI,9,1-4 of how Bishop William who was a close friend of king Svend Estridsen (c 1020-1074) met the king's funeral procession in a forest on the way to Roskilde and prayed that he might also die, now that the king was dead. His wish was fulfilled. The account is a legend, as the bishop died 3 years before the king.

## Simon Peter Tilemann

Lemgo 1601-Vienna 1668/70

259
*King Eric Ejegod (c 1956-1103) received by the Emperor in Constantinople*
Inscribed "S. P. Tilman fecit 1637"
Pencil, pen, brown and black ink, brush, brown and black ink wash. 26.4×38.4 cm
Den kgl. Kobberstiksamling Tu 121-27. Old no. 18
In Saxo XII,7,3, Pontanus p. 204 and Lyschander 217, Eric Ejegod's pilgrimage to the Holy Land and his death on Cyprus is mentioned; on the way, he arrived at Constantinople where he was received by the Byzantine emperor.

## Crispin de Passe II

260
*Canute Lavard (c 1096-1131) concludes friendship with Duke Henry of Wendland*
Not inscribed. After 1637.
Pencil, pen, brown ink, brush, black ink wash. 25.8×41.0 cm
Den kgl. Kobberstiksamling Tu 121-28. Old no. 35
Saxo XIII,2,1-9 has several anecdotes in his account of Canute Lavard's youth as a duke in Schleswig, which was looted by the Wends under his cousin Duke Henry. On their eventual agreement it is stated, XIII,3,5 that Canute sent men to a house where Henry was holding a feast but immediately after walked in at the door himself, showing that he could have attacked him, but would rather be friends.

261
*Harold Gille's ordeal by fire*
Inscribed "crispin de pas inven. 1639"
Pencil, pen, brown ink, brush, brown and black ink wash. 23.7×38.1 cm

Den kgl. Kobberstiksamling Tu 121-29. Old no. 25
The literary source for the drawing is Saxo XIII,11,3. The scene shows how Harold Gille travelled from Ireland to Norway to prove by ordeal by fire that he was son of the Norwegian king Magnus Barfod (1073-1103).

262
*Radulf outwits the Wends at Roskilde*
Not inscribed. After 1637
Pencil, pen, brown ink, brush, brown and black ink wash. 27.0×39.2 cm
Den kgl. Kobberstiksamling Tu 121-30. Old no. 23
The events are described by Saxo XIV,15,3 and mentioned by Pontanus p. 224. While King Svend Grathe (c 1127-1157) is in Roskilde, Radulf alone discovers that the Wends are coming. He attacks them while they are inattentive, beats them back and summons help from the town, which is described as "Rodtschildt" in the inscription above. The drawing is a study for cat. 285 by Adriaen van Nieulandt.

263
*Cavalry battle*
Not inscribed. After 1637
Pencil, pen, brown ink, brush, brown and black ink wash. 28.0×33.5 cm
Den kgl. Kobberstiksamling Tu 121-31. Old no. 14
The Print Cabinet's catalogue from the end of the 18th century and F. R. Friis identified this motif as: "King Valdemar II's victory over the Estonians and Livonians 1219". A painting of "The Valdemar Battle" by Nic. Knüpfer which belonged to the Kronborg series, was destroyed by fire at Christiansborg in 1794. Another possibility is the battle at Fodevig 1134.

## Gerrit van Honthorst

264
*Valdemar Atterdag (c 1320-1375) marches into Visby in the year 1361*
Inscribed "G. Honthorst fecit". After 1637
Pencil, pen, black ink, brush, black ink wash. 28.2×39.2 cm
Den kgl. Kobberstiksamling Tu 121-32
After the conquest of Gotland 1361 and the bloody battle outside Visby, which then capitulated, Valdemar Atterdag humiliated the town as described by Huitfeldt (p. 524): "When he came to the town, is was willingly opened for him, but he would not go in by the gate, but had a part of the wall knocked down and came through it with all his kin".

265
*King Albrecht hands over the Swedish crown to Queen Margrethe in the year 1389*
Inscribed "G. Honthorst fec.". After 1637
Pencil, pen, brown ink, brush, brown ink wash, white colour. 27.6×40.1 cm
Den kgl. Kobberstiksamling Tu 121-33. Old no. 3
The sources here are Huitfeldt (p. 584) and Pontanus (p. 519). During the struggle to unite the three Scandinavian kingdoms (the Union of Kalmar 1397), Queen Margrethe defeated the Swedish King Albrecht at Åsle 24.2.1389. The king and his son were taken prisoners and were imprisoned for several years. The drawing is a study for cat. 286.

## Crispin de Passe II

266
*Christian I occupies Gotland in the year 1449*
Inscribed "C. de pas delin. 1639"
Pencil, pen, brown ink, brush, brown and black ink wash. 27.3×39.4 cm
Den kgl. Kobberstiksamling Tu 121-34. Old no. 22
The Print Cabinet's catalogue from the end of the 18th century and F. R. Friis named this theme "The Fetalie Brothers land and plunder the peasantry". (Huitfeldt 1652 p. 585 and 1281). Since the details of the motif do not confirm this description, it must be regarded as doubtful. The source is Huitfeldt, who mentions the ravaging of the fetalie brothers under Eric of Pomerania. The high cliffs on the coast could perhaps indicate Gotland.

267
*Queen Philippa defending Copenhagen against the Hanseatic fleet in the year 1428*
Not inscribed. After 1637
Pencil, pen, brown ink, brush, brown and black ink wash. 26.8×39.2 cm
Den kgl. Kobberstiksamling Tu 121-35. Old no. 19
All details agree with Huitfeldt's story (p. 741) about Erik of Pomerania's queen, Philippa, who defended Copenhagen successfully against the Hanseatic fleet in 1428. The inscription above reads: "Coppenhaven".

268
*King Hans at the battle of Rotebro before Stockholm in the year 1497*
Not inscribed. After 1637
Pencil, pen, brown ink, brush, brown and black ink wash. 27.9×40.4 cm
Den kgl. Kobberstiksamling Tu 121-36. Old no. 2
The source may be Meursius' account (1630 p. 82ff) of King Hans' war in Sweden 1497. At Rotebro, he defeated the Dalecarlians who had sent reinforcements and then defeated Sten Sture outside Stockholm. The inscription above right reads: "Stockholm". The theme was previously wrongly identified (Friis, Beckett) as: "The citizens of Stockholm open the city gate to the rebel Engelbrecht and his company against the wishes of the lord of the manor 1436". The present identification was by M. Bligaard 1978. The drawing is a study for cat. 287.
*Literature:* Friis 1890-1901 198. Beckett 1937 121f. Bligaard 1978 29f. Langberg 1985 92 and 95f.

270

269
*Christian I meets Prince Maxmilian at Rothenburg ob der Tauber in the year 1474*
Inscribed "Crispin de pas 1639"
Pencil, pen, brown ink, brush, black ink wash. 27.7×33.5 cm
Den kgl. Kobberstiksamling Tu 121-37. Old no. 13
The source may be Meursius (1630 p. 51-53), who describes Christian I's journey to Rome 1474, and Huitfeldt (p. 940), who mentions Prince Maximilian who met the king outside Rothenburg on the emperor's behalf. The inscription in the centre above the background reads: "Rothenburg afu(!) der Tauber".

270
*The double bethrothals or nuptials of 1502*
Inscribed "Crispin de pas delin": After 1637
Pencil, pen, brown ink, brush, brown and black ink wash 26.2×38.9 cm
Den kgl. Kobberstiksamling Tu 121-41. Old no. 21
The previously unidentified scene is probably the celebration of the engagements between Duke Frederik, the later Frederik I, and Anna of Brandenburg and the Elector Joachim I and Elisabeth of Denmark. The explanation for this theme was suggested by Ulla Houkjær in 1987. Friis called it "A distinguished gentleman, lying in bed, will not allow his son to marry the lady standing beside him and therefore pulls his arm from her hand". The literary source is Huitfeldt (p. 1029-30 and 1240). The drawing was the study for a painting by Salomon Koninck (1609-56), which is now in Skokloster, cf. cat. 288.

## Adam Willaerts

Antwerp 1577-Utrecht 1664

271
*Christian II leaves Copenhagen in the year 1523*
Inscribed "Adam Wilers fecit". After 1637
Pencil, pen, brown ink, brush, brown and black ink wash. 27.6×39.1 cm
Den kgl. Kobberstiksamling Tu 121-38. Old no. 4
Huitfeldt (p. 1208) writes: "In the year 1523, on 20th April, die S. Tiburtii, King Christian sailed from Copenhagen with the queen and his children and was on the ship Løffven". He never regained his power, but was imprisoned on his attempt to return.

## Crispin de Passe II

272
*Frederick I at the siege of Copenhagen in the year 1523*
Not inscribed. After 1637
Pencil, pen, brown ink, brush, black ink wash. 27.8×34.1 cm
Den kgl. Kobberstiksamling Tu 121-39. Old no. 17
Huitfeldt (p. 1253) writes: "On 10th June, the feast of St. Barnabas, he came to Copenhagen and pitched camp north of the town, at Sersløf Marck, in order to make a defence of the sea. The 18 ships of the Lübeck Fleet were strongly placed out in the roads, and he dug an entrenchment to Valby to the west of the town, so that the town was covered both from the sea and the land. At the same place ten years later, Copenhagen was again besieged by his son Christian III". The inscription above

to the left reads: "Coppenhaven". The drawing is a study for cat. 289.

## Palamedes Palamedesz.

London? 1607-Delft 1638

273

*Daniel Rantzau in the battle of Falkenberg against the Swedes in the year 1565*

Inscribed "Palamedes Palamedessen". Before 1638

Oil on paper. Brush, white, grey, brown and black colour. 27.8×40.3 cm

Den kgl. Kobberstiksamling Tu 121-40. Old no. 1

The source may be unpublished material for the history of Frederik II printed by P. H. Resen in 1680 (p. 137-38). Only this sheet and cat. 249 are painted with a brush in thick colours. An inscription in German beneath the drawing identifies the theme as the Battle of Falkenberg. Palamedes Palamedesz. is the only artist represented in the series who had no connection with the Utrecht school. He worked in Delft among other places and in his short life, was regarded as a specialist of battle-pieces.

## Crispin de Passe II

274

*Cavalry battle before Maastricht*

Not inscribed. After 1637

Pencil, pen, brown ink, brush and black ink wash. 28.1×33.8 cm

Den kgl. Kobberstiksamling Tu 121-42. Old no. 16

The inscription "Maestricht" indicates that this and the next drawing were executed as illustrations for Meursius: Gulielmus Auriacus, Amsterdam 1638, which deals with the Dutch War of Independence. P. 123-24 describes Frederick of Nassau's mounted battle around Maestricht in 1574. The banner with the three toads (?) also appears in Honthorst's painting in Drottningholm, which has been mistakenly identified as the Valdemar Battle 1219.

275

*The conquest of Liège (Luyck) in the year 1577*

Not inscribed. After 1637

Pencil, pen, brown ink, brush, brown and black ink wash. 24.1×38.3 cm

Den kgl. Kobberstiksamling Tu 121-43. Old. no. 32

The inscription "Luÿck" points to the possibility that this drawing along with the previous one was executed for Meursius work on the Dutch War of Independcence. Friis' tittle "Lüttich is stormed and occupied, probably 1577" may therefore be correct.

## Gerrit van Honthorst

276

*King Valdemar the Victorious arrives in Lübeck in the year 1202*

Inscribed "G. Honthorst". After 1637

Pencil, pen, brown ink, brush, brown ink wash. 25.7×45.4 cm

Den kgl. Kobberstiksamling Tu 121-44

The drawing is undoubtedly one of the Kronborg series, but was not handed down with the others and was not, therefore, listed by Friis. The literary source is Huitfeldt (I p. 171) who writes: "In August of the same year, he went to Lübeck with a great company, honourable and magnificent: everyone, learned and unlearned, went to meet him and accompanied him into the town with great honour: the people of Lübeck swore obedience and submission to Denmark as lord of Vagria and North Albingia".

*Provenance:* Bought at an auction in 1768, inserted into the folio after 1901.

## Crispin de Passe II

277

*Lisbon besieged by Rollo*

Not inscribed. Previously attributed to Pieter de Wit Candid (c 1548-1628)

Pencil, pen, brown ink, brush, black and blue ink wash. 23.9×42.3 cm

Nationalmuseum, Stockholm NMH 353/1973

The drawing has not previously been connected to the Kronborg series, but is thematically related to it. This sheet is closest to the drawings cat. 253-55. Numbered 41 at the bottom right.

*Provenance:* Prince Charles de Ligne. From 1749 Duke Albert of Saxe-Teschen. From 1801 Duke J. G. De la Gardie. Presented to the Nationalmuseum 1973.

*Literature:* Exhibition "The Age of Breughel", Nationalmuseum, Stockholm 1984-85. (cat. 306).

278

*Baptismal scene. An adult king is baptised* [Not exhibited]

Not inscribed. Mistakenly listed under Pieter de Jode (1570-1634)

Pencil and chalk, pen, white colour. 24.5×36.8 cm

Kupferstichkabinett, Berlin, Dahlem

The drawing has not previously been connected to the Kronborg series. There can be little doubt, however, that it belongs to it as the visual source of the painting by Claes Moeyaert now in Östra Ryd church, Sweden. Cf. cat. 284.

*Literature:* Katalog Boch-Rosenberg 1930 no. 2829.

## Claes Moeyaert

Amsterdam 1592 or 1593 – Amsterdam 1655

279

*The baptism of Harold Bluetooth*

Pen brown ink, brush, brown ink wash on blue paper. 27.0×43.7 cm

Prentenkabinet der Rijksuniversitet, Leiden. PK 3838

This drawing is undoubtedly the final study for Moeyart's painting cat. 284.

*280*

## *Paintings*

### Claes Moeyaert

280
*The funeral of a heathen King* 1643
Signed C ... Mo ... yaert 1643
Oil on canvas. 162×341 cm
Skokloster, Sweden. Inv.no. 3633
Beckett (1937 p. 114) identifies this picture, presumably mistakenly, with a picture in the Frederiksborg inventory of 1650 (p. 86): "1 painting showing how a heathen king, who has died, lies on a pyre and is to be burned. Nearby stands a man with an ochide on his head and a mace in his hand".
*Provenance:* Kronborg. Skokloster castle; mentioned first in inv. 1728: The burial of a heathen Emperor. The 1756 inventary notes "Taken to Stockholm"; presumably back in Skokloster 1832.
*Literature:* Granberg 1912 104 (the signature here reads C. L. Moeyaert 1683). Beckett 1937 110, 113f.

### Isaac Isaacsz.

283
*Harold Klak received by Emperor Ludwig (778-840) in the year 826*
Signed: "Isaac Isaacsen Fecit A° 1640"
Oil on canvas. 163×345 cm
Skokloster inv.no. 1954
For the corresponding drawing, see cat. 251.
*Provenance:* Kronborg. Swedish war booty 1658-60. Carl Gustaf Wrangel's estate 1676. Mentioned for the first time in Skokloster's inventory 1756.
*Literature:* Beckett 1937 127 130.

### Claes Moeyaert

284
*The baptism of Harald Bluetooth*
Oil on canvas. 194×373 cm
Östra Ryd church, Sweden
The Frederiksborg inventory from 1650 lists four historical paintings as having hung between 1636 and 1650 (p. 91) in the room by the bedroom beside the Winter Room: Hagbard and Signe, "a scene in which King Harald is baptised", a picture of a king carried in triumph and another of a king riding on a piebald horse with his knights through water. Cat. 284 can probably be identified with the second of the paintings mentioned above. In Östra Ryd church in Uppland, there is a very fine collection of paintings, mostly Karl Gustav Wrangel's war booty, which was presented to the church by his grandson Abraham Brahe, in addition to war booty brought home by Nils Brahe. Much of this may originate from Denmark. The church owns a version of "Christian IV's Vision" (cat. 186), which perhaps came from Frederiksborg Castle (sight 68×58 cm. Not previously published). In 1978 a replica of this painting was owned by the Astoria Gallery, Munich. The picture was signed by Moeyaert and dated 1643 (measurements given as 170×350 cm). The painting has not been traced

283

since and unfortunately no photograph was brought to Denmark. It is therefore impossible to evaluate its authenticity.
*Provenance:* Executed as part of the decoration of Kronborg. Frederiksborg 1650? Swedish war booty 1658-60. Karl Gustav Wrangel. Per Brahe. Abraham Brahe. Östra Ryd church (presented to the church in 1702 inv. 1705 "Clodowi's" baptism, when, as the very first Christian king in France, he allows himself to be baptised, done by the famous master Moyart").
*Literature:* Granberg 1930 184. Norberg 1918. Sveriges Kyrkor Uppland I 1928. Beckett 1937 131 (as Isaac Isaacsz.?). Tümpel 1974 268. Cf. cat. 278-79.

## Adriaen van Nieulandt

285
*Radulph outwits the Wends at Roskilde*
Signed centre left: "Adriaen van Nieulandt Anno 1643"
Oil on canvas. 164.5×315.0 cm
Skokloster inv.no. 1953
For the corresponding drawing, see cat. 262.
*Provenance:* Kronborg. Swedish war booty 1658-60. Carl Gustav Wrangel's estate 1676. Mentioned for the first time in Skokloster's inventory 1793.
*Literature:* Friis 1890-1901 no. 30. Granberg 1911 I no. 450-52. Same 1930 55. Beckett 1937 120. H. D. Schepelern 1951 22.

## Gerrit van Honthorst

286
*King Albrecht hands over the Swedish crown to Queen Margrethe in the year 1389*
Oil on canvas. 247×504 cm
Frederiksborg G31 (A 7157)
The corresponding drawing is cat. 265. The painting may have been in Copenhagen during the booting of Kronborg. It suffered considerable damage during the fire at Christiansborg Castle in 1794, when it had to be cut from its frame. It was restored by Nicolai Abildgaard.
*Provenance:* The Royal Danish Kunstkammer 1689, 135. 1737. 892/88. 1827 To the Royal Picture Gallery as Spengler 377. Presented to Frederiksborg in 1914.
*Literature:* Hauber 1777 96. Hertz 1924-1925 331. Beckett 1937 120f. Braun 1966 2294 (W21, as Willem van Honthorst). Stein 1984 378. Langberg 1985 96ff.

287
*King Hans at the battle of Rotebro before Stockholm in the year 1497*
Oil on canvas 290×288 cm
Kronborg 423
For the corresponding drawing, see cat. 268. The painting was at some time given the erroneous title: Engelbrecht outside Stockholm. It was reproduced in etching by Anders Hultgren.
*Provenance:* Kronborg. Swedish war booty 1658. Afterwards at Sjöö in Uppland, Kesäter in Södermanland and Näs in Småland. Kronborg.
*Literature:* Beckett 1937 121ff. Judson 1959 200. Braun

1966 293 (cat. W18 as Willem van Honthorst). Bligaard 1978 no. 8. Heiberg 1983 18. Stein 1984 378. Langberg 1985 92, 95f.

## Salomon de Koninck

Amsterdam 1609 – Amsterdam 1656

288
*Festivities in a palace on the occasion of an engagement*
Oil on canvas. 164×345 cm
Skokloster inv. 1955
For the corresponding drawing, see cat. 270. The previously unidentified scene is probably the celebration of the engagement between duke Frederik, the later Frederik I, and Anna of Brandenburg.
*Provenance:* Kronborg. Swedish war booty 1658-60. First mentioned in the Skokloster inventory 1756.
*Literature:* Beckett 1937 128ff.

## Gerrit van Honthorst

289
*King Frederik I at the siege of Copenhagen in the year 1523 c. 1649*
Oil on canvas. 274×286 cm
Frederiksborg A 6482
H. Langberg suggests (op.cit. 1985) that the painting might perhaps represent "Christian III before Copenhagen 1536". The painting has been trimmed from its original quadrilateral shape. For the corresponding drawing, see cat. 271. An engraving was made from the painting by Anders Hultberg.
*Provenance:* Kronborg. Swedish war booty 1658-60. Presented 1941/42 by the Royal Swedish ambassador, Baron C. F. H. Hamilton of Hageby and Baronness, b. Duchess de la Gardie, in whose estate Kesäter the picture was.
*Literature:* Beckett 1937 125. Styhr 1945 54. Judson 1959 cat. 113 201f. Braun 1966 294 (cat. W20, as Willem van Honthorst). Eller 1973 212. Stein 1984 378f. Langberg 1985 92, 95f.

# *Paintings. Alphabetically after artists*

## Dirck Barendz.

Amsterdam 1534 – Amsterdam 1592

290
*The prodigal son*
Oil on panel. 122×66 cm
Statens Museum for Kunst inv. 952
Engraved by Johann Sadeler, cf. G. K. Nagler. Neues allgemeines Künstler-Lexicon. XIV, Munich 1845 p. 144, no. 142: "Die Menschen in ihren Lastern von der Sündfluth überrascht" (nach Th. Bernard).
*Provenance:* Otto Thott's auction 1787, no. 11. Bought by Spengler, cf. Kort Udsigt over den Spenglerske Malerie Samling, Copenhagen 1809 10. Prinsens Palæ. Inventoried 1870/71.
*Literature:* Blomberg and Andrup 1935 119.

*285*

*286*

## Batholomeus van Bassen

d. The Hague 1652

291
*Interior with backgammon players at table.* C 1625
Oil on panel. 21.5×28.5 cm
Statens Museum for Kunst inv. 1968

*289*

Pendant to cat. 292. The figures probably painted by Esaias I van de Velde (Amsterdam c 1591 – The Hague 1630).
*Provenance:* From Gottorp Castle 1759, cf. exhibition Schloss Gottorf, cat. 1965 260. At Fredensborg 1848, Stroe 196. To Statens Museum for Kunst 1906.
*Literature:* Jantzen 1910 64, Cat. 1946 no. 35. Keyes 1984 171, cat. VI
*Exhibitions:* Kunstforeningen October 1896 no. 5. Schloss Gottorf, May 31-July 31, 1905 no. 364. Kunstindustrimuseet October 11-November 2, 1969 no. 36.

292
*Interior with party at table* C 1625
Oil on panel. 21.5×28.5 cm
Statens Museum for Kunst inv. 1969
Pendant to cat. 291. The figures probably painted by Esaias I van de Velde.
*Provenance:* From Gottorp Castle 1759? cf. exhibition, Schloss Gottorf, cat. 1965 260. At Fredensborg 1848. Stroe 200. To Statens Museum for Kunst 1906.
*Literature:* Jantzen 1910 64, 159. Cat. 1946 no. 34. Keyes 1984 170f. cat. V.
*Exhibitions:* Kunstforeningen October 1896 no. 6. Schloss Gottorf May 31-July 31, 1965 no. 363. Kunstindustrimuseet October 11-November 2 1969 no. 35.

290

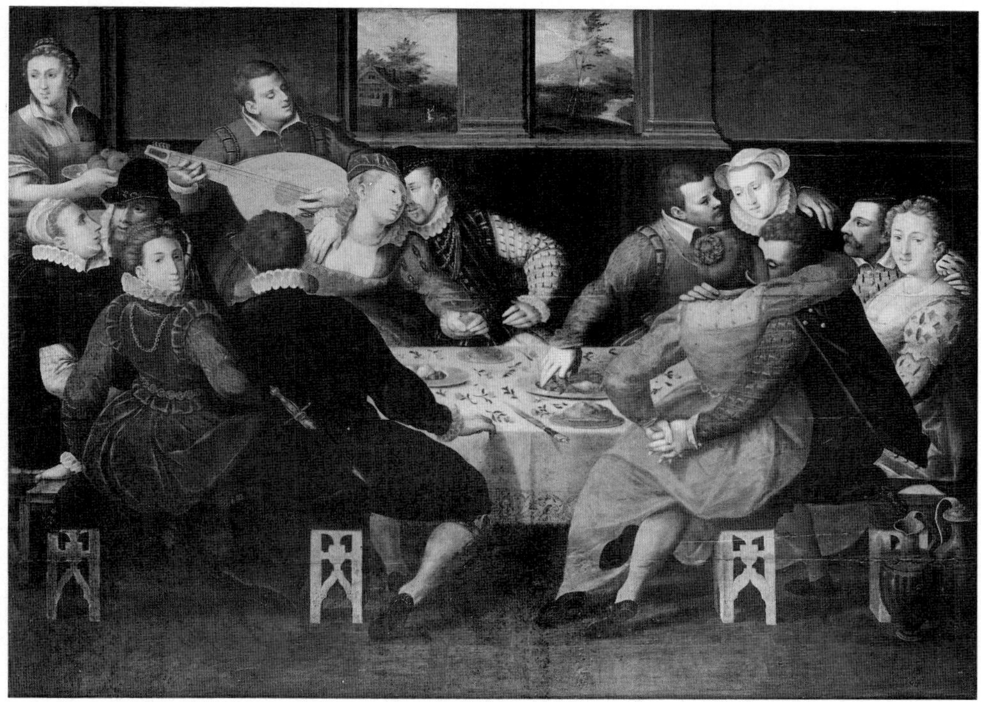

## Attributed to Bartholomeus van Bassen

293
*Party scene. Allegory of the five senses*
Oil on panel 73×104 cm
Statens Museum for Kunst Sp. 353.
*Provenance:* To the Royal Danish Kunstkammer 1827 from Fredensborg (Inv. 1827 12/a 1113). The same year to the Royal Picture Gallery.
*Literature:* Cat. 1946 no. 36. Frimmel 1904 70. Jantzen 1910 64, 159, no. 58. Bauch 1960 89.

## Louis de Caulery

Cambrai before 1582 – Antwerp 1621/22

294
*Tilting at the ring in a park*
Oil on panel 58×79 cm
Stockholm University's Art Collection
Louis de Caulery was represented by several paintings in the collections of Christian IV and a few are still in situ in the Winter Room at Rosenborg. Tilting was one of the most important features at courtly festivals and Christian IV often took part in these tournaments, both at home and on visits abroad.
*Provenance:* Count Clas Fleming until 1831. S. U. Palm, Berg. Stockholm University 1884.
*Literature:* E. Michel 1933 224 ff. Legrand 1963 76ff. C. van de Velde 1966 211ff.

## Franz Cleyn?

295
*Aeneas carrying his father Anchises on his back. In the background, the Sack of Troy.* C 1620?
Oil on canvas
Frederiksberg Castle, Copenhagen
The attribution to Franz Cleyn is based on the stylistic resemblance to his Rosenborg paintings (particularly the Fireworks picture, cat. 218). Cleyn was in England by 1622 and settled there in 1624 or 1625. The original location for the painting is unknown. At Frederiksberg Castle there are 4 paintings with themes from the Aeneid, some of which may be attributed to Reinhold Timm.
*Provenance:* Glückstadt (before 1701). From 1701, Frederiksberg Castle.
*Literature:* F. Weilbach 1936 19 23 26.

296
*Oriental horsemen. In the background, a battlefield.* C 1620?
Oil on canvas
Frederiksberg Castle, Copenhagen
Attributed to Franz Cleyn, on the same evidence as in the previous catalogue number. Meir Stein interprets the picture as the prophet Daniel's prophecy on the four kingdoms.
*Provenance:* Glückstadt (before 1701). Frederiksberg Castle.
*Literature:* Weilbach 1936 19 23f. Stein 1987 65.

## Jacob van Doordt

d. Stockholm 1629

297
*One of Christian IV's sons as a boy (Frederik III?)*
Oil on canvas. 47.0×38.0 cm
Nivaagaard Samlingen
*Provenance:* Johan Bülow, Sanderumgaard; C. A. Jensen. From Hage's collection to Nivaagard.
*Literature:* Catalogue Nivaagaard 1908. Karl Madsen refers to an engraving by Adr. Matham of P. Isaacsz.: Portrait of the Heir Apparent as a child. Leo Swane, cat. 1949: Jacob van Doordt: Frederik III as a young boy?

298
*Christian IV 1611*
Dated top left "A° 1611"
Oil on copper. 87×66 cm
Gripsholm 1875. On permanent loan to Malmö Museum
A half length version of van Doordt, cat. 151.

## Willem Cornelisz. Duyster

Amsterdam 1598 or 99 – Amsterdam 1635

299
*The officer's visit*
Oil on panel. 58×45 cm
Statens Museum for Kunst inv. 318
Another version with approximately the same dimensions is known, see Christie's auction December 12, 1980, cat. 20 (repr.).
*Provenance:* Bought by the Museum at Bugge's auction August 21, 1837, no. 219 (as Jan le Duc).
*Literature:* Cat. 1946 no. 194. Rawert 1829 no. 249. Bode 1883 150 (as P. Codde). Martin 1935 364. Plietzsch 1960 31.

## Albert Freyse

?-Wolfenbüttel 1652?

301
*Duke August of Braunschweig-Wolfenbüttel 1579-1666 and his family*
Oil on canvas 120×168 cm
Braunschweigisches Landesmuseum no. VBM 3278
Musical entertainment at the court of Duke August the Yonger of Braunschweig-Wolfenbüttel: the Duke at the table in the middle of the room is looking out at the observer. The Duchess is playing an Italian spinet of the same type as cat. 400 and her six children make up a consort of viols. Facing the observer are a bass viol and a treble viol of the same type as cat. 409. On the table among the music books can be glimpsed an alto lute, which appears to be related to cat. 404. There is also the end of a recorder and behind the Duchess a flute which is peeping out from under a large lute, presumably a theorbo.

## Marcus Geraerts the Younger

Bruges 1561 – London 1639

302
*Anne of Denmark*
Oil on canvas 211.2×127.0 cm. Colour-plate XXXII
Marquess of Tavistock, Woburn Abbey, inv. 1377
Christian IV owned several portraits of his sister, some of which were signed by Marcus Geraerts, but they have all been lost, some of them in the Frederiksborg fire of 1859. For a particularly brilliant example, cf. cat. 109.
*Provenance:* Probably a gift to Lucy Harrington, third countess of Bedford. Inherited through the family down to the present owner.
*Literature:* Scharf 1890 42. Lionel Cust 1914 26. Kelly 1916 359. Strong 1969 299
*Exhibitions:* The Tate Gallery 1969 no. 160. Victoria and Albert Museum May 1979.

303
*Christian IV. 1614[?]*
Oil on canvas. 200×130 cm
Private collection, Great Britian
The painting is of the same type as the portrait of Christian IV in the Princeton Art Museum (cat. 3) only slightly differing. For example, Christian IV is wearing the chain of the Order of the Garter, but not the garter itself. The painting belongs to the large group of portraits of English court and nobility, which were executed by artists such as Marcus Geraerts, Robert Peake and John de Critz. English court painting was well represented in Christian IV's collections because of his family connections with James I, cf. cat. 109.
*Provenance:* Woburn Abbey. Christie's 25.6.1965 no. 11. Auction Bonham's London, 17.4.1980 no. 52. Lane Fine Art Ltd., London. Present owner.

## Cornelis Norbertus Gijsbrechts

-1659-1672-

304
*Trompe l'oeil with musical instruments*
Inscribed "F of Gijsbrechts"
Oil on canvas. 169×115 cm
Statens Museum for Kunst inv. 3073
The painting shows 11 musical instruments. By 1672, a number of them had more or less gone out of use. They belong to the instruments of Christian IV's time and 8 examples of similar types can be seen in the exhibition: 2 small descant recorders cat. 415-16, basset-recorder cat. 417, curved cornett cat. 424, orpharion cat. 407 and cittern cat. 406. In addition, there are violin and kit with bows, double harp, baroque recorder and straight cornett.
*Provenance:* One of a series of 12 (possibly 18) paintings commissioned for the Royal Danish Kunstkammer. On permanent loan to the Musikhistorisk Museum 1911 (depot no. X 82).

*301*

*Literature:* Gammelbo 1956 125. Mirimonde 1971 154 and 256ff.

## Pieter Isaacsz.

305

*Roman matrons on the Capitol*

Oil on copper. 41.5×62 cm

Rijksmuseum, Amsterdam. Inv.no. A 1720

The literary source is Aulus Gellius' Noctes Atticae and the scene the angry Roman matrons preparing to protest in the Roman Senate. The rogue Papirius has tricked them into thinking that the Senate was going to discuss whether each Roman citizen should have two wives.

*Literature:* Beckett 1937 82ff. Cat. Rijksmuseum 1976.

306

*Barbara Wittrup 1591-1653, married 1614 to Chancellor Christen Friis*

Oil on canvas

Private collection, Sweden

Isaacsz.' elegant portrait of the noblewoman Barbara Wittrup clearly demonstrates the influence of the Mannerist art of the court of Rudolf II as represented by his teacher Hans von Aachen (1552-1615). The magnificent hair is a "Venetian" reddish fair colour and the greenish carnation is reminiscent of von Aachen.

307

*Portrait of a noblewoman, here identifed as Kirsten Munk*

Oil on canvas. 100×80 cm

Private collection, Great Britain

The identification of the sitter is based on comparison with known portraits of Kirsten Munk, which are all of a later date, however (cf cat. 133). It can be compared to Isaacsz.' painting of Barbara Wittrup (cat. 306) with the red-gold hair and the slightly green carnation. The rich clothing and magnificent jewellery indicate the sitter's high social status. As the painting belonged to Anne of Denmark, Christian IV may have sent it to his sister in England, shortly after his marriage to Kirsten Munk, perhaps as a pendant to an Isaacsz. portrait of the king.

*Provenance:* Anne of Denmark, Oatlands, 1618. Charles

*305*

I. Northwick Park. Northwick Park Sale, 1964. Present owner.

## Attributed to Pieter Isaacsz.

308
*Judith with the head of Holofernes*
Oil on canvas. 214×154 cm
Statens Museum for Kunst inv. 981
Harald Olsen formerly attributed this painting to Denys Calvaert. A picture by him of Judith and Holofernes was in Rudolf II's collection in Prague (inventory 1621 no. 1315). The similarities between the "Judith" and some of the documented Danish works by Isaacsz. form the basis of the present attribution. Two paintings of Judith are listed in Isaacsz.' estate but we cannot be certain that they were painted by Pieter Isaacsz. himself. (A. Bredius: Künstler-Inventare, 1918 1474, inv.no. 60 and 68). There were many pictures of Judith, a popular contemporary motif in Christian IV's collections: at Frederiksborg Castle alone, there were seven versions of this Old Testament heroine. There is a replica or copy in Parma, Pinacoteca Stuard, cat. 1926 no. 52 pl. 12.
*Provenance:* Previously Kronborg. 1871 inventoried as the property of Statens Museum for kunst.
*Literature:* H. Olsen 1961 45.

## Karel van Mander III

309
*An old mand. Allegory of Sight.* 1639
Inscribed "K. V. Mander 1639"
Oil on panel. 58×44.5 cm
Statens Museum for Kunst Sp. 799
Three out of five paintings on the senses are extant, cat.no. 310, an allegory of Taste, previously Sadolin's collection, Arne Bruun Rasmussens's Auctions 371/270 (Nov. 1977) and the present painting. Hearing, cf. Arne Bruun Rasmussens's Auctions 123/283 (Nov. 1960) cat. no. 283, and Taste, Gaunø 103, are copies or replicas.
*Provenance:* Purchased by J. S. Wahl 1740 from Poul Løvenørn's collection. Wahl's auction, March 1766, cat. no. 16: "The 5 Senses in original works". Bodendick's collection, cat. 1825, no. 100. Purchased 1810 with Bodendick's collection by Den kgl. Malerisamling.

*Literature:* Friis 1890-1901 78. Gerson 1942 464. Sthyr 1945 28 Eller 1973 168, 182.

310
*An old woman. Allegory of hearing.* 1639
Oil on panel 58×44.5 cm
Statens Museum for Kunst Sp. 800
Pendant to cat.no. 309
*Provenance:* Cf. the previous entry.
*Literature:* Friis 1890-1901 78 Gerson 1942 464. Sthyr 1945 28.

311
*Prince Christian, the Heir Apparent*
Oil on canvas. 213×111 cm
Gaunøfonden no. 225
*Provenance:* Ibstrup 1732? Gavnø.
*Literature:* Eller 1971 169.

312
*The finding of Prince Svend's Body.* C 1642
Oil on canvas 235×56.5 cm
Statens Museum for Kunst Sp. 795
The literary source is Torquato Tasso: Gerusalemme liberata VIII, 32-33: Back in the crusaders' camp outside Jerusalem, the Danish knight Karl (Carlo) is reporting on how he found the body of his countryman Prince Svend (Sveno) with two hermits. He had been killed at the hand of the nomadic Moslem chief Suliman. Sven's sword is handed over to Rinaldo who is enjoined to carry out revenge. The style in this night scene is Caravaggesque particularly in the pronounced chiaroscuro and the torch flame shielded by a hand. Two copies in cabinet size are known: Aarhus Kunstmuseum, inv. 40 and the former Sadolin collection (with the inscription: "Prince Svend of Denmark, famous in the Crusades", cf. Raadhusudstillingen 1901, cat. no. 1212, and Kunst i Privateje III, 1945 168f. Engraved by Haelwegh, cf. Jørgen Sthyr, Dansk Grafik 1500-1800, 1043 77.
The painting can possibly be dated before 1642 on the basis of the correspondance between the historian Steffen Hansen Stephanius in Sorø and Ole Worm, in which the identity of Prince Svend is discussed: Stephanius to Worm 2.2.1642: "He cannot be other than Sweyn Forkbeard's grandson ..." and Worm to Stephanius 7.2.1642: "This painting must depict the man you describe and not the other". (See H. D. Schepelern ed.: Ole Worms Breve II, 317f.). That "this painting" is by van Mander is not stated in the letters.
*Provenance:* Purchased from J. S. Wahl March 28 1753 for the Royal Danish Kunstkammer. Inv. 1775, 273/3. The Royal Picture Gallery in 1872.
*Literature:* Hauber 1777 119. Ramdohr 1792 110. Friis 1890-1901 78. Friis 1904 26. Hertz 1921-1923 373. Hertz 1924-1925 302. Sthyr 1938 20, 53, Andrup 1939 108. Gerson 1942 465. Sthyr 1945 28. Eller 1971 133f. Schepelern 1980 12ff.

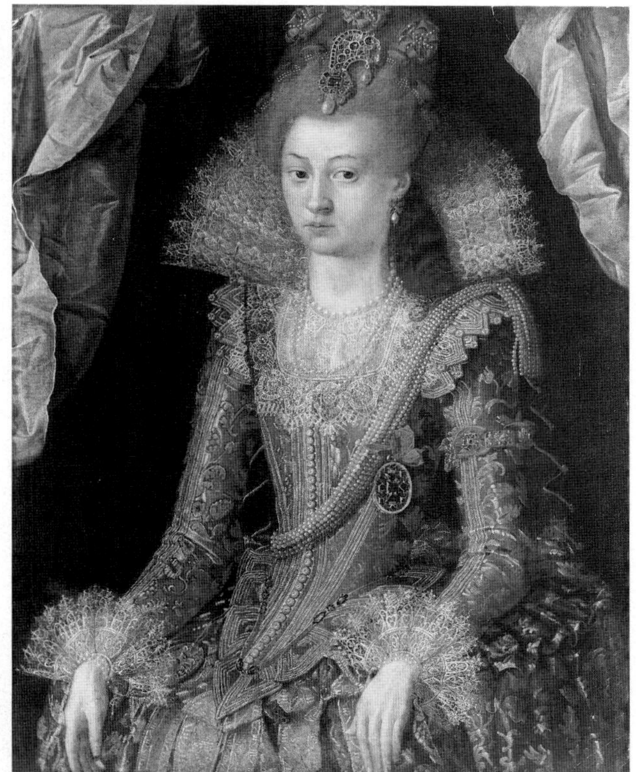

*307*

313
*A Tartar legation visiting Copenhagen 1655*
Oil on canvas. 218×282 cm
Statens Museum for Kunst Sp. 796
Inscribed on cartellino at the lower right: "SVLTAN. KOLSEHATTAFALCK. NVRAALLE. ELCHEBY. MURSA. DERVSS. HASSAN. BABA. ARRAMASAN 1655". In addition to the portraits, the execution of a Tartar envoys's servant is shown on the rigtht. One of the envoys has a bow and arrow, which suggests a particular event: "On Sunday Hs. M. (His Majesty) went hunting on Amager and desired that they (i.e. the envoys) should go with him to show their skill in riding and archery", Becker 1847, p. 61. The occasion for the visit of the envoys of "the Precopensian Tartar prince" was a petition "that the King of Denmark will invade Russia from Norway, or at the least, will not send the Grand Duke any munitions".
*Provenance:* The Royal Danish Kunstkammer 1689, 165. 1737, 888/54. 1827 to the Royal Picture Gallery.
*Literature:* Hauber 1777 96. Ramdohr 1792 129. Becker 1847 61. Friis 1877 19ff and 1890-91 7ff. Eller 1971 257 and 1984 386.

314
*The artist with his family.* 1660s
Oil on canvas. 136.5×111.5 cm
Statens Museum for Kunst Inv. 3824
The group portrait shows the artist, his wife Maria Fern and, most probably, his mother-in-law. A replica or copy of the picture at Frederiksborg, inv.no. 2163 is inscribed "Carl van Mandern His Wife and Wife's Mother" and "Ipse pinxit" and "From the collection of Klevenfeldt". An earlier date of c 1640 is based on a connection between the picture and the marriage of Mander and Maria Fern at that time. The age of the sitters discounts this, however and the style can be compared with later works such as the Gamborg family portrait. Engraved by Coenrad Waumans (Westergaard 7641).
*Provenance:* Kunsthalle, Hamburg 1876. Statens Museum for Kunst December 1927.
*Literature:* Falck 1926-1928 182f. Gerson 1942 464. Tidens Konsthistorie 1950 212.

315
*The Elector of Saxony's Italian dwarf Giacomo Favorchi with Princess Magdalena Sibylla's dog Raro*
Oil on canvas. 163.2×103.8 cm
Statens Museum for Kunst Sp. 798.
Inscribed "Giacomo Favorchi Nano Italiano" and "Raro". On the dog's collar can be seen the initials "MS" (Magdalena Sibylla). The picture may have been painted on the occasion of Magdalena Sibylla's visit to Denmark 1663. Eller 1971 does not consider the painting to be by van Mander.
*Provenance:* The Royal Danish Kunstkammer 1689 143. To the Royal Picture Gallery 1827.
*Literature:* Friis 1890-1901 79. K. Madsen 1915 181. Hertz 1924-1925 343. Krabbe 1930 114-117. Sthyr 1945 34 López-Rey 1950 284 note 15. Tietze-Conrat 1957 100. Eller 197.
*Exhibtions:* 330. Raadhusudstillingen 1901 no. 1216.

*313*

*315*

318
*An allegory of the Sense of Hearing*
Oil on canvas. 1668×202 cm (oval)
Nasjonalgalleriet, Oslo inv. 1099
At Holsteinborg, a manor house on Zealand, there is a cycle with the 5 senses, originally a ceiling decoration, in which "Hearing" is almost identical to the Oslo picture in iconography and composition, but rectangular in shape. On Mander's interest in the senses as allegorical pictures, see cat. 309-310 and 385.
*Provenance:* Rosenborg(?): (cf. Friis 1872-1878, p. 117). Presented to Count A. G. Moltke 1751 (?). Fredensborg Castle (?) Bequeathed by Sophus Larpent to Nasjonalgalleriet 1914.
*Literature:* Cat. 1973 no. 128. Friis 1872-1878 116f.

319
*Hydaspes and Persina beside Andromeda's picture*
Oil on canvas. 110×220 cm
Staatliche Kunstsammlungen Kassel, Gemäldegalerie Alte Meister (Leihgabe der Verwaltung der Staatlichen Schlösser und Gärten Hessen) inv. GK 1028a
The literary source is Heliodor: Aethiopica IV, 8, see p. 83. Unlike Honthorst's decoration of the King's Chamber at Kronborg, (cat. 229-32), van Manders's series of 10 pictures (now 9, all in Kassel) cannot be linked to a wedding.
*Provenance:* Swedish war booty 1648-50? Landgrave William VIII of Hessen-Kassel before 1749 (cf. inv. 1749: "Nr. 435-444, Zehen Stück, so der Baron von Stein aus Schweden anhero bracht."). Löwenburg, Schlosspark Wilhelmshöhe, late 18th century. Landgrafenmuseum Kassel 1937-39.
*Literature:* Andrup 1939 102. Gerson 1942 465. Stechow 1953 151f.

316
*Priests by a globe*
Oil on canvas. 114×142 cm
Gavnø no. 96
Four paintings at Gavnø may be part of a ceiling decoration. They all show the same characteristic pronounced foreshortening. The literary source for the decoration is inknown.
*Literature:* Andrup 1914 no. 96.

317
*A Turk accompanied by two warriors and five servants*
Oil on canvas. 141.5×111.5 cm
Gavnø no. 97
See the previous entry
*Literature:* Andrup 1914 no. 97.

*318*

*319*

320
*Thyamis takes Chariklea and Theagenes prisoners*
Oil on canvas. 109×199 cm
Staatliche Kunstsammlungen Kassel, Gemäldegalerie Alte Meister (Leihgabe der Verwaltung der Staatliche Schlösser und Gärten Hessen) inv. GK 1028e
The literary source is Heliodor: Aethiopica I, 4, see p. 84.
*Provenance:* see previous entry.
*Literature:* Andrup 1939 104. Gerson 1942 465. Stechow 1953 151f.

## Daniel Mytens the Elder

Delft c 1590 – The Hague before 1648

321
*Charles I of England (1600-1649) as Prince of Wales.* 1624
Inscribed on the wall below the window "Carolus magnae Britanniæ Princeps ætatis suæ, XXIII, anno D 1624"
Oil on canvas. 207×125 cm
Statens Museum for Kunst Sp. 72
Studio replica of the signed picture in Ottawa, National Gallery of Canada, Cat. 1961, Vol. I, no. 768.
*Provenance:* Frederiksborg 1636. Inv. 1650 ed. A. Petersen 1866 39. Inv. 1677. To the Royal Danish Kunstkammer 1793. Inv. 1807,13/a 788. 1827 to the Royal Picture Gallery.
*Literature:* Cat. 1946 no. 461. Ramdohr 1792 137f. Bredius and Moes 1907 90. Kelly 1920 84. Drost 1926 255. Toynbee 1939 121f. O. ter Kuile 1969 55f.

## Reinhold Timm

322
*Group of Musicians (c 1620)*
Signed "RT"
Oil on canvas. 207×113.5 cm. Colour-plate XXI
Private collection, The Netherlands
4 musicians are playing instruments of a type to be found in the exhibition: tenor flute, alto lute, Irish harp and bass viol. Of particular interest are the harpist and his instrument. 17th century Irish harps are characteristic because of the very curved broad front pillar. The instrument rests on the player's left shoulder and the strings are plucked with the nails as can be seen in the painting from the position of the left hand and fingers.
*Provenance:* Otto Thott's auction 1787 no. 562. Gaunø 169. Christies 9.7.1976.
*Literature:* Beckett 1937 69f. (ill). Friis 1872ff 117. Holst 1984 149f (ill.).

323
*A Roman general before a besieged city.* 1620s
Oil on canvas
Frederiksberg Castle
The painting belongs with cat. 296, here attributed to Franz Cleyn. Both are mounted in the ceiling at Frederiksberg Castle. The attribution to Timm rests on the stylistic similarities with the Rosenborg series, especially cat.no. 216. Meir Stein regards the picture as part of a series on Daniel's prophecy of the four kingdoms.
*Provenance:* Glückstadt (before 1701). Frederiksberg Castle.
*Literature:* F. Weilbach 1936 23f. Stein 1987 65.

## Frederick van Valckenborch

Antwerp 1570 – Nuremberg 1623

324
*Carnival*
Oil on canvas. 52.0×88.0 cm
Munich, Alte Pinakothek. Inv. 7118
A night scene depicting various masked figures. To the right is a waggon with musicians, behind that, a group of acrobats. Paintings with similar themes were at Frederiksborg 1636, for example "one night piece showing masked persons holding a banquet" and "two paintings in which some masked persons are acting" (Frederiksborg's inventory 1650 (1636) ed. A. Petersen 1866 63, 111). There were several paintings by the Valckenborch family at Frederiksborg, even though the inventory does not permit identification of each member of the familiy, but simply lists "Falckenberig". With this identification are listed a painting of animals fighting, a night scene of Nero burning Rome and three battle scenes. Jonas Charisius purchased two paintings "De bello Amazonum" by "Valkenberg" in the Netherlands 1607 for Christian IV. (Nystrøm 1908 229).

*321*

## Werner Jacobsz. van den Valckert

Amsterdam 1581-Amsterdam after 1627

325
*Galathea (1619)*
Oil on canvas. 93.5×124 cm
Private collection, Oslo
van den Valckert was one of the painters who provided pictures for Christian IV's Oratory at Frederiksborg (destroyed by fire 1859). The provenance of the pictures of Galathea and Neptune exhibited here is not known, but they have been identified by van Thiel as two paintings from among the many which were offered to Christian IV in 1621 by Frans Bastiaensz: no. 228: "de Triton van Valckart RD 50" and 229: "de Gallette (= Galathea) van Valckart RD 50" (see F. Beckett 1949 259 "reghijster vand DHr fransoes bastijansens schildery binnen Koppenhagen"). A painting of the mocking of Christ by van den Valckert was formerly in the University Library, but is presumably lost. It is copied in a woodcut by Chr. I van Sichem (?), Amsterdam, Rijksprentenkabinet.
*Provenance:* Offered to Christian IV by Frans Bastiaensz. 1621?
*Literature:* van Thiel 1983 128ff, 147.

326
*Neptune 1619*
Oil on canvas. 93.5×124 cm
Private collection, Oslo
See the previous entry.

## Sebastien Vrancx

Antwerp 1573 – Antwerp 1647

327
*Festival in a palace garden*
Oil on panel. 72×106.5 cm
Statens Museum for Kunst inv. 1059
The painting is perhaps identical with a picture in the Frederiksborg inventory 1650: (the room beside the Duchess of Pomerania's room:) "one long picture on which is painted a castle and a garden, below this some gentlemen, ladies walking, in a gilded frame". At Frederiksborg there were several paintings with musicians in gardens, courtly gatherings and masked figures i.a. "one painting showing some gentlemen with ladies banqueting and making music in garden".
*Provenance:* At Fredensborg 1848 (Stroe 318). 1864 to the Royal Museum of Fine Arts.
*Literature:* Cat. 1946 no. 788. Frimmel 1907 193. Tacács 1961 52. Legrand 1963 190. Winkler 1964 327.

331

## Danish School c 1634(?)

328
*Christian, the Prince Elect*
Oil on canvas. 204×107 cm
Gripsholm 1121
The artist who worked most for the Prince Elect at his court in Nykøbing was Morten Steenwinckel, but other painters were also active at the court of the heir to the throne.

## Danish School c 1634

329
*Princess Magdalena Sibylla*
Oil on canvas. 207×105 cm
Gripsholm 1122
See cat. 328.

## English School, 17th Century

330
*James I*
Oil on canvas. 196×114 cm
Statens Konstsamlingar, on permanent loan to Malmö Museum, Sweden
Christian IV's collections naturally included many portraits of his brother-in-law, Mary Stuart's son James. At Kronborg, for example, about 1590, there was an equestrian portrait of James (Friis 1890-1901 169f). A three quarter portrait on panel and a painting on copper were lost in the Frederiksborg fire in 1859.
*Provenance:* Swedish war booty 1658-60?
*Literature:* Friis 1890-1901 169f.

## French School, late 16th century

331
*"Bal à la Cour des Valois"*
Oil on canvas. 163×194 cm
Musée des Beaux-Arts, Rennes no. 794.1.135
Picture of a celebration in a princely environment: there is riotous dancing. The musicians at the front of the platform are playing 3 violins and a double bass: the violin family is winning popularity in ensembles for entertainment and dancing. In theme and detail, the picture is almost identical to a painting in the Lord of L'Isle and Dudley collection, in which the central couple represent Queen Elizabeth and Lord Leicester.
*Provenance:* President de Robiens. Revolutionary confiscation. Musée des Beaux Arts, Rennes 1794.
*Literature:* Lesure 1966 156-157. Musée des Beaux-Arts,

Rennes 1978 no. 83. Musée de Picardie, Amiens 1983 no. 54.

## Danish School c 1630. Previously attributed to Remmert Petersen

332

*"Ball at the Ruds"*

Oil on canvas. 132×200 cm

Frederiksborg A 7770

The picture shows a ball at the home of a Danish noble family. According to the inscription, Corfitz Rud til Sandholdt is sitting at the table and his wife Birgitte Rosensparre is standing beside him. The three couples dancing are their three daughters Mette, Helvig and Birgitte Rud and their husbands, Niels Trolle, Gregers Krabbe and Christen Skeel. The woman on the far right is Margrethe Rosenkrantz, who was brought up by Corfitz Rud. The music is supplied by trumpeters on a trumpeter stand.

*Provenance:* From Ryegaard 1970.

*Literature:* Holst 1983 151.

## Danish School c 1616

333

*Musical scene*

Oil on panel. 64.6×48.5 cm

Musikhistorisk Museum and Carl Claudius' Collection no. OB 46

Chamber music scene with spinet, lute and flute. The man with the flute has a striking resemblance to the young Christian IV. This together with the date, has given rise to the supposition that this might represent the king with Queen Anna Cathrine and the heir apparent. Proof of this supposition would be of importance as we lack information on whether Chr. IV simply promoted music or was himself a practising amateur.

*Provenance:* Carl Claudius before 1925.

*Literature:* Seiffert 1925 293.

## Danish School, before 1620

334

*Portrait of a family. Previously called The Schiønning family picture*

Oil on canvas. 217×117 cm

Frederiksborg R94

The costume of the sitters shows that the picture must have been painted before 1620. The artist in Denmark at that time who had the greatest knowledge of the group portrait tradition was Pieter Isaacsz., but whether he painted the picture on exhibition and who the sitters are cannot be clarified at present. The group portrait shows similarities to a group picture with as many as 22 sitters at the Schleswig-Holsteinisches Landesmuseum at Gottorp Castle, "Family group from Rüllschau". The picture comes from the little church in Rüllschau near Flensborg, but the identity of the sitters has not been established. The similarity between the two paintings was noticed by Wolfgang J. Müller.

*Literature:* Wolfgang J. Müller 1960 159f.

*333*

## Dutch school?

335

*Lute player at a table*

Inscribed "Jeltop pinxit"

Oil on panel. 32.3×26.5 cm

Statens Museum for Kunst inv. 1394

*Provenance:* To Statens Museum for Kunst from Frederiksborg 1890.

## Dutch School?

336

*Caritas(?)*

Unknown artist after 1617. Inscribed below "VB" (?)

Oil on panel. 99×68 cm

Statens Museum for Kunst Stroe 382

The most important iconographic feature in the representation of Charity, the suckling child, is omitted here. The aspect of earthly love is stressed by the fruit. On the back is the mark of the panel maker, perhaps Hans van Haaecht.

*Provenance:* To the Royal Danish Kunstkammer 1785.

*338*

## Artists unknown

337
*Tower of Babel*
Oil on panel. 56.8×106.0 cm
Rosenborg 3247
*Provenance:* Rosenborg inv. 1718, 594 no. 1.

338
*Lot and his daughters*
Oil on panel(?) 48.5×39.3 cm
Rosenborg 32.72
The painting illustrates Genesis chap. 19, verses 30-38, where Lot's daughters could not get husbands after the destruction of Sodom and therefore made their father drunk and slept with him. In Karel van Mander's estate, an engraved copperplate of Albert Haelwegh's "Lot and his daughters" (Sthyr 136a) was found along with other copperplates by Haelwegh from compositions by van Mander. The painting might therefore be an early work by Karel van Mander.
*Provenance:* Rosenborg inv. 1718, 246 no. 32
*Literature:* Sthyr 136a

339
*Lot and his daughters*
Oil on panel. 38.8×59.5 cm
Rosenborg 33.11
*Provenance:* Rosenborg inv. 1718, 251 no. 52.

340
*Joseph and Potiphar's wife*
Oil on panel. 16.3×24.2 cm
Rosenborg 32.65
*Provenance:* Rosenborg inv. 1718, 249 no. 42.

341
*Christ at Emmaus*
Oil on copper. 46.5×55.8 cm
Rosenborg 33.12
*Provenance:* Rosenborg inv. 1830 D 19

342
*Christ on the cross*
Oil on canvas. 53.9×38.0 cm
Rosenborg 32.68
The painting has been attributed to the painter Heinrich Janssen (1625-67) by Erik Moltke (verbally), because of similarities to his work in Flensborg.
*Provenance:* Rosenborg inv. 1718, 392, no. 5.

343
*Landscape with a nymph fleeing from Neptune*
Gouache on panel. 13.5×19.7 cm
Rosenborg 33.52
*Provenance:* Rosenborg inv. 1718, 242 no. 10.

344
*Morning. Allegory*
Oil on copper. 42.5×28.5 cm
Rosenborg 30.11
*Provenance:* Rosenborg inv. 1718, 392 no. 6.

345
*Noon. Allegory*
Oil on copper. 48.5×38.8 cm
Rosenborg 30.10
*Provenance:* Rosenborg inv. 1718, 391 no. 3.

346
*Evening. Allegory*
Oil on copper. 42.5×28.5 cm
Rosenborg 30.12
*Provenance:* Rosenborg 1718, 392 no. 7.

347
*Night. Allegory*
Oil on copper. 48.7×38.5 cm
Rosenborg 30.9
*Provenance:* Rosenborg 1718, 391 no. 4.

348
*The Sack of Troy*
Oil on canvas. 131×238 cm
Rosenborg 30.28
*Provenance:* Rosenborg 1696, 133 no. 6.

349
*Group playing board games*
Oil on panel. 18.0×28.0 cm
Rosenborg 32.58
*Provenance:* Rosenborg 1718, 248 no. 36.

350
*Landscape with recumbent female nude*
Water colour on paper. 16.0×15.9 cm
Rosenborg 32.67
*Provenance:* Rosenborg 1718, 251 no. 49.

351
*Landscape with seated female nude*
Oil on copper. 23.5×16.9 cm
Rosenborg 32.63
*Provenance:* Rosenborg 1718, 247 no. 35

352
*Standing female nude*
Oil on panel. 23.3×16,8 cm
Rosenborg 32.64
*Provenance:* Rosenborg 1718, 247 no. 35.

353
*Landscape with figures*
Gouache on panel. 14.3×20.1 cm
Rosenborg 33.51
Pendant to cat. 343
*Provenance:* Rosenborg 1718, 242 no. 10.

354
*Frost scene*
Oil on panel. 20.2×37.8 cm
Rosenborg 32.2
*Provenance:* Rosenborg 1718, 246 no. 27

355
*Mountain landscape with river*
Oil on canvas. 18.0×23.5 cm
Rosenborg 32.46
*Provenance:* Rosenborg 1797, 194 no. 39.

*339*

357

356
*Landscape with a lake*
Oil on panel. 18.6×28.1 cm
Rosenborg 32.32

## Drawings

### Franz Cleyn

357
*Satyr spying on a sleeping woman*
Signed lower left "Francesco Clein" and dated lower right "1615"
Pencil, pen, black ink. 9.9×15,9 cm
Den kgl. Kobberstiksamling Td 503,3
Inscribed "L.S." (Lorenz Spengler's collector's mark). Verso inscribed lower right "Fr. Clein"; fragment of a letter in German (the paper has been folded like a letter). The Italianate signature suggests that the drawing was made while Cleyn was in Italy, cf. Horace Walpole: Anecdotes of Painting in England, Vol. II, Strawberry Hill 1762 127.
*Provenance:* Lorenz Spengler catalogue 1812 9.
*Literature:* Beckett 1936 4. Cat. Br. Dr. I 286.

358
*Apollo flaying Marsyas*
Signed "Zur frewndlichen Gedächtnuss (sic) gemacht in Copenhagen. Franz Clein. 1617".
Pencil, red chalk, pen, black and brown ink, heightened with white body colour. 12.3 × 15.9 cm
Den kgl. Kobberstiksamling Td 503,2, inv. 13097
Presumably a page from an album amoricum. The literary source is Ovid: Metamorphoses I 382-400. The Phrygian satyr Marsyas challenged Apollo to a musical competition. He lost and as punishment for his arrogance, he was flayed alive by the god. The tears of his friends became a river.
*Provenance:* Schaper, auction Sept. 26 ff 1853 (postponed to Dec. 5), no. 48.
*Literature:* Beckett 1936 4. Beckett 1937 43f. DT I 29; II 9. Cat. Br. Dr. I 286.
*Exhibitions:* Staatsgalerie Stuttgart 1979-80 N 30.

359
*A collector or a sculptor*
Inscribed "Fr. Klein"
Pen, brown ink. 27.3×18.4 cm
Den kgl. Kobberstiksamling Td. 503,9
Lower right "115" and lower left stamp "L.S." (Lorenz Spengler's collector's mark). Verso: draft of accounts and light sketches.
*Provenance:* Lorenz Spengler catalogue 1812 9.
*Literature:* Cat. Br. Dr. I 286. (The date listed here "1608" cannot be found on the drawing).

360
*Anatomical studies.* Drawn in Italy?
Pen, brown ink, 39.2×25.3 cm
Den kgl. Kobberstiksamling Td. 503,6
Top left study of a right arm. Top right two men wrestl-

ing. Lower left two men leaning slightly forward, half length. Lower right seated man leaning far back.
*Literature:* DT I 29. Cat. Br. Dr. I 286. Hjorth Nielsen 1979 19.
*Exhibitions:* Staatsgalerie Stuttgart 1979-80 145.

361
*Anatomical studies.* Drawn in Italy?
Pen, brush, brown ink. 28.3×20.0 cm
Den kgl. Kobberstiksamling Td. 503.7
Top left study of a right and a left leg. Top right and lower left, sketches of five standing figures (from sculptures). Lower right a smiling face and three feet. In addition, pen trials and fragments of Italian text (draft of a letter). Verso: three large figure compositions, a few sketches of figures, pen trials and handwriting specimens in Italian. The character of the studies and the text indicate that the drawing was made in Italy.
*Literature:* DT 29. Cat. Br. Dr. I 286.

*359*

362
*Figure composition*
Inscribed lower right "fr. Klein"
Pen, black ink. 17.1×21.9 cm
Den kgl. Kobberstiksamling Td 503,13
Lower left stamp "L.S." (Lorenz Spengler's collector's mark) and lower right "108".
*Provenance:* Lorenz Spengler catalogue 1812 9.
*Literature:* Cat Br. Dr. I 286.

363
*Adam and Eve*
Pen, brown and black ink. 31.6×18.0 cm
Den kgl. Kobberstiksamling Td 503.12
*Literature:* Cat. Br. Dr. I 286.

364
*Study of Christ*
Inscribed "Fr. Klein" at the bottom
Pen, black ink. 20.7×18.1 cm
Den kgl. Kobberstiksamling Td 503,15
Lower left "L.S." (twice; Lorenz Spengler's collector's mark).
*Provenance:* Lorenz Spengler catalogue 1812 9.
*Literature:* Cat. Br. Dr. I 286.

365
*The Descent from the Cross*
Inscribed lower left "Fr. Klein fe."
Pencil, pen, brown ink, brush, red water colour. 33.3×21.4 cm
Den kgl. Kobberstiksamling Td 503.10
Verso: a tracing of the figure of Christ.
Top left "No. 16".
*Literature:* Cat. Br. Dr. I 286.

366
*The dead Christ with an angel*
Inscribed lower left "Fr. Klein"
Pen, brown ink. 30.6×19.8 cm
Den kgl. Kobberstiksamling Td 503,8
Below right "110" and stamp "L.S." (Lorenz Spengler's collector's mark).
Verso: tracing of Christ's right arm and leg.
*Provenance:* Lorenz Spengler catalogue 1812 9
*Literature:* Cat. Br. Dr. I 286.

367
*The Assumption*
Inscribed "Fr: Klein"
Pen, brown ink. 25.5×19.0 cm
Den kgl. Kobberstiksamling Td. 501,11
Verso: accounts.
*Literature:* Cat. Br. Dr. I 286.

*372*

368
*The martyrdom of St. Sebastian*
Pen, black ink, heightened with white body colour 27.9×37.1 cm
Den kgl. Kobberstiksamling Td 503.5
Top left "Rembrant". Verso lower left "No. 22". Along the left side "Renbrandt" (sic), deleted. Lower right "F. Kleyen" and "No. 42." (or 47?). A crucified thief and lettering including "Amsterdam".
*Literature:* Cat. Br. Dr. I 286.

369
*Man standing with an axe*
Pen, black ink. 26.9×16.6 cm
Den kgl. Kobberstiksamling Td. 503,14
Lower left "L.S." and lower right "114" (Lorenz Spengler's collector's mark and number). Verso "Fr. Cleijn" (added later in pencil).
*Provenance:* Lorenz Spengler catalogue 1812 9.
*Literature:* Cat. Br. Dr. I 286.

*370*
*Female nude*
Inscribed "Fr. Klein"
Pen, brown ink. 22.0×17.4 cm
Den kgl. Kobberstiksamling Td. 503,4
Lower right sketches of two nude male models. Inscribed lower right "109" (Lorenz Spengler's collector's number?). The female figure cannot be definitely identified; perhaps a representation of Fortune, perhaps of Venus on a shell.
*Provenance:* Lorenz Spengler catalogue 1812 9 (?). The catalogue lists "nine studies and pen drawings" by Cleyn, nos. 107-115.
*Literature:* Cat. Br. Dr. I 286.

371
*The Last Judgement*
Pen and brown ink. 19.2×17.9 cm
Den kgl. Kobberstiksamling Td. 503,16
Verso: falling devil (traced through the paper). Lower left "L.S." (Lorenz Spengler's collector's mark).
*Provenance:* Lorenz Spengler.

372
*Heraldic composition*
Inscribed "f: Klein"
Pen, brown ink. 29.9×20.9 cm
Den kgl. Kobberstiksamling Td. 503,17
Lower left "L.S." and lower right "113" (Lorenz Spengler's collector's mark and number). Verso male herma, studies of male arms, studies of horses' legs, accounts and lettering. The coat of arms can be assigned to the family van Swieten of Leiden, cf. the epitaph of the family van Swieten, 1552, in Stedelijk Museum de Lakenhal, Leiden, cat. 1983, inv. no. 250. The drawing was possibly copied from a sepulchral statue. It can be argued from this that Cleyn travelled or settled in Holland.
*Provenance:* Lorenz Spengler catalogue 1812 9.

## Karel van Mander III

373
*Laughing youth* 1631
Inscribed "K.VM 1631", lower left "Karl von Mandern 1631." (in a later hand)
Black and white chalk on grey-blue paper. 25.5×24.5 cm
Den kgl. Kobberstiksamling Td. 503,19
Lower left "L.S." (Lorenz Spengler's collector's mark). Lower right "99".
*Provenance:* Lorenz Spengler catalogue 1812 99.
*Literature:* Andrup 1933-1934 152f. DT I 35.

374
*Danish Nobleman?* 1632
Inscribed lower right "C. v: Mandern" (later addition?) and "1632" (in pencil)
Black chalk on greyish paper. 28.6×15.5 cm

*378*

Den kgl. Kobberstiksamling Td. 503,28
Part of the paper has been cut off at the left, so that the edge follows the contours of the hat and breast. Lower left "L.S." (Lorenz Spengler's collector's mark). Verso "N: 55: W. Riboldtz" (old ink inscription).
*Provenance:* Wilchen Riboldt (died 1711). Lorenz Spengler catalogue 1812 100.
*Literature:* Andrup 1933-34 159f. Hjort Nielsen 1979 17.

375
*Vertumnus and Pomona.* 1635
Inscribed lower left "Mander en Coppehage le 17.de Maj 1635"
Pencil, pen, ink, brush, brown and grey-blue water colour, heightened with white. 23.8×21.3 cm
Den kgl. Kobberstiksamling Td. 503,31
The literary source is Ovid: Metamorphoses XIV 623-771: the nymph Pomona had her heart set on cultivating and caring for King Proca's orchard and she had no time for her many suitors, including Vertumnus. Dressed as an old woman, he wins Pomona's confidence and when he throws aside his disguise, she is captivated by his youth and beauty.
*Literature:* Andrup 1933-34 156 ff 161. Gerson 1942 464 note 1. DT I 35.

376
*Old woman with a recorder. Half length oval.* 1639 (?)
Inscribed on the left side "K: V. Mander"
Red, black and white chalk. 55.3×39.7 cm
Den kgl. Kobberstiksamling Td. 504,14
The paper is pieced together horizontally in the middle. Below left "L.S." and below right "98" (Lorenz Spengler's collector's mark and number). Verso left "Copie. Carl v. Mander jun. Spenglers Catalog 98". On the right "Copie. Carl v. Mander junior Spengls Catal. 98" (two different hands).
*Provenance:* A. van Steenwinckel, auction Dec. 4 ff 1688 no. 79: "One octagonal painting of an old hag with a flute". Lorenz Spengler catalogue 18 12 98.

377
*Christian V (1646-99), King of Denmark, as a child.* 1650s
Inscribed "König Cristian der finfte als Printz"
Black and white chalk on bluish paper. 21.0×25.2 cm
Den kgl. Kobberstiksamling Td 503,20
Inscribed verso in broad black chalk "König Christianus Quintus als Cron Printz von Dannemarck". Underneath in smaller writing "C.v. Mander?". Study for Manders's oil painting at Rosenborg (inv. 9179).
*Literature:* DT I 35; II pl. 13.

378
*Standing male figure in a cloak and turban.* C 1655
Inscribed "K V Mander Fecit Copenhagen A 1670"
Black and white chalk on greyish prepared paper. 43.3×26.6 cm
Den kgl. Kobberstiksamling Td. 503,24
Verso below with charcoal "119". The signature and date are not in Mander's handwriting and from a stylistic viewpoint, the dating is improbable. The dress and position of the figure show some relation to the central figure in Mander's oil painting. "The Tartar legation in Copenhagen 1655", (The Royal Museum of Fine Arts, Sp. 796, cat. 313). The drawings Td. 503,21 – Td. 503,25, cat. 376 to 379, would appear to date from the same period. A drawing in Leipzig, Museum der bildenden Künste, Graphische Sammlung undoubtedly belongs to this series; cf. Zeitschrift für bildende Kunst 1913. The inscription may have appeared when Karel van Mander's estate was inventoried prior to its auction.

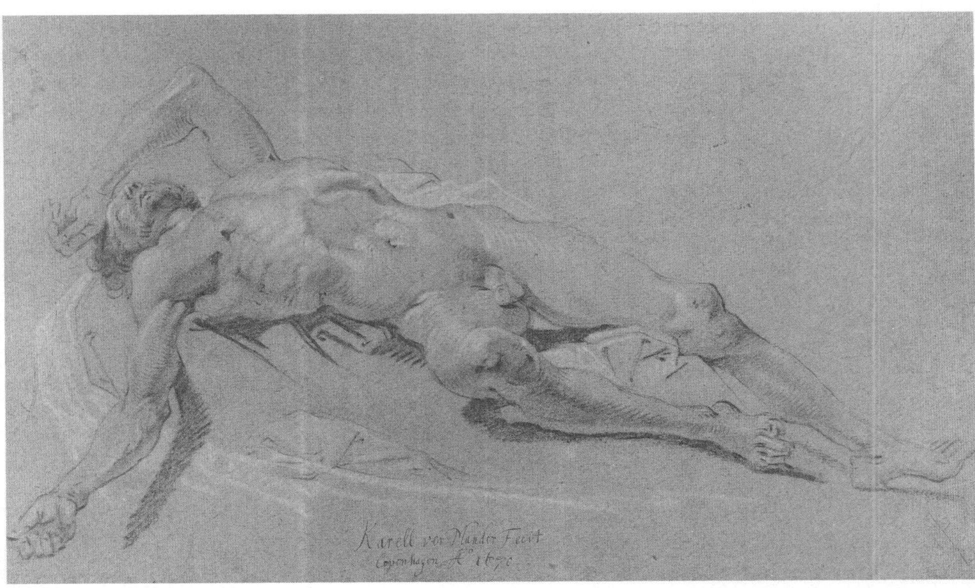


379
*Standing figure in cloak and fur hat leaning on a staff.*
C 1655
Black and white chalk on greyish prepared paper. 40.7×23.5 cm
Den kgl. Kobberstiksamling Td. 503,22
Verso lower left "C. v Mander" and above "27" (added later in pencil).

380
*Kneeling female figure with a turban.* C 1655
Inscribed lower left "K: V Mander Fecit Copenhagen A 1670"
Black and white chalk on greyish prepared paper. 42.5×26.5 cm
Den kgl. Kobberstiksamling Td. 503,23
Verso below (in pencil) "120".

381
*Seated figure in cloak and turban holding a book.* C 1655
Inscribed below "K: V Mander Fecit. Copenhagen A 1670"
Black and white chalk on greyish grounded paper. 42.7×26.2 cm
Den kgl. Kobberstiksamling Td. 503,21
Verso below in pencil "119" (corrected to "118").
*Literature:* Voss 1913 223.

382
*Seated figure in cloak and fur hat.* C 1655
Inscribed below "K: V Mander. Fecit Copenhagen A: 1670"
Black and white chalk on greyish prepared paper. 41.7×26.5 cm
Den kgl. Kobberstiksamling Td. 503,25, inv. 11847
Lower right "Gr" inscribed in a half circle (August Grahl's collector's mark). Verso below "125" (corrected to "124") and "Hof". Lower left "1010" (J. Rump's inventory no.). Lower right "42.265 II".
*Provenance:* August Grahl (died 1868). Engineer J. Rump bequest 1932.
*Literature:* Andrup 1932 36f.

383
*Male figure in Oriental Dress*
Black and white chalk on greyish prepared paper. 24.1×16.1 cm
Den kgl. Kobberstiksamling Td. 503,29
Verso above "een man die rust op syn stok", lower left "G. Terburg", centre "C. v. Mander" and below right "56".

384
*Apollo flaying Marsyas.* C 1635-39
Inscribed lower left "Karl v. Mander f. Roma"
Pen, brown ink, brush, brown wash. 27.8×18.8 cm
Den kgl. Kobberstiksamling Td. 503,30
Top left "No. 27" and in pencil "69". The signature is unlikely to be genuine. Cf. cat. 358.
*Literature:* DT I 35.

385
*Recumbent male model*
Inscribed at the bottom "Karell ver Mander Fecit Copenhagen A° 1670"
Black and white chalk on grey-green paper. 26.2×43.0 cm
Den kgl. Kobberstiksamling Td. 503,32
The date is not written in Mander's hand and from a stylistic viewpoint improbable.
*Literature:* DT I 35; II pl. 15.

## *Tapestries*

In his use of woven tapestries, Christian IV was following the predominant European fashion. As a child, he saw the completion of his father's monumental decorative project, 40 large tapestries for the new Banqueting Hall at Kronborg, woven in Elsinore at the workshop of Hans Knieper from Antwerp, court painter and tapestry weaver. Christian IV himself was the sitter along with his father for the last tapestry in the series, representing the youngest member of a glorious line of royal ancestors. Knieper died in 1587 in Elsinore and with his death, the first Danish production of tapestries ceased; no Danish workshop was able to attain such quality again.

Christian IV's extensive castle building programme created a need for woven tapestries, which could not be fulfilled from Danish workshops. Jan Claesz. van Wijk, a Dutchman, was appointed court painter in 1598 and in 1608 and 1609, he was paid for designs from which to weave tapestries. The work was entrusted to the workshop in the prison of the Holy Spirit in Copenhagen but at the same time, designs were sent to Holland to be woven in workshops there, through the aegis of Isaac Pietersz. the King's commissioner and agent in Elsinore.

When the new Frederiksborg Castle was being furnished, a large number of tapestries were procured from abroad. During 1614 and 1616, payments were made to Adam Baseler (Basilius), a merchant from Antwerp who later settled in Hamburg, for delivery of several series of "Tapetzerie" of varying quality. Motifs such as "Scenes from Roman History", the "Story of Diana", and the "History of Troy", which were bought for Frederiksborg and Copenhagen Castles, are presumably stock goods from Flemish workshops, but the decoration of the Great Hall at Frederiksborg was quite a different matter. Christian IV wanted to create a counterpart here to his father's Banqueting Hall at Kronborg with a magnificent series of tapestries in which the King himself would figure at the centre of a monumental national epic. The subjects were to be the Kalmar War which had just been successfully brought to a close and the coronation of the King. Christian IV turned to a Dutch workshop for this project, that of Frans Spierings in Delft, presumably partly because he looked to Holland in all his art policies, partly because of the high quality of Spierings' workshop. It is possible that, during his visit to England, he might have seen Spierings' great series "The Victory of the English Fleet over the Spanish Armanda", commissioned by Lord Charles Howard from drawings by Cornelisz Vroom. Frans Spierings arrived in Denmark in May 1614 for negociations with Christian IV, bringing various tapestries with him, but the project was given to his competitor, Karel van Mander II, who had been the designer for Spierings since 1604. The Scipio series (cat. 388), which has all the characteristics of van Mander, is from this period. Van Mander delivered the great series of 26 tapestries in 1619 and 1620. The whole series was lost in the Frederiksborg fire of 1859 together with the remainder of other series of tapestries from Christian IV's time.

The great majority of the King's tapestry commissions were for Frederiksborg Castle, as can be seen from the surviving inventories (1636 and 1650). Tapestries were often requisitioned from Frederiksborg when the King went to stay in his other castles. There was probably a small collection of tapestries in Copenhagen Castle, but normally, the rooms here were clad only in gilt leather and cloth. No other decoration is mentioned in the inventory from 1638 or from 1654. But if there was to be a celebration at the castle, the tapestries were brought out and the King requisitioned tapestries from far and near. For the coronation, for example, about twenty noble ladies received letters in May 1596 inviting them to attend and to bring "the very best tapestries, Flemish bedclothes, curtains for beds etc". For The Royal Nuptials in 1634, Knieper's ancestral tapestries were brought from Kronborg and suspended under the ceiling of the "Old Hall". This arrangement was repeated for Leonora Christina and Corfitz Ulfeldt's wedding in 1636; for the decoration of the walls, the King had requisitioned "the best tapestries which are at Frederiksborg that are suitable".

Out of Christian IV's entire large collection of tapestries, only the King's portrait (cat. 393), "The Stag Hunt" (cat. 392) and possibly "The Wild Boar Hunt" (cat. 389) appear to be extant, and of these, only one is in a Danish collection.

*Vibeke Woldbye*

## Hans Knieper

386

*Abel, King of Denmark 1250-1252*

Elsinore 1581-85. Mrk. with rebus: Crown B (for Kronborg).

Wool and silk. Tapestry. 409×304 cm.

Nationalmuseet, deposited at Kronborg Castle T.4.

The painter and weaver Hans Knieper from Antwerp was summoned to Elsinore in 1577 by Frederik II. 1581-85 he executed 40 tapestries for the Banqueting Hall at Kronborg, depicting 100 Danish kings from the legendary Dan to the King himself with little Prince Christian (IV). 14 are extant, 7 in Kronborg and 7 in the National Museum. The series was supplemented in 1586 with a magnificent canopy (Swedish war booty 1658, now in the Nationalmuseum, Stockholm).

*Provenance:* Banqueting Hall at Kronborg Castle. Cf. cat. 758.

*Literature:* Mackeprang & Flamand Christensen 1950. Langberg 1985 29ff.

## Frans Spierings' style

387

*Orpheus charming the Beasts*

Delft beginning of the 16th century.

Wool and silk. Tapestry. 250×194 cm

Kronborg Castle K.B. 425

The tapestry belongs to a small group of decorative compositions with floral elements above and a figure section below made in Spierings' workshop in Delft. Frans Spierings was in Denmark in 1614 to negociate the decoration of the Great Hall at Frederiksborg Castle with Christian IV.

*Provenance:* Bernheimer Munich 1985.

*Literature:* Böttiger 1928 51 pl. 38. Ysselsteyn 1936 287f, LXXIX, fig. 167-169. Cavallo 1967 141ff.

## Karel van Mander II

388

*The Magnanimity of Scipio*

Signed: Franciscus Spiringius fecit. Frans Spierings' workshop, Delft c 1617, design by Karel van Mander II. Wool and silk. Tapestry. 426×538 cm.

Statens konstmuseer, Stockholm. NM 19/1918.

From the series "The History of Scipio", originally 13 tapestries. Two other episodes are in: Bank voor Handel en Scheepvaart, Rotterdam and Palazzo Communale, Cagliari. Christian IV kept part of a set of Scipio-tapestries after the design of Giulio Romano at Frederiksborg Castle.

*Provenance:* Gustav II Adolf. Queen Christina. Donated to the National Museum, Stockholm in 1918.

*Literature:* Göbel 1923 540ff. Ysselsteyn 1936 249f. Nationalmusei exhibition cat. 250 1958 no. 2. Nationalmusei exhibition cat. 305 1966 no. 1 213.

*388*

388a
*Orlando saves Angelica from the Sea Monster Orca*
Signed: Franciscus Spieringus fecit. Frans Spierings' workshop, Delft c 1609-1620. Design attributed to Karel van Mander II.
Wool and silk. Tapestry. 400×328 cm
Private collection, England
From one of two series woven in Spierings' workshop with scenes from Ariosto's Orlando Furioso. The same scene without the border was sold at an auction in Amsterdam in 1923 and 1933 (F. Müller), provenance now unknown. Two other scenes are in the Rijksmuseum, Amsterdam, and Los Angeles County Museum.
*Provenance:* Private collection, Italy.
*Literature:* Ysselsteyn 1936, 303, fig. 66. Erkelens 1962, 68, 84f., fig. 8.

## Karel van Mander II?

389
*Wild Boar Hunt*
Delft 1620s? Design and execution attributed to Karel van Mander II.
Wool and silk. Tapestry. 281×307 cm
Colour-plate XXX.
Kungl. Husgerådskammaren, Stockholm. HGK 12. The scene is derived from one of a series of engraved hunting scenes after David Vinckboon, "Has venationis, aucupu et piscatori formulas" Amsterdam n.d.
*Provenance:* Purchased by the Kungl. Husgerådskammaren 1864. According to Böttiger, the tapestry may have been taken as war booty in Denmark.
*Literature:* Böttiger II 1895 46. Ysselsteyn 1936 I 252f, II XLIVf.

## Aert Spierings' workshop

390
*The Story of Tobias*
Delft. Signed: Arnoldus Spieringius fecit Anno 1626. Citymark of Delft.
Wool and silk. Tapestry. 272×260 cm
Kungl. Husgerådskammaren, Stockholm. HGK 423
Aert and Pieter Spierings carried on their father, Frans Spierings' workshop in Delft until about 1640. Adam van Noort may have been the artist who delivered the designs for a group of similar tapestries from the workshop.
*Provenance:* Purchased for Kungl. Husgerådskammaren 1896.
*Literature:* Erkelens 1962 53ff. Cavallo 1967 no. 43. Statens Museum for Kunst 1977 no. 18.

## Francis Cleyn

391
*Leander swimming up to Hero's Tower*
Cartoon 1636. Woven at the Mortlake manufactory under the direction of Francis Crane. Signed FC.
Wool, silk, gold and silver thread. Tapestry. 440×455 cm
Kungl. Husgerådskammaren. Stockholm. HGK 52
From a series of 6 tapestries depicting Hero and Leander's love story. In the border are oval medallions, cartouches, garlands and putti. Above centre, the coat-of-arms of James I. In 1623, James I appointed Francis Cleyn designer to the Mortlake manufactory and when he returned from Denmark in 1625, Cleyn continued his work here until at least 1657.
*Provenance:* The series was originally woven for James I, from whom it came into the possession of the Duke of Buckingham. It was later acquired by Count Johan Oxenstierna and presented by him to Karl X Gustav on the occasion of his wedding to Hedvig Eleonora in 1654.
*Literature:* Böttiger II 1895 40ff.

## Maximilian van der Gucht's workshop?

392
*Stag Hunt with Diana*
Delft 1640s.
Wool and silk. Tapestry. 366×455 cm
De danske kongers kronologiske samling på Rosenborg. 31r.9a.
A tapestry woven from the same cartoon with only small divergences is part of one of the hunting series which was delivered in 1647 from Maximilian van der Gucht's workshop in Delft for the coronation of Queen Christina.
*Provenance:* The stag hunt hung with other hunting tapestries in the King's bedchamber at Nykøbing Castle, when it was Queen Sophie Amalie's jointure. They may have been there before her time. Transferred from Nykøbing Castle to Christiansborg Castle in 1767 and hung in Rosenborg Castle in 1773.
*Literature:* Böttiger II 1895 28.

## Karel van Mander III

393
*Christian IV*
Delft? around 1645
Wool and silk. Tapestry. 132×101 cm
Kunstsammlungen der Veste Coburg, Coburg. GR. Cat. XX,5
There is reason to believe that the tapestry portrait was woven in Delft, possibly in Maximilian van der Gucht's workshop. The previous owner of this workshop had been Frans Spierings with whom Christian IV had been dealing in 1614. There is also evidence that designs were sent from Denmark to Holland to be woven.
*Provenance:* Presented by Christian IV to Magdalena Sibylla, who took the tapestry with her when she remar-

391

ried Duke Friedrich Wilhelm II of Saxe-Altenburg. Altenburg later came under Saxe-Gotha, which was united with Saxe-Coburg in 1826.
*Literature:* Andrup 1920 107. Eller 1971 143 444. The prototype is a picture of the same type as cat. 5.

## *Furniture*

394
*Chest*
Denmark 1608. Oak covered with leather and mounted with iron. H. 58 cm, L. 93 cm, W. 48 cm
Private collection, England
Rectangular with slightly arched lid. Divided externally into squares by the fittings. In the top squares of the front is the date 1608, combined with Christian IV's crowned monogram. The other squares are fitted with 28 double roses (the united Tudor roses, James I's symbol?). The front can be lifted with two small rings; handles on the sides. Inside there is one large compartment lined with salmon coloured silk, quilted in several patterns. In the centre of the lid, Christian IV's crowned monogram in a circle.
*Provenance:* The chest may have contained gifts from Christian IV for James I, along with a similar chest (cat. 395) which is also in an English collection. Purchased by the present owner from Christie's, London in 1974.

395
*Chest*
Denmark 1608. Oak, covered with leather and mounted with iron. H. 100 cm, L. 150 cm, W. 100 cm
Private collection, England
Rectangular with slightly arched lid. Divided externally into squares by the fittings. In the top squares of the front, the date 1608 combined with Christian IV's crowned monogram. The other squares are fitted with square open work ornaments. The front can be lifted by two small rings; handles on the sides. Inside there is one deep compartment and two shallow drawers beneath it with silvered handles. Lined and quilted like cat. 394,

also with Christian IV's monogram in the lid. A similar chest, dated 1599 but without the monogram, lined in green velvet and damask, is at Rosenborg Castle.
*Provenance:* See cat. 394. Bought by the present owner from an art dealer in London.

## Francis Cleyn?

396
*Armchair*
C. 1630. Oak, carved and painted; traces of original gilding. H. 116 cm, W. 68 cm, D. 65 cm
Victoria and Albert Museum, London, W9-1953
So-called *sgabello.* The back is in the shape of a shell, the armrest is of the "caquetoire" type, semicircular seat with a circular depression. In front trestle shaped support carved with mask suspended from garlands and scrollwork. Italian type of chair, probably introduced into England by Francis Cleyn. Horace Walpole mentions Cleyn as designer of similar chairs at Holland House, Kensington. Chairs of the same type are to be found in Lacock Abbey and Petworth House. The "sgabello "chair can also be seen in Daniel Mytens' portrait of the Countess Arundel in the picture gallery at Arundel House (National Portrait Gallery), built by Inigo Jones and in a painting of Ham House (Henry Dancerts), where Cleyn had decorated two of the rooms.
*Provenance:* Purchased as one of a set of five chairs from Christie, Manson & Wood Ltd. 1953. Two more of the set were acquired in 1984.
*Literature:* Fitzgerald 1970 no. 14. Thornton & Tomlin 1980 27ff. The Treasure Houses of Britain 1985 no. 57.

## Antonius Meiding (died 1641)

397
*Doorway*
Made 1627-28, delivered 1635
Ebony, ebonized wood, boxwood and rosewood. H. 420 cm, W. 280 cm
Kronborg Castle
Built up architecturally with carved columns, consoles, cornices, broken gables and inlaid ornamental details. Antonius Meiding immigrated from Augsburg and became cabinet maker to the Danish court in 1620.
*Provenance:* Originally made for the Queen's Chamber at Kronborg, but moved in 1928 to the Banqueting Hall, in front of the stairs in the Trumpeter's Tower.
*Literature:* Langberg 1979 40f. Woldbye 1986 66f.

# Christian IV and Music

Music flourished greatly at the court of Christian IV throughout the greater part of his reign. Except in the worst war years, Danish court music during this entire period had a stable organization and included a large complement of distinguished native and foreign musicians.

When Frederik II died, Christian IV took over his corps of *singers, instrumentalists and trumpeters* – the three main groups comprising the court music. This body was enlarged in the years around 1600 – for Christian IV's coronation in 1596, for example. On this occasion – as also later in connection with "Det store Bilager" (the lavishly celebrated wedding of the heir apparent, Prince Christian, and Princess Magdalena Sybilla of Saxony) – music played a central part. From 1596 and throughout nearly all of Christian IV's life, the quality as well as the quantity of the music at his court was the equal of that at most of the courts of Europe. Numerous internationally known musicians were in Christian IV's service during this time and the king also created opportunities for the most gifted of native talents to be educated abroad, particularly in Venice. Under Christian IV valuable contacts were made abroad, notably with Italy, Germany, the Netherlands, England and Poland. King Christian became known throughout Europe as a patron of music and several composers who never set foot on Danish soil dedicated their works to the Danish king.

From the long list of names of those connected with the Danish court for varying lengths of time from the

*394*

end of the 16th to the middle of the 17th centuries can be mentioned: Vincentius Bertholusius, Melchior Borchgrevinck, William Brade, John Dowland, Melchior Schildt, Johann Schop, Thomas Simpson, Jan Tollius, Gregorius Trehou, Gabriel Voigtländer and, foremost of all, Heinrich Schütz. Most prominent among contemporary Danish musicians were Hans Brachrogge, Hans Nielsen and, especially, Mogens Pedersen.

Angul Hammerich's doctoral thesis, *Musiken ved Christian den Fjerdes Hof* (Music at the Court of Christian IV), from 1892, remains the only extented work to date on this important period in the history of Danish music. Any succeeding activity touching on this theme, whether in the form of research, the preparation of exhibitions or of musical publications, must of necessity be based on this impressive work. Hammerich describes in detail the structure of musical life, the people involved, the music itself, the king's interest in it, his position and importance as a patron of music – even such social considerations as the position, protection, housing, etc. of his musicians are not overlooked. In everything he is thorough and alert to the significance of the material in the context of musical and cultural history.

Even so, and exhibition in 1988 will be different from one which Hammerich would have been able to present almost 100 years ago. Subsequent research has added much to our knowledge and even though the basic view of the age of Christian IV has not been altered with regard to music, our position in respect to a number of areas has been adjusted with the passage of time. There are thus good reasons for revising Hammerich's pioneer work and bringing it up to date and for, in exhibition and publications, giving an account of what is new and of what we can learn from it.

In the exhibition "Kongen og Kunsten" (Christian IV – Patron of Arts) at Kronborg Castle all the types of sources which, since Hammerich's study, have helped to influence our understanding of music and its circumstances in Denmark at the time of Christian IV are represented: archival documents, books, music, pictures, musical instruments. Often one experiences an incredibly inspiring interplay between these factors, which together can help to localize the problems or even to expose previously undefined relationships. In the following paragraphs some examples are given of the results achieved by the research activities, increasing in intensity as the jubilee year of 1988 has approached, of Danish and foreign scholars.

When dealing with *archival documents,* we meet Hammerich on home ground, as it were, since the main sources for his book were the treasurer's accounts and the concurrent board-allowance accounts in the National Archives, which exist for the entire period from 1588 to 1648. Since 1892 a number of dates have been corrected and many new biographical details about Christian IV's musicians have been discovered. Perhaps the most important addition of this kind, however, is documentation showing that Christian IV was himself an active practitioner and hence not merely interested in music as a representative art. Accounts from 1590 and 1591 in the National Archives reveal the purchase of cittern and lute strings, as well as of a "symphony" (a clavichord, or perhaps rather a spinet) for Christian IV's "own use"; such purchases must be interpreted as evidence that the young monarch, still a minor, received instruction on these instruments.

One realizes, moreover, that it is probably in such matters as *access to the repertoire* and *performance practice* that the greatest advances have been made. Much of the music which Hammerich wrote about he had never had the opportunity to study personally and only very seldom in his day was it possible to hear these works performed. Today a considerable amount of this music has been published and described. One may note in this regard that most of the works composed by the Danish composers of the time: Mogens Pedersen, Hans Nielsen, Truid Aagesen, Hans Brachrogge, Melchior Borchgrevinck and Nicolo Gistou, have been published in the series DANIA SONANS (see bibl.). In 1988 this series will be supplemented by a set of 7 booklets with the title MUSIC IN DENMARK AT THE TIME OF CHRISTIAN IV, which contain, for the most part, works previously unpublished in modern times, including music by, among others, Voigtländer, Schildt, Pedersen, Mancinus, Prætorius, Trehou, Tollius, Bertholusius and Schattenberg. In the exhibition, furthermore, it will be possible to see a number of works which have first come to light after Hammerich's time, such as the Clausholm fragments,[1] the Tregian manuscript[2] and Mogens Pedersen's two pavans.[3] The studies and editions which accompanied these discoveries have, together with international research and the world wide computer registration of recent years, resulted in a much easier access to the repertoire of this period than was possible 3 or 4 generations ago.

*Music iconography* too can make a considerable contribution to our knowledge of the musical practice of former times. Reinhold Timm's picture of musicians from Christian IV's chapel (cat. 322) was tentatively dated to ca. 1622 by Francis Beckett[4] in 1937 on the basis of a comparison with another work by Timm. On the other hand, Beckett was unable to identify what he called "the now unknown instrument" in the picture; musical research has since been able to explain that it is an Irish harp. Hammerich states that Christian IV engaged the harpist *Darby Scott* from England in 1621 and that he remained in Denmark until his death in 1634. We know that he played the Irish harp, and since until 1627 he was the only harpist in the king's chapel, there is every reason to believe that it is Scott who is depicted in Timm's picture. The viol player is a man in the prime of life. It would seem obvious to identify him as either *William Brade* or the equally highly esteemed *Thomas Simpson,* who suceeded Brade at the court in 1622. Both these Englishmen were colleagues of Scott, and their own periods of service overlapped between May and September 1622. By this times Brade had been employed by the king during three periods and was therefore an old acquaintance. His prominent position in the musical life at court – a previously unknown report from the envoy of the Gottorp court in Copenhagen mentions Brade in 1622 as the leader of a consort of viols[5] – speaks in favour of seeing Brade in the picture. Against him is undoubtedly his age in 1622, namely ca. 62. Simpson's 40 years are more in keeping with the erect and self-assured violist who dominates the foreground of the painting; but if it really is Simpson who confronts the observer with a cool look from the surface of the painting, we must assume that Timm's work was done after Brade's departure in September 1622 – and before Simpson's in March 1625.

It is more difficult to suggest identities for the two very young musicians in the background of the painting. The lute player may be *Jørgen Rasch,* who was engaged by the king in 1618, whereas the flute player remains unknown to us; but perhaps there is no particular reason to seek out individual portraits in these cases. Beckett pointed out a strong resemblance between these heads and a couple of figures in Timm's painting "Young men wrestling on a bridge" at Kronborg (cat. 214).

The diplomatic report mentioned above from the envoy of the Gottorp court, Gosche Wensin, tells of an exquisite banquet at Rosenborg at which was heard solo music by an Irish harp with brass strings. In Timm's painting, however, it is part of a small ensemble with lute, transverse flute and bass viol. In 1622 the Irish harp was normally a diatonic instrument whose repertoire was limited with regard to variety of keys. What place did it have in the performance of consort music at a princely court?

It is such questions as this that are being asked by the steadily growing circle of musicians and scholars who concern themselves with *performance practice.* One can try to approach the sound which characterized the music of that time by studying the music itself, by a renewed study of contemporary theoretical treatises and, finally, as has been done in recent years, by examining the instruments of the period which have been preserved. The answer to our immediate question which is emerging from all this seems to confirm the suspicion that the Irish chromatic harp was probably more widespread and built in a greater variety of forms than has previously been suspposed. The main evidence is provided by the fragments of the so-called Dalway harp, signed 1621, in the National Museum in Dublin. It was the subject in 1987 of a new qualified suggestion for reconstruction, which is of particular interest in connection with Reinhold Timm's painting. This suggestion for a model of the Irish harp is a complicated construction in which, among other things, the middle section presents a close accumulation of string-levels which overlap each other. In the diatonic bass section nearest the pillar, on the other hand, the tuning pegs are placed very far apart – in both respects exactly as can just be made out in Timm's instrument.

The harp has always been a favourite motif, rich in symbolism and beautiful in shape. Why then did Timm choose to show it from an angle which makes it almost unrecognisable? Perhaps it was because Scott's harp was a chromatic model and therefore might seem to fit uneasily in the midst of the otherwise pure forms and colours. This may be an heretical thought, which perhaps is contrary to all that the art historians have to say about the composition of the painting, but it may nevertheless offer an explanation worth taking into account. Reinhold Timm's painting has long been valued in Denmark as a precious testimony to the time of Christian IV. However, it is also unique as documentation of the 17th-century harp as a consort instrument and for this reason it has become world famous.

The music section of the Kronborg exhibition has tried to present old, well-established knowledge side by side with new research results and discoveries from one of the most important periods in Danish music history. If, by way of conclusion, we try to assess the value of the new material which has been brought to light since musical research "discovered" Christian IV and music, the conclusion must be following: the most important advance has occurred in and with our knowledge of both the national and the international repertoires of music of the period; this insight has in turn raised a number of questions for musicology and musicians, among them those related to a reasonable modern way of performing old music. Such questions are just what archival documents, books, music, pictures and surviving instruments, and in particular the interplay between them, can help to answer.

*Mette Müller* and *Ole Kongsted*

1. See bibliography: Glahn and Sørensen 1974.
2. See bibliography: Bergsagel 1976 and art. "Francis Tregian" in *The New Grove Dictionary of Music and Musicians* XIX (London 1980). 126f.
3. See bibliography: Bergsagel 1976 and art. "Mogens Pedersøn" in *The New Grove Dictionary of Music and Musicians* XIV (London 1980), 328ff.
4. See bibliography.
5. The authors wish to thank Jørgen Hein, curator of Rosenborg Museum, for information concerning "Bericht Gosche Wensins über den Kopenhagener Hof", dated April 24, 1622 (Landesarchiv Schleswig-Holstein, Kurt Hector: Findbuch no. 74).

397a

## Heinrich Schütz (1585-1672), German composer

Engraving by August John (Dresden 1602- after 1678)
Ratschulbibliothek, Zwickau
A few years ago the German musicologist Eberhard Möller found this hitherto unknown engraving of the Director of the Royal Chapel in Copenhagen, Heinrich Schütz. The 42-year old composer is depicted at a time only few years before entering Royal Danish service.

398

398

## Organ with reed stops: Bible regal

Unsigned. Presumed built in 17th Century
Keyboard: L. 63.4 cm. Bellows, lid: 20.3×30.6 cm
Musikhistorisk Museum, no. Cl.596
1 manual (range C-b2C sharp). Composed of 9 parts: keyboard + wooden pipes with brass reeds (4 sections), 2 wedge shaped bellows joined by a leather hinge, 2 weights and 2 wind feeders which connect the bellows and the keyboard part. The regal can be folded up and looks like a Bible with clasps and fittings. Rebuilt in probably both the 18th and 19th centuries. Restored 1958 by Anders Persson and 1972 by Ture Bergstrøm. Regals were used in church services and for secular entertainment with music and dancing.
*Provenance:* Acquired by Carl Claudius before 1931.
*Literature:* Claudius and Skjerne 1931 337 340. Bergstrøm 1972 and 1980 5. Menger 1973 119ff. Van der Meer 1983 166f.

399

## Harpsichord

Signed Andreas Rvckers me fecit Antverpiae 1648
In addition, maxims in block letters and inside on the bottom of the case, Ruckers' number: St/69
Case: L. 182.5 cm, B. 71.0 cm, H. 24.1 cm
Musikhistorisk Museum no. 1968-54
1 manual (range C/E-c3). 32 registers (8′+8′+4′). Divided lute stop. Stand missing. Restored in 1965 by Frank Hubbard, USA. In its present form, it is an instrument of the Flemish school with features which can be partly assigned to the 17th century, partly to the 18th century. This harpsichord is very suitable as both solo and continuo instrument in works written for Christian IV's court music or dedicated to the Heir Apparent and Frederik III by Heinrich Schütz, Melchior Schild and Gabriel Voigtländer.
*Provenance:* C 1923 purchased in Holland by cellist Otto van Koppenhagen, USA. 1965 sold to harpsichordist Gustav Leonhardt, Amsterdam. 1968 sold by Leonhardt to Musikhistorisk Museum.
*Literature:* Boalch 1956 98; 1974 145. Grove III 1984 267 274. Van der Meer 1971 112 115.
*Recordings:* Telefunken "Das alte Werk" with Gustav Leonhardt (SAWT 9512-B).

400

## Spinet

Signed Brvneti al organi Veronesis mdlviii (probably identical with Brunetto Pontoni)
Case: L. 155.5 cm. B. 42.5 cm. H. 18.5 cm
Musikhistorisk Museum no. A51
1 manual (range C/E-f3). 1 register (8′). Pentagonal case with mouldings and sound board with rose, all in cypress wood. The key bed extends half way into the case, which is unusual. The stand and outer case are missing. The instrument is typical of the Italian school: an extremely light construction, the case made of very thin wood and in comparison to the spinet's size, a surprisingly bis tone.
*Provenance:* Acquired in 1932 from the harpsichord and piano builder Johann Georg Steingräber in Berlin.
*Literature:* Boalch 1974 20f.

401

## Harp

Unsigned, Ireland, beginning of 18th century (?)
H. internal on straight 111.8 cm. D. (on straight between external points) 75.6 cm. Soundbox total L. 99.1 cm
National Museum of Ireland, Dublin no. 121-1945

Big high-headed Irish harp. Stringing: 36 tuning pins. Below these, corresponding bridge pins, probably an alteration to the instrument's original form. The harp is of the late Irish type: the pillar bends outwards only slightly in comparison to the instrument in Reinhold Timm's painting cat. 322. Irish harps at Christian IV's court are documented in the records by information about the purchase of brass strings.
*Provenance:* Previously in Major Sirr's collection. Belonged to a bard of the O'Neill dynasty.
*Literature:* Rimmer 1964 45 47ff and 1977 56 77.

402

## Small descant lude

Not signed. First part of the 17th century
Total: L. 41.5 cm. Body: L. 24.6 cm. B. 13.2 cm
Vibrating l. of strings: 35.6 cm
Musikhistorisk Museum no. X50
The body of ivory ribs with balck/white inlay. Ivory and ebony covering on other parts. Belly of spruce with carved rose. Pegbox at a right angle to the neck. Strings: 3 double courses + 1 single. The instrument is in its original state and is probably the only known extant example of its kind.
*Provenance:* The Royal Danish Kunstkammer (inventory 1690). On permanent loan from Nationalmuseet, Copenhagen 1898.
*Literature:* Hammerich 1911 66. Baines 1966 34.

403

## Mean lute

Indistinct signature: "Peve Rozzi". Italy c. 1600?
Body: L. 49.7 cm. B. 34.2 cm
Musikhistorisk Museum no. C44
The body is of yew ribs. The belly is spruce with carved rose. Pegbox at a right angle to the neck. Strings: 7 double courses. The neck has been rebuilt. The "mean" lute is part of the ensemble which in England was attached to the theatre and which had a repertoire called broken music.
*Provenance:* Purchased from Stefan Zatelli in Munich 1898
*Literature:* Hammerich 1911 67f.

404

## Lute

Signed "Christofolo Cocho all 'Aquila d'Oro in Venetia" (probably a south German builder). C 1640. On the fingerboard, the coat-of-arms of the Austrian baronial family von Rödern and the initials CMVR
Total: L. 75.3 cm. Body L. 48 cm. B. 30.2 cm. Vibrating length of strings: 66.5 cm
Musikhistorisk Museum no. C1.96A
The body is of ivory ribs with black inlay. Ivory and ebony covering on other parts. Belly of spruce with carved rose. Pegbox at a right angle to the neck. Strings: 9 double courses + 1 single. The instrument was repaired by Johann Chr. Hoffmann, Leipzig 1712 and by Voss in Berlin 1926. A lute player can bee seen in Timm's painting of the Royal musicians cat. 322. One of the greatest contemporary virtuosos on the lute, John Dowland, was employed by Christian IV from 1598 to 1606 and several of his compositions were written in Denmark.
*Provenance:* Acquired by Carl Claudius from Wildhagen's collection in Berlin before 1931.
*Literature:* Claudius and Skjerne 1931 103f. Young 1980 44. Pohlmann 1982 325.

405

## Lute: Zweikragenlaute

Signed: Sixtus Ravwolf Avgvstanvs 1958 (or 1599?)
Total: L. 106 cm. Body: L. 47.5 cm. B. 32.8 cm. Vibrating length of strings 96.4 and 67.5 cm respectively
Musikhistorisk Museum no. C1.93
The designation indicates that the lute has two pegbox-

*400*

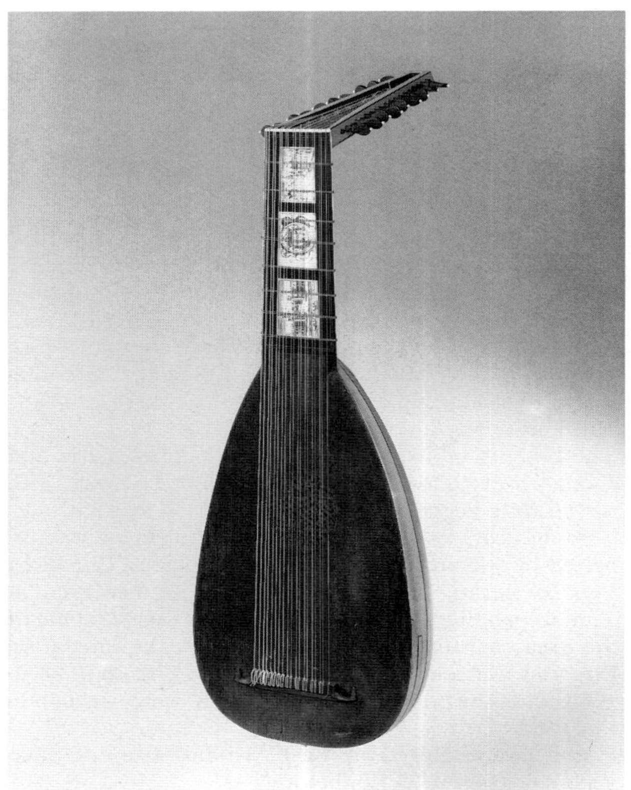

*404*

es, both at an angle to the neck. Short neck: 6 double courses played on the fingerboard. Long neck: 4 double courses which are tuned in a diatonic scale and plucked as open strings. The stringing was possibly changed during the baroque period "Laute mit zween Krägen" is described in the inventory from 1566 of the Raimund Fugger collection. It is also known from Flemish paintings. Can be seen in the costume drawing "Entry of Music" from c. 1620 (cat. 548). The Zweikragenlaute on exhibition is the only known extant instrument of this type.
*Provenance:* Acquired by Carl Claudius before 1931.
*Literature:* Claudius and Skjerne 1931 97 100ff. Hellwig 1980 479f.

406
## Cittern

Not signed. Italian, 17th century?
Total: L. 85 cm. Body: L. 39 cm. B. 26 cm
Musikhistorisk Museum no. C1.141
The instrument appears to have been thoroughly rebuilt, but can illustrate a plucked instrument which was popular in Christian IV's time. It is, for example, part of the theatre ensemble for "broken" music, where a type with shorter strings would have been used, but no known examples of this type have been preserved.
*Provenance:* Acquired by Carl Claudius before 1931.
*Literature:* Claudius and Skjerne 1931 134f.

407
## Bandora: Orpharion

Signed: "Francis Palmer Dwelling in ... 1617"
Total: L. 100.2 cm. Body: L. 43 cm. Vibrating L. of strings, bass side 60.5 cm, treble side 51.5 cm
Musikhistorisk Museum no. C1.139. Colour-plate XX
Stringing: 9 double courses. Nut, bridge and 15 metal frets on the fingerboard are placed in a fan shape with greater distance towards the bass side to achieve greater variance in the length of strings and thus a greater range of tone. The name is derived from Orpheus and Arion, and the scalloped contours of the body should suggest the mythology associated with the shell. This type was invented about 1590. The repertoire is the same as for the lute and it was very popular in Christian IV's time. Presumed to be reproduced in the ceiling painting of the Royal musicians (Rosenborg) and in Gijsbrechts' painting from 1672 (cat. 304).
*Provenance:* Acquired by Carl Claudius before 1931.
*Literature:* Claudius and Skjerne 1931 132f. Gill 1960 14 25. Segerman and Abbott 1976 48 56. Grove II 1984 972 974.

408
## Treble viol

Not signed. Probably built by Würfl in Greifswald (first part of 17th century)
Total: L. 74 cm. Body: L. 41 cm. B. 21.5 cm
Musikhistorisk Museum no. C1.261A
The body's contour has a double lower bout. 6 strings. The pegbox ends in a lion's head. The neck seems to have been rebuilt. The treble viol can be part of the English "broken consort" and was also played in works such as William Brade published for 4, 5 or 6 instruments.
*Provenance:* Acquired by Carl Claudius before 1931 from Wildhagen's collection in Berlin.
*Literature:* Claudius and Skjerne 1931 210ff. Young 1980 120.

409
## Treble viol

Signed: "Paulus Hiltz Noriberga me fecit Anno 1656"
Total: L. 73.3 vcm. Body: L. 43.5 cm. B. 24.8 cm, side: 5 cm
Musikhistorisk Museum no. C 261
The body's contour has a triple lower bout. Flame shaped sound holes. 4 strings. The pegbox has a scroll with a carved face. The neck has been rebuilt. Repaired by Hansz Conradt Pfeifferz c 1700. The instrument's

very low sides indicate that it was played in the arm: perhaps an early form of viola d'amore without sympathetic strings.
*Provenance:* Acquired by Carl Claudius before 1931.
*Literature:* Claudius and Skjerne 1931 211f.

410

## Alto/tenor viol

Signed: Paulus Hiltz in Noriberga fecit Anno 1656
Total: L. 99 cm. Body: L. 48 cm. B. 28.5 cm
Musikhistorisk Museum no. C1.266
The body's contour has a triple lower bout. Flame shaped sound holes and rose. 6 strings. The neck has been rebuilt.
*Provenance:* Acquired by Carl Claudius before 1931.
*Literature:* Claudius and Skjerne 1931 214 217.

411

## Alto/tenor viol

Signed: "Ernst Busch in Nuremberg 1617"
Total: L. 96 cm. Body: L. 51 cm. B. 30.3 cm
Musikhistorisk Museum no D24
The body's contour has a double lower bout. Stylized F holes. 6 strings. The neck has been rebuilt.
*Provenance:* Presented by Carl Claudius to Musikhistorisk Museum 1898.
*Literature:* Hammerich 1911 88f. Young 1980 54.

412

## Bass viol

Not signed. Possibly built by Barak Norman, who was active in London c 1700
Total: L. 122 cm. Body L. 66.5 cm. B. 39 cm
Musikhistorisk Museum no. 1986-5.

413

## Large bass viol

Signed: "Ernst Busch in Nuremberg 1638"
Total: L. 154 cm. Body: L. 88 cm. B. 50 cm
Musikhistorisk Museum no. C1.280
The body's contour has a triple lower bout. Flame shaped sound holes and rose. 6 strings. The neck is probably rebuilt. The viola da gamba was an instrument for the aristocratic amateur. In Albert Freyse's painting cat. 301, Duke August the Younger of Braunschweig-Wolfenbüttel can be seen with his family. The duchess is playing the spinet, the children form a consort of viols. Amongst the instruments are a bass viol and a treble viol of the same type as instruments by Ernst Busch.
*Provenance:* Acquired by Carl Claudius before 1931.
*Literature:* Claudius and Skjerne 1931 244f.

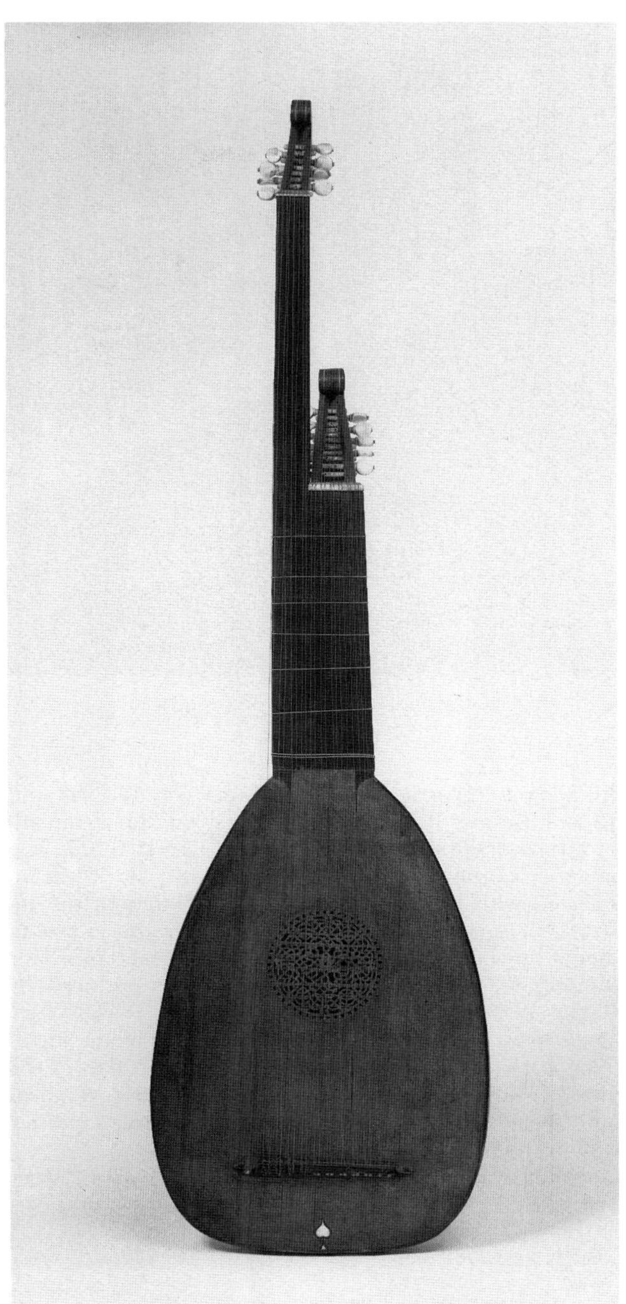

*405*

414

## 2 tenor transverse flutes

Probably made by Hans or Caspar Rauch von Schrattenbach in Hamburg in the 1530s.
Total: L. 13.282: 65.9 cm. Total: L. 13.283: 68.4 cm.
Diameter: 13.282: 0.82 – 1.7 cm. Diameter: 13.283: 0.81-1.77 cm

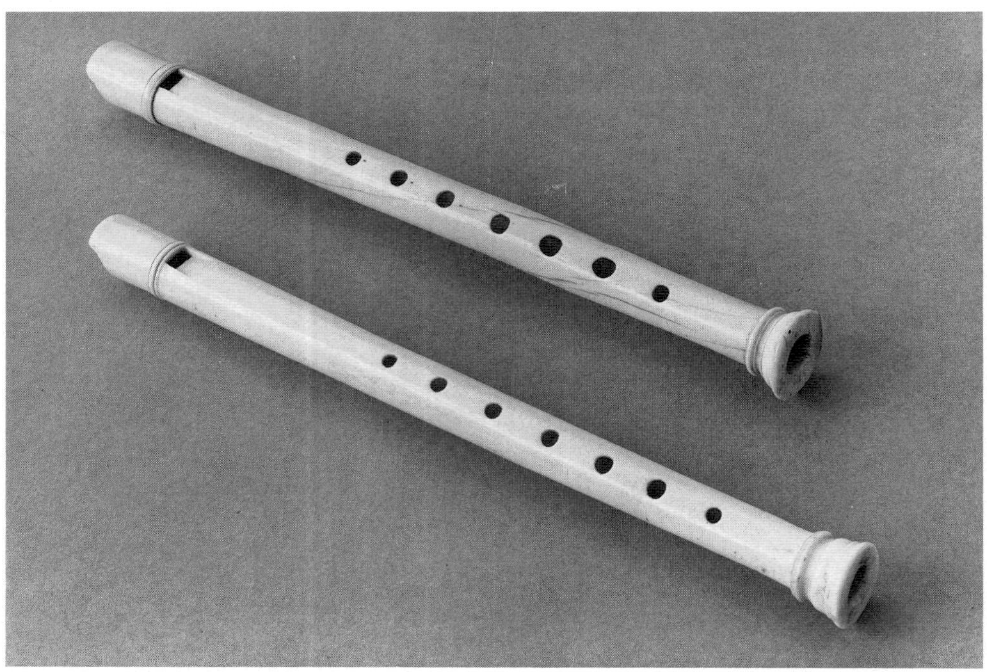

*415-416*

Accademia Filarmonica di Verona no. 13.282 and 13.283. Besides its role as a military musical instrument, the transverse flute was used in Christian IV's time as a member of the English "broken consort", which was associated with theatre music. In this exhibition, the instrument can also be seen as a chamber music instrument in Timm's painting of the Royal musicians (cat. 322). The two flutes exhibited were restored by Rainer Weber, Bayerbach 1971-72.
*Provenance:* The instruments were acquired by the members of the Accademia Filarmonica in the first part of the 16th century. They were used in concert performances and have been in the Accademia Filarmonica's possession ever since.
*Literature:* Van der Meer and Weber 1982. Van der Meer 1983 64.

415

## Small descant recorder

Unsigned. Made before 1674
Total: L. 30 cm. Sounding length: 26.55 cm
Rosenborg no. 1.75
Made of narwhal tusk in one piece with ornamented bell ring glued to the end of the recorder. Simple ornamented turnery adorns the beak above the window. Partially reversed conical bore. 7 finger holes in the front and a thumb hole in the rear. Tuning: a′ = 488. A transitional form between the renaissance and the baroque recorder and as such, remarkable in covering the technical requirements in connection with the repertoire in Jacob van Eyck's two volume work "Der Fluyten Lust-Hof", which appeared during the 1640s. 2 recorders of this type can be seen in cat. 304. Together with cat. 416, these are the only known extant examples of a type which could accomodate van Eyck's music.
*Provenance:* Appears as one of the "Tve Fløyter af Eenhorn" in the inventory of the Royal Danish Kunstkammer from 1674. In Rosenborg's inventory 1696.
*Literature:* Legêne 1984 50ff. Morgan 1984 47f.

416

## Small descant recorder

Unsigned. Made before 1674
Rosenborg no. 1.74
Same type as cat. 415 but made by an amateur. The Danish royal family were interested in turnery and it is known that Christian IV made a tobacco jar from narwhal tusk. It has been suggested that the king made this recorder using the other, professionally made example at Rosenborg as a pattern. Cf. cat. 415.

417

## Basset recorder in G

Signed: "AA". A member of the Schnitzer family
Nuremberg/Munich. Mid 16th century
Total L. 86 cm
Musikhistorisk Museum no. E78

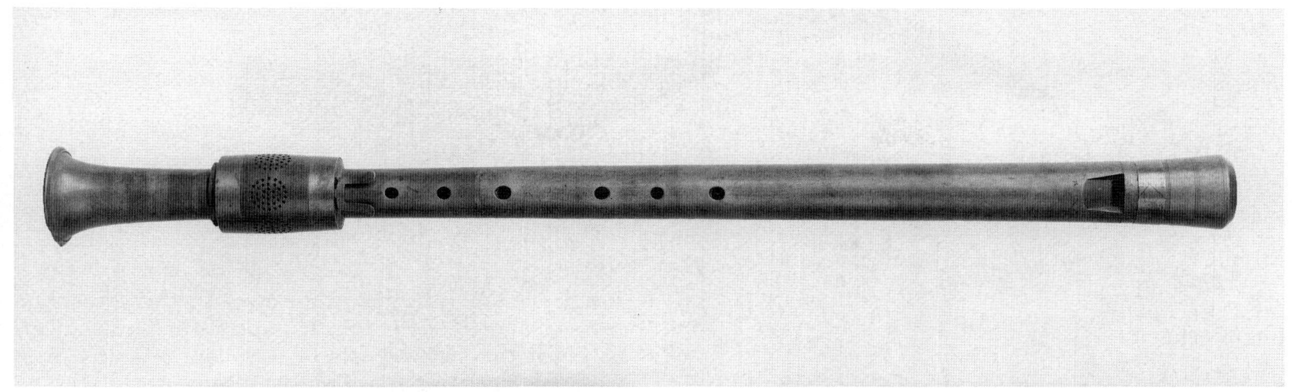

*417*

Made in one piece. Rings and keys of brass. Loose fitting wind cap. Swallowtail key protected by barrel shaped fontanelle. The edge of the end has been repaired in 4 places. The side walls of the window have been altered so that the recorder is pitched about a quarter tone higher than originally. The Schnitzer family was one of the most important instrument maker dynasties of its time. Several of its members had a double A as signature.
*Provenance:* Purchased 1903 from Hans Hahn in Munich.
*Literature:* Hammerich 1911 20. Nickel 1971 48-77. Fjordside 1986. 6-16.

418

## Soprano shawm

Signed: "D" (at the upper end) and "HGK" (at the lover end)
Germany, 17th century
Total L. 60.5 cm
Staatliches Institut für Musikforschung Preussischer Kulturbesitz no. 65
The oboe of the early 17th century was called pommer or, in the case of the small instruments, shawm. It was a loud, robust instrument, suitable for very large rooms or in the open air. They were important as part of processions and other outdoor arrangements and in pictures of Christian IV's coronation, they can be seen in several situations. C.f. cat. 48.
*Provenance:* Became part of the national music collections in Berlin before 1892.
*Literature:* Sachs 1922 271.

419

## Soprano shawm

Unsigned. The Netherlands c 1700
Total L. 62 cm
Staatliches Institut für Musikforschung Preussicher Kulturbesitz no. 2929.
*Provenance:* Came from the lawyer César Snoeck's collection, which was sold in the 1890s to the national instrument collection in Berlin.
*Literature:* Sachs 1922 271.

420

## Alto-tenor pommer

Unsigned. Germany c 1600
Total L. 92 cm
Staatliches Institut für Musikforschung Preussicher Kulturbesitz no. 290
*Provenance:* From Marienkirche in Danzig (Gdansk). Part of the national music collections in Berlin before 1892.
*Literature:* Sachs 1922 271.

421

## Curtal: Choristfagott

Not signed. Germany, 16th century
The instrument's L. 104 cm (the bore, incl. the S-tube, 210 cm)
Museum für Hamburgische Geschichte no. 1928, 389
Double bore in one piece of boxwood, separate bell. 2 keys, protective cap, S-tube and fittings on the instrument and the bell are all of brass. The curtal can be seen as a bass instrument in consort playing in Franz Cleyn's ceiling painting of Christian IV's musicians (Rosenborg).
*Literature:* Schröder 1930 71. Young 1980 38.

422

## Curved cornett

Signed with the mark: two Xs. Probably Venice c 1600
Bore L. 62.4 cm
Germanisches Nationalmuseum Nürnberg no. MIR 41
Made of wood, 2 halves lengthwise, covered with leather.
*Provenance:* Purchased from Sammlung Rück 1962.
*Literature:* Van der Meer 1979 29 149ff.

*425*

423

## Curved cornett

Unsigned. C 1600
Total L. 55 cm
Staatliches Institut für Musikforschung Preussicher Kulturbesitz no. 580
Made of ivory.
*Provenance:* Part of the national music collections in Berlin before 1892.
*Literature:* Sachs 1922 199.

424

## Curved cornett

Not signed. 17th century
Mahogany covered in leather. Total L. (longest curve): 58 cm
Musikhistorisk Museum no. F48
Restored 1969 by Rainer Weber in Bayerbach. A curved cornett can be seen in the painting by Gijsbrechts 1672 (cat. 304) and in the ceiling painting of Christian IV's musicians (Rosenborg).
*Provenance:* Purchased from S. Zatelli in Munich in 1898.
*Literature:* Hammerich 1911 44. Overton 1981 130 250.

425

## S-shaped cornett: tenor

Not signed. 17th century
Total L. (curve): 97.5 cm
Musikhistorisk Museum no. F58
Wood covered in leather. Swallowtail key of brass. Restored by Rainer Weber in Bayerbach c 1970.
*Provenance:* Purchased from Franciolini in Florence in 1899.
*Literature:* Hammerich 1911 44. Overton 1981 130 250.

## Trumpets

The trumpets on exhibition are all made of brass. Several of the instruments have been rather roughly repaired and are not in their original state. None of them can be dated to Christian IV's time, but this is of minor importance since the trumpet in many respects remained unchanged until c 1800. Trumpets played a prominent part at the court and the stock of instruments was regularly supplemented with new purchases. In the coronation procession of 1596, 9 of the trumpeters had instruments of silver, the next year 24 of the more ordinary brass trumpets were purchased and at "Det store Bilager" in 1634, no fewer than 24 silver trumpets took part. The trumpeters Heinrich Lübeck and Magnus Thomsen each compiled his own music book, presumably for teaching purposes (cat. 480).

426

Signed Hans Geyer in Wienn 1684
Total L. (bent): 57.5 cm
Musikhistorisk Museum no. F88.
*Provenance:* Purchased at an auction in Stockholm 1907.
*Literature:* Wörthmüller 1955 428. Wheeler 1965 19. Hammerich 1911 36. Langwill 1980 59.

427

Signed Macht Pavl Hainlein Nvrnberg 1685.
Engraved maker's mark cock + P.H.
Total L. (bent): 67 cm
Musikhistorisk Museum no. C1.528.
*Provenance:* Acquired by Carl Claudius before 1931.
*Literature:* Claudius and Skjerne 1931 314 317. Wörthmüller 1955 448. Langwill 1980 69.

428

Signed Johann Wilhelm Haas Nurnberg and maker's mark: hare + J.W.H. (c 1700)
Total L. (bent): 60.5 cm
Musikhistorisk Museum no. F87.
*Provenance:* Presented to the museum 1906 by the secretary to the opera in Stockholm Johs. Svanberg.
*Literature:* Wörthmüller 1955 428. Wheeler 1965 19. Hammerich 1911 36. Langwill 1980 68f.

429

Signed Johann Wilhel.. Haas Nurnberg and maker's mark: hare + J.W.H. (c 1700)
Total L. (bent): 75 cm
Musikhistorisk Museum no. F105.
*Provenance:* Acquired 1922 from V. Simonsen in Copenhagen.
*Literature:* Wörthmüller 1955 428. Wheeler 1965 19. Langwill 1980 68.

430
Signed JOHANN WILHELM HAAS IN NURNBERG and maker's mark: hare + J.W.H.
(c. 1700)
Total L. (bent): 62.7 cm
Musikhistorisk Museum no. C1.529
*Provenance:* Acquired by Carl Claudius before 1931.
*Literature:* Claudius and Skjerne 1931 315 317. Wörthmüller 1955 431. Wheeler 1965 19. Langwill 1980 68f.

431
Signed MACHT GEORG FRIDERICH STEINMEZ IN NVRNBE..
Mark: Orb + GFS (c 1700)
Total L. (bent): 56 cm
Musikhistorisk Museum no. X70.
*Provenance:* On permanent loan from Nationalmuseet, Copenhagen 1899.
*Literature:* Hammerich 1911 36. Wörtmüller 1955 469. Langwill 1980 59.

432
Signed MACHT PHILIPP SCHÖLLER IN MÜNCHEN 1753 and TST LANDSHUT
Total L. (bent): 58.5 cm
Musikhistorisk Museum no. F78.
*Provenance:* Acquired by the Museum from Hans Hahn in Munich in 1904.
*Literature:* Hammerich 1911 36. Langwill 1980 160.

433
Signed IOHANN IOSEPH SCHMIED MACHTS IN PFAFFENDORFF 1760
Total L. (bent): 69 cm
Musikhistorisk Museum no. C1.530.
*Provenance:* Acquired by Carl Claudius before 1931.
*Literature:* Claudius and Skjerne 1931 315. Langwill 1980 159.

434
Signed I. GEORG ESCHENBACH A NEUKIRCHEN 1808
L. (bent, with mouthpiece): 59 cm
Musikhistorisk Museum no. F42.
*Provenance:* Purchased for the Museum from L. Helbing in Nuremberg 1898.
*Literature:* Hammerich 1911 36.

435
## Trumpet mouthpiece
Not signed. Probably from the 17th century
Brass. L. 10.5 cm. Diameter external rim 3.4 cm
Musikhistorisk Museum no. X64
Trumpet mouthpieces from the 17th century are larger and deeper than the type which were normal in the high baroque period (18th century).
*Provenance:* From the fragment of a trumpet, found in wreckage at Skagen. On permanent loan from Nationalmuseet, Copenhagen to Musikhistorisk Museum 1898.
*Literature:* Hammerich 1911 36.

436
## Trumpet mute
Unsigned. C 1700
Reichsstadtmuseum der Stadt Rothenburg, no number.
*Provenance:* On permanent loan from the museum in Rothenburg to the instrument collection in Germanisches Nationalmuseum Nürnberg.
*Literature:* Van der Meer 1983 141.

437
## Tenor trombone
Signed CUNRAT LINCZER ME FECIT NURM 1587 and Nuremberg's coat-of-arms twice.
Made of brass. L. (1st position): 124 cm
Museum für Hamburgische Geschichte no. 1928, 328.
*Provenance:* The instrument was found in the St. Annen chapel at the beginning of the 19th century.
*Literature:* Schröder 1930 58. Wörthmüller 1955 454. Young 1980 43.

438
## Tenor trombone
Signed SEBASTIAN HAINLEIN II 16. NVRMBERG. 42 and maker's mark: a cock and 3 Nuremberg coats-of-arms
L. (1st position): 107.5 cm
Germanisches Nationalmuseum Nuremberg no. MI 169
Brass, richly ornamented with engravings and decorations.
*Provenance:* Part of Germanisches Nationalmuseum's original collection (begun 1852).
*Literature:* Van der Meer 1979 92 205.

439
## Bass trombone
Signed MACHT ICH ISAC EHE NVRMBE 1612 and various Nuremberg coats-of-arms etc.
L. (1st position): 149 cm
Germanisches Nationalmuseum Nuremberg no. MI 168
Brass with sections in silver plate and gilding and richly ornamented with engravings and attached decorations. A so-called quint bass trombone with an extra slide which can lower the pitch by two semitones. From the 16th to the end of the 18th centuries, Nuremberg was an important headquarters for making brass wind instruments, which could, however, be made of more precious metals too: early in the year 1596, Christian IV sent the musician Kortenberg to Nuremberg to buy 4 silver trombones which were to be used at the coronation.
*Provenance:* Part of Germanisches Nationalmuseum's original collection (begun 1852).
*Literature:* Van der Meer 1979 93f 205.

440
## Pair of kettledrums (a+b)
Unsigned. 18th century
a) bowl diameter incl. ring: 48.5 cm. bowl curve incl. ring: 88 cm
b) bowl diameter incl. ring: 50.5 cm. bowl curve incl. ring: 92 cm
Musikhistorisk Museum no. H 10
Copper bowls. The skin is tightened by a metal ring with screws.
*Provenance:* Originally from a church in Bavaria. Purchased for the Museum from Neumann in Nuremberg in 1898.
*Literature:* Hammerich 1911 17.

441
## Pair of drum sticks for kettle drums (a+b)
Unsigned. Germany c 1700
L. (handle + head) 36.65 cm. Diameter of head: 4.3 cm
Sammlung historischer Musikinstrumente des Germanischen Nationalmuseums Nürnberg no. MI 188 a-b
Plum wood, turned in one piece. Handles pierced for attaching ribbons or leather strips.
*Provenance:* No information.
*Literature:* Van der Meer 1979 104.

442
## Side drum
Unsighed. The cylinder is painted with heraldic signs. France c 1700
Height: 73 cm. Diameter: 29.5 cm
Germanisches Nationalmuseum Nürnberg no. MIR 636
Cylinder and rings of wood. The skin is tightened by cords.
*Provenance:* Purchased from F. Wildhagen's collection in Berlin for Sammlung Rück 1933. To Germanisches Nationalmuseum 1962.
*Literature:* Van der Meer 1979 105 208.

443
## –: Verzeichnus der Reise ... Anno 1595
Det kgl. Bibliotek, Copenhagen 35, 194 4°
Description of a journey to Germany by Christian IV in Sept.-Nov. 1595. On this journey, for the first time, the king encountered tournaments, fireworks, music of all kinds on a large scale and there is reason to believe that his experiences in Germany were, amongst other things, the inspiration for later large celebrations in Denmark such as his own coronation.

444
## Christian Hunno(?): Relatio Oder Wahrhaftiger vnd eigentlicher Bericht ... Hamburg 1595
Det kgl. Bibliotek 35-194 4°
Description of the coronation in 1596, both the processions and the ceremonies in Vor Frue Kirke which differs slightly from other accounts. C. H. provides proof that the other sources' statements concerning the number of musicians involved in the procession of "inventions" (eleborate settings for 'tableaux vivants' built on horse-drawn wagons) are not correct. It is also clear from the account that the various tableaux were of a national character with regard to colours, dress and music.

445
## Johann Maria Nossenius: Inventio. Mons Virtutis. Kbh. 1596
Det kgl. Bibliotek 35-194 4°
Explanation of Christian of Brandenburg's "invention" at the coronation 1596. The Italian architect Nosseni had constructed it in Dresden and had had it transported to Copenhagen. Nosseni was famous for designing inventions, allegorical pageants and mummeries. On this occasion musicians played on "the mountain of Virtue" and the song "Virtutis Alloquium" was thrown out to the people.
*Literature:* Machowsky 1904.

446
## Dennemärckische Krönung gedruckt bey Friedrich Hartmann 1597
Det kgl. Bibliotek 35-195 4°
Description of the coronation 1596 with 3 prints: a) the young king, b) the procession to Vor Frue Kirke, the actual coronation in the church and the procession from the church, c) the tilting and pageants in connection with the coronation. Print b) provides us with the first picture of an organ in Vor Frue Kirke; b) and c) show numerous musical scenes.
*Provenance:* Høeghs samling. Possibly the only extant example of this book.

447
## Caspar Klingner: Des durchlauchtigsten Hochgebornen Fürsten vnd Herrn/Herrn Christiani des vierdten glückliche geschehene Krönung zu Kopenhagen ... Anno 1596. Görlitz 1599
Det kgl. Bibliotek 35-195 4°
Description of the coronation in 1596 in 192 verses, "im

Thon/Hertzlich thut mich erfrewen die liebe Sommerzeit/Oder/ Vom Graffen zu Rom/ Auch wie man den alten Hildebrand singt". – The verses make an acrostic (Christian IV's name and style in German) with the following conclusion: "... godlobgelicklich gekronet zu Koppenhagen".

448

## Johan Kraft: Musicae Practicae Rudimenta. Kbh. 1607

Det kgl. Bibliotek 35-195 4°
Elementary textbook in Latin in the form of a catechism, patterned on German textbooks of the 16th century. Kraft was headmaster at Vor Frue School and lector musices at Copenhagen University.
*Provenance:* Grams Samling no. 794.
*Literature:* Hammerich 1892 147f. Schiørring 1977 212ff.

449

## Hans Bang: En liden Kriegs Sang oc Bøn Kbh. 1611

Det kgl. Bibliotek 35-200 8°
One of several songs and prayers to God, published by Danish clergymen in 1611 on the occasion of the outbreak of the Kalmar war, some with indications of the tune. This one, "Denmark's Head and Lord", is bound together with 5 others from the same period. 23 of the 24 verses form an acrostic: DANMARKIS WNDERSA(A)TERS BØN (Prayer of the Danish subjects). The last verse has H, a prayer for *help* in need. Included in Moltke's hymn book 1647, where it is stated, that it should be sung with its usual tune, a variant of "Wilhelmus van Nassouwe".
*Provenance:* Suhm's book collection.
*Literature:* Schiørring 1950 167.

450

## Bernhard Meier: Lampades. Hamburg 1621

Det kgl. Bibliotek 55-10 4°
Latin school play about the 5 wise and the 5 foolish virgins with 8 songs in 5 or 6 parts and one for 4-part double chorus. Lampades is one of the relatively few examples of a school play from this time the music of which has been preserved. The author was pastor of Skt. Petri Kirke in Copenhagen from 1616-1634.
*Literature:* Schiørring 1977 224f.

451

## Anders Christensen Arrebo: Kong Davids Psalter. Kbh. 1623

Det kgl. Bibliotek 1-103 8°
"... arranged as songs to more than one hundred tunes and tones which are used and well known in our Danish churches and Christian houses". On the whole, the author uses traditional melodies for the translation of the Psalms of David, but there are also tunes which had not been previously printed (2nd edition 1627 provides notated melody-lines for most of the psalms).
*Literature:* Hammerich 1892 65f. Schiørring 1977 112f. Rørdam 1857. Davidsen and Glahn 1981.

452

## Jørgen Pedersen Hegelund: Tvende nye Sange, 1629

Det kgl. Bibliotek 35-222 8°
In the war years, several pastors published songs which, like the first of these "describe the pitiable and deplorable state and circumstances of the homeland" or, like the second, are "... to sing and pray against the enemies of the Christian church". (Tune: "Fader vor udi Himmerig" and "Aff Adams Fald er plat forderfluit").
*Provenance:* Hielmstierne 1359.

453

## En kaart Beskriffuelse ... Kbh. 1634.

Det kgl. Bibliotek 35-276 4°
Description in Danish of "Det store Bilager" 1634. (f. cat. 454).

454

## Eine Kurtze Beschreibung ... des ... Herrn ... Christian V ... Beylager (place of publication unknown) 1634

Det kgl. Bibliotek 35-276 4°
Description in German of "Det store Bilager" 1634. Cf. previous entry.

455

## Cartell Vnd Articull des Ring-Rennens

Det kgl. Bibliotek 35-276 4°
Tournament book for tilting at the ring, Copenhagen 1634, with rules for participation etc. contained in 19 articles. The basic idea is as follows: the king as "mantenador" invites his guests, the so-called "aventurirer", to try to wrest from him a prize (Danck), put up by himself, in tilting. These "Däncke" could be wreaths, rings, sometimes silver and gold jewellery. The tournament was begun with a splendid procession of "inventions" (tableaux), in which the king and his guests themselves participated in various disguises".

456

## Christian Cassius: Relation von dem Hochfürstlichen Beylager ... Hamburg 1635

Det kgl. Bibliotek 35-276 4°
Detailed description of Princess Magdalena Sibylla of Saxony's entry into Copenhagen in 1634, of the wedding itself and the celebrations, including the 18 "inventions" which comprised the procession before the tilting. It appears that music had a central position in this connection and the description allows of diverse conclusions as to the type and number of musicians.

457

## Johannes Lauremberg: Zwo Comoedien. Kbh. 1635

Det kgl. Bibliotek 35-276 4°
Two dramatic plays in mythological-allegorical style performed at Copenhagen Castle on the occasion of "Det store Bilager" in 1634. The first, "Aquilo", describes how the ruler of the midnight lands (Prince Christian) brings home the noble princess Orithyia (Magdalena Sibylla). The other, "The Harpies", tells a story of how the winged goddesses of death are banished by two Nordic heroes. In both plays, the prose dialogue alternates with songs; the music for these is now lost.
*Literature:* Hammerich 1892 115f. Krogh 1939 22ff. Schiørring 1977 187ff. Kongsted 1985 10.

458

## Laurentz Schröder: Ein nützliches Tractätlein. Kbh. 1639.

Det kgl. Bibliotek 17-67 8°
L.S., organist at Helligåndskirken 1639-45, praises Christian IV, to whom the book is dedicated, for his "liberality" towards music, the one of the "sieben freie Künste" which the author considers to be held in the lowest esteem. The work is a warm, somewhat naive, defence of music, which Schröder, in agreement with "the scholars", divides into 4 groups: Musica mundana ("the Music of the Spheres"), Musica humana (the music made by the human voice), Musica instrumentalis (instrumental music), Musica avicularis (the music made by the birds).
*Literature:* Hammerich 1892 131ff. Schiørring 1977 216.

459

## Lauritz Pedersen Thura: Canticum Canticorum Salomonis. Kbh. 1640

Det kgl. Bibliotek 1-129 8°
Retelling in Hebrew, Latin and Danish of the Song of Solomon. The collection includes 40 psalms, 31 of which have melodies in 4-part settings; it was completed in connection with "Det store Bilager" and is dedicated to Prince Christian (in Latin) and to Magdalena Sibylla (in Danish), but was not published until 6 years later.
*Provenance:* Luxdorph's library.
*Literature:* Hammerich 1892 181ff. Schiørring 1977 113f.

460

## Johannes Meursius: Collectanea de tibiis. Sorø 1641

Det kgl. Bibliotek 29-128 8°
Short account of what authors of antiquity wrote about wind instruments.
*Literature:* Hammerich 1892 148. Schiørring 1977 216.

461

## Hans Mikkelsen Ravn: Heptachordum Danicum. Kbh. 1646

Det kgl. Bibliotek 17-71 4°
Textbook on musical theory intended for use in the upper classes of the grammar school. The book includes a resumé of the history of Danish music, deals with various disciplines in the theory of music, gives an account of various forms of contemporary music and an explanation of diverse musical terms; it deals finally with the teaching of figured bass.
*Literature:* Hammerich 1892 143ff. Johnsson 1977. Schiørring 1977 212ff.

462

## Letter from Nicolaus Zangius to Christian IV. Danzig (Gdansk) August 2, 1599

Rigsarkivet. Da.Kanc., B 160
Letter sent with an accompanying composition, not preserved, dedicated to Christian IV by N.Z., director of music in Danzig (Gdansk). In the same letter, Zangius offers to act as a kind of impresario; if the king is interested, he will ensure that good musicians come to Copenhagen.
*Literature:* Hammerich 1892 21 169f.

463

## Aksel Gyldenstierne's diary 1602

Rigskarkivet. TKUA, Rusland A II
Diary written by Aksel Gyldenstierne, member of the King's Council, on a journey to Moscow in 1602. He was leader of the delegation which accompanied Duke Hans in connection with his forthcoming marriage to be Grand Duchess Zenia, daughter of the Russian Tsar Boris Godunov. Included in the retinue were 8 instrumentalists, 7 trumpeters and 1 tympanist.
*Literature:* Hammerich 1892 29.

464

## Petition from the King's musicians c 1627

Rigsarkivet. Da.Kanc., B 160
Petition in German from the King's musicians to the King that, in spite of the war, they might be paid their salaries.
*Literature:* Hammerich 1892 192.

465

## Heinrich Schütz: Autograph letter to Friedrich Lebzelter. January 6/16, 1633

Rigsarkivet. Kongehusets arkiv, AI
Friedrich Lebzelter, the Saxon envoy in Hamburg, acted as intermediary in the appointment of the Saxon director of music Heinrich Schütz as the royal director of music in Copenhagen in 1633. On Feb. 15, 1633 Lebzelter wrote a fine reference for Schütz to Prince Christian and enclosed Schütz' letter to himself: this letter was written in such a way that it could be used as it stood as proof for the prince that Schütz was interested in coming to Copenhagen. Circumstances in Dresden had become unbearable because of the Thirty Years War, and the letter expresses a strong desire to escape from the events of the war, at least for a time.
*Literature:* Hammerich 1892 104ff. Kongsted 1985 8 15.

466

## Autograph letter from Christian IV to the treasurers. Dec. 18, 1633

Rigsarkivet. Kongehusets arkiv
The King informs treasurers that he has engaged a new director of music (Heinrich Schütz), and that there are to be practice rooms in the castle chapel and in the room outside the king's apartments; the treasurers must also find a house for the director of music in the town. The deputy director of music (Jacob Ørn) must ensure that the "chapel boys" attend and finally, that the musicians "as far as possible" (!) should have their money, so that the new director of music "can use coercion when he wants them to rehearse".
*Literature:* EB III no. 235. Hammerich 1892 108.

467

## Letter from Jacob Mores to Prince Christian (V) August 12, 1637

Rigsarkivet. Kongehusets arkiv
Mores, the royal factor in Hamburg, sends the Prince an art book, which is being brought by "the servant of the Elector of Saxony's musician". This was cited by Kongsted in 1985 as the most important argument against (the Saxon musician) Heinrich Schütz being in Copenhagen in 1637, as has previously been generally supposed.
*Literature:* Marquard I 1952 377f. Kongsted 1985 12ff.

468

## Court accounts May 3, 1642

Rigsarkivet. Revised civil accounts, Hofmønsterskriverens regnskab 1628-1661
Schütz was re-appointed as the royal director of music in Copenhagen in 1642: according to these accounts, he received the same salary as his first appointment (1633-35): 800 rigsdaler.
*Literature:* Hammerich 1892 128. Kongsted 1985 16.

469

## Letter of appointment as director of music (draft) for Heinrich Schütz May 3, 1642

Rigsarkivet. TKIA no. A13
Draft letter of appointment for the Saxon director of musici Heinrich Schütz in connection with his second period of office in Copenhagen 1642-44. The king hereby appoints "our dear faithful Henricum Schultzen" and entrusts him with responsibility for instrumentalists and singers; he must be prepared to serve in the church and elsewhere, where he is required to do service, and furthermore, he must report any disobedience to the Lord Chamberlain or to the king himself, so that suitable measures can be taken.
*Literature:* Kongsted 1985 14ff.

470

## Payments list from Nykøbing Castle 1643-44

Rigsarkivet. Accounts for Christian (V)'s household 1643-35
The payments list from Nykøbing Castle shows the payment of salaries to 6 trumpeters and 6 instrumentalists, 3 of whom (Stolle, Weckmann and Werner) were from the Electoral chapel in Dresden. After "Det store Bilager" in 1634, the prince established a chapel on the Saxon model at Nykøbing Castle.
*Literature:* Hammerich 1892 178ff.

471

## Pietro Joanelli: Novi atque catholici thesauri musici ... Venezia 1568

British Library K.4.e.3
38 4-12-part motets by 16 different composers, including the only complete extant work by Christian IV's director of music from 1590-1611, Gregorius Trehou, the motet "In dedicatione templi" for 6 voices. Like several of the other important musicians at the court, Trehou was from the Netherlands, where he was born in the 1540s; he died in Copenhagen at the beginning of 1619.
*Literature:* Hammerich 1892. Schiørring 1977 144fg. Bergsagel 1988. Kongsted 1988.

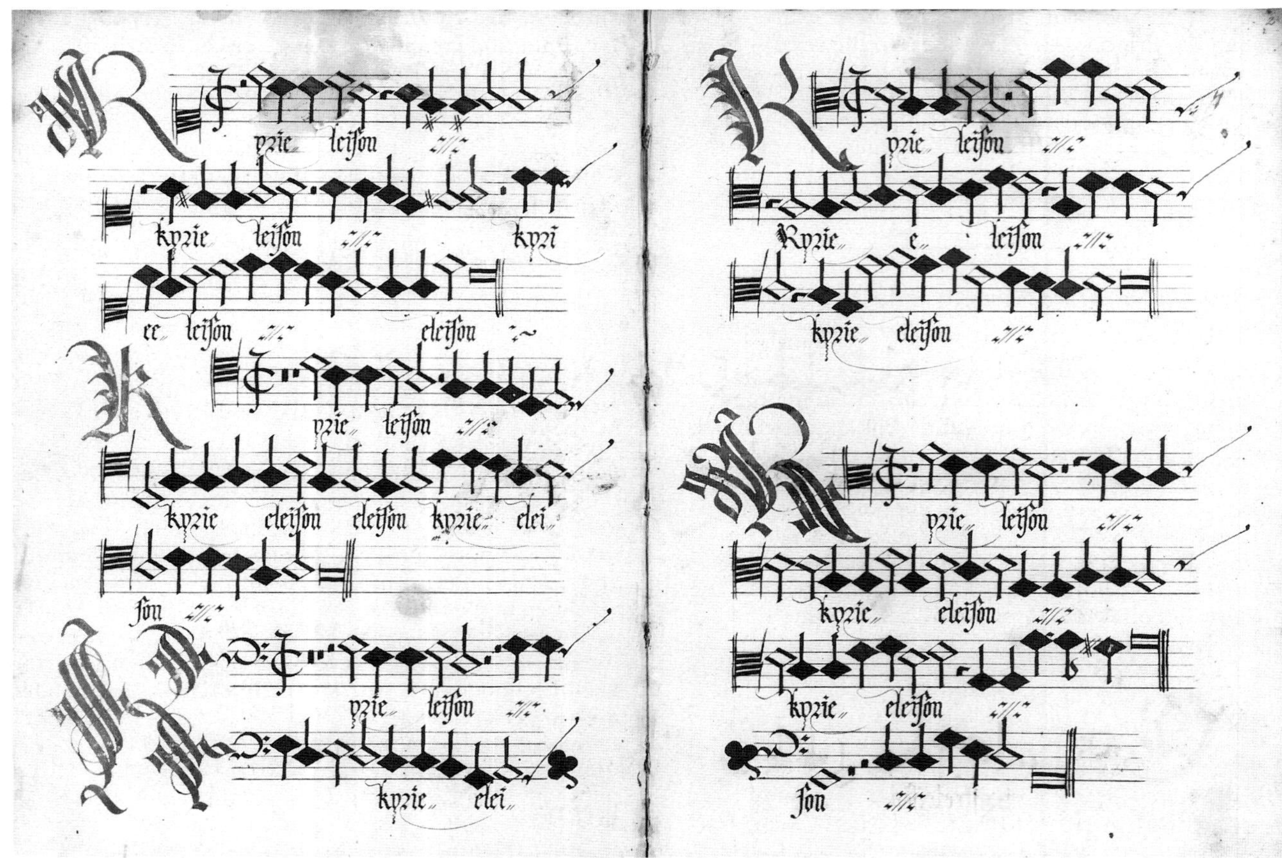


*473*

472

## Thomas Mancinus: Cantio funebris, Helmstedt 1585

Landesbibliothek and Murhardsche Bibliothek der Stadt Kassel, Mus 54f 4°

The earliest printed work by Duke Heinrich Julius' director of music in Wolfenbüttel. T.M. was presumably a member of the retinue when the duke was married to Princess Elisabeth of Denmark in 1590, since it can be seen from a Danish source that Christian IV presented the singers whom the duke had brought with him with a sum of money. The pamphlet contains a woodcut of T.M.

*Literature:* Hammerich 1921 188. Ruhnke 1963. Glahn 1988.

473

## Anonymous mass 1590

Det kgl. Bibliotek, Thott Ms.152 Fol

Anonymous 5-part "missa sine nomine"; de luxe binding in brown calf with Christian IV's apparently youthful autograph signature on the inside of the binding. The outer sides of both covers are decorated with blind-tooled ornamentation; on the front, a compound coat-of-arms for Frederik II and Sophie, in addition a crowned C and the date 1590. It has been suggested that the work may have been an inaugural work by Gregorius Trehou on taking up his appointment as royal director of music, but this attribution is uncertain.

*Literature:* Hammerich 1892 18. Schiørring 1977 145. Bergsagel 1988.

474

## Abraham Praetorius: Harmonia gratulatoria. Kbh. 1590

Det kgl. Bibliotek 35, 184 4°

The earliest printed set of part-books in the history of Danish music printing, though unfortunately only the Altus and Sexta Vox in Denmark; a complete set is, however, to be found in the British Library. A.P. was a singer in the royal chapel c 1587-1593, and the work was com-

posed for the occasion of the marriage of James VI of Scotland to Princess Anne in 1589. On the reverse of the title page, the Royal coat-of-arms of Scotland and the Order of the Thistle are reproduced.
*Literature:* Hammerich 1892 217. Glahn 1988.

475

## Jan Tollius: Liber primus motectorum ... Venezia 1591

Landesbibiothek und Murhardsche Bibliothek der Stadt Kassel, Mus. 21 4°
22 motets for church use for 5 voices by one of the many Netherlanders Christian IV had in his chapel. Liber secundus – which appeared in the same year – comprises 21 motets; the style is progressive, particularly as to harmony and melody, and it is reasonable to describe J.T. as a master who has been unjustifiably forgotten.
*Literature:* Hammerich 1892 26, 220. Kongsted 1988.

476

## Thomas Mancinus: CANTIO NOVA ... in honorem Domini Christiani IV

Det kgl. Bibliotek, Ny kgl. s. 633 g fol.
Motet composed by the director of music at the court of Christian IV's brother-in-law, Duke Heinrich Julius of Braunschweig-Wolfenbüttel, dedicated to Christian IV before 1596. The motet may have been presented to the as yet uncrowned Christian IV in 1590, at which time Mancinus was in the duke's retinue on the occasion of his marriage to Princess Elisabeth at Kronborg; it is more probable, however, as suggested by Glahn in 1988, that the presentation was made when Christian IV visited the duke in 1595.
*Literature:* Hagen 1893 24. Ruhnke 1963 76. Glahn 1988.

477

## Alexander Orologio: Intradae. Helmstedt 1597

Det kgl. Bibliotek, mu 6512.1431
Collection of 28 5- and 6-part pieces "... quarum in omni genere instrumentorum musicorum usus esse potest"; the work carries a dedication to Christian IV with whom O. corresponded.
*Literature:* Hammerich 1892 169. Hagen 1893 23. Schiørring 1977 161. Bergsagel 1988.

478

## Jan Tollius: Madrigali a sei voci. Heidelberg 1597.

British Library A.352
Tollius' skill in composing madrigals interested even Monteverdi, who quoted one of the madigals from this collection "Zefiro torna", in his 6th madrigal book, 1614. The collection contains 21 6-part pieces in Italian.
*Literature:* Seiffert 1901. Kongsted 1988.

479

## Jan Tollius: Moduli trium vocum. Heidelberg 1597

Herzog August Bibliothek, Wolfenbüttel 62.1-3 Musica
22 3-part compositions by J.T., who was a tenor singer in Christian IV's chapel from 1601-03. The individual pieces in the collection are short, sometimes in several parts, in shorter, sometimes imitative phrases with clear cadences.
*Provenance:* Probably Duke August the Younger's (1579-1666) library.
*Literature:* Hammerich 1892 26, 220. Kongsted 1988.

480

## Magnus Thomsen: Trumpeter's book (undated, c. 1600)

Det kgl. Bibliotek, Gl. kgl. Saml. 1875a, 4°
M.T. was employed as a trumpeter from 1596 to 1612, when he fell at Elfsborg. This book, which is presumed to have been prepared by him because it has MT printed on the front page, contains 281 "sonnadas", pieces which might have been used as table music, for example; at the end of the book, some of the pages indicate that it was used for teaching purposes and finally there are a number of pieces called "Tocceda".
*Litterature:* Hammerich 1892 7f, 203. Schiørring 1977 166f.

481

## John Dowland: The Second Book of Songes or Ayres, London 1600

British Library K.2.i.5,2
The foreword to this book by J.D. is dated "from Helsingnoure in Denmarke the first of June, 1600". The collection contains 8 duets, 12 songs for 4 voices and 2 for 5 voices, with tablature for lute or opharion and accompanied by a viol. The manuscript for this collection was prepared in the first two years of J.D.'s stay in Denmark and were sent to England by the composer to be printed.
*Literature:* Hammerich 1892. Schiørring 1977 148-151. Poulton 1972.

482

## Vincentius Bertholusius: Sacrarum cantionum, Venezia 1601

Uppsala Universitetsbibliotek
Collection of 29 motets for 6, 7, 8, 9 and 10 voices by Christian IV's most highly paid musician, the organist

V.B., who was employed at the court for 1½ years, 1607-08. He was Italian by birth and had been employed by King Sigismund of Poland before he came to Copenhagen.
*Provenance:* War booty from Mainz. Has belonged to the prince-bishop Johann Schweickhardt von Cronberg's (1604-26) library. Given to Uppsala University in the 1620's by Gustav II Adolf.
*Literature:* Hammerich 1892 39f, 212. Kongsted 1988.

483

## Thomas Robinson: The schoole of musicke, London 1603

British Library K.2.d.1.
From the foreword to "The school of musicke", it appears that the English lutenist T.R. had given Princess Anne of Denmark lessons in Elsinore; this was probably in 1589 before her marriage to the King of Scotland.

484

## John Dowland: Lachrimae, or Seaven Teares, London 1604

British Library K.2.i.16
J.D., the most famous lutenist of the period, was engaged by Christian IV in 1598 at a salary of 500 rigsdaler per annum – quite a considerable sum for an "ordinary" musician. With the exception of one lengthy interruption, he was employed at the Danish court until 1606. He composed his "Lachrimae" or "tear pavans" while he was court lutenist in Copenhagen. He dedicated this work to Queen Anne of England with the chivalrous observation that the work was begun where she was born (in Denmark) and completed where she was queen (in England).
*Literature:* Hammerich 1892. Schiørring 1977 148-151. Poulton 1972. Bergsagel 1988.

485

## Orazio Vecchi: Le Veglie de Siena, Venezia 1604

Landesbibliothek und Murhardsche Bibliothek der Stadt Kassel, Mus. 20 n.
A madrigal comedy for 3-6 voices in 2 parts dedicated to Christian IV by O.V., who says in the foreword that his new work is difficult to perform, but that it will be easy for a chapel such as Christian IV's. Vecchi's dedication is one of many indications of the reputation which King Christian had as a patron of music throughout much of Europe, a reputation which had arosen in connection with the coronation in 1596 and had continued to increase since.
*Literature:* Hammerich 1892 170ff.

486

## Melchior Borchgrevinck: Giardino novo ... I-II. Kbh. 1605 and 1606

British library K.4.e.1,2
The first collection of polyphonic music to be printed in Denmark, edited by Christian IV's court organist M.B.; in two parts, the first dedicated to the King of Denmark, the second to the King of England. This anthology of madrigals contains 28 + 28 pieces by popular contemporary Italian composers, with the exception, in the first part, of one madrigal by B. himself, in the second part, of 4 works by musicians attached to Christian IV's court 1 by B., 3 by Nicolo Gistou, 1 by Hans Nielsen.
*Literature:* Hammerich 1892. Dania Sonans III 1967. Glahn a.o. 1983.

487

## Niels Jespersøn: Gradval. Kbh. 1606

Det kgl. Bibliotek 17-111 2°
Together with Hans Thomissøn's hymn book from 1569, the Gradual by Bishop N.J. from Funen is the most important monument of the early Lutheran period for the history of church music and hymns. The first edition was in 1573. Late editions in 1606 and 1637 indicate consistent use of the book in Danish churches. The Gradual contains music for the communion service ordered according to the church calendar. The Latin and musically demanding Gregorian chants were presumably performed where it was possible to do so – for example, in the market towns by the grammar school pupils – whereas the Danish hymns could be used in places where the parish clerks alone were responsible for the singing.
*Provenance:* The cover of parchment has printed on it "Kiøbenhaffns Slodt", this copy must therefore have been used by Christian IV's musicians at services in the Castle church.
*Literature:* Dal and Glahn 1986 489 no. 34.

488

## Michael Praetorius: Musarum Sioniar: Motectae et Psalmi Latini. Nürnberg 1607

Det kgl. Bibliotek, mu 6602.2131
M.P., who was director of music for Duke Heinrich Julius in Wolfenbüttel, sent the above work and four parts of his Musae Sioniae to Christian IV with a dedication in his own hand.
*Literature:* Hammerich 1892 173. Schiørring 1977 163f.

489

## Zacharias Füllsack und Christian Hildebrand: Ausserlesener Paduanen und Gaillarden erster Theil. Hamburg 1607

Herzog August Bibliothek, Wolfenbüttel 36.5. Musica, 8°

Collection of 5-part pavans and galliards with several composed by musicians attached to Christian IV's court: Melchior Borchgrevinck, William Brade, John Dowland, Benedictus Grep, Matthaeus Merker "... auff allerley Instrumenten vnd insonderheit auff Fiolen (viols) zu gebrauchen". The collection's importance lies in its presentation of a number of compositions by English musicians on the continent.

*Literature:* Hammerich 1892 47. Engelke 1930 Bergsagel 1988.

490

## Teoderico Sistino: Cantiones trium vocum. Hamburg 1608

British Library K.3.k.6.

Collection of 22 3-part canzonet type songs by T.S. (Truid Aagesen). He was Danish by birth and was appointed organist at Vor Frue Kirke in 1593 and remained in this position until he was dismissed in 1613 by the rector of the University because of his Roman Catholic leanings.

*Literature:* Hammerich 1892 177f. Dania Sonans II 1966. Schiørring 1977 160-163.

491

## Mogens Pedersen: Madrigali a cinque voci. Venezia 1608

Landesbibliothek und Murhardsche Bibliothek der Stadt Kassel, mus. 20$^{d}$, 4°

M.P.'s "graduation exercise" after his studies in Venice with the organist of St. Mark's Church, Giovanni Gabrieli, 1599-1600 and 1605-1609. The collection consists of 21 5-part pieces with Italian text in the style which, M.P., the most important Danish composer of Christian IV's time, had learnt from Gabrieli.

*Literature:* Hammerich 1892. Dania Sonans I 1933. Dania Sonans III 1967. Bergsagel 1972. Bergsagel 1976. Schiørring 1977. Glahn 1988.

492

## Christian Hildebrand: Ander Theil, ausserlesener lieblichen Paduanen ... und Galliarden ... Hamburg 1609

Herzog August Bibliothek, Wolfenbüttel 40.3 Mus. 8°

Part 2 of no. 489; between them the two collections comprise 84 dance movements (pavans and galliards) of which 34 are composed by musicians associated with the court of Christian IV. In this collection, in addition to Borchgrevinck, Brade, Grep and Merker, also Nicolo Gistou is represented.

*Provenance:* Presumably the library of Duke August the younger.

*Literature:* Hammerich 1892 47. Engelke 1930. Bergsagel 1988.

493

## William Brade: Newe ausserlesene Paduanen ... Hamburg 1609

Herzog August Bibliothek, Wolfenbüttel. 41.3 Musica

Collection of 46 5-part dance movements by the Englishman William Brade, who was a member of the royal music in Copenhagen during 3 periods, totalling 11 years in all. Brade's music, according to the titles of the collections he published, is supposedly suitable for all instruments but was primarily for viols, on which instrument he was a famous player at Christian IV's court.

*Provenance:* Presumably Duke August's library.

*Literature:* Hammerich 1892 68f, 210. Engelke 1930. Schiørring 1977 149. Herzog August Bibliothek Wolfenbüttel 1986 190-191. no. XIV. 5.

494

## "Tregian-manuscript". England 1609-1619

British Library, Egerton MS 3665, ff 458v-463

10 5-part madrigals in Italian with the following attribution: "Magno Petreo Dano, Libro secundo 1611" – a second collection of madrigals by Mogens Pedersen which has not otherwise survived. M.P. was in England from 1611 to 1614, but we do not know if Tregian copied from a printed source of from the composer's manuscript, nor for that matter, if Pedersen's work was ever published. Tregian was imprisoned during these years because of his Roman Catholic faith, yet must have been in contact in some way with the works of the Danish musician.

*Provenance:* Acquired by the British Museum in 1950.

*Literature:* Dania Sonans III 1967. Bergsagel 1976. Schiørring 1977 158f.

495

## Abraham Schadaeus: Promptuarii musici. Strasbourg 1611

Det kgl. Bibliotek, mu 6610.0731

Collection in three parts of 83, 100 and 121 motets for church use; each part is divided up according to the church year. The work contains several pieces by composers who had some connection with the Danish court: Bertholusius, Orologio, Zangius.

*Provenance:* The volume has the ducal arms of Holstein-

Gottorp as super-exlibris and presumably came to the Royal Library when the library at Gottorp Castle was transferred there in 1735-49.
*Literature:* Kongsted 1988.

496

## Mogens Pedersen: Two pavans. 1611-14?

British Library Add. MS 30826, ff 10v-11
These two 5-part pavans for viols by M.P., the only known instrumental music from his hand, presumably date from his stay in England, 1611-14. Only 3 of the 5 parts Cantus, Altus and Tenor, have survived.
*Literature:* Bergsagel 1976.

497

## Antonius Mors: Etzliche Schone vnd Liebliche Fantasien ... mit V Stimmen. Rostock 1615

Det kgl. Bibliotek Gl. kgl. Saml. 1875b, 4°
The only one of the 5 part-books to have survived. A.M. manu propria with dedication to Christian IV. The book contains a number of fantasias to be played on "allerhandt Instrumenten ... Insonderheit vff Fiolenn" and at the end, 3 galliards. – A.M. was one of the organ builder/organist family M.; he was organist at the court in Güstrow 1573-1575 and at Jacobikirche in Rostock 1583-1613.
*Literature:* Hammerich 1892 173. Ruhnke 1963 188, 196. Schiørring 1977 163.

498

## Thomas Simpson: Opus newer Paduanen, Gaillarden, Intraden ... Hamburg 1617

Staats- und Universitätsbibliothek, Hamburg: Scrin. A/578
Collection of 22 pieces for 5 viols by T.S., who succeeded to William Brade's position as viol player at Christian IV's court in 1622. He remained in Copenhagen until 1625, when he left. The latest biographical entry on him (Grove 1980), which states that he died after 1630, is inaccurate since it is clear from Danish sources that he died in or before 1628.
*Literature:* Hammerich 1892 69f, 214. Grove 1980. Bergsagel 1988.

499

## Hans Brachrogge: Madrigaletti a III voci, libro primo. Kbh. 1619

Det kgl. Bibliotek, mu 6311.1432
The only known work by H.B., who was employed at Christian IV's court from 1602-1638 with af few interruptions. The three part-books, Canto primo, Canto secundo and Basso, contain 21 short pieces, 2 of which are by Mogens Pedersen. The collection's Italian foreword dedicates the work to Christian IV.
*Literature:* Hammerich 1892 59f. Dania Sonans II 1966 XV, 127-161. Bergsagel 1976 9ff. Schiørring 1977 160.

500

## Mogens Pedersen: Pratvm Spiritvale. Kbh. 1620.

Det kgl. Bibliotek 17-111 4°
"Pratum spirituale" is the principal work of Danish music from the period of Christian IV; it contains 31 5-part settings of Danish hymns, responses in Danish, a mass for 5 voices, 3 Latin motets and responses in Latin. The work is dedicated to the Heir Apparent and it appears from the Danish foreword that M.P. has been the prince's teacher, as a consequence of which he is not only able to "give his judgement on hearing, but can take the book in his own hand and demonstrate it in practice. The collection is published" ... for the service of the fatherland and for the further practice of youth in the schools".
*Literature:* Hammerich 1892 60f. Dania Sonans I 1933. Schiørring 1977 298. Glahn 1988.

500a

## Thomas Schattenberg: Jubilus S. Bernhardi ... Kbh. 1620

Herzog August Bibliothek Wolfenbüttel, 165, Musica diversa
Apart from Mogens Pedersen's "Pratum spirituale", this is the only large collection of Danish vocal church music from Christian IV's time; the work consists of 39 4-part Latin motets composed by T.S., who was organist at Nikolaj Kirke in Copenhagen from 1604.
*Literature:* Hagen 1893 5. Schiørring 1977 161. Esther Barfod, Bo Foltmann, Lisbeth Ahlgrenn Jensen, Poul Anders Lyngberg Larsen, Henrik Palsmar and Claus Røllum-Larsen 1988.

500b

## Thomas Schattenberg: Jubilus S. Bernhardi. Kbh. 1620

Per Brahegymnasiet, Jönköping.
Proofs of S's work which turned up when the material used in the binding of a copy of C. C. Lyschander's "Synopsis historiarum Danicarum" (Kbh. 1622) was examined in the 1960s. Proofs from this time are very unusual; in this case, S.'s care in the division of the syllables of the text beneath the notes is revealed.
*Literature:* Davidsson 1966.

500

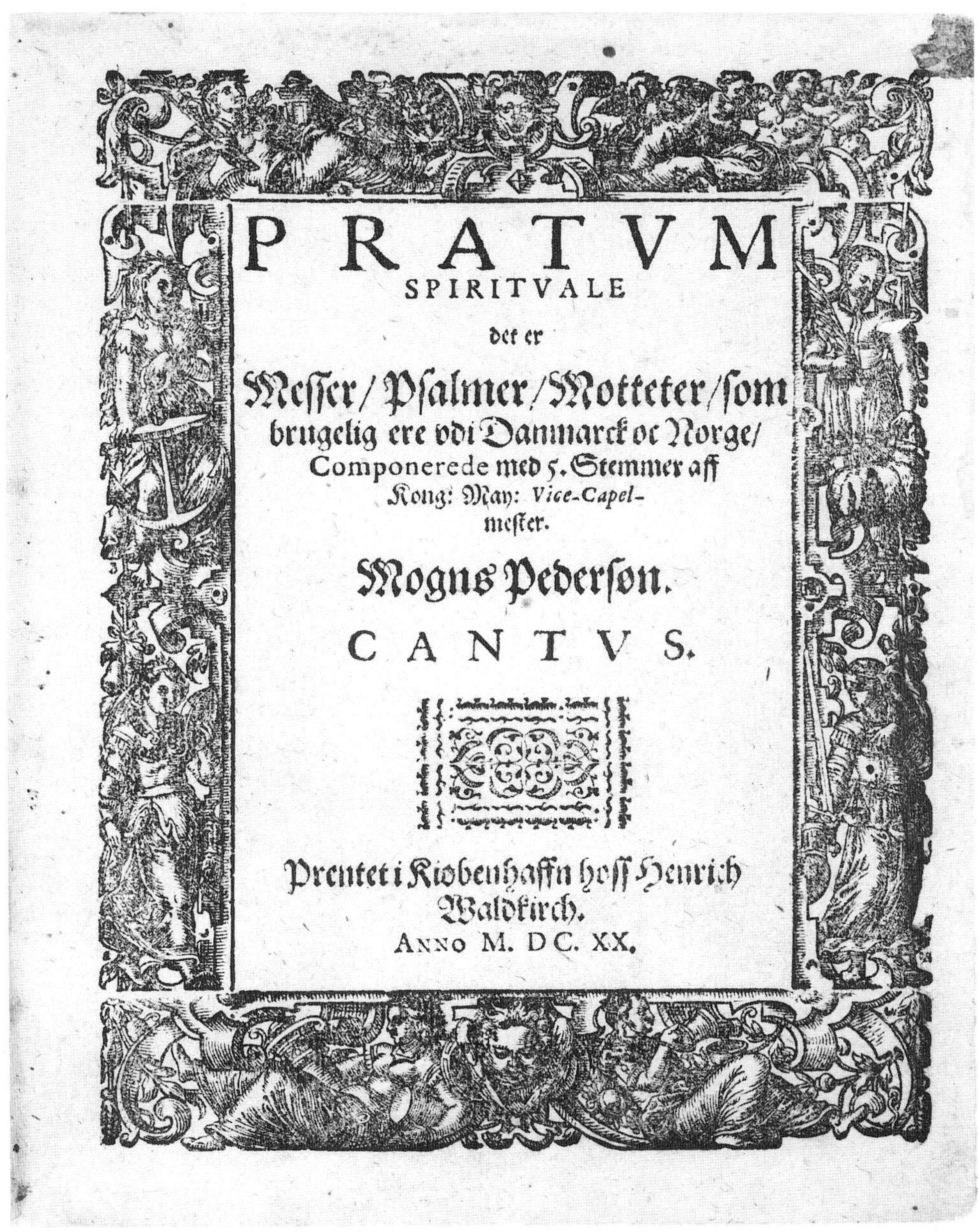

PRATVM
SPIRITVALE
det er
Messer/Psalmer/Motteter/som
brugelig ere vdi Danmarck oc Norge/
Componerede med 5. Stemmer aff
Kong: May: Vice-Capel-
mester.
Mogns Pederson.
CANTVS.
Prentet i Kiøbenhaffn hoss Henrich
Waldkirch.
ANNO M. DC. XX.

501
## Thomas Simpson: Taffel Consort, Erster Theil. Hamburg 1621.

Uppsala Universitetsbibliotek, Utl. instr. mus. tr. 26. 50 pieces for 4-part viol consort edited by T.S., 7 of which are his own compositions which he presumably had with him to perform at the court in Copenhagen, to which he was appointed the next year.
*Literature:* Hammerich 1892 69f, 214. Bergsagel 1988.

502
## Heinrich Schütz: Gesang der Venuskinder. Kbh. 1634

Schleswig-Holsteinisches Landesbibliothek Ms 13
Song for 4 sopranos, 2 violins and basso continuo for one of the "inventions" ("Thronus Veneris") at "Det store Bilager" 1634. This piece, which is dedicated to 6 Danish noblemen, is the only work from the Bilager to survive.

*Literature:* Hammerich 1892 104ff. Larsen 1969. Gudewill 1984. Kongsted 1985 10.

503

## Heinrich Schütz: Erster Theil kleiner geistlichen Concerten. Leipzig 1636.

Staatsbibliothek Preussischer Kulturbesitz, Berlin: Mus. ant. pract. S 780.
Schütz may have composed some of the movements of this collection of church music for 1-5 parts" ... sampt gefügtem Basso Continuo vor die Orgel" during his first stay in Denmark 1633-35.
*Literature:* Hammerich 1892 129. Schiørring 1977 192.

504.

## Clausholm fragment no. XI c 1640

Det kgl. Bibliotek, Håndskriftafd., dep. 1965/117
Tablature fragment containing works by Heinrich Schütz, who was the royal director of music in Copenhagen for two periods, 1633-35 and 1642-44. The fragment is part of the find made in 1964 in the chapel of Clausholm Castle, where a number of closely written sheets of music had been used to seal the organ's bellows.
*Literature:* Glahn and Sørensen 1974.

505

## Johann Schop: Johann Risten H. P. Himlischer Lieder. Lüneburg 1641-42

Staatsbibliothek Preussischer Kulturbesitz, Berlin: Eh 7400a
Johann Schop was employed as an instrumentalist from 1615 to 1619 in Copenhagen, which he visited briefly again in 1634 in connection with "Det store Bilager". He collaborated with the Holstein poet/priest Johann Rist, whose songs became very popular in Scandinavia, where they are considered significant as a source of inspiration for Søren Terkelsen's "Astree Siunge-Choer".
*Literature:* Hammerich 1892 53, 168, 213. Schiørring 1977 168, 251.

506

## Gabriel Voigtländer: Allerhand Oden vnnd Lieder (Erster Theil). Sorø 1642

Det kgl. Bibliotek, Hielmstierne 110, 2°
Collection of ballads and songs in German written by Prince Christian's trumpeter G.V. From the title page it appears that he took the melodies for the collection from Italian, French, English and German sources; there are about 100 tunes in the collection, which he adapted to a greater or lesser degree by adding a bass part. The collection is dedicated to Christian IV, the Heir Apparent and Princess Magdalena Sibylla.
*Literature:* Hammerich 1892 183ff. Schiørring 1950 365ff. Schiørring 1977 248ff.

507

## Gabriel Voigtländer: Allerhand Oden vnd Lieder. Sorø 1642

Det kgl. Bibliotek, mu 6610.2631
As cat. 506. In a supplement after the last of V.'s songs there is a tablature manuscript (mu 6703-2131) containing keyboard variations by Melchior Schildt, organist at the court and teacher to the royal children from 1626 to 1629, on 2 melodies: the first is Dowland's "Paduana lagrima", the second "Gleich Wie dass feuwr". At the end of the supplement there are 6 works which include pieces by Johann Rudolph Radeck and Heinrich Scheidemann – 2 of the composers to be found in the Clausholm fragments, as identified by Glahn and Sørensen in 1974.
*Literature:* Hammerich 1892 81ff. Schiørring 1950 307. Glahn and Sørensen 1974 34ff. Schiørring 1977 180f. Glahn 1988.

508

## Heinrich Schütz. Symphoniarum sacrarum secunda pars. Dresden 1647.

British Library F.21
Schütz presented the manuscript of this work to the Heir Apparent Prince Christian immediately before he concluded his second stay in Denmark 1642-44; the foreword with the dedication to the prince is dated Dresden, May 1, 1647. We do not know if the prince managed to see the work in print, since he died, while on a trip for his health, in Dresden itself on June 2. The work contains "Deutsche Concerten Mit 3.4.5. Nehmlich einer, zwo, dreyen Vocal, und zweyen Instrumental-Stimmen, Alsz Violinen, oder derogleichen Sambt beygefügtem geduppelten Basso Continuo", and is composed in "the new Italian manner".
*Literature:* Hammerich 1892 130f. Schiørring 1977 193. Kongsted 1985 18.

509

## Agostino Fontana: Exurgat Deus

Ms. dat.: Hamburgi 15. Junij 1647
Ratsbücherei Lüneburg: Mus. ant. pract. 206, 4°
The only known composition by A.F., who was the director of the Danish royal chapel 1647-1650, after having been an alto singer since 1638; he died in Copenhagen in 1650 and was buried in Vor Frue Kirke. The volume, which is bound up in pages from an old mass book, contains 73 vocal pieces in all.
*Provenance:* Apparently came to Ratsbücherei, Lüneburg, in the middle of the 19th century, from St. Johannis Lüneburg.

502

An Hoch Printzlicher Durchläuchtigkeit
zu Dennenmarck vnd Norwegen/ etc.

# Beylager/

# Gesang der VENUS-
Kinder in der Invention
genennet

# THRONVS VENERIS

Mit 4. *Discanten* vnd zweyen *Violini* über den
*Bassum Continuum* gestellet
Durch

## Henrich Schützen/
Capellmeistern.

## BASSO CONTINVO.

Gedruckt zu Kopenhagen / bey Henrich Krusen/
Im Jahr M. DC. XXXIV.

*Literature:* Hammerich 1892 127, 135f, 163, 185, 223. Schiørring 1977 192, 256.

510

## Søren Terkelsen: Astree Siunge-Choer. Første Snees. Glückstadt 1648

Det kgl. Bibliotek. V. Bruuns Samling

Transplantation into Danish of Johann Rist's and Gabriel Voigtländer's German songs. The collection contains 11 pieces from Voigtländer's "Oden und Lieder" and 9 pieces from Rist's "Galathee". The purpose of the collection was to promote the use of the Danish language for such songs at a time when German was dominant. Terkelsen was no genius, but his collections were apparently issued at a favourable moment since they became very popular.

*Literature:* Schiørring 1950 367. Sønderholm 1976. Schiørring 1977 251f. Hatting og Krabbe 1988.

# Christian IV and Drama

Various forms of entertainment commensurate with European development are known to have existed in Denmark during the reign of Christian IV: school drama, court ballet and the wandering players. Research into this genre is, however, hampered by the paucity of material evidence. Plays connected to Danish grammar schools provide the richest sources.

School drama, which is closely connected to European humanism, came to Denmark in the 16th century. The topics of these plays were largely taken from the Bible and the language was primarily Danish. The authors of the school plays were recruited in Denmark from amongst the headmasters of the grammar schools and the clergy. The most highly esteemed are the works of Hieronymus Justesen Ranch, three of whose plays are extant, including "Solomon's Homage", which was created for Christian IV's journey round Denmark in 1584 to receive homage from his subjects. School drama was performed at important celebrations at court, such as Christian IV's baptism and the engagement of his sister Anne to King James of Scotland. Grand occasions at European royal courts in the Renaissance were celebrated with sumptuous ceremonies, at which the entertainment in addition to drama, consisted of music, song and dance – the so-called court ballet-processions and fireworks.

Danish court culture in Christian IV's earlier years was strongly influenced by the Imperial court in Prague. After the Thirty Years War, the influence of Western Europe, especially France, was greater. One of the things which came to Denmark from France was the court ballet "ballet de cour". The form of the genre was laid down in a work of 1581 entitled "Ballet comique de la Reine", in which the constituents of court ballet were expounded. Only one complete Danish court ballet has survived in written form; it was performed at Copenhagen Castle on the occasion of the wedding of Christian IV's eldest son, the Prince Elect and Princess Magdalena Sibylla of Saxony in 1634. The ballet was written down by the dancing master Alexander von Kückelsom.

In "Regiae Nuptiae", a Danish description from 1637 of the wedding celebrations, the equipment for the court ballet is given in great detail but if we want a clear idea of the mythological and allegorical figures in ballets of this type, we have to turn to England and France. In the years from 1605 to 1640, the author Ben Jonson and the costume and scenery designer Inigo Jones created a number of masques, as court ballets were called in England. Collections of drawings for costumes and scenery are still in existence from these performances, in which Christian IV's sister, Anne of Denmark, was a keen participant. From the French court ballets too, we have today a remarkable collection of material consisting of 188 costume drawings which were found in 1985 in a private library in Germany. These drawings and the drawings which were already known in France and England are the most important source of our knowledge of the costumes used in court ballets in the time of Louis XIII. The drawings found in 1985 are by the Frenchman Daniel Rabel who died in 1637. They were mounted from the start as pages in an album and they all have water marks from the 1580s.

We can conclude from the numbering that the original collection must have had at least 239 drawings. Materials, colours and sometimes the names of the actors are listed on the drawings, which stem from court ballets performed between 1614 and 1634. In comparison with Inigo Jones' drawings, Rabel's show a much richer, sparkling imagination.

In addition to the school plays and court ballets, the Italian Commedia dell'arte was also known in Denmark in Christian IV's time, as seen in von Kückelsom's ballet in which, after a certain scene, 3 Pantalone figures have to collect up "dead animals" (dancers in costumes of hides and skins) and clean the (ball)room. The King could in fact see these figures every day, since a painting with Commedia dell'arte figures was – and is – mounted in one of the wall panels of the Winter Room in Rosenborg. In the second half of the 16th century groups of wandering professional actors, who entertained mostly with dance and mummery, could be found in Europe. English actors had been in the Danish King's service since 1579, but during the reign of Christian IV, foreign groups were very infrequent visitors. We do, however, know af two occasions when foreign actors took part in the entertainment. Christian IV's brother-in-law, the Duke of Braunschweig-Wolfenbüttel, sent his troupe to Copenhagen for the coronation celebrations in 1596. It is now believed that this troupe was led by the Englishman Thomas Sackville. The other occasion was the wedding of the Prince Elect in 1634, for which the King had engaged a troupe from abroad. This group performed two plays in the Great Hall of Copenhagen Castle and a "Tragoedia von den Tugenden und Lasten" in the castle yard, which included an impressive firework display. In this case too, we can only guess at the troupe in question. It was probably a group of actors who had been working at the court in Dresden. The performance of this tragedy is recorded in an engraving in the book "Triumphus Nuptialis Danicus" from 1648.

*Lisbet Grandjean*

511

## Hieronymus Justesen Ranch: Kong Salomons Hyldning. Kbh. 1585

Det kgl. Bibliotek, LN 1363, ex. 3

A merry and profitable comedy on King David and King Solomon, written by request of chancellor Niels Kaas and performed as part of the festivities in Viborg in 1584, on the occasion of Prince Christian's journey to receive homage from his subjects.

*Literature:* Krogh 1940

512

## Hieronymus Justesen Ranch: Samsons Fængsel. Aarhus 1633

Det kgl. Bibliotek 55-145,4
A Biblical play probably performed as early as 1599. The text is taken from the Old Testament, the Book of Judges chapter 16
*Literature:* Krogh 1940.

513

## Hieronymus Justesen Ranch: Karrig Nidding. Kbh. 1633.

Det kgl. Bibliotek 55-145 8°
A domestic comedy, probably from 1599, about Nidding, a miserly husband.
*Literature:* Krogh 1940.

514

## Anders Kieldssøn Tybo: Absalon. Kbh. 1618

Det kgl. Bibliotek, Hielmst. 1832 8°
A Biblical play about the rebellion of Absalon and his followers and their terrible punishment.
*Literature:* Krogh 1940.

515

## Erich August: ... Beskriffuelse om den ... kgl. Kroning. Kbh. 1598

Det kgl. Bibliotek LN 574, ex.1
"A clear and true description of the high and mighty Prince and Lord Christian the Fourth's ... royal coronation on 29th August 1596". The book contains detailed descriptions of the ceremony itself, the procession with scenery and costumes, fireworks, musical instruments, jousting.

516

## Jørgen Jørgensen Holst: Regiae Nuptiae. Kbh. 1637

Det kgl. Bibliotek 35-276 4°
The work is in two parts. The first part contains the book Regiae nuptiae, which describes the celebrations surrounding the nuptials. The second part consist of the text of the Tragedy of the Virtues and Vices, which was performed in the outer yard of Copenhagen Castle on 10th October 1634.
*Literature:* Memoirer og Breve XX, 1914.

517

## Jørgen Jørgensen Holst: Triumphus Nuptialis. Kbh. 1648

Det kgl. Bibliotek 35-276 4°
Description of the celebrations in connection with the wedding of the Prince Elect in 1634.
*Literature:* Memoirer og Breve XX, 1914.

518

## Charles Ogier: Ephemerides sive iter danicum svecium polonicum. Paris 1656

Det kgl. Bibliotek 31-193 8°
Travel journal which includes a description of the celebrations in 1634 in connection with the wedding of the Prince Elect and Magdalena Sibylla of Saxony.
*Literature:* Memoirer og Breve XX, 1914.

519

## Alexander von Kückelsom: Kurtzer Einhalt und Bedeutung des Ballets ... Kbh. 1634

Det kgl. Bibliotek 35-276 4°
Programme for the first court ballet known in Denmark, performed at Copenhagen Castle in 1634 in connection with the celebrations on the occasion of the marriage of the Prince Elect and Magdalena Sibylla of Saxony. The programme was intended as directions for the audience.
*Literature:* Krogh 1939.

520

## Pantalone's Serenade

Anonymous, end of the 16th century, probably Dutch
Oil on panel. 35×47.2 cm
Drottingholm's Teatermuseum, Akvis.nr. DTM 4797/1939
Pantalone's Serenade is one of three paintings of the same size with *motifs* from the Commedia dell'arte. All three correspond with woodcuts reproduced in Recueil Fosard, Stockholm.
*Literature:* Liljevalchs Konsthal 1973 nr. 2.

*520*

## *Drawings by Inigo Jones for masques*

About 450 drawings from the hand of Inigo Jones are known today. They were carried out between 1605 and 1640 for the theatre at the Stuart court. Most of these drawings belong to the Duke of Devonshire's collection in Chatsworth, England. The drawings were acquired in the 18th century by Lord Burlington, whose only daughter married the 4th Duke of Devonshire. Some of the drawings were done by Jones' assistents from drafts which have now disappeared. The English masques were usually performed around Christmas and New Year.

521

### Niger's Daughter (1605)

Drawing, water colour, silver (now whitened) and gold. 29×15.9 cm. Colour-plate XXXI
The Trustees of the Chatswoth Settlement
Inigo Jones' drawing is a costume design for his and Ben Jonson's play "The Masque of Blackness", performed at the Whitehall Banqueting House on 6th January 1605 for Twelfth Night. One of the performers in the masque was Queen Anne, Christian IV's sister.
*Literature:* Simpson & Bell 1923-4, no. 1. Orgel & Strong 1973 no. 1. Festival Designs USA 1967-8 no. 4. King's Arcadia London 1973 no. 39.

522

### A torch bearer (1605)

Drawing, water colour, silver (now black) and gold. 28.5×18.7 cm
The Trustees of the Chatsworth Settlement
Inigo Jones' drawing is a costume design for his and Ben Jonson's play "The Masque of Blackness", performed at the Whitehall Banqueting House on 6th January 1605 for Twelfth Night. One of the performers in the masque was Queen Anne, Christian IV's sister.

*Literature:* Simpson & Bell 1923-4 no. 4. Orgel & Strong 1973 no. 4. Festival Designs USA 1967-8 no. 5. King's Arcadia London 1973 no. 40.

523

## Winged masquer (c 1605)

Drawing, water colour, silver (now black) and gold. 27.6×18 cm
The Trustees of the Chatsworth Settlement
The masque for which this costume was designed by Inigo Jones is not known. It is a costume for a dancer and may be from a masque performed as early as 1603, in which Queen Anne was one of the dancers.
*Literature:* Simpson & Bell 1923-24 no. 418. Festival Designs USA 1967-8 no. 1. King's Arcadia London 1973 no. 41. Orgel & Strong 1973 no. 5.

524

## The House of Fame (1609)

Wash drawing, black ink. 27.8×19.9 cm
The Trustees of the Chatsworth Settlement
The earliest surviving design for scenery by Inigo Jones, for the 2nd scene of "The Masque of Queens", a Christmas masque performed at the Whitehall Banqueting House on 2nd February 1609. Queen Anne was one of the players.
*Literature:* Simpson & Bell 1923-4 no. 14. Orgel & Strong 1973 no. 15. Festival Designs USA 1967-8 no. 8. King's Arcadia London 1973 no. 44.

525

## Penthesileia (1609)

Wash drawing, black ink. 27.6×15.6 cm
The Trustees of the Chatsworth Settlement
Costume drawing for "The Masque of Queens". The design was for Lucy Harington, Countess of Bedford, one of the queens in the House of Fame.
*Literature:* Simpson & Bell 1923-4 no. 18. Festival Designs USA 1967-8 no. 9. Orgel & Strong 1973 no. 16.

526

## Camilla (1609)

Wash drawing, black ink. 28.3×17.2 cm
The Trustees of the Chatsworth Settlement
Costume drawing for "The Masque of Queens". The design was for Catherine Somerset, Lady Windsor, one of the queens in the House of Fame.
*Literature:* Simpson & Bell 1923-4 no. 19. Festival Designs USA 1967-8 no. 10. Orgel & Strong 1973 no. 17. King's Arcadia London 1973 no. 46.

527

## Design for Camilla's head dress (1609)

Pen and ink drawing, black ink. 10×7.4 cm
The Trustees of the Chatsworth Settlement
*Literature:* Simpson & Bell 1923-4 no. 20. Orgel & Strong 1973 no. 18.

528

## Thomyris (1609)

Wash drawing, black ink. 28.6×17 cm
The Trustees of the Chatsworth Settlement
Costume drawing for "The Masque of Queens". The design was for Susan de Vere, Countess of Montgomery, one of the queens in the House of Fame.
*Literature:* Simpson & Bell 1923-4 no. 21. Festival Designs USA 1967-8 no. 11. Orgel & Strong 1973 no. 19.

529

## Artemisia (1609)

Wash drawing, black ink. 30.5×18.7 cm
The Trustees of the Chatsworth Settlement
Costume drawing for "The Masque of Queens". The design was for Elizabeth Somerset, Lady Guildford, who was one of the queens in the House of Fame.
*Literature:* Simpson & Bell 1923-4 no. 22. Festival Designs USA 1967-8 no. 12. Orgel & Strong 1973 no. 20.

530

## Design for Artemisia's head dress (1609)

Pen and ink drawing, black ink. 9.5×7.5 cm
The Trustees of the Chatsworth Settlement.
*Literature:* Simpson & Bell 1923-4 no. 23. Festival Designs USA 1967-8 no. 17d. Orgel & Strong 1973 no. 21.

531

## Berenice (1609)

Wash drawing, black ink, 29.7×18 cm
The Trustees of the Chatsworth Settlement
Costume drawing for "The Masque of Queens". The design was for Lady Anne Clifford, one of the queens in the House of Fame.
*Literature:* Simpson & Bell 1923-4 no. 24. Festival Designs USA 1967-8 no. 13. Orgel & Strong 1973 no. 22. King's Arcadia London 1973 no. 47.

532

## Design for Berenice's head dress (1609)

Pen and ink drawing, brown ink. 10.6×7.3 cm
The Trustees of the Chatsworth Settlement.
*Literature:* Simpson & Bell 1923-4 no. 25. Festival Designs USA 1967-8 (18b). Orgel & Strong 1973 no. 23.

533

## Candace (1609)

Wash drawing, black ink. 30×18.5 cm
The Trustees of the Chatsworth Settlement
Costume drawing for "The Masque of Queens". The design was for Lady Anne Winter, one of the queens in the House of Fame.
*Literature:* Simpson & Bell 1923-4 no. 26. Festival Designs USA 1967-8 no. 14. Orgel & Strong 1973 no. 24.

534

## Zenobia (1609)

Wash drawing, black ink. 30×17.3 cm
The Trustees of the Chatsworth Settlement
Costume drawing for "The Masque of Queens". The design was for Elizabeth de Vere, Countess of Derby, one of the queens in the House of Fame.
*Literature:* Simpson & Bell 1923-4 no. 27. Festival Designs USA 1967-8 no. 15. Orgel & Strong 1973 no. 25.

535

## Design for Zenobia's head dress (1609)

Pen and ink drawing, brown ink. 9.5×7.2 cm
The Trustees of the Chatsworth Settlement.
*Literature:* Simpson & Bell 1923-4 no. 28. Festival Designs USA 1967-8 no. 17b. Orgel & Strong 1973 no. 26.

536

## Atalanta (1609)

Wash drawing, brown ink. 27.7×15.4 cm
The Trustees of the Chatsworth Settlement
Costume drawing for "The Masque of Queens". The design was for Alathea Talbot, Countess of Arundel, one of the queens in the House of Fame.
*Literature:* Simpson & Bell 1923-4 no. 29. Festival Designs USA 1967-8 no. 16. Orgel & Strong 1973 no. 27.

537

## Design for Atalanta's head dress (1609)

Pen and ink drawing, brown ink. 9.5×6.8 cm
The Trustees of the Chatsworth Settlement.
*Literature:* Simpson & Bell 1923-4 no. 30. Festival Designs USA 1967-8 no. 17a. Orgel & Strong 1973 no. 28.

538

## Bell-Anna, Queen of the Ocean (1609)

Pen and ink drawing, brown ink. 18.4×13 cm
The Trustees of the Chatsworth Settlement
The design for the head dress is presumed to have been for Queen Anne, one of the queens in the House of Fame.
*Literature:* Simpson & Bell 1923-4 no. 422. Orgel & Strong 1973 no. 29.

539

## Unidentified queen (1609)

Wash drawing, black ink. 28.5×16 cm
The Trustees of the Chatsworth Settlement
Costume drawing for "The Masque of Queens". The design must have been for one of the queens in the House of Fame, since she carried a sceptre in her left hand.
*Literature:* Simpson & Bell 1923-4 no. 31. Festival Designs USA 1967-8 no. 27. Orgel & Strong 1973 no. 32.

540

## Naiad (1610)

Wash drawing, brown ink. 30×17.7 cm
The Trustees of the Chatsworth Settlement
The costume drawing belongs to Inigo Jones and Samuel Daniel's masque "Tethys' Festival", which was performed at the Whitehall Banqueting House on 5th June 1610, when Prince Henry was nominated Prince of Wales. Anne of Denmark had the title role in the masque.
*Literature:* Simpson & Bell 1923-4 no. 37. Festival Desings USA 1967-8 no. 32. Orgel & Strong 1973 no. 53.

541

## Tethys or a nymph (1610)

Wash drawing, brown ink, 33.5×17.8 cm
The Trustees of the Chatsworth Settlement
Costume drawing for "Tethys' Festival". The design was for Anne of Denmark, who had the part of Tethys.
*Literature:* Simpson & Bell 1923-4 no. 38. Festival Designs USA 1967-8 no. 31. Orgel & Strong 1973 no. 54. King's Arcadia London 1973 no. 50.

542

## Design for a head dress, presumably for Anne of Denmark (1610)

Pen and ink drawing, brown ink. 22×17.8 cm
The Trustees of the Chatsworth Settlement.
*Literature:* Simpson & Bell 1923-4 no. 39. Orgel & Strong 1973 no. 55.

548

*Costume drawings from Daniel Rabel's studio, Paris*

543

## Monster in the shape of a dog

Pen and ink drawing with water colour. 28.5×20 cm
The Board of Trustees of The Victoria and Albert Museum, London.
Costume drawing for the "Ballet de la Délivrance de Renaud", first performed on 29th January 1617. The literary source for the ballet was Torquato Tasso's work "Gerusalemme Liberata" 1575 and it had parts for Louis XIII and the Duke of Luynes amongst others.
*Provenance:* Purchased 1985. Cf. p. 142.
*Literature:* McGowan 1986 no. 4. Theatre Museum London 1987.

544

## A soldier

Pen and ink drawing with water colour. 29.3×20,8 cm
The Board of Trustees of The Theatre Museum, Victoria and Albert Museum, London
Cf. the previous entry.
*Literature:* McGowan 1986 no. 6. Theatre Museum London 1987.

545

## Ismen

Pen and ink drawing with water colour. 32.5×20.5 cm
The Board of Trustees of The Theatre Museum, Victoria and Albert Museum, London
Costume drawing for the "Ballet de Tancréde", performed in the Louvre on 12th February 1619 by Louis XIII, the Duke of Luynes and members of the court on the occasion of the King's sister's wedding to the Duke of Savoy. The literary source for the ballet was Torquato Tasso's work "Gerusalemme Liberata" (1575).
*Literature:* McGowan 1986 no. 7. Theatre Museum London 1987.

546

## Four wood spirits

Pen and ink drawing with water colour. 32×21 cm
The Board of Trustees of the Theatre Museum, Victoria and Albert Museum, London
Cf. the previous entry.
*Literature:* McGowan 1986 no. 8. Theatre Museum London 1987.

547

## The shepherd Apollo

Pen and ink drawing with water colour. 26.5×19 cm
The Board of Trustees of The Theatre Museum, Victoria and Albert Museum, London
Costume drawing for the "Ballet du Roy" or "Ballet d'Apollon", performed in the Louvre on 18th February 1621. The part of Apollo was played alternately by Louis XIII and the Duke of Luynes amongst others.
*Literature:* McGowan 1986 no. 38. Theatre Museum London 1987.

548.

## Entry of Music

Pen and ink drawing with water colour. 31×21 cm
The Board of Trustees of The Theatre Museum, Victoria and Albert Museum, London
Costume drawing from the "Ballet des Fées de la Forest de Saint-Germain", performed on 9th February 1625.
*Literatur:* McGowan 1986 no. 47. Theatre Museum London 1987.

549

## A player

Pen and ink drawing with water colour. 30,5×21 cm
The Board of Trustees of The Theatre Museum, Victoria and Albert Museum, London
Cf. the previous entry
*Literature:* McGowan 1986 no. 53. Theatre Museum London 1987.

550

## A saraband dancer

Pen and ink drawing with water colour. 29,7×19 cm
Theatre Museum, Victoria and Albert Museum, London
Costume drawing for the "Ballet Royal du Grand bal de la Douairiére de Billebahaut", performed in February 1626 in the Louvre for the court and at the Hotêl de Ville for the citizens of Paris.
*Literature:* McGowan 1986 no. 86. Theatre Museum London 1987.

551

## La Douairière de Billebahaut

Pen an ink drawing with water colour. 31,5×19 cm
The Board of Trustees of The Theatre Museum, Victoria and Albert Museum, London
Cf. the previous entry.
*Literature:* McGowan 1986 no. 88. Theatre Museum London 1987.

552
## Summer

Pen and ink drawing with water colour. 32×21 cm
The Board of Trustees of The Theatre Museum, Victoria and Albert Museum, London
Costume drawing for the "Ballet des quatre saisons de l'Année", performed during the carnival in 1626.
*Literature:* McGowan 1986 no. 91. Theatre Museum London 1987.

553
## A bonnetted bottle

Pen and ink drawing with water colour. 29×20.5 cm
The Board of Trustees of The Theatre Museum, Victoria and Albert Museum, London
Costume drawing for the "Ballet du Sérieux et du Grotesque", performed in February 1627 at the Louvre for the court and at the Hotel de Ville for the citizens of Paris.
*Literature:* McGowan 1986 no. 103. Theatre Museum London 1987.

554
## Astrologer

Pen and ink drawing with water colour. 32.5×21 cm
The Board of Trustees of The Theatre Museum, Victoria and Albert Museum, London.
Cf. previous entry.
*Literature:* McGowan 1986 no. 106. Theatre Museum London 1987.

555
## Grotesque ladies

Pen and ink drawing with water colour. 32.5×20.5 cm
The Board of Trustees of The Theatre Museum, Victoria and Albert Museum, London
Cf. cat. 553.
*Literature:* McGowan 1986 no. 115. Theatre Museum London 1987.

556
## Harmony

Pen and ink drawing with water colour. 26×20.5 cm
The Board of Trustees of The Theatre Museum, Victoria and Albert Museum, London
Costume drawing for the "Ballet de l'Harmonie", performed in 1632.
*Literature:* McGowan 1986 no. 148. Theatre Museum London 1987.

557
## Nine muses

Pen and ink drawing with water colour. 26×20.5 cm
The Board of Trustees of the Theatre Museum, Victoria and Albert Museum, London
Cf. cat. 556.
*Literature:* McGowan 1986 no. 149. Theatre Museum London 1987.

558
## The Prince Elect's clothing

Coat, breeches, cloak etc. 1635
Wool, silver embroidery
Rosenborg 7.21 11a-c
Chocolate brown clothing with silver embroidery. Cloak and coat are lined with topaz yellow silk velvet. The coat has long skirts and ¾ length wide sleeves with a slash along the front edge. It has a centre fastening of stitched silver thread buttons. The breeches narrow at the knee and fasten with silver buttons and loops of silver cord. Round cloak with collar stitched on separately. The breeches are lined with the same cotton flannel as is found in the sleeves of the Kolberger Heide coat.
*Provenance:* Rosenborg inv. 1718 471,1. 1648, List of the Heir Apparent's clothing, no. 11.
*Literature:* Flamand Christensen 1940 I 52, II Plates 17-18.

559
## Balet comique de la Reyne

Baldassazrino da Belgiojoso
British Library, London
In this work which was performed in Paris in 1581 at the wedding of the Duke of Joyeuses and Margrethe of Lothringen, the form of the court ballet is established.
*Literature:* Panum & Behrend I 1905. Krogh 1939.

560
## Trufaldino de Bentruffati, servant figure in Commedia dell'arte

Engraving by Stefano Scolari (1650-87)
Den kgl. Kobberstiksamling. On loan to Kunstindustrimuseet KKS 124
*Exhibitions:* Kunstindustrimuseet 1958 no. 38.

561
## Two Commedia dell'arte figures, the servant types Brighelle and Trivelin

Engraving by Gregoire Huret
Den kgl. Kobberstiksamling. On loan to Kunstindustrimuseet KKS 129
*Exhibitions:* Kunstindustrimuseet 1958 no. 37.

*Prince Frederik's invention at the Tilting on occasion of The Grand Wedding (Det store Bilager) 1634. Engraving in Triumphus Nuptialis Danicus, Hafnia 1648. (Cat. 517).*

562

# Rosenborg

## *Treasures of Christian IV*

The exhibition is divided up into 8 "Kammern" (Rooms) which show aspects of Christian IV as King and as private individual. In the first 3 Kammern the official function is dominant: the King as personification of society (Treasury), as the head of the Church (Oratory), and as War-commander (Armoury). In the remaining Kammern – the Jewel Cabinet, the Kunstkammer, the Silver Cabinet, the Furniture Cabinet and Wardrobe – official and private elements are combined. The "Kammern" are reconstructions, not recreations of original arrangements. Our limited knowledge cannot take us further.

From the time before 1650 almost all Danish inventories have been lost. The conspicuous exception is the Frederiksborg Castle inventory of 1636, and Johan Adam Berg's printed description from 1646.[1] With the Kunstkammer's inventory of 1674 and Rosenborg's of 1696 an unbroken series begins which permits us to follow the objects forward to the present day.[2] The loss is in part counterbalanced by inventories – of dowry objects, confiscated articles and estates left on death – for female members of the Royal house.[3] To these can be added treasury accounts, but the descriptions of objects given there are brief, and as regards more detailed accounts from artists or goldsmiths sent to the King's own chamber, only a few are preserved.[4] Mention should finally be made of Prince Christian of Anhalt's travel-diary from 1623, which gives important information about the furnishing of Frederiksborg and of Rosenborg.[5]

The paucity of sources is particularly to be regretted because the craftmanship of that period is anonymous, lacking the signature which a painting would have, the master's stamp on silver, or the marks on porcelain. Of the objects exhibited, many have inscriptions describing how they came into the possession of Christian IV and his family. The majority have been chosen because they come from the time of the King's rule and be traced uninterruptedly through the inventories of Rosenborg and the Kunstkammer.

Although written sources give scant information about Christian IV's treasure, the King's letters – over 3000 of them – allow us insight into his personality. Not an intellectual, but not without talents either. Well-educated, endowed with strong emotions and temperament, a large appetite for work and restless energy, the King's strengths seem more directed towards practical business, mechanics and technology than towards book-learning and philosophical reflection. Perhaps because of this it was architecture and music that were closest to his heart. Instruction in drawing and practice at the lathe formed part of his education and helped to develop his eye, but beyond ordinary pleasure in beauty Christian IV never really became interested in art and craftsmanship.[6] On the other hand the procurement of e.g. the series of tapestries for Frederiksborg's Long Hall, the ceiling paintings in Rosenborg's Long Hall and Honthorst's pictures of Denmark's history demonstrate his appreciation of the usefulness of art as political propaganda and official representation.

In relation to Christian IV's clear sense of prestige, one may ask why the King did not unite his art treasures and precious objects in a Kunstkammer as became fashionable among the north European princes after 1600.[7] Prompting to take such action was not lacking. The art dealer Philip Hainhofer, for example, who worked in Augsburg as art adviser on the setting up of Kunstkammern, eagerly but without success tried to contact Christian IV.[8] If the King was not prepared to be a customer for one of Hainhofer's Kunstschränke, the reason was without doubt that he did not wish to see the Danish-Norwegian King's art collection made into a replica of those of the minor North German princes who were Hainhofer's usual clients. The splendour and dimensions of the silver altar in Frederiksborg Castle Chapel are indications that Christian IV preferred to commission works himself.

With his collections of weapons and riding equipment at Sparepenge Christian IV may well have anticipated the Kunstkammer idea; in any event, he left it to his son to realise the project. Kept politically without influence, the Prince Elect, Christian, had a free rein as patron of art and culture. After his marriage his father transferred to him the collections at Sparepenge, and there, as in his residence at Nykøbing Castle, the Prince had a Kunstkammer set up. Among his prize acquisitions was the Golden Horn found at Gallehus in 1639, a gift from his father.[9] After the Prince's sudden death, the widow was forced by Christian IV's stubbornness, to return the Prince's valuables, which "should remain with the Crown". The King entrusted them to the new heir to the throne, the future Frederik III, who thus acquired the nucleus of the Kunstkammer, which was set up in Copenhagen Castle in 1652, and of the treasure collection at Rosenborg.[10]

Many of the exhibited objects are princely gifts and foreign purchases. The Danish/Norwegian economy was based on agriculture and shipping, but did not involve any mining or metal-working industry worth mentioning. The trading companies established by Christian IV did not achieve his ambition of making Copenhagen the international centre of trade in overseas goods, nor did the King's silkworks established in 1620 with the help of Dutchmen called in for the purpose, last for long. There was only one commodity – unicorn horn, or narwhal tusk – of which the Danish King had a monopoly for use in exchanges of princely gifts.[11] The question of origin – Danish or foreign – should thus be easy to answer.

The exceptions are works produced by travelling carpenters and goldsmiths. The pews in Frederiksborg Castle Chapel, made by the court carpenter Hans Barchmann in 1611-16, are of European quality, but are unfortunately the only preserved intarsia furniture (apart from cat. 91a) and makers of the few pieces of ebony and silver furniture are not known.

Christian IV's crown is a crucial departure-point for an understanding of the Danish goldsmiths' craft of that time. By great good fortune the receipts for the making of the Crown have been preserved; the receipts and the crown itself demonstrate what Dirich Fyring's court workshop was capable of producing around 1600. We must suppose that the master had apprentices. But since his successors' corresponding accounts have all been destroyed we do not know their works.[12] The question is therefore for what length of time did Christian IV have money to occupy goldsmiths of international standard? There was certainly money up till the time of Denmark's entry into the 30 Years' War in 1625, and it should be stressed that even in these "good years" the King's prestige buildings and art purchases cost less than the defence budget. Neither the expenditure on the war nor the occupation of Jutland had serious economic consequences. What weighed heavily after 1630 was the military re-arming, but this was covered by increased imposition of taxes, raising of the Sound toll, and taking out loans. Only in the 1640s, as a result of the Torstensson War and the lowering of prices for Danish agricultural products, did Christian IV seem to be without capital.[13] By then his stock of inherited valuables which could be melted down and re-used had also been exhausted. During those years the Crown's purchases in Hamburg were increased – a trend which continued in the 1650s.[15] The reason was not any difference in quality, but rather in liquidity. The Hamburg trading companies could offer the Crown credit in exchange for landed property or for exemption from future toll charges, while the Copenhagen goldsmiths needed direct supplies of materials and capital in order to be able to work. In this way the lack of finance became a threat to the Danish jewellers' craft, but this did not happen until the last years of Christian IV. Then the proudest treasure of Danish goldsmiths' crafts was no longer to be found in the capital of the Kingdom. Christian IV's crown had been pawned in Hamburg.[16]

1. Frederiksborg Castle inventory of 1650. Berg, 1646.
2. Rosenborg inventories: 1696, 1718, 1731, 1781, 1784, 1797, 1802, 1812, 1824, 1830, 1836, 1839, 1851, 1877, 1910. Gundestrup & Lundbæk 1980 259.
3. The most important are: Queen Anna Catherine's dowry inventory of 1597; the estate of the deceased Queen Sophie, 1631; the estate of the deceased Prince Elect Christian, 1647; list of confiscations from Kirsten Munk, 1658, and from Leonora Christina, 1661; the estates of the deceased Queen Sophie Amalie, 1685, Princess Sophie Hedevig, 1735, Queen Anna Sophie (Reventlow), 1743, Queen Sophie Magdalene, 1770, Princess Charlotte Amalie, 1783 (RA).
4. Liisberg 1929 76. Boesen 1986 104.
5. Christian des Jungeren 1858 90-103.
6. E.g. the goldsmith Willum Fransos mounted objects of whale-bone made by the King in 1592. Liisberg 1929 133 16.
7. Impey & MacGregor 1985.
8. Hainhofer 1984 nos. 448, 583 (1619 and 1621).
9. Christian V's letters I 1952 188. II 1956 574. Hermansen 1960 16-44.
10. RA. TKUA Sachsen II Pakke 25, concerning the estate of the Prince Elect, 1647-53. Staatsarchiv Dresden Loc. 10546.
11. Bencard 1985 114-125.
12. Among discarded bills from important Copenhagen master-craftsmen listed in 1720, mention is made of e.g. Niels Truidsen 1599-1614, Morten Wechsel 1602-17, Steen Pedersen 1620-23, Mathias Clausen 1632-34, Christen Thomsen 1631-41. RA Rentekammeret, A I 34 Revision of 14.5.1720.
13. Heiberg 1976, 25-58.
14. Liisberg 1929 61ff. 73.
15. Gabriel Gomez in Hamburg. RA. Afregninger 216.220 (G 20).
16. Boesen, 1986 86.

Jørgen Hein

## The Treasury

In the Treasure-Chamber, which was sited in the "Vault" of Copenhagen Castle, the Regalia were kept: the King's crown, sceptre, orb, and sword as well as the Queen's crown and other valuable objects. This is recounted e.g. in the inventories from 1549 and 1557. After the construction of Frederiksborg some of the precious objects were moved there, but there is every reason to believe that the Regalia remained in Copenhagen.

In the present reconstruction the main piece is Christian IV's crown, a chef d'oeuvre of goldsmiths' art from Renaissance Europe (cat. 562). Gudmund Boesen sees in the open crown a reflection of the crowns of the Kings of the Nordic union, and thus an expression of the wish for a reunited Scandinavia under Danish rule. From the beginning of the 1620s the King surrounded himself with closed crowns, the more prevalent type of King's crown in Europe.

The orders of chivalry were symbols of the glory of the crown, to be worn as a sign of royal favour. They also give insights into Christian IV's mentality. "The Mailed Sword-Arm", a new military order initiated in 1616, testifies to the King's pride in having defeated Sweden in the Kalmar War in 1611-13 (cat. 563). The Order of the Elephant, instituted by the first King of the House of Oldenborg, was given virtually the appearance it has today by Christian IV. In any case here the white enamel elephant is met for the first time, in contrast to the oldest preserved, that of Frederik II, which is of gold. It was varied, however, a couple of times in Christian IV's lifetime. After the defeat in the 30 Years' War it was amalgamated with the Mailed Sword-Arm (cat. 564). When Sweden was well on the way to conquering Denmark in the 1640s the Mailed Sword-Arm disappeared from the Elephant's cover and was replaced by a flaming heart beneath "The Lord" in Hebrew – an expression of Christian IV's Old Testament faith in the righteousness of his cause.

As a young man the King received the Order of the Garter from his brother-in-law, James I, in 1603. The cape (cat. 568) is the oldest preserved. The chain (cat. 565) and "The Great George" (cat. 566) have until now been assumed to be his father's, but those were in fact returned in 1597. Irrespective of whether Christian IV took his father's insignia or not, this is the oldest preserved example. The reason it was not returned after 1648, as Frederik II's and Christian V's were, was probably connected with the Civil War in England.

562

### Christian IV's Crown

Denmark 1596, Dirich Fyring (-1580-1603)
Gold, enamel, diamonds, pearls. H. 17.8, Diam. 20.8. – Frontispiece p. 152
Rosenborg 6.2

Circlet and gables of gold with multi-coloured enamel, table-cut stones and pearls. The circlet is divided up into 12 segments with stars of table-cut stones and enamelled cherubs. Onto the circlet are soldered 12 small voluted gables with pearls. 12 leaf-shaped points made of two layers of open "Schweifwerk"-ornamentation are fastened to the circlet with bars. The 6 smaller ones have stars of table-cut stones, the 6 larger have allegorical figures. On the inner side of the points sit enamelled eschutcheons bearing the different quarterings from the Royal coat of arms. The number 12, which occurs repeatedly in the crown's construction, links it to both the Old and the New Testaments: the 12 tribes of Israel; the 12 apostles – a number mysticism which was found already in the Holy Roman Emperor's crown from the 10th century. The figures of the points illustrate the virtues which a good king should possess, and at the same time his functions as a sovereign: fortitudo (manlihood, strength – the king as warlord), justitia (righteousness – the king as judge), and caritas (love, both to God – the king as head of the church – and to his subjects). Love is also symbolised by the pelican repeated on 3 of the points, which pecks at its chest in order to revive its young with its blood. Originally a symbol of Christ's sacrifice, it became used at that time for the king's duty to defend and redeem his people with his very blood.
The crown's open form may cause surprise. Contemporary European kings had long before switched to hoop-crowns. Perhaps the explanation may be found in the symbol of union in the national coat of arms: the three open crowns. Christian IV's crown could be perceived as a crown of the union, and thus as an expression of the young King's dream of uniting the Scandinavian countries. The crown later had hoops added to it, probably for Frederik III's coronation i 1648. The enamelled coats of arms came from that occasion. The hoops had been removed again at the time of the inventory of 1696.
*Provenance:* Rosenborg inv. 1696, 45 no. 2.
*Literatur:* Liisberg 1922. Liisberg 1929. Boesen 1986 57 ff.

563

### The Mailed Sword-Arm

Denmark? Dated 1617
Gold, enamel, diamonds, iron L. 6.8 Colour-plate X
Rosenborg 3.119 b
Armour-clad right arm with raised sword in hand. Blue *champlevé* enamel with a curvilinear design in gold. On the upper arm is the crown and "C 4" in red and white enamel. Sword with gold hilt and steel blade. The chain has a white-enamelled quatrefoil. Arm, sword, and flower are studded with table-cut stones.
In 1616 Christian IV awarded the new Order of the Mailed Sword-Arm to 12 noblemen who had distinguished themselves in the Kalmar War (cat. 179). As pointed out by H. D. Schepelern, the idea for the emblem of the order probably came from a description of

the Danish Prince Svend's exploits in Torquato Tasso's poem "The liberated Jerusalem" (1550). In 1633 and 34 the Mailed Sword-Arm was combined with the Order of the Elephant (cat. 564).
At Rosenborg there are 3 further emblems of the Order of the Mailed Sword-Arm. They appear to have been made later and were probably connected with a projected revival of the Order under Christian V in the 1670s.
*Provenance:* Acquired in 1818 from the Countess Rosencrone.
*Literature:* Schlegel 1771 58. EB III 280. Grandjean 1903 34 94. Frederiksborg 1980 12-16 40.

564

## The Order of the Elephant

Denmark? 1633-34
Gold, enamel, diamonds. Colour plate XI
Rosenborg 3.119a
Elephant of white-enamelled gold. Blue cover with the mailed sword-arm between 4 table-cut stones on the front; back plain. The elephant carries a tower of gold with paler blue enamel. On the front, portrait of Christian IV between 4 table-cut stones, on the back the crowned emblem "C 4". On the head sits a blackamoor in multi-coloured enamel. On the rump a black leaf decoration.
Frederik II (1559-88) revived the Elephant Order, originally a Christian Brotherhood initiated by Christian I (1448-81). Conflicting opinions have been put forward concerning the appearance of the Order's emblem in Christian IV's time, but it seems certain that Christian IV only performed 3 ceremonies of appointments to Orders, in 1616 awarding the Mailed Sword-Arm and in 1633 and 1634 the Elephant with the Mailed Sword-Arm on the cover as on the present emblem of the Order. This is to be seen on the portrait of Jørgen Brahe, Knight 1633 (Eller, p. 433). After that the Mailed Sword-Arm seems not to have been awarded any more. On the portrait of Christian IV from the 1640s the Elephant is without blackamoor. Instead of the cover there can be seen inscribed the Hebrew word for "Lord", above a flaming heart or a decoration of table-cut stones (Sthyr, no. 1,6,119).
The colour of the enamel and the leaf decoration on the rump can be recognized on Christian IV's hourglass from 1633 (cat. 640) and on covered cup (cat. 658).
*Provenance:* as above.
*Literature:* See above. Eller 1971 433. Sthyr 1965

565

## The Collar of the Order of the Garter

England 1603 (1582?)
Gold, enamel. L. 55 cm. Colour-plate VIII
Rosenborg 1.37
The collar consists of 26 links with the emblem of the Garter and 26 connecting links with double bows. On the collar hangs "The Lesser George" (erroneously, but since before 1696?) – normally worn on a blue band. This, according to the inventory of 1696, belonged to Frederik II. The "Great George" (cat. 566) must have belonged to the collar.
According to the Rosenborg inventory of 1696 the collar is the one which Frederik II received from Elizabeth I in 1582. This was however returned in 1597 (Slange, RA). In 1603 James I appointed his brother-in-law Christian IV as a Knight of the Garter (Slange). Is the explanation that Christian received his father's collar?
*Provenance;* Rosenborg. Inv. 1696 46 no. 13
*Literature:* RA. TKUA, England AI, 11. Slange 1749 125 and 351. Hackenbroch 1979 304. Victoria and Albert Museum, London 1981 97.

566

## Insignia of the Order of the Garter; "The Great George"

England 1603 (1582?)
Enamelled gold. Diamonds. Pearls. Wood mounting H. 4.5 cm. Colour-plate VIII
Rosenborg 1.40
The group consists of the white-enamelled, rearing horse, harnessed, a green- and white-enamelled St. George, and green- and blue-enamelled dragon. The horse has an enamelled gold caparison and a black saddle, to which is attached a mounting-loop. St. George is standing at the horse's side and raising his sword against the dragon, which is lying on its back. Behind the horse is a flowering green-enamelled bush. Mounted on a wooden base. "The Great George" belongs to the collar of the Order (cat. 565), but has been displayed on the stand since before 1696. The King was appointed a Knight of the Order in 1603, but was probably given his father's insignia. Frederik II was appointed in 1579 and was presented with the Order in 1582. Ascribed by Liisberg to Corvianus Saur.
*Provenance:* Rosenborg inv. 1696 75 no. 15
*Literature:* Liisberg 1929 pl.I. Flamand Christensen 1940 31.

567

## Insignia of the Order of the Garter "The Lesser George"

England 1603
Enamelled gold. H. 5.4 cm. (without chain). Colour-plate VIII
Rosenborg 3.128
On an oval blue-enamelled garter, a blue-enamelled St. George riding a white horse and triumphing over a green dragon. Hanging on 3 gold chains connected in a gold ring.
*Provenance:* Rosenborg inv. 1696 46 no. 46
*Literature:* Flamand Christensen 1940 31.

568

## Cloak of the Order of the Garter

England 1606
Silk velvet, silk taffeta. L. 356 cm
Rosenborg 7.200
Dark mauve velvet, lined with pale taffeta. The cloak is semicircular, with a long tapering train. Short, stiff ruff. James I's command for delivery of the costume of the Order is dated 28 September 1606, which was a month after Christian IV left England. This caused Flamand Christensen to surmise that there had been 2 costumes. However, there is also the fact that the delivery of Frederik II's Order-costume is dated September 1582 (Arnold), which again is after the date of the delegation's departure to Denmark with the costume (Molbech).
*Provenance:* Copenhagen Castle inventory 1666. Rosenborg inv. 1696 46 14
*Literature:* Molbech 1823. Flamand Christensen, 1940 I 21ff; II tbl.1-2. British Museum 1978 cat. 249. Arnold 1980 76.

569

## Garter of the Order of the Garter

England 1606
Velvet, rubies, pearls, gold, enamel. L. 53.0 cm. Colour-plate VIII
Rosenborg 3.126
Garter of mauve velvet. Lettering and eyelets of gold, studded with rubies. The garter is edged and ornamented with pearls. Buckle and mounting of gold, table-cut stones and rubies on the front; back and edges enamelled with ribbon-ornaments, flowers, and a parrot.
*Provenance:* Rosenborg inv. 1696 46 no. 13.
*Literature:* Flamand Christensen 1940 30.

570

## Star of the Order of the Garter

England. After 1627
Silver thread. Velvet. Satin. H. 31 cm
Rosenborg 7.199
8-point star, mounted on cardboard. The rays are embroidered with silver thread, the garter is pale blue satin, the cross in the middle red velvet.
The star was introduced in 1627 by Charles I and was meant to be worn with everyday clothing. It was first mentioned in 1718 together with the cloak (cat. 568), and is therefore linked to Christian IV.
*Provenance:* Rosenborg inv. 1718 470.
*Literature:* Flamand Christensen 1940 29.

# Armoury

Precious weapons, examples of the latest technical advances as well as exotic types of weapon from the Orient, were favourite princely gifts and must have inspired their owners to provide them with a worthy setting.

The precious weapons displayed here are the remains of Christian IV's collections at Sparepenge, the small garden palace at Frederiksborg which was pulled down in 1720. It was probably modelled on foreign armouries such as that of Duke Ferdinand in Ambras, but since the Sparepenge inventory has been lost it cannot be ascertained whether functional use or museum interests were the guiding principle of the organisation of the collection. In 1634 Christian IV handed over Sparepenge to the Prince Elect, and after his death it went to the future Frederik III.

Our knowledge about Sparepenge comes from Prince Christian of Anhalt's travel-journal of 1623. In the armoury room he observed guns, pistols, and swords. He particularly noted the room with pearl- and gold-embroidered riding trappings, among which were some from Hungary as well as Russia, England, Italy, and Spain. His eye was especially caught by a horse harness with stirrups and spurs of gold, decorated with sapphires and diamonds. This without doubt was Christian IV's coronation harness, of which parts were re-used in a new harness for the wedding of the Prince Elect in 1634 (cat. 571 and 576). Other display-weapons mentioned include a dress-sword richly studded with diamonds, worth 36,000 *rigsdaler*. Possibly the so-called "wedding-sword" (cat. 579). Also displayed was a Muscovite coat of mail, a gift from the Tsar the year before. Perhaps the Persian dagger (cat. 592) also came from there. The only gifts preserved from the King's coronation are the two wheel-lock guns (cat. 586-87). The so-called "Admiral's sword", with mathematical instruments which show the knowledge of artillery technique, was without doubt a gift from the court in Dresden (cat. 577). Worthy of note is the Prince Elect's serpent-and dragon sword. Made of enamelled gold, in France or Denmark, the fabulous animal-heads are without equal elsewhere (cat. 581-82).

571

## Christian IV's Coronation Riding trappings

Caparison
Peter Paul Perlestikker, Denmark 1596
Velvet, gold, pearls. L. 274 cm. W. 71 cm.Colour-plate XXXIV
Rosenborg 3.28
Caparison with flowers, foliage and planets in cartouches, embroidered in gold and pearls on black velvet. A caparison is a cover which is laid over an unadorned saddle and hangs down over the horse's sides.

572

Stirrups and Spurs
Denmark 1596
Gold, iron, enamel, diamonds. H. 20.8 cm. L. 11.5 cm
Rosenborg 3.23 and 3.26
2 stirrups of gilt iron with "Schweifwerk" ornamentation and ribbons in polychrome enamel, studded with table-cut stones. Above, "C 4" under an open crown. Above and below, 4 holes, in which sapphires were set. 2 spurs with star-shaped wheels of gold. On the surfaces, wave-patterned decoration and single-mounted table-cut stones.

*Pistols*
Pommels and mounts: Denmark 1596. Pistols signed "Heinrich Kappel Kopenhagen" (1674-1718), c. 1690
Gold, enamel, sapphires, diamonds, L. 55.3 cm.
Rosenborg 3.25
2 pistols. On the locks the signature is engraved along with 2 female figures – war and peace. The pommels of gold with varicoloured enamelled scrolls, studded with 3 sapphires and table-cut stones. On each stock, 2 gold mounts with varicoloured enamelled drums, trophies and a banner with a crowned "C". In 1702 the pommels and mounts formed part of 2 ivory pistols, which were described as defective. About 1830 they were transferred to present pistols.
The caparison was earlier considered to belong to the riding trappings which were made for the wedding of the Prince Elect, in 1634 (cat. 576). Recent investigations show, however, that there was mention of a separate set of riding gear made for Christian IV's coronation.
In 1596 Peter Paul Perlestikker received payment for a caparison of black velvet with gold and pearls. In 1598 Nicolaus Schwabe (1570?-1629) made the coronation medallion. It shows Christian clothed and ornamented on his ride from the Cathedral and on this the caparison can clearly be seen. The stirrups, spurs, and pistols can be recognized from the description of dress riding trappings seen by Prince Christian of Anhalt at Sparepenge in 1623. These trappings were pawned in 1628, but redeemed in 1633, and certain pieces, including the stirrups, spurs, and pistols, were transferred to the new riding trappings for the Prince's wedding in 1634. On these are also to be found 5 figure-shaped jewels which probably came from the coronation outfit's harness. The architecture and scrolls of the framework around the figures are related to Erasmus Hornich's patterns for jewellery from around 1565. In 1594 Dirich Fyring received payment for the repair of an older jewel from Frederik II's riding trappings. Were the 5 jewels re-used for the coronation of the son in 1596?
The decoration of the riding trappings plays on the theme of the King as the master of the universe; e.g. the caparison's planets and the jewels: Chronos, the father of the Gods and of time, surrounded by 4 allegorical figures.
*Provenance:* Rosenborg inv. 1718 157 no. 11.
*Literature:* Liisberg 1929 59 ff 65 f 68 103 f 154. Hoff, Schepelern and Boesen 1956 no. 53-54. Boesen 1986 86 ff.

572

## Sword Belt (a) with Sword-hanger (b)

Denmark 1596?
Silk, gold, silver, pearls, iron. a) L. 95 cm b) L. 35 cm
Rosenborg a) 7.212 b) 7.172
a) Sword belt of leather, covered in dark silk, embroidered with stylized foliage in gold thread and pearls. Strap-end with hooks, buckles, and sliding loops of iron with gilt flowers. b) sword-hanger with 2 supports each with 5 suspension-straps. Leather with dark silk, embroidered with multi-coloured silk, gold and silver thread and studded with pearls and spangles. In leaf-cartouches can be seen the pelican, which pecks its own chest until it bleeds in order to feed its young (symbol of Christ's martyrdom and of the king's duty to defend his people) and trophies of arms. Mountings as those on the sword belt. Hook at the top in the shape of a swan's neck.
Kept together with Christian IV's blood-stained clothing

573

(cat. 745). Perhaps belonging to the coronation riding trappings.
*Provenance:* Rosenborg inv. 1696 123 no. 2.

573

## Rapier with Sheath

Mogens Winter, Denmark (-1595-1620), 1596
Gold, champlevé enamel. L. 110.3 cm, blade L. 94.5 cm
Rosenborg 7.213
Double-edged blade with circular stamp. Gilt hilt with varicoloured enamelled arabesques and animals. On the pommel the "C 4" with crown and Danish coat of arms. The painted chape and suspension-hook on the leather sheath are later additions. Possibly identical with a "gilt side arm" made by M. Winter and worn by Christian IV at his coronation in 1596.
*Provenance:* Rosenborg inv. 1696 77 no. 13.
Literature: Hoff, Schepelern and Boesen 1956 31f., no. 7. Boesen 1986 61f.

574

## Helmet

Denmark 1596?
Velvet with gold embroidery. H. 37 cm
Rosenborg 3.29
Probably worn by Christian IV when he rode from the Castle to the Cathedral to be crowned. In 1696 kept along with the blood-stained clothes (cat. 745).
*Provenance:* Rosenborg inv. 1696 123 no. 2.

575

## Sword-hanger

Denmark 1596?
Sealskin, silk, silver, pearls. H. 35 cm
Rosenborg 7.164
Sword-hanger with 2 supports, each with 5 suspension-straps, and 1 tightening-strap. Sealskin, the front covered with mauve silk, the back with pale silk-velvet. On the front, entwined foliage with cornucopia, flowers, and leaves, embroidered in silver thread and spangles and partly studded with pearls. Top mounting and buckle of smooth gilt iron.
*Provenance:* C.f. preceding entries.

576

## Christian the PrinceElect's Riding trappings

Gert Osserijn (-1633-1636). Denmark 1633-34
Velvet, gold, pearls, gems. Caparison L. 95 cm. Colourplates XXXIV-XXXV
Rosenborg 3.16-3.22
Riding trappings consisting of: saddle, caparison, 2 pis-

574

579

580

tol holsters, headstall and harness. Black velvet with closed crowns, dragons, and star-rosettes in acanthus decoration, embroidered in gold and studded with pearls and jewels. With this were used the stirrups, spurs and pistols from Christian IV's coronation riding trappings. Made in 1633-34 under the direction of pearl-embroiderer Gert Osserijn, partly re-using pieces from older cut-up riding outfits, among them the harness from Christian IV's coronation riding trappings. From there, probably, came the 5 figure-shaped jewels on the breast-strap and crupper and also perhaps the headstall's nose band, the table-cut stones in single-mountings, and the red-and-white 6-petalled flowers. The abundant use of table-cut stones and the enamel date the other jewels to 1633-34. The quality and style sub-divide them into a coarser and a finer group. The former includes the rosettes with 7 stones on multi-coloured foliage and the rosettes on the bit, whose enamel is reminiscent of a mirror and hour glass (cat. 639f). The latter, finer group includes the ovals with stones on a ground of open-work leaves together with the harness's buckle and strap-ends. The ovals form counterparts to the bracelets (cat. 632), the buckles to the cameo of the Prince-Elect (cat. 608). Modelled on the pea pod style and ascribed by Liisberg to Corvianus Saur.
The goldsmith Jochum Feige worked on the headstall. It has, however, been altered. In 1634 the big sapphire which now decorates the front of the Absolute Monarch's crown sat on the headstall. This sapphire, too was transferred from the coronation riding trappings, which is apparent from Prince Christian of Anhalt's travel-journal from 1623. After the wedding of the Prince Elect in 1634, Christian IV presented his son with this riding outfit and the collection at Sparepenge. In 1646 the Prince had the sapphire taken out of the riding outfit and mounted as a jewel for his wife. After the Prince's death the widow's envoy returned the sapphire and on the same occasion saw the riding trappings at Sparepenge.
*Provenance:* Rosenborg inv. 1718 157 no. 11 and list of deficiencies from 1702 to inv. 1696.
*Literature: As cat. 571.*

577

## Rapier with Scabbard

Christoff Trechler (1571-1623). Dresden 1617. Blade Toledo?
Iron, leather, gilt. L. 95 cm. Blade L. 79 cm
Rosenborg 2.38
Hilt of gilt metal. Oval pommel. On the front Venus and Cupid surrounded by tracery; on the back a herm and a

heart between cupped hands in foliage and flowers. Two cherub's heads on the edges. Grip bound with gilt wire. Diagonally curved quillons with foliage and dragons' heads. On the cross a mask with scrollwork. Black velvet scabbard. Chape of metal gilt with infants and birds. Leather sheath with the following instruments: 2 ordnance gauges, 1 pointer, 1 priming needle, 1 awl, 1 file, 1 knife, 1 pair of compasses, 4 of these marked 'C.T.D.E.M. 1617' (Christoff Trechler Der Eltere Mechanicus). The instruments are thought to be related to the King's activities as colonel with the artillery. Possibly a gift from the Court in Dresden.
*Provenance:* Rosenborg inv. 1696, 78 no. 22.
*Literature:* Hoff, Schepelern and Boesen 1956 no. 9 Hægstad 1984.

578

## So-called Accolade Rapier

Denmark c. 1600? Blade stamped 'De Tomas De Ayala', Toledo
Gold, enamel, diamonds. L. 115.8 cm. Blade L. 100 cm
Rosenborg 6.3
Double-edged hollow ground blade with struck stamp. Hearthaped pommel. Diagonally curved quillons, curved ring guards and finger guards; terminals with heart-shaped indentation. Hilt with foliage in gold on blue *champlevé* enamel set with table-cut and pointed diamonds. Pommel edged with a row of table-cut stones, and in the indentation leafwork in gold on white enamel. The grip wound with gold wire, twisted and smooth. According to the 1718 inventory, used by the kings for conferring knighthood.
*Provenance:* Rosenborg inv. 1718, 95 no. 3.
*Literature:* Hoff, Schepelern and Boesen 1956 no. 8.

579

## So-called Wedding Rapier of the Prince Elect

Denmark c. 1620-1635?
Gold, enamel, diamonds. L. 97.8 cm. Blade 82 cm
Rosenborg 3.27
Blue-enamelled gold hilt with table-cut diamonds, singly and in C-scrolls. Grip with white enamel diaper. Quillons with foliage in gold, white pearls in C-scrolls, and at the terminals varicoloured foliation. On the reverse foliage of gold only. On the cross a star in table-cut diamonds with varicoloured foliation on one side, and on the other a trophy in polychrome enamel. On the blade gilt foliage above and below. Black velvet scabbard. On the chape table-cut diamonds, singly and in C-scrolls, set in polychrome enamel. The traditional assumption that this weapon was worn as the 'Wedding Rapier of the Prince Elect' was first established by Stouenberg in 1828.
*Provenance:* Rosenborg inv. 1696, 80 no. 40.
*Literature:* Hoff, Schepelern and Boesen 1956 no. 15. Stouenberg 1828 30.

580

## Hunting Knife belonging to the Prince Elect

Ascribed to Gabriel Gipfel (-1591-) or his workshop (1596-1650)
Dresden c. 1630
Staghorn. L. 44.7 cm, blade L. 31.8, sheath L. 33.5 cm
Rosenborg 6.139
Grip of staghorn with figures of animals in silver gilt. Front quillons in silver gilt shaped like an elk's head, above which Orpheus and the Animals in relief. In front, a smooth ring guard. Blade marked with 3 and 4 crosses. Along the back a deep fuller. Leather sheath bound in green velvet. On the front a pocket with 4 knives and a file, all with grips matching the hunting knife. On the sheath 3 large silver gilt mounts: above, two hunting scenes from antiquity, in the middle a crowned coat of arms flanked by two woodhouses and, surrounded by the 14 quarterings of the Danish coat-of-arms, the Prince's monogram 'C5' and his motto 'P.E.C.' (Pietate Et Constantia). On the chape Actaeon and Diana, and on the back a bear hunt scene. The matching leather belt has remnants of green velvet and 15 small animals. The weapon is depicted in a still-life by Cornelis Gijsbrects (1659-1672), dated 1672 (Rosenborg 33.28).
*Provenance:* From Frederik VI 1828. Given to Christian IV after the Prince's death in 1647.
*Literature:* Hoff, Schepelern and Boesen 1956 44-46, no. 18. Hoff 1977 212-221. Petit Palais, Paris 1978 no. 69. Sophienholm 1983.

581

## Rapier with Snake's Head belonging to the Prince Elect.

France or Denmark c. 1634
Gold, enamel, diamonds. L. 109.8 cm, blade L. 93 cm
Rosenborg 7.204
Double-edged blade with high central ridge. The hilt's grip, knuckle guard and ring guard formed as 3 snakes with red hearts in their jaws. The snakes are in gold, painted with 'scales' of black enamel and with light opaque enamel heads. The red hearts are translucent enamel. On each snake's head and down the back is a row of table-cut diamonds. Wooden scabbard covered in leather. Chape and hook with snake motifs. The snake symbolizes wisdom, controlling the emotions, symbolized by the heart, and this quality was attributed to the owner of the rapier, the Prince Elect. The polychromy of the snakes' heads shows the influence of French enamel work 1630-40. There is some doubt as to whether this rapier dates from the Prince's wedding in 1634. Snake devices are found on several rapiers made for the Danish prince from 1625-1630. Corfitz Ulfeldt had a 'steward's' version of this magnificent rapier. (cat. 1332).
*Provenance:* Rosenborg inv. 1696 77 no. 9. Mentioned in the Prince's estate.

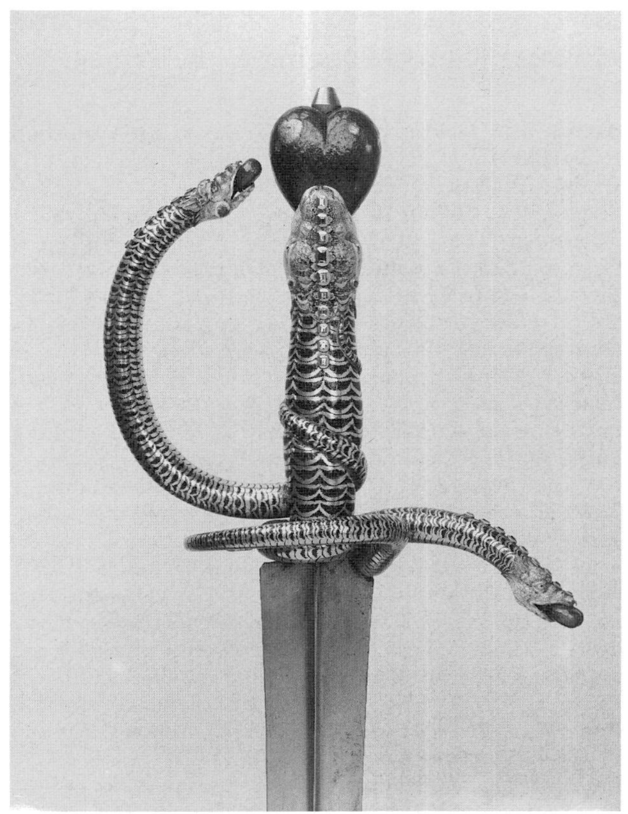

581

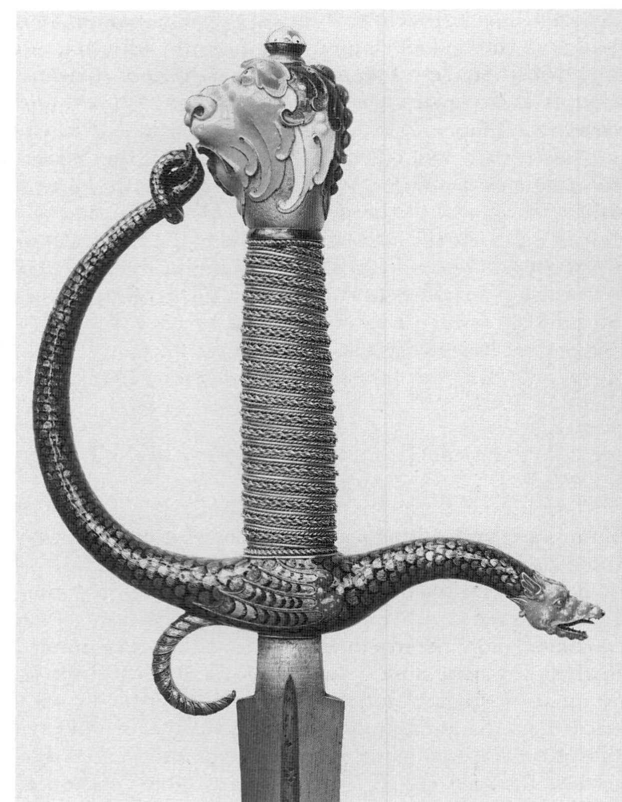

582

*Literature:* Hoff, Schepelern and Boesen 1956 no. 16. Boesen 1957 1f. Nielsen 1985 87 f.

582

## Rapier with Dragon belonging to the Prince Elect

France or Denmark c. 1634? Blade marked 'Peter Munich', Solingen.
Iron, gold, enamel. L. 93.3 cm. Blade L. 86.4 cm
Rosenborg 7.208
Double-edged blade; fuller with signature. Hilt of gold covered with polychrome opaque enamel. Pommel formed as a monster-like head in blue, violet, white, green, and gold. The grip is wound with plain and braided gold wire. Knuckle guard and quillons formed as a winged dragon with a green scaly body and a violet head with yellow dots. A striped finger guard curves down from the belly of the dragon in blue and gold. Classified in 1696 as belonging to the Prince Elect.
*Provenance:* Rosenborg inv. 1696 77 no. 10.
*Literature:* Hoff, Schepelern and Boesen 1956 no. 17. Thomas 1963 no. 73.

583

## Snake Spurs belonging to the Prince Elect

Ascribed to Henrik Langemack (-1634-1657). Denmark
Iron, gold, enamel. L. 12.5 cm
Rosenborg 7.220
A pair of spurs with rowel, chain (replacing arch-strap) and buckle (for the missing leather instep strap). Iron covered with gold. The heelpiece and rowel arm decorated with black snakeskin in hatched enamel on gold, and three green enamelled snakes in relief. On the 7-pointed rowel a heart in red enamel.
*Provenance:* Rosenborg inv. 1696 77 no. 10. Mentioned in the Prince's estate.
*Literature:* Boesen 1957 1-7.

584

## Sword Belt with Snake Mounts belonging to the Prince Elect

Denmark 1634-1647?
Iron, gold, enamel, diamonds. L. 107 cm
Rosenborg 7.205

Belt of yellow leather with 7 mounts of iron covered with gold and enamel, all shaped as masks and with pairs of intertwined snakes. The green snakes have blue heads. Mounts and buckles are blue with green or black, and violet with blue or green; the slider is green.
Two table-cut diamonds on the mounts, 4 on the buckles and one on the slider. Presumably matching the rapiers with snakes' and dragons' heads (cat. 581-82). The ornamentation on the masks is influenced by Netherlandish Mollusc style.
*Provenance:* Rosenborg inv. 1696 77 no. 11.

585

## A Pair of Spurs

Denmark 1640's?
Iron, gold, enamel. L. 13.5 cm. Colour plate XVIII
Rosenborg 7.166
Rowel spurs with 5-point stars. On the front of the heelpiece holes for leather straps. Iron covered with partially chased gold. Upon this in bas-relief naturalistic flowers in polychrome opaque and translucent enamel. In the cross between the heelpiece and the rowel arm a lion couchant in polychrome enamel. The flower enamel matches the bookbinding and the knife (cat. 721, 642).
*Provenance:* Rosenborg inv. 1696 77 no. 17.

586

## Wheel-lock Gun

Halle? 1596. Marked 'C.L.' (Støckel no. 2240)
Silver, horn, fruit wood, walnut. L. 138.9 cm
Rosenborg 7.155
Chiselled on the barrel the Danish coat-of-arms, the date 1596 and the master's mark 'C.L.' with bagpipes. Behind the barrel tang the engraved letters 'H.G.' The butt with inlaid tracery, animal and human figures in horn. On the butt plate engraved coat-of-arms and 'HIRONYMUS SCHLICK G.Z.P.U.H.Z.W.' (Graf Zu Bassano Und Herr Zu Weisskirchen, both in Bohemia). Schlick was a member of Joachim Friedrich of Brandenburg's retinue to Christian IV's coronation. This gun and the following were gifts for the King in 1596.
*Provenance:* Rosenborg inv. 1696 111 no. 13.
*Literature:* Støckel 1938 no. 2240. Hoff, Schepelern and Boesen 1956 no. 2.

587

## Wheel-lock Rifle

Halle? 1596
Silver, horn, fruit wood. L. 124.2 cm
Rosenborg 7.161
As the previous gun but shorter and with rifled bore. Engraved on the barrel 'J. (Jørgen) Bielke' (1621-1696, officer). The gun illustrates how royal possessions could be given to faithful retainers but could later come back into the Royal Family's possession. In this case with Bielcke's collection of arms 1693.
*Provenance:* Rosenborg inv. 1696 111 no. 13.
*Literature:* Hoff, Schepelern and Boesen 1956 no. 3.

*583*

588

## 2. Wheel-lock Pistols

France c. 1610. François Poumerol (-1580-1630-)
Silver, fruit wood, walnut. L. 57.5 cm
Rosenborg 7.137 and 7.147
Gilt strapwork on the barrels and fore stocks. On the locks the letters F.P. (almost Støckel 2512). Pear-shaped pommel with 12 silver bands ending in a silver plate. The ramrods are marked A. and C. respectively (Anna Cathrine and Christian IV). A similar pistol, signed by F. Poumerol in the Musée de l'Armée, Paris, is dated c. 1610.
*Provenance:* 1839 from Det partikulære Rustkammer.
*Literature:* Støckel 1938 no. 2512. Hoff, Schepelern and Boesen 1956 no. 5, 6. Reverseau 1982 98.

589

## Wheel-lock Gun

Max Wenger? (c. 1630-1670) Saxony
Steel, gold, horn, cedar? L. 112.5 cm
Rosenborg 7.145
The barrel mark is attributed to Max Wenger (Støckel 4077). On the lock Samson and the Lion. On the butt in inlaid horn 3 deer united in a single head, and a crowned F (Frederik III). Above a gold monocle. The 1775 inventory notes that the trigger plaque was dated 1618. The crowned F was later misconstrued as Frederik II (1534-1588), and the date was consequently altered to 1585.
*Provenance:* 1839 from Det Partikulære Rustkammer, inv. 1775, 224 no. 325.
*Literature:* Støckel 1938 no. 4077. Hoff, Schepelern and Boesen 1956 no. 10. Hoff 1977.

590

## Wheel-lock Rifle

Hans Kaluza (-1620-1640-). Teschen, Silesia 1632
Steel, horn, mother-of-pearl, fruit wood. L. 95.5 cm
Rosenborg 7.138
Barrel and lock engraved with parrots and arabesques, originally in gilt. On the butt, inlaid figures, flowers and strapwork in horn and mother-of-pearl. Engraved signature 'H.K.' At the ramrod a carved date '1632'.
*Provenance:* 1840 with Frederik VI's effects.
*Literature:* Hoff, Schepelern and Boesen 1956 no. 4.

591

## Two Dog Collars

Saxony 1611-1641 and 1602-1611
Leather, cloth-of-gold, brass. L. a) 36.2 cm b) 48 cm
Rosenborg a) 1.80 and b) 1.81
Leather with end mounts and rings of brass. Front covered in cloth-of-gold. (a) fringed with gold thread with silver spangles. The other (b) embroidered with stylised flowers. a) is engraved on the top mount with a crowned '8' (for the letter h: Electress Hedevig of Saxony 1581-1641, the sister of Christian IV) and on the bottom mount with a princess's electoral hat and a king's crown; b) is engraved 'CH' (for Christian II of Saxony, 1583-1611, and Hedevig) on the top mount, and on the bottom mount with ornamental fruit.
*Provenance:* 1858 from the Kunstkammer inv. 1737, 828/66.

592

## Oriental Arms

Persia – Turkey c. 1600?
Nationalmuseets 4. afd. inv. E.b.15,16-18, 21-22a.
*Provenance:* 1859 from Rosenborg inv. 1696 78 nos. 19-20, 76 no. 1 and 4, 78 no. 18.
*Literature:* Pope III 2 1973 2561. Rosenborg 1986 no. 170.

*Armbrace*
Steel, gold, gems, silk. L. 58.5 cm.
Right arm brace consisting of a hinged over and under section fastening with leather straps; the over section covers wrist to elbow, the under section only the wrist. Blued steel, inlaid partly with smooth gold in leaf patterns and partly with chased gold rosettes and foliage. Set with turquoises and rubies. Terminating in a half gauntlet in chainmail, lined inside and out with red silk.

*3 fencing and close-combat shields*
Steel, gold, gems, velvet. Diam: 22.8, 22.5, 25 cm
Circular, convex shields of blued steel, inlaid with gold and set with gems like the armbrace above.
Edged with fringes of gold thread. Lining of vari-coloured velvet with birds and plants on gold ground.

*Dagger with sheath*
Gold, turquoises, gems. L. 36.5 cm and 37.4 cm
Dagger with steel blade. Hilt covered in gold with leaf and rosette patterning with inlaid table-cut turquoises. Pommel set with rubies and turquoises. Sheath covered with gold, set with rubies, rose quartz, turquoises and pearls.

*Dagger with sheath*
Agate, silver gilt, gems. L. 32.5 cm and 40.6 cm
Originally with etched blade. Hilt of agate formed like a crown with wedge-shaped indentation at the top. Below, a silver gilt ring of rope-filigree set with rubies and turquoises. Wooden sheath covered in shagreen (rough goatskin). Locket and chape mountings like the ring of the hilt.

*Brow ornament for a horse*
Silver gilt, jade, turquoises, rubies. L. 31.5 cm
Transverse-oval domed plate with leaves and scalloped edge. Silver gilt, set with 8 turquoises surrounding centre plate of jade with 6 rubies. Fastened to the plate by rings and shaped like eagles' beaks are 4 double chains with a turquoise at each link.

Oriental arms, in the past called 'Persian, Turkish or Polish', were the fashion in 1550-1750, and were often used as princely gifts. In 1622 a Russian envoy, among other gifts from the Tsar and the King of Poland brought Christian IV and the Prince Elect a saddle, riding trap-

*593*

*594*

pings, a suit of armour, a tent, some sabres and daggers. Some of these went to 'Sparepenge', where the Duke of Anhalt observed a 'Muscovite' suit of armour the following year. Some of the items mentioned above possibly originate from this same Russian envoy. In reciprocation, Christian IV gave the Tsar objects of silver and silk tablecloths.

## The Jewel Cabinet

In 1623, Prince Christian of Anhalt (1599-1656) was shown the rich collection of arms and saddlery in the "Sparepenge" at Frederiksborg. He was, however, not permitted to see the Jewel Cabinet in the castle itself. We have, nonetheless, some idea of its contents. From the printed description of Johan Adam Berg, we learn that the Royal jewels were kept in two great wall cupboards, later known as "cabinets", of ebony and silver. The Jewel Cabinet also contained a "unicorn's horn" (narwhale tusk) some eight feet in length (4 "alens"), a jewel case, and a dragon of rock crystal. Thus, in addition to jewellery, the Jewel Cabinet also contained Kunstkammer pieces, or curiosities.

The present reconstruction displays both jewels and objects of a personal nature such as amulets, vinaigrettes and toilet articles. There are, moreover, a number of "likenesses" – painted, carved or wax miniature portraits of the King and other members of the Royal Family. Such miniatures enjoyed a great vogue at the time as gifts exchanged between members of the Royal family; there was also a well-established custom of presenting portraits to both foreign envoys and deserving servants, as a mark of royal favour, the value of the gift being proportionate to the rank and importance of the recipient. The examples of foreign origin were presumably gifts received by the Danish King from visiting ambassadors. (Cat. 595).

The jewels exhibited here are all that remains of a sadly diminished former splendour: contributory factors to this state of affairs were partly changes in fashion, which led to "outmoded" articles being sold or "realised", and partly the need to finance Christian IV's costly but often unsuccessful military campaigns, which necessitated the melting down of a large number of valuable items, especially in the period after 1628.

Several pieces are especially worthy of note: those enamelled in white, with "broken" colours and black, and those embellished with floral designs in the pea-pod style which drew its inspiration from French ornamental engraving. (Cat. 564, 639-40 and 601, 604, 608). Were these produced in Copenhagen workshops, or by a goldsmith especially commissioned for the wedding of the Prince Elect in 1634? There is one group, dating from the 1640's, which bears naturalistic floral motifs in polychrome enamel (cat. 585, 642, 721). These have been attributed to several different artists, among them Henrick Langemack (-1634-1657), Jørgen Mortensen (-1623-1655) and Caspar Herbach (c. 1600-1660). Even the sparsity of the information we have about these jewels cannot rob them of their beauty. Especially delightful are the so-called 'baroque' pearls, where the point of the joke was to allow the natural shape of the pearl or mother-of-pearl to dictate the overall form of the rest of the design (cat. 620). Evocative, too, is the personal note struck by the idea of having the hair of a lover mounted in a bracelet for the beloved to wear (cat. 631), or in endowing Time with wings, as a promise of undying affection (cat. 630).

593

### Cameo of Christian IV

Unknown artist c. 1596
Mother-of-pearl, silver. H. 2.8 cm
Rosenborg 3.74
Oval. Head-and-shoulders portrait, in profile. Ruff and patterned dress. Inscription; CHRISTIANUS 4 DA(niæ) N(orvegiæ) REX'. Silver setting, with loop and lobed rim.
*Provenance:* Accession 1867. Transferred to the Kunstkammer from Den kgl. Mønt og Medaillesamling, 1795. Inv. 1807, 47/P44.

*596*

594

## Wax Portrait of Christian IV 1595

Signed "G. H. Rapp fecit" for Henrich Rappusch the younger (1616)
Wax, dyed and painted, on glass, in wooden case. Diam. 12.2 cm
Staatl. Museen, Preuss. Kulturbesitz, Berlin. Inv. 885
Bust portrait in profile to the right. Hat and doublet, encrusted with paste and pearls, with ruff and sash. On black glass ground, in gold "CHRISTIAN 4 D(ei) G(ratia) REX DANI(ae) VAN(dalorum) GOTT(orum) EL(ectus) Z (15)95", and the signature of the artist. Mounted in a case of turned wood.
*Provenance:* In the Brandenburgisch-Preussische treasury 1769. Gift presented by Christian IV to Anna Cathrine on his visit to Berlin 1595?
*Literature:* Bange 1923 148. Pyke 1973 117. Theuerkauff 1981 no. 74.

595

## Chain with Medal of Christian IV

Signed "NIC.SC.F" for Nicolaus Schwabe "1597"
Gold. Diam. 3.8 cm L. of chain 145.3 cm
Rubenhuis, Kunsthistorische Musea, Antwerpen
Obverse: Christian IV, profile. The monarch is portayed wearing a crown, armour and a ruff. Inscription: "CHRISTIANUS IIII DANIÆ NOR VAN GOT REX" and "ÆTA XX AN.O" (Christian IIII King of Denmark, Norway, the Wends and the Goths, in his 20th year). Reverse: Elephant, with tower and warriors, and a crowned "C" on the saddle cloth. Inscription: "REGNA FERMAT PIETAS" (Piety fortifies the Realms), the King's personal motto. In the loop a chain of plain links. Traditionally held to be a gift presented by Christian IV to the painter Peter Paul Rubens (1577-1640), 1620. It appears unlikely, however, that at this date Rubens should have received a portrait of the King in his youth.
*Provenance:* Presented to the city of Antwerp in 1927. Acquired by the Rubenshuis in 1945.
*Literature:* Galster 1936 27f. Baudouin 1958 29. Kunstindustrimuseet 1960 no. 68 A.

596

## Locket with Miniature of Anna Cathrine

Miniature ascribed to Jacob van Doordt
Dated 1612
Watercolour, parchment, gold, enamel. H. 4.5 cm
Rosenborg 3.85
Oval. Bust portrait *en face,* head turned slightly to the left. Mounted under rock crystal in a locket of gold. On the reverse, grotesques in red, green and white champlevé enamel. The case is contemporary with the Queen's portrait. Similar volutes may be seen on ornamenal engravings by Corvinianus Sauer (1560?-1605).
*Provenance:* Rosenborg inv. 1696 62 no. D 5.
*Literature:* DMP IV 13. Liisberg 1929 plate 14. Colding 1953 14. Rosenborg 1970 no. 10.

597

## Silver Reliefs of Christian IV and Anna Cathrine

Jacob van Doordt 1612
Silver, ebony, H. 4.0 cm
Rosenborg 1.114
Ovals, bust portraits, profiles to right and left, with inscriptions "CHRISTIANUS 4 D(ei) G(ratia) DAN(iae) NORV (egiæ) REX" and "ANNA CATHAR(ina) K(önigin) Z(u) D(ennemarck) G(eborene) A(us) C(hurfürstlichen) S(tamm) Z(u) B(randenburg)". On her breast Anna Cathrine wears a crowned 3 (for C(hristian). Ebony frame adorned with oak leaves and crown.
*Provenance:* Accession 1844 from Christian VIII.
*Literature:* Galster 1936 31 f.

*596*

598

## Silver Reliefs of Christian IV and Anna Cathrine

Jacob can Doordt, before 1617
Silver. H. 3.6 cm
Rosenborg 3.86 a-b
Similar to the previous piece, with minor changes in coiffure, costume and inscription. The fact that the Queen is here depicted wearing her own crowned monogram "AC" suggests that her portrait may have been posthumous. Mounted on mirror cat. 725.
*Provenance:* Acquired 1884 through purchase
*Literature:* Galster 1936 31 f.

599

## 3 Cameos of Christian IV

Ascribed to Nicolaus Schwabe in the portrait style of Jacob van Doordt from c. 1612
Carnelian, gold. a) 2.4×1.7 cm, b) 1.5×1.3 cm, c) 1.4×1.2 cm
Rosenborg 3.89, 3.87, 3.79
Ovals. Bust portraits in profile to the right. On the reverse, a crowned "C4". The gold mountings: a) ropework rim with loops at top and bottom, knobs on either side b) plain ring with loop and "crabs" c) plain edge on eighteenth-century ring of openwork foliate design with rocailles.
*Provenance:* 1858 and 1867 from the Kunstkammer.

600

## Cameo of Christian IV

Denmark 1644, in an ornamental mounting of later date
Cornelian, silver gilt, paste. 1.5×1.3 cm
Privately owned, Vienna
Oval. Bust portrait in profile to the right. On the reverse a crowned "C4". Mounted in silver gilt a) wreath with chased points (19th century?) on b) ornament, openwork in foliate design, with crown, decorated with red, green and white paste, and with opals and pearls (18th century?)
*Provenance:* Purchased 1986 from dealer

601

## Locket with Miniature of Christian IV Denmark ca. 1638

Gold, rock crystal. H. 3.8 cm
Rosenborg 3.73

*602*

*603*

Bust portrait, half-profile to the right. Mounted under rock crystal in a plain gold locket, enriched with an openwork border of foliate design in the pea-pod style. The border has been chased in preparation for an enamelling process that was never completed.
*Provenance:* 1824 from the Kunstkammer inv. 1775, 248/599,5. Originally Queen Sophie Magdalene's estate 1772.
*Literature:* DMP IV 8.

602

## Design for "Likeness Locket"

Hans Hollænder (-1604-1645-) 1635
Pencil drawing on paper
Rigsarkivet
Oval portrait container with closed crown. The crown and border encrusted with table-cut gems. Along the edge openwork ornamentation. Inscription: "Inden udi K:M: Conterfaict med en Cristall Sten(bjergkrystal) for", "om denne affriidz (tegning) K:M: Naadigst Kand gefallde, ("Within the likeness of the King's Majesty with a crystal stone (rock crystal)" "for if this sketch (drawing) graciously shall please the King's Majesty"). The drawing was enclosed in a letter written by Christian IV on 17.5.1635, from which it is clear that the design did in fact meet with the monarch's approval. Over the rock crystal cover the King wished there to be a further front casing of openwork, bearing his name executed in large diamonds. This sketch is the only example of a Danish design for jewellery which has been preserved, from the period.
*Literature:* Holck Colding 1953 74f. Boesen 1986 83. EB III no. 453.

603

## Ivory Box with portrait of Christian IV

Ca. 1633. Ascribed to Karel van Mander
Turned, painted ivory. Oil on silver. H. 4.9 cm.
Kungl. Husgerådskammaren, Stockholm, inv. 518:31
Oval. Bust portrait. Mounted in profiled box, turned in ivory and painted reddish-brown, green and yellow to resemble agate. On the cover the inscription: "KÖNIG CHRISTIAN IV IN DENEMARCK".
*Provenance:* From the estate left by Queen Ulrika Eleonora the Younger of Sweden (1688-1741), daughter of Ulrika Eleonora the Elder (1656-1693), granddaughter (by his son) of Christian IV.
*Literature:* Nationalmuseum Stockholm 1930 no. 632. Eller 1971 117f. Kungl. Husgerådskammaren 1982 no. 264.

*606*

*608*

604

## Locket with Miniature of Christian IV

1638-40? Case Danish?
Gold, enamel. H. 2.8 cm
Rosenborg 3.77
Oval. Bust portrait. Mounted under rock crystal in oval locket case of gold. Reverse decorated with pea-pod and floral ornamentation in blue, green and yellow champlevé enamel on a white ground. The enamel is reminiscent of the ovals on the ceremonial saddle mountings of the Prince Elect, (cat. 576).
*Provenance:* Rosenborg inv. 1696 62 no. 6.
*Literature:* DMP IV 12.

605

## Miniature Case: Unknown young Man

Denmark c. 1640?
Oil on copper. Gold and enamel. H. 0.8 cm
Rosenborg 3.109
Oval. Bust portrait of unknown young man. The front cover is of gold with a floral motif in light colours and a pea-pod design in black on a white enamel ground. On the lid a pointed diamond.
*Provenance:* Rosenborg inv. 1784 25 no. 204

606

## Christian IV ca. 1640

Tinted, painted wax on glass, pearl, wood. 12.6×10.4 cm
Rosenborg 3.60
Bust portrait. The braid decorated with genuine pearl, on the breast a chain with wax conch-shell. Cartouche of foliate ornamentation and the King's personal motto "REGNI FIRMAT PIETAS". Back-plate of black-painted glass. Wooden frame with notched edges.
*Provenance:* 1867 from the Kunstkammer (Inv. 1673 163).
*Literature:* Liisberg 1897 163.

607

## Christian IV in later Life

Signed "DVHB", dated "A(nn)o 1648"
Tinted painted wax, wood, lustre lacquer. 11.2×8.6 cm
Rosenborg 3.83
Bust portrait, half-profile to the right. The King wears armour, a white collar with tassels and the blue ribbon of the Order of the Elephant. Mounted back-plate of black-painted wood, inscribed with signature and date at the bottom. 1696 in a tortoiseshell frame, the lustre lacquer frame dating from before 1718.
*Provenance:* Rosenborg inv. 1696, 128 no. 14.

608

## Cameo: the Prince Elect

C. 1630? Mounting Danish?
Jasper, gold, enamel. H. 4.5 cm
Rosenborg 3.134
Oval. Bust. Portrayed as a military commander. Beneath the shoulder the inscription "PEC", standing for the Prince's motto "Pietas et Constantia". The mounting adorned with multicoloured flowers and foliage on a white ground; suspension ring and loop. Similar in style to medal portrait ca. 1620. The enamel technique employed on the mounting echoes that of the buckles on the ceremonial saddle-mountings, (cat. 576).
*Provenance:* Rosenborg inv. 1718 42 no. 1.
*Literature:* Galster 1936 fig. 40. Rosenborg 1986 no. 174.

609

## Cameo Case: Venus, Cupid and two Putti

Mounting Danish? C. 1630?
Jasper, gold, enamel. H. 6.1 cm, and 5.2 cm
Nationalmuseets 2. afd. inv. DFa 117 and 139
Obverse: Venus, concealing Cupid. Inscription: "LATET ATQUE VIDETUR" (He is unseen, yet he is present). On the reverse, two putti frolicking amidst symbols of the 4 elements. Inscription: "CRESCIT AGITATUS ARDOR" (Be love once kindled). The obverse is framed similarly to the previous cat.no., while the reverse has a foliate design. The hinges on the mounting indicate that the two cameos originally formed the front and back of a locket

*609*

case. The locket's message is an erotic one. Did it once conceal a lock of Prince Christian's hair, and was it perhaps intended to be worn as a pendant to the portrait cameo?
*Provenance:* Rosenborg inv. 1718, 53 no. 17 and no. 10. Sophie Amalienborg inv. 1680, 10 no. 13.
*Literature:* Rosenborg 1986 no. 175f.

610

## Locket with Portrait of Frederik (III)

Ascribed to Karel van Mander 1644-1648
Oil on metal. Silver-gilt rock crystal. H. 8.1 cm
Rosenborg 5.90
Oval. Portrayed in profile. Fashionable dress, with Order of the Elephant. Plain case. After he lost the sight of his right eye in the Battle of Kolberger Heide, Christian IV would only permit himself to be painted in profile. Is it conceivable that Frederik had himself painted in profile also, as a reminder of his own position in the order of succession?
*Provenance:* Rosenborg inv. 1696 62 no. D 11
*Literature:* DMP IV 16. Eller 1971 239. Rosenborg 1986 no. 4.

*610*

611
## Cameo of Philip II of Spain

Ascribed to Jacopo da Trezzo (1514-1589) or his Madrid workshop, c. 1560?
Onyx, gold. H. 4.0 cm
Rosenborg 3.133
Oval. Bust portrait, profile to the right. Armour, ruff and sash. About the King's neck the "Golden Fleece". Inscription: the King's name and title. On the back three holes bear witness to the presence of a mounting, which has since been lost. Framed in a fluted gold border. Possibly a gift from a member of the Spanish embassy to Copenhagen in 1594?
*Provenance:* Mentioned in the inventory of the Royal family's private hosehold at Christiansborg Castle 1784, 9 no. 2.

612
## Locket with Cameo of Emperor Rudolf II

Cameo of South-German origin, c. 1600. Locket Danish, 1650's?
Conch shell, glass, gold, enamel, rubies. H. 2.3 cm
Rosenborg 3.140
Bust portrait, profile to the right. Laurel wreath, armour, ruff and sash. About the Emperor's neck collar of the "Golden Fleece". Chain of Order. Oval back-plate of black-painted glass encircled by an openwork foliage wreath in white and black enamel, surmounted by ditto crown, both studded with rubies. Behind the glass plate a hinged lid, enamelled blue with a floral design, white on the outside and green on the inside. There is a matching cameo in the Kunsthistorisches Museum in Vienna.
*Provenance:* Rosenborg inv. 1718, 27 no. 4.
*Literature:* Eichler and Kriss 1927 no. 430.

613
## Cameo of Gustavus II Adolphus before the City of Nuremberg

Nuremberg 1632?
Conch shell, gold. H. 2.6 cm
Rosenborg 3.121
Oval. Obverse shows the King, mounted on a rearing steed, in front of a city and the monogram "GA" "RS" (Gustavus Adolphus King of Sweden). On the reverse a lion *passant* with shield and raised sword. Below, the legend "CUM DEO ET VICTIBUS ARMIS" (With God and the Victorious Arms). Below the horse the King's monogram, written as one word: "GAR". Set in a gold mount with two loops and two knobs. During the Thirty Years War the city of Nuremberg placed itself under the protection of Gustavus Adolphus.
*Provenance:* Rosenborg inv. 1696, 69 no. 13.
*Literature:* Strömbom 1932 no. 173.

*613*

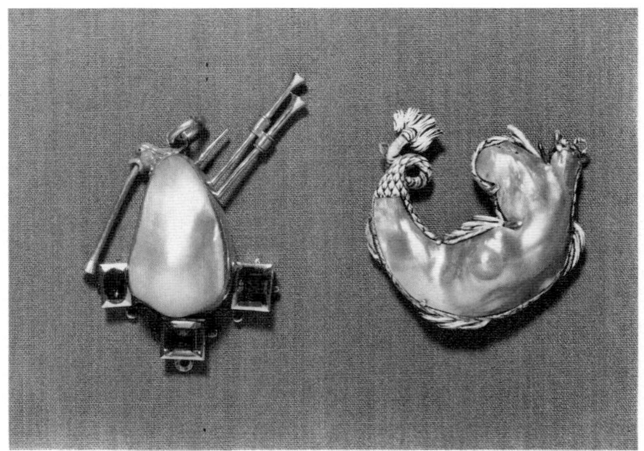

619

614

## Portrait Relief of Gustavus II Adolphus

Executed after a medal by Sebastian Dadler (1586-1657), Nuremberg 1630's?
Gold, enamel. H. 4.3 cm
Rosenborg 3.120
Bust portrait, profile to the right. Laurel wreath, armour with lace collar. Loop at top. Green, blue and white enamel on gold. On the reverse, the crowned monogram "GASR" (Gustavus Adolphus, King of Sweden) over palm leaves in gold on black enamel. The King's position as the official Defender of the Protestant Faith resulted in a veritable spate of commemorative medals after his death in the Battle of Lutzen, 1632.
*Provenance:* 1824 from the Kunstkammer, inv. 1775, 248/599,4, originally in the estate of Queen Sophie Magdalene.
*Literature:* Victoria and Albert Museum, 1981 no. 124

615

## Cameo of Emperor Ferdinand III

By an unknown artist, after medal by George Schweigger c. 1650
Ivory on conch shell, gold, enamel. H. 3.1 cm
Rosenborg 3.132
Bust portrait of the Emperor as a man advanced in years. Profile to the right. Laurel wreath, cuirass and ruff. The "Golden Fleece". Oval back-plate of conch shell, bearing the legend: "FERDI ROM IMP SE AVGE HUN BO REX". (Ferdinand Roman Emperor, King of Hungary and Bohemia). The reverse emblazoned with the imperial coat of arms, with crowned eagle and the collar of the Golden Fleece. Framed in pierced wreath of polychrome flowers, with loops at top and bottom. Presumably a gift from the Imperial Court. Matching cameos may still be seen in Kunsthistorisches Museum, Vienna.
*Provenance:* Mentioned in the inventory of the estate left by Princess Sophie Hedevig (1677-1735).
*Literature:* Eichler and Kriss 1927 no. 440.

616

## Christian IV's Signet Ring

The signet stone c. 1623. The ring made in Hamburg 1641
Sapphire, gold, enamel. H. 1.7 cm
Rosenborg 3.127
Octagonal sapphire, cut in *intaglio* with crowned national coat-of-arms, flanked by the coats-of-arms of the provinces, and two woodhouses. The crown flanked with the monograms "C4" and "R". Set in a plain gold ring with niello foliate ornamentation. Used on correspondence from 1623-31. In 1641 the King commanded the signet stone to be more deeply cut and set in a new ring in Hamburg.
*Provenance:* Rosenborg inv. 1696, 12 no. 51.
*Literature:* Liisberg 1929 207. Grandjean 1950 20 no. XX.

617

## Signet Ring of the Prince Elect.

Copenhagen c. 1625?
Sapphire, gold. H. 1.5 cm
Rosenborg 3.129
Octagonal sapphire, cut in intaglio with the Prince's crowned monogram "C5". Within the "C" the national coat-of-arms, flanked by the coats-of-arms of the provinces. Set in a plain gold ring.
*Provenance:* Rosenborg inv. 1696, 50 no. 43. Mentioned in the inventory of the estate left by the Prince in 1647.
*Literature:* Grandjean 1951 29 no. IV.

618

## 3 Necklaces

Denmark c. 1600
Gold a) L. 167 cm. b) L. 235.6 cm c)L. 108.8 cm
Rosenborg a) 1.38, b) 5.144, c) 5.145.
3 thin gold chains. The links in a) consist of quatrefoil rosettes, in b) and c) they form a basic rectangular shape. Of the countless chains like these familiar to us from the portraits and estate inventories of the renaissance, only a handful have survived – possibly because they functioned as a financial reserve for their owners.
*Provenance:* Rosenborg inv. 1784, 16.
*Literature:* a) Rosenborg 1970 7.

619

## 2 Pendants: a) Dolphin, b) Bagpipes

Northern Europe ca. 1600
Mother-of-pearl, gold, enamel. Dolphin. H. 5.5 cm. Bagpipes H. 4.7 cm
Rosenborg 5.130 (dolphin), 5.128 (Bagpipes)
Curved dolphin with open jaws. Body: mother-of-pearl, set in enamelled gold with white and black design on blue ground. Jaws and tail bear traces of red enamel. A stone is now missing from the eye. Bag of mother-of-pearl, set in gold. Above a dragon's head in blue enamel, below a ruby, emerald(?) and sapphire. On the back foliate ornamentation in niello.
*Provenance:* Rosenborg inv. 1696 no. 5 and 6. Sophie Amalienborg inv. 1680 10 a nos. 13 and 12.
*Literature:* Rosenborg 1986 nos. 172 and 171.

620

## 2 Pendants: a) Mermaid, b) Merman

Northern Europe ca. 1600
Pearls, gold, diamonds, enamel, silver. H. a) 4.5 cm b) 2.8 cm
Rosenborg 5.129 and 5.131
Mermaid: Body of pearl, set in gold and enamel. Arms and legs flesh-coloured, bifurcate tail green. The left hand holds a mirror set with a facetted diamond. Loops on head and tail. Merman: Body of pearl. Hair of chased gold, head, arms and tail enamelled pastel blue. On the stomach a pointed diamond mounted in silver, possibly a later repair? Head and tail connected by a golden chain.
*Provenance:* Rosenborg inv. 1718 5 no. 27 and 28 no. 13.

621

## 3 incomplete pieces

Northern Europe (Denmark?) 1585-1600
Gold, enamel. a) 2.3 cm, b) 2.1 cm, c) 2.0 cm
Rosenborg 1.141-1.143
3 scenes with figures in gold and polychrome enamel, no backing or mounting. a) Mars, with shield, and Venus, seated, facing one another. Between them Bacchus on a wine cask, behind the figures windswept chased drapery. b) Cupid with dog, behind him drapery of the same type, which again forms a frame for c), warrior flanked by two female figures, one holding a glass, the other a wine-pitcher formed from double pearl. Ascribed by Liisberg to Corvinianus Sauer.
*Provenance:* Discovered when the regalia cabinet was being put in order in 1906.
*Literature:* Liisberg 1929 66 plate 1.

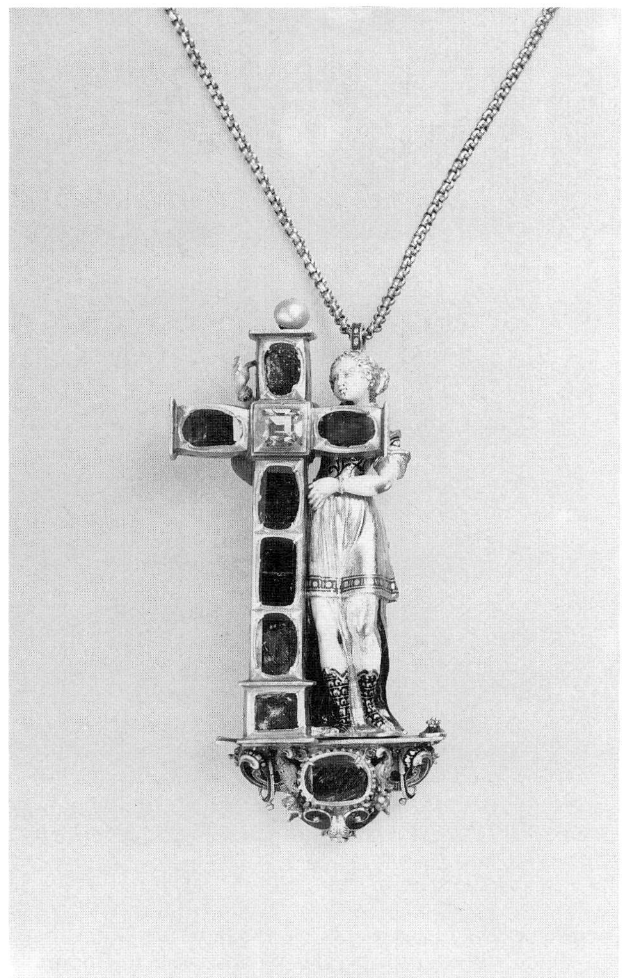

*624*

622

## Ornament of Escutcheons

Denmark, 1596. Dirich Fyring (1580-1603)
Gold, enamel, wooden plaque with velvet. 1.8 cm.
Rosenborg 3.114. (Illustration on back cover)
Topmost, beneath the crown, the three Danish lions, held by genii. Forming a wreath, the crowned arms of

625

the provinces: (clockwise) Norway's lion, the Goths' lion, the Union's three crowns, the Wends' wivern, Gotland's lamb, Iceland's stockfish, Schleswig's two lions, Holstein's nettle, Stormarn's swan, Ditmarsk's horseman, Oldenburg's beams, Delmenhorst's cross and Oesel's eagle.
The genii are the same as the ones on the circlet of Christian IV's crown. The escutcheons are presumably those originally fastened to the inside of the points. They must have been replaced before the coronation of Frederik III in 1648 since Denmark relinquished Gotland and Oesel in 1645.
*Provenance:* Rosenborgs inv. 1784 193 no. 24.

624

## Pendant on Chain. Woman with Cross

Northern Europe 1585-1589
Gold, enamel. precious stones. H. 7.5 cm. Chain L. 65.6 cm
Rosenborg 3.142
Latin cross studded with 5 rubies, emerald, table-cut diamond and surmounted by a single pearl (one setting empty). The cross is supported by the standing figure of a woman. Pedestal with one small emerald surrounded by ornamental fittings. On the head of the figure a loop for the gold chain, which consists of individual rings. The figure of the woman supporting the Cross symbolizes Faith.
*Provenance:* Rosenborg inv. 1696, 45 no. 6.
*Literature:* Rosenborg 1970 no. 3, Hackenbroch 1979 206.

625

## Pendant: Flying Cupid

Northern Europe (the Netherlands?) c. 1600
Gold, enamel, rubies, table-cut diamonds, pearls. L. 6.1 cm
Rosenborg 3.110
Hair, wings, bow and arrows, quiver, of chased gold. The rest of the figure enamelled white, with polychrome ornamentation, encrusted with table-cut diamonds and with rubies. In the ear a pearl. From loops on the head and foot a gold chain. Another ornament, which may have been pearls, was originally suspended from the three loops on the leg, quiver and wings. A similar Cupid is mentioned in the inventory of Queen Anna Cathrine's dowry, in 1597.
*Provenance:* Rosenborg inv. 1696, 69 no. 3. Sophie Amalienborg inv. 1680, 10 a no. 8.
*Literature:* Rosenborg 1986 no. 164.

626

## Pendant: Lion *passant*

Denmark c. 1600?
Gold, enamel, diamonds. L. 4.1 cm
Rosenborg 3.111
Crowned lion *passant* with extended tongue. Gold, partially chased, partially enamelled blue and encrusted with pointed and table-cut diamonds. Claws and genitals chased with black enamel. Gold crown with fields of red and green enamel. From loops on the neck and tail a gold chain with a ring. Similar lions adorn the serpentine cup of Princess Magdalena Sibylla (cat. 665). These lions may have been taken from older pieces or they may have been executed by the Princess's court goldsmith Heinrich Langemack (1634-1647), who wrought "Lions with diamonds" for the princely couple's journey to Eger in 1647.
*Provenance:* Rosenborg inv. 1696 45 no. 7.
*Literature:* Boesen 1957 1 RA. Reg. 108B Prince Christian. Accounts pertaining to the journey to Eger, 1647.

627

## Pendant: Lion *Statant*

Denmark c. 1600? The centre piece Danish, c. 1635?
Gold, enamel, diamonds. H. 3.8 cm
Rosenborg 3.108
Crowned, lion *statant* with open jaws (tongue missing).

626 og 627

Chased gold, enamelled brownish-green, studded with table-cut diamonds. On the gold crown table-cut diamonds and green and blue enamel. From loops on crown, tip of tail and root of tail three gold chains are connected to the pierced centre-piece of polychrome enamelled gold with a table-cut diamond and surmounted by a ring. Similar pieces may be seen in Residenz and Bayerisches Nationalmuseum, Munich.
*Provenance:* Rosenborg inv. 1784 15 no. 87 or 88.
*Literature:* Hackenbroch 1979 146 170.

628

## Pendant: Crane

Northern Europe (Denmark?) c. 1620
Pearls, gold, enamel, precious stones. L. 6.5 cm
Rosenborg 3.103
Crane with spread wings holding a stone in its claw. Head, neck, body and stone of pearls, secured in gold settings, encrusted with rubies, diamonds and emeralds. On the wings blue enamel feathers and alternate rows of rubies and emeralds. On the reverse foliate ornamentation with pointed leaves in translucent and opaque *champlevé* enamel, in green and yellow, and white, pale blue and black. Loops on the head and the wings, from the wings chains run to the C-shaped openwork centre-piece decorated with diamonds and fruit. On the reverse, foliate ornamentation in niello. The centre-piece is older than the bird and was incorporated at a later date. The crane symbolizes vigilance. If it were to fall asleep, it would drop the stone and awake. Ascribed by Charles Beard to Corvinianus Sauer.
*Provenance:* Rosenborg inv. 1718, 29 no. 15.
*Literature:* Beard 1938 72 ff. Hackenbroch 1979 212.

629

## Pendant: Cameo Noah's Ark

Ascribed to Alessandro Masnago or his workshop in Milan ca. 1575. Mounting Danish c. 1640
Onyx, gold, enamel. H. 3.7 cm
Rosenborg 3.123
Transverse oval cameo showing the embarkation of the animals in Noah's ark (part of the sky has broken off and been replaced by blue enamel). Mounted in a gold case with lop. On the reverse in *champlevé* enamel a crowned "K" standing for Kirsten Munk, wreathed in polychrome flowers. Border edged with enamelled foliate ornamentation in black and white. The Cameo carved after an engraving by Bernard Salomon (1510?-1561?) 1554.
*Provenance:* Rosenborg inv. 1718 43 no. 9. Leonora Christina's catalogue of valuables, 1661 34 no. 6? (Det kongelige Bibliotek Kall 540,4°).
*Literature:* Rosenborg 1970 no. 12. Rosenborg 1986 no. 166. Boesen 1986 101.

*629*

630
## Bracelet

Denmark? c. 1600
Cast and chased gold, niello, diamonds. L. 20 cm
Rosenborg 3.137
18 hinged links of gold with niello. On the outside, alternately, crowned heart with a single ruby, and hour-glass with 2 table-cut diamonds. The hour-glass on the clasp is winged. On the inside, in niello, alternately a crowned monogram "C4" and an hour-glass. The bracelet be-

*630*

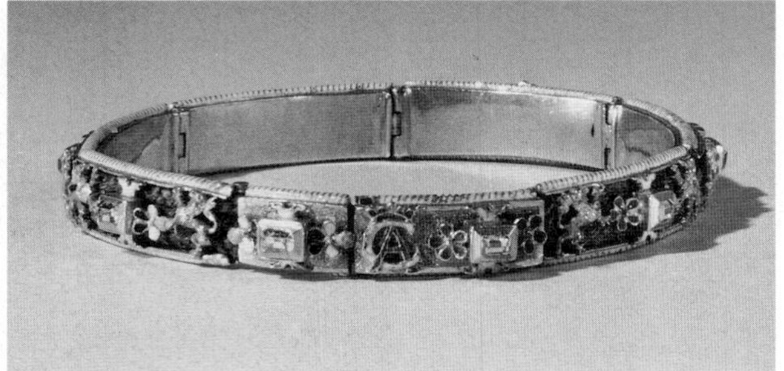

*631*

longed to Christian IV's mother and is assumed to have been a gift to her from her son. Do the wings on the clasp perhaps symbolize the ability of the son's filial affection to withstand the passage af time, thus prevailing even after his mother's death?
*Provenance:* Rosenborg inv. 1696 50 no. 3. Estate left by Queen Sophie 51. Inherited by Christian IV's sister Hedevig and bequeathed to him by her in her will in 1641. (RA, – the Royal Family Archives).
*Literature:* Rosenborg 1970 no. 8.

631
## Bracelet containing Christian IV's Hair

Denmark? c. 1600
Gold, enamel, diamonds. Diam. 5.5 cm.
Rosenborg 3.99
7 hinged links of cast and chased gold. Openwork with polychrome enamel. On 5 links flowers and lions *statant* flank a table-cut diamond, while on the 6th link these are replaced by a heart-shaped diamond with a crown and two crossed arrows. On the clasp, flowers and table-cut diamonds flank a crowned "AC" which stands for Queen Anna Cathrine. Beneath the arrows and the monogram lies a lock of hair, plaited. Perhaps a gift from Christian IV to his Queen?
*Provenance:* Rosenborg inv. 1696 50 no. 4.
*Literature:* Kunstindustrimuseet 1960 no. 82, Rosenborg 1970 no. 9.

632
## Pair of Bracelets

Denmark? 1635-1645
Gold, enamel, diamonds. L. 19.3 cm. Colour-plate XVIII
Rosenborg 3.135-136
8 hinged links, rectangular and box-shaped, of gold, enamelled on inner sides and edges. On the outside, openwork, alternately 4 reliefs of the seasons in gold, and naturalistic floral ornamentation in polychrome enamel, each link having 13 table-cut diamonds, 52 in all, representing the 52 weeks of the year. On the inside, multi-coloured flowers, birds and hunting scenes on a

white ground. The bracelets were worn as a pair. They may have been a wedding present to Queen Sophie Amalie. The floral ornamentation is identical to that found on the ceremonial saddle-mountings from 1634 (cat. 576) Ascribed by Liisberg to Corvinianus Sauer.
*Provenance:* Rosenborg inv. 1696 50 no. 2. Catalogue of the estate of Sophie Amalie, 1685, 103 no. 2.
*Literature:* Liisberg 1929 plate 6. Steingräber 1957 139f. Rosenborg 1970 no. 11. Rosenborg 1986 no. 179.

633

## Ear-rings from the Battle of Kolberger Heide

Denmark 1644
Gold, enamel, iron and bronze. H. 1.8 cm
Rosenborg 2.37
A pair of ear-rings in the form of white-enamelled hands (both right hand). One hand holding a splinter of iron, the other a splinter of bronze. These splinters (from a Swedish cannon ball and a Danish cannon) were respectively removed from the wounds sustained by Christian IV in the naval battle of Kolberger Heide in 1644. The ear-rings were a present to the King's mistress, Vibeke Kruse.

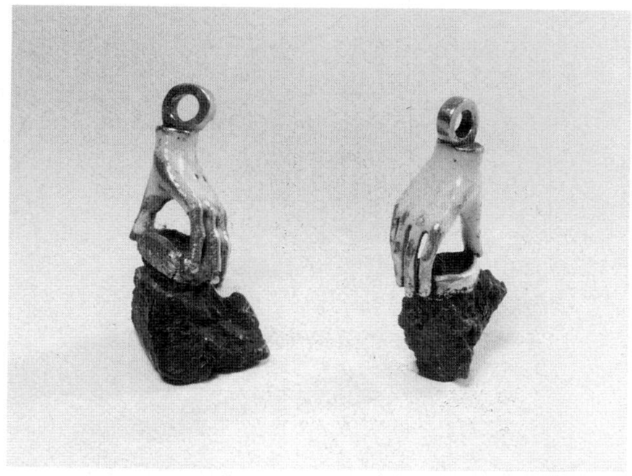

*633*

*Provenance:* Accession 1839. Mentioned in the inventory of Vibeke Kruse's estate, at Frederiksborg, 1648.
*Literature:* Bruun 1879 237. Fang 1960 5-13. Johannsen 1985.

*637*

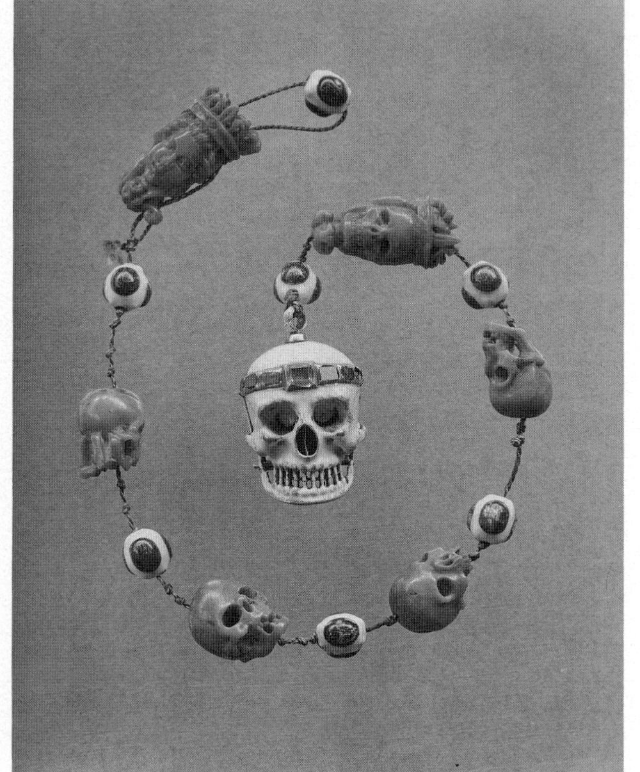

636

## Christian IV's Jade Amulet

Jade, silver. Diam. 2.7 cm
Rosenborg 3.94
Square plate of jade, set in a plain silver mounting with a loop. Engraved: "1648, 28 February, King Christian the 4th died with this gold chain about his neck and the stone within". The chain has since been lost. Jade was reputed to protect the wearer against gallstones.
*Provenance:* 1874 from the estate left by the Countess Danner (1815-1874), wife of Frederik VII.

637

## Vinaigrette and Chain, with Death's Heads

Denmark? c. 1600
Gold, enamel, rubies, coral. H. 3.0 cm
Rosenborg 1.33
Skull of white enamelled gold with a wreath of rubies. Chain with 7 red and white enamelled balls and 6 copal heads: 4 skulls and 2 crowned heads with smiling women's faces and skull. Inside the skull a sponge and six lidded compartments for balsam. Lid engraved: "Schlag B, Citronen, Rosen, Caneel B, Maiora, Negeler". The skull is the symbol of human vanity and is intended as a memento mori, to remind the owner that even that which is sweet smelling has no power against death.
This vinaigrette belonged to Queen Sophie Amalie; two similar examples were owned by Leonora Christina and Ellen Marsvin.

*639*

*Provenance:* Rosenborg inv. 1696 51 no. 12, Sophie Amalienborg inv. 1980 18a no. 2.
*Literature:* Bøje 1950 no. 6. Rosenborg 1970 no. 13. Rosenborg 1986 no. 173.

638

## Vinaigrette in Form of an Ape's Head

France 1647?
Cat's eye (sapphire variant), silver-gilt. H. 3.4 cm
Nationalmuseets 2. afd. inv. D 232
Ape's head cut in cat's eye, mounted in silver-gilt. On the reverse a mirror. Inside, two lids with painted miniatures and inscriptions. In the first section a gentleman points to his head while he contemplates another who appears deep in thought. The inscription reads: "Les hommes sont des miroirs les uns aux autres pour se contempler à la raison". In the second section an ape and a gentlemen consider their reflections in a looking-glass. "Mains la plus part s'itent par phantasie semblable aux singes". "Mankind are reflections of each other in their admiration for reason, but most of them look at their own reflection with the vanity of apes". The ampulla belonged to Leonora Christina. She may have purchased it when she accompanied her husband Corfitz Ulfeldt on his diplomatic mission to Paris in 1647.
*Provenance:* 1781 from Rosenborg to Den kgl. Mønt- og Medaillesamling. 1797 til Kunskammeret.
*Literature:* Rosenborg 1986 no. 186.

639

## Mirror with Rebus

Denmark 1630s?
Glass, enamelled gold, velvet. H. 13.2 cm
Rosenborg 1.115
Oval mirror. The frame hinged at sides, with palmettes on front and rear edge, loop-and-bow at top. Back covered with black velvet, decorated with a crowned C4 and the legend "Dirige Meum", above a burning heart. The inscription, which is intended to be understood in the sense of "Jehovah, direct thou my burning heart" has its parallels on hour glasses (cat. 640) and in the Rundetårn (the Round Tower) as well as on coins minted after the Peace of Brømsebro in 1645. The Lord's name used in connection with a rebus also occurs in inscriptions on objects executed around 1633 for the King's sister, the Electress Hedevig of Saxony.
*Provenance:* Rosenborg inv. 1696 46 no. 9.
*Literature:* RA TKUA Sachsen A II 22. Hedevig's estate (inventory) 1641. Liisberg 1929 pl. 3. Dunér 1965 12. Boesen 1986.

640

## Hourglass

Denmark 1633?
Glass, gold, translucent and opaque enamel. H. 12.6 cm
Rosenborg 1.111
Two hourglasses wound in cloth and gold wire. Frame with 6 pillars, connecting profiled upper and lower pedestals, each with 2 circular grooves and 4 ball feet. The pedestals decorated on the inside with foliate design in enamel and beaded edges. On the outside, in enamel, edged with foliate design, and in the two circles the inscription in Hebrew "Jahve" in flames above a burning heart, "DIRIGE MEUM AO 1633" and the crowned monogram "C4" within a wreath of berried foliage. Both rebus and enamelling (light colours and black on a white ground) match cat. 639.
*Provenance:* Rosenborg inv. 1696, 49 no. 31.
*Literature:* Liisberg 1929 pl. 2. Petit Palais, Paris 1978 no. 84.

641
## Scissors with Rebus

Saxony 1636
Iron blades, gold frame with niello. L. 114 cm
Rosenborg 3.105
One blade hall-marked with oakleaf surmounted by a crown. Handles in the shape of an 8. On the upper loop, in niello, the Hebrew inscription "Jahve" and 1636, flanking a crowned "H". "H" and "8" stand for the Electress Hedevig of Saxony, who bequeathed her personal possessions to her brother.
*Provenance:* Rosenborg inv. 1696 52 no. 4.

642
## Knife with Sheath

Denmark c. 1650
Iron, gold, enamel, table-cut stones, emeralds, rubies, velvet. L. 17.9 and 15.8 cm. Colour-plate XVIII
Rosenborg 6.219
Grip and sheath of gold with chased ground and naturalistic flowers, animals and insects in bas-relief covered with translucent and opaque enamel and set with table-cut stones, emeralds and rubies. Blade of iron with stamped crown. The sheath lined with velvet.
*Provenance:* Sophie Amalie's estate 1685, no. 71.10. Rosenborg inv. 1696 51 no. 11.
*Literature:* Rosenborg 1986 no. 183.

# The Kunstkammer

The Kunstkammer originated in Italy and spread by way of the Emperor's Court to Northern Europe, where it became fashionable around the year 1600. In it reposed collections of valuables and rarities. Goblets of rock crystal and semi-precious stones, clocks and technical instruments, animals and porcelain from foreign lands, or fossils and freaks of nature. The idea was to arrange the objects according to material and function, resulting in a world picture in miniature. Christian IV also bought 'curiosities'; Rosenborg could boast a Japanese sedan chair and Japanese arms in 1623. But strangely enough, he never became obsessed by this fashionable prestige phenomenon. It seems as though the Prince Elect, however, collected at 'Sparepenge' the beginnings of a cabinet of curiosities, but this only manifested itself during the reign of Frederik III in 1652.

The present reconstruction consists of items of applied art and some few clocks, the exhibits in rock crystal and semi-precious stones being the most noteable. Only rarely are they signed, as in the case of the splendid goblet by Hans Kobenhaupt in Stuttgart, 1620 (cat. 652). Some items can be determined by features of style, such as the almost erotic forms that came from the Emperor Rudolf II's royal workshops in Prague, c. 1610 (cat. 650). In other cases it is the material, such as Saxony serpentine, which provides a clue to its origin. (cat. 662).

But we lack information as to whether or not jewellers sold their semi-manufactured pieces. The enamelled settings do not help us much either since they are unstamped. Added to this, the reproduction of printers' engravings was prolific and widespread. Only archival documentation can determine whether, for instance, the group of bowls with enamel settings in pea-pod style was made in France, in Denmark, or elsewhere. (Cat. 655, 656, 658). One thing is certain, however, and that is that subsequent generations of the Royal Family cherished these works of art, handed them down or placed them in the Family Treasury, Rosenborg. Splendour served not only as pomp and spectacle; it was an inherent part of the family identity. Also in our own time the spectator is impressed by their exquisite materials and the artistic workmanship. But it should be borne in mind that in Christian IV's time, these objects were also ascribed supernatural powers and human attributes. It was believed, for example, that the unicorn's horn (narwhal tusk) (cat. 667) and serpentine (cat. 661) gave protection against poisoning, and that light blue sapphires were a symbol of female fidelity (cat. 687). Coupled with this was the desire to control the forces of nature and to

*640*

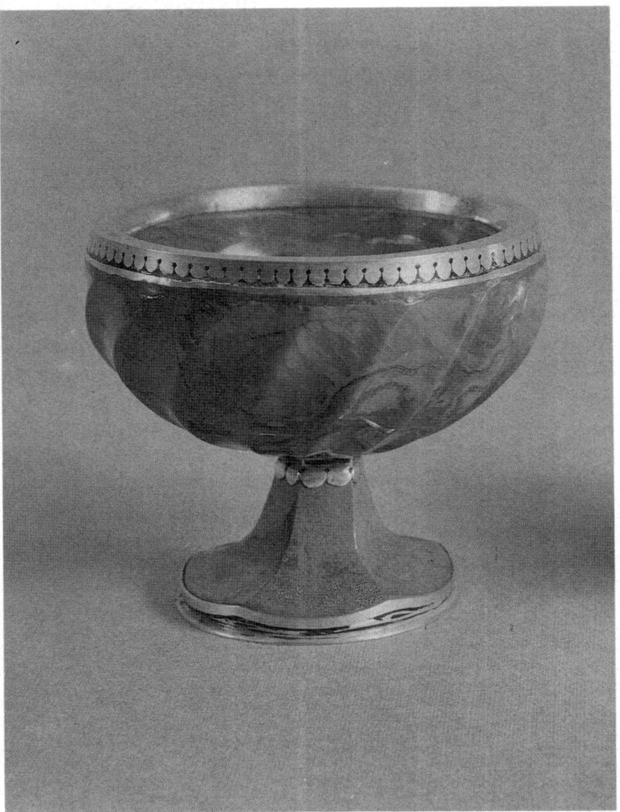

*644*

demonstrate the capacities of Man. For this reason, inanimate minerals were burnished into life and shaped into beauty by virtuose exploitation of technical aids. These masterpieces are a manifestation of the human spirit's eternal quest for challenges which poise delicately on the verge of the impossible.

643

## Pitcher with Handle, 'Lekytos'

Roman Empire 1st Cent. BC or AD. Mounting Northern Europe 1620-50?
Onyx, gold. Carved in one piece. H. 16.1 cm
Rosenborg 5.219
Body circular in section, broadest in the middle, with flared rim. From here to the middle an openwork looped handle with foliate ornaments. Terraced, hinged cover with flower knob and foot stand with 3 volutes. Both of smooth gold.
*Provenance:* Rosenborg inv. 1718, 69 no. 7. Sophie Amalienborg's inv. 1680, 13 no. 5. Leonora Christina's inv. 1661, 23 no. 10.
*Literature:* Petit Palais, Paris 1978 no. 44. Grand Palais, Paris 1984 129-135. Rosenborg 1986 no. 151.

644

## Chalice

Venice c. 1350. Mounting Denmark 1627
Red jasper, gold, niello. H. 6.1 cm
Rosenborg 1.95
Hemispherical diagonally facetted cup. Circular cinquefoil foot. Mounting and inside bottom of gold with niello work. On the base plate a crowned 'K' for Kirsten Munk. Cf. cat. 687.
*Provenance:* 1858 from the Kunstkammer inv. 1775, 262/810. Came from Queen Sophie Magdalene's estate 1770. Leonora Christina and Corfitz Ulfeldt's inheritance after Kirsten Munk, 1658: 'Et lidet Jaspis begger'?
*Literature:* Petit Palais, Paris 1978 no. 43. Hahnloser 1985 no. 442. Rosenborg 1986 no. 157.

645

## Bowl with Dragon Handle

Executed at the Court of Samarkand? C. 1425-1450
Filigree mounting Turkish c. 1600
Jade, gold, gems, rock crystal. L. 13.8
Nationalmuseets 4. afd. inv. E.c. 18
Oval bowl on foot ring, on the one broad side a dragon's head, all carved out of a single piece of jade. On the rim folded gold engraved with leaf and scale patterns. On the handle a garnet. On and under the foot, eagles' heads with scaling, set with rubies and inside a table-cut stone. On the shoulder fronds of leaves in inlaid gold filigree with turquoises, rubies, emeralds, table-cut stones and rock crystal. The gold edge and eagles' heads could be original. The filigree and gems are probably a Turkish addition to a Persian booty.
*Provenance:* Accession: 1859 from Rosenborg, inv. 1696 70 no. 2. Sophie Amalienborg's inv. 1680 14 no. 11. Leonora Christina's inv. 1661 no. 4 or 8.
*Literature:* Rosenborg 1986 no. 159.

646

## Covered Vase

Executed at the Court of Samarkand? C. 1424-50.
Mounting Danish c. 1600
Jade, gold, enamel, pearls, emerald. H. 7.4 cm.
Rosenborg 1.109
Cylindrical terraced neck on spherical body with stand ring. At the shoulder two handles carved out of the mass. Openwork cover and foot ring of filigree gold with enamel in red, green, blue and white. On the cover 7 pearls (two missing) and 6 emeralds. The enamel is reminiscent of the flowers on cat. 631.
*Provenance:* Rosenborg inv. 1696, 75 no. 17. Sophie Amalienborg's inv. 1680, 15 no. 7. Leonora Christina and Corfitz Ulfeldt's inheritance after Kirsten Munk 1658: 'Een Hvid Steen Krucke med Guld laag och Perler'.
*Literature:* Kunstindustrimuseet 1950 no. 665. Petit Palais, Paris, 1978 no. 42. Rosenborg 1986 no. 158.

*645*

647

## Covered Goblet

Cover and foot ascribed to Francesco Tortorino (-1550-1595), c. 1560. Goblet South German, c. 1600?
Lapis lazuli and gold. Relief and intaglio. H. 27.5 cm
Rosenborg 1.126
On the cover and foot carved tritons in waves and leaves in relief, on the shoulder of the cup architecture, leaves and tritons in intaglio. On the cover a silver gilt Pallas Athene (spear missing), knob with grotesque masks. This goblet was probably made up of assembled pieces. The carving of the cover's muscular gods and waves is also to be found on a rock crystal goblet in Vienna, signed by Tortorino. The knob can be contemporary with the cup, but bears traces of repair.
*Provenance:* Rosenborg inv. 1696, 71 no. 11. The pieces possibly come from Sophie Amalienborg, inv. 1680 10 no. 2.
*Literature:* Kriss 1929 I no. 336-337. Petit Palais, Paris, 1978 no. 47. Rosenborg 1986 no. 162.

648

## Neptune Bowl belonging to the Prince Elect.

Milan? 1580-1610. Under the base an engraved 'C5' for the Prince Elect.
Jasper, gold, enamel, gems. H. 14 cm
Grünes Gewölbe, Dresden inv. VI 36
Bowl of jasper, mounted with gold and enamel, set with emeralds, rubies, diamonds and pearls. The oval bowl is borne by a dolphin resting on a circular foot. Sitting on the rim, Neptune, casting his trident at a dolphin at the bottom of the bowl. Neptune is white enamelled, the dolphins blue and green. The edges and mounts have white and blue ornaments and black foliage with blue and red. The 'C5' has been identified as Christian V (1670-1699). The bowl was nevertheless part of his mother Sophie Amalie's estate, 1685, and was inherited by her daughter, Wilhelmine Ernestine, who bequeathed it to her sister, the Electress Anna Sophie of Saxony. Presumably a gift from Christian IV to the Prince Elect as dauphin. The Neptune motif allegorizes the Danish King's claim to mastery of the Baltic and the North Sea.
*Provenance:* Grünes Gewölbe, inv. 1725, 52. 1717 from the estate of Electress Anna Sophie (1647-1717).
*Literature:* Menzhausen 1970 no. 24c.

650

## Bowl

Ascribed to the Miseroni workshop in Milan c. 1610
Smoky topaz, gold, enamel. Carved. L. 12 cm
Rosenborg 5.229
Mussel-shaped cup on circular stand. On the front a lion's mask surrounded by foliage. On the sides and the tri-partite moulded rim, curved fluting; over this ribboning with terminal volutes around flared rim. Terraced foot ring of gold, black and green enamel. From 1607-1611 the Miseroni family supplied three similar bowls to Rudolf II, whose Kunstkammer was renowned for its lapidary pieces. The bowl's lustre is due to the varying thicknesses of its walls, which exploit the material's capacity for absorbing and reflecting light.
*Provenance:* Rosenborg inv. 1696 64 no. 9.
*Literature:* Petit Palais, Paris, 1978 no. 35. Distelberger 1978 102-106. Hein 1985 40.

651

## Vase

Ascribed to Ottavio Miseroni (-1588-1624) in Prague c. 1620.
Smoky topaz, gold. Carved. H. 9.8 cm
Rosenborg 5.228

*646*

648

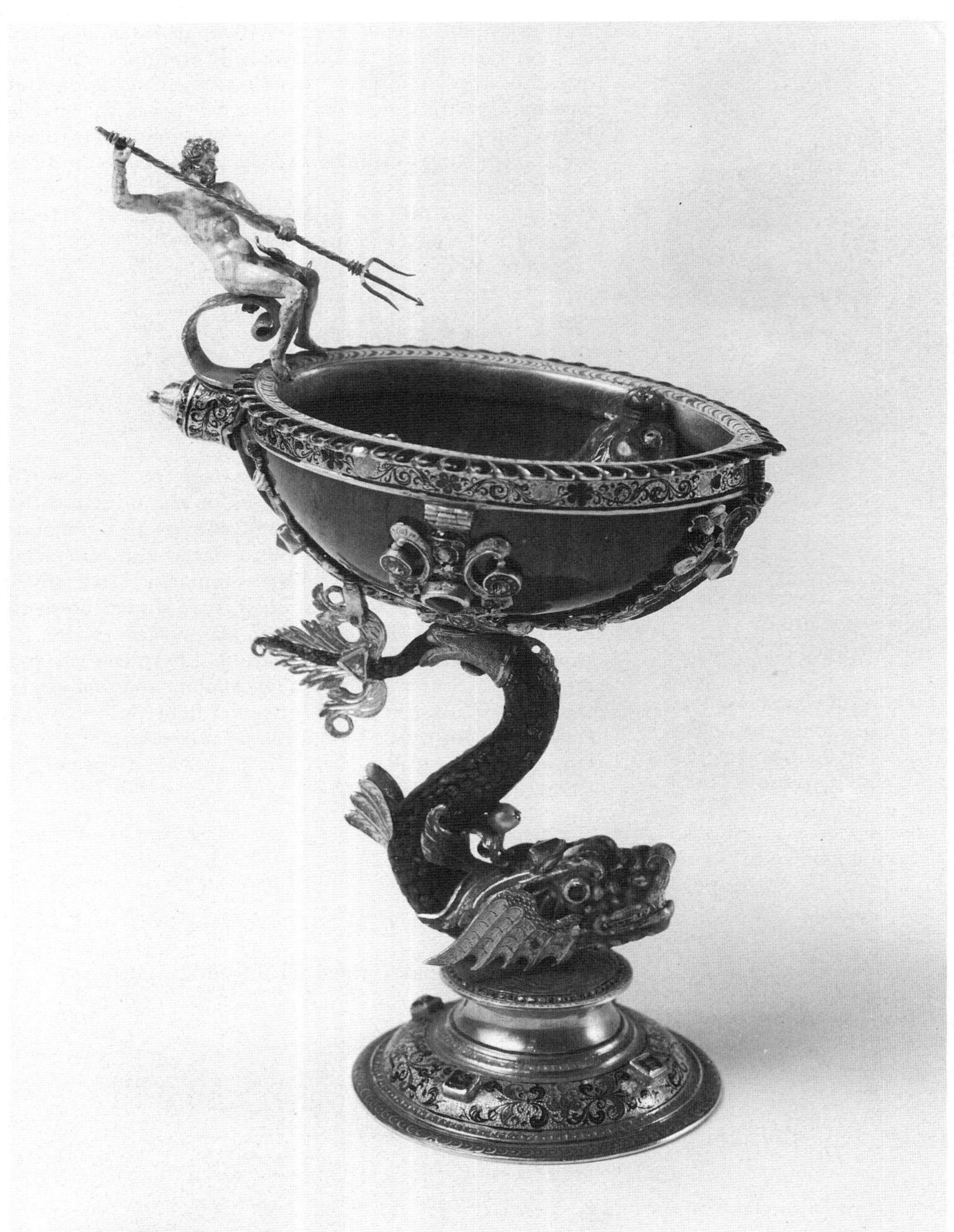

Ovoid body on stem. Rim and bottom carved with fluted wall and pointed rhomboids. Oval foot with stem edged with rhomboids and fluting. Profiled stem ring and stand rim of gold. Ottavio Miseroni left Milan for Prague to work for Rudolf II. In his latter years he departed from the smooth transitions and moulded profiles of the lion bowl (previous cat.no.) in favour of concise and well-defined forms as on this vase.

*Provenance:* Rosenborg inv. 1696, 58 no. 39. Sophie Amalienborg inv. 1680, 14 no. 12.

*Literature:* Distelberger 1978 146 151-152. Hein 1985 40. Rosenborg 1986 no. 168.

*650*

652

## Covered Goblet

Signed on the stem 'HK' and '1620' for Hans (Johann) Kobenhaupt, Stuttgart 1609-23.
Agate, gold, enamel, rubies, diamond. H. 29.8 cm
Rosenborg 1.121
Eliptical quatrefoil-curved cup, baluster stem, foot and cover. Lacquer-red agate with grey and blue-white, shot with yellow, covered with trophies in bas-relief. On the cover the 4 quarters of the Württemberg coat-of-arms. Mounting of gold and polychrome enamel partly in openwork, set with rubies. On cover and foot rim female half-figures which on the cover alternate with dolphins. As cover knob a diamond-embellished Roman warrior with sword and shield, upon which the Württemberg coat-of-arms with the inscription 'IO FRIED H Z WIRTEM V DECKH G Z MUN HEI' (Johan Friedrich Herzog zu Württemberg und Taeck. Graf zu Mömpelgard. Her zu Heidenheim). Presumably a gift from Duke Johan Friedrich to his brother-in-law, Christian IV. Or possibly identical with the 'meget smukke ... drikkekar' (very beautiful drinking vessel) which Frederik III received when he had bestowed the Order of the Elephant upon Johann Friedrich's son in 1654. (Haupstaatsarchiv Stuttgart, A.202 Buch 1202).
*Provenance:* Rosenborg inv. 1696, 71 no. 20. Offered as a prize for tilting at the ring by the Dowager Queen Sophie Amalie and won by Christian V in 1680.
*Literature:* Fleischauer 1970 284. Heidelberg 1986 II no. L 1. Rosenborg 1986 no. 107.

653

## 3 Goblets

Ascribed to Hans Kobenhaupt or his workshop. 1609-23.
a) Agate. H. 19.6 cm b) red jasper. H. 8.4 cm c) heliotrope. H. 10.3 cm

*651*

*653c*

*655*

a) Nationalmuseets 2. afd. inv. MNOD 81. b-c) Rosenborg inv. 5.291, 5.290 a)funnel-shaped gadrooned baluster stem, circular foot and domed cover. Mounting of polychrome enamelled gold. Stem ring with dolphins and ornaments. Cover rim with marine and hunting scenes between white fields. As cover knob, Venus Anadyomene with a dolphin. The variation in colour and working of the agate indicates that the baluster stem and foot were a later addition. b) oval, boat-shaped cup. Terraced baluster stem on oval foot, turned. Enamelled openwork stem mounts of gold with polychrome enamel. On the foot rim, between white fields, four rustic and marine scenes. c) Mussel-shaped cup with gilt grooves. Terraced baluster stem. Egg-formed stand with grooves. Two stem rings and stand edge of gold with polychrome enamel. On the upper stem ring a collar of leaves and two dolphins. Similar goblet in the Kunsthistorisches Museum, Vienna, inv.no. 1820. In the carving, polishing and enamelling Kobenhaupt's work approaches the quality of Rudolf II's royal workshops in Prague.
*Provenance:* a) and b) Rosenborg inv. 1718, 50 no. 4 and 59 no. 61. c)1867 from the Kunstkammer inv. 1775, 262/800, 1770 from Queen Sophie Magdalene's estate. Like the foregoing cat.nos. presumably gifts from the Ducal House of Württemberg.
*Literature:* Fleischauer 1970 287 (b). Petit Palais, Paris, 1978 no. 58 (c) and no. 59 (b). Heidelberg 1986 II no. L 6 (a) and L 10 (c).

655

## Covered Goblet

Agate turned in the 1500s? Mounting Danish?
Agate, gold enamel. H. 16.8 cm
Rosenborg 5.345
Cup, baluster stem and cover knurled. Gold mountings. Stem ring, stand plate and cover knob in openwork foliation and fruit in blue, green, yellow, black and white. The beading seen in the pointed, openwork leaves on the mounting has given the name "pea-pod style" to this decoration. Developed as surface ornamentation in France c. 1620, it is characterizised by a certain naturalism and by a colour scheme of pale or strong colours with a moderate use of red. Examples are known from France, Holland and Moscow. Had the style reached Denmark in 1634?
*Provenance:* Rosenborg inv. 1718 50 no. 3.
*Literature:* Petit Palais, Paris 1978 no. 60.

*658*

656

## Goblet

Mountings in pea-pod style 1620-40
Heliotrope, gold, enamel. Turned. H. 9.9 cm
Rosenborg 5.240
Egg-shaped cup. Stem knob, spiral cut, terraced foot. Openwork mounting in white enamelled gold with yellowish-red flowers.
*Provenance:* Rosenborg inv. 1696 75 no. 28.
*Literature:* Petit Palais, Paris, 1978 no. 56.

658

## Covered Goblet

Mounting in pea-pod style. Denmark 1620-1640?
Brownish agate, enamelled gold, rubies. H. 11.7 cm
Rosenborg 5.230
Hemispherical cup with flat stand ring. Oval stem knob. Circular foot. Cover with circular centre plate surrounded by 10 oval agate pearls. Terraced cover knob. Mounting in openwork. Set with a total of 64 rubies. White enamel with black foliage ornaments, otherwise turquoise, blue and green. The stand ring's tracery similar to that on the King's hourglass (cat. 640).
*Provenance:* Rosenborg inv. 1718, 51 no. 7.
*Literature:* Petit Palais, Paris, 1978 no. 45.

660

## 3 Drinking Vessels with Cameos and Intaglios

The Netherlands? 1635-1650
Gold with painted enamel. H. a) 43.3 cm, b) 31.4 cm, c) 36.5 cm
Rosenborg 6.78, 6.80, 6.76.
a) Goblet. Cup, foot and cover enamelled with varicoloured flowers on blue ground. On these in gold settings, cameos and intaglios (205), some blue-enamelled ovals with flowers and birds, some white ovals with profile heads (115). Pale blue cover knob with flower in black and white. Stem in the form of a seated blackamoor on a dragon, enamelled in natural colours and set with table-cut stones (24). On the foot a painted signature: dark blue oval with 2 c's? b) Oval covered bowl with 2 dragon

660a

660b

660c

handles, oval foot with 4 dolphins. On the surfaces enamelling and stone settings (267) as the above, and white ovals with blackamoor heads (8). Dragon handles and serpents green-enamelled, heads and tails light blue, green and red on white ground. c) Oval covered bowl, 2 volute handles with blackamoor heads, 4 volute feet on ball-pads. Body and cover blue-enamelled, the cover with acanthus design in black. Stone-setting as the foregoing (121). Handles and feet enamelled in pale colours on white ground. The blackamoor heads have earrings and necklaces of pearls.

The Renaissance prized each and every cameo or intaglio for its beauty, and revived antiquity's lapidary art. After 1600, however, it became fashionable to use these stones as decorations on objects, which led to a commercial production. The enamelling of the handles and feet of these drinking vessels dates them at between 1635 and 1650, usually thought to have originated in the Netherlands. Similar examples are preserved in Stockholm, Kassel and the Hague.

All three are former royal possessions. Christian IV's daughter, Leonora Christina, owned a similar goblet. It was confiscated by Queen Sophie Amalie and sent to Rosenborg. In 1716, Frederik IV gave it to Tsar Peter the Great. In 1785, Catherine the Great had the cameos prised off and the goblet melted down.

*Provenance:* a) Rosenborg inv. 1781, 137 no. 11. b) 1876 from the Kunstkammer. 1795 (c 976G) from Den kgl. Mønt- og Medaillesamling. c) Rosenborg inv. 1718, 73 no. 28.

*Literature:* c) Petit Palais, Paris 1978 no. 111. Kungl. Husgerådskammaren Stockholm 1982 no. 22. Link w/o year pl. 13. Neverov 1985 57.

661

## Butter Bowl

Mounting, and possibly bowl, ascribed to Caspar Herbach (1600-1664) 1643

Saxony serpentine, silver gilt. L. 16 cm

Rosenborg 1.122

Oval octofoil bowl on 4 animals paws, carved in one. Hinged cover with loop handle, bolt and openwork mounting of silver gilt. On the cover engraved flowers, Hebrew inscription 'Jahve', crowned 'C4 1643' and 'Friedrichsburg'. Caspar Herbach came to Denmark in 1642 with the legacy from Christian IV's sister, the Electress Hedevig of Saxony. In 1643 he made for the King 'a butter dish and two bowls of gold'. Did he bring the bowl or did he carve it here in Denmark? He later ran a stone mill and was paid, among other items, for Queen Sophie Amalie's crown in 1648. This bowl was formerly considered to be Byzantine.

*Provenance:* Rosenborg inv. 1696 58 no. 33. Sophie Amalie's estate description 1685, 311 no. 2.

*Literature:* Petit Palais, Paris 1978 no. 106. Grand Palais, Paris 1984 no. 286-91. Rosenborg 1986 no. 181. Boesen 1986 104 fol.

662

## A Pair of Slippers

Saxony 1635-1647?

Saxony serpentine. L. 30.5 cm

Nationalmuseet 2. afd. D 170-171.

Each slipper is carved in one piece. On the uppers and heel an engraved ornamental border, inlaid in white. Signs of wear show that the slippers were used. Was this because serpentine was thought to have prophylactic powers? A pair of serpentine slippers was found in 1694 in the Gottorp Kunstkammer. Probably both pairs were gifts from the Court at Dresden to the sons-in-law, the Prince Elect and Duke Frederik III of Gottorp.

*Provenance:* From the Kunstkammer, inv. 1674, 28b

*Literature:* Kiel 1965 no. 293.

663

## Head of a Woman
## Saxony or Denmark c. 1640-1650?

Serpentine, silver, gilt, enamel. H. 16 cm

Nationalmuseets 2. afd. D 88.

Back of the head carved in one piece of serpentine. Cover of silver in the form of a young woman's head with gilt border edging in braiding and openwork. On this, 3 green and red enamelled bows. Around the back of the head matching borders and stand bows. Drinking vessel. Possibly a reliquary, provided with a new cover?

*Provenance:* Rosenborg inv. 1718 75 no. 35.

664

## Princess Magdalene Sibylla's Gold Horn

Denmark 1650. Perforated crowned 'M(agdalene) S(ybilla) 1650'

Gold with enamelled castwork. L. 49.5 cm.

Grünes Gewölbe, Dresden, inv. IV 45

Slightly curved horn. Chased curve. On it, 8 smooth

*661*

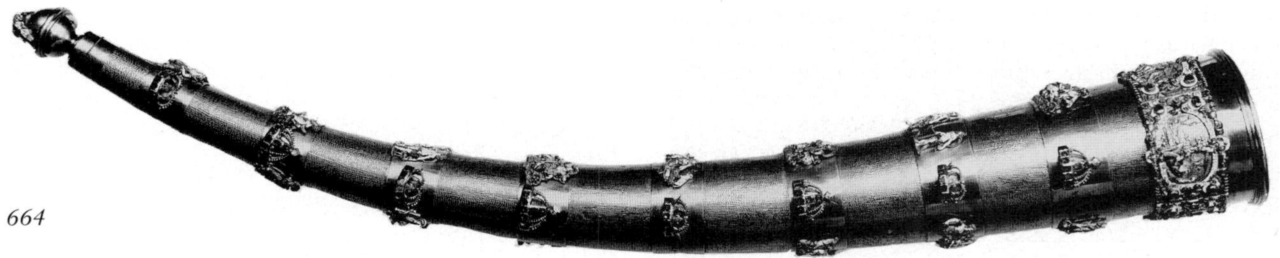

664

bands with crowns, set with rubies, in 2 different forms. Between the crowns enamelled figures, some human (the 8 virtues) and some animal (the 7 planets). Nearest the rim a broader band of 4 oval reliefs with Old Testament scenes of slaying (Goliath, Holofernes, Sennacherib and Sisera) in scrollwork with enamel and rubies. The horn is loosely modelled on the gold horn from Gallehus which Christian IV gave the Prince Elect, and which he allowed Magdalene Sibylla to keep in her widowhood. Like its model, the copy was equipped with a screw stopper to be used either to drink from or to blow on. Gudmund Boesen has shown that the enamelled figures are almost certainly made over from older pieces of jewellery from the Princess' dowry, presumably c. 1580.
*Provenance:* Accession Grünes Gewölbe 1746 by order of Augustus the Strong from Magdalene Sibylla's grandson.
*Literature:* Sponsel II 1928 15.17. Boesen 1957 13.23.

663

665

## Princess Magdalene Sibylla's Serpentine Bowl

Ascribed to Henrik Langemack (-1635-1657). On the ridge in enamel: crowned 'M(agdalene) S(ibylla) 1651'
Serpentine, silver, gilt, gold, enamel. H. 23 cm
Grünes Gewölbe, Dresden, inv. V 381
Bowl on a foot. Oval, octofoil cup. Vase-shaped stem. Oval foot plate. All of serpentine, mounted with silver gilt, partly enamelled silver. On the ridge of the bowl a nautilus-shaped baldachin with monogram and date. To the sides and on the rim animals in gold enamel, set with diamonds: 2 blue-green dragons (The Wendish Wyvern), 2 white swans (Stormarn). Under the baldachin in a curve of rubies, 1 blue lion with neck ring and crown of diamonds. To each side 4 similar lions, every other one with a crown, and 1 gold lion with an axe (Norway). After the death of the Prince Elect in 1647, Magdalene Sibylla remained a widow for five years until she married Duke Johan Adolf of Saxony-Weissenfels in 1652. She presumably had an existing bowl set with animals from the Danish coat-of-arms, possibly from pieces of older jewellery (cat. 626-27). Diamond-studded lions were made by Henrik Langemack for the Prince to use as gifts on the journey during which he died.
*Provenance:* Grünes Gewölbe 1746 by order of Augustus the Strong from Magdalene Sibylla's grandson.
*Literature:* Ibid.

668

## Bell

South Germany c. 1600
Rock crystal, gold, metal. H. 4.5 cm
Rosenborg 1.100
Bell, eye and loop carved in one piece. The bell is engraved with ornamental leaves. Eye and loop wound with gold. Inside the bell a metal thread holds the rock crystal tongue.
*Provenance:* Rosenborg inv. 1696 65 no. 17. Sophie Amalienborg inv. 1680 16 a no. 15. Leonora Christina's inv. 1661 25 no. 8.
*Literature:* Rosenborg 1986 no. 152.

*668*

670

## 2 Oil Lamps in the Form of Ships

a) unmarked b) marked 'CF' and '12' Northern Europe (Denmark?) c. 1600?
Silver, gilt, rock crystal. a) H. 13 cm, b) H. 12.5 cm
Rosenborg 1.87 (a) and 1.88 (b)
Hull of facet-cut rock crystal mounted with silver gilt (a) and silver (b). Single masted ships with square sail and split flag, painted with the cross of Dannebrog. On (a) warriors. The hull serves as an oil holder, in the bows a lip for the wick, on the deck a screw-stopper for refilling. The stand plates were added later. Ship forms were very popular, especially for salt cellars and musical boxes.
*Provenance:* Rosenborg inv. 1797 75 no. 34. Saved from the Christiansborg Palace fire in 1794.

671

## Goblet

The rock crystal is ascribed to the Saracchi workshop c. 1580 Mounting Danish c. 1620-1640?
Rock crystal, gold, niello, turquoises. H. 12.7 cm
Rosenborg 6.61.
Oval cup. Round the cup a border of engraved leaf work, under which carved piping on baluster stem. Oval stem and foot of gold with niello work, set with 52 turquoises. Through the bottom of the cup can be seen a bunch of fruit in polychrome enamel.
*Provenance:* Rosenborg inv. 1797 39 no. 20. Saved from the Christiansborg Palace fire in 1794. Possibly identical with the goblet with turquoises in the estate of Frederik IV's second wife, Anna Sophie Reventlow (1693-1743).
*Literature:* Petit Palais, Paris 1978 no. 41.

673.

## Bobbin

Christian IV
Ivory. Turnery and carving. L. 11.3 cm
Rosenborg 1.73.
Reel with end rosettes hollowed to accomodate a spindle, which is fastened to the vertical side-pieces with ivory nuts, one of which is missing. Head with mounts of blue-enamelled forget-me-nots and a ring of metal gilt fastened to the sides with metal studs. Traditionally held to have been made by the King. In 1592 and 1600, the treasurer's accounts note expenses in connection with the mounting of Christian IV's turnery. The 1696 inventory has this bobbin as the King's work.
*Provenance:* Rosenborg inv. 1696 73.
*Literature:* Brock 1892 105. Liisberg 1929 133 100.

674

## Penknife and Paper Folder

c. 1600
Ivory, brass, iron. a) L. 38.6 cm, b) 16.5 cm
Rosenborg 1.76, 1.77
Knife blade of iron, stamped with crowned C(?). Ring of brass gilt. Turned conical ivory handle, twist-turned. Paper-folder. End knob, twist-turned handle, 3-forked point. Traditionally held to have been turned by Christian IV.
*Provenance:* Rosenborg inv. 1718,7 no. 15-16
*Literature:* Borck 1892 105

675

## Covered Mug

Christian IV? c. 1600?
Ivory. Turnery. H. 12.5 cm
Private collection
Cylindrical, basket-turned body with laciniated foot and mouth. Laciniated, flat-domed cover with rosette-shaped knob. Smooth loop handle and ball-shaped thumb-piece. 3 reeded ball feet. Under the base a turned rosette and black wavy lines. In the bottom an inscribed rosette surrounded by three flowers, all in black. In the cover, black flowers around a crowned C4. Familiy tradition holds the mug to have been turned by the King. A certain disharmony in the turnery of the body and the

*670a*

somewhat primitively executed black line drawing suggest amateur work, supporting the theory. The open crown on the cover indicates an early work.
*Provenance:* Inherited by his daughter Hedevig, married to Ebbe Ulfeldt in 1642. The mug is now owned by the descendants.

676

## Covered Mug

Mounting stamped 'AW' for Andreas I. Wickert (c. 1600-1661) and Augsburg's hall mark 1640-1645
Ivory, silver gilt. H. 37.5 cm
Rosenborg 5.313
Silver gilt with cylinder, lid cover and knob of ivory. The cylinder carved with a Silenus and Bacchus drinking orgy, lid cover with putti on sea-horses, and on lid knob a kneeling Bacchus. The silver gilt mounting is engraved with grapes and vines. On the handle a winged female figure, on the foot rim 8 winged putti (2 missing).
The Bacchanalia was a favourite theme of Peter Paul Rubens (1577-1640) and was executed in ivory on a covered pitcher carved by Georg Petel (1601/2-1634) in Augsburg c. 1630. Petel's covered pitcher (in the Städtische Kunstsamlung in Augsburg) was the prototype for a series of jugs and mugs, including this one, presumably an Augsburg work from 1640-45. In 1645 the Prince Elect bought an ivory jug, carved with figures and mounted with silver gilt, from his Court goldsmith Henrik Langemack. Perhaps this covered mug?
*Provenance:* Rosenborg inv. 1696 57 no. 18.
*Literature:* Georg Petel 1973 78 (Theodor Müller) and cat. 19 (Alfred Schädler). Seling III 1980 no. 1451 and 63-65. Knutsson 1983 6.

677

## Walking Stick

Copenhagen 1641
Narwhal tusk, iron. Carved. Turnery L. 129 cm
Rosenborg 1.129
The stick consists of 10 different carved and turned pieces, pierced and held together by an iron rod. Ferrule of iron. Above, the inscription 'VON GOTTES GENADEN WILHELM HERTZOG ZU SACHSEN 1641'. Duke Wilhelm of Saxony-Weimar (1598-1662) was an ally of the Swedes. The King's letters reveal that in 1641 there was a good deal of dissatisfaction with the Swedes among the Weimar soldiers. Was the stick intended as a gift (or bribe) to the Duke?
*Provenance:* 1867 from the Kunstkammer inv. 1737, 765/319.

678

## Serpent and Hare

Coral L. 4.8 cm and 23.1 cm
Rosenborg 24.24 and 24.31
Coiled serpent with gaping jaws. Jumping hare. The overseas coral was much prized. Sicily was one of the centres of production. Leonora Christina owned 30-40 items of coral, including the Apostles and some angels.
*Provenance:* Rosenborg inv. 1696 69 no. 4 and 7. Sophie Amalienborg inv. 1680, 18 no. 17 and 18a no. 3. Leonora Christina's inv. 1661 30 no. 3?
*Literature:* Rosenborg 1986 no. 207-208.

*673 og 674*

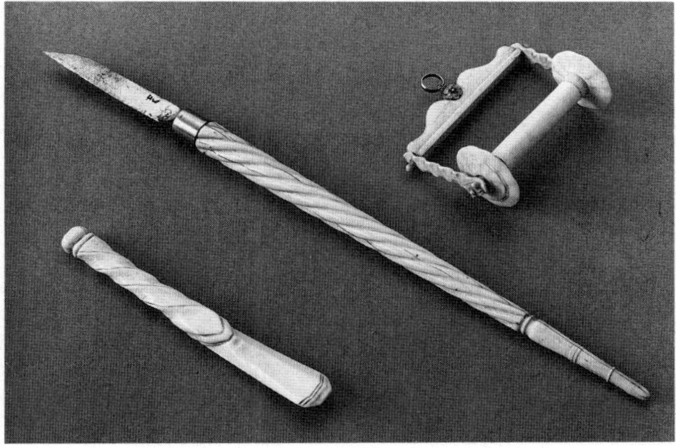

*676*

679

## Bird-shaped drinking Vessel

Stamped 'MB' and 'N' for Meinrad Bauch the elder (Master in Nuremberg 1575, died 1623)
Silver, gilt, mother-of-pearl, garnets. H. 31 cm
Nationalmuseets 2. afd. D 103
Standing bird with mother-of-pearl feathers. On breast and wing a rosette with inset garnets (missing on the breast). By the bird's feet 2 frogs and a lizard. Circular, terraced foot, silver gilt and partly gilt cartouches and mounts. On these, two more frogs and two lizards. Earlier ascribed to Melchior Bayer (Nuremberg 1525-1575).
*Provenance:* Kunstkammer inv. 1807, 48/c978, saved from the Christiansborg Palace fire in 1794.
*Literature:* Olrik 1909 58. Rosenberg III 1925 46 and 119. Kunstindustrimuseet 1984 no. 115.

680

## Nautilus Goblet

Stamped 'W' and 'N' for Peter Wiber(s), Master in Nuremberg 1603, Geschworener 1623. From c. 1620
Nautilus framed in silver gilt. H. 48 cm
Nationalmuseets 2. afd. D 450
Lip rim with engraved marsh landscape and ledge with female herm. Suspended from here to the foot, garlands of openwork leaves and fruit: Actaeon, kneeling surrounded by 3 hounds, 2 frogs, a serpent, a tortoise and a bird. Terraced foot with bosses and mounts. Similar cover. As cover knob, Diana with 3 hounds, and as thumb-piece Minerva. According to the inscription on the base, the goblet saw service as a banqueting goblet for farmers in Kedingen, south of the Elbe. The inscription is dated 1640. It is not known when the goblet came into Royal possession.
*Provenance:* Kunstkammer inv. 1775, 250/627, from the estate of Queen Sophie Magdalene 1770. Rosenborg inv. 1696 74 no. 18.
*Literature:* Olrik 1909 70. Rosenberg II 1911 535. Kunstindustrimuseet 1984 no. 73.

681

## Two Salt Cellars

Wanli porcelain, c. 1610. Mounting Netherlands?
Porcelain, brass gilt, pearls, turquoises, gems. W. 7.7 cm
Rosenborg 5.209 and 5.211
Two circular cups on a stand of blue and white porcelain, outside net pattern, and inside, in the bottom, a flower. Rim mounts in castwork and openwork, set with pearls, turquoises and gems. Base mount on 3 feet, set with pearls. Matching cups found on the East India vessel Witte Leeuw, which sank in 1613.
*Provenance:* 1867 from the Kunstkammer, inv. 1775, 250/614, from Queen Sophie Magdalene's estate 1770.
*Literature:* van der Pijl-Ketel 1982 165.

682

## Covered Mug

Chinese. Cover dated 1644
Porcelain. Cover of silver. H. 20.3 cm (w/o thumb-piece)
Private collection
Cylindrical mug with handle. Blue painted landscape with 2 figures and frieze on foot and rim. On the cover

*678*

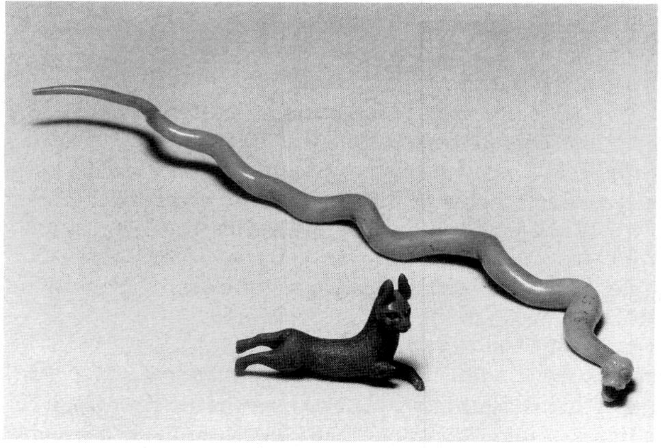

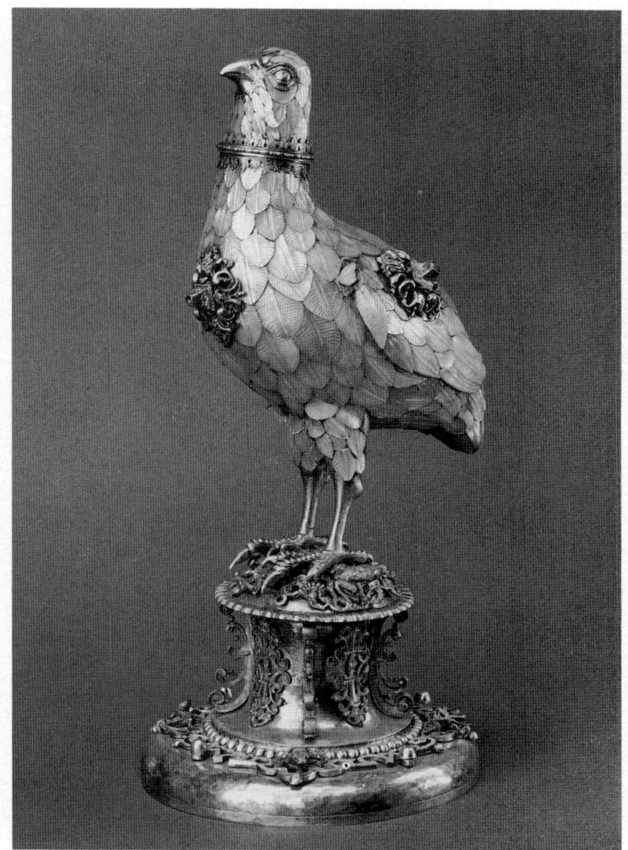

679

680

engraved a wreathed crowned Munk coat-of-arms and '1644'. Above, 'K(irsten) M(unk) G(revinde) T(il) S(lesvig) H(olsten)' (Kirsten Munk, Duchess of Schleswig Holstein).
*Provenance:* Inherited by her daughter Hedevig, married to Ebbe Ulfeldt in 1642. The mug is owned by the descendants.

683

## Butter Bowl

Saxony 1639
Stoneware, mounted in silver gilt. H. 7.2 cm
Rosenborg 1.93
Circular bowl. Around the bowl cherub heads and masks. On the cover, the Hebrew inscription for God-Messiah-Holy Ghost. On the base a crowned '8' and '1639'. 8 signifies H for Hedevig, Electress of Saxony, Christian IV's sister. Presumably the King inherited it from his sister in 1641.
In Saxony a consistent production of stoneware led to Meissener porcelain. As an early prototype, this bowl was given a costly mount, and came into the possession of the Electress.

*Provenance:* Rosenborg inv. 1696 58 no. 34. Sophie Amalie's estate inventory 1685 311 no. 3.
*Literature:* Rosenborg 1986 no. 178.

684

## Figure group

Venice c. 1600
Polychrome glass on a wire skeleton. H. 28 cm
Rosenborg 5.225
Two Commedia dell'Arte figures on a dark wooden base. The position of the fingers indicate that they are playing 'morra'. Between the figures is a stool with a table-cloth upon which is a glass of wine, some bread, biscuits and sausage. Similar figures in the Kunsthistorisches Museum in Vienna.
*Provenance:* 1867 from the Kunstkammer, Museum Regium Part II, sec. I, no. 54. From the painter Karel van Mander's (1609-1670) Kunstkammer. Possibly acquired in the 1630's.
*Literature:* Schlosser 1908 61 and 64. Krogh 1938 145. Boesen 1960 14-18. Leithe-Jasper and Distelberger 1982.

681

686

## Spoon, Knife, and Fork

Ascribed to Johan Kobenhaupt's workshop, Stuttgart, 1609-23
Agate, gold, enamel, iron. L. 16.0 cm, 20.0 cm, 17.3 cm
Rosenborg 3.61, 3.62, 3.63
Handles and bowl of spoon brown agate. Knife blade of iron, fork of gold. Mounting in coloured gold enamel. On fork and spoon a female herm. The stem of the spoon is terminated with a standing youth.
*Provenance:* Rosenborg inv. 1718 47 no. 3. Like cat. 652-53 presumably a gift from Württemberg to Christian IV or Frederik III.
*Literature:* Fleischauer 1970 287. Petit Palais, Paris 1978 no. 108. Heidelberg 1986 no. L. 13.

687

## Spoon

Denmark? 1615-1630
Sapphire, gold, enamel. L. 9.8 cm
Rosenborg 3.124
Bowl in the form of a circular facetted sapphire. Handle of gold with polychrome enamel with crowned lion's mask and crowned 'CK' for Christian and Kirsten. A gift from the King to his beloved? The light blue sapphire was the symbol of female fidelity. Ascribed by Liisberg to Corvinianus Sauer.
*Provenance:* Rosenborg inv. 1696 50 no. 1. Sophie Amalie's estate inv. 1685, goldsmith's evaluation list 12 no. 28.
*Literature:* Liisberg 1929 plat 9. Petit Palais 1978 no. 120. Rosenborg 1986 no. 165.

688

## Spoon

Denmark c. 1640? Crowned 'K' for Kirsten Munk
Onyx, gold, enamel. L. 16 cm
Grünes Gewölbe, Dresden, inv. V. 2yy.
Spoon. Heart-shaped bowl of sardonyx. Flat handle of gold with polychrome floral and pea-pod designs in opaque and translucent enamel, both in *champlevé* and relief. Over the bowl a crowned 'K' wreathed in forget-me-nots (?). The crowned 'K' and the floral design match those on Kirsten Munk's cameo. (cat. 629) Cf. also cat. 644.
*Provenance:* Gift from a Princess of Teschen to Augustus the Strong of Saxony (1694-1732).
*Literature:* Menzhausen 1970 no. 62a

689

## Spoon

Mounting Danish 1600-20?
Gold, enamel, coral. L. 17.2 cm
Rosenborg 3.66
Circular bowl with rat-tail and cuff of gold with foliage design in polychrome *champlevé* enamel. Handle of polished red coral.
*Provenance:* Rosenborg inv. 1696 51 no. 4. Sophie Amalie's estate inv. 1685 128 no. 8.
*Literature:* Rosenborg 1986 no. 177.

690

## Spoon

Rock crystal from Freiburg? Mounting Henrik Langemack (1634-1657)?
Rock crystal, silver gilt. L. 16 cm
Rosenborg 5.65

Oval bowl with flat bottom, carved in rock crystal. Handle in the form of a coiled serpent biting the bowl. One of a set of four spoons. The serpent appears to have been a favourite theme of the Prince Elect cf. cat. 581, 583.
*Provenance:* Rosenborg inv. 1718 15 no. 3. One of the '5 gilt spoons' in the Prince's estate?
*Literature:* Petit Palais Paris 1978 no. 123.

692

## Knife handle

Saxony? 1632
Gold. L. 6.9 cm Colour-plate XXII
Rosenborg 3.112
Smooth, octagonal in section. On the one side a perforated crowned '8' (cipher monogram for the letter H for Hedevig of Saxony, the King's sister), and on the other side '43'6K 1.6.3.2' (reference to alchemistic experiments?) Gift from his sister? Kept in 1696 in the Regalia Cabinet, where the description 'knife handle' originated.
*Provenance:* Rosenborg 1696 52 no. 12

*682*

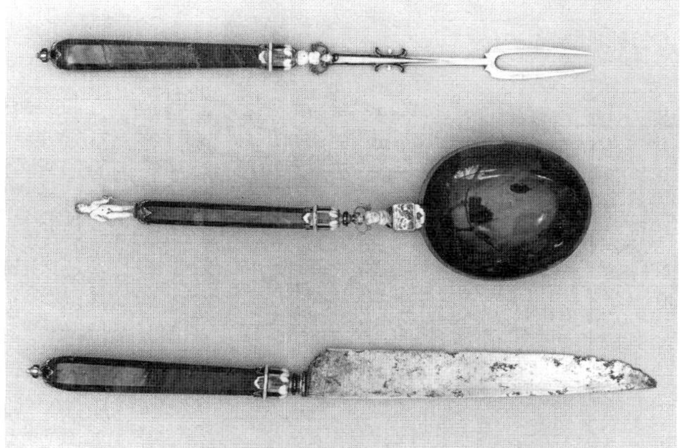

*686*

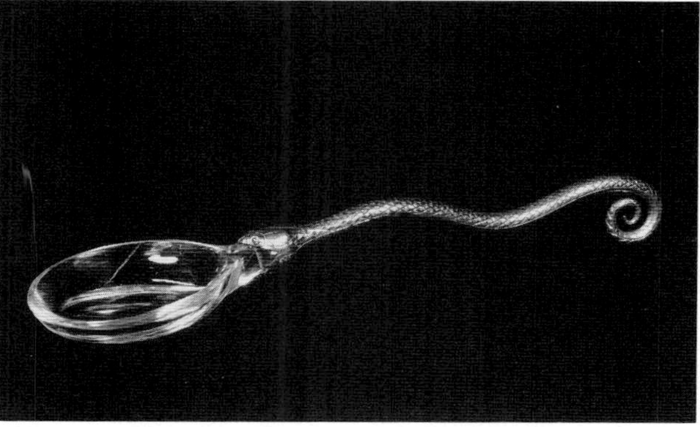

*690*

693

## 2 Covered Cups

Stamped 'IW' and 'MB', and 'D' for Jacob Watzky (1641-1679) and Martin Börisch (1613-1649), Dresden
Silver gilt, staghorn, coral. H. 19.2 cm and 20.9 cm
Rosenborg 25.108 and 25.113
Hollowed stag antlers mounted with silver gilt: ring, rim and stand ring, base mount with 3 ball feet. As cover knob on leaf work, a springing stag and a red coral branch respectively. Presumably a gift to the Prince Elect from his in-laws in Dresden 1641-1649.
*Provenance:* Accession 1867. Kunstkammer inv. 1674 p. 23 and 21.
*Literature:* Rosenberg II 1911 no. 1139, 1131 and 1053.

694

## Travelling Clock

Steffen Brenner (1556-1602) Denmark 1561
Metal gilt, enamel. H. 6.4 cm
Rosenborg 1.102
Square case on lion's feet. Dolphins on the corners. Leaf

693

ornamentation and grotesques on the sides. On top, clock face 18th century with black enamel ciphers. Hands with Frederik V's (1723-1766) monogram. Masks in the corners. At the bottom of the works grotesques, leaf ornamentation and hands with the numbers 1-6. Engraved in the base plate 'ANNO 1584 GAF KONNING FREDERICK DEN ANDEN TIL DANEMARK OCH NORGE SIN SØN KRISTIAN DETE SEGEVERK' and '1561' (In the year 1584 King Frederik II of Denmark and Norway gave his son Christian this clock).
*Provenance:* 1827 from the Kunstkammer, inv. 1775, 242/b244.
*Literature:* Liisberg 1908 151. Slomann 1931 178.

696
## Neck Watch

Clockwork signed 'Caspar Cameel'. Strasbourg c. 1620. Enamel Strasbourg? Case Freiburg?
Metal, enamel, diamonds, rock crystal. L. 6.5 cm
Rosenborg 3.130
Mechanism of metal. Hour hands of steel. Dial of gold with rustic scenes and ornaments in polychrome *champlevé* enamel, the reverse in blue enamel with stars and clouds in gold. On the openwork edge 7 table-cut diamonds. Octagonal case with hinged covers, of facetted rock crystal, hinge and openwork clasp of gold enamel.
*Provenance:* Rosenborg inv. 1696 63 no. 20
*Literature:* Petit Palais, Paris 1978 no. 83. Liisberg 1908 150. Maurice 1976 no. 446. Hein 1985 42.

697
## Table Clock

Clockwork marked 'ZLA' Signature? Germany c. 1625
Iron, brass gilt? H. 19.6 cm. Key L. 3.5 cm
Rosenborg 1.90
Works only. Dial of silver (hour hand missing) with planetarium of silver gilt. Works (damaged) with silver gilt ornaments. Octagonal case with pointed rock crystal sides. The case wreathed in openwork foliage with animal heads, and mounted on steel stands attached to octagonal foot on 4 silver dolphins. Inside, striking train and iron chimes. Key on chain.
*Provenance:* Rosenborg inv. 1718 19 no. 19.

# The Silver Cabinet

There are two sources from Christian IV's time that tell us about his Silver Cabinet: Christian of Anhalt's diary from 1623, and the Keeper of the Royal Silver's accounts from 1622-1636. During his stay at Rosenborg, the diligent foreign visitor observes that 'Die Silberkammer Zum gartenhaus gehörig ist Zimlich versehen, damit diejenige im Schloss nicht angetastet werde'. Rosenborg could thus function independently of the actual Silver Cabinet, which was kept at Copenhagen Palace. In this sense, Rosenborg was apparently specially privileged in comparison with the other royal residences, which had to 'borrow' silverware (and napery, which was also the domain of the Keeper of the Royal Silver) from Copenhagen as required. This is best illustrated by a list of the silverware that was stolen while on loan during the period 1622-28. The residences where these losses occurred include Frederiksborg, Kronborg and Haderslev. However, no simple conclusion can be drawn from this. A comparison of the 'in' and 'out' lists drawn up by the Keeper of the Royal Silver and the goldsmiths' invoices published by Bering Liisberg brings only one delivery to light. Perhaps the various residences had a certain amount of silver in hand for everyday use, and only requested deliveries from Copenhagen for the more important occasions.

The accounts comprise 3 stock lists: one from 1622, one from 1628, (after considerable amounts were sent away to be melted down), and one from 1636, following

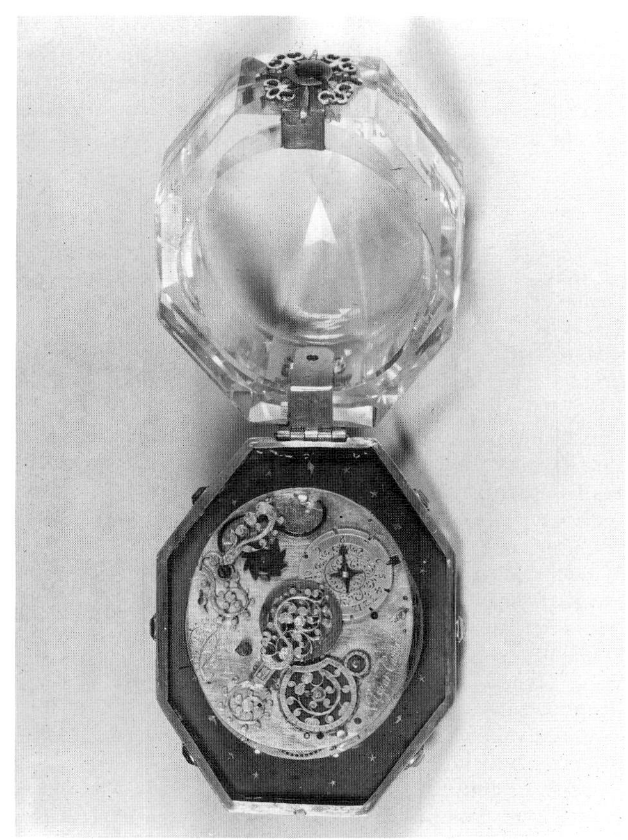

*696*

*694*

the wedding of Prince Christian. As the accounts have never before been published, the most significant items are recorded below, not only to give an impression of the Silver Cabinet's stocks but also to show their movements during these important years.

| | 25/10 1622 | 20/11 1628 | (undated) 1636 |
|---|---|---|---|
| Dishes | 218 | 140 | 196 |
| Plates | 191 | 136 | 224 |
| 'Kommentken' (Bowls) | 25 | 14 | 42 |
| Spoons | 63 | 41 | 83 |
| Salt cellars | 11 | 9 | 29 |
| Quart cups | 21 | 11 | 45 |
| Pint cups | 11 | 7 | 26 |
| Half-pint cups | 39 | 15 | 19 |
| Quarter-pint cups | 83 | 36 | 24 |
| Jugs, ass.sizes | 13 | 10 | 8 |
| Wine goblets | 0 | 0 | 51 |
| Large dishes | 8 | 8 | 8 |
| 'Musselschalen' (Musselbowls) | 14 | 13 | 13 |
| 'Eggeschalen' (Eggbowls) | 12 | 6 | 6 |
| Sweetmeat bowls | 80 | 60 | 141 |
| Sweetmeat dishes | 26 | 20 | 4 |
| Sweetmeat plates | 18 | 18 | 18 |
| Hand basins and pitchers | 4+4 | 4+4 | 13+11 |
| Pairs of serving knives | 5 | 5 | 12½ |
| Pairs of carving knives and forks | 5 | 4 | 11 |
| Pairs of snuffers | 5 | 1 | 1 |
| Candlesticks | 15 | 7 | 28(?) |
| Covered goblets | 0 | 0 | 21 |

1628 was the year when the King had to sell huge amounts of his valuables (including the silverware which is now in the Armoury in Moscow) in order to liberate Jutland from Imperial occupation. However, it appears that the Silver Cabinet was rehabilitated in ample measure by 1636. Notwithstanding the many goldsmiths' invoices unearthed by the tireless Bering Liisberg, it is important to remember that these only represent a fraction of the purchases the King must have concluded. And as further documentation has not been preserved, one can only conjecture as to the stocks of silver at his Court. A division of Liisberg's accounts according to year rather than to the particular purveyor brings to light that the large concentrations fall between the years 1589-91 for the sisters' dowries, 1596 for the Coronation, and around 1640 for the children's dowries. Numerically, just as in the accounts of the Keeper of the Royal Silver, the dishes, plates and spoons constitute the main body. In 1589-91, for instance, 100 dishes were purchsed, and for the Coronation 150 dishes. Each weighed about 70 lod (à 15 grammes). 140 plates were purchased, and 120 for the Coronation, weighing about 20 lod each. Purchase of spoons in 1589 amounted to 4 dozen à 4.5 lod, and 4 dozen of unspecified weight: in 1591 2 dozen à 3 lod and in 1596 3 dozen à 3 lod. The many dishes for the Coronation were ordered from various goldsmiths (through the offices of the Master of the Guild, Hans Pedersen), but as the weight is the same, one must conclude that the dishes were identical.

Plates and spoons were ordered by the dozen. The King's sisters as well as the King himself could thus set their tables with pure silverware. Goblets were bought singly or in pairs as a rule. Nevertheless 6 and 12 were bought for his sisters, and 6 at a time crop up several times during the years. On one occasion, in 1636, a purchase of 2 dozen goblets occurs. Knives appear as the broad-bladed 'kredens' knives used for serving, together with carving knives and forks. But there are no table knives, apart from a possible item in 1596 of '60 silver cases for small knives', neither are there any forks (although 12 forks from the Silver Cabinet were repaired in 1642). Although Christian IV's tablecloth (cat. 732) shows a knife and a 2-pronged fork at each cover, these were usually brought along by each guest for his own personal use.

After this survey of the available written records, it will be apparent that the silverware in this exhibition was not in fact in the Silver Cabinet. There was, it seems, a difference between the silverware used at table and the showpieces, which are largely the items preserved. Contemporary paintings confirm that the showpieces were displayed on shelves behind the guests. An example of this can be seen in Pieter Isaacs' 'Banquet of the Gods' painted on the ceiling in Rosenborg's Winter Room. In the light of this, it is more than likely that the display silver was kept at Frederiksborg, the King's representation castle above all others. Silver objects of this kind were conventionally used for presentation purposes; at coronations, weddings, christenings and as presents to foreign envoys. From August Erich's description of the Coronation in 1596 (pp DII and OII) it can be seen that the legations of Lübeck, Hamburg, Danzig, Rostock and Stralsund presented the King with camels, horses and precious gilt goblets. Coronation gifts now preserved in Moscow include magnificent goblets that were gifts from Oesel's Order of Knights, from the cities of Krempe, Malmø and Wilstermarsk (pieces), and from the Cathedral Chapter of Lund. These the King sold in the critical year of 1628. The goblet from Ribe's Cathedral Chapter (cat. 699) was unfinished and therefore not given up. A particularly notable example of an envoy gift is the list of purchases for Christian IV's son Valdemar Christian's wooing expedition to Moscow in 1644. In 1642, one of the King's agents in Hamburg, Albert Baltzer Berns received payment for 51 silver goblets weighing between 33 and 352 lod, 'so nach Muscuvien gekommen', as the invoice reads. In 1643 there were also purchases from the Hamburg goldsmiths Hans Lambrecht (III) and

Hans Georg Deszler (Silbergeschirr nachher Moscow). The invoice comprises 90 goblets of various sizes, 6 pitchers with dishes, 12 jugs, 10 chased sweetmeat bowls, 16 flasks, 10 bowls, 6 nautilus goblets, 2 sugar shakers, 1 ship on four wheels, 1 ostrich's egg and 1 mountain with corals, 1 Bacchus and 1 polar bear. In 1644 a Dutch broadsheet published a list of the Prince's gifts, which was considerably more modest than the actual purchases, but which on the other hand corresponds accurately to many of the items now preserved in Moscow. (Cf cat. 706). The explanation must lie in the fact that two of the transport ships stranded on the way, necessitating new purchases in Poland. There could be no question of economising when a favourable impression had to be made.

Notes:
Christian des Jüngeren 1858 95
Silver Cabinet accounts, RA.Reg.108b, pk. 10
R. R. Martin published a list of Christian IV's silver, dated 1635 (Martin, 1900 20). It is taken from the above accounts, but reproduces the collected accessions from 1628-1635 according to the Keeper of the Royal Silver. When the deliveries are subtracted, the result is the list shown above from 1636.
Liisberg 1929
The Dutch list is published by Martin 1900 8.
Bernard Heitmann refers to the invoices of 1643, but without including Hans Georg Deszler (Schliemann II 1985 103 and 554).

*Mogens Bencard*

698

## Christian IV tilting at the Ring

Heinrich Beust (mentioned 1584-99). Braunschweig 1598
Silver gilt. The figure H. 71.5 cm. Pillars. H. 130 cm.
Colour-plate V
Rosenborg 2.75
The statuette depicts the King with a lance in his right hand on a rearing horse, supported by a tree trunk and with a kneeling groom. The King is wearing a Spanish costume with a plumed hat. On the horse's brow the Royal coat-of-arms. On the 2 pillars between which hangs the ring, engraved arms and names.
The equestrian statuette lost its history early on (KK 1674: 'En som rider til rings ...' Mus Reg.: Gift 1596 from Hamburg), but in all subsequent literature it was referred to as a prize won by the King at the Coronation. This is refuted by August Erich's description of the Coronation. The King won much, but nothing that corresponds in description to this statuette. He refused to accept the 3 prizes that he himself had offered. The arms and names on the pillars refer to all those who took part in the tilting in 1596 (Cf August Erich). This proves that the engraving, at all events, was done after the event. Bering Liisberg (p. 120) interpreted a bill of purchase from Henrik Beust (dated 1598) erroneously. It does not say 'En Hest af Sølv og zwo philern' (A horse of silver and two elephants) but 'Ein pferde ... sampt zwo philaren' (A horse and two pillars). According to the bill, dated 7th June 1598, the King commissioned the figure from Heinrich Beust and Lyder Grevink. The King thus ordered a momento of the event.
*Provenance:* 1824 from the Kunstkammer, inv. 1674, 17b.
*Literature:* Erich 1598. Museum Regium 1710 Part.II, Sect. I, no. 1. Brock 1870 18f (arms and names). Liisberg 1929 27 118f. C. Hernmarck 1975 115, plate 175. Petit Palais, Paris 1978 no. 1.

699

## Covered Goblet

Master mark of Hermann Bordesloe (1579-1613), Hamburg c. 1590?
Silver gilt, castwork, chasing, tooled.
National Museum 2nd dep. inv. D 75
Circular in section. Domed foot. Baluster stem. Cup with bulging base, circular middle and flaring bowl-like lip. Domed cover with corbelled ledge. The decoration consists of scrollwork with clusters of fruit, cartouches, masks and herms. On the cover cartouches, the virtues Faith, Hope and Charity. Around the stem and top of the cover 3 handles (one missing). As cover knob a standing warrior with a smooth shield (for an inscription?). Inside the cover a medaillon with portrait bust of a woman in relief.
According to the guild mark, the goblet must have been made in 1591 or before. It was received by Ribe Cathedral in January 1597. Tradition has it that the goblet was intended as the Cathedral's coronation gift to the king in 1596, but as it was not delivered on time, it was kept and used by the Cathedral at various gatherings.
*Provenance:* Kunstkammer accession 1740.
*Literature:* Schliemann, II p. 51-52.

700

## The Temperance Cup

Gabriel Brockmüller (mentioned 1586-1619). Hillerød 1600
Silver. H. 17 cm
Rosenborg 1.117
Covered cup. Gilt inside. On the lid engraved frieze of strapwork and fruit. On the cover knob an engraved crowned C4. On the body under the hunting frieze an inscription dated 1600, referring to a wager between the King and 4 courtiers as to whom could remain sober longest. Stamped under the base GB in a shield-formed frame. (Bøje no. 2076) for Gabriel Brockmüller. The King, who won the wager, commissioned the cup (Liisberg).
*Provenance:* To Rosenborg 1824 from Kunstkammer, inv. 1775 c 554. Given from the Court 1768. From Rosenborg 1754, inv. 1696 121 no. 4.

*699*

*Literature:* Brock 1870 26 (inscription). Liisberg 1929 116 fol., plate II.

701

## Bossed Goblet

Christoph Jamnitzer (1563-1618). Nuremberg c. 1600
Silver, chased, cast, partly gilt. H. 55.5 cm
Kunstindustrimuseet B56/1933
Circular in section. Domed foot with 3 rows of bosses between which fastened scrolling and masks. Hexagonal stem with 3 herms in castwork, each supporting the cup with one hand. Cup same as foot. Smooth rim engraved with flowering ramblers and birds. Between the bosses on the cover, winged figures fastened with bolts. On the cover, floral bouquet. On cover rim engraved 'Arild Hvitfeld' (1546-1609, historian, King's Chancellor). Stamped with Nuremberg's hallmark and Christoph Jamnitzer's mark. (Rosenberg[3] no. 3839). Under the foot, engraved Russian inscription and weight.
*Provenance:* 28th June 1607, the King bought this i.a. from the Chancellor (Liisberg). Sold in Archangelsk in 1628. Counted among Tsar Michael's silver treasures in 1634. Acquired 1933 from the Armoury in Moscow.
*Literature:* Martin 1900 plate 8 inv. 1067. Liisberg 1929 41. Slomann 1936. von Falke 1937 11. Rückert 1960 187.

702

## Covered Goblet

'HM' Nuremberg c. 1600
Silver, chased, gilt. H. 24.7 cm
Rosenborg 1.82
Terraced, domed foot. Stem with knob. Cylindrical cup with flared lip. Shallow-domed cover with knob bearing traces of a broken figure. Decorated with mountings, fruit groups and masks in flat relief. On one side of the cup an engraved C4. Stamped on cover and cup Nuremberg's hallmark. (Rosenberg[3] 3061), and on cover, foot and cup 'HM' (Rosenberg[3] 4019). The type is common in Nuremberg around the end of the century. A similar goblet, also Nuremberg work, was presented to Copenhagen's University in 1590 by James VI of Scotland (the King's brother-in-law, later James I of England).
*Provenance:* 1824 from the Kunstkammer, inv. 1775, 230/556.
*Literature:* Germanisches Nationalmuseum, Nuremberg 1985 no. 42. Olrik 1909 no. 5 plate 15-16.

703

## Sweetmeat Bowl

Hinrich Lambrecht I (c. 1570-1628). Hamburg c. 1605
Silver, gilt, cast, chased, engraved. H. 15.5 cm
Private Collection
Smooth oval bowl on the back of a lion *passant.* Oval foot with man's heads on the long sides. Inside the bowl Danish coat-of-arms in flat relief.
*Provenance:* Presumably sold 1628. Recorded in the Tsar's inventories for the first time in 1631. Sold in 1930's. Sold at Sotheby's in Geneva, 1980.
*Literature:* Martin 1900 fig. 2. Scheffler I 1965 413. Schliemann II 1985 70 no. 5.

704

## Lantern

Hans Trægård (1609-34). Copenhagen c. 1620
Silver. H. 29 cm
Rosenborg 1.84

Body in square section with vertical sides. Framework of silver and panes of glass. One side hinged with catch. 4 ball feet and 4 balls above. Inside at the bottom 1 candle holder. Conical openwork top-piece on which stamped C4. Stamped 'HT' in shield-formed frame for Hans Trægaard (Bøje, no. 21). Presumably a night light, as there is no handle for carrying. The lantern is not mentioned in existing accounts (Liisberg).
*Provenance:* 1824 from the Kunstkammer, inv. 1674 18a.
*Literature:* Museum Regium 1710 Part II Sect. I no. 12. Liisberg 1929 172 fol. pl. 3.

705

## The King's Gold Spoon

Denmark. After 1624
Gold, enamel. L. 15.5 cm
Rosenborg 3.68

Smooth square handle, smooth oval bowl with engraved crowned C4, inlaid with red enamel on the back. Gold spoons were for the personal use of the King and

700

703

*709*

Queen. A series of these, from later regents, can be seen at Rosenborg. The crown on the spoon is the closed crown used by the King after 1623. In the incomplete accounts of purchases (Liisberg) are 10 enamelled gold spoons in 1601 (Jørgen Kreutz) and the same year 10 other gold spoons (Jørgen Prytz). In 1618 1 gold spoon was bought from Hans Bruun, a Copenhagen goldsmith.
*Provenance:* Rosenborg inv. 1696 51 no. 3.
*Literature:* Liisberg 1929 plate 13. Boesen 1948 fig. 419.

706
## Spoon

Denmark c. 1640
Silver L. 11.3 cm
Skokloster inv. 250
Pine-cone knob, smooth laciniated handle, smooth pear-shaped bowl, with engraved crowned C4 on the reverse, and 'Kronenburck' (Kronborg). So-called 'grape spoons' with knob in the form of a bunch of grapes or a pine-cone were popular from 1600-1650.
*Provenance:* Mentioned for the first time in Skokloster inv. 1756.

707
## Sweetmeat Bowl

Hans Lambrecht II (c. 1600-33). Hamburg 1631-34. Ambrosius Sommer (c. 1590-1647). Hamburg 1614-1647
Silver, partly gilt, chased, punched. H. 19 cm
Det danske Kunstindustrimuseum 16/1969.
Oval bowl with laciniated rim, chased mask in the middle wreathed in auricular style ornamentation. Stem formed as a female figure with a burning heart and holding (the remains of) an arrow. Quatrefoil foot with chased cartouches. The bowl is stamped by Sommer, the foot by Lambrecht.
*Provenance:* From a set of 18 bowls presented to the Tsar by Valdemar Christian in 1644. Most of these are still in the Armoury in Moscow. Sold in the 1930's. Bought by Kunstindustrimuseet in 1969.
*Literature:* Scheffler 1965 I 441. Schliemann 1985 I 29.

*710*

708

## Covered Cup

North Germany? 1635
Silver, chased. H. 38.8 cm
Rosenborg 21.27
Conical body with wreath of leaves round the middle. Above, ovals with riders tilting, surrounded with masks; below masks and mussel shells. The terraced lid is decorated with masks and palmettes, and on the knob, leaves. Under the cover an engraved Danish coat-of-arms, 1635, and Frederik III's titles as Archbishop of Bremen (abbreviated, in German). On the middle of the cup his corresponding titles, abbreviated, in Latin. Under the rim an inscribed legend to the effect that Frederik had the cup made with the prize money he won in a tilting contest on June 7th 1635 at the princely nuptials in Oldenburg (Duke Anthon Günther's marriage to Sophia Catharina).
*Provenance:* 1858 from the Kunstkammer, inv. 1775, 226/540. Transferred from the Court 1768. R. A. Copenhagen Palace inv. 1673 (after Silver Cabinet).
*Literature:* Brock 1870 42 (inscriptions). Rosenborg 1986 no. 94.

709

## Cup

Ascribed to Caspar Herback (1600-1664) 1644
Gold, engraved. H. 7.0 cm
Rosenborg 1.123
Smooth cup with gently flaring rim. On the shoulder engraved crowned 'C4' and '1644'. The ascribing is owed to the crown's similarity to that on the butter bowl. (cat. 661), and that Caspar Herbach is known to have made gold cups in 1643.
*Provenance:* Rosenborg inv. 1696 48 no. 29.
*Literature:* Petit Palais, Paris 1978 no. 3. Boesen 1948 no. 48.

710

## Rosewater Fountain

Hans III Peters (c. 1600-72), Daniel Zech (1587-1657)
Augsburg 1640-45
Silver, ebony. H. 186 cm
Rosenborg 21.122, 24.25, 29-30, 92, 116, 120-22
Underpart on 3 legs, middle part with 3 drawers, upper part with baldachin on 3 columns, each of which with taps and basins. Under the baldachin Diana with bathing nymphs and Actaeon. Top figure Actaeon with hound. The top section is perforated and has served as an incense vessel. Beneath, a container for rosewater to be drawn from the taps. In 1681 there were 51 toilet and writing articles in the drawers. Of these the following are preserved: 1 hammer with profiled head and handle, 1 pair of scissors with gilt handle, 1 iron signet, unengraved, 1 double comb of ivory with silver gilt mount, 1

*711*

*712*

glass bottle with silver gilt stopper, 1 ink and 1 sandpot of silver gilt.
Fountains for rinsing the fingers during the meal were normally used as table centrepieces. This is the only known example of a fountain as a separate standing piece. The contents of the drawers make it a kind of commode but it also incorporates certain features of the "Kunstschrank". Showpiece clocks from Augsburg c. 1700 are also found with drawers containing similar articles for writing and toiletry. Bernhard Heitmann has identified this rosewater fountain as the one presented to Frederik III by the City of Hamburg at his coronation in 1648. The recorded weight and description, however, do not tally with this. This one, which was one of several fountains in the king's possession, was possibly a wedding present from 1643.
*Provenance:* Rosenborg inv. 1696 90, no. 18. Sophie Amalienborg's inv. 1681 18 no. 6-10.
*Literature:* Boesen and Lassen 1958 32 fol. Seling I 1980 no. 1360 1322/64. Schliemann II 1985 103. Rosenborg 1986 no. 147.

711

## Cup

Hermann Lambrecht (c. 1610-67). Hamburg c. 1650
Silver, chased. H. 14.6 cm
Rosenborg 1.119
Conical body with moulded rim. On the sides vines and 3 oval mask frames containing Ceres, Bacchus and the crowned Munk coat-of-arms. Above, the inscription 'KISSTINA M(unk) G(räfin) Z(u) S(chleswig) H(olstein)' Gilt inside. Under the base Hamburg's hallmark and 'HL' for Hermann Lambrecht (Schliemann no. 188-5). Also an engraved 'S.R.', entwined 'AH' and an indistinct inscription. The 3 ovals are a play on the proverb 'Without Ceres and Bacchus, Venus shivers', with the spouse Kirsten in the role of Venus.
*Provenance:* From Nationalmuseet 1889 (mus.no. D2276), which had bought it shortly before. Stated by previous owner to have been bought at an auction at Boller, where Kirsten Munk lived from 1630.
*Literature:* Copenhagen 1879 37f. Illustrated Tidende 19th Oct. 1876, and 4th Nov. 1894. Nyrop 1885 44. Liisberg 1929 225. Schliemann II 1985 134f.

712

## Covered Mug

Daniel Harder (c. 1600-69) Odense 1653
Silver, partly gilt. H. 9 cm
Rosenborg 1.120
Cylindrical body with gilt terraced stand ring. Gilt loop handle with thumb piece in gilt castwork, depicting a harp player. Shallow-domed cover, partly gilt. On the body, 3 engraved incidents from the life of Lucretia (rape, suicide and death), with gilt columns between. On the cover, engraved, partly gilt, wreath of flowers within which the crowned arms of the Munk family surrounded by K.M.GT.S.H. (Kirsten Munk, the year, Duchess of Schleswig Holstein). Under the gilt base, stamped 1) lily for the town of Odense, Bøje no. 4005, and 2) master mark for Daniel Harder, Bøje no. 4071.
*Provenance:* Bought 1900/1901
*Literature:* Boesen 1948 fig. 14. Lassen 1964 114 fig. 68. Boesen 1968 fig. 28.

# The Oratory

Throughout his life Christian IV retained his simple unshakeable faith in God. As Head of the Church he supported the orthodox Lutheran majority against a Calvinistic-oriented minority. In return the church preached absolute obedience to the King as the deputy of Christ. In foreign affairs he regarded himself, albeit closely challenged by the King of Sweden, as the rightful defender of the true faith against Papism. The chief monument to this conviction is the Frederiksborg Castle Church, a kind of Protestant Emperor's Chapel. The emphasis in its decoration lies characteristically enough not on Christian IV himself but on the office of the king and, singularly important in an Electoral State, on the heir to the throne in the same family. The magnificent altar of ebony with gilt reliefs and figures of silver was bought from Jacob Mores of Hamburg. It is a Northern European Protestant counterpart to contemporary Augsburg altars, but with certain features reminiscent of the "Kunstschrank". The pulpit, also with figures of silver, is likewise bought from Mores, while the pews display the high standard of craftsmanship of the domestic cabinetmakers. Adjoining the Castle Chapel, the King had his magnificently appointed private oratory. Alterations to the appointments after his defeat in the Thirty Years' War reveal that Christian IV now identified himself with Christ the Rejected.

The present reconstruction shows a modest version of the Frederiksborg altar from the Oratory of the Duchess Augusta of Gottorp (1580-1639), the King's sister. (cat. 713). The altar set was also bought for Augusta, who was an ardent Lutheran, probably out of her mother's estate. The cranium on the chalice is worthy of note – it serves as a reminder both of Adam's grave at Golgotha and the popular Memento Mori theme of the time: 'Live today as though you were going to die tomorrow'. (cat. 714). A symbol of a woman's piety was the prayer book wherein she entered quotations from the Holy Scriptures and her children's dates of birth. (cat. 716f.). The beauty of these books ranges from the enamelled grotesque ornamentation of c. 1600 to the flower enamelling of the 1640's, which is also seen on the gold jug from 1650 belonging to Princess Magdalene Sibylla (cat. 723).

713

1. Hugo Johannsen: Regna Firmat Pietas. Hafnia. Copenhagen Papers in the History of Art 1974 67-140.
2. Frederiksborg Slotskirke, 1796-1816 (Bodil Busk Lausen). Bernard Heitmann und Renate Scholtz: Die Ebenholz-Silber-Arbeiten in der Schlosskapelle von Frederiksborg bei Hillerød 78-89. Cf. Schleimann I, Hamburg 1985.
3. Hugo Johannsen: Den ydmyge konge. Kirkens bygning og brug. Festskrift til Elna Møller, 1984 124-157.

713

## The Duchess Augusta of Gottorp's House Altar

Stamped with Augsburg's hall-mark and the master mark of Albrecht von Horn (1581-1665). Dated 1620
Ebony, partly silver gilt. H. 260 cm
Nationalmuseets 2. afd. D70
The two panels are hung on Corinthian columns of

714

silver. The panels have on the outside 4 engraved, and on the inside 4 chased, silver reliefs with scenes from the Passion after engravings from 1596-1598 by Hendrick Goldtzius (1558-1617). Behind the panels, in the niche, the crucifixion in three planes. Under the altarpiece a frieze in relief with Veronica's Sudarium. Gabled openwork toprail with figure of Christ Triumphant. Above the columns, angels with symbols of the Passion; below, frieze with masks and fronds of acanthus. Predella of marble with inlaid foliation. In the centre, on the door of the cabinet, a silver relief with the Last Supper. Husum Castle was the dower residence of the Duchess Augusta, Christian IV's sister and confirmed Lutheran.

*Provenance:* Kunstkammer inv. 1775, 112/c20. Transferred from Husum Castle 1751.

*Literature:* Kiel 1965 392f. Seling 1980 57 and no. 1307. Pause 1981 177-186. Johannsen 1984 101.

714

## Duchess Augusta of Gottorp's Altar Set

North Germany or Denmark 1632

Gold, enamel, gems. H. 20.5, 5.1,23 cm. Diam. 17 cm

Rosenborg 1.105-1.108

Wine jug, oblate box, chalice and paten of gold, engraved and inlaid with niello. Covered jug. Pear-shaped body, fluted neck, S-shaped lip and looped handle. Domed foot and cover. Smooth neck engraved with crowned 'A(ugusta)' and '1632'. Around the jug in ovals, the Scourging, the Mocking, the Walk to Calvary and the Crucifixion. In between, cherub's heads, cartouches and foliage. On the lip and the handle, pea-pod style tracery. The lip has a mask as finial, the handle a shield. Smooth footstem set with 6 rubies (1 missing), moulded edge engraved with 4 scenes from the Gospels, and fruits. Cover and thumb piece with foliage. On the cover, 4 sapphires. Engraved under the stand rim: Wigt 267 Cronne'.

Oblate box. Octagonal, sides with profiled edges top and bottom. Hinged domed lid with a sapphire on top. Engraved with the Passion and leaves. On the sides, the Sudarium, 'HS' (Iesus Hominorum Salvator), Scourging post, crossed torches, cross and crowned 'A', '1632' and Danish coat-of-arms. Lid panels show a scourge, St. Peter's cockerel, a sword and an axe, a lantern, a crown of thorns, a jug, nails, a ladder and dice. Engraved on the bottom of the box 'Wygt 40 3/4 Cronne'.

Chalice. Cup on ringed stem. Knob formed as a skull with crossed bones, white-enamelled with red outlining and diamonds as eyes. Scallloped sexfoil foot with ribs of table-cut stones and sapphires. Around the cup, ovals with scenes from the Passion: washing Jesus' feet, the Last Supper, and Jesus in the Garden of Gethsemane. In between, a crowned 'A', '1632' and the Danish coat-of-arms on leaves. On the foot, Jacob's Dream, the Crucifixion, Jacob and the Angels, Samson and the Lion, the Exaltation of the Serpent, and Samson bearing the City gates. On the moulded rim, leaves and fruit. Under the stand ring engraved 'Wigt 340½ Cronne) Paten, circular. In the well, Christ on the Cross, with Mary, Mary Mag-

dalene, and John. Over the cross, 'INRI', at its foot, skull and bones. On the ledge crowned Danish coat-of-arms in pea-pod frieze, set with 3 sapphires. On the reverse, crowned 'A' of branches, 'An(n)o 1632' and 'Wycht 54 314 Cronne'.
The Duchess Augusta, Christian IV's sister, received a large inheritance after her mother, the Dowager Queen, 1632, which included gold and silver pieces of jewellery. The difference in the cutting of the stones indicates that these were 'second-hand' pieces from the inheritance. The skull on the chalice is to remind the onlooker of Calvary (Golgotha), where the Cross stood upon Adam's grave and thereby suggested eternal life. The engravings on the chalice are nearly all based on illustrations done by Matthæus Merian in 1625-1628 to the Strasbourg edition of Luther's translation of the Bible (1630).
*Provenance:* Rosenborg inv. 1781 233 no. 1, 234 no. 4. Presumably having come into the Royal family's possession after the Great Northern War in 1720.
*Literature:* Brock 1870 18. Garde 1961 278 (cartoon etching). Hernmarck 1975 310 (chalice).

715

## Table

Top made in Prague 1600-1620? Frame Danish 1660-1670?
Marble, stone. Top 158×98 cm
Rosenborg 5.49
Top of black stone (marble?), inlaid with fruit, flowers, birds and insects in naturalistic colours, composed of semi-precious stones. Frame of ebony with corner legs, cross struts and pad feet. In ivory on the frame Frederik III's (1648-1670) monogram and motto 'Dominus Providebit' (By God's Providence). The pietra dura technique, which employs inlaid semi-precious stones to achieve a naturalistic effect, was developed in Florence and was much prized at the Imperial Court in Prague. In 1646 the top rested upon an 'Indian' frame in the King's oratory at Frederiksborg. The present frame was probably made after the Swedish Wars in 1658-1660.
*Provenance:* 1858 from the Kunstkammer. 1695 from Frederiksborg. Mentioned in Johan Adam Berg's description of Frederiksborg 1646.
*Literature:* Frederiksborg Slotskirke 1973 1894-1896. Waagepetersen 1980 no. 237.

716

## Prayer Book

Hamburg or Copenhagen? 1613
Gold, enamel. H. 12.7 cm
Rosenborg 3.95
Binding with clasp, of gold with opaque and translucent *champlevé* enamel in delicate foliation and mountings with fruit, birds and insects. On the front a crowned Schleswig-Holstein coat-of-arms and the inscription 'I A H Z S H 1613' for Iohan Adolf Herzog Zu Schleswig Holstein. On the back a crowned Danish coat-of-arms and the inscription 'A G A K S Z D H Z S H' for Augusta Geborene Aus Königlichem Stamm Zu Dänemark Herzogin Zu Schleswig Holstein. Ascribed by Liisberg to Corvenianus Sauer (c. 1560-1635). However, the style, and especially the fruits, are more like David Altenstetter's work.
*Provenance:* Rosenborg inv. 1784 10 no. 27.
*Literature:* Liisberg 1929 plate 10. Kiel 1965 no. 287.

717

## Prayer Book

Bound (in Copenhagen) c. 1615
Velvet, gold, enamel H. 18.2 cm
Private collection
Bookbinding green striped velvet. Corners of gold enamel with white Agnus Dei on red, green and blue mountings. In the book the following texts: 1) 'Heuptstücke Christlicher Lehre ...' with etching of Christian IV's maternal grandfather, Ulrik of Mecklenburg, who had the book printed. 2) Luther's translation of the Book of Psalms, Copenhagen 1610, 3) Luther's Sacred Songs, Leipzig 1589, 4) 146 Psalms, Copenhagen 1610. First in the book quotations from the Holy Scriptures, the first signed 'Kirstine g(räfin) z(u) s(schleswig) h(olstein)', the second, dated Boller 20th September 1646, from The Book of Revelations, ch.7, under the heading 'Denne Tekst vill Jeg nest guds hielp haffue forklarit till min Ligprediken' (This text will I with the Grace of God have read as my funeral sermon). In the back Kirsten Munk has entered the years, dates, and hour of births of her 10 children. Then, 'Anno 1630 den 16 Januari drog ieg mett stor Hierttens Bedrøffuelse fraa Fresborig, saa Gud husuahle mig for din store barmhiertigheds Skyll...' (Anno 1630, with great sadness in my heart, I left Frederiksborg, may God comfort me for your great pity's sake ...). Also the years when the 5 of her children who died in her lifetime, died. The last entry is Sophie Elisabeth, 1657. In addition, a copy of Kirsten's maternal grandfather's and her own mother's entries on their respective children's births.
*Provenance:* Inherited by her daughter Hedevig, who married Ebbe Ulfeldt 1642. The prayer book is owned by the descendants.

718

## Kirsten Munk's Large Prayer Book

1617. Mounting Danish?
Paper, parchment, velvet, gold, enamel. 15.6×11.5 cm.
Rosenborg 3.64
On the title page Christian IV has written his motto and the date, 22.10.1617. Also the monogram of Kirsten Munk, who filled 225 pages of the book with prayers before 28.11 of the same year. There are also entries by Leonora Christina, 1637-1638. At the front and back of the book drawings on parchment in ink and gold of

*718*

Christ before the Cross with the instruments of His martyrdom at His feet, and Christ as Man of Sorrows. Binding of black velvet with mounts of polychrome gold enamel. On the corners the Agnus Dei on openwork mounts. Centre front and back a crowned cipher monogram 3.4.10.12 for C(hristian 4 – K(irsten) M(unk). The mounting was previously attributed to Corvinianus Sauer (c. 1560-1635).
*Provenance:* Rosenborg inv. 1696 53 no. 5. Presumably confiscated from Leonora Christina by Frederik III.
*Literature:* Molbech 1828 587-592. Liisberg 1929 pl. 11. Bencard and Hein 1985 148. Rosenborg 1986 no. 35.

719
## Kirsten Munk's Small Prayer Book

1625-30. Mounting Danish?
Paper, velvet, gold, enamel. 5.7×5.0 cm.
Rosenborg 3.65
Probably written by Kirsten Munk. Illustrated with 14 scenes from the Scriptures, colour engravings and drawings, marked '29' (1629?). First in the book entries of Christian IV's three sons of his first marriage, dated 1625, and at the back entries by Birgitte Ulfeldt 1635-36. Bound in black velvet with mounts of polychrome gold enamel. Corner mounts with symbols of the Evangelists. Centre front and back two lions holding a crowned 'CK' for Christian and Kirsten.
*Provenance:* Rosenborg inv. 1696 53. Presumably confiscated from Leonora Christian by Frederik III.
*Literature:* Molbech 1828 592. Bencard and Hein 1985 148f. Rosenborg 1986 no. 36.

721
## Almanac

France 1647?
Printed paper, gold, enamel 3.2×1.7 cm. Colour-plate XVIII
Rosenborg 3.97
'Almanach Curieux, Pour L'Année 1647' printed by 'Thomas la Carriere, rue S. Iacq.pres S. Yuce' Paper scroll with end rods, wrapped over a roller in cylindrical case, enamelled on the outside with coloured flowers on white ground; opposite the handle of the roller a forget-me-not.
*Provenance:* Rosenborg inv. 1696 50 no. 9. Bought 1647 in Paris by Leonora Christina and confiscated by Frederik III?
*Literature:* Petit Palais, Paris 1978 no. 26.

722
## Prayer Book

Prayers written 1633, Danish binding c. 1648?
Paper, gold, enamel 7.6 × 9.8 cm
Rosenborg 3.96
First page signed 'Anna Cathrine – 1633' by Christian IV's favourite daughter (1618-1633), who has written prayers in French in the book. Binding with clasps of smooth gold, upon which openwork in bas-relief with naturalistic flowers in polychrome opaque and translucent enamel. On front and back, chased ovals with Vanitas motifs and legends. On the front, a book with cross and skull with hourglass and 'DURABIS IN ETERNUM' (Thou shalt be eternal) and 'VERBUM DOMINI MANET IN ETERNUM' (The word of the Lord remains eternal). On the back a skull with serpent, and 'TE NUNQUAM TIMUI' (Fear not). On the clasps Anna Cathrine's crowned monogram and on the back her arms as Duchess of Slesvig and Holstein. The flower enamel is similar to cat. 642.
*Provenance:* Rosenborg inv. 1696 47 no. 16.
*Literature:* Petit Palais, Paris 1978 no. 25. Boesen 1986 102 fol.

723
## Princess Magdalene Sibylla's Gold Jug

Denmark 1650?
Gold, enamel, diamonds, rubies. H. 24.7 cm
Kunstindustrimuseet 75/162
Pear-shaped body. S-shaped spout and looped handle

with herms, scallops and lion masks in castwork. Bossed and scalloped sexfoil foot and cover; as thumbpiece a castwork satyr's mask. The jug is engraved with flowers, stalks and petals in composite inflorescence, chase-edged. On foot and cover, 6 settings with pointed and table-cut diamonds and rubies in blue and white grained enamel. On the cover, the remains of blue-enamelled leaves. Under the spout an engraved oval with a crowned 'MS 1650' for the Prince Elect's widow, Magdalena Sibylla. Under the base inscribed '248', 'C'? and 'TA 744'.
*Provenance:* Bought in the antique trade 1962.
*Literature:* Lassen 1964 41.47.

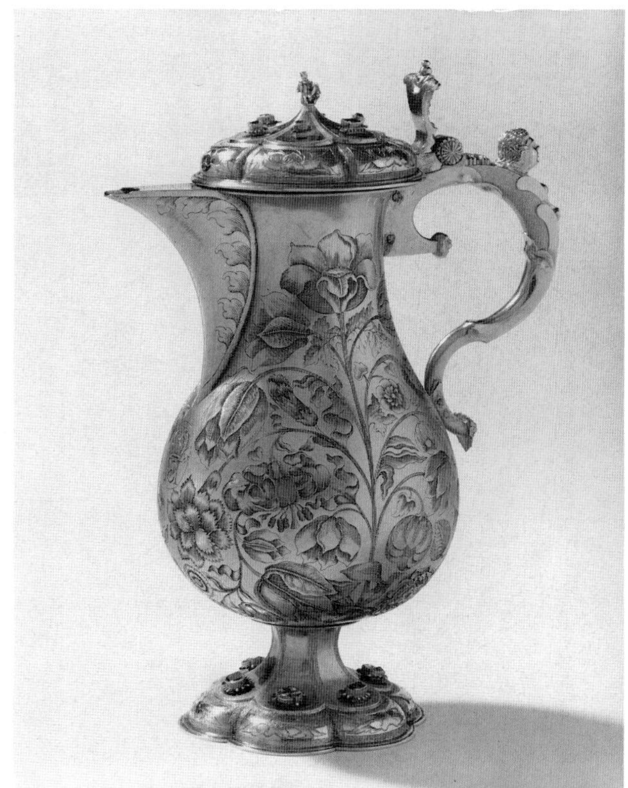

*723*

## Furniture Cabinet

Palace fires have left us with very few Christian IV interiors and furniture. The only original rooms at Rosenborg, the King's Writing Closet and the Winter Room, are without their original furnishings. Fortunately we get a vivid insight into Court life at the King's most splendid residence from the Frederiksborg Castle inventory of 1636, and from Johan Adam Berg's description of 1646. Berg, in particular, describes the decorative fixtures: ceilings of stucco or wood, floors of marble or tile, walls lined with tapestries, textiles or gold leather, closely hung with paintings, and fire-places and architraves of polychrome marble. The furniture was specially designed to this framework of glowing colours and joyous contrasts. The inventory indicates that beds, chairs and tables were mainly of slender construction similar to the travelling furniture of the Middle Ages, in which the textiles outshined the wood, whereas the showpieces – beds, tables and mirrors of ebony, silver and gems – were early examples of the new type of furniture.

Obviously, the King's, the Queen's and the Dowager Queen's suites were the most lavishly appointed. Here were beds, cupboards, chairs and couches, tables and mirrors.

The bed was the prestige piece of the period, and in 1621 Christian IV followed the fashion. For 8,000 rix dollars he purchased from Jacob Mores in Hamburg a bed of ebony, richly mounted with silver. The trimmings were black velvet with gold embroidery in pearls and garnets on blue satin.[1] The other beds were hardly less spectacular. The canopy of Queen Anna Cathrine's bridal bed is preserved (cat. 730). Other examples of ebony and silver furniture are the 2 tables and the mirror (cat. 724f). Similar pieces were purchased in other places, including Brussels and Hamburg, although these could well have been made in Denmark.[2] In 1607 the goldsmith Johan ter Borch (1613-1623) received payment for silver plating made for the valuable ebony cupboard, which the Royal Cabinetmaker Gregers Greus (1600-1616) was working on. The sumptuous decoration was an expression of the prevailing dislike of smooth, empty surfaces. Another example is the intarsia decoration on pews and on the Royal chairs in the Castle Chapel, carried out in 1611-1616 by Greus' successor, Hans Barchmann (1588-1648)[3]

Exotic woods do not appear to have been used for chairs, couches or the more humble tables. These were most often gilt, or painted and upholstered, or covered with brilliantly coloured textiles; for example, the cushion cover of silk brocade with the Royal coat-of-arms from the Dowager Queen's dining room, and the chair cover with Christian IV's monogram and motto (cat. 733-35). They exist in a number of colour combinations, and probably all come from Christian IV's silkworks, started as part of the King's mercantile policies in 1620. One of the leading lights, Paschier Lammertijn (c. 1563-1621) had already been a purveyor of napery, including table napkins from Haarlem (cat. 731). His tablecloths from the silkworks were now counted among the ceremonial gifts such as those presented to the Tsar in 1622 (cat. 732). The rich colouring culminated with tablecloths, chair and cushion covers in embroidered satin for the princesses' dowries in 1642. (cat. 737). These are high quality craftsmanship, whereas the worn tablecloth (cat. 736) is probably a child's work.

Lastly, the chafing and pewter dishes. These demon-

724

strate that the 'use again' principle was put into effect in the children's dowries (cat. 740). Without frugality there could be no luxury. Both the 'young ladies' and Duke Frederik had beds of ebony with ivory and silver, made by the Court Cabinetmaker Bertil Møller (1617-1684).[4]

1. Frederiksborg inv. 1650 156-58. Liisberg 1929 159.
2. Home from Brussels, the Court Tailor Willum Carron in 1602 supplied an ebony dresser with drawers of cypress, mounted with chased and engraved silver and 32 'large stones' of lapis lazuli, jasper and agate. RA.Dan. Kanc. Invoices B 223 III C.
3. Liisberg 1929 169. Frederiksborg Slotskirke 1973 1828 fol. 1844.
4. RA.Dan.Kanc. B.189. Kontraktbog 1633-1647 Christian IV's letters V 1883-1885 nos.319-320. VIII 1947 nos. 200 and 209. August 1643.

724

## Table

Engraved silver panels after engravings by Bartholomaeus Spranger (1546-1611) 1600-1619
Pine, ebony, silver. Top 107×131.3 cm
Nationalmuseets 2. afd. D147
In the centre of the table a square silver panel engraved with motifs from Spranger's Wedding of Psyche and Fama leading the Muses to Olympus. Surrounding this in ebony veneer framed with silver, 4 engraved silver panels: Neptune and Amphitrite, Phaeton and the Sun Chariot, Pan and Syrinx, and the War of the Titans. Newer frame. As Hugo Johannsen has demonstrated, the goldsmith combined various 'borrowed' models: from a Spranger-inspired engraving by Hendrick Goltzius (1558-1628) from 1587, and from Jan Muller (1571-1628) from 1597. Mythological themes in art were very popular at Court. Pieter Isaacsz (1567-1625) borrowed from the same source when painting the Marriage of Psyche on the ceiling in Rosenborg's Winter Room, 1619.
*Provenance:* Kunstkammer inv. 1737, 882/158, first recorded 1704
*Literature:* Johannsen 1984 90f.

725

## Mirror

Augsburg/Copenhagen? Reliefs of the King and his consort ascribed to Jacob van Doordt (1610-1640) c. 1610
Mirror glass, ebony, silver 121.5 × 72.5 cm
Rosenborg 3.36
Rectangular mirror with bevelled beading at edges and corners. Ebony veneer frame with pilasters between the tripartite top and the base. On the gable portal and in the velvet-lined niches, figures in silver with name en-

graved on plinth: 'Charitas', 'Fides', and 'Spes'. On top portal, putti holding reliefs in silver of Christian IV and Anna Cathrine (as cat. 597), on the base, the Queen's monogram. The frame is mounted with cherub heads, foliage and rosettes in silver castwork. According to J. F. Hayward the mirror is Augsburg work. It could also have been made in Copenhagen, perhaps with imported silver mountings. In 1607 Johan ter Borch (1613-1623) received silver for mountings on 'the valuable cupboard', which the Royal Cabinetmaker Gregor Greuss (1600-1616) was making in ebony.
*Provenance:* Rosenborg inv. 1718 153 no. 18
*Literature:* Liisberg 1929 169 43. Galster 1936 31 fol. Hayward 1958 72 fol.

726
## Table

The engraved silver panels ascribed to Simon de Pas (1595-1647).
Denmark c. 1624
Pine, ebony, silver, mother-of-pearl. Top 95 × 114 cm
Rosenborg 3.39
Rectangular table-top of ebony, inlaid with engraved silver panels and leaves in silver, mother-of-pearl and ebony. Oval centre panel with lovers in a rustic scene surrounded by an edged border and leaves. In the corners a square, and at middle sides a round panel depicting the Virtues. Newer frame with drawer, corner legs and cross. J. W. Frederiks ascribed the silver panels to the engraver Simon de Pas, and also found the cartoons. The central oval is by Daniel Vinckboons (1576-1632/33) and Hendrick Goltzius (1558-1617), the others, with the exception of Peace, also Goltzius. If the ascribing is correct, the table must have been made in c. 1624, when de Pas came to Denmark. It was probably made here.
*Provenance:* Rosenborg inv. 1718 382 no. 5.
*Literature:* Frederiks 1985 22 26 fol.

727
## 4 Reliefs in silver 1620-1650?

1) 31×26 cm, 2) 26×21 cm, 3) 25×21 cm, 4) 25×20 cm
Rosenborg 5.20, 5.32-5.34
Oval reliefs in repoussé, chased and embossed silver.
Unframed. 1) Christ, bound to the scourging post in architectural niche with drapery. 2) Naked youth with shepherd's crook and drapery in rustic landscape like 3) and 4) Two naked female figures with drapery (Venus and Diana?) Liisberg wondered if perhaps the reliefs came from Christian IV's silver bed at Frederiksborg, bought from Hans Mores 1621. The inventory description of the bed provides no answer. B. Heitmann and R. Scholz ascribed the reliefs to Heinrich Lambrecht I (1582-1631) in Hamburg, who supplied figures for the altar at Frederiksborg. The figures on the reliefs are, however, short and compact, not delicate and long-limbed like the altar figures. The art here lies in the virtuosity of the repoussé work. This changing of the flat to the round was much admired at the time. Were the reliefs intended as 'pictorial' decorations in one of the private chambers?
*Provenance:* Rosenborg inv. 1696 125.
*Literature:* Liisberg 1929 39 fol. Schliemann II 1985 70 fol.

728
## Chest (letter casket)

Denmark 1599
Oak, iron, pewter, velvet. 60.5×81×56 cm
Rosenborg 3.173
Chest with 2 drawers in front. Oak covered with green velvet and pewtered iron mounts. On the front Christian IV and Anna Cathrine's combined crowned monograms 'C4-AK', flanked by lions and '15-99'. Lining of velvet and silk damask. Similar chests in private collections in England (cat. 395).
*Provenance:* Recorded 1882 as a gift. Is believed to have come from Gråbrødre Kloster in Odense.

*725*

731

729

## So-called Kirsten Munk's Jewel Case

Denmark? Dated 1648
Oak, leather, brass. 23.5×37.3×26 cm
Kunstindustrimuseet B 103/1939
Lid compartment with two loose trays and a drawer in the side. Oak covered with leather and brass fittings and mounted with engraved roses and rosette studding. Keyhole engraved with acanthus leaves, 2 brass handles and 4 pad feet. On the lid a wreathed Munk coat-of-arms and '1648'. Over this is scrolled: "LUNA VICES ORBEM IMPLENDO DEPLENDO REUOLIT SIC HOMINUM VITAM FATA VICESQUE MANENT.' 1649." (The moon waxes and wanes in its shining orb, thus the turn of destiny is the fate of mankind) Brass corners with the phases of the moon.
Is the inscription a reflection on her own fate? With the death of Christian IV, adversity for Kirsten Munk and her family was a growing reality.
*Provenance:* Acquired 1939.

730

## Coat-of-arms and Canopy from Anna Cathrine's Bridal Bed

Berlin? 1597
1) H. 36.4 cm, 2) 341×128 cm, wings H. 54 cm
Rosenborg 1.149 and 24 roll A17-18
The coat-of-arms of the Electorate of Brandenburg embroidered with coloured silk, gold and silver thread and braid, set with pearls, rubies and turquoises. Winged canopy. Gold brocade with patterns of flowers and palmettes in red silk. Framed border with vines in pearls and gold embroidery. Among the items of Anna Cathrine's dowry brought to the wedding was the bridal bed, consisting of a gilt four-poster bed, which could be assembled, 6 drape curtains with palmets, a canopy (exhibited here) and a bedspread, both with the name of Jesus embroidered with pearls and, in the centre of the bedspread, the bride's coat-of-arms. In 1650 the bed was at Frederiksborg Castle.
*Provenance:* Rosenborg inv. 1718 164 no. 3. Frederiksborg inv. 1650 176-177. Zentrales Staatsarchiv, Merseburg. Kgl. Haus Archiv. Kurf. Joa. Fr. Kinder, Anna Katharina, 1597-1603, bl. 265-265a.

731

## 4 Napkins

Dated '1602'. Ascribed to Paschier Lammertijn (c. 1563-1621), Haarlem.
Linen, damask. 100×70 cm
Rosenborg 31D 14 bc, D23, 25.1005
White linen woven with crowned Danish coat-of-arms, '1602' and combined monograms 'C(hristian) 4 A(nna) K(atharine)' in wreathed Province arms. Edged with trophies. Damask weaving was a Dutch speciality and Lammartijn was prized for his superb pictorial patterns. His work for Christian IV was often used for official presentations. He worked with the weaver Karel Thijssen at the Copenhagen Silkworks founded in 1620.
*Provenance:* Acquired 1897, 1910, 1917.
*Literature:* Mygdal 1913 160. Burgers 1965 144.

732

## Tablecloth

Signed 'KT'. Ascribed to Karel Thijssen after design of Paschier Lammertijn c. 1621
Linen, damask 407×217 cm
Rosenborg 31 roll 26
White damask. In the centre a laid table. On the long sides a hunting scene and a naval battle. On the short sides a crowned C(hristian) 4 and Danish coat-of-arms. At the corners, putti. Fields divided by leaf borders. On the table, shellfish, fish, fruit and tart. The peacock is a show-dish of sugar and fat. When serving, dishes of widely differing type were handed on the same service. By each plate is bread, a knife, and the 2-pronged fork

fashionable at the time. Similar silk tablecloths were presented to the Tsar in 1622.
*Provenance:* Accession 1859. Belonged to Kirsten Munk, perhaps.
*Literature:* Boesen and Bøje 1948 28.

733

## Cushion Cover

Woven 'KT' and '1623' Ascribed to Karel Thijssen.
Silk brocade. 61×64 cm. Colour-plate XV
Rosenborg 31. D. 28
Front of patterned woven coloured silk on red ground. Crowned royal coat-of-arms in the centre. Christian IV's motto around the closed crown. Above and below his name and titles in German and Latin. Lined with beige damask with pomegranate design. Matching cushions found in the Dowager Queen's dining room at Frederiksborg.
*Provenance:* Gift 1859
*Literature:* Flamand Christensen 1940 I 40f.

734

## Chair Cover

Copenhagen Silkworks 1620-1623?
Silk velvet brocade. Repeat 80×60 cm.
Rosenborg 131.12, 2.50, 2.54
Loose seat cover of purple (now dark brown) velvet brocade with woven gold and silver thread. The background is satin with a pattern of cut and uncut velvet. In the center a crowned C4 in cartouche, wreathed with crowned sprays. On this, the King's motto 'RFP'. The seat cover comes from a set of 6 contemporary oak chairs at Frederiksborg. On the backs can be seen the cut-off part of the repeat: the crown with the motto on sprays in another version.
*Provenance:* Transferred 1859 from Frederiksborg.

735

## Stool Covers

Copenhagen Silkworks 1623-?
Silk brocade with velvet pattern. 50×45 cm
Rosenborg 2.42, 2.44
Silk brocade with a crowned C4 and leaves in cut and uncut velvet on a ground (now lost) of silver thread. Fringes of red silk and gold thread. Same fabric as Christian IV's slippers and nightcap. (cat. 746). The covers were transferred c. 1859 to oak stools, probably for the King's Chapel at Frederiksborg, c. 1690.
*Provenance:* Transferred 1859 and 1839 from Frederiksborg.
*Literature:* Flamand Christensen 1940 40-42

736

## Table Cover

Child's work 1620's?
Taffeta, silver embroidery. 102×64 cm
Rosenborg 31.A.10
Bedside table cover of blue taffeta. Border with floral design, in the centre a crowned 'C4' and 'RFP' motto, worked in appliqué silver braid. Edged with narrow silver lace. Lined with green taffeta. Pattern of embroidery visible in several places where the sewing is missing, or diverges. Both pattern and sewing indicate that the cover is not the work of a professional. Stained and faded.
*Provenance:* Rosenborg inv. 1696 123 no. 2.

737

## Christian IV's Daughter Hedevig's Dowry Items?

Denmark 1642?
Private collection
*Embroidered cushion cover*
Petitpoint, silk. 59×56 cm
In each corner a naturalistic flower (2 roses, 2 tulips). A delicate spray of naturalistic flowers surrounds single blooms at the centre. Varicoloured silks, untwined. The background in black is worked with staggered rows of loop stitch in different directions.

*737*

*Embroidery*
Petit point, silk, silver thread
215.5×13 cm
Embroidered coat-of-arms flanked by putti in blue or red drapery. In between, naturalistic flowers. Petit point in varicoloured silk, ground of silver thread in loop stitch. Lined with light blue satin with red selvedge. For mounting on canopy or altar? By tradition used as swathe. The coat-of-arms was used by Kirsten Munk's children as dukes and duchesses of Schleswig-Holstein.

*2 sheets and 2 pillowcases*
Linen, 1642. 280×300 cm and 79×79 cm
Sheets of fine linen c. 50×50 thr/cm. Edged on all sides with 12 cm wide Tønder lace with broad scallops interspersed with figures. In the corners 1 scallop is gathered, otherwise the lace is sewn on flat. The material, as fine as silk, has a loom breadth of 78 cm, the selvedges of the lengths being cast finely together. At the edge, 'A°1642' embroidered in chain stitch. Pillowcases with one side seam, of finest linen 40×40 thr./cm. 8 cm wide scalloped Tønder lace at one end; scallop flaps sewn together like Christian IV's pillowcase (cat. 745). At the other end 6 pairs of sewn loops to tie tapes through. At the top embroidered crowned 'JR MSUF 1698' (Johan Ridderchans and Marie Sofie Ulfeldt).

*Chair cover*
Satin, embroidery. 45×45 cm
Cover for chair seat of ruby-red satin (same as following tablecloth). Embroidered crowned C4 in middle, wreathed in arabesques in flat stitch, couching, appliqué gold and silver braid, purls and gold paillettes sewn down with purling. Varicoloured silk, gold and silver thread. Edged with 1 cm wide gold lace in openwork pattern. Unlined. The satin has the same green border in the selvedge, 1.5 cm wide, divided into 3 single-thread stripes, as the tablecloth.

*Tablecloth*
Satin, embroidery. 166×166 cm, fringes 9 cm
Embroidered tablecloth with crowned 'C4' and 'RFP' in centre, wreathed with vines. Embroidered edge and strewn floral sprays in gold, silver and polychrome silks. Techniques: flat stitch, couching, braiding. Edged with a twilled possement fringe of gold and silver, under this another fringe of terra cotta silk. The ground material is made up of 3 seamed lengths, loom breadth 55 cm. Lined with topaz-yellow taffeta. Christian IV's daughter Hedevig (1626-1678) married Ebbe Ulfeldt in 1642. The above exhibits are owned by her descendants. Tradition has it that they were part of her dowry.
*Literature:* Nationalmuseet 1953. Garde 1961 140 215 illustr. 216.

738
## Tablecloth
Copenhagen 1642?
Satin, embroidery. 166×166 cm, fringes 9 cm
Frederiksborg B 2690
Embroidered tablecloth with crowned 'C4' and 'RFP' in the centre wreathed with vines. Embroidered edge and strewn floral sprays in gold, silver and polychrome silks. Techniques: flat stitch, couching, gold and silver braiding. The cloth is lined with linen edged with yellow silk taffeta. Almost identical with the previous cloth. Most probably from Christiane's (Hedevig's twin sister) dowry. She was married the same year (1642) to Hannibal Sehested.
*Provenance:* Purchased 1924-5.
*Literature:* Garde 1961 140 215.

739
## Mug
Denmark 1633
Pewter H. 26 cm
Rosenborg 1.4
Cylindrical mug with terraced foot; handle and cover missing. Smooth. Under the lip rim and over the foot ornamental ribboning. Around the body engraved crowned 'C4'. Above, 'Kopenhagen Slot' and under this, 'Sophie Elisabeth'. The drinking water was unclean and

*740*

frequently unhealthy and consequently everyone took a jug of ale with him when retiring for the night. Whether Sophie Elisabeth (1619-1657), eldest daughter of Christian IV and Kirsten Munk, used the mug at Copenhagen Palace or whether it was part of her dowry at her marriage to Christian Pentz (1600-1651) in 1634 is not known.
*Provenance:* Found 1890 during excavations in Gothersgade, Copenhagen.
*Literature:* Boesen 1968 104.

740
## Chafing Dish

Stamped with 2 S's and a pair of scissors for Stephen Schirmer, master in Nuremberg 1593.
Brass. H. 12.5 cm
Rosenborg 1.6
Circular chafing dish on a foot. Ring of vents on stem and round the body. Looped handles. Flared rim with 3 knobs. Round the body an engraved crowned 'CIV 1636 Elinore Kierstine'. In 1636 Leonora Christina married Corfitz Ulfeldt. Presumably part of her dowry.
*Provenance:* 1870 from the Museum of Nordic Antiquities, to which it was given in 1818.

741
## Dish

South German c. 1625
Brass, hammered. Diam. 60.0 cm
Rosenborg 1.5
In the well, Diana with crescent on her brow on a background of tracery with fruit and flowers. On the ledge, tracery with fruit, dogs and deer. On the edge an engraved crowned 'C4' and '1636 Elinora Kierstine'. Presumably from her dowry. In Rosnæs Church (Holbæk amt) there is a (christening) paten with 'c4' and 'Elisabeth Augusta' and the year '1639' when Leonora's sister was married to Hans Lindenow (1616-1659).
*Provenance:* Purchased 1889/90.
*Literature:* DK Holbæk Amt 1987.

742
## Dish

Denmark? 1638
Pewter. Diam. 36.5 cm
Rosenborg 1.3
Circular dish with broad ledge and profiled edge. On the ledge engraved crowned 'C4 1638' and 2 coats-of-arms with 'H.V.G.' and 'R.G.' for the King's illegitimate son Hans Ulrik Gyldenløve (1615-1645) and Regitze Grubbe (1618-1689). Also stamped crowned mark. On the bottom the later owner's initials and inscriptions. Hans Ulrik Gyldenløve and Regitze Grubbe were married in 1641. Was the dish 'used again' at the wedding?
*Provenance:* Gift 1870.

# The Wardrobe

In addition to clothes, the Wardrobe contained various arms and items for personal hygiene such as combs and clothes brushes (cat. 743). Only a few of the costumes are preserved, since in former times used clothes from royal personages were a part of servants' remuneration, except in cases where the materials contained so much gold or silver that the articles were burnt and the metal melted down. Re-use or 'sewing over' for the children was also practised. Costumes were only kept when they were related to events of particular importance.

The background for this tradition was probably the blood-stained clothes of Christian IV from the battle of Kolberger Heide in 1644, although these are not the oldest to be preserved (cat. 743). The King must have seen a parallel in his blood-stained clothes to those that were preserved almost as religious relics in Stockholm, worn by his great rival, Gustav II Adolf when he was killed in the Battle of Lützen in 1632.

The remaining costumes on exhibit belonged to the King's sons, Prince Christian, the Prince Elect, and Duke Frederik (III). All the costumes consist of breeches, doublet and cape. One group shows the fashion around 1634: rather than emphasize the figure's natural shape, the doublet and breeches are wide at the waist and form a rhomboid silhouette (cat. 749f). Another group from around 1645 illustrates the trend towards a loose-fitting, more flowing costume, especially regarding the leg-width of the breeches (cat. 751). Both groups are richly supplied with lace collars and cuffs.

The 3 sets of coats and under-coats show a costume type of Persian origin which reached Northern Europe by way of Poland (cat. 756). In the inventory they are called Persian, Indian and Polish. They were originally used when Europeans dressed in 'oriental style'. The long wide coat with loose sleeves was so comfortable, however, that it gained popularity as a 'housecoat' and became the prototype of the dressing gown. On the other hand, the rest of the costume, consisting of under-breeches, made up of breeches and hose sewn together, did not find favour. It is not known whether the Polish costumes were presents from foreign envoys or were made in Denmark. Signs of wear show that they have been used.

743
## 2 Clothes Brushes?

Northern Germany or Denmark 1597
Silver gilt, hogs' bristle. Silk fringes. H. 20.5 cm
Rosenborg 1.85-1.86
Conical handles, oval and circular. Engraved with fruit and flower ornamentation. On one side the Brandenburg arms beneath 'K.G.M.Z.B.' and surrounded by '97' ((Anna) Katharina Geborene Markgräfin Zu Brandenburg (15) 97). Opposite, 'FK' in a crowned heart in front

743

of crossed arrows (for Anna Cathrine's parents). Above, crowned 'C4' in rosette on 1.85. Christian IV and Anna Cathrine were married in 1597. Possibly a wedding present.
*Provenance:* Rosenborg inv. 1696 123 no. 2.
*Literature:* Boesen 1956 105-106. Petit Palais, Paris 1978 no. 114.

744
## Sash

1610-20
Silk taffeta, gold and silver embroidery. 414×97 cm
Rosenborg 31. D.24
Sky-blue silk taffeta. Embroidered flowers and ornaments in flat stitch and outline stitch worked in gold and silver. Crowned monogram 'C4' framed by palm and laurel branches. 15 different floral motifs repeated.
*Provenance:* Rosenborg inv. 1718 472. Frederik III's Wardrobe 1651 no. 80.
*Literature:* Flamand Christensen 1940 I 31, II pl. 5.

745
## Christian IV's blood-stained Clothes from the Battle of Kolberger Heide 1644

Colour-plate XL

*Doublet c. 1635*
Velvet, taffeta, cotton. Colour-plate XXXX
Rosenborg 2.31a
Black and plum-coloured patterned velvet. The pattern is sea horses and small sprigs of flowers. Lilac taffeta lining at front edges. Cut to the figure above the waist, with short jutting skirts and long inserted sleeves buttoned at the wrist. 19 spherical buttons of gold thread. Inside the waist, six straps for fastening to the breeches. The cut is emphasized with gold and silver braid. Shot holes in right sleeve and over right shoulder.

*Collar, 1635-40*
Line, lace. Br. 5.6 cm
Rosenborg 2.31b
Pleated collar sewn into a narrow neckband. Edged with 1 cm wide lace in front, elsewhere with 5.6 cm wide Tønder lace with broad scallops and symmetrical leaves of cloth stitch. Blood-stained and torn on right side.

*Cuff, 1635-40*
Linen, lace. Br. 5.6 cm
Rosenborg 2.31c
Linen strips laid double with narrow stitched pleats. Edged with 5.6 cm wide Tønder lace, like the collar. Blood-stained. Corresponding blood stains on the right sleeve of the doublet show that this must have been the right cuff.

*Shirt, 1644*
Linen, lace
Rosenborg 2.36
White bleached linen. Without shoulder seams, with inserted sleeves and gussets at shoulders and under the arms. Gathered at the neckband to a narrow collar which, like the cuff and the neck opening, has 4 cm wide Tønder lace. Below the lace at the neck an embroidered '1644' and (concealed) a crowned 'C4' monogram. Blood stains at the neck and at right shoulder. The lower edge of the shirt is partly ripped and cut off. Fastens at the neck with two sets of side bands.

*Pocket handkerchief, 1644*
Linen, lace. 61×59.5 cm
Rosenborg 2.35
White bleached linen, 37×37 thr./cm. Narrow rolled seams on three sides, the fourth is the selvedge. Crowned 'C4 1644' embroidered in one corner in chain stitch. Edged with 1.3 cm wide Tønder lace with cloth stitch pattern. Many holes and blood stains.

*Cap, 1642*
Brocade, gold lace, linen lining
Rosenborg 2.33
Black brocade with floral pattern in red, green, and white with interwoven silver threads. Sewn in 8 sections. Seams covered with gold lace. Loose white linen lining (42×42 cm) with a crowned 'C4' 1642 in outline stitch embroidery. Edged with 11 cm wide Tønder lace to fold up round the cap edge. Many holes and blood stains.

*Cap, c. 1640*
Satin, silk and gold embroidery, loose linen lining.
Rosenborg 2.34
Pale green satin with flowers embroidered on each of the 8 sections in silk and gold. The crowned flowers include carnations, pansies and fritillaria. The sections are framed with gold embroidery. Loose white linen lining (62×50 thr./cm) with 9 cm wide Tønder lace to fold up round the cap edge. A green silk patch (13.5×11.5 cm) is attached to the edge of the cap to cover the King's injured eye.

*Pillowcase, c. 1644*
Linen 55×70 cm, lace W. 10 cm
Rosenborg 2.40
White bleached linen oblong pillowcase, edged at one end with broad scallops of Tønder lace with floral pattern. The other end fastens with 5 sets of linen tapes. Crowned 'C4' monogram in outline stitch. Blood stains.

*Metal splinters, 1644*
Iron, 1×3 mm and 6×8 mm
Rosenborg 2.31d
Two iron splinters found during conservation of Christian IV's doublet in 1984. The larger of them was entangled in bloodsoaked linen threads from the lining of the collar. The smaller was found in the right sleeve.

Parts of the clothing worn by Christian IV when he was wounded in the naval battle at Kolberger Heide on July 1st 1644. The clothing was subsequently preserved as a relic at Rosenborg, where Johannes Lilienskiold saw it in 1668. Gustav II Adolf had sent his field dress in a similar manner to Stockholm, where it became a national symbol after his death.
*Provenance:* Rosenborg inv. 1696 123 nos. 1-2. The embroidered cap was also mentioned in Copenhagen Palace's inv. in. 1666.
*Literature:* Lilienskiold 1916 6. Flamand Christensen 1940 I 34 fol., II plates 6-10. Johansen 1985.

746

## Cap and Slippers

Denmark 1630's?
Patterned silk velvet with silver thread
Rosenborg 2.32, 2.41
Velvet brocade with yellowish-brown silk ground, originally covered with interwoven silver thread. Flowers and crowned 'C4' in cut and uncut dark red velvet. Cap with 8 sections, the seams covered by 0.5 cm silver braid. Lining of pale blue silk taffeta. Inner lining of coarse linen with painted motifs (re-use of discarded wall coverings). Slippers with velvet brocade uppers, lined with red leather. Soles welted and double, square toes, low heels. Identical lasts. Same material as stool coverings (cast. 735)
*Provenance:* Rosenborg inv. 1696 123, 1. Always kept with Christian IV's blood-stained clothes.
*Literature:* Flamand Christensen 1940 I 39 41 fol. II pl. 10. Johansen 1985.

747

## Under-waistcoat

Velvet L. 71 cm
Rosenborg 2.39
Black velvet. Double-sided under-waistcoat, same front and back. On the neck points black strings to tie round the neck. Very worn. For Prince Christian's wedding in 1634, Christian IV had two under-waistcoats of double green plush made.
*Provenance:* Rosenborg inv. 1696 p. 123 no. 1. Always kept with Christian IV's blood-stained clothes.
*Literature:* Flamand Christensen 1940 I 37 44. Johansen 1985.

748

## Costume: Casaque, Breeches and Cape

1625?
Black silk brocade with gold thread
Rosenborg 31. A.8 and 31. B.8 ab
Black costume of flower-patterned gold brocade. Characteristic 'Spanish' style. The casaque, (jacket with wing sleeves) has long skirts, and fastening slantwise across the breast from neck to left armhole. Smooth wide breeches with 6 iron hooks on the inner waistband for fastening to a doublet, and tying at waist and knee. Circular cape could be fastened at the collar or worn hanging loose from the shoulders. Belonged to the Prince Elect.

*746*

*Provenance:* The deceased Prince Elect's costumes, 1646, no. 25. Rosenborg inv. 1718 472,4.
*Literature:* Flamand Christensen 1940 I 45, II pl. 11-12.

749

## Costume: Doublet, Breeches and Cape

c. 1634
Gold brocade
Rosenborg 7.201
Ivory coloured silk with woven gold thread. Short-waisted doublet with long skirts and high stand-up collar. Fastens with buttons and loops of silver cord. Slashing at back seam. Sleeves open at the front and buttoned at the wrist. 6 inside tabs with iron eyes to hook on to the breeches. All seams edged with gold thread. Breeches: straight, tied with bows at waist and knee, with horizontal pockets in front, and two side pockets. Circular cape with collar. Possibly worn at the wedding of the Prince Elect in 1634.
*Provenance:* Rosenborg inv. 1718 472, 3. The deceased Prince Elect's costumes, 1648, no. 7
*Literature:* Flamand Christensen 1940 I 49, II pl. 13-14.

*749*

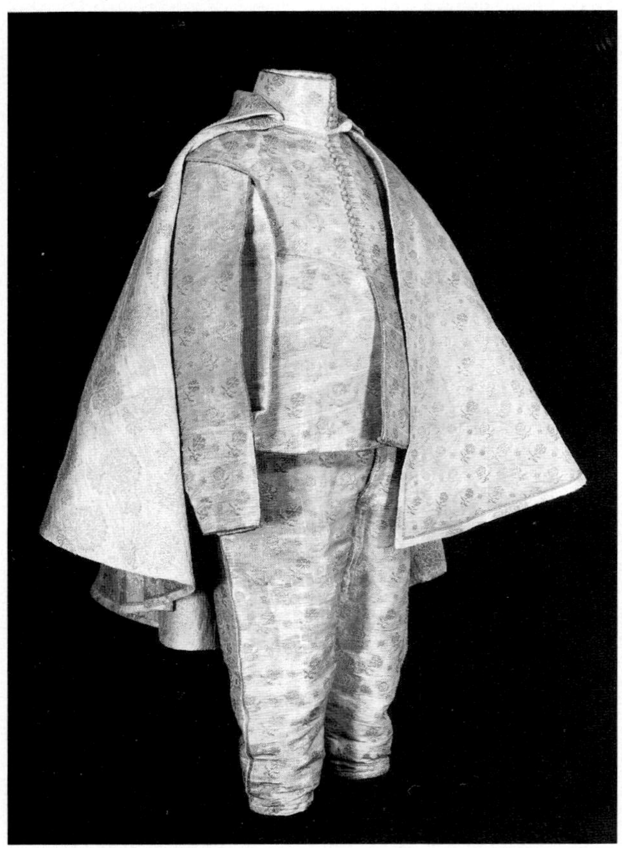

750

## Costume: Cape and Breeches

c. 1634?
Rosenborg 31. A.7
Silver-woven silk (very tarnished) with flowers worked in gold thread. Similar lining, but different, smaller pattern. Semicircular cape with collar. Cape and collar edged with narrow gold lace. Breeches straight, tight, with vertical inserted pockets in front. Shortened at knee. Possibly worn by Prince Frederik (III) at the wedding of the Prince Elect in 1634. The matching doublet was already very worn in 1651, and from 1718 was no longer mentioned in the inventory. Some remnants, possibly from the doublet, are exhibited here.
*Provenance:* Rosenborg inv. 1718 472. Frederik III's Wardrobe 1651 no. 52
*Literature:* Flamand Christensen 1940 I 51, II pl. 15.

751

## Costume: Doublet, Breeches and Cape

c. 1645
Satin, closely sewn over with silver band
Rosenborg 7.207
Light turquoise (very faded) satin sewn over with close rows of narrow silver bands. Originally lined with light blue watered silk with interwoven silver thread. Short tight-fitting doublet with short skirts and high stiff collar. Sleeves open along front seam. Wide straight breeches, buttoning in front with covered silver braid buttons. Circular cape with collar. Edged with silver lace. Belonged to the Prince Elect.
*Provenance:* Rosenborg inv. 1718 471, 6. The deceased Prince Elect's costumes, 1648, no. 44?
*Literature:* Flamand Christensen 1940 I 57, II pl. 21

752

## Costume: Doublet, Breeches and Cape

c. 1645
Brocade
Rosenborg 7.203 a-c
Gold brocade on black silk. Doublet and cape are lined with ruby-coloured gold brocade. Short tight-fitting doublet with short skirts and high collar. Sleeves slashed at front seams. 32 covered gold buttons in front. Wide knee-length breeches. Bows of floral silk ribbon in front. Circular cape with collar. All trimmed with gold lace edging. Belonged to the Prince Elect.
*Provenance:* Rosenborg inv. 1718 741, no. 7. The deceased Prince Elect's costumes, 1648, no. 50?
*Literature:* Flamand Christensen 1940 I 55, II pl. 19.

753

## Sash

1630-40
Silk taffeta, embroidery, gold lace. 266×71 cm
Rosenborg 31. D. 25

*751*

*752*

Salmon-pink silk taffeta, richly embroidered with flowers, birds and insects in coloured silk, gold and silver. The long edges finished with narrow gold lace, the short ends with 27 cm wide gold and silver lace with wheel pattern and scallops. On the lace small pearls and silk tassels in different colours. Possibly a gift from Charles I to Christian IV or his sons.
*Provenance:* Rosenborg inv. 1749 209. Royal Wardrobe, Christiansborg 1784.
*Literature:* Flamand Christensen 1940 I 61, II pl. 23-4.

754
## Sash
1634-40
Silk taffeta, embroidery. 344×99 cm
Light green silk taffeta. Embroidered military symbols in gold, silver and silk: harness, standards, swords, trumpets and an 'S'. Possibly a gift from Princess Magdalene Sibylla (1617-68) to the Prince Elect. Can have been transferred to Frederik III from the Prince Elect's estate in 1648.
*Provenance:* Rosenborg inv. 1718 472, 5. Frederik III's Wardrobe 1651 no. 81.
*Literature:* Flamand Christensen 1940 I 58, II pl. 22.

755
## Sword-belt
1630's
Silver embroidery, velvet
Rosenborg 31 E.24
Crossbelt in silver embroidery with fringes of silver thread. Lined with gold-coloured velvet. Mounts of silvered iron.
*Provenance:* Rosenborg inv. 1718 473, no. 10? Frederik III's Wardrobe 1651, no. 88?

756
## 'Polish' Costumes
1640's

*Coat*
Velvet, gold and silver braid
Rosenborg 31. L. 1a
Cardinal red velvet, lined with moss green velvet. Hooked together in front, decorative fastenings and trimmings of gold and silver braid and tassels. Sleeves open from shoulder seams to allow arms to come through. Inserted pockets in front widths, trimmed with lace.

Deep red coat of velvet lined with white silk taffeta. The coat is very wide – both front and back widths have been cut from whole lengths of velvet. Long sleeves, wide at the top, narrow forearm, slashed from elbow upwards to allow arms to be put through.

*Breeches*
Silk damask
Rosenborg 31. A.1
Red silk damask. Very wide at the top, tight below the knee, ending in two flaps. Lined with linen. Inside pockets at the top. Judging by the large waist measurement, these were made for the Prince Elect or for Christian IV, rather than for Frederik III.

*Hose*
Silk damask
Rosenborg 31. L.1d
Yellow silk damask like the sleeves of the under-coat (above). Sewn as tights with large waist measurement (154 cm) and with a drawstring casing and button fastening in the front. Underwear of this age and type is rarely preserved.
*Provenance:* Rosenborg inv. 1718. Copenhagen Palace inv. 1666. L.1a, A.2, and A.3 also in Frederik III's Wardrobe 1651.
*Literature:* Rosenborg 1986. Flamand Christensen 1940 I 84-93, II pl. 40-49.

*Under-coat*
Silk damask
Rosenborg 31. A. 3
Pink silk damask coat with extra under-sleeves of yellow Chinese silk damask. Lined with sky-blue silk. Centre fastening with hooks and eyes. The front widths are trimmed with borders of silver thread like the previous coat.

*Coat*
Velvet, silk taffeta
Rosenborg 31. C. 2

*Under-coat*
Silk damask, silk taffeta
Rosenborg 31. L. 1b
Yellow silk damask with vines and rose pattern. Buttoning at front with 10 covered buttons of gold thread, trimmings of gold braid. Tight sleeves ending in a tongue to turn up or wear over the back of the hand. Lined with yellow silk taffeta.

*Coat*
Gold brocade
Rosenborg 31. A.2
Wine-red brocade coat with flowers worked in silk and gold thread. Lined with bright yellowish-green silk damask, visible when front widths fall open. Sleeves joined to back only. Lacework borders of gold thread. Worn open, no fastening.

756

*759, 760*

# Nationalmuseet
## (The National Museum)

## *Christian IV – the Enterprising King*

The title gives an indication of the main theme of this exhibition: Christian IV's personal involvement in the finances of the realm and his role as initiator of a whole series of business enterprises, of which only a few were to outlive the King himself. Throughout the whole time of his reign Christian IV was vitally engaged in matters of state finance, because it was only through his economic liberty of action that he could set up his large-scale political initiatives. The King's interest in trade and commerce in Denmark was however limited to a short period – approximately 1610-1625. The "Emperor's War" – i.e. Denmarks's brief participation in the 30 Years' War – not only led to defeat, the impoverishment of the Crown (and the State), the occupation of Jutland and the imposition of heavy additional taxes, but also effectively brought to a premature end what one might term the King's policy of commercial enterprise.

The Crown's difficulties did not automatically lead to impoverishment of the *whole* population. The worst afflicted were the farmers, who had to bear the brunt of the tax-burden. The major noble families – as exclusive and aristocratic as could be found anywhere in Northern Europe – experienced, as far as many of them were concerned, a continued growth of prosperity, together with increased political influence. And among the bourgeoisie – especially in Copenhagen – there were individuals who managed to work themselves forward into leading positions in society.

Supplies to the King and court and for the conduct of the war made some, such as Mikkel Vibe, the son of a farmer, the imigrant Braem brothers, and later Hans Nansen and Henrik Muller, into extremely rich men who carried on many of the King's commercial initiatives, e.g. the overseas trading companies. They were owed vast sums by the Crown. As a result of the introduction of absolutism in 1660, the nobility's monopoly of ownership of manorial land was abolished. This made it possible for Henrik Müller, at a single stroke, to become the country's largest land-owner.

The King's direct involvement in the setting up of trading companies and manufactories was not just an expression of Christian IV's restless entrepreneurial drive. It was an element in a policy directed towards the strengthening of the power of the State, above all in military and foreign-policy respects. Considerations of the welfare of the citizens were secondary. The scarcely concealed motives are revealed in the expression of Christian IV's desire that a newly created company should become "to Us, an honour, and, with God's help, to the merchants, not to their disadvantage".

Despite the fact that the King on many occasions spoke disparagingly of the Dutch "republics of shopkeepers", he nevertheless chose – at any rate for a certain period – to give his personal support to commercial life in Denmark. In this he was following a development which had been in process in Europe for a long time. The principal idea was to lessen the individual country's economic dependence on others. Only by this means could that country's political position in relation to its neighbours be maintained and strengthened. The more-or-less explicitly formulated theories which Christian IV became familiar with through his adviser Jonas Charisius later came to be grouped under one term: *state mercantilism.* Although individual contries adapted economic policy-measures to this end according to national conditions, it could be said that there were common basic concepts which were reflected in homogenous measures. For all, it was a matter of sharing in the wealth of the newly-discovered regions of the world, not just by trading through the middle-men in Lisbon or Amsterdam, but by venturing out on one's own behalf down to "where the pepper grows". For that purpose it was necessary to have a fleet with both trade and warship capacity, built in one's own dockyards. These ships could moreover very well be of decisive importance for the political balance of power between the sea-faring nations. In the case of Denmark the underlying concern was that of dominance in the Baltic.

Making the country self-sufficient – predominantly for these military-political reasons – became the main goal. Even in Frederik II's time tentative efforts had been made to lay the foundations of a metal industry and gunpowder- and paper-mills. In the early years of Christian IV's reign these developments were followed up by the construction of the cannon foundry at Elsinore. The "raw" material for the foundry consisted of church bells collected from village churches. The bell-metal supply of course was soon exhausted. While the search for metal on Sealand and in Scania was in vain, a mining industry was launched in Norway. There the iron, copper and lead factories were run by miners called in from Germany. As early as 1623, however, these industries became privately-owned. The beginning of salpetre-production and powder-mills must also be seen in a military context, and a major reason for interest in trade with Iceland was the island's sulphur deposits; in 1602 the King awarded the monopoly of this trade to the towns of Copenhagen, Malmø and Elsinore. In 1619 the Icelandic Company was founded, and for a long time Iceland was the main supplier of sulphur for gunpowder-production in Europe.

In accordance with mercantilism's demands for a positive balance of trade and protection of domestic commerce – including the monopolies – an active customs policy had to be implemented. An embargo on imports was one of the means; prohibitively high customs duty was another. During the first decades of the 17th. century a stricter customs control was introduced in all towns. It was, however, widely neutralized by corruption and ineffectiveness. The Øresund toll, which was put on goods transported through the Sound, was considerably increased in 1618; together with the incomes from the royal estates it constituted the most important source of income for the King.

It was precisely those two main sources of income, from the estates and from the Øresund toll, which made it possible for the King to embark on economic adventures. The reform of the system of payment from the royal estates, which doubled the revenue from the enormous properties which the monarchy had confiscated at the time of the Reformation, and a doubling of the income from the Øresund toll during Christian IV's reign, had made him one of the wealthiest rulers in Europe. The surplus on the state budget, together with the revenue from the Øresund toll, which was regarded as a "regale" (a royal prerogative) resulted in very large sums being at the King's personal disposal. In 1605 the King's wealth was calculated at over 1 million rigsdaler; by the 1620s it had grown to about 1.5 million.

In political respects the wealth of the King meant that he could, to a large extent, act independently of the Rigsråd (Council). And the Rigsråd, dominated by the high nobility, refrained from active particiption in the King's business projects. The nobility, and the craftsmen too, stood for conservative attitudes. There was fear, partly justified, that the banning of imports would result in scarcity of goods and increased prices. Moreover, could it be wise, in a long-term perspective, to make Danish industry and trade dependent on immigrant merchants and craftsmen?

The investment capital which the King placed in the different businesses was therefore simply essential for the initiatives to be carried out. But in this fact lay major hazards for the future conduct and survival of the operations. Just as the King had given intensive personal support to the establishment of manufactories and the founding of overseas trading companies in the decade from 1610-20, in the 1620s he became absorbed in placing his personal capital in foreign-policy adventures instead. As already mentioned, some of the enterprises slid into private ownership, and were more or less successfully continued, but the mercantilist policy as a whole had to give way to traditional royal power-politics and aristocratic agrarian conservatism. The mercantilist experiment, which from the start was beset by lack of experience, capital, raw-materials, trained man-power and by an under-developed marketing structure, was doomed in advance to go wrong. Danish society, structured in separate estates, was not yet mature enough to follow the rest of Europe. The greatest lasting consequence of this decade of royal involvement in economic policy was probably that Copenhagen from then on, to a much greater extent than previously, took on the status of capital city. There were people in Malmø, Odense, Flensborg and in Glückstadt, which the King had founded, who were immensely proficient and able (e.g. like Jens Bang in Aalborg), but the more far-reaching economic enterprises were run by the new bourgeois class in Copenhagen.

In the autumn of 1629 a meeting of citizens was held in the little market-town – now village – of Rye near Skanderborg. The purpose was to complain to the King about the burden of taxation and the economically catastrophic situation of the country after the "Emperor's War" and Wallenstein's occupation of Jutland. The criticism was directed both at the King – and his mercantilist policy – and at the nobility for its inability to defend the country against its enemies. Was it not precisely the duty of the nobility, in return for freedom from tax, to protect the kingdom and its inhabitants? Instead, the nobilty in Jutland had run away with its tail between its legs and sought refuge with relatives on estates in Sealand and Scania. The meeting's resolution is vibrant with indignation, but at the same time it presents a picture of the estate-society which reflects strict Lutheran teaching about static class-structures:

"Each estate should hold to its own place [i.e. rank] and support itself acoording to its own privileges and freedoms; that is to say: the *nobility* from their manors and tenants' farms, and other benefices from the Crown [the economic advantages they were granted as the King's royal representatives]; the *clergy* from their tithes, offerings and interest; the *farmers* from their crops and stock-breeding; *craftsmen* in the towns form their crafts and trade; so that each in unity can do his work with joy as demanded by God, and so that among the estates there can always be and remain concord and good correspondence, to the reciprocal benefit and contentment of all".

But what did this contentment consist of in reality for the lowest of the estates – the peasants – who made up roughly 80% of the population? Looked at as a whole, Christian IV's reign marks a lowering of the living standard of the Danish farmer. He was not, like the squire, directly dependent on the vagaries of the Dutch and German cattle- and corn-markets, but the deterioration of the financial situation of the nobility and of the State after the "Emperor's War" marked a water-shed. Tenants' dues were from the onwards to a large extent paid in kind and by villeinage, because all ready money was absorbed in payment of special taxes. There was no question, however, of a total starving-out of the peasantry. Numerous treasure-hoards of silver objects testify to this; they were hidden away be peasants during the "emperor's War" and the "Torstensson War" (1643-45), and again during the following war (1657-60). These wars led to the long-term occupation of Jutland with consequent plundering and extortion.

The Rye resolution did not particularly concern itself with the duties of the clergy; it dealt rather with the sources of the clergy's income. Tithes and offerings came from the peasantry, who also provided subsistence for the parish clerk. The "interest" referred to, however, was from invested capital. To the ordinary clergyman this source of income was probably rather limited, even if certain families produced a growing number of clergymen in sucessive generations, and no doubt accumulated sizeable fortunes, often invested in land. The professors of theology, on the other hand, held the most important positions in the University of Copenhagen, and several of them appear as partners in manufactories and companies.

The clergy's most important role was to keep the fatih to the narrow road of Lutheran orthodoxy – the "true faith". Dissenters – e.g. followers of other reformers such as Calvin – were regarded as heretics. Supported by people such as Professor Jesper Brochmand and Hans Poulsen Resen, the Bishop of Sealand, the King worked through decrees and ordinances for the victory of orthodoxy. The King's motto, "R.F.P." – "Regna firmat pietas" (Piety strengthens the realms) – bears witness to the true piety of the King, although even during his lifetime this abbreviation was interpreted by his contemporaries as "Riget fattes Penge" (the realm is short of money).

For the nobility the time of Christian IV's reign meant a certain polarization. A growing proportion of land in Denmark was collected in the hands of a few "old" families. For others the war and the economic fluctuations resulted in impoverishment. From the royal accounts it can be seen that after agricultural crises in 1605-08 and again in 1618-21 the King had to advance substantial loans to the nobility. After the "Emperor's War" he was no longer able to assist the hard-pressed nobility, and through new kinds of loans or mortgages bourgeois capital was channelled into agriculture.

At the Rigsdag (Parliament) in 1536, the Assembly of the Estates had been deprived of its role as the kingdom's highest political institution. Rule was thus placed in the hands of the King and the Rigsråd, which consisted exclusively of nobles. Assemblies of the Estates were summoned only a few times during this period, and then chiefly to approve the imposition of special taxes. Christian IV, on his accession to the throne, had to sign a charter, defining his powers, which was not significantly different from that signed by his father. But the fact, discussed above, that Christian IV possessed substantial private means, gave him corresponding political freedom of manoeuvre. His fortune was an important lever in foreign policy, and inter alia resulted in several North-German princes becoming economically dependent on him.

The income of noblemen came from their own land, which was constantly augmented through marriages within their own class. But noblemen embodied earlier royal power throughout the country, where as *lord-lieutenants* (lensmænd) they managed the Crown's land and directed the local administration. Conditions for such noblemen could vary considerably, but the reform of the administration of Crown land resulted in many small fiefs being combined into larger ones, and the noblemen responsible were eventually treated as officials on fixed salaries.

The bourgeoisie did not consist only of *craftsmen,* as referred to in the Rye resolution, even if they set the stamp to a large extent on the business life of the market town. Since the Middle Ages, kings had sought to limit craft and trade activities to the towns – partly for fiscal reasons, and partly to control quality and secure coverage of the populations's needs at reasonable prices. Christian IV was no exception in this respect. In the slightly larger towns these conditions in themselves were supposed to be regulated by the guilds which were controlled by the mayors and magistrates. But numerous complaints about price-fixing resulted in the King, in 1613, banning the guilds. It seems, however, that this prohibition was to no avail. In 1621 a new order was issued which regulated the rules of the guilds and in practice brought to an end their previous role as production- and marketing-cartels. At the same time it is possible to trace a higher degree of specialization of guilds within individual crafts.

The bourgeoisie also included the *merchants*. It was their function to act as middle-men in the marketing of Danish agricultural products south of the border and in Norway, and they handled the distribution of the imported goods – first of all beer, cloth and small metalware – whether imported on the merchant's own ships or by foreigners. The import of luxury goods for the nobility and the court was handled by special commissioners.

Deliveries to the State, especially during the King's "mercantilist period" and in times of war, grew to colossal dimensions. They included e.g. deliveries to Denmark's largest place of employment – *Holmen* in Copenhagen. Throughout his reign Christian IV gave high priority to Holmen and the naval dockyard, out of concern both for foreign trade, for which the Danish merchant fleet was never sufficient, and for the navy. During the period 1596-1611 the number of naval ships built there was trebled, and Frederik II's rope-walk, the sail-house and the anchor-smithy (which was converted in 1619 into Holmens Church) steadily hummed with business. In this respect the great merchants of Copenhagen shared the King's interests, and they eagerly supported the construction of *Børsen* (the Stock Exchange) in 1624 and Christianshavn, as well as the extension of the harbour. In the King's last years the harbour reached from the present Toldbod (Customs point) in the north to the Tøjhus (Armoury) with naval arsenal, provision-house and naval port (the present-day garden of the Royal Library) in the south. The goal, which was never reached, was to make Copenhagen the leading commercial town of the Baltic.

In accordance with the basic ideas of mercantilism, the King worked for the strengthening of Danish foreign trade and sea-faring. Danish merchants should handle a larger proportion of trade, and a larger proportion of import and export goods should be carried by Danish ships. But the ships were also the pre-condition for bringing home raw-materials and other riches from far-distant regions. During the first years of the King's reign the interest focused on the *North Atlantic*. In 1599 Christian IV himself particpated in an expedition to the North Cape, using the alias of "Captain Christian Frederiksøn". In their search for the "North-East Passage" to India, England and Holland had observed large numbers of Greenland whales at Spitsbergen. The English called the place "Greeneland" (i.e. they thought it was Greenland), and their presence there was therefore a theoretical violation of Danish-Norwegian sovereignty. To this could be added that the English and Dutch whaling deprived the Danes of important resources. Whale-oil was used for lamp-oil, for soap production, paint, preservation of natural materials, etc. The baleen of the whale was used for corset-bones, knife-handles, riding-whips, brushes, upholstery – in fact virtually everything where today synthetic materials are used. From 1617 onwards the Danish *whaling* at Spitzbergen got under way. The Hamburg-born merchant Johan Braem took over leadership in the following year, and in 1620 he became director of the *"Nordlandske"* or *"Grønlandske" Kompani.* When the King a couple of years later withdrew from the whaling operations, Johan Braem and his brother Goedert extended their business, which by 1630 also included actual *Greenland,* to which the King had sent an expedition in 1605. In recent years the National Museum, together with Norwegian archaeologists, has carried out investigations on Spitsbergen, and in this exhibition some of the finds are shown to the public for the first time.

The *"Petsoriske Kompagni"* was established in 1619 with the purpose of exploiting the resources of Northern Russia, particularly the fur trade. Russian coins – "denninge" were struck in Denmark for this trade, and a ship was sent off from Copenhagen. The Tsar, however, feared that the established trading-station would develop into an actual colonisation, and therefore confiscated the ship and arrested its crew. A couple of years later Jens Munk and Hans Nansen were sent to the White Sea, officially to catch pirates but in reality to claim compensation for the confiscated ship. The trade with Northern Russia was never to become a success, but these attempts, as well as the whaling, meant that Danish sea-captains acquired valuable experience in navigation in the North Atlantic. This had a lasting significance for the *Iceland trade* and was decisive for Jens Munk's dramatic expedition to the North American continent.

The English and the Dutch had led the search for the "North-East Passage". In 1619 Christian IV sent Jens Munk and two ships out to find the "North-West Passage" to India. With his 64-man crew he reached Hudson Bay in Canada, where he had to spend the winter. The whole crew except for two men died of cold and scurvy, but Jens Munk succeeded in sailing one of the ships back to Copenhagen. The expedition was of no lasting economic significance, but the legend of this unique sea-faring exploit is preserved in Jens Munk's own diary, which in 1624 was printed with the title: "Navigatio Septentrionalis".

If Danish ships were to reach India and later on the Far-East, they had to follow the route already opened by other nations – the route south of Africa. By the establishment of *"Det ostindiske Kompani"* in 1616 and by the sending out of the first ships two years later, Denmark showed its flag as the fourth European nation in the East. The English and the Dutch had previously broken the Portuguese monopoly. In November 1617 a Dutchman, Marchelis de Boshouwer, who had joined the service of the "Emperor" of Kandy, approached Christian IV to ask for military support against the Portuguese. When the Dutchman Roland Crappé, with Ove Giedde, reached Ceylon in 1620, it turned out that the "Emperor" in the meantime had become King, and had in fact given up opposition to the Portuguese. Pursued by the Portuguese, Crappé sought refuge with the Nayak (the Prince) of Tanjore, who offered Denmark one of the best trading places on the Coromandel coast – Tarangambadi ("the town at the singing waves"), which the Danes corrupted to *"Trankebar"*. In the name of the Danish King, Ove Giedde constructed a mighty castle which still exists today, *Dansborg,* for the supervision of the trade. The colony was in Danish possession for about 200 years, but only a few ships were sent out there and even fewer succeeded in reaching Copenhagen again with the sought-after spices from the East. The King himself had invested around 200,000 rigsdaler in the Danish East India Company, and was far from seeing a return on his capital. This perhaps explains his reluctant attitude with respect to the establishment of another colonization attempt – a West Indian Company, in 1625. The main stockholders in the East India Company – the Dutchmen Johan de Willem and Herman Rosencrans – nevertheless offered tempting prospects of large profits from the import of West Indian sugar to the European market. This project – like the plans for colonies in Africa – did not reach fulfilment, however, until the end of the century and the beginning of the next.

One can sense Christian IV's disappointment over the lack of eagerness to invest in these different enterprises, especially on the part of the nobility. On the other hand, many of the initiatives appear, from the perspective of the present day, to have been extremely bold, not to say naively optimistic or unrealizable from the outset. This is true not only of the overseas exploits, but to a large extent also of the State's commercial undertakings in Denmark. Potentially the most viable of these for a long time was the *Prison and Orphanage,* set up in 1605. Criminals and vagrant children were put in custody there and occupied in the production of textiles. The solution of social problems was thus combined with economic interests. When the Orphanage House was reconstructed in 1620 the criminal element was separated off, and the House then came to function as a training-place for textile craft-workers. The production methods were not technically different from craftsmanship. It was only because of the large number of workers collected in one place – 500-600 children in 1625 – that the term "industry" came to be used in connection with it. At first the materials were delivered to the "Royal Clothes Chamber", from where they were distributed for clothing the army and the navy. But by setting up the *"Cloth Company"* in 1620 and the *"Silk Company"* in 1621 the King sought also to modernize the whole marketing system. The Silk Company however failed as early as 1626, and the Cloth Company was dissolved two years later. By that time all manufactories – apart from the Children's House, which survived until 1649 – were run by private individuals under royal privilege.

The purpose of this fostering of Danish commercial life, as previously mentioned, was to create a surplus in the balance of trade. By doing so it was hoped, inter alia, to share the wealth which the Spaniards and Portuguese in particular were bringing to Europe from the silver mines in South America. For a royal ruler who issued coins it was essential to have access to precious metals. One can therefore understand that Christian IV immediately set out for Norway when an earthquake in Numedalen in 1623 laid bare a vein of silver. Mine-workers were called in from Germany, and the mines were dubbed *"Kongsberg"* (Royal Mountain) by the King. Throughout the two kingdoms thanksgiving ceremonies were held, and the King financed from his own coffers the starting-up of the mining operations. The yield however came too late to cover the losses incurred in the "Emperor's War", and the King was therefore not in a position to develop the mines to full capacity. Instead a partnership was set up, with the King as a participant. In 1624 the first silver arrived in Copenhagen from the Kongsberg mines, and at once daler were struck from it with the eloquent inscription "SEGEN GOTTES: BENEDICTIO DOMINI: HERRENS VELSIGNELSE" (Blessed be the Lord). The silver mining at Kongsberg was to continue for more than 300 years.

# The King

758

## Tapestry, Frederik II and prince Christian (IV)

Hans Knieper's workshop at Kronborg 1581-85

Wool, silk and linen thread, tapestry weave with 6-7 warp threads per cm., woof 8 threads per cm. 394×367 cm

The National Museum, Second Dep't., CLXXIII

Prince Christian, who had been acclaimed as the heir to the throne in 1584, is depicted together with his father, King Frederik II. In the background are Kronborg and Frederiksborg. The historical rhymes were written by the king's fief-holder at Ringsted Abbey, Ivar Bertelsen. The tapestry was probably hung at the east end of The Long Hall at Kronborg, next to the table canopy under which royalty sat on festive occasions. (Cf. cat.nos. 1, 10, and 36).

*Provenance:* Long Hall at Kronborg, for which this, at well as 39 other royal tapestries, were ordered by Frederik II (cf. cat. 828). On the occasion of the wedding festivities of prince Christian (V) (Den store Bilager) in 1634, the tapestries were placed in "the old hall" in Copenhagen Castle. On 13.11.1819 they were moved by royal order from Det kgl. Møbelmagsin (the Royal Furnishings Storage) to the Museum of Northern Antiquities, now the National Museum.

*Literature:* Mackprang and Flamand Christensen: 1950 33f., Pl. 14; Heiberg 1984; Langberg 1985 40, fig. 57.

Victoria & Albert Museum 1948-49 nr. 174; Malmö no. 50.

*758*

759

## "Rosenblommen" (rose), a tankard of gilded silver

Unknown silversmith, maker's mark AE, probably German or Dutch. 1570's.
Gilt silver, cast and chased. Height with lid, 37.5 cm. Diameter at greatest 25.3 cm., at least, 17.6 cm.
Frontispiece p. 220
The National Museum, Second Dep't., 14926

*Rosenblommen* (The rose) has the shape of a barrel with four rows of bands with reliefs between them. Hunting scenes, cartouches with scrolls, leafy ornaments and fruits. A smooth section has the following inscription in verse:

MIT . NAFFN . THET . KALDES . EN . ROSENBLOMME
BILLIGT . BØR . MAND . AT . FAVGNE . IN . KOMME
GIESTERNE . WILL . IEG . MET . KONSTERNE . MIN
NAR . VDI . MEG . SCHIENCKIS . THEND . KLARE . WIN
TROLIG . TILHIELPE . SORGEN . FORDRIFFVE
SAA . THE . ALLE . SCHVLLE . GLADE . BLIFFVE
THI . THAGE . MEG . VP . OCH . DRICK . PAA . LOFFVE
THET . ER . THEND . RET . GAMLE . WISS . TILL . HOFFVE.

[MY NAME IS CALLED A ROSE / MY COMING SHOULD BE APPROVED / GUESTS WITH MY TALENTS I WILL, / WHEN THE CLEAR WINE IS POURED INTO ME, / TRULY HELP TO DRIVE AWAY SORROW / SO ALL WILL BE JOYOUS: / SO TAKE ME UP AND DRINK IN FAITH / THIS IS THE ANCIENT CUSTOM.]

At the bottom of the one side a cartouche with the names: HANS SKOVGAARD – ANNE PARSBERG 1577, on the other side their coats of arms. The tankard weighs nearly 6 kg., and has a volume of almost 8 litres. On its inside there are markings for the *pægl,* a volume measure of about half a pint. According to tradition, substantiated by the year 1577, a christening present to Christian IV from his godfather Hans Skovgaard, the earlier highest secretary in the Danish Chancellery, and Anne Parsberg.
*Provenance:* May 5, 1768 from the court to Det kgl. Kunstkammer as part of "valuables ... over which it has not been possible to keep lists"; inv. 1775, 226/c539. 1826 to the Royal Kunstkammer, D (Dv) 313; 1855 to Museum of Nordic Antiquities, now the National Museum.
*Literature:* Nyrop 1885 26; Olrik 1909 59-62; Axel-Nilsson 1959 45-72; Lassen 1964 59-63.

760

## Christian IV's display dagger

Unknown goldsmith, blade marked S; c. 1575
Gilt silver, cast and engraved, steel blades. L. 45.4 cm.
Frontispiece p. 220
The National Museum, Second Dep't., 10102

Gilt sheath of solid silver with reliefs: St. George and the Dragon, Hercules and Fortuna, etc. In the sheath is enclosed another, smaller knife, and a hunting spike?, both with silver inlaid wooden handles. In the end of the knife's silver mounting is engraved a crowned C. The dagger perhaps originally belonged to Frederik II, since he wears a similar one – perhaps the same – on the painting by Hans Knieper from 1581, cat. 10, cf. the Knieper tapestry, cat. 758.
*Provenance:* The Royal Kunstkammer, inv. 1689, 59; 1737, 863/96. 1824 to The Royal Museum of Art, BDc65, to Museum of Northern Antiquities 1848.
*Literature:* Victoria & Albert Museum 1948/49, no. 197.

761

## Procession at Christian IV's Coronation, 1596

?Phillip Uffenbach, 1597
Copper engraving, cut, plate edges 20.5×27.5 cm
Københavns Bymuseum, 1934: 117
Cf. cat. 48.

762

## Tilting at the quintain at Christian IV's coronation, 1596

?Philip Uffenbach, 1597
Copper engraving, plate edges 23×29.5 cm.
Københavns Bymuseum, Aa 743.
Cf. cat. 49.

763

## Accounts from the Sound Tolls from May 1 (Phillipi Jacobi day), 1587 to the same day in 1588

Two volumes (income and expenditures), mss. on paper, bound in leather, folio.
Rigsarkivet, Reviderede regnskaber

The dues imposed for sailing through the Sound were collected in Elsinore. Originally the dues were imposed on the ships, from 1567 it was the cargo – in part calculated from the width of the cargo deck. To lessen the costs the Dutch built a special type of ship, "fløjten", with an extremely narrow deck. The one volume of the accounts gives the dues for the individual ships; the other records expenditures. The King had personal control over the substantial income from the Sound tolls. The accounts are preserved from 1497. The Sound tolls were abolished in 1857/58.

# The Peasants

764

## Jacob Ulfeldt's manorial roll

C. 1588, the illustrations probably made in October-November 1588
Ms. on paper, bound in vellum, 156 pp. (including uncut pages) of c. 20.2×15.75 cm.
Private collection
"JACOB WLFELS JORDEBOG PAA WLFELSHOLM, SELSO OC BAELS" (Jacob Ulfeldt's manorial roll of Ulfeldtsholm, Selsø and Bavelse) is a register of the peasant holdings on Jacob Ulfeldt's (d. 1593) three estates: Ulfeldtsholm (now Holckenhavn) near Nyborg, Selsø and Bavelse on Zealand. The book is divided according to each manor, and next by villages, and for each farm or house is listed the name of the peasant, the rent he owes, as well as information on how and from whom Ulfeldt had acquired the property. The book may well have been compiled in regard to the coming disposition of the property after Jacob Ulfeldt's death; Ulfeldt himself apparently wrote much of the text.
The book has coloured drawings of 1) Ulfeldtsholm 2) an often reproduced scene showing ploughing and sowing under the text "Wlfelsholm gods" (Ulfeldtsholm Estate), 3) the arms of the Ulfeldt family, 4) the arms of the Flemming family (for Ulfeldt's wife Anne Flemming of Bavelse (1544-1570) with the caption "Bauelse", 5) The manor af Bavelse, 6) the Ulfeldt arms with the caption "Selsø Gods" (Selsø Estate) and 7) the manor at Selsø. Coloured ink has been used for both the illustrations and the text of the roll: green, various degrees of clarity of red, yellow, yellowish and "dark". In addition blue in the prospects of the manors.
*Provenance:* Bought for 3 mark by Baron Fr. C. Holck of Holckenhavn (the earlier Ulfeldtsholm) at an auction in 1820 of the collection of books and mss. of the historian, judge G. L. Baden. Most likely belonged to a "Per Knusen" c. 1800 (from Funen?).
*Literature:* Gissel 1964.

765

## Wheel plough

Reconstruction of a Danish wheel plough from the 1500's from pieces found in the soil
Oak wood with a share and coulter of iron. L. 350 cm
Curator Grith Lerche, The international secretariat for research on the history of agricultural implements.
*Provenance:* The original parts o the plow came from Navndrup north of Viborg, Andbjerg (cat. 766), Tømmerby and Linå near Silkeborg, Gl. Lindholm voldsted west of Roskilde, Nyborg castle's demesne, Rind å near Herning and from finds from the Dannevirke in The National Museum, First and Second Dep't.
*Literature:* KLMN 13 330-350; Glob 1951 73-74; Lerche 1970 131-150 and 131-156; Michelsen 1959. On dating see Lerche and Steensberg 1980 81-86.

766

## Fragment of a plough; sole and sheath

Danish, 1400-1500's
The conjoint sole and sheath made out of a bifurcated piece of beech wood. Length of the sole 72 cm., height of the sheath 67 cm., Distance between the top end of the sheath and the underside of the sole 55.5 cm.
The National Museum, First Dep't., C25913 (the Andbjerg plough)
The sheath has been scarfed onto the beam. At the point of the sole is a hole for the tang of the share. This has been supported by the outermost flat point of the sole. On the left side of the sole, the landside, 24 pebbles of granite, quartz and flint.
*Provenance:* Found in 1945 during peat digging in Andbjerg bog, Dover parish, near Silkeborg.

767

## Silver hoard from the Thirty Years' War, the Danish period 1627-29, eight spoons and a belt

One spoon from Augustinus Jacobsen in Århus; other workshops unknown. c. 1600
Silver, bossed and/or cast. Spoons 15.2-16.7 cm., belt, 93.5 cm.
The National Museum, Second Dep't., D635-43
"There wasn't a peasant so poor, but that he had spoons, tankards and cups of silver", related the Italian Torquato Recchia, who participated in Wallenstein's occupation of Jutland in 1627-29. In the course of the 1800's and 1900's numerous silver hoards have been delivered to the National Museum which were dug down during the wars of Christian IV and Frederik III. Some are made up of coins (daler), others of coins and silverware, or, as with this one, silver spoons with cherub heads and the housewife's silver belt – typical peasant silver from the time of Christian IV.
*Provenance:* Found in 1870 under ploughing of heath in Åstrup, Føvling parish, west of Horsens.
*Literature:* Olrik 1909 117 no. 4.

768

## Domestic utensils

Some of the pewter produced by a Flensborg master after 1637
Brass, copper, iron and pewter
The National Museum, Second Dep't., D63-D74/1951 and D749-D758/1979; deposited at Haderslev Museum.
Six large pots, three bowls and a sieve of sheet brass, two three-legged pots and a pair of candlesticks of?, an iron

768

pot, and five plates, four mugs and a salt cellar of pewter. The salt cellar has the initials HN engraved on it, perhaps for Hans Nielsen, c. 1630 the owner of Hørløkkegård, who could have hidden his valuable utensils during one of the wars, unless the items are stolen goods.
*Provenance:* Found in 1950 and 1951 during ploughing in Hørløkke, Skrydstrup parish, west of Haderslev.
*Literature:* Liebgott 1980 no. 34

## The Clergy

769

### Silver spoon. Betrothal gift?

Mark HP for Hans Plancke, Elsinore and Copenhagen, or Hans Paludan, Copenhagen, c. 1600
Silver, cast handle and wrought bowl. L. 17 cm
The National Museum, Second Dep't., D 8858

*772*

Handle in the shape of a pillar with a betrothal hand-clasp and Leda and the Swan. In the bowl is engraved the spies in Canaan carrying a cluster of grapes, and on the back Cimon and Pero and H. CHRISTIANVS BRVN, probably the vicar of Hillested on Lolland, Christen Madsen Brun (1599-1639).
*Provenance:* Purchased 1916 at the auction of F.A. Lorck's estate sale.

770

## Silver spoons

One spoon by Hans Olufsen, three by Didrik Seede, Vejle, one by Hans Buch, Kolding. The others without marks
Silver, bossed, cast, engraved. L. 14.8-18.5 cm
The National Museum, Second Dep't., 16081-90
One of these spoons deserves to be singled out, a gift from the vicar in Seest, Anker Buch (1631-62), to his bride. A Latin verse translates:
Pray, Bride, and work/ and the Lord will to you from Heaven/ send strength/ and much desired gifts./ If you love the Lord, you, little Bride, will/ flourish like a green olive branch./ From the Earth you will gather platters of fruit/ and from the Waters you will drink cups of liquid/ in bed you will see in peace your love pledges ... etc.
*Provenance:* Found 1856 at Ørum vicarage, east of Vejle
*Literature:* Olrik 1909 121 no. 1.

771

## Silver hoard from Errindlev vicarage

A tankard by Hans Matzen, Vejle; two spoons by Hans Olufsen, Vejle; the others without marks; 1640/44
Silver, bossed, cast, engraved. Tankard h. 23 cm., cup, h. 9.3 cm., lid diam. 7 cm., spoons l. 17-17.5 cm
The National Museum, Second Dep't., D11436-40
Just like the peasants, the clergy were exposed to plundering during the wars of their houses, as did the vicar of Errindlev; two spoons with the year 1644 engraved on them could be wedding presents.
*Provenance:* Found in 1929 at Errindlev vicarage, South Lolland.
*Literature:* Mackeprang 1930 57-60.

772

## Gilded ewer, Nysted Church

Stamp with mark (Bøje 8007), master from Lolland-Falster? Dated 1593, perhaps older
Gilded silver, bossed, chased and engraved. H. 16.6 cm., diam. 7.8 cm
The National Museum, Second Dep't., 4061
The nobility had to make sure that churches whose livings were in their gift were suitably equipped. Inscriptions with the name of the giver, as here, are therefore not uncommon. In the middle of the lid are the arms of Hobe and Urne and a FH-SW for Frederik Hobe of Boserup, lord-lieutenant of Nykøbing and Ålholm and his wife Sidsel Urne, who, according to the inscription on the sides of the chalice (which has the shape of a secular tankard), gave it to the church in 1593.
*Provenance:* Bought in 1837 through Smith, Korselitse.
*Literature:* Olrik 1909 64 no. 6.

773

## Chasuble from St. Nicholas Church, Copenhagen

Gert and Jacob Osserin's workshop, Copenhagen. 1640's
Silk with embroidery in silk, gold and silver thread. 122 ×98 cm
The National Museum, Second Dep't., 9207
A crucifix in raised embroidery. A wide border with heads of angels alternating with scenes from the Passion of Christ (Gethsemane, the Entombment, the Descent to Hell, the Resurrection, the Ascension).
*Provenance:* Bought in 1661 for 300 rigsdaler by the verger of St. Nicholas Church, Hendrik Jacobsen, from the estate of Kirsten, wife of the late Jacob Osserin. After the first at the church the chasuble was transferred to the Church of the Holy Ghost in 1806, and from there to the Museum of Northern Antiquities (now the National Museum).
*Literature:* DK I, 1 532 f.

774
## Chasuble from Hirsholmene

Date embroidered as 1641, but older
Patterned black velvet, borders and embroidery in silver threads, fringes, 95×87 cm.
The National Museum, Second Dep't., D5827
The church on the island of Hirsholm was built about 1640, through royal grant in 1632 to the owner, Councilor of the Realm, Otte Skeel of Hammelmose and Bangsbo (1576-1634), lensmand at Aalborghus 1631-34 (cf. cat. 809) The church was appointed with older furnishings: the chasuble – with the arms and initials of Otte Skeel and Birgitte Lindenov (1581-1648) and the year 1641 – is sewed of cloth from the beginning of the 1500's and had a late medieval cut with broad shoulders and a slit at the neck.
*Provenance:* Given to the National Museum 1904

775
## Chasuble from Church of St. Peter, Næstved

Professional beadwork, 1594
Dark red Italian velvet, gold lace, gold braid and gold embroidery. 112.5×84 cm
The National Museum, Second Dep't., D2243
Over a cross of gold braid a ribbon with the inscription: FRW INGER BASSIS – F OC M VABEN (Fru Inger Basse's F(ather)'s and M(other)'s arms); under this the coats of arms for the Basses and Emmiksens and 1594.
*Provenance:* To the Museum of Northern Antiquities 1886

776
## Christian IV's Bible 1647

Title page engraving by Hans Andreas Greijs. Printed in Copenhagen 1647, bound there before 1657
Title page engravings, 18×14 cm; full binding with open-work silver clasps and initials, 4°
The National Museum, Second Dep't., D776; Bible deposited from the Church of the Holy Ghost, D1587/1983
Surrounding the title: "Biblia Paa Danske ..." (the Bible in Danish). On each side a panel with respectively Christ giving a Blessing and Moses with the Tablets. Above, middle, a cartouche with the animals from Noah's Ark, below the Day of Judgement. The oval panels in the corners depict the Baptism in Jordan, the Circumcision, the Last Supper and Judas taking the 30 pieces of silver. On the verso of the title engraving an oil painting from c. 1730 depicts a prophet(?) surrounded by angels; frame from the end of the 1600's.
*Provenance:* The title page engraving was a gift to the museum from a private collector in 1873. The Bible was given to St. Nicholas Church in 1657 by the churchwardens; after the fire at the church in 1795 to the Church of the Holy Ghost, deposited in the National Museum in 1983.
*Literature:* DK I, 1 682.

*773*

777
## Vicar Jens Jegind's two memorial tablets, c. 1675

Oil on wood. 85×116 cm. and horizontal oval 85×79.5 cm
The National Museum, Second Dep't., XVII: 128
The one painting depicts the vicar of Lemvig, Jens Legind (1632-75) and his wife, Cathrine Olsdatter, and her deceased husband, curate at Lemvig, Bertel Nielsen Fæstler (or Fistler). It was common that a pastor on assuming and incumbency married the widow of his predecessor. Note that the clergyman's dress, which had its origins in bourgeois fashion, had already in the 1600's assumed the style which is still in use today. The other painting, of a unusual shape, shows Jegind's fourteen children – seven boys and seven girls. According to the custom of the time, both the surviving and the deceased children are depicted on the same picture, though the deceased children can be identified by their wimples. In this case only half of the children survived past the age of toddlers.
*Provenance:* Lemvig Church, to the National Museum, 1917.
*Literature:* Sandvad 1915 135.

## The Nobility

778

### Clausholm bed, "the bridal bed in the hall"

Presumed made by Peder Jensen Kolding, who joined the Horsen's joiner's guild in 1646
Carved out of oak. 240×175×320 cm
The National Museum, Second Dep't., D8472
As the carvings and inscriptions indicate, it served as a symbolic bridal bed in the hall at weddings among the nobility. On the headboard: the Shepherds worshipping the Child between figures representing Love and Justice; on the footboard: the Annunciation between Faith and Hope, flanked by the apostles Peter and Paul. On the canopy a quotation from the Song of Solomon: 5,2.
*Provenance:* Purchased for the Museum of Northern Antiquities in 1842 from a tenant farm near Randers; had been purchased at Clausholm "many years ago".
*Literature:* C. A. Jensen 1911 86-89; measurements by V. Koch in Dahlerup and others 1872-80, IV. rk. 1; Troels-Lund ed. 1969 82f.; Liebgott 1975 38f.

779

### Bed sheet and pillow case

Denmark, 1600's
Fine linen cloth, drawn thread work, lace and embroidery. Sheet 375×270 cm. with lace 8×270 cm.; pillow case 71×101 cm., with lace 5.5×142 cm. and 68.5×96 cm.
Kunstindustrimuseet, B36/1917, B64/1918 and A33/1931
The sheet has a border in drawn thread work in satin stitch, outline stitches and knots with tulip, rose, carnation and grapes in a twining vine between two narrow borders of flowers; Tønder lace of the Christian IV type from the first Tønder period. The pillow cases have – as is typical for the 1600's – a border with reticella stiching and insertions of lace and borders with rosettes and diamond shapes in the one seamed end, while they have ties at the other end. Thus the ornamentations show to advantage when the bed is made.
*Provenance:* The sheet was a gift to The Museum of Decorative Arts in 1917, the cases: 1) used at a wedding in Ballerup 1913, 2) from Stensgård, Langeland.
*Literature:* Hannover 1911 31, Kunstindustrimuseets Virksomhed 1917 45 and 1918 35. Kunstindustrimuseet 1980-81 and 1983 no. 185.

*777*

*780-795*

White table linen, tablecloths, napkins and towels, woven of linen in damask or drill, became fashionable from the last half of the 1500's. These finely woven cloths, often decorated with embroideries, were imported from Holland. In the time of Christian IV they were imitated in Slesvig-Holsten, and foreing weavers were called in to the kingdom of Denmark – especially to the *Silkeværket* (cf. cat. 734-35 and 792) to produce excellent products in silk and linen damask.

780

## Ellen Marsvin's blue silk wall hanging 1648

Blue silk satin with silk embroidery. 98×96 cm
The National Museum, Second Dep't., 9244
In the middle of the rug "EMS 1648", written in a laurel wreath encrusted with Ellen Marsvin's four ancestral coats of arms. Surrounded by flowers and animals, among them a dog with "EMS" embroidered on its collar.

*778*

*Provenance:* Purchased in 1846 in Horsens.
*Literature:* Berner-Schilden-Holsten 1925 346f.; Garde 1961 215.

781

## Else Marsvin's silk embroidered "langserviet" (long cloth) 1598

Belongs to a group of cloths from the nobility associated with manors on South Funen (1581-1619)
Linen embroidered with red silk. 71×323 cm
The National Museum, Second Dep't., 13204
At one end are the coats of arms of the paternal ancestors of Enevold Kruse (1554-1621) and his wife Else Marsvin (1575-1632), at the other end the maternal. Year 1598. Else was a younger sister of the famous Ellen Marsvin. May have been used as a long cloth on a table, or in church as a christening cloth. The original sources for these cloths from noble families are often German or Dutch engravings.
*Provenance:* Gjerum Church, Vendsyssel.
*Literature:* Garde 1961 27 no. 12 and 1962 8f.

782

## Dorte Daa's silk embroidered table cloth

Belongs to the same group as the previous number. Originally dates 1614, the year changed to 1654
Linen with red and yellow silk embroidery. 296×185 cm
The National Museum, Second Dep't. 22017
The original owner's name has later been altered, but is revealed in the cryptogram repeated all around the border: two number fours. This suggests the fourth letter of the alphabet, and is to be read as DD for Dorte Daa (d. 1624). At each end the arms of the Hundermark and Daa families; above the shields there has been a K HM, IHS and DD. The couple lived at Øxendrup, South Funen.
*Provenance:* Donated to the Museum for Nordic Antiquities (now the National Museum) in 1864 by a photographer in Jutland.
*Literature:* Garde 1961 27 no. 13 and 1962 9f.

783

## Silk embroidered cloth, presumed to be a christening cloth

Denmark 1620
Linen with red silk embroidery. 60×128 cm
The National Museum, Second Dep't, D9457
Within a large wreath, embroidered with outline stitches in red silk, a shield with IHS and 1620. Above is the death of Abel and the sacrifice of Isaac, below the Judgement Day with the Archangel Michael as the weigher of souls in the middle. The leitmotif of Christ triumphant over death gives grounds for assuming that it is a christening cloth. The sacrifice of Isaac is similar to the woodcut by Erhardt Altdorfer in Christian III's Bible.
*Provenance:* Donated by tax collector Wilckens Heiberg 1917.
*Literature:* Garde 1961 31 no. 16 and 1962 10f.

784

## Eiler Høg's and Else Krabbe's cloth

Dated 164- (last digit missing)
Linen with red silk embroidery. 180×272 cm., original length 370 cm.
The National Museum, Second Dep't., D8072
Most of a wreath in the center is preserved; within EH and E(K) for Ejler Høg and Else Krabbe and the four ancestral coats of arms of the couple: Høg, Krabbe, Bryske and Friis (chequered) and the year 164-. One of the large panels shows the Procession of the Cross, drawn from Hendrick Goltzius' series on the Passion c. 1596. The evangelists are placed in the middle panel, only Matthew and John remain. Flowers, fruit and animal motifs. In the outer border are the implements of torture used on Christ, among other motifs. The cloth has been trimmed, presumably to fit the altar in Lynderup Church.
*Provenance:* Lynderupgård, to Lynderup Church. 1912 to the National Museum, from landscape painter H. Foss.
*Literature:* Garde 1961 94 no. 43 and 1962 16f.

785

## Anne Gyldenstjerne's antependium for Horne Church

Emerenze Clausdatter, 1640 and 1641
Damask cloth with silk embroidery. 102×180 cm
The National Museum, Second Dep't., D10489
In the middle are the coats of arms of the Brahes and Gyldenstiernes, IB and AGS, for Jørgen Brahe and Anne Gyldenstierne, and 1640. In one of the frames:

Anno 1641, Christmas Day, I, Anne Gyldenstierne, wife of Mr. Jørgen Brahe of Hvedholm, have presented this cloth for the altar of Horne Church, and I have ordered sewn thereon what I considered would best give rise to the Fear of God by one of my girls, named Emerenze Clausdatter.

The Cruxifiction, the Resurrection and the Ascension are among the many scenes on the cloth, modelled on engravings by artists of the 1500's.
*Provenance:* Horne Church near Fåborg, acquired for the National Museum from Hvedholm Manor.
*Literature:* Berner-Schilden-Holsten 1925 344; Garde 1961 90 no. 42 and 1962 15f.

786

## Vibeke Friis' cloth, c. 1650

Linen with colourful silk embroidery. 165×165 cm
The National Museum, Second Dep't., 6058
In the middle the four coats of arms of the (Egern) Friis, Ulfeldt, Gyldenstierne and Brockenhuus families.

Above the inscription: IESPER FRIIS ELSEBE VLFELD; below: WIWEKE FRIIS. Flower and fruit motifs, drawn from Crispin de Pas: "Hortus Floridus", 1614; the pairs of birds and fourlegged animals have their roots in old animal books such as Jost Ammans "Thierbuch" 1579.
*Provenance:* Vibeke Friis, (d. 1655), was the daughter of Jesper Friis of Ørbæklunde and Elsebe Ulfeldt, a sister of Corfitz Ulfeldt. Acquired for the Museum of Northern Antiquities in 1841 with the Lassen Collection.
*Literature:* Berner-Schilden-Holsten 1925 349-50; Garde 1961 126 no. 56 and 1962 19f.

787

## Falk Gøye's and Ide Ulfstand's tapestry

Professional workshop, presumably c. 1575
Wool, tapestry in dull brown, blue and yellow-gray colours. 197×184 cm
The National Museum, Second Dep't., D11601
Is believed to have been made on the occasion of Falk Gøye's and Ide Ulfstand's daughter Mette's wedding with Councilor of the Realm Axel Brahe 1575. Center motif Lot and his daughters. The 16 ancestral coats of arms in the border documented noble rank.
*Provenance:* Acquired in 1930 from Hvedholm near Fåborg with support from the New Carlsberg Foundation
*Literature:* Berner-Schilden-Holsten 1925 313f; Garde 1949 26f.

*787*

788

## Dorthe Giedde's pillow case, 1644

Linen with silk embroidery in petit point and Holbein stitch (double running stitch), human hair has been used for the hair of the female figures. 47×49 cm
The National Museum, Second Dep't., 10553
Middle panel: Christ with Mary and Martha. Text: "MARIA HATH CHOSEN THE GOOD PART WHICH SHALL NOT BE TAKEN AWAY FROM HER LVKE X CHAP". Surrounding, twice sixteen ancestral coats of arms, beginning with Dorte Giedde's paternal side "DGF" and the maternal, "DGM", and the year 1644. Dorte was the daughter of Admiral Ove Giedde (cf. cat. 891, 894 and 994) and Dorte Urne.
*Provenance:* 1849 from Det kgl. Danske Selskab for Fædrelandets Historie og Sprog (The Royal Danish Society for the History of the Fatherland) via prof. Tyge Becker.

789

## Tapestry woven pillow sham showing Esther and Ahasueras, or the Queen of Sheeba and King Solomon.

"Slesvig tapestry weaving", 1640's
Wool and silk, tapestry weave. 50×50 cm
The National Museum, Second Dep't., D2177
In the middle, on a throne, a king with a crown and scepter, while the queen, with a crown, kneels before him. Around this a flower motif typical of the period.
*Provenance:* Bought 1886.
*Literature:* Garde 1949 22.

790

## Drill tablecloth

Woven in drill, single thread linen in warp thread and woof, 20/18 pr. cm. 238×151 cm.
The National Museum, Second Dep't., D79/1986
As was common, sewn together of two equal lengths. In the seam selvages, at the outer edges, a 5 mm. double folded hem. Wowen in pavé pattern; in the middle an embroidered shield with the monogram for Jesus and OMK – IK 1645.
*Provenance:* Gift to the National Museum, Nov. 1986. Claimed to have come from a farm near Allindelille, north of Ringsted.

791

## Hunting tablecloth

Flemish workshop, 1594
Damask woven linen, three repeating patterns across the width, each 17.8 cm. 209×112 cm
The National Museum, Second Dep't., D1536
Hunting scenes: riders with horns, standing hunters, deer and dogs in front of a castle with three towers. The arms and initials of Otto Banner (of Asdal) and In-

geborg Skeel (d. 1604) are embroidered in white thread. The museum owns a similar cloth (dated 1596), which is believed to have belonged to Councilor of the Realm Predbjørn Gyldenstjerne and Mette Hardenberg. – The white cloths were placed over coloured tapestries of cloths when the tables were laid.
*Provenance:* Presumed to be from Voergård.
*Literature:* Mygdal 1913 9.

792

## Lap robe

Courtrai (Kortrijk) in Flanders, end of the 1500's
Damask woven linen. 153×66 cm
The National Museum, Second Dep't., D100/1984
Woven motif: The temptation of Abraham and the sacrifice of Isaac. In clouds in Hebrew letters "Jehovah" and with Gothic minuscules "adsum d(omi)ne". Wide insertion of reticella stitching and lace.
*Provenance:* Purchased 1984, originally from Toftekærgården by Roskilde Inn, Tåstrup. Similar lap robes are found in the National Museum, Third Dep't., Dansk Folkemuseum.
*Literature:* Cf. van Yesselsteyn 1962 no. 68.

793

## Cloth from Slesvig or Holsten decorated with the Creation, 1614

Damask woven linen, 6-shaft satin. 265×166 cm
The National Museum, D3345
"Genesis chap 22" woven in cloth. The motifs include Our Lord, the Creation of the Earth, the Creation of Eve, Eve by the Tree of Life and the Expulsion from Paradise; unicorns, peacocks and eagles, lilies, etc. In one corner, 1614.
*Provenance:* Purchased 1896
*Literature:* Mygdahl 1913 9f.; Paludan and Wieth-Knudsen 1987.

794

## Dutch? cloth with the Creation, 1632

Damask woven linen, middle section with three repeated patterns; 5-shaft satin. 335×182 cm
The National Museum, D13412
The motifs include the Creation of Earth, Adam and Eve by the Tree of Life, the Angel with the Flaming Sword and the Expulsion from Paradise; the sun, moon, and stars, deer and birds. In the corners, coats of arms and H.R.A.R. 1632; presumably a wedding tablecloth for Frantz Rantzau of Salzau and Anna Rantzau.
*Provenance:* Purchased at Charlottenborgs Kunstauktioner Sept., 1945, cat. 292.
*Literature:* Mygdahl 1913 10.

795

## Dutch tablecloth with the parable of the Prodigal Son, 1640

Damask woven linen. 185×75 cm
The National Museum, D3137
"Luke ch. xv" woven into the cloth, as well as scenes from the story of the Prodigal Son. Two coats of arms embroidered, and the initials MG LGS 1640, for Mogens Sehested of Holmegård and Lisbeth Gyldenstjerne.
*Provenance:* Bought in 1895.
*Literature:* Mygdahl 1919 12

796

## Prospect of Maltesholm, 1638

Oil on canvas. 140×230 cm
Private collection, Sweden
Malte Juul of Gjessinggård (1594-1648) – of the then still very wealthy high aristocracy – acquired by his marriage to Anne Ramel in 1625 (1610-1661, daughter of Councilor of the Realm Henrik Ramel (cf. cat. 39)) a good deal of scattered land holdings in southeast Scania. Juul consolidated the holdings around the parish town Sønderslev, which in 1633 had to give up land for the creation of the manor Maltesholm, which Juul established at the same time that he re-built Birkholm (now Løvenholm) on Zealand. The painting shows both the new manor house – with the barns over the bridge – and the Italian-inspired gardens laid out according to the current fashion in the 1600's.
*Literature:* Kristianstad 1977 no. 110. Illustration in Ladewig Petersen 1981 270.

797

## Caritas Fountain, c. 1600-1650

Cast bronze, figure 55 cm. high, base 19,7×15,5×14.5 cm., faucet 19×47.5×7.8 cm. Water pipe of drilled hollow pine, orig. l. 4.72 m.
The National Museum, Second Dep't. D152/1982, D971-72/1984 and D974/1984A-B
Caritas (Charity or Benevolence), symbolized with a burning heart in the woman's left hand. The flame may have been the water gushing through the hole at the top of the heart, where a nozzle appears to have been broken off. Water sprayed out in addition through holes in the figure's mouth, breasts and navel, and through the Medusa, or troll, masks of the base. Closely related to the Caritas fountain on the Old Square in Copenhagen, by Statius Otto 1608-10. – The fountain in the form of a dolphin or dragonhead; the slightly conical form of the pipe suggests that it has been placed on a wooden basin or wooden pipe. The water pipe was found together with a covered trough, also of wood. In the pipe was a piece of a measuring stick, probably an "alen" stick.
*Provenance:* From Tulstrup Hovegård, pulled down around 1700 – now Tulstrup Møllefarm – between

*797*

Århus and Viborg. Found in the ground 1982 and 1983.
*Literature:* O. Olsen 1984 20.

798

## "Tresor", silver cupboard with two doors and two drawers

Work from Funen?, c. 1610
Oak with carved reliefs. 185×214×65 cm
The National Museum, Second Dep't., no number.
In the panels shields with the paternal and maternal coats of arms of Jacob Ulfeldt of Egeskov and his wife Birgitte Brockenhuus (Flemming, Ulfeldt, Brockenhuus and Skram). This type of silver cupboard belonged among the furnishings of the hall, cf. the painting Dance of the Ruds [Rud family] cat. 332. On the top of the cupboard were placed particularly fine tankards, "Welcomes", e.g. made in the shape of gilded animals (colourplate XVII):
a) *Horse;* two marks: a Nürnberg mark and that of Wolf Christoff Ritter (Rosenborg 1925, 3880), c. 1620. H. 19.5 cm., inv. no. D120. From the estate of Queen Sophie Magdalene to the Royal Kunstkammer 1772, inv. 1775, 249/c604.
b) *Cock;* two marks: town mark for Zwolle (Rosenberg 1928, 7736) and datemark D, c. 1650. H. 22.5 cm., inv. no. D11602.
c) *Bossed goblet;* two marks: one for Hamborg and one for Braunschweig? c. 1625, h. 52 cm., inv.no. D76. From the court to the Royal Kunstkammer 1750, inv. 1775, 128/c172.
d-e) *Goblets* of coconut in gilded mountings of silver and brass respectively. H. 24.5 and 26 cm.; d) belonged to Otte Brahe, who fell at Kalmar in 1611. Inv.no. D2528 and 3751.
*Literature:* Olrik 1909, a): 70 no. 23, c) 69 no. 22, d-e): 65 no. 8 and 9; b) Olrik 1932 25.

799

## Sophie Steensdatter Brahe, 1588-1659

Designated Sophie Brahe, ætatis suæ 14, Brahe- and Rosenkrantz arms, 1602
Three-quarter portrait. 115×86.5 cm
Frederiksborg, A 2590
Sophie, daughter of Councilor of the Realm Steen Brahe, is fashionably dressed in a black dress, which serves as background for her gold jewelry, her circular collar, the red scallopped cuffs and her matching beaded gloves and cap.
*Provenance:* Acquired from Ryegård 1970.

800

## Sophie Rosenkrantz Holgersdatter ~ 1646 with Steen Brahe of Knudstrup

Presumably Johan Thim, 1642
Oil on canvas. 107×77 cm.
Frederiksborg, A 5677
Sophie, daughter of the learned Holger Rosenkrantz (cat. 177) and Sophie Brahe, was painted before marriage – therefore so much of her hair was allowed to be visible. She wears a red dress with a wide lace collar; the gold chain marks her noble rank.
*Provenance:* Rosenholm.

*802*

801

## Ingeborg Ulfstand, 1598-1652

After 1644
Oil on canvas. 97.5×82 cm
Frederiksborg, A 4277
The painting shows Ingeborg Ulfstand in white widow's mourning clothes. She had been married to Admiral Jørgen Vind, who died of his wounds after Kolberger Heide in 1644.
*Provenance:* Vernø Cloister in Norway, which was deeded to Ingeborg Ulfstand's two sons by the king in 1675. Acquired by Frederiksborgmuseet 1928.

802

## A group of children of the nobility

C. 1620
Oil on canvas. 120×94 cm
The National Museum, Second Dep't., D12604
The children are all dressed like small adults; the big boy is in golden trunk hose, which cover the knee, similar buttoned doublet with short peplum and a silver mounted sword belt for a rapier. A high felt hat with a feather and polished shoes with laces complete his dress. The older girl is in a blue brocade dress, whereas the small girls are in red and wear bonnets. The little boy wears a lace collar typical of the period just like the girls.
*Provenance:* 1929 exchange from Frederiksborgmuseet, which had purchased the painting from an antique dealer, who apparently acquired it from the manor Nakkebølle, South Funen.

803

## Elsebet Brockenhuus' hope chest

Presumably workshop on Funen. Dated 1595
Oak with carvings and paint. 81×189×75 cm
The National Museum, Second Dep't., D8473
On the front the paternal arms of Elsebet Brockenhuus, Brockenhuus and Skram, flanked by the maternal, Tinhuus and Krabbe. Below this her initials, EBH and 1595. Elsebet was the sister of Birgitte, cf. cat. no. 798. The chest, which contained her personal belongings, apparel etc., was finished for her wedding at Koldinghus in 1596 with Corfitz Ulfeldt of Bavelse.
*Provenance:* Bought in 1843 from a farmer in Lem near Randers; is said to have been at Mariager cloister.

*804*

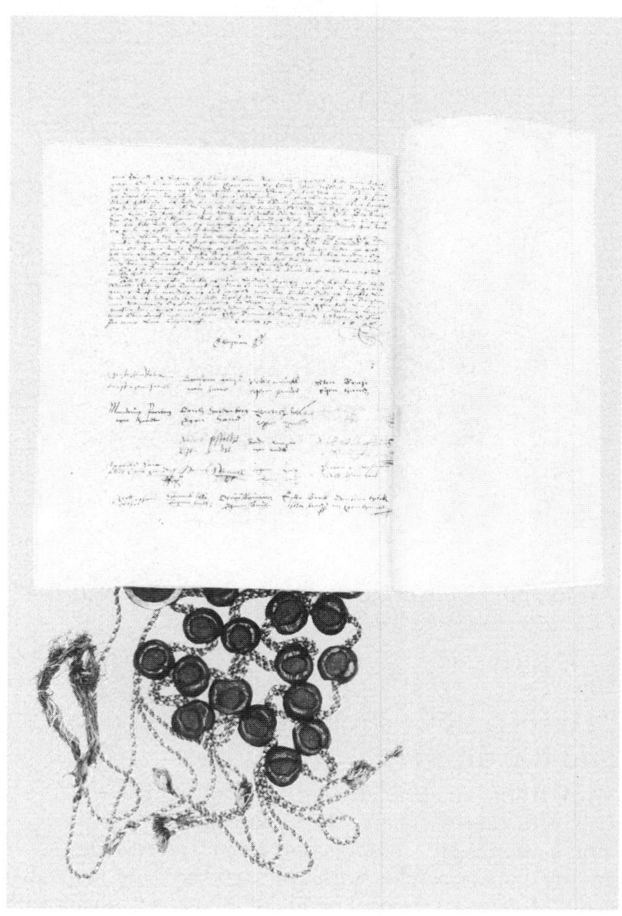

804
## Christian IV's coronation charter, August 17, 1596

Rigsarkivet
The charter, which was prepared in several copies, secured the rights of the Council of the Realm to their share of governing power and guaranteed the priveleges of the nobility. Among the signatories is Manderup Parsberg, cf. cat. 809.

805
## Lord Seneschal Christoffer Valkendorf's brass canister

Presumably a workshop in Copenhagen, 1594
Brass, engraved. Diam. c. 8 cm
The National Museum, Second Dep't., MCCCCXLIX
This gilded brass canister has engraved Moresque decoration on the outside; inside on the lid are Christoffer Valkendorf's coat of arms and initials, CW, and the year 1594. The canister was probably used to store Valkendorf's signet.
*Provenance:* Gift from Councilor Saabye in 1826

*807*

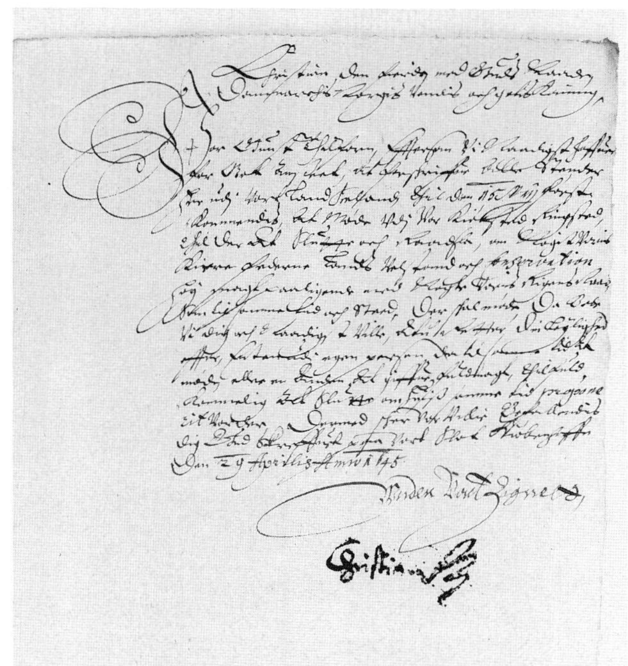

*806*

806
## Summons to the Estates 1645

Danish Chancellery, April 29, 1645
Paper, folded sheet
Rigsarkivet, Da.Kanc. A 9
The letter is an official – but never sent – royal summons to a meeting of the estates in Ringsted on May 15, 1645. Such letters were routinely written in the secretariat of the chancellery. The king did not take the trouble to sign the many identical letters in his own hand, but let them be signed with a signature stamp, cat. 807. From the year of the Danish Reformation in 1536 until the last year of Christian IV's reign, the Estates were only summoned on extraordinary occasions – as a rule to provide confirmation of tax levies.

807
## Christian IV's signature stamp

Earlier than 1645
Wood, iron, lead and pewter. Length of case 23.2 cm
Rosenborg, 3.147
The iron mounted wooden case, which can be locked, contains an ink tin of pewter, two leather-covered ink pads and a stamp with the king's signature in facsimile. Used in connection with dispatching letters of the type of cat. 806.
*Provenance:* The Royal Kunstkammer, no number, to Rosenborg 1827.

*810*

808

## A lensmand (noble lord-lieutenant's) letter cabinet c. 1600-25

Oak, painted in part, fittings of iron. 94×72×44.5 cm
Aalborg Historiske Museum, 19828
The hanging cabinet's doors have carved panels and moldings with dentils and egg and dart ornamentation. Elaborate hinges and carrying handles of wrought iron. The cabinet contains nine drawers with partially preserved black labels: "ruller, Reg., Assignationer, Quitantzer, tin[gs] [W]inde, Sende Bref, Obligationer, Con[tracter] ... kongebref ... Leenit wed komende!" which indicates that it is the letter cabinet of a lensmand; the presumed initials CMK have, however, not been identified. The two carrying handles show that the cabinet was transportable; it must have contained papers regarding the current administration of the len (territorial fief). Inventories from Aalborghus mention several document cabinets, cf. cat. 809.
*Provenance:* Purchased from a private party 1937.
*Literature:* Riismøller 1951 39f.

809

## Accounts from Aalborghus len (territorial fief)

Kvittanciariumbilag 1597, accounts from 1622 and 1644/45
Rigsarkivet, Reviderede Regnskaber
Aalborghus len was an accountable fief (in contrast to a security or a charge or free type of fief) which had to send in its accounts each year to the central auditing in the Rentkammeret (exchequer). The accounts cover both the accounting itself and manorial rolls, extra tax levies and the kvittanciariumbilag (receipts), which contain, in part, the annual receipts from the treasurers for their accounts delivered, the charters and inventories. Such inventories were compiled in particular in the case of transfers, as when Manderup Parsberg took over Aalborghus len after Ove Lunge in 1597, and again when Tønne Friis assumed control in 1622. In 1644/45, when the fief was impoverished after two enemy occupations of Jutland, Gunde Lange of Brejninge was lensmand – the seventh and last during Christian IV's reign.
*Literature:* Jexlev 1976 293f.

810

## "Trésor" and letter cupboard from Tisselholt

Workshop on Funen? C. 1610-20
Cupboard of oak with intarsia of maple and pear. 185×87×44.5 cm.
The National Museum, Second Dep't., D2661
The cupboard is completely decorated with intarsia. Behind the doors in the upper section are two shelves, whereas ten drawers are placed behind the wooden lattice of the lower section.
*Provenance:* The cupboard was at the manor of Tisselholt, on South Funen until 1806. Purchased in 1892 in Odense.
*Literature:* C. A. Jensen 1911 21.

811

## Glass tankard mounted in silver

Southern German or Bohemian? Danish mounting, 1605
Glass with enamel painting and cutting, silver with engraving. H. without lid 13 cm., diam 8 cm
The National Museum, Second Dep't., D880
Painted Danish and Brandenburgian arms; between these has later been cut Christian IV's and Anna Cat-

hrine's crowned names, and "Rex et Regina Daniæ et Norvegiæ Vandalorum Gothorumque". In the lid, the arms and initials of lensmand Ebbe Munk and his wife Sidsel Høg with the date.
*Provenance:* Exchange with a private party, 1874.
*Literature:* Olrik 1909 67 no. 18.

812

## Two bossed goblets

Georg Koler and Andreas Michel, Nürnberg (Rosenberg III, 4170 1 and 4165 u); between 1617 and 1623
Gilded silver, bossed and engraved. The lidded goblet 30 cm high, the smaller 16.1 cm
The National Museum, Second Dep't, 6877 and 6878
On the lidded goblet are pricked in the Rosenkrantz and Krabbe arms and the initials HRK – KK – 1647 for Holger Rosenkrantz of Glimminge and his wife Karen Krabbe. She may have given the goblet to the couple who owned it when their initials and the year 1655 were pricked into both goblets.
*Provenance:* Part of a "hoard from the Swedish wars", found in 1842 whilst ditch digging in a field in Dræby, Munkebo parish, northeast of Odense. May have belonged to the vicar of Munkebo, Claus Hansen Naschou, and his wife, whose initials are on some of the items. He was hunted to death by the Swedes in 1659.
*Literature:* Olrik 1909 133 no. 4.

813

## Gilded silver cup

Unknown goldsmith, presumably Danish, 1631
Silver with fire-gilding, chased, cylindrical cup. H. 13 cm
The National Museum, Second Dep't. D 1558
Rud and Rosensparre coats of arms and CR – BRS 1631 for Corfits Rud and Birgitte Rosensparre. Made at her instance after her husband's death in 1630.
*Provenance:* Bought 1880
*Literature:* Danske Magasin 1884; Olrik 1909 72.

814

## Small silver bowl, "salsirken"

No maker's mark. Engraved coat of arms from first half of the 1600's
Silver, chased, engraved and with a soldered on edge. H. 2.4 cm., diam. 12.3 cm
The National Museum, Second Dep't., D1204/1982
Bowl with smooth border and an edging which has been soldered onto the rim. In the middle a raised boss, on which is engraved a divided shield with a helmet decoration, now nearly worn away, perhaps for Jørgen Arenfeldt, owner of Voergård 1611-58. Later FF scratched in.
*Provenance:* Found in the 1950's during digging in the courtyard at the manor Voergård, Voer parish, Dronninglund herred in Vendsyssel. Later handed over as national treasure.

*815*

815

## Display coins as presents

Gold and silver
Den kgl. Mønt- og Medaillesamling
At christenings and wedding it was the custom to give display coins as presents, either Danish or foreign gold coins, *dalere, crowns* or the splendid, large *breddalere* which had the weight of several dalere. The king himself gave his handsome gold coins as presents or, e.g. as payment of gambling debts.

816

## Two "kristenhuer" christening caps

Denmark 1620-30, mounted c. 1700
Rep silk, raised embroidery in gold and silver thread, briad and sequins
Boy's cap 14 cm. h., girl's cap 10 cm
Kunstindustrimuseet, 22-23/1972
The clergy often rented out "christening clothes", but the families of the nobility had their own, which – like these caps – became heirlooms. The boy's cap is embroidered with roses, pomegranates, and the fore half of a unicorn; two gold lace bands laid in a cross on the crown. The girl's cap is worked of three pieces, and in addition to roses and pomegranates, it has a pelican attacking its breast to feed its young, a symbol of Christ's death for the sake of mankind.

*Provenance:* Gift from Mrs. Eggers-Krag 1972
*Literature:* Kunstindustrimuseet 1983 no. 9.

817

## Lace

Tønder? Flanders? c. 1640
Linen, lace with twisted and braided brides. 263×9.5 cm
Kunstindustrimuseet, 25/1975
Flat lace collars became fashionable c. 1630, as is demonstrated by the many contemporary pictures of Christian IV (cf. cat. 191). This lace with the blunted scallops, each filled out with a motif of a vase with three carnations, is typical of the period.
*Provenance:* Gift from Helge Jacobsens fund 1975
*Literature:* Kunstindustrimuseet 1980-1.

818

## Jewelry and other accessories to apparel

Colour-plate XVII
The National Museum, Second Dep't
a) Heavy *gold chains* – often with medaillons – were a symbol of rank and were typical of the dress of the nobility during the first decades of Christian IV's reign. Later wide drooping lace collars became fashionable and the chains become less noticeable. Women began to wear short gold chains tight at the throat, while the longer chains followed the edges of the collar, as can be seen on Beate Rosenkrants' portrait, cat. 819.
*Belts,* usually made of gilded silver, circled the ladies' waists. The gold chains and gold belts of the nobility have been melted down in the course of time, but from wealthy clergymen's and peasants' wives, who imitated the fashion, there exist preserved gold chains and silver belts.
*Gold chains,* L. c. 50 cm. The Trinity is engraved on the front of the fastener, the initials of the owner IBF BPD 1641 on the back. 8312.
*Gold necklace.* L. 47.5 cm. A leaf ornament engraved on the front of the fastener, on the back SKDF. Found in Vemmelev vicarage near Korsør. 18894. *Chain* of gilded silver with oval links. L. 105 cm. In the chain a cast medal with 1552 under a depiction of the Wedding in Canaan; on the other side the creation of Eve. Found with other jewelry and dalere (coins) at Eltang Farm near Kolding. D 13122.

b) *Jewels,* necklaces with diamonds and other precious stones surrounded with colourful enamels often bore the monogram of Jesus, IHS. These were worn in the middle of the chest.
*Pendant,* 1575-1600. Enamelled gold with amethyst, peridot, and pearls. 3.8×2.85 cm D224.
*Pendant,* late 1500's, gold with table cut diamonds and enamelled edelweisses. Three interior compartments for balsam. Found in Købmagergade 49 in Copenhagen. D867.
*Pendant,* c. 1600. C. 2×2 cm. Gold, IHS. Parsberg's chapel in Hyllinge Church near Næstved. D12629.
*Pendant,* c. 1600. 2.6×2.8 cm. Gold, IHS in openwork and engraving. Vetterslev cemetery near Ringsted. 2353.

c) *Finger rings* were worn by both sexes. Signet rings could be placed on either the thumb or pointer finger, whereas betrothal rings, often a spiral ring with an inscription, were worn on the fourth finger. Rings with jewels could be worn on all fingers.
*Signet rings* of gold from noble families:
EVA engraved above the arms of the Podebusks. 1500's. Benløse cemetery near Assens. D2669
INGBORG.SCHEL engraved in rock crystal. Late 1500's. Found at Voergård. D49/1962.
F(rederik) G(ans) above a coat of arms with a goose. 1500's found near Blæsbjerg. D 1432.
K(aren) B(ille) M(arqvards) D(atter) in cornelian. C. 1620. from Hvidkilde. D200/1964.
*Spiral finger rings* of gold. Late 1500's. Inscription ATS IHK. Rønninge, West Funen. 6601. C. 1600. No inscription. From Bogø. D13528.
Enamelled gold finger rings with precious stones: D7753, from Hvidovre; D8386, Store Heddinge; D1704, Roulund near Viborg and D7021, found in Århus near the creek.

d) *Bracelets* could be worn in pairs, and, like finger rings, be spirals or made of wide chains, sometimes of braided silk, gathered in engraved or enamelled fasteners.
*Spiral bracelet* of gold from the late 1500's. Heirloom in the Sehested family. 5885.
*Bracelet* of braided silk with enamelled gold fastener. On the back side of the fastener: H(enrik) W(ind), the monogram of Jesus, and M(argrete) L(ax) M(and) 1630. On the front symbols of weddings and vanity. Found in Henrik Vind's grave, Hjembæk Church near Holbæk. 8960.
Enamelled gold fastener from a bracelet, with the Annunciation. Dated 1653. 1.7×2.8 cm. D7438.

e) Other jewelry items such as enamelled *buckles, earrings, pomanders,* "desmerknopper" (cf. cat 838 and 910), shaped into balls or skulls, and a knitting sheath could hang from the belts of the women. Men might have a jeweled toothpick, a *hunting knife* or hunting *whistle. Gold buttons* and shoelace tags were also fashionable.
Two enamelled *gold buckles* with rubies. 1.2×2.1 cm. D243.
2½ pairs of *earrings* with dolphins, remains of enamel. D3794, D12755, D1000/1959.
*Pomander,* engraved and gilded silver. H. 4.5 cm. Attached chain. for six kinds of spices and perfume. *Pomander,* in the form of a skull, copper with remains of gilt. Attached chain. Inside a spoon and compartments for six spices. 5460.
*Knitting sheath* of silver, late 1500's. L. 19 cm. Inscription

ELLIN GLAMBEK. from the Århus area, perhaps "Trods Katholm". D13497.
*Toothpick jewel,* gold. Late 1500's. L. 6.8 cm. Shaped like a dolphin with table cut stones and enamel. Asmild near Viborg. D436/1972.
*Hunting whistle* of gilded silver. L. 8.7 cm. Five compartments for spices etc. Near Jægerspris. 1 3763.
Two small *gold buttons,* connected by a brace. With enamelled flowers. 19026.
*Spherical button* of gold with engraved interlacing and the initials MVW. D 2729.
Two *shoelace tags* of gold with enamelled flowers and bunches of grapes. 2665.
Dagger *with silver shaft.* dated 1579. The shaft c. 10 cm. long, the hilt 6 cm., the blade broken. Ornaments in Floris style. St. Dyrehave (deerpark) near Hillerød. D106/1954.
*Literature:* a) Olrik 1909 124 no. 6; Lindahl 1980 no. 6; b) DK V2 1055: c) Lindahl 1980 no. 50; d) Lindahl 1975 190f., DK IV, 2 706; e) Warburg 1980 and 1982, Lindahl 1962.

819

## Beate Rosenkrantz, 1608-47

Presumably Johan Timm, painted c. 1642
Oil on canvas, glued to wood. 31×22 cm
Frederiksborg, A 615
The dress is reminiscent of her sister Sophie's (cf. cat. 800), and the jewelry is also of a similar type. The IHS pendant is typical, as are the spiral-shaped bracelets (cf. cat. 818d). The portrait has the same type of face as a lifesize portrait (Frederiksborg A7778), dated 1642, which, together with a pendant of Henrik Thott, can be presumed to have been made on the occasion of their wedding the same year.
*Literature:* Heiberg 1979 79 f.

820

## Otte Rosenkrantz, 1610-39, brother of the above

Presumably Johan Timm, painted c. 1635-39
Oil on canvas, glued to wood. 31×22 cm
Frederiksborg, A 614
The large soft collar, trimmed with Tønder lace, and the matching cuffs (cf. cat. 817) are typical of male apparel. Study for a life-size portrait at Rosenholm. The yellow buffcoat indicates that he was an officer; he died in a duel in 1639.
*Literature:* Heiberg 1979 79f.

821

## Jørgen Brahe and Anne Gyldenstjerne's hymnal

Printed by Henrich Waldkirch, Copenhagen 1627, bound 1637.
Bound in black velvet, gilded buckles and enamelled mountings. 9×5.8 cm.
The National Museum, Second Dep't., D11598
On the front and back covers, the enamelled Brahe and Gyldenstierne coats of arms and 1637. Belonged to Councilor of the Realm Jørgen Brahe, married to Anne Gyldenstierne, 1695-1677.
*Provenance:* Purchased in 1930 from Count Bille-Brahe-Selby, Hvedholm near Fåborg, (cf. cat. 787 and 822).

822

## Lisbeth Bryskes prayerbook

Printed in Copenhagen 1645, presumably also bound there
Bound in back velvet, gilded buckles and enamelled coats of arms. 15×8.8 cm.
The National Museum, Second Dep't., D11599
"Brandenburgian Prayerbook in Danish". Copper engraving of Christian IV by H. A. Greijs. The first owner of the book was Lisbeth Bryske, who on the 17th of August, 1647, at Tirsbæk, wrote in it that was given to her by her dear daughter Margrethe Lunge.

*823-828 Hunting and hunting weapons*

"Peasant folk may not shoot animals" reads the text of an order from the late 1500's. By "animal" was to be understood deer, which only the king was allowed to hunt, though the nobility might do so on their own lands, and noble fief-holders with royal permission might also. That the decree was meant to be taken seriously is demonstrated by the execution in 1634 of Laurids Karup, who had shot deer in the king's game preserves. The most prestigious form of hunting at the time was carried on in this fashion: the game was driven together by hundreds of beaters into a gigantic trap made up of extremely long pieces of canvas, called "hunting cloths". On the shooting range these formed a passage narrow enough to shoot across with ease as the beaters and dogs drove the game past the hunters.
Another popular form af hunting employed nets which were strung on posts in the forest. The game was chased into the nets by fast running dogs, followed closely by hunters on horseback. When the deer was caught in the net, it was killed with a hunting spear. Riding to the hounds was first intoduced into Denmark after 1650.

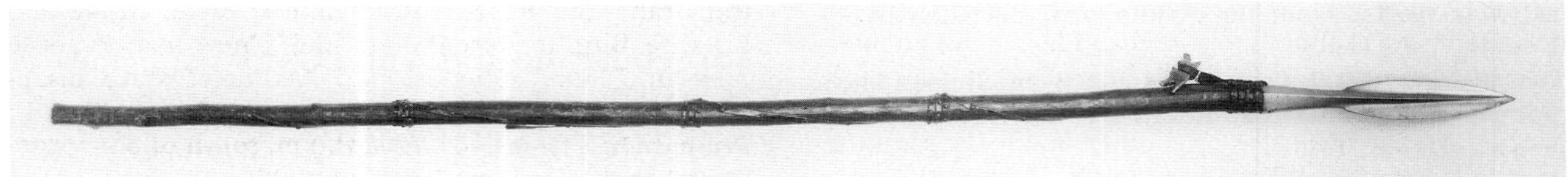

*823*

823

## Hunting spear c. 1600

Iron and wood. L. 205 cm.
The National Museum, Second Dep't., 10171
This spear type is known as a wild boar spear, and has a very heavy double edged iron blade on a staff of wood wound around with leather. At the blade is a cross guard of antler which serves to limit the depth to which the spear pierces the boar's jaws. Similar spears are depicted in the hunting scenes on Knieper's tapestries from the Ballroom at Kronborg, (cf. cat. 757 and 828).
*Literature:* The Royal Kunstkammer, inv. 1737, 865/134. 1827 to the Royal Museum of Art, BDc 149; to the Museum of Northern Antiquities 1848.

824

## German hunting crossbow, c. 1580

Steel and wood with bone and horn inlay. 72×75 cm
The National Museum, Second Dep't., 5131
The crossbow has a bow of steel with a bowstring of waxed hemp. The stock, of wood, has inlaid hunting scenes in bone. On both sides are wild boars, bears, deer and hares and a kneeling rifleman with a dog. On the end surface: noble weaponry and the initials HGHVS.
*Provenance:* Bought for the Museum of Northern Antiquities 1839

825

## German crossbow windlass c. 1575

Steel with golden metal ornaments. 10×35 cm
The National Museum, Second Dep't., 21660
"German windlass" for a crossbow of the same type as cat. 824. The jack has a bifurcated hook to hold the bowstring, a drum with a cogwheel, a crank and a heavy loop of hemp rope. The loop is placed on the stock, the notch holds the bowstring and it is then pulled back in place with the crank.
*Provenance:* King Frederik VII's weapon collection, inv. c49/590. To the Museum of Northern Antiquities 1864.

826

## Two hunting rifles (paired rifles)

Hieronimus Borstorffer and Georg Müller, München, c. 1600
Wheel lock with double cocks; calibre 15.5. L. 113 and 119 cm
The National Museum, Second Dep't., 10423-23
Two nearly identical full stocked rifles with octagonal barrels. Marks HB and GM on the stock and bore. The wheel locks have smooth lock plates, double cocks and wheels with domed covers. The trigger has a hair trigger and the trigger guard has finger grips. The stocks are inlaid with bone in volutes and vines. The cheek rests have exotic fruits and parrots respectively, and other engravings of hunting dogs and game birds.
*Provenance:* The Royal Kunstkammer, inv. 1737, 843/43 and 44; 1826 to The Royal Museum of Art, BDc 106 and 107; 1848 to the Museum of Northern Antiquities.

827

## Powder horn

German, first half of the 1600's
Gilded brass on wood, covered with velvet. 28×23 cm
The National Museum, Second Dep't., 10461
Intended to be hung from a shoulder strap. On the front an illustration of an Oriental lion hunt, such as the European imagination envisioned it. The three horsemen and the lion are shown in the instant before the hunters spear and kill the raging beast of prey. The back has arabesques and trophies on a background of green velvet.
*Provenance:* From the Oldenborg Armory at the Arsenal to the Royal Kunstkammer 1692, inv. 1737, 844/61, 1825 to The Royal Museum of Art, BDc 131; 1848 to the Museum of Northern Antiquities.

828

## "The Wild Boar Hunt"

Hans Knieper, 1585
Woven tapestry. 394×160 cm
The National Museum, Second Dep't., CLXXIV
One of three tapestries, which belong with the series of 40 royal tapestries, which – by the order of Frederik II – were woven in 1581-85 for the Ballroom at Kronborg, (cf. cat. 758). The other two have not survived. The horseman on the white horse is presumably Frederik II, the

younger rider can be Christian IV. At the top tapestry has Frederik II's initials (F 2 RD) and below this an intertwined F(redericus) S(ophie), a reference to the king's wife – flanked by the initials of the king's and the queen's mottos. Below Frederik II's other motto, T(reu) I(st) W(ildbrat) (Game is Great) – an expression of the king's interest in hunting.
*Provenance:* From The Royal Furniture Storage to the Museum of Northern Antiquities (now the National Museum) 1819.
*Literature:* Mackeprang & Flamand Christensen 1950 38 and plate 15; Langberg 1985 57.

829

## Ceiling painting from Næsbyholm

Painted shortly after 1585
Oil on lathing of three rows of boards
The National Museum, Second Dep't., D2745
Originally the four seasons in medaillons surrounding the monogram for Jesus. The main figures in "Spring" and "Winter" are thought to be portraits of members of the Brahe and Rosenkrantz families; Steen Brahe and his wife Birgitte Rosenkrantz had a new manor house built in 1585. "Summer" and "Autumn" have disappeared, the latter in the fire at the manor in 1932.
*Provenance:* The Manor Næsbyholm, south of Sorø; presented to the National Museum 1892.
*Literature:* Beckett 1901-07 62ff.; C. A. Jensen 1935 385.

*826*

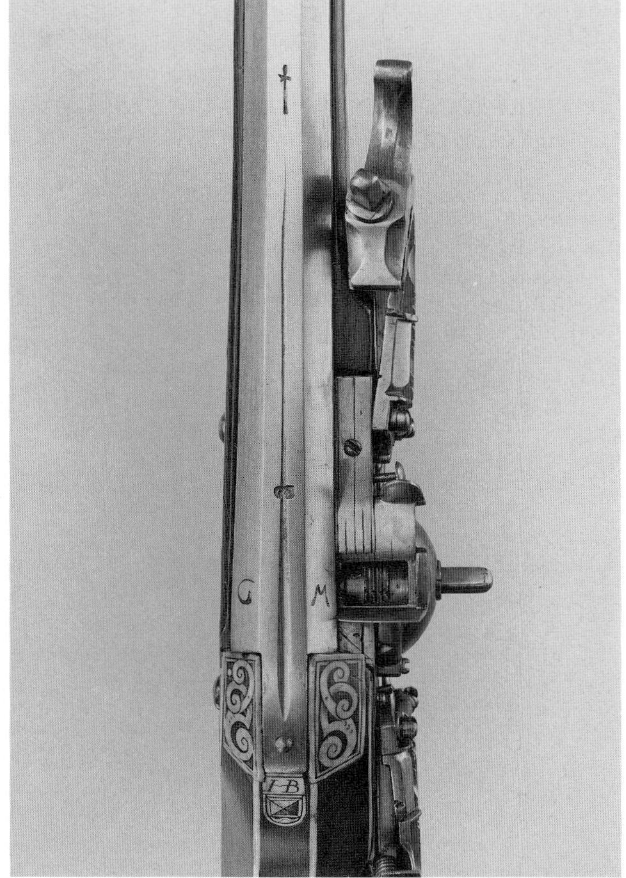

# The Bourgeosie

830

## Malmø Saint Knud's Guild Cup

Alexander Trægaard, Copenhagen 1648; engraved 1652 (Bøje 44 and Copenhagen mark)
Chased, engraved silver, cast figure on lid. H. 47.5 cm
St. Knud's Guild in Malmö, deposited at Malmö Museum
Engraved with the arms and names of seven noblemen: Holger Vind, Johan Friederich Marschalk, Hugo Lützow, Mathias Budde, Frantz Brockenhuus, Christian Urne and Philip Barstorf. Also a full-figure picture of the crowned Blessed Knud holding a halbard and stepping on the Dragon of Evil. On the lid a Roman warrior with a drawn sword.
*Provenance:* Believed to have been presented to the Saint Knud guild in Malmø on the occasion of Frederik III's admission in 1652.
*Literature:* E. Lassen 1964 92-96; J. Kruse 1895.

831

## Four "Mayoral" cups

Marked MH, Bøje 8024, and Copenhagen mark 1610
Silver, chased and engraved. H. 25.8 cm
Københavns Bymuseum og Det kgl. kjøbenhavnske Skydeselskab og Danske Broderskab. The four lidded cups in the shape of goblets are nearly identical: decorated with engraved birds and other animals, the year 1613 and the mark and initials MW for Mikkel Vibe – a Danish peasant's son, who became a great merchant with interests in whaling, trade with Iceland and the North, and in the East India Company. He became councilman in Copenhagen in 1602, mayor from 1609. In 1621 he became the overseer of the salt companies; he was involved in the construction of Christianshavn.
*Provenance:* According to Resen presented by Mikkel Vibe to the Danish Company. The inventory list in the Copenhagen city treasury for 1725 states that they were in the city hall; they escaped the fire of 1728. The Royal Shooting Club and The City Museum of Copenhagen each own two.
*Literature:* A. Linvald 1927-28; Langeland-Mathiesen 1934 240f.; Boesen and Bøje 1948 no. 39-39; Lindahl 1980; Erichsen 1984 17.

*830*

832

## The money box of the City of Aalborg

Early 1600's
Wood, iron. H. 19.5, diam. 13.5 cm
Aalborg Historiske Museum, no number.
The cylindrical money box is painted green and mounted with red painted iron bands. Locked with two padlocks. On the back the arms of Aalborg are painted twice.

833

## Writing implements

Bernt Mathisen, Aalborg (mark: crowned rose), 1647
Pewter, glass, and wood. 12.4×20.1×25.4 cm
City of Aalborg, deposited in the Aalborg Historiske Museum, 9323
The rectangular tray holds an inkwell of glass with a wooden lid and a sand castor. In the corners, four identical figures of Pallas Athena. The tray rests on four reclining lions. On the sides the names of the mayors of Aalborg and the councilmen, and the year 1647. On the bottom the inscription: This has been given to Aalborg City Hall by pewtersmith Bernt Mathisen in the year 1647.
*Provenance:* The inkwell was used at Aalborg City Hall in the mayor's office from 1647 to 1942.

834

## Tankard which belonged to the mayor of Copenhagen, Iver Poulsen, and Karen Munck

Mark MH and Copenhagen mark 1610, engraved 1615
Silver, gilded on the inside, chased, engraved. H. 19 cm
The National Museum, Second Dep't., D1039/1982
A piece typical of the first decades of Christian IV's reign, with its chased and engraved ornamentation. An engraving in the bottom shows that it belonged to Iver Poulsen.
*Provenance:* Believed to have been in England for a period. Arne Bruun Rasmussen's auction 212 (1967), no. 863, and 430 (1981), no. 175. Gift from The New Carlsberg Foundation on the occasion of the National Museums anniversary in 1982.
*Literature:* E. Lassen 1964 75ff. and Lindahl 1982 103ff.

835

## The mayor of Odense Jacob Let's tankard

Mark for Jacob Christensen (Bøje 4065) and for Odense (Bøje 4004); engraved with the year 1618
Silver, chased and engraved. H. with lid lever 26.5.
The National Museum, Second Dep't., D1538
Let was councilman from 1599 and mayor 1607-22.
*Provenance:* Part of a "Swedish wars" hoard from Mesinge north of Kerteminde, found in 1880.
*Literature:* E. Lassen 1964 75ff. and Lindahl 1982 103ff.

*836*

836
## Lidded bowl with handles

Mark of Geert Hermans, Aalborg 1594
Silver, chased and engraved. H. 11 cm., d. 15.5 cm
The National Museum, Second Dep't., D9/1961
Belonged to the mayor of Randers, Niels Jacobsen and his wife; initials and coats of arms on the lid and the handles. The domed lid with three ball feet is in itself a bowl.
*Provenance:* Purchased in 1961; inscriptions on the bowl indicate that it has been an heirloom in Niels Jacobsen's family for several hundred years.
*Literature:* Boesen and Bøje 1948 no. 312

837
## Fire guild drinking horn from Bysum

Drinking horn from the late Middle Ages, North Frisian, "renovated" 1604
Tame ox horn from southern Europe, the silver mountings cast and engraved; three crystals cut en cabochon. L. 65 cm., diam. at the top 14 cm.
The National Museum, Second Dep't., CMLIX
Acquired by the fire guild of Bysum, Ditmarsken, in 1604 from the Huddingman family, who had gotten it from Hans Hesk and the Wittingman family. A new mouthpiece mounting with inscriptions, the middle band and carved ornaments done in 1604; the griffin's head with the little lion above and the feet with claws may be older.
*Provenance:* 1823 sent to the Museum of Northern Antiquities (now the National Museum) by royal order through bailiff Griebel in North Ditmarsk.
*Literature:* Olrik 1909 27 no. 4.

838
## Bourgeois silver hoard

Silver rummer presumed to be made by Gert Hermansen, Århus; imported pomander, whistle with a chain, and ornaments. 1640's
Silver, chased, engraved, niello. Rummer h. 8 cm
The National Museum, Second Dep't., D310 and D312-15
Belonged to a well-to-do citizen of Horsens, Hans Munk, and his wife. The initials KID on the rummer suggest it belonged to the wife; a little pomander – a scent box with compartments for spices, (cf. cat. 818e and 910) – hung on her belt. The filigreed basket with a little frog was probably also hers, just as the two silver coins from 1624 and 1638 may have been maternity gifts. Hans Munk wore the silver chain around his neck when he went hunting.
*Provenance:* Found in 1868 in Søndergade, Horsens, under a hollowed out foundation stone in a cellar wall. Assumed to have been hidden during the Torstensson War in 1644 or the Swedish Wars with Carl Gustav 1657-60.
*Literature:* Olrik 1909 121 no. 11.

*839*

839
## Christianshavn's seal, 1641

Bronze, 6.1×4.8×2.4 cm
The National Museum, Second Dep't., D2747
In the central section the arms of Christianshavn: a tower with a round arched gate below, in which there is a lion rampant. Above the gate Christian IV's crowned monogram. The building has a spire with three crowns stacked above each other. The spire is flanked by the year 1641. Inscription encircling the design: CHRISTIANSHAFNSSTADZWAPEN SI DEVS PRO NOBIS QVIS CONTRANOS (The arms of the town of Christianshavn. If God is with us, who can be against us).
*Provenance:* Bought in 1893 from estate owner Riise, Hedehusene. Believed to have belonged to Assistenshuset.
*Literature:* P. B. Grandjean 1937 21

*840-845*

The separate provincial laws from the Middle Ages, together with the municipal regulations of the boroughs, made up the nation's legal basis until the introduction of Christian V's Danish Law of 1683. Before this, however, a steady stream of national laws, recesses, etc. were promulgated which were in force both in town and country. The boroughs had their own jurisdiction and the city gate represented the transition to the laws of the borough, with its council elected by the citizens, the city court as the judicial branch and the royal appointee (byfoged) as the executive. The administration of justice was strict. Capital and other physical punishments were common; prison was almost exclusively custodial, keeping the prisoner until judgement was passed in his case. Theft was in principle punishable by death, if the stolen goods had a value of over one half mark; men were hanged and women buried alive under a tub. When these laws were made one half mark was a sizable amount, but with the fall in the value of money, by c. 1600 even petty theft could mean execution – however pardons were common in minor cases.

840

## The Ribe Municipal Law

Ribe, early 1400's, binding from the early 1600's
Ms. on vellum, full binding with silver mountings, 4°
Den antikvariske Samling i Ribe, 200X1
The manuscript, from, the first half of the 1400's, contains, in addition to the Ribe municipal law from 1269, The Jutish Law from 1241, Erik Klipping's National Law from 1284 and various local historical notes. The binding has silver clasps and ornaments from the early 1600's; two identical clasps, in the shape of a shield with the town of Ribe, held by two angels, and on the front cover there is a medallion with the head of Christ in profile.
*Provenance:* Ribe Raadhussamling
*Literature:* P. Kr. Madsen 1983.

841

## Christian IV's Court signet 1630

Silver. D. 4 cm
Rosenborg, 3.139
Round signet of silver with a hinged handle and an engraved plate. In the middle the Danish national coat of arms with a cross overlaid by three lions. Around the shield an ornamental scrollwork, from behind which the ends of arms of the cross are visible. The upper end of the cross is surmounted by the king's crown, which is closed above by an arched band. Encircled by an inscription: "Sigillum Regni Daniae ad Causas". At the outer edge, a wreath motif consisting of interesecting triangles. On the hinged handle is engraved "1630".
*Provenance:* Rosenborg's inventory 1877, p. 23, no. 35. 1867 transferred from the Museum of Sculpture and Handicraft.
*Literature:* P. B. Grandjean 1951 21.

842

## Two beggar's badges, Copenhagen 1605 and Elsinore 1649

Cast lead. 4.5×3.8 cm. and 3.5×4.1 cm
The National Museum, Second Dep't., D6929 and 19765
The beggar's badges, here with the city arms of Copenhagen and Elsinore respectively, were intended to be sewn onto the clothing of the beggars. Beggar's badges were introduced in Spain in 1393, in Scotland in 1424-25 and in Denmark for the first time under Christian II 1521/22, again in 1537 and at numerous later points. The purpose was to limit beggary, so that only actual charity cases, who were chartered and controlled by the authorities, had the legal right to beg within a town, or in the rural areas within a parish, whose badge the beggar was to wear visible on his chest.
*Provenance:* Earth-find, Christian IX's Gade, Copenhagen, 1908 and under the construction of Elsinore harbor, respectively.
*Literature:* Matthiessen 1925 115

843

## Executioner's sword from Ribe

Presumably North Italian, c. 1550-1600
Iron. L. 114.4 cm
Den antikvariske Samling i Ribe, 200 X 21
Long handle sheathed in wood, broad and powerful blade with a short hollow grind. The width of the blade narrows slightly towards the tip, which is broken off. Near the tip three holes, presumably to hold lead balls to increase the weight of the sword when in use. On each side of the blade is a seal design, and on one side a

*844*

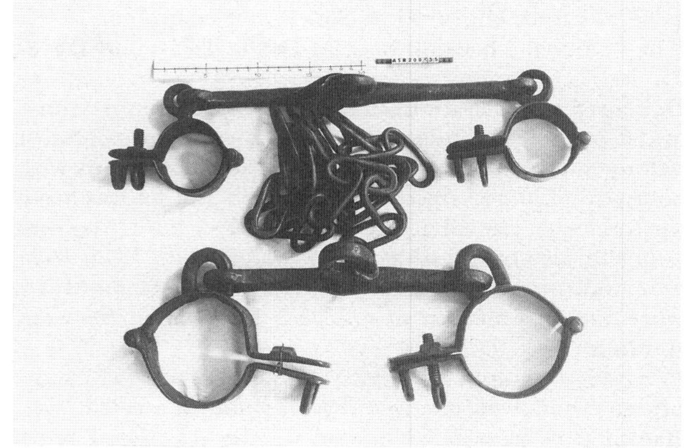

*842*

square stamp with the letters ST (the smith's mark?). To be beheaded was more honourable than hanging. It even happened – at times on the way up to the gallows – that a sentence could be commuted from the gallows to the sword.

*Provenance:* Ribe Raadhussamling.

*Literature:* P. Kr. Madsen 1983 35; Matthiessen 1910 52 ff.

844

## Hand and foot irons, 1600's

Iron; bar to the hand iron l. 34.3 cm., bar to the foot iron 27 cm

Den antikvariske Samling i Ribe, 200 X 35

Made up of four holders, each made of two flat hammered iron pieces, bent into half circles. These are hinged on the one side and bent on the other into flanges with holes for a lock. The hand and foot irons are fastened through eyes to iron bars, joined by chain. The prisoners in the prisons of the period often bore such irons, at times supplemented by neck irons, to prevent escape.

*Provenance:* Ribe Raadhussamling

*Literature:* P. Kr. Madsen 1983; Matthiessen 1915 100-120.

845

## Executioner's tools, 1600's

Iron; tongs l. 76 cm., thumbscrew 7.5 cm

The National Museum, Third Dep't., 382/1943 and 393/1943

The *pincers,* with three and two "claws", that interlock – were, when red hot, used to pinch criminals, either as torture or as part of the punishment. Last used in 1753 in connection with an excution. The *thumbscrew* consists of three pieces linked together with a screw in the middle, with which the two hinged parts can be pressed together towards the centerpiece. The piece has depressions, equipped with blunted points, for the thumbs. According to a tariff from 1612 the executioner of Copenhagen was payed ½ daler to "... to torture, when so ordered".

*Provenance:* The pincers was fastened to the old City Hall in Kolding, demolished in 1839. The Museum of Northern Antiquities 1852 (now the National Museum), inv.no. 1280; thumbscrew purchased for The National Museum, Second Dep't., in 1904, inv.no. D5471. Both later delivered to The National Museum, Third Dep't., Danish Folk Museum.

*Literature:* Eliassen 1923. Matthiesen 1910. H. Rasmussen 1986.

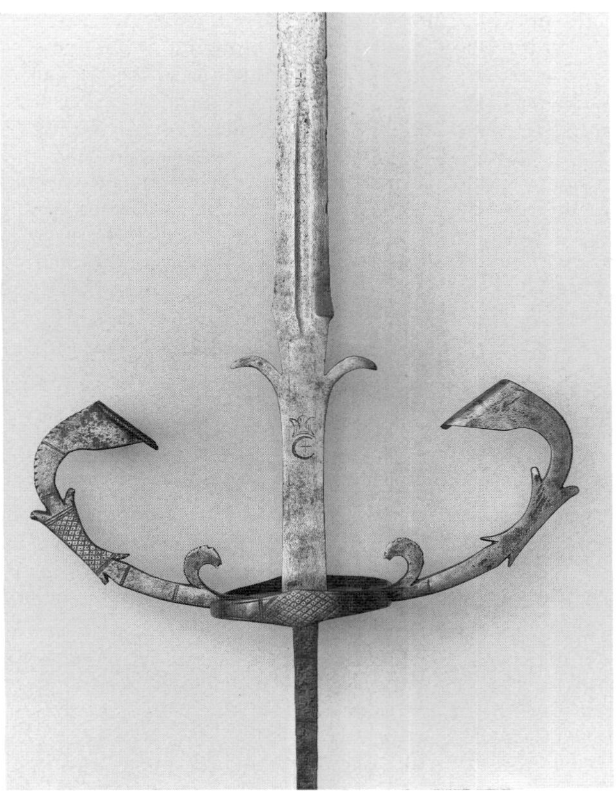

*846*

846

## Nine ceremonial broadswords from Copenhagen

Solingen (?) – presumed from Wilm Kleins – and perhaps Passau, c. 1600, one (18969) with the year 1598 on the blade.

Iron blades and iron, one blade (18965) has traces of brass decorations, total length 159-234 cm

The National Museum, Second Dep't., 18965-71 and -73 and D85/1955 (18965 and -69) deposited at the City Hall in Copenhagen)

The two handed broad sword was originally a military weapon, which most likely was used first in Switzerland at the beginning of the 1400's. Mercenaries equipped with the two-handed broad sword received twice as much pay as others; their duty was to hack a path through the pikes of the enemy into the infantry ranks. Towards the end of the 1500's the broad swords became so heavy that they were impractical as actual weapons; instead they were used ceremonially, e.g. by colour guards and honor guards for officers and other important persons. The broad swords shown here – of which two bear the inscription"Christian / der vierte" on the blade, the one also has the king's crowned monogram on the ricasso – have presumably been borne by the town marshalls as a mark of dignity for the town judge in Copenhagen. Similar swords with the king's name is known from Malmø (hanging in the mayoral office) and from Ribe (cat. 847). These towns were, like Copenhagen, outside the jurisdiction of the *landsting* (court), which meant that the town judge had the same rank as the judges of the landsting; cases decided by him could be appealed directly to the highest level, the King's Court. One of the swords (D85/1955) has had a separate fate from the others. It was presented to the English general, Baron Thomas Blomefield, leader of the English artillery corps that bombarded Copenhagen in 1807 – according to tradition because he did not confiscate the bells of the city. While in English hands it has been provided with a secondary hilt covering.

*Provenance:* Copenhagen City Hall. The swords can be traced in the city hall inventory in the accounts of the treasury from 1673 and on. Survived the City Hall fire of 1795, when they must have lost their hilt coverings. Found during the cleaning of the attic of the next city hall building, now the court house, presented to the Museum of Northern Antiquities (now the National Museum) in 1859. Two of the swords have been deposited in Copenhagen's new City Hall since 1902, hung in the room where the city council meets; one is a present to the National Museum in 1955 from Sir Thomas Blomefield, London. (cf. above).

*Literature:* Engberg 1962-64. Re: confiscation of the bells, see also Grinder-Hansen 1982 and 1985.

847

## Three ceremonial broadswords from Ribe

Solingen ?, c. 1600

Iron blades, of which the two are broken, and iron hilt, with partly preserved wooden covering. L. 112.6-155.4 cm

Den antikvariske Samling i Ribe, inv.nr. 100 X 7, X 9 and X 20

The collection of Ribe City Hall has seven ceremonial swords; of the three exhibited here, two have the inscription "CHRISTIAN / DER VIERDTE" on the blade, while the third has "C4" under an acanthus-stylized crown (cf. cat. 846). Just as Copenhagen and Malmø were, Ribe was outside the jurisdiction of the *landsting* (court) according to the decree by Frederik II in 1586.

*Provenance:* Ribe Raadhussamling, perhaps from the armory in the previous city hall in Grønnegade (1394-1709).

*Literature:* P. Kr. Madsen 1983; Engberg 1962-64 459-498.

848

## Nine high hats

Professional work 1600's

Knit, coarse wool. 17-27 cm. high, diam. 29-35, brim width 7-7.5 cm.

Københavns Bymuseum 1941/140A, 1947/169 and no number; The National Museum, Second Dep't., 2×D6711, D9776, D9819, D12062
The hats are of high quality knitting technique. Knit from above in one piece with the brim, which is double-knit and cast off at the edge. Originally the hats have been fulled so that they ressembled felt, and perhaps they were dyed.
*Provenance:* Earth-find in Copenhagen
*Literature:* Warburg 1987.

849

## 14 gloves, 1600's

Wool knit in stockinette stitch. 26-39 cm. long
Københavns Bymuseum 1941/144B and two without nos.; The National Museum, Second Dep't., D1118, D4215, D8936, D9822, D9823, D9825, D9826, D40/1985, D41/1985, D42/1985 D45/1985
*Provenance:* Earth-find in Copenhagen.
*Literature:* Warburg 1981 and 1987.

850

## Three children's stockings and a long "winter" stocking, 1600's

Wool knit in stockinette stitch. 22-28 cm. and 53 cm. long
Københavns Bymuseum 1941/146c and no number
One of the children's stockings was probably white; "winter" stocking has sown on raised nap.
*Provenance:* Earth-find in Copenhagen.
*Literature:* Warburg 1987.

851

## Copenhagen seen from the land side and from the water

Coloured copper engraving from Braunius and Hogenberg IV, Köln 1588. Perhaps from an original drawn by Hans Knieper, (cf. cat. 758 and 828)
Det kgl. Bibliotek
This double prospect is the oldest known reproduction of Copenhagen. The prospects show the city – the upper from Valby Hill, the lower from the island of Amager – before Christian IV's considerable construction program. The road in the foreground on the upper prospect leads over the bridge at St. Jørgen's Lake into Vesterport (the West gate of the city). Outside the city in the foreground is on the left, St. Jørgen's Hospital, several post mills, the gallow's hill and a few buildings just under the medieval city wall. On the left the tower of St. Petri Church, the tall spire belongs to the Church of Our Lady. On the right, the monasteries of St. Gertrud and St. Clara, and Nicolai Church with its little roof spire. Directly to the left of the castle complex one sees the end wall of the Naval Dockyard's anchor smithy, and masts from the ships anchored at the Dockyard Bridge. On the right of the castle, Christian III's arsenal and furthest out on the point, the two mills belonging to the castle. – On the lower picture ships lie at anchor in Grønnegård's harbour. From the spit on the right there is a ferry connection over to the castle island (Slotsholm), roughly at the location where Christian IV later established the bridge. Just across from the spit is the entrance to the old harbour in the stream bed between the castle island and the city. On the right of this, the anchor smithy, St. Nicolai Church and at the extreme edge of the picture Østerport (East gate) on the site of the present *Kongens Nytorv.*
*Literature:* Grove 1908 10-11; Mollerup 1912 2-3; Lorenzen 1937 63-70; Erichsen 1974 16.

852

## Map of Copenhagen, c. 1600

Wash drawing
Det kgl. Bibliotek
Plan of the city with the label: "Oldest plan of Copenhagen c. 1585", which shows the medieval city in its last phase before Christian IV's expansion. The city lies like an island, closely surrounded by its ramparts and moats. Above, *Vesterport,* to the right, *Nørreport,* and at the bottom *Østerport* on the site of the present *Kongens Nytorv.* Within the ramparts are the old churches, streets and squares of the city; of the other buildings only the City Hall is shown. – The left side of the map shows the harbour, the Naval Dockyard and the buildings on the *Slotsholm.* Furthest to the left (D) is Christian IV's new arsenal, built in 1598-1604. But the building built facing it in 1602-1606, the Naval Stores, is missing. Thus the drawing must be dated to c. 1600.
*Literature:* Grove 1980 7-10; Lorenzen 1937 64f.; Gamrath 1980 18-26

853

## Copenhagen seen from the Southeast

Jan Dirichs van Campen from a lost painting by Jan van Wijk, 1611
Copper engraving. C. 35×100 cm
The Antiquarian Topographical Archive of the National Museum
"HAFNIA METROPOLIS ET PORTVS CELEBERRIMVS DANIÆ" (Copenhagen, Denmark's very celebrated city and harbour), is the headline on this well-known prospect. The city and the harbour are viewed from an imaginary point above Amager after Christian IV's first extensive construction phase. The left side of the picture is dominated by the king's new Naval Arsenal (1602-06), with the arsenal and the naval stores in front of the old Copenhagen Castle. In the middle ground the city itself with Christian IV's new city hall (1610) and the spires of the Church of the Holy Ghost and Nicolai Church's new spire (1594 and 1610). On the right the Dockyard with the Naval Shipyard, which in 1606 was separated from the city by the construction of the new rampart on the

854

east, Østervold. In the foreground, immediately behind the rampart, the old anchor smithy, which in 1619 was converted to Holmens Kirke (the Naval Church). Furthest to the right Frederik II's long ropewalk with the sail house, the remains of which can still be seen behind Charlottenborg.
*Provenance:* The original was destroyed in the City Hall fire of 1728. The engraving is only known to exist in three copies, of which the National Museum owns one.
*Literature:* Grove 1908 11-14:; Mollerup 1912 6f.; Lorenzen 1937 63-70; Erichsen 1974 17f.

854

## Bourgeois interior from Aalborg

Wainscoting and ceiling built in 1602 for Aalborg concilman Niels Christensen's home on the corner of Østeraa and Stranden
The National Museum, Third dep't. Dansk Folkemuseum; furnishings belong to The National Museum, Second Dep't

The councilman's house had storage rooms in the ground floor and the living quarters above. *The wainscoting,* of which sections are found i Aalborg Historiske Museum, are typical examples of the work of the cabinetmaker workshops of the town. – The furniture is from various parts of the country, and shows a style which the provincial cabinetmakers mastered for decades. The furnishing corresponds more or less to what would be found on a prosperous farm. *The table,* dated 1644, is placed in front of *a bench fixed to the wall* under the windows. The man of the house sat by the *corner cupboard. The four-poster* 1642, was often placed in the parlor. In the one corner is a "*trésorskab*" (cupboard) of Northern Jutish type, carved in coffering. Heating was done by a *stove* fed from another room, here built from plates from a Jutish iron foundry. The windows have the typical Renaissance form with inset *glass paintings* – remembrances with the names and marks of the donors.

# Navigation and Shipping

856
## Church ship, the warship "Randers"

Danish, 1632
Painted wood. L. c.100 cm
Skt. Morten sogns menighedsråd, Randers
Presumed to be the oldest preserved church ship in Denmark, this model depicts a warship from the beginning of the 1600's. Repaired 1704, c. 1700, 1826 and most recently in 1976 by Customs Officer Nissen, Varde.
*Provenance:* According to a painted inscription given in 1632 by councilman, later mayor of Randers, Jesper Lauritzen.
*Literature:* Henningsen 1950 42f., 149.

857
## Fregate for table decoration, 1600's

Silver filigree work. 35×30×10 cm., weight c. 735 gr.
The National Museum, Second Dep't., D150
Model, made as a table decoration, of a three masted warship from the 1600's. The ship – a frigate with 30 canons at full sail and with the wind abaft the beam – has a crowned lion as a figurehead. The flag has three vertical sections (Dutch?), from the mast tops wave smooth penants, on the mast a smaller smooth square flag. The hull and deck are made of filigree, the rigging of spun silver thread, the sails of silver sheet. At the front hang three large and one smaller anchor, the port stern lights are missing. In 1751 it was mounted in a black case, in 1775 in a black box with gold edgings and glass on three sides.
*Provenance:* From the Court (via valet Braun) to the Royal Kunstkammer, 17. Sept. 1751, inv. 1775, 124/c130; The Royal Museum of Art, CBb 13; the Museum of Northern Antiquities 1867.

858
## Dutch ships at the Copenhagen waterfront

After 1634; signed B.P., for Bonaventura Peeters I (1614-52). On the back the seal of the St. Luke Guild of Antwerp
Oil on oak. 72.5×101.5 cm
Københavns Bymuseum 1984:71
A lively activity among Danish, Swedish and several Dutch ships in front of a rather inaccurate version of Copenhagen, seen from the East – i.e. c. 45° further north than van Wijk's panorama (cat. 853). In the middle a Dutch warship, saluting and about to set sail or unrig, behind it a Danish warship at anchor.
*Provenance:* Gift from New Carlsberg Foundation 1984
*Literature:* Erichsen 1985 130f.

*857*

859
## Two pane glass painting with ships, 1600's

Painted pane glass in new lead frame. 17×12.5 and 16.5×12.8 cm
The National Museum, Second Dep't., D11055
Both are joined, a) of two different paintings: above the superstructure and rigging of a warship of an early 1600's type; from the mast tops fly the Oldenborg colours, and in the rigging there is lively activity of sailors setting the topmast's mainsail. Below the hull of a cog-like trading vessel or fishing boat with a man dressed in black at the rudder. b) two versions of apparently the same warship, which flies the Danish flag from the masts; the piece with the spanker is a newer repair job. On the hull an anchor is visible, and a pair of canon; below the inscription: "...tikren (?) Raszmussön." See also the glass painting of a three masted warship in the middle-class parlour (cf. cat. 854).
*Provenance:* From Chr. A. Jensen's collection, to the National Museum 1927.

*859a*

860

## Atlas supporting celestial globe

Raphael Custodis (1590-1651)
Bronze and brass, partly gilded. H. 64.5 cm
The National Museum, Second Dep't., D146
The figure and the globe, which perhaps did not originally belong together, are believed to have been part of a large pyramid-shaped clock – made by Heinrich Habrecht in 1630 – in the Ducal Art Collection at Gottorp Castle. The figure could be Italian from the end of the 1500's and as such older than the globe, which is signed "Raphael Custodis scalpsit [sic]".
*Provenance:* 1734 and 1743 in the Ducal Art Collection at Gottorp Castle. The Royal Kunstkammer, inv. 1775, 108/b200; 1826 to the Royal Art Museum, D(G) 440; 1867 to the Museum of Northern Antiquities (now the National Museum).
*Literature:* Schlee 1975, 91f. Gottorf 1965 no. 263; Aarhus Kunstmuseum 1971 no. 19.

861

## The warship "Hannibal", built 1646

Willem van de Velde the younger, perhaps from an original by the elder, 1659(?)
Pencil and wash, outlined with fine pen and brown ink on paper. 35.5×62.8 cm.
National Maritime Museum, London, Robinson 58
The warship "Hannibal" with 63 canons, built on Hovedøya outside Christiania (Oslo) in 1646, named for the vice-regent, Hannibal Sehested. 1658 renamed "The Swan", when Hannibal Sehested declared his neutrality in the war, scrapped 1716.
*Provenance:* Messing's collection, acquired by the National Maritime Museum 1932.
*Literature:* Robinson 1958/74 no. 58. National Maritime Museum 1982 no. 62.

862

## The warship "Trekroner"

"I.D.S.", presumably Jan Dirichs van Campen (cf. cat. 853) from original by Christian Møller, 1616
Copper engraving. 57×66 cm
Det kgl. Bibliotek, Kortsamlingen
This very large engraving depicts Christian IV's flagship, "Trekroner" (Three Crowns), which in 1606 brought him to England. There the 1500 ton, lavishly decorated ship – "gilded aft and stern, carved with pictures, which are painted in all manner of colours" – received deserved attention. Thousands of people made the excursion to Gravesend to see what at the time was indeed a very large ship, built by the Scot David Balfour (b.1574). He worked in Denmark from 1597 (from 1601 as a resident ship builder) to his death in 1634. There is a Latin poem in praise of Christian IV's mastery of the sea at bottom of the engraving.
*Literature:* Styhr 1943, 60; Lind 1889, 368f.; Glarbo 1956.

863

## Christian IV's compass

Unknown, Copenhagen (?), 1595
Gilded silver. Diam. 20.9 cm
Rosenborg, 1.78
Dry compass with a handpainted rose in a gilded silver box with a hinged lid. On the inside of the lid are engraved the Danish national arms. Over the crown the initials C.R. (for Christianus Rex), under the elephant, which is suspended in a wreath of leaves, the year 1595. On the round sides of the box, the arms of the Danish provinces under inscriptions: "Dennenmarck. Norwegen. Gothen. Wenden. Unio 3 Regi. Gotland. Schleswig. Island. Holstein. Stormarn. Ditmers. Femern. Oldenburg. Delmenhorst. Oesel", and an empty oval section. The dial of the compass is made of several layers of paper glued together. The rose is drawn with ink and

painted with colours and gold. A lily indicates North, the variation is indicated with thin ink lines.
*Provenance:* Rosenborg's inventory 1830. Lit. A 120.
*Literature:* Henningsen 1980 138ff.; Liisberg 1929, pl. VIII.

864

## Bagge Wandel: Det vaagendis Øye

Printed by the university printer Melchior Martzan, København 1649
Full binding with gold tooling on the back, 8°
Marinens Bibliotek, 46 (nr. 14)
One of the oldest Danish textbooks in navigation. Bagge Wandel, 1622-83, was named head of the Navigation School on Bremerholm on June 6, 1647 by Christian IV.
*Literature:* Ehrencron-Müller VIII 404ff.; Lind 1889 432 ff.

865

## Astrolabe. Nautical instrument for measuring the altitude of stars

Perhaps produced by Champlain, dat. 1600
Cast in brass. Half circular shape, diam. 34 cm., h. 33 cm., 0.16-0.18 cm. thick
Handels- og Søfartsmuseet på Kronborg, K3573
On the half circle's outer edge is engraved an arc of 180° (2×90°), subdivided into half degrees. Under the center of the arc is a half round metal disk with four fleur-de-lis, stamped in a rhomboid pattern. Under 90° the year "1600". A 5-6 cm. thick metal pointer (alhidade) pivots at the center of the disk. Two plates are attached at right angles to the pointer, and each has a fine perforation (sight vane) placed so that the sighting line through the holes can be aligned with the outer edge of the pointer, which marks the position to be read. Above there is an arched band, which revolves on two axes, one parallel to, and the other at right angles to the plane of the instrument. The astrolabe, which is very heavy, is suspended from the arched band during use, so that it rights itself vertically with the baseline parallel with the plane of the horizon. The instrument is unique in its form, since the few other remaining nautical astrolabes are all formed as full circles.
*Provenance:* Purchased in the antique trade in 1928.
*Literature:* Price 1956 338 ff.

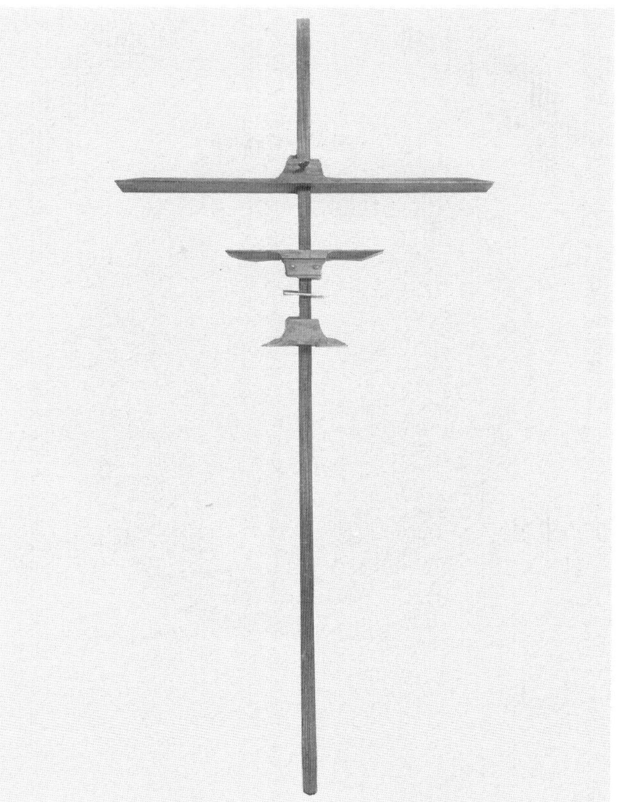

*866*

*865*

866

## Cross-staff. Nautical instrument used to take the altitude of the sun or stars, c. 1600

Staff of ebony. Length 82.8 cm. with wooden slides, 8.8, 16.3 and 38.9 cm.
Württembergisches Landesmuseum Stuttgart, KK 80

*870*

Long squared edged ebony staff with degrees on all 4 sides. On the staff 3 right-angled wooden slides of varying lengths, edged with narrow beveled mouldings. On the slides positioning screws of brass, on the smallest an inlay of bone along the one side.
*Provenance:* From the Dukes of Württemberg's Kunstkammer at Altes Schloss in Stuttgart.
*Literature:* Zinner 1956 210.

867

## Marine atlas: "Speculi Marini", 2nd part

Drawn by Lucas Janszoon Waghenaer, engraved by Jan van Deutecum. Printed 1586
Printed with hand coloured maps, bound in red velvet with gold tooling, 42.5×29.5 cm
Det kgl. Bibliotek, Kortsamlingen
36 pages of text and 25 maps on 50 unnumbered pages. At the very beginning a printed dedication to Frederik II. Latin edition of the first printed marine atlas, "Spiegel der Zeevaerdt", Leiden 1584-85, which was widely used and in the following decades was reprinted in numerous editions and in many languages. The maps, which cover the northern and western European waters, are plane charts, which do not take the curvature of the earth's surface into account and thus make it impossible to plot a course as a straight line.

868

## Marine atlas: "Het Licht der Zee-vaert"

Willem Janszoon Blaeu, 1571-1638, Amsterdam 1618
Printed. 25.7×29.5 cm
Det kgl. Bibliotek, Kortsamlingen
Blaeu was a pupil of Tycho Brahe; his atlas appeared for the first time in 1608. The maps are plane charts with a system of compass lines. At the beginning a guide to navigation, various tables and views of shorelines. On the first pages a handwritten survey of the voyages made by Admiral Henrik Vind in the service of the king from 1616 to the conclusion of the peace in 1629. Among others, he lead a convoy in 1622 made up of the warships Rytteren, Nellebladet and Fides, which conducted trading vessels such as those from the Salt- and Wine Company to Spain and back.
*Provenance:* Admiral Henrik Vind, 1594-1633. Transferred to The Royal Library from the University Library.

869

## Marine atlas: "Arcano del Mare", vol. 3, 2nd part

Robert Dudley, Florence 1647
Printed. 56.5×45.5 cm
Det kgl. Bibliotek, Kortsamlingen
The whole work is made up of three volumes and is the first marine atlas which covered the whole of the then known world. Whereas Waghenaer's and Blaeu's charts are plane, Dudley's are Mercator's charts, i.e. the distance between the latitudes increases between the Equator and the Poles, and the relationship between longitude and latitude remains correct at all times. The geographer Gerhard Mercator invented this method in 1569, but its use first became widespread on sea charts much later, and Arcano del Mare is the first marine atlas in which all the charts are in Mercator's projections.

870

## Armillary sphere; terrestrial globe surrounded by 11 hoops

Caspar Vopel (1511-1561), 1543
Paper maché and brass, largest diam. 12 cm
The National Museum, Second Dep't., D1656
11 spherical hoops which show the paths of the stars, with the Earth at the center. Signed by the Cologne cartographer Vopel (Vopell) in 1543, the same year in which Copernicus published his proof that the Sun is the center of the Universe; the last year of Copernicus' life. Leather covered wooden case.
*Provenance:* Belonged to Tycho Brahe according to a tradition probably founded on a more recent inscription in

*871*

the case. Bought for the Museum of Northern Antiquities (now the National Museum) by a physician in Randers in 1881. Zinner 1696 40 and 579.
*Literature:* Zinner 1956 40 579; Aarhus Kunstmuseum 1971 no. 18; Mosteiro dos Jerónimos, Lisbon 1983 no. 70.

## Clocks and Watches of the Renaissance

871

### Table and console clocks and pocket watches

European clockmaker art from the 1500's and 1600's
Gilded brass, silver and enamel
The National Museum, Second Dep't.,
The collection of watches and clocks is small, but exquisite; only a few will be given particular attention. In the 1500's and the early 1600's the finest watches were made in Germany, especially at Augsburg. Several of the works of these masters are represented in the exhibit. *Carol Schmidt* (1590-1635/36): small table clock in a crystal ball, inv.no.r D114. *Hans Buschmann* (d. 1662): table clock with the weights of the balance in the shape of birds, fluttering around an owl in the middle, D118. *Nicolaus Radeloff,* from 1647 employed by the court at Gottorp: spherical clock 1654, D106. Two console clocks, D1064 and D138, – the latter with three cross beats and with engravings on the lids showing: Copernicus and Tycho Brahe, each pointing at his own astronomical system – credited to Radeloff. *Stephan Brenner* (1553-1597): a table clock with the Bille arms, 6031. Examples of Danish masters are *Hans Stenbuch,* Copenhagen: table clock, 1629, D678/1960, and *Jacob Slange,* Helsingør: a hanging globular clock 1642, D2500, and a pillar table clock, 1647, D108.
*Provenance:* Most of the clocks on exhibit came from the royal Kunstkammer. Many can be traced back to the Kunstkammer at Gottorp Castle, where clockmaking flourished through the ducal connections to Hessen.
*Literature:* Liisberg 1908 151f., 164-66; Stiesdal 1951 and 1987. The National Museum, Second Dep't., 1971 e-i and k; Gottorf 1975 96f., no. 100 and 106.

## The North Atlantic

872

### Pieces of clothing from graves of whalers on Svalbard (Spitzbergen)

First half of the 1600's. Colour-plate XXXVIII
Kulturvernet for Svalbard og Jan Mayen

a) *Double knitted cap* of wool, presumably machine knit. Made of two slightly fulled, doubleknit pieces, sewn together. On the outside a pattern of natural coloured stripes alternating with dark and pale green – originally blue – stripes, dyed with indigo or wadje. Grave 4-1.

b) *A pair of long knitted stockings* of natural coloured wool, heavy grade. L. c. 64 cm. Fulled, roundknit with a marked "seam" at the back. Stocking garter edge at the top. Both stockings patched on the heels with sewn on pieces of woven material. Near the top of the leg of the stocking weak dye remnants from a shirt of plant content (probably line), which had been fastened to the upper edge of the stockings with brass pins. The shirt was checked, white and blue, dyed with indigo or wadje. Grave 14-1 & 2.

c) *Double button of brass.* Diam. 1.6. and 1.2. cm. Hollow and ornamented with a geometric pattern: on the front 6 radially placed pointed ovals on a circle. The buttons, which are throughly worn, are held together with an S-shaped brass wire (similar to a modern cufflink) and have been used as a throat closing in a shirt. Grave 15-2.

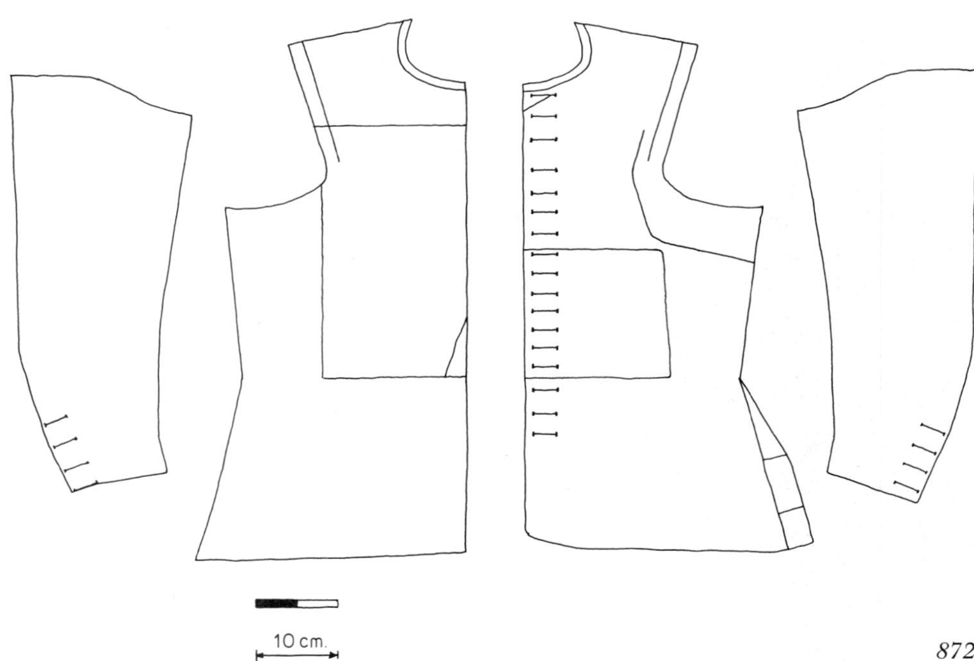


872

d) *Two pairs of long knit stockings* of natural coloured wool. The outer stockings have darned places on the underside of the foot. L. c. 66 cm. At the top weak dye remnants from a shirt presumably made of linen, which had white and blue stripes; the dye is indigo or wadje. The inner stockings have an arrow pattern at the ankles made with purl stitches. L. 62 cm.; at the top edge a 3.5 cm. wide garter edging. Grave 19A-1, 2 & 3.

e) *A pair of canvas woven garters* of natural coloured wool. Width c. 2 cm. Finished with a hem at the ends. Have been tied on the outside of the stockings just under the knee with three turns and closed with bows at the front. Grave 19A-4 & 5.

f) *Knitted hat with a narrow brim* of wool. Original colour probably yellowish-brown/brown. The edge of the brim has been lined with a c. 1.8 cm. wide woven band of natural coloured wool. The crown's h. c. 13 cm., dia. c. 62 cm, the brim's width c. 6.5 cm. Grave 19A-6 & 7.

g) *A pair of long knitted stockings* of natural coloured wool, lightweight grade. L. c.64 cm. On the ankle on each side an arrow pattern in purl stitches, partly in seed stitch. At the top a c. 2 cm. wide stocking garter edging. Very worn, darned on both the knee and feet. On the right stocking three canvas woven strips of c. 10×3 cm. have been sewn under the ball of the foot, curving up over the toes.

h) *Short form-fitting lined jacket,* wool. Darts in the sides, round neck. The outer material, which originally has been a lining in a jacket with a damask woven red outer material, is twill, and was originally red, presumably dyed with madder red. The lining is canvas woven, buttons, of which 9 were buttoned at the burial; at the sleeve openings there are four button holes. The jacket is very worn and has many darnings and patches; on the shoulders and the upper part of the back is a sewn on reinforcement/patch of a canvas mixed material (wool and a now disintegrated plant material). Grave 19B-4, 5, 6 & 7.

i) *20 turned buttons* of wood and bone from jacket h). 13 of hawthorn (diam. c. 1.5 cm.) from the front of the jacket. Four of wood (diam. c. 1.5 cm.) and three of bone (diam. c.1.5 cm) from the sleeves. Grave 19B-8 & 9.

j) *Knitted cap, ear-lap style* wool. Slightly fulled, presumably originally pale gray background colour, with a pattern in alternating blue, red and natural stripes, for which wadjeindigo and cochineal have been used. At the lower edge a 6.5 cm. cuff with ear-laps. Grave 19C-1.

k) *Doubleknit cap,* wool. The outer cap, presumably machine knit, is made of two identical pieces sewed together, with a pattern of two narrow green (originally blue) stripes; between these is a greenish (blue) "cloud pattern" on a background of natural colour. Lower down the pattern consists of alternating greenish and brownish (org. blue and red) stripes; the dyes are wadjeindigo and cochineal. The inner cap is of natural coloured wool and has its lower edge turned up and sewn to the outer cap. Grave 21-1.

l) Fragments of a pair of knee length pants of twill, slightly fulled, red woolen material, presumably dyed with madder-red. Under a narrow waistband of canvas woven material a series of narrow pleats. In the legs,

875

which are finished with an edging and a woven band, gussets at the crotch. No fly or other closing, the front pieces presumably just overlapped each other. Grave 38-1, 2, 3, & 4.
*Provenance:* Gravplads 2. Jensenvannet. Danskøya, Northwest Spitzbergen.
*Literature:* Albrethsen 1985; Lütken 1986.

873

## Whalers on Svalbard (Spitzbergen)

ABR(aham) Speeck, 1634
Oil on canvas. 122×197 cm
Skoklosters Slott, 11865
The painting depicts a Danish whaling station on Svalbard (Spitzbergen). The Danish flag waves above a couple of buildings in the background; on the end of the large building in the middle of the picture, under the flag, is a crowned "C4" in white on a red background. To the left whaling is carried on from small boats and in the foreground a Greenland whale is being flensed. On the right a whale oil works; on a keg on the lower right the signature ABR Speeck. A similar work in the Rijksmuseum, Amsterdam, by Cornelis de Man, 1639, with af Dutch flag over the whaling station, must be based on Speeck's picture.
*Provenance:* Estate inventory of Carl Gustaf Wrangel 1676; mentioned for the first time in Skokloster's inventory 1728.
*Literature:* Dalgård 1962 381.

874

## "Greneland", map of Svalbard (Spitzbergen)

English, c. 1625
Copper engraving. 33.5×41 cm
Det kgl. Bibliotek, Kortsamlingen
The illustrations in the margin depict whaling, boiling whale oil, the hunting of walrus and polar bear, and other activities.

875

## Johan Braem, 1595-1646, merchant, shipbuilder

Simon de Pas after a painting now at Frederiksborg, 1646
Copper engaving. 17.5×11.4 cm
Den kgl. Kobberstiksamling
Braem, who was from Hamburg, traded in Lisbon and Amsterdam before he came to Copenhagen in connection with the establishment of the Ostindiske Kompagni, of which he became the director in 1624. He was already involved in 1618 in whaling activity, which the next year was organized in the Nordlandske or Grønlandske Kompagni, a partnership between the king and a group of whaling shipowners. In 1620 he became – together with the merchants Mikkel Vibe (cf. borgmesterbøgerne, cat. 831) and Thomas Lorck – a director of the company; between 1619 and 1621 he visited Biscaya four times to enlist Basque whalers. When the king's praticipation in the whaling ended in 1622, Braem expanded his activities to Spitzbergen, where he and his brother, Goedert (cat. 876), obtained monopolies on the best whaling locations with royal privileges handed out in 1624, 1630, 1631 and 1634; he annexed a section of coastline, which he named Copenhagen Bay. In 1630 he is said to have called at Greenland. – Braem kept up his merchant trading as well as his whaling; he exported oxen and grain and had interests in trade with the Far East. In addition, he and his brother had plans for forming a Guinean and African company. Braem became one of the most prominent merchants with deliveries of all manner of luxury goods to the king and the Prince Elect and of wares to state institutions like the naval stores, the armory and the orphanage. In 1634 he received the con-

tract for all the copper from the works Gudsgave at Trondheim; in 1634 he became the administrator of the postal service and in 1639 judge of the admiralty.
*Literature:* Westergaard no. 1364; Schepelern 1951 no. 42; Dalgård 1962; DBL (Braem).

876

## Goedert Braem, 1601-55, merchant, shipowner

Albert Haelwegh from a painting by Karl van Mander, after 1655
Copper engraving. 17.4×11.2 cm
Den kgl. Kobberstiksamling, 7502
Goedert Braem, brother of Johan Braem (cf. cat. 875), became a citizen of Copenhagen in 1631 and a member of the Nordlandske or Grønlandske Handelskompangi. In 1631 he settled in Elsinore, where he was a customs official from 1639 to 1641 at the Sound toll. He participated in his brother's trading and whaling activities, and after Johan's death in 1646, moved to Copenhagen in order to take over his business and property. – On the engraving, to the left of Braem, is a view to the sea with a whaling scene.
*Literature:* Westergaard 1930 no. 1361; Sthyr 1965 no. 150.

877

## Christoffer Iversen (1580–d. after 1641) accountant at the exchequer, shipowner

Simon de Pas, 1633
Copper engraving. 13.3×8.8 cm
Frederiksborg
Iversen, who worked at the exchequer, was sent in 1617 to England to negotiate in the dispute over whaling near Spitzbergen. From the 1620's on he apparently had economic interests in whaling in addition to his public employment: for example he shipped whale oil from Copenhagen. In the 1630's he and his son-in-law Johan Ettersen competed in whaling with both the Islandske Kompagni and the Braem brothers. In 1636 he was the first to conduct whaling operations from the open sea without stations on land, which led to accusations from Johan Braem that Iversen had violated his monopoly north of the 71st degree latitude; Braem had Iversen's shipments attached in Amsterdam. – Iversen was fired as the head accountant in 1640 because of confusion in the accounts; an audit showed that 80.000 rigsdalere were missing. But Iversen avoided punishment since he was able to repay the king the missing amount.
*Literature:* Westergaard no. 5700; Schepelern 1951 no. 19; J. Jørgensen 1957; DBL (Iversen)

878

## Map of the Artic: "NOVA ET ACCURATA ATLAS POLI ARTICI et terrarum Circum Iacentium DESCRIPTIO"

Johannes Janssonius, Amsterdam 1650
Copper engraving, hand coloured. 41×52 cm
Det kgl. Bibliotek, Kortsamlingen
Published for the first time in 1637, exists in many editions. In the polar regions it is not possible to use the Mercator's projection (cf. cat. 869); instead the map has the North Pole as its center and the latitude degrees are placed as concentric circles.
*Literature:* Koeman 1967-85 IV 273, Me 164.

879

## Tusk of a narwhale (Monodon monoceros)

L. 188.4 cm
Rosenborg, 25.236
In the first half of the 1600's the tusk of the narwhale was still believed to be the much sought after and costly horn of the unicorn, which was thought to be an effective antidote to poisons. And when experiments apparently proved the assumption, the belief held, also long after Ole Worm had proved that the "horn" was merely the tusk of a sea mammal. The material was therefore often used for drinking cups and such. Expeditions to Greenland in 1605-1607 and 1635 brought back large quantities, and whalers occasionally were able to acquire these tusks.
*Provenance:* Greenland, most likely brought back in the 1600's. Rosenborg's inventarium 1718, p. 536 no. 68.
*Literature:* Bencard 1985 114-125.

880

## Cranium with tusks from a walrus (Odobenus rosmarus L.) Greenland

L. 60 cm.
Zoologisk Museum, CN10
Cranium of a large male walrus, lower jaw missing. The tusks are called the "ivory of the North".

881

## Two baleens (whalebones) from a Greenland whale (Balaena mysticetus L.)

320×25×4 cm
Zoologisk Museum, no number
The Greenland whale – which is a large lethargic and slow baleen whale ("right whale") with a very thick layer of blubber and baleens up to four meters long – can reach up to 18-20 meters in length and attain a weight of c. 100 metric tons. From one such whale up to 160 bar-

882 and 883

884a

rels of whale oil and 700-750 pieces of whalebone could be obtained, though from an average whale only about half of that was to be expected. The whalebone was a strong, elastic and light material, which could be formed in nearly any shape; it served the purposes that synthetic materials do today, and was used in the 1600's as stays in corsets and parasols, for bed springs and knife handles, riding whips and lanyards, in several types of crafts (cf. cat. 884) and as bristles in brushes and brooms. The whalebone fibers were used for wigs and feather decorations on hats and soldiers' helmets and also for furniture upholstery. The whalebone did not have any particular economic value, but for short periods the price might be high enough that an animal's whalebone gave just as much profit or more than its oil. This was – as is crude petroleum today – used for lighting, soap production, greases and paint, and for waterproofing leather and textiles. The whale meat was of no interest – perhaps the whalers themselves ate it.
*Literature:* Dalgård 1962.

Examples of objects (cat. 882-884), manufactured from raw material – narwhale tusk (unicorn, walros tusk and baleen – brought back from the whaling grounds in the North Atlantic.

882

## Two boxes of turned narwhale tusk

Danish?, 1600's
a) H. 6 cm., D. 6 cm.; b) H. 6.9 cm., 5.8 cm
The National Museum, Second Dep't., D436 and D453
The one box has a double rose of thin plates of narwhale tusk on its lid; the other is a double box, since a smaller box makes up the lid of a larger one.

*Provenance:* 1695 from Rosenborg to the Royal Kunstkammer; inv. 1737, 766/329 and 330. 1826 to the Royal Museum of Art, later Museum of Sculpture and Handicraft, inv.no. CCb25 and CCb19; 1869 to the Museum of Northern Antiquities (now the National Museum).

883

## Icelandic box with lid, 1600's

Walrus tusk and turned ivory. H. 11.8 cm. largest dia. 9 cm.
The National Museum, Second Dep't., D431
The staves in the body and bottom of the box and the knob on the lid are made of walrus tusk. The lid and the rings around the upper edge and bottom are of ivory.
The Royal Kunstkammer, inv. 1674, 21; 1689, 31/7; 1690, 47/27; 1727, 757/174. 1826 to Royal Museum of Art, later Museum of Sculpture and Handicraft, inv. no. CCa78. 1869 to the Museum of Northern Antiquities.

884

## Two reliefs made of whalebone

Attributed to John Osborn's workshop, c. 1626
Pressed whalebone, oval, a) 14.4×11.3 cm. b) 15.1×12 cm
a) The National Museum, Second Dep't., CAd163;
b) Statens Museum for Kunst, inv. 5517
a) depicts Henri IV of France, 1589-1610, and the companion piece b) can be assumed to be his mistress Gabrielle d'Estrées, 1573-99.
*Provenance:* The Royal Kunstkammer, inv. 1674, 19a; 1690, 59/44 and 43; 1737, 767/348 and 349. 1825 to Royal Museum of Art, CAd163 and 164. a) later to the

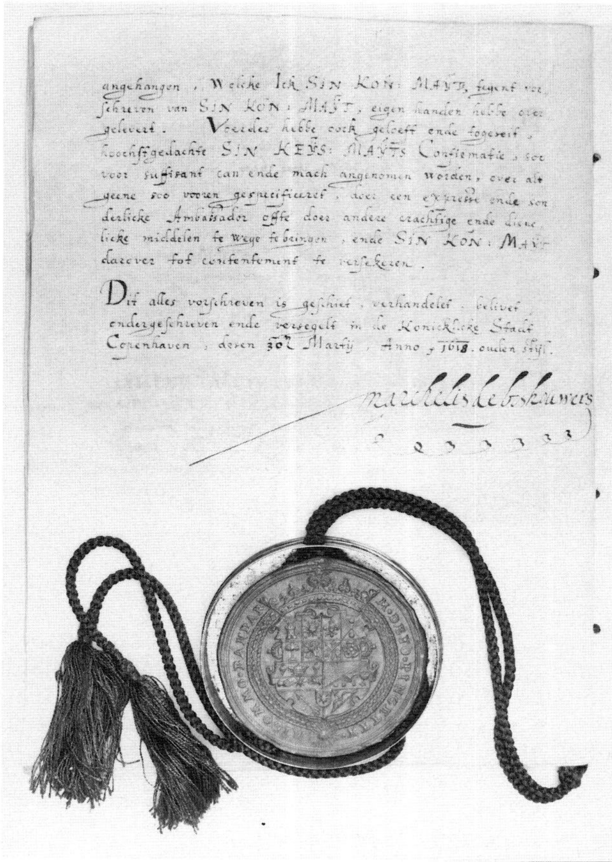
angehangen , Welcke Ick SIN KON: MAYT, tegent vor
schreven van SIN KON: MAYT, eigen handen hebbe over
gelevert . Voerder hebbe oock geloeft ende togeseit ,
hoochstgedachte SIN KEYS: MAYTS Confirmatie , soo
voor suffisant can ende mach angenomen worden , over alt
geene soo vooren gespecificeert , door een expresse ende son
derlicke Ambassador offte door andere crachtige ende diene
licke middelen te wege tebringen , ende SIN KON: MAYT
daerover tot contentement te verseekeren .

Dit alles vorschreven is geschiet , verhandelet , belivet ,
ondergeschreven ende versegelt in de Koninckliche Staet
Copenhaven , deren 30t Martij , Anno 1618 . ouden stijl .

*889*

Museum of Sculpture and Handicraft, and in 1869 to the Museum of Northern Antiquities; b) 1886 to The Royal Art Academy and in 1905 to the State Museum of Art.
*Literature:* H. Olsen 1980 I 87; II fig. 115

885

## Jens Munk's diary 1619-20

Munk's handwriting on paper
Det kgl. Bibliotek
In June of 1619, navy captain Jens Munk (1579-1628) was ordered by the king to undertake a voyage of discovery to the North Atlantic in order to find the "Northwest Passage" to India. With the warship "Enhjørningen" (the Unicorn) and the yacht "Lamprenen", he reached the Churchill River in Hudson's Bay in September the same year, where he set up a winter harbour, "Nova Dania". Of the 64 crew members, 61 died of the cold and scurvy in the course of the winter. With only two men Munk managed to sail the "Lamprenen" back to Denmark. He kept a diary throughout the whole voyage, which gives a detailed account of the adventures and trials of the expedition. The entry from June 8th, 1620, reads: "Since I now no longer could save myself from the bad smell and stench of the dead bodies, which had been lying around the ship for a good while, I got out of my bunk, any way I could ...". "And on land we had our shelter for a time under a bush ... and made a fire for ourselves during the day". ... "Towards the end we crawled all around, and wherever we saw the least bit of greenery growing up from the earth, we dug it up and sucked intensely on the root ..."
*Literature:* Printed illustrated edition "Navigatio Septentrionalis", Haffnia 1624. P. Lauridsen 1883.

886

## Finds from Jens Munk's winter harbour in Hudson's Bay

The National Museum, Second Dep't., without numbers.
Among other items, two iron cannon balls, a stone ball and an iron bar, all of which are definite traces of the Munk expedition. The remaining finds are less certain, because since the 1700's the English Hudson's Bay Company had a trading station on the site.
*Provenance:* From Thorkild Hansen and Peter Seeberg's memorial expedition to Jens Munk's winter harbour in 1964.
*Literature:* T. Hansen and Seeberg 1965

887

## East India

Dansborg and Trankebar, c. 1650
Oil on canvas. 132.5×273.5 cm
Skokloster slott, Sweden, 9626
The Danish trading station Trankebar on the Coromandel Coast in Southeast India. The rendering of the fort of Dansborg is particularly precise; the main aspects of the city plan of Trankebar are also correct, though schematic. The key to the letters and numbers is not known in its entirety.
*Provenance:* Presumably from one of the royal castles, war booty of the Swedish Admiral Karl Gustav Wrangel 1657-58; mentioned in his testament in 1676. In the Skokloster inventory from 1728.
*Literature:* Brøndsted 1952 61; Feldbæk and Justesen 1980 49; Hjelm 1987.

888

## Reconstruction model of Fort Dansborg, c. 1650

Architects Lars Bjørn Madsen and Torben Hjelm, 1987
Wood, scale 1:100
The National Museum, Second Dep't.
Reconstruction based on surveying and measurements, archaeological investigations in 1985 and archive studies.
*Literature:* Hjelm 1987

889

## Treaty between Christian IV and the "Emperor of Ceylon", Copenhagen, March 30, 1628.

Rigsarkivet, Traktatsamlingen, Ostindien nr. 2a
Alliance and trade treaty in Dutch, signed by the "emperor's" (rajah Cenviradt Adasyn of Kandy) envoy, the Dutchman Marchelis de Boshouwer, "prins of Migomme". The corresponding copy, written in German and with Christian IV's signature, was also preserved in Copenhagen (no. 2b), since Ove Giedde discovered in 1620 that the rajah neither could nor would keep the terms of the treaty. The seal was cut off the latter copy and reused on the peace treaty in Lübeck in 1629.
*Literature:* DNT III; G. Olsen 1952 20ff., and 20ff.; Feldbæk and Justesen 1980 43ff. and 53 ff.; Rise Hansen 1980 231.

890

## Gold foil message from the nayak of Tanjore, April 2, 1620

Gold foil, stamped inscription in Tamil. L. 41 cm.
Colour-plate XVI
Rigsarkivet, Traktatsamlingen, Ostindien nr. 4
Official messages to reigning princes were stamped in gold foil, while important documents were stamped in silver. The message from the nayak (prince) Ragunatha (1600-1634) to Christian IV gives his envoys Ove Giedde and Roland Crappé permission to settle in Trankebar.
*Literature:* DNT III; Feldbæk and Justesen 1980 60ff.; Rise Hansen 1980 231.

891

## Ove Giedde's report from his voyage to East India

Rigsarkivet, Danske Kancelli, Indlæg til registre og tegnelser samt henlagte sager
Ove Giedde's (cf. cat. 894) own handwritten "Record of all that which happened on this trip to India from the beginning the 14th of November 1618 and up to the 4th of March the year 1622" written on his flagship "Elefanten" (The Elephant).
*Provenance:* Sent to the Danish Chancellery as an official report, January 24, 1623.
*Literature:* Schlegel 1772.

892

## Travel or invalid chalice

Steen Pedersen, Købmagergade (Bøye no. 24) and Copenhagen mark 163(.)
Silver, partly gilded; h. 21 cm dia. above 6 cm
The Tamil Evangelical Church, Ny Jerusalemskirken, Trankebar

*892*

The cup is hexagonal at the top, and below that bosses. The knob and base are also hexagonal. In the upper part of the chalice is an engraved, unidentified coat of arms. Originally secular bossed goblet.
*Provenance:* Brought to Trankebar, at the latest at the beginning of the 1600's. Still belongs to the furnishings of the Ny Jerusalemskirken.

893

## Lead "kas" (coin) from Trankebar

Den kgl. Mønt- og Medaillesamling
When the colony of Trankebar was founded, the need was felt for small coins for use in trade with the local population, and the small lead coins called "kas" were minted for that purpose. Many different types were minted, of which a good many have the crowned C4 monogram. One group has the inscription DANSBORG; the ground plan of the fort was also used as a motif. Many coins have the names of ships which sailed on the route to India.
*Literature:* U. B. Jensen 1978

894

## Ove Giedde (1594-1660), Admiral of the Fleet

Albert Haelwegh, after 1660
Copper engraving. C. 52×38.8 cm
Frederiksborg
Ove Giedde, later Councilor of the Realm and Admiral of the Fleet, led the expedition to Ceylon and Trankebar in 1618-1621
*Literature:* Westergaard no. 3616; Styhr no. 231.

895

## "Abriss des Castehls Dannebourg in Ostindien", c. 1650

Coloured drawing on paper
Privately owned
Presumed to be the earliest known representation of Dansborg. The somewhat primitive drawing –with the buildings and the earthworks shown in profile despite the birds-eye perspective – does however give a good and correct impression of the set-up of the fort.
*Literature:* Brøndsted 1952 91.

896

## Tanjore, capital of the Indian state Tamil-Nadu

Governor Peter Anker, between 1787 and 1806
Coloured drawing on paper. 28×50 cm
Universitetets etnografiske Museum, Oslo, Peter Ankers Samling
Tanjore, at that time the capital of the princely state Tamil-Nadu, viewed from the southwest. The city had not altered in appearance between Ove Giedde's visit in 1620 and Peter Anker's arrival 150 years later. Behind the heavy walls of the city can be glimpsed the many pagodas of the Chola dynasty's golden age, 900-1200; the largest, the Brihadeswara temple, is sacred to Shiva and has a hight of c. 63 m.
*Literature:* Felbdæk and Justesen 1980 59.

The items which follow are all examples of European use and processing of imported goods from overseas regions, from raw materials like ivory, coconuts, rhinoceros horn and nautilus shells to Chinese porcelain and spieces and the balsam for pomanders.

897

## Tusk from an African elephant (loxodonta africana)

L. 220 cm., weight c. 72 kg
Zoologisk Museum CN8
Unusually large tusk from a male elephant. Ivory was used in the Renaissance to make various types of art objects, goblets, sculptures, powder horns, jewelry etc.
*Provenance:* The Royal Kunstkammer, inv. 1674, 1b; 1690, 4/37; 1737, 649/39. 1826 to The Museum of Natural History, now the Zoological Museum.

898

## The horns of black African rhinoceros (Diceros bicornis).

Longer horn 48 cm., shorter horn, 22 cm., largest diam. 15 cm.
Zoologisk Museum CN33
*Provenance:* From the Royal Kunstkammer, no number; 1826 to the Royal Museum of Natural History, now the Zoological Museum.

899

## 1½ shell of Nautilus Pompilius

The whole shell: largest diam. 19 cm., width 9.5 cm., the halft shell: largest diam. 21 cm.
Zoologisk Museum, the half; j.no. 98. Shells of multi-armed, shelled mollusk.
*Provenance:* Molucca Islands, 1908.

900

## Powder horn with a watch (and lost compass?)

German, c. 1620
Ivory with gilded and engraved brass, pewter. 22.5×11 ×7.5 cm
The National Museum, Second Dep't., 10466
Both the ivory front and back sides and the caps are decorated with hunting scenes. The watch works has a pewter wreath with the numbers, and is signed MK on the back (presumably for Michael Klenck, Augsburg, 1570-1632, independent from 1598). Perhaps there was a compass opposite the watch.
*Provenance:* To the Royal Kunstkammer Nov. 16, 1692, inv. 1737, 844/63; 1826 to Royal Museum of Art, inv. no. BDc135. 1848 to the Museum of Northern Antiquities.
*Literature:* Philippovich 1962 130f.; Abeler 1977 342.

901

## Powder horn without bottom or mountings

Signed HME under the base, and the year 1647 on each side of the base Ivory. L. 19.8 cm
The National Museum, Second Dep't., D472
Encircling the opening are carved two battling snakes; on the sides animals, birds and mounted hunting nymphs.
*Provenance:* Placed in the royal Kunstkammer between

*902, 903, 904*
*901, 905*

1737 and 1765, inv. 1775, 148/c379; 1826 to Royal Museum of Art, later Museum of Sculpture and Handicraft, inv.no. CDb51. 1869 to the Museum of Northern Antiquities (now the National Museum).
*Literature:* Philippovich 1961 210.

902

## Danish (?) coconut goblet, 1600's

Body and lid of coconut shell, turned base and mounting of ivory, knob of amber on lid. H. 26.5 cm
The National Museum, Second Dep't., 716
*Provenance:* 1811 to the Commission for the Preservation of Antiquities, later the Museum of Northern Antiquities from Kammerherre v. Krogh, Odense.

903

## Goblet with lid

The Holy Roman Emperor Rudolph II (1577-1612) Prague
Turned horn from an East African rhinoceros, lid and base of mahogany, mounted in gold. H. 23 cm
The National Museum, Second Dep't., D406
The gold edges on the lid and base have black enamelled inscriptions in Latin and Greek in italics: "Divi Rudolphi II Rom: Imperat: poculum deletorium προφυλαχτίχόν – Polydædala manus Invict: Imperat: Toreuma hoc finxit (The exalted Roman Emperor Rudolph II's goblet, which protects against poison – The unconquerable emperor's hand shaped this ingenious goblet)". Emperor Rudolph was known as an eager lathe operator.
*Provenance:* The Royal Kunstkammer, inv. 1674, 20a; 1690, 63/24; 1737, 766/339. 1826 to Royal Museum of Art, later Museum of Sculpture and Handicraft, CDa 209. 1869 to the Museum of Northern Antiquities.
*Literature:* Olrik 1909 65 f.

904

## Nautilis goblet

The Bellekins' workshop in Amsterdam? mid-1600's, silver mountings assumed to be more recent.
Shell of Nautilus Pompilius with a silver mounting and base. H. 27 cm.
The National Museum, Second Dep't., CCXIX
The shell has at the front of each side three riders engraved and drawn in India ink with pistols and sabres, at the back carved ornaments. The inside curvature has a carved crowned double eagle over a helmet with a visor.
*Provenance:* 1820 gift to the Museum of Northern Antiquities from Baroness Rantzau-Lehn of Hvidkilde on Funen.
*Literature:* Olrik 1909 77 no. 43; cf. Woldbye 1985 53-59.

905
## German or Dutch spoon. c. 1600

Ivory and mother of pearl with gilded silver mountings. L. 22 cm
The National Museum, Second Dep't., D212
An example of the use of different imported raw materials: the bowl is of mother of pearl, the handle is of ivory, which has been partly painted green, and it has an agate bead at the tip.
*Provenance:* The Gottorp Kunstkammer, inv. 1743, 89a; c. 1750 to the Royal Kunstkammer, inv. 1775, 102/b139; 1826 to Royal Museum of Art, DAd81; 1867 to the Museum of Northern Antiquities.
*Literature:* Kunstindustrimuseet 1983-84 no. 116.

906
## Porcelain bowl with a Danish mounting

Bowl: China, Wanli (1573-1619). Mounting in silver by Jacob tor Borch;
Copenhagen mark 1608
Dia. at upper edge 22 cm., at bottom 12 cm
The National Museum, Second Dep't., D 1696/1961
C. 1890 found at jægermester Schøller's at Marfård, Funen; later sold to Holger Drucker. At the auction of the latter's estate in 1961 purchased by the New Carlsberg Foundation as a gift to the National Museum.
*Literature:* Clemmensen and Mackeprang 1980 23ff.

907
## Chinese bowl with a European mounting

Bowl: late Ming (c. 1500-1644). Mounting perhaps German, c. 1620
Porcelain with gilded silver. H. 7 cm., dia. without handle. 11 cm.
The National Museum, Second Dep't., D9035
*Provenance:* 1773 to The Royal Kunstkammer from the estate of Queen Sophie Magdalene, inv. 1775, 249/c613. 1826 to Royal Museum of Art, EBc101, from there to the Ethnographic Museum and thus to the National Museum; 1916 from the Fourth Dep't., Ethnographic Collection, to the Second Dep't.

908
## Tankard with lid

Tankard: China, "Transition period", 1640's. Mounting Danish, mid-1600's Porcelain, blue/white; lid and base edging of silver. H. with lid lever 22 cm.
Aalborg Historiske Museum, 5825
The shape of the tankard is European and is called "Snelltje". On the lid are engraved the arms and initials of Henrik Bielke (1625-83) and his wife Edele Ulfeldt (1630-76), married 1649.
*Provenance:* Purchased in 1895 from either Bjørumgård eller Gl. Vrå, both north of Aalborg, by A. Jacobsen, F. Obel, I. Strøyberg and L. K. Kier and presented to the Aalborg Historiske Museum.
*Literature:* Clemmensen and Mackeprang 1980 39ff.

909
## Bowl

China, Wanli (1573-1629)
White porcelain with remnants of painting, lined with gold foil. H. 10 cm.
The National Museum, Fourth Dep't., EAc117

On the bowl the Eight Daoist Immortals and pierced decoration (ling-long). Probably painted in Europe, where it also has been lined with gold foil on the inside and around the base.
*Provenance:* The Royal Kunstkammer, inv. 1690, 77/28; 1737, 805/105. 1826 to the Royal Museum of Art, EAc177, from there to the Ethnographic Museum and later to the National Museum.
*Literature:* Hornby 1980 168. Berlin 1985 219 no. 4/5

910

## Pomander

German or Dutch, early 1600's
Silver with niello ornamentation, sachet. H. at highest 4 cm., diam. 2.3 cm.
The National Museum, Second Dep't., D3092
The six sections have sliding lids, on which the contents are indicated: ROSEMERN·B, ROSEN.B, VIOL·B, MUSKAT·B, GIRAN·, SLAG·B. (Rosemary, Rose petals, Violet petals, Nutmeg, etc.). In the base, where the plate at the bottom is open, a sachet. (cf. cat. 818e and 838).
*Provenance:* Purchased from an antique dealer in 1895.

The following items are examples of Danish imports from the Far East, imported either via the Danish trading stations in the area or through trade in European harbours, especially in Holland, where large quantities of goods arrived before being spread out over Europe. The majority of the items was both produced and introduced into Denmark during the reign of Christian IV.

911

## Indonesian coins

Banten and Pelembang, 1600's
Tin. Diam. 2-3 cm. Colour-plate XVI
The National Museum, Fourth Dep't., EDc99-100
Used at trading stations in Indonesia. Until 1682 Denmark had its most important Indonesian trading station in Banten, which was one of the most eminent states on Java.
*Provenance:* The Royal Kunstkammer, inv. 1674, 32a; 1775, 161/d141. 1826 to the Royal Museum of Art, EDc99-100, from there to the Ethnographic Museum and later to the National Museum.
*Literature:* Wulff 1979 37; Wulff and Rishøj Pedersen 1980 141.

912

## Lance point with sheath

Java, before 1647
Spear point, damascened iron with gildingæ L. 47 cm; sheath: painted wood.
The National Museum, Fourth Dep't., EAb9
When in Ole Worm's possession, it had a staff of 2.5 m.; Worm assumed that it had belonged to an "Indian" king or prince.
*Provenance:* A present from Laurids Ulfeldt to Ole Worm in 1647, Museum Wormianum 1655, s. 356. 1655 to The Royal Kunstkammer, inv. 1674, 29b; 75/53; 1737, 802/59. 1826 to The Royal Museum of Art, EAb9, and from there to the Ethnographic Museum and later to the National Museum.
*Literature:* Wulff 1979 37 f.; Wulff and Rishøj Pedersen 1980 142 f.

913

## Geomantical compass

China, first half of the 1600's
Wood and brass. D. 10 cm. Colour-plate XVI
The National Museum, Fourth Dep't., EBc36
The Chinese used the compass to determine the locations of their houses and graves.
*Provenance:* Before 1653 to Ole Worm's collection, Museum Wormianum 1655, s. 372f.; 1655 to The Royal Kunstkammer, inv. 1674, 29b; 1690, 84/43; 1737, 814/275. 1826 to 1826 to The Royal Museum of Art, EAc36, and from there to the Ethnographic Museum and later to the National Museum
*Literature:* Hornby 1980 216; Clemmensen and Mackeprang 1980 35ff.; Berlin 1985 216 no. 7/21.

914

## Erotic group of figures, a youthful couple in an embrace

China, late Ming (c. 1500-1644)
Ivory, European base of marble. H. 11 cm. Colour-plate XVI
The National Museum, Fourth Dep't., EBc191
To Worm the group of figures was interesting because it depicted the dress and hair styles of the Chinese.
*Provenance:* Before 1654 to Ole Worm's collection, Museum Wormianum 1655, s. 378f; 1655 to The Royal Kunstkammer, inv. 1674, 30a; 1690, 81/53; 1737, 809/194. 1826 to The Royal Museum of Art, EAc191; and from there to the Ethnographic Museum and later to the National Museum.
*Literature:* Hornby 1980 181; Justesen 1979 57; British Museum 1984 no. 131.

915

## Box

China, Ming dynasty (1368-1644)
Red lacquer, carved. Diam. 4 cm
The National Museum, Fourth Dep't., EDc47a
*Provenance:* The Royal Kunstkammer, inv. 1689, 45; 1690, 74/37; 1737, 801/38. 1826 to The Royal Museum of Art, EAc 47; and from there to the Ethnographic Museum and later to the National Museum.
*Literature:* Hornby 1980 195.

916

## Wanli porcelain

China, Wanli (1573-1619)
a) diam. 11 cm., b) h. 18 cm., c) h. 71 cm
The National Museum, Fourth Dep't, EBc99-100, 160 and 180
a) Two bowls with pierced decoration ("ling-long"), b) jug and c) a lidded jar, of which the original knob has been replaced by a small porcelain box, also Wanli. Colour-plate XVI.
*Provenance:* The Royal Kunstkammer, a) and b) inv. 1690, 72/26 and 74/28 – c) 1691 to The Royal Kunstkammer from Rosenborg – inv. 1737, 805/103, 800/30 and 821/392. 1826 to The Royal Museum of Art, EBc99-100, 160 and 180, and from there to the Ethnographic Museum and later to the National Museum.
*Literature:* Hornby 1980 160ff.; c) Justesen 1979 55ff.

917

## Namban toilet case

Japan, Momoyama (1573-1615)
Lacquered wood (maki-e), inlaid with mother of pearl. H. 17 cm.
The National Museum, Fourth Dep't., EAc139
In 1621 Christian IV wrote in his calendar diary that he "paid ... 25 dalere for a comb case". It is a reasonable guess that the king's was of this same type, perhaps even the same one.
*Provenance:* The Royal Kunstkammer, inv. 1690, 79/7; 1737, 807/146. 1826 to The Royal Museum of Art, EAc139, and from there to the Ethnographic Museum and later to the National Museum.
*Literature:* Boyer 1959 79f. Hornby 1980 228f. Tokyo 1981 no. 35-46.

# Trade

918

## Two female and two male sandstone hermas from the Stock Exchange

Lorenz and Hans van Steenwinckel, c. 1620
H. 100-105 cm
The National Museum, Second Dep't., D11426
Removed in connection with restoration in 1902-06, when most of the sandstone ornaments on the facade were renewed
*Literature:* Lassen 1858: Wancher 1937 114-123.

919

## The Copenhagen Stock Exchange, erected in 1620, facade facing the canal and the end of the building with the portal

Lauritz de Thurah: Den Danske Vitruvius I, 1746, Tab. LIV-LV
Copper engraving. C. 26×43 cm.

*921*

The National Museum's Antiquarian Topographical Archive
Christian IV's Stock Exchange, a monument to Mercantile economic policies. In the upper storey domestic and foreign merchants were to meet in 40 offices and booths, whereas the grocers' goods were on sale in the smaller booths downstairs.

920

## Balance scale, 1650

Iron. L. 282 cm
The National Museum, Second Dep't., D12247
A very heavy-duty scale, made of a beam and a holder, for weighing large items. The holder has the year 1650 and the initials FB.
*Provenance:* Gift 1933: believed to come from a warehouse on Christianshavn.
*Literature:* Hermansen 1936 162-74.

921

## Foreign textile seals, 1600's

Lead, partly on wool textile
The National Museum, Second Dep't
Quality control of textile production in European cities went on under the supervision of the guild master in the "Cloth Hall". After being controlled the bolts of cloth were "hallmarked", i.e. provided with a seal with the city arms and the mark of the manufacturer. When Christian IV in 1620 reorganized the Prison and Orphanage and established the "Cloth Company", it was to decrease imports of cloth from England and the Hanseatic Towns. The seals a-e come from German and Dutch manufacturers. They are still attached to a narrow strip of the original bolt of cloth. f-h) Cloth seals stamped in Amsterdam in 1647. i-l) English seals with the national coat of arms and the Tudor rose. i) has London's city arms. m) Seal with the city arms of Lubeck and the year 1614.
*Provenance:* Mainly earth-find in Copenhagen.
*Literature:* Liebgott 1975a.

922

## Scales for weighing gold coins, c. 1644

Guilliam de Neve, Amsterdam (1575-1654)
Scales with brass bowls, steel balance beam and brass weights in a carved wooden box with ornamentation. 12.1×6.8×3.6 cm.
Den kgl. Mønt- og Medaillesamling, no number
The weights indicate with motif and inscription which gold coins they represent. Merchants and brokers used this type of scale to check the gold coins they received; coins often were below their stated weight because the edges were illegally clipped. On the weights – some of which are missing – the date 1644.
*Literature:* Poperinge 1980.

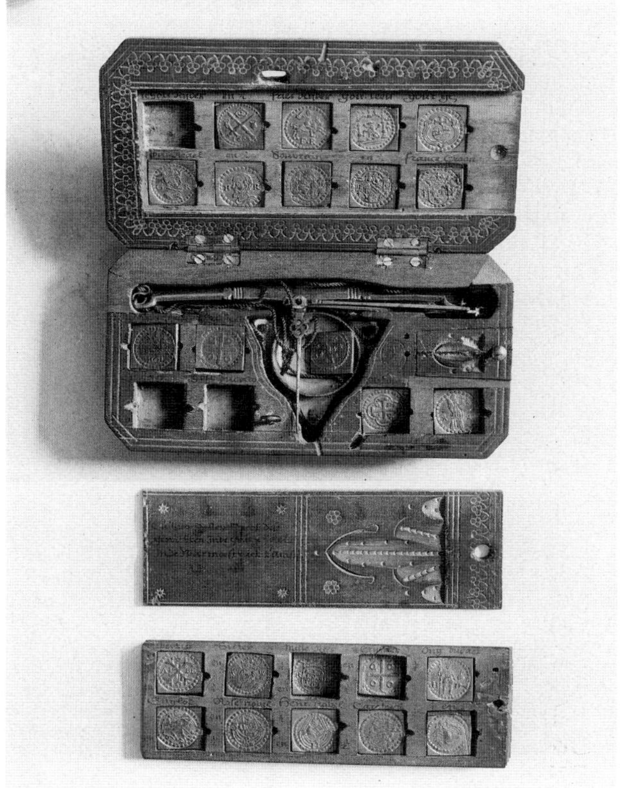

*922*

923

## Hans Nansen, 1598-1667, merchant, shipowner, mayor of Copenhagen in 1644

Oil on canvas. 102×80 cm
Frederiksborg, A 1178
Already in 1614 Nansen had participated in a trade expedition to the Kola Peninsula and visited Russia several times after that. There Nansen learned the language so well that the government used him as an interpreter. In 1619-20 he went with the Petsor Company's expedition to establish trade with Northern Russia. His experience in arctic areas lead to his employment in the Icelandic Company, where he was director from 1639 to 1649. Through his marriage he came in contact with politically and economically influential circles in Copenhagen, where he became the fourth vice-mayor in 1644, and in 1654 the head mayor. He never became, as did Johan Braem (cf. cat. 875) or Henrik Müller (cf. cat. 924), a large-scale contractor with the state, but his interests in the trading companies – especially the Icelandic – made him a wealthy man. He apparently played a prominent role in the introduction of the absolute monarchy in 1660. He was named president in

*924*

Copenhagen and in 1661 he was given control of the city's trade and marketplace.
*Literature:* DBL.

924

## Henrik Müller, 1609-92, merchant, treasurer of the Exchequer

Copy from an original by Abraham Wuchters at Ledreborg
Oil on canvas. 83×66 cm
Frederiksborg, A 1174
Müller, who was born in Itzehoe, started service in the German Chancellery (for the duchies), became Christian IV's secretary from 1632 to 1641, and purchasing agent on behalf of the Court and the Copenhagen state institutions. From 1634 he carried on independent trading activities, and in 1641 became the customs officer for Copenhagen. In this capacity he made contacts with the great merchants of the city and soon became himself one of the large purveyors to the state. In return for the substantial balances due to him he received mortgages on the crown's landed properties, and when the crown lands were foreclosed after 1660 he became all at once the largest landowner in the country. In the capital he built, among other projects, a magnificent house in Østergade, which in 1915 was demolished to make way for the department store Illum. At his establishment on Christianshavn Müller had his own quay, and he controlled numerous rental properties and a mill near Vesterport. As an industrialist he made his mark under Frederik III and Christian V; Norwegian mining interests (in the period 1673-80 he owned Kongsberg Silverworks) and salt refining, Scanian alum and vitriolic acid production as well as sugar refining were all part of his activities. The latter was connected to the West Indian trade; he also had an interest in the African and the Icelandic Companies. Henrik Müller was the undisputed leader of the businessmen of his time, a position he retained long into the period of Absolutism, just as he retained his influential official position until 1679.
*Literature:* Johan Jørgensen 1966; DBL 3. ed. (Müller).

925

## Map of Iceland

Abraham Ortelius, 1585, reprinted 1612
Copper engraving. 46×64 cm
Det kgl. Bibliotek, Kortsamlingen
In the sea around Iceland a wealth of fantastical animal life is depicted. The Icelandic trade, encouraged under Frederik II and Christian IV, brought fish, whale oil, mutton, homespun woolens and sulphur to Denmark. In 1602 the citizens of Copenhagen, Malmø and Elsinore were given a monopoly on this trade for 12 years.

926

## Icelandic or Færoese mitten with one thumb, 1600's

Guard hair of sheep's wool, knit. 1.28 cm., w. over the back of the hand, 9.5 cm.
Københavns Bymuseum, no number
*Provenance:* Earth-find, Copenhagen
*Literature:* Warburg 1987.

927

## Five Icelandic mittens with two thumbs, 1600's

Stockinette stitch knitted wool. 1.19-31 cm., width across the back of the hand, 12.5-15 cm
Kæbenhavns Bymuseum, no number, 1. nr. 28, 98, 99, 121; The National Museum, Second Dep't., D6711
One of the Icelandic export products was knitted wares. The mittens are typical in having two thumbs, which made it possible to extend their life by wearing them on both sides. Mittens knitted of two ply yarn were the most expensive. Light coloured wool was preferred, with the darker reserved for the cuffs and borders. Most were fulled.
*Provenance:*Earth-find in Copenhagen.
*Literature:* Adils 1926-27; Warburg 1987

# Crafts and Guilds

Guild items illustrate life in the craft guilds and the life of the artisan both on weekdays and Sundays. An artisan had to be member of the guild, if he did not want to spend his life beyond the pale. Attendance was required at the guild meetings, which were held three to four times a year. The casket played an important role at the meetings. The meeting opened with the guild master knocking three times on the lid, which then was opened. "With an open lid" the guild's concerns were discussed and new journeymen were admitted. The meeting ended with the closing of the lid, and the closed lid was again knocked. The casket usually had more than one lock, and the guild master and "the vice-masters" had keys. The precious belongings of the guild, e.g. the signet and protocol were kept in the casket. The "welcome", a tankard, was used when taking in a new journeyman. After proper ceremonies, he was toasted by the guild master; in return the journeyman presented a silver sign which was hung on the "welcome". The signet was used on documents and on journeymen's certificates, so that the wandering journeyman could prove his successfully completed apprenticeship wherever he travelled. At gatherings the skaffer (a waiter and monitor of sorts) carried the skafferstok (a staff) as a symbol of dignity. His task was to keep order during the meetings and keep the mugs filled with beer. The poor box demonstrates the social aspect of the guild system: the duty toward the poor and ill guild brothers.

928

## Contemporary printings of three royal decrees, 1613, 1621 and 1622

Print on folded paper
Det kgl. Bibliotek
1613, June 19: *On guild laws and privileges.* All guilds are suspended; the laws and privileges must be deposited with mayors and councilmen. – 1621, Dec. 10: *On apprentices and journeymen.* The standard of the crafts must be raised by improving the recruitment of good journeymen. The guilds are formally reintroduced; the artisan masters and the city magistates are together to draft "certain conditions" – i.e. new guild laws. Children of the poor are to be given easier access to a craft – to avoid being left in idleness. 1622, Aug. 26: *On freedoms allowed and given to those who settle in the market towns, also foreigners who would move into the country.* Intended to promote movement to the towns by promising new townsmen – merchants, pedlers, artisans and coastal traders – tax exemptions etc in the first year; specialists in textile and weapon production up to six years. Foreigners were also subject to other lenient conditions.
*Literature:* Secher III, 1894, no. 401 and 607; IV, 1897, no. 23.

*927*

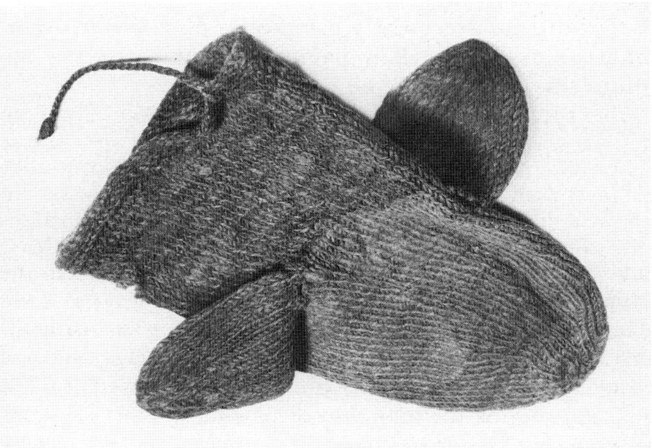

929

## The casket of the Elsinore Smith's Guild, 1606

Wood and iron. C. 31.6×45×27 cm
Helsingør Bymuseum, HM 4809
Painted green, iron bottomed wooden casket with 1606 in iron numbers and traces of gilt on iron bands. Secondary painted text: "Klein og Grovsmed / Mæsternis Lade. Anno 1792". (Lock smiths and blacksmiths / the master's casket. Anno 1792". Iron handles on the sides, three key holes, but only one key preserved. Painted red on the inside.
*Literature:* L. Pedersen 1910 24 and 1929, vol. 2, 253; Riismøller 1940 37.

930

## Documents from the Elsinore Smith's Guild

Landarkivet for Sjælland
*Privileges of the journeyman smiths,* granted by the mayors, councilmen and town justice in 1591, consisting of 45 articles. At the beginning are listed the 18 master smiths who requested that this new set of guild privileges replace the old one. Ends with the approval of the masters' guild. – *The Guildbook* begins with the articles of the smiths' guild (renewed in 1574) the 6th of January 1592 and with 11 smiths' seals as authorization. Up until 1651 ordinary guild business, accounts, enrollment of masters and changes in guild masters. Later less thorough accounts, but up to 1682 an annual inventory. Ends in 1702.
The protocol is bound in white vellum binding with stamped borders; the binding has a flap and ties for closing. In the middle panel of the front cover is a pattern representation of justice, JUSTITIA, with a quotation from Vergil's Aen. 6.620; "DISCITE JUSTICIAM, ET NON

TE[MNERE DIVOS]. On the back cover LUCRETIA, who points a dagger at her heart, symbolising the corruption of chastity: CASTA FUIT C[LA?] RUM CAPIT MINO LUCRETIA. On front and back respectively has later been tooled SMEDERNEIS LAVGS BOG? VDI HELSINGØER and ANNO CHRISSTI 1592.
*"Thegne Registers Bogh"*, which has a jacket cover made of an older manuscript on parchment, contains the accounts of the journeymen's casket's income 1592-1609. – *The "black book"*. The foreward, dated April 22, 1610, makes clear that the masters in the guild set up this book, "with thoroughly considered courage and for reasons of necessity". The foreword is later repeated in German. The book contains the names of journeymen who in one way or another have violated the rules of the guild in Elsinore or other places – e.g. leaving before their time or running away from debts. A "drivebrev" entered into the book from the guild in Danzig on April, 22 1610, giving the names of such journeymen, exemplifies the use made of the blacklist.
*Literature:* L. Pedersen 1910 and 1929, vol. 2, 250; Degn and Dübeck 1983 144.

931
## The Smiths' Guild Regulations from Roskilde

Booklet in the original red leather binding
Landarkivet for Sjælland
Issued by the mayor and council on Feb. 23, 1623; contains 33 articles. Seal of the town attached.
*Literature:* Nyrop 1886 55ff.

*932*

932
## The Sign of the Smith's Guild of Kolding, 1601

Painted oak. 33×35.5×4 cm
Museet på Koldinghus, MKH 2161
Carved oak plank; in the middle panel a vertical hammer, crossed by an open smith's tongs. Encircled by the year 16 01. Newer painting.
*Provenance:* From the discontinued guild house and journeyman's home, Låsbygade 69, Kolding, to which this sign, and other signs from the Smith's Guild, were delivered in 1858. Presented to Museet på Koldinghus by plumber Th. Dohm, Kolding.
*Literature:* P. Eliassen 1910 375f; Bruun and Jacobsen 1939 and 1940; Rissmøller 1940 28.

933
## Signet from the Holbæk Smiths' Guild 1626

Iron stamp. Diam. 4.5 cm
The National Museum, Third Dep't., D650
On the surface of the signet a hammer, a key and a tongs encircled by a large horseshoe; the tools and products of the smith. Encircling text: HOLBECKS SMEDERS LA S 1626 (Holbæk's Smiths' Guild 1626). This guild was apparently one of those which included several crafts; in the 1640's the belt makers were included.
*Provenance:* Presented in 1887 by Holbæk mastersmiths' guild to Dansk Folkemuseum (now the National Museum's Third Dep't.).
*Literature:* Nyrop 1897 201; Grandjean 1950 60; A. Thomsen 1936-37 260; Strømstad 1976 46.

934
## The beer bowl of the Odense Smiths' Guild, 1600

Carved wood. H. 24 cm. diam. 62 cm
Museet Møntergården, 12-1861
Beer bowl with secondary gray paint, under which remnants of red and yellow painted ornamenting. On the inner side of the edge the inscription:
"ANNO / 1600 : PINDTZ : DAGH: GAF ERLICH OCH WELACHT MAND HANS NIELSØN LANDTZTHINGSCHRIEFVER RAAD MAND I OTTHENSZE / OCH BESI[DDE]R WDI SMEDE LAVGIT DENNE SKAAL WDI LAVGET WO[RRIS LAVG THIL] ÆRRE OC HANNEM [TH]IL I HUKOMMELSE" (In the year 1600 on Whitsun the honest and respected man Hans Nielssøn provincial court recorder and councilman in Odense and "vice-master" in the Smiths' Guild gave this bowl in the guild to our guild's honor and to his remembrance).
Hans Nielsen was provincial court recorder and councilman 1584-1607, and together with Niels Bager he was "vice-master" in the smiths' guild 1600, and died 1607. – C. 1600 the fee for initiation of new masters was 6 daler in cash, one two-man bowl and two mark's worth of wax

for lighting; among the most common fees otherwise were beer and barley for brewing.
Delivered to Fyens Stiftsmuseum from spur maker Petersen 1861, inv.no. 653 Lavsbog 1564-1631 in Odense Smedelavs archive, Landarkivet, Odense J. Lauritzen 1806; Riismøller 1940 21; Sv. Larsen 1965; Grandt-Nielsen 1969 17.

935
## The shoemakers' guild regulations from Nysted

Ms. on parchment. 40×50 cm
Landsarkivet for Sjælland, parchment collection
Issued by the mayor and council on January 3, 1634; consists of 15 articles. The city seal is attached, though only fragments of it remain.

936
## "Welcome" (tankard) from the shoemakers' guild in Svendborg?

Rostock 1641
Pewter. H. 41 cm

*936*

*934*

The National Museum, Second Dep't., D8702
On the mug is engraved a drinking verse in German and the year 1641. On the base is stamped an indistict maker's mark. H D (?) and the city mark of Rostock. A markedly contoured lower section with a circle ring, which has space for the hanging on of signs.
*Provenance:* Traded in 1915 from Lolland-Falsters Stifsmuseum, who had received it from grocer Lauritz Schrøder. Believed to come from Svendborg Shoemaker's Guild.
*Literature:* J. Olsen 1919 450; Bro-Jørgensen 1959 vol. 1 255.

937
## Signet of the Shoemakers' Guild in Assens, 1608

Brass, turned handle of wood. Diam. 3 cm.
The National Museum, Third Dep't., D 573
In the cartouche in the middle a shoemaker's knife. Text encircling: ASSENS SKOMAGERLAF 1608 (Assens Shoemaker Guild 1608). In this year Prince Christian was chosen as heir to the throne; on this occasion numerous guilds – among them the Assens shoemakers – had new signets made with which to seal the electoral letters.
*Provenance:* Delivered to Dansk Folkemuseum (the National Museum's Third Dep't) by the Shoemakers' Guild in Assens in 1887.
*Literature:* Nyrop 1897 169, Grandjean 1950 47; Strømstad 1976 61.

938
## The Seal of the Elsinore Glovemaker's Guild, 1645

Iron and brass. H. 12.2 cm., the plate 3.1×3.2 cm
Helsingør Bymuseum, HM 1698
Iron stamp with a brass plate seal for the glove and purse makers' guild in Elsinore. The plate is square, rather

*941*

worn. In the middle section a glove next to a round shape; most likely a purse. Along the edge the incription: "HANSKEMAGER LAUS STEMPEL J HELSINGOR 1:6 4 5" (Glovemakers' Guild Stamp in Elsinore 1:6 4 5).
*Literature:* Laurits Pedersen 1926-29 vol. 2 241. Riismøller 1940 19.

939

## "Welcome" (tankard) from the furriers' guild in Copenhagen

Presumably Southern German, 1604. Figure on top added later
Pewter (6 parts tin to 1 part lead) with engraving. H. 47 cm., greatest diam. 15 cm., diam. at edge, 10 cm
The National Museum, Third Dep't., 4016/1955
On the lid are engraved the names of the donors and the date, April 1, 1604; six of the names are known from the period 1581-1633, and of these five were furriers. On the tankard the guild symbols of both the furriers and glovemakers: fur and gloves. The two crafts were only in the same guild during the period around 1670, but the furriers had the right from olden days to make gloves.
*Provenance:* Auctioned into private hands at the dissolution of the guild in 1857. Presented to the National Museum along with two tankards in 1955.
*Literature:* Strømstad 1956 and 1976.

940

## Signet for the Tailors' Guild in Ribe, first half of the 1600's

Brass stamp with a bone handle. Diam. 3.8-4 cm., l. 7.4 cm.
Den antikvariske Samling i Ribe, 200×55
On a cartouche in the middle is an opened shears, above the arms of the town. Encircling text: "SCHREDER EMBETS PVSIER VDI RIBE" (Tailors' craft's signet in Ribe). The tailors of Ribe received in 1636 royal recognition of their entrance requirements; thereafter a prospective tailor in Ribe had to chalk out a woman's cloak, and woman's jacket and a man's suit in order to become a member.
*Provenance:* Ribe Raadhussamling; tidl. inv.no. ASR 689
*Literature:* Grandjean 1950 56; Degn 1981 184.

941

## Casket from the Tailors' Guild in Copenhagen

Heinrich Ringerinck, Flensborg, early 1600's; back side, however by another, later master
Oak. 56×32.5×31 cm
The National Museum, Third Dep't., D 646
On the front, the Annuciation and the Birth of Christ. Figures in the corners, on the left, Caritas (Charity), on the right, Spes (Hope); on the ends, The Fall and the Baptism of Christ.
*Provenance:* To the Dansk Folkemuseum (now the National Museum, Third Dep't.) in 1857 from the Journeymen Tailors' Guild.
*Literature:* Strømstad 1976; C. A. Meier 1984.

*943*

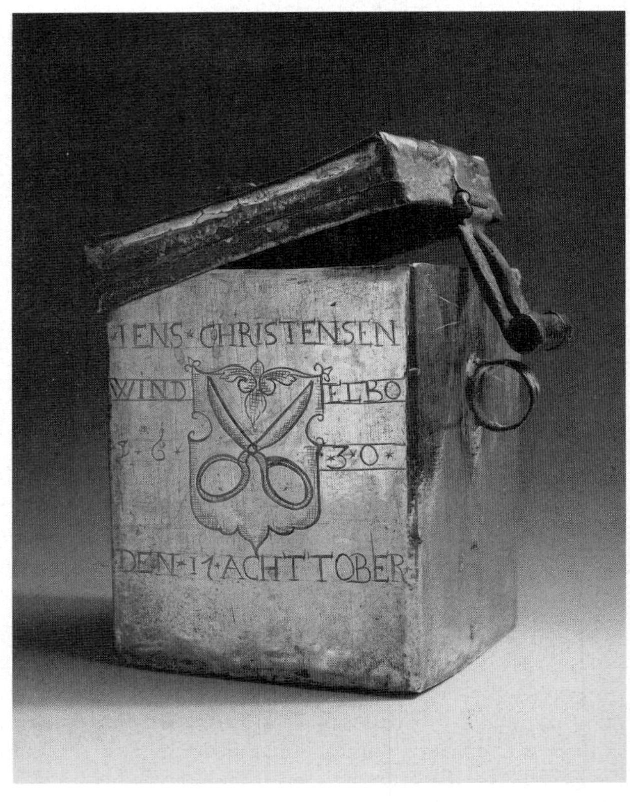

942
## Staff from the Master Tailors in Aalborg, 1600's

Pine with remnants of paint. L. 62 cm
Aalborg Historiske Museum, AHM 5938k
*Provenance:* Gift from the Tailors' Guild in Aalborg.

943
## Money box from the Tailors' Guild in Aalborg, 1630

Engraved copper. H. 9 cm., bottom 7.2×7,2. cm
Aalborg Historiske Museum, AHM 5938 c
Brass hinge, hasp of sheet iron; on the front engraved in a cartouche an open shears and "JENS CHRISTENSEN WIND / ELBO 1630" The money slot has a strip of red leather on the inside, to prevent anyone slipping coins out again.
*Provenance:* Gift from the Tailors' Guild in Aalborg.

944
## Poor box from the Tailors' Guild in Copenhagen, 1640

Engraved brass. H. 18 cm., dia. 13 cm
The National Museum, Third Dep't., D 645
A lock hung on each of the three hasps on the slightly domed lid. On the side is engraved:
"Give with your generous hand, remember the poor just as the Lord has been gracious unto you. Andreas Matsen Hans Olefsen 1640"
*Provenance:* Purchased in 1906 from a grandchild of the guild's last guild master.
*Literature:* Strømstad 1976.

945
## Pewter tankard from the Coopers' Guild of Copenhagen

Bartels Løhnebeck, Kiel 1617
Cast pewter. H. 34 cm., largest diam. 15.8 cm
The Coopers' Guild, Copenhagen, deposited with Dansk Folkemuseum (The National Museum, Third Dep't.) D 177
A "pibekande" ("pipe tankard") with a spout from which to drink; the bulging shape was common in Christian IV's time. Later engraving: Andreas Tech 1665.
*Literature:* Olrik 1906 67 f.

946
## Sign from the Millers' Guild of Copenhagen 1648

Engraved silver. 10×8.5 cm
The National Museum, Third Dep't., D 485
Shield shaped sign with a chain for hanging. On the front a mill with a peasant's cart, in the background a town. On the back side: "PETER / BERENSEN /MÖLLER / GESEL / ANNO / 1648". Signs of this type were given by the newly admitted members to the "welcome" (tankards); when there was no longer space for more, they were melted down to make to new "welcomes" (tankards).
*Provenance:* Presented to Dansk Folkemuseum (The National Museum, Third Dep't.) by the Journeymen Millers' Association in Copenhagen in 1888.
*Literature:* B. Olsen 1889 182ff.: Strømstad 1976 57.

*946*

947
## Casket from the Master Bakers' Guild of Copenhagen

C. 1640. The sides of the lid with open tracery and a painted inscription MDCXXXI added later

949

Wood with mixed, gilded decorations. 62.5×43×46 cm
The National Museum, Third Dep't., D 1
Richly carved with Biblical motifs in late Renaissance style. On the front three key holes with corresponding keys, kept by the guild master and the two "vice-masters".
*Provenance:* Presented to Dansk Folkemuseum (The National Museum, Third Dep't.) by the Guild in 1887.
*Literature:* B. Olsen 1888 41f; Strømstad 1976.

948

## Money box from the Copenhagen Goldsmiths' Guild

Goldsmith workshop in Copenhagen, Jacob Mavritsens?, 1576-78
Engraved sheet brass. H. 15 cm., dia. 8.2 cm
The National Museum, Second Dep't., D13609
According to the engraving started in 1575 and first used in 1578; the names of the nine guild members from these years are given. Pictures of a workshop, the use of tools and the correction of apprentices by the masters. Originally the penalty box of the guild, later the poor box. The picture of the goldsmiths' patron saint, St. Loye (St. Eligius), shows that he was revered even after the Reformation.
*Provenance:* Purchased in 1948.
*Literature:* T. E. Christiansen 1965 7-24. Nationalmuseet 1979.

949

## Poor box, 1605

Engraved brass. H. 16.5 cm., dia. 8.5 cm
The National Museum, Second Dep't., D78/1986
Engraved shield with the engraved mark and name of the donor, Wilvm Haversak, mentioned in Copenhagen in 1620. In addition pictures from the story of the Rich Man, flower and fruit ornaments and a scroll with both a Danish and German inscription. One of a series of identical poor boxes from the early 1600's, presumed to have been produced in Denmark. The price is given on the lid as 3.5 mark.
*Literature:* DK XIX, 2 964f.; Hermansen 1943.

The following items [nos. 950-52] are examples of tools used in the many skilled crafts found in the towns – and in some cases also in the countryside – in Christian IV's time. Tools are poorly represented in the museum collections, both because they simply wore out, and because the immediately succeeding generations saw no reason to preserve them. Much has thus been lost, and that which turns up usually comes from broken tool pieces found in the ground. Dating can also be difficult since tools often alter only slightly. Many of the carpentry tools used 30-40 years ago are nearly identical to those used in the 1600's. – Most of the items exhibited here are finds from the ground in areas of the Copenhagen fortifications which were demolished in the 1600's.

950

## Tools for working metals, 1600's

Iron, wood, graphite, clay and limestone
The National Museum, Second Dep't., diverse nos.
The many crafts that dealt with metals were divided in part by materials – the braziers worked in brass, the pewterer in pewter – and in part by product – the locksmiths made locks, the armourers made armour, etc. Here are shown crucibles in which to heat the metal and tongs with which to hold the crucibles; a ladle to pour the hot metal into the mould and moulds for buttons and pewter plates (cf. cat. 956). In addition hammer heads, a hacksaw, files and tongs.
*Provenance:* The soldering iron D8266 is an individual find from Støvring near Randers in 1913, the others are earth-find in Copenhagen.
*Literature:* Schiørring 1979 64-73.

952

951

## Tools for leather crafts, 1600's

Iron and wood
The National Museum, Second Dep't., diverse nos.
The leather artisans – shoemakers, furriers, belt makers and skin dressers – were partly diversified by their products, partly by the types of leather they used, and finally by the tanning methods they employed. Here are shown in particular tools used by shoemakers: a shoemaker's knife with its half-moon shaped blade; a wooden last; a tongs for stretching the leather over the last; an awl to prepare the holes for seams; a smoother to smooth seams, which could also have been made of bone; a scraper to form the edges of the leather before sewing or for cleaning rawhides before tanning. Until 1635 – when the leather dressers in Copenhagen received the privilege of tanning hides for resale – the shoemakers were also tanners; now they were only allowed to tan for their own production.
*Literature:* Jäfvert 1932 75-76 and 1938; L. Pedersen 1935 68.

952

## Tools for wood working, 1600's

Iron and wood
The National Museum, Second Dep't., diverse nos
Wood workers were divided according to their major tools; carpenters used axes, joiners used planes etc. Here are shown the head of an axe, with a transverse blade, used for hewing planks, etc. and saws, of which there were several types, e.g. the buck saw which is still in use. Also a hammer head, plane, gimlet, auger, chisel and level. The gouge belongs to the carver's tools – joiner and carver were actually often the same person. Examples of the carving and cabinetwork of the period are seen in cat. 778, 941 and 965-70.
*Provenance:* Hammerhead and drill D1107 and -8 are gifts 1876, the compass D9691 a gift 1919, the bow saw D336/1977 found in a well in Herlev. Rest found in the ground in Copenhagen.
*Literature:* Goodman 1964; C. A. Jensen 1911.

953

## Wrought iron railing

Caspar Fincke's smithy, Elsinore, 1643
The National Museum, Second Dep't., no number
Samples of royal locksmith Caspar Fincke's iron railing at the Round Tower; from a staircase now removed.
*Literature:* Kn. Holm 1983 47-61.

954

## Danish door lock, c. 1600

38×15×6 cm
The National Museum, Second Dep't., D2902
Decorated box lock of iron with Christian IV's monogram and remnants of red and blue painting.
*Provenance:* Bought from an antique dealer 1894.

955, 956

957

955

## Two cast bronze mortars

Presumably Northern German, dated 1606 and 1607
a) H. 11.7 cm., Diam. above 12.3 cm.; b) H. 19.8 cm. Dia. 17 cm.
The National Museum, Second Dep't., D3733 and 20736
The form is typical of the period 1550-1600; inscription on a); "LOF GODT VAN AL A 1606", b): "ANO 1607 N R S NR A B D"
*Provenance:* a) purchased in 1898, believed to have come from Funen; b) gift from 1863, heirloom in the Gamborg family in Roskilde.
*Literature:* Dexel 1981 no. 201.

956

## Pewter plate

Bernt Mathisen, Aalborg, 1637
Diam. 30.8 cm
The National Museum, Second Dep't., 4673
Example of pewterer's work. Engraved arms for Lange (one rose) and Vognsen of Hæstrup; the initials NL (Niels Lange of Skrumsager) and JJ (Jolind Jespersdatter (Vognsen)).
*Provenance:* Found in 1838 in the moat of Rønnowsholm which was purchased by Niels Lange in 1620
*Literature:* P. H. Kristensen 1983 99.

*960, 958, 961, 962, 959*

957
## Communion set for giving the sacrament to invalids

Jacob Otter (or Otto) (Bøje 1662), Elsinore, first half of the 1600's
Chalice and paten of gilded silver, wine bottle of silver. Chalice H. 18 cm, wine bottle, h. 13 cm.
Skt. Olai kirke, Elsinore Cathedral
The base of the chalice is from c. 1600, the rest is Baroque. The base and cup are six-lobed; the cup chased, along the edge are engraved Latin verses and the year 1650. Under the bottom a plate has been attached with the donor's name, arms and the year, as well as the Elsinore city mark and the master's mark "i o 27"; the six-lobed paten and the pear-shaped wine bottle have the same name, arms and marks.
*Provenance:* Presented in 1650 by Mads Mortensen [Rosenvinge, customs official] and Catrine Christophersdatter. In the inventories of 1717 and 1745 it is mentioned as an invalid set, chalice and paten of 64 lod (a weight), the wine bottle with oblate compartment of 25 lod.
*Literature:* DK II, 142f.

958
## Cherub cup

Hans Hollænder, 1606-45, Copenhagen. Engraved year 1607 corrected to 1667 Chased silver. H. 12.6 cm. D. 7.7-8.4 cm.
The National Museum, Second Dep't., D13289
*Provenance:* Purchased at general director Ole Olsen's auction in 1943 (Winkel & Magnussen), Earlier in the collection of F. A. Lorck (Auktionskat. 1915 nr. 407).

959
## Drinking tankard

Unknown, Bøje 8013 and Copenhagen mark 1610
Chased silver with embossing and engraving. H. 22.6 cm., Dia. 10 cm.
The National Museum, Second Dep't. D7311
Domed lid with embossed ornaments: fruits and foliage surrounding the monogram for Jesus, IHS. The base also has chased Renaissance ornaments; on the smooth body are engraved the initials of later owners.
*Provenance:* Purchased at Frohne's auction in 1910
*Literature:* Olrik 1909-11 466f.

963

960
## Wedding tankard

Ove Nielsen, citizen of Aarhus 1623, mentioned 1628 (Bøje 5843); Århus mark (Bøje 5810). Later engraved: 1665
Chased silver with set in gilded medallion. H. 20.8 cm. Diam. 10.5 cm
The National Museum, Second Dep't., D7312
Embossed diamond-shapes and later engraved decoration. On the lid a German wedding medallion.
*Provenance:* Purchased at Frohne's auction in 1910, no. 902.
*Literature:* Olrik 1909-11 468f.

961
## Drinking tankard

Unknown master, Copenhagen (?), mark (Bøje 8015). Engraved 1636
Chased silver with cast ornaments. H. 20.8 cm., Diam. 10.5 cm
The National Museum, Second Dep't., D5147
An eight shilling piece with Christian IV's bust is set in the domed lid, which also has three cherubs, fruit and foliage ornaments. Engraved: I(ØR(GEN NIELSSEN – ELSE KERISTENS DATTER – 1636. Between the engraved baroque ornaments on the sides the initials of a later owner couple have been added: ANS – KTD – 1690.
*Provenance:* Testamentary gift 1902.
*Literature:* Olrik 1909 72 no. 30.

962
## Ole Worm's silver tankard given to Johannes Schelderup

Borchart Rollufsen 1637 (Bøje 32); Copenhagen mark 1641
Cast and chased silver. H. 13 cm., Diam. 11.5 cm.
The National Museum, Second Dep't., D739
On the lid and sides, arms and initials, OWD (D=doctor) and MMF, for Ole Worm's and his third wife, Magdalene Motzfeldt; Latin inscription with Worm's congratulations to his son-in-law Johannes Schelderup, on the occasion of his elevation to Bishop of Bergen.
*Provenance:* Purchased in Kristiania (Oslo) in 1872.
*Literature:* Olrik 1909 75 no. 36.

963
## Altar chalice and paten from Ellensborg's Chapel

Jørgen Jørgensen Prytz, Copenhagen (Bøje 38); engraved with the year 1639
Chased silver, gilded and engraved. Chalice: h. 21.8 cm., paten: diam. 14.2 cm.
Private collection.
Made for Christian IV's mother-in-law, Ellen Marsvin, while she owned the manor, which earlier was named Ulfeldtsholm (cf. cat. 764), but which she called Ellensborg. The chalice is engraved with the twelve apostles from original copper engravings by Hans Sebald Beham or his successor; the paten has a representation of the Holy Eucharist.
*Literature:* Grandt-Nielsen 1983 89.

964
## Altar candlesticks

Probably a master from Elsinore, prior to 1643
Cast brass. H. with the lions 75 cm., without, 69 cm
St. Marie's church, Elsinore
Baroque form; with engraved capitals on the bowl:
A. 1643 den 2. aprilis haben Iohann Hansen vnd Iohann Wilders beyde fvrsteher der tevtschen Kirchen dise 2 leucheter Gott zv Ehren vnd der Kirchen zvr Zirde vnd Gedachtnvs verehret ("A. 1643, 2nd of April, Johann Hansen and Johann Wilders, both vergers of the German church, have presented these two candlesticks to the glory of God and to adorn the Church and in thanksgiving").
*Literature:* DK II. 1 392.

965

## Carved cabinet panels

Early 1600's; ascribed to Hans Gudewerth the Elder, c. 1570-1640
Oak. The largest: 80×55.5, the smallest: 13×47.5 cm
The National Museum, Second Dep't., no numbers
In total nine panels from several cabinets. Two of the reliefs depict, respectively, a man and woman playing the lute in a portal panel with volutes (whorls) and fruits in the corners. In a third panel a man and woman with a hare playing the lute. Of the remaining six – presumably related panels – four depict Biblical scenes: above the Creation of Adam and of Eve, the Fall, and the Departure from the Garden of Eden. Below the Crucifixion and the Resurrection. The framing of the upper panels depicts hares playing both the bagpipes and the lute.
*Literature:* C. A. Jensen 1911 100ff.

966

## Fragment of a chest front

Gudewerth's workshop (Lorents Jørgensen or Hans Gudewerth the younger?), 1630's-1640's
Oak. 90×113 cm
The National Museum, Second Dep't., D8972
Two panels – with the Creation of Adam and Eve – between framing with a cartouche and scrollwork and two herma figures: on the left a man with a cane, in the middle a lady with a muff and on the right a loving couple; perhaps the persons are the heir apparent Christian and his wife Magdalena Sibylla. – Within the panel base mouldings a cartouche ornamentation in early auricular style.
*Provenance:* From the collection of C. A. Jensen 1915; believed to come from Højet, Væggerløse parish, South Falster.
*Literature:* C. A. Jensen 1911 101 and 1925.

967

## "Tresor" cupboard with five compartments

Credited to Brix Michgell, c. 1610-20
Oak. 196×219×71 cm
The National Museum, Second Dep't., 5082
Late-Renaissance style; originally painted, restored in the 1900's
Ascribed to the cabinetmaker Brix Michgell, mentioned in period 1611-27, whose works are related to the "Øresund" (The Sound) style; he was perhaps the teacher of Peder Jensen Kolding, (cf. cat. 778).
*Provenance:* Gift from Councilor Brinck Seidelin in Hjørring 1839, org. from distiller Thomas Pedersen, also Hjørring.
*Literature:* C. A. Jensen 1911 83f. and 1928; Liebgott 1975 34f.

*965*

968

## Panel with bas relief of the Circumcision

Ascribed to Brix Michgell, c. 1610-20
Oak. 36×29 cm
The National Museum, Second Dep't., 18093
Perhaps from a cupboard; originally painted and gilded.
*Provenance:* From Jersore in Klinte parish on Northern Funen. To the Museum 1858 from the collection of the historian Vedel-Simonsen on the manor Elvedgård on Funen.
*Literature:* C. A. Jensen 1911 83f. and 1928 52; Liebgott 1975 37f.

969

## A section of a pulpit

Jørgen Ringnis' workshop, 1631
Oak
The National Museum, Second Dep't., D11039
Made in 1631 by Jørgen Ringnis for 80 sletdaler. He was presumably from the area around Flensborg and perhaps a pupil of Hinrich Ringerink (cf. cat. 941). Ringnis' style is marked both by the Renaissance and the incipient auricular style.
*Provenance:* From Vaalse Church on Falster, to the museum in 1927 from C. A. Jensen's collection.

*970*

*Literature:* C. A. Jensen 1911 97f.; DBL: Jørgen Ringnis; DK VIII 1211f.; E. Skov 1979 21f.

970

## Double door from a cupboard

Ascribed to Hans Dreier, 1642
Oak. 130×107 cm
The National Museum, Second Dep't., D10796
The upper panel on each door has the arms and initials of Henning Valkendorf (left) and Anne Brockenhuus respectively, the year 1642 and the letters G E MT ("God is my comfort" ?); all in raised relief. In addition reliefs showing the Sacrifice of Isaac, Ruth and Boza (left), as well as Jacob wrestling with the Angel and Jesus healing the haemorrhaging Woman. On the check, a herma for Hope (an anchor) under foliage and a crane (perhaps Vigilance). The back side is painted red with golden rosettes, the monogram for Jesus and the initials mentioned above. – Hans Dreier, 1572-1631, is best known for the furnishings at the Chapel in the castle at Holckenhavn. He worked extensively for the Danish nobility; these doors are an example of this work.
*Provenance:* Purchased in 1925. Have been at the manor of Rørbæk by Kerteminde; originally from Glorup on Funen.
*Literature:* C. A. Jensen 1911 and 1931, DBL: Hans Dreier.

971

## Two floor tiles

Næstved, c. 1575-1600. ascribed to potter Laurits
Fired red clay with slip of pale yellow clay and polychrome glaze. 19.5×19.5×3 cm.
The National Museum, Second Dep't., D12168
The contour lines of the ornamentation have been stamped into the surface with a wooden plate, which contained thin metal bands; the motifs are emphasized by a glaze containing tin, in the colours white, blue, green, violet and yellow. Similar floor tiles are known from other churches on Southern Zealand, e.g. Skt. Bendt's in Ringsted, and unsuccessfully fired tiles have been found among the refuse from a pottery in Næstved which was in production in the last quarter of the 1500's.
*Provenance:* Vallensved Church near Næstved, acquired by the National Museum 1932.
*Literature:* Uldall 1934.

# Manufacturing

972

## Vouchers, etc. part of the Silk Works' accounts 1622-23

Rigsarkivet, Rentekammeret
The vouchers deal with deliveries to the King from Aug. 11, 1622 to May 11, 1623.
*Literature:* A. E. Christensen 1943 54 ff.

973

## Letter from Christian IV to Corfitz Ulfeldt

Glücksborg, Sept. 1, 1642
Rigsarkivet, Corfitz Ulfeldt's private archive
In the letter the King orders canvas woven for a large equestrian painting (cf. p. 2). The cloth is to be woven in the "Orphanage" on the large "getou" (loom), which stands in the attic where canvas is made.
*Literature:* EB VIII 207 no. 160.

974

## Accounts from the "Orphanage" 1639-43

Rigsarkivet, Rentekammeret
From the accounts for the "Prison and Orphanage" established in 1605 it is apparent that – at Ulfeldt's orders – 40 alen (c. 80 ft.) of portrait canvas was delivered on Sept. 15, 1642 Karl van Mander, the royal portrait painter. (cf. cat. 973).
*Literature:* O. Olsen 1952 319f.

*971*

975

## Textile seal, c. 1620

Lead. Diam. 2.2 cm
Københavns Bymuseum, 1646
Half of a textile seal stamped with Christian IV's crowned monogram. As a step towards attaining self-sufficiency for the country and to create a market for the textile products of the Prison and Orphanage, the King established "Klædekompagniet" (The Textile Company) in 1620. Just as was done abroad, the textiles were quality controlled and given a seal (cf. cat. 921).
*Provenance:* Found in the ground in St. Kongensgade, Copenhagen.
*Literature:* Liebgott 1975a.

976

## Cropper's shears, 1600's ?

Iron. L. 124 cm., weight 13 kg
Københavns Bymuseum, 1934: 55A
The raw woold had to be put through a long series of processes – carried out by artisans organized in each their guild – before it could be cut for clothing. When the cloth was woven and fulled, it was brought to the cropper, who raised and sheared the nap from the cloth. The shears were moved vertically, with the brace resting around the waist of the cropper.
*Provenance:* Gift 1934.
*Literature:* Gamle danske haandværk 1971.

977

## Paper with Christian IV's monogram as watermark

Aarhus Papirmølle, c. 1635-1648
Paper with watermark, double sheet
The National Archive
August 21, 1635, Christian IV gave Bishop Dr. Morten Madsen and the canons Paaske Jensen and Hans Hansen Skaaning a 10 year monopoly during which to establish a paper mill in Århusgårds len. In 1638 they received the deed to the mill, which was built as the uppermost of four industrial mills at Skambæk (later Varnabæk) south of Århus. The King had – to encourage the domestic paper industry – supported the establishment of the mill and the collection of rags, which were the raw material for paper; on Nov. 8, 1636 the mill received the right to use the King's crowned monogram as a watermark. – On Sept. 15, 1637 a grant was made to establish a paper mill in Scania; this also received the right to use the King's monogram as a watermark. The paper is, however, easily distinguished from the two mills, both of which had only local distribution. The earliest date found on paper from Århus Papirmølle is April 18, 1638; the most recent is March 16, 1651. – Hans Hansen Skaaning also had a print shop in Århus, and he used paper from his own mill in the books.
*Literature:* Rottensen and Waaben 1986; C. Nyrop 1878; Kraglund 1981.

*978b*

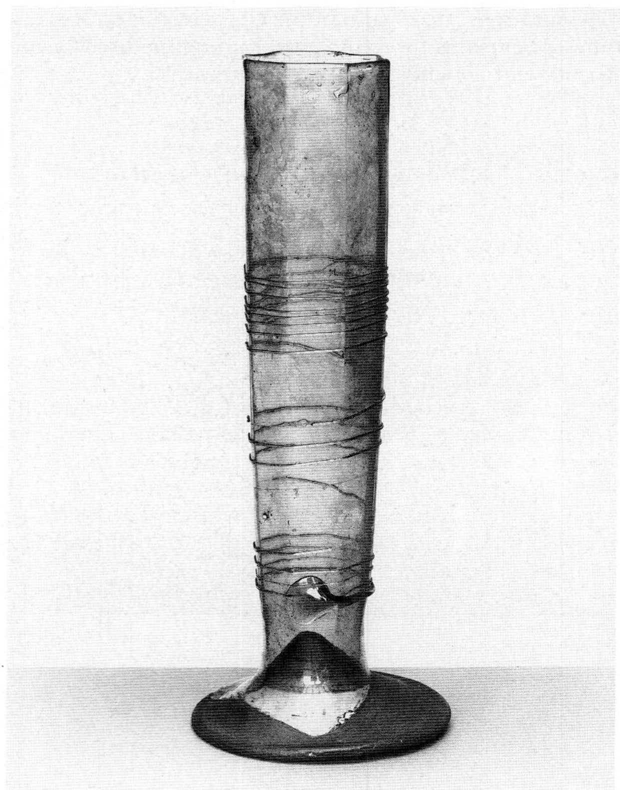

*978c*

978

## Glass from Danish Glassworks

The large glass production that started when Frederik II established his glassworks in the heavily forested areas around Skanderborg was only briefly continued under Christian IV. Though a Danish glass production reduced the costly import of German glass, in part for the collossal amounts of glass used by the Court, nevertheless the felling of the Jutish forests was too high a price to pay. In the 1630's and 40's there were still glassworks in production in Jutland and Scania, but they were run by private initiative. a) Pasglas of thin, greenish glass (Waldglass), c. 1600. H. 22 cm., base dia. 10.4 cm. Found under digging in 1970 in Bremerholm, Copenhagen (downtown Copenhagen). The City Museum of Copenhagen, no number. b) Mug of thin Waldglass, c. 1600. Handle melted on and thin glass threads. H. 13.8 cm. largest dia. 11 cm. Purchased from private party 1964. Aalborg Historiske Museum, 14.326. c) Pasglas of Waldglass c. 1600, base heavily restored. H. 22 cm. From digging in Købmagergade, Copenhagen (downtown Copenhagen). The National Museum, Second Dep't., D3520. d) Collection of pieces of broken glass from the glassworks in Svejbæklund near Ry, in production 1582-98. The pieces are from Pasglas of the type mentioned above. From a dig in 1957. The National Museum, Second Dep't., D26/1957-D42/1957.
*Literature:* Jexlev, Rissmøller and Schlüter 1970.

# Mining, silver and monetary policy

979

## Prospect of Kongsberg, c. 1695

From the printed inventory of the Royal Kunstkammer, "Museum Regium", written in Latin, København, 1710
Copper engraving
Det kgl. Bibliotek, Kortsamlingen
Kongsberg after the fire in 1652,; in Christian IV's time it appeared almost like this.
*Literature:* Moen 1967 79 and 95ff.

980

## Georg Agricola: De Re Metallica, 1621

Det kgl. Bibliotek, Second Dep't
This famous work was originally published in Basel in

1556 and reprinted – also in the German edition – many times. It explains thoroughly the mining methods of the period, and is richly illustrated with woodcuts.

981

## Kurze Doch wahrhaftige Beschreibung der Silber und anderer Bergwercke in Norwegen so viel derselben im Jahr 1630 bekandt gewesen. Durch einen Liebhaber Der Bergwerck an Tag gebracht

Dr. Johan Friderich Norman 1631, published 1649
Det kgl. Bibliotek
The Oldest specialized description of the Norwegian mines. Dr. med. J. F. Nor(t)man, who had been a mining doctor in Ober-Harz, emigrated in 1627 to Norway, where he became the viceregent Jens Juel's advisor in mining matters. In 1628 Juel hired him as the mine overseer (the King's representative) at Kongsberg, which lead to Juel's transfer to Aalborghus len in 1629 (cf. cat. 809).
*Literature:* Moen 1967 36ff.

982

## Mining tools, 1600's

b) and c) wrought iron
Norsk Bergverksmuseum, Kongsberg, a) BVM 459/-85, b) no number c) BVM 74
The silver was mined by a combination of two methods. The rock wall a) has on the one side stripes from "cold chisling", and on the other soot from "firing". The rock-face was "exploded" by heating it up. Split fir poles of roughly a meter's length were stacked up against the wall of the mine and lit afire. The heat itself was sufficient to split off a layer of rock. Then the chiseling could be used again to follow the lodes of silver into the rock face with hammer and pick b), in such a way that the pick (the pointed hammer) functioned as a chisel. The wear on the tools was great, and every miner had numerous picks – enough for the day's work – hanging from his belt. With the pick axe c) the miner hit directly on the rock face. The crossed hammer and pick is the international symbol of the miner's work.
*Provenance:* Individual finds in the silver mines i Kongsberg.
*Literature:* Berg 1983 56f. and 1984.

983

## Christian IV's monogram 1624

Modern silicon cast of monogram cut in stone, c. 106×115 cm
Norsk Bergverksmuseum, Kongsberg
Christian IV visited Sandsvær in Numdalen in 1624, where silver had been found a year earlier. At the same time the town was founded, which he named "Kongsberg" (King's Mountain). The King's crowned monogram and the year were cut into the rock face at "Kongens Grube" (the King's Mine). – At the same place is Christian V's similar crowned monogram; he visited Kongsberg in 1673 and 1685.
*Provenance:* Casting from Norsk Bergverksmuseum 1987.
*Literature:* Sælebakke 1975.

984

## Miner's and logger's axes

Norway, two dated: 1619 and 1644
Length 61.5-166 cm
The National Museum, Second Dep't., 10181, 10033, 10176, and 10179
Axes were symbols of dignity for the loggers and the miners, recruited from Germany, whose axes – "Hackeler" – were usually in the shape of inv.no. 10181. In the 1600's the axes had become display weapons – as are these – and often carried inscriptions and other decorations, later they became pure symbols without sharp edges; even examples with wooden blades carved as one with the shaft are known.
*Provenance:* The Royal Kunstkammer, inv. 1737, 866/154 and 867/161 as well as inv. 1775, 92/b13. 1826 to The Royal Museum of Art, BDe8, 3 1 and 5; 1848 the Museum of Northern Antiquities (now the National Museum).

985

## "Serepta", sermons for miners

Johan Mathesius, 1578
Det kgl. Bibliotek
Mathesius was pastor in "the free mining town" in St. Jochimsthal, from which many miners were recruited to Norway. In his sermons the Bible is explained and interpreted with concepts and examples from the miners' daily experience in the mine.

986

## "Portrait" of a lump of silver, found in Kongsberg 1630

Adam van Breen, 1631
Oil on canvas. 121×171 cm
Kongsberg Church, Norway
The large lump of silver is reproduced on a red clothed table standing below a red drapery with braid and tassels. Above Christian IV's crowned monogram under the letters R F P, below an inscription in German and Latin:
BENEDICTIO DOMINI DIVITES FACIT. Anno 1630 den 31 Aug: Ist alhier zu Königsberg in SEGEN GOTTES grube der gleichen Stück gediegen Silber gewon(n)en, so gewogen 409 marcke und taxirt worden vor 3272 Reichs thaler. SOLI DEO GLORIA." (The blessing of the Lord creates wealth. In the year of our Lord 1630 the

31st of Aug. here in Kongsberg in the mine "God's Blessing" was found this piece of high quality silver, which weighed 409 mark and is valued at 3272 rigsdaler. The Glory is God's alone. April 21., 1631 the painter Adam van Breen was paid 24 rdl. by the order of viceregent Christopher Urne for two paintings of the great lump of silver. The one was hung up in the church in Christiania (Holy Trinity Church in Oslo) – where it must have burned in 1686 – the other in the church in Kongsberg, where it hangs in the sacristy of the present church. Restored in 1986.
*Literature:* Bugge and Alsvik 1962 20.

987

## Silver

Geologisk Museum
a-b) Two lumps of silver, a) massive fibrous silver; fan shaped. Weight 1600gr., 16×14×12 cm.; no number; b) fibrous silver. 50 gr., 13×41 cm.; inv.no. 142. – c) A piece of matrix of mainly calcite, a little quartz; considerable fibrous silver is crystallized between and on the calcite crystals. 640 gr. 10×9×5 cm.; inv.no. 130. – d) vein with silver; a piece of matrix made up of hornstone, calcite and flourite with thin sheets of silver. 784 gr., 10 ×9×5 cm.; inv.no. 1979.522.
*Provenance:* Kongsberg, Norway, d) from "Christian IV's mine".

987

## Selection of Danish coins: daler, mark, and skilling

Silver and copper
Den kgl. Mønt- og Medaillesamling
Minting was royal privilege, i.e. only the king had the right to mint. In order to maximize the profit from this right it was common to mint coins that were devalued either by adding copper to the silver or simply underweight. The difference between the established intrinsic value and the real value of the coins gave the king a profit. Only the standard coin, the speciedaler, was always minted at full value, and that rarely in very great numbers. One speciedaler had a value of 6 marks (the mark was a coin that gave the king high profits until the Council of the Realm interfered). The daler was worth 96 skillinge. The most common coins in circulation were the 4, 2 and 1 skillinge.
*The mints* were Copenhagen (from 1593), Elsinore (from 1607), Frederiksborg castle (from 1622), Haderslev (from 1590), Glückstadt (from 1619) and Christiania (Oslo, from 1628).
*Literature:* Wilcke 1919 and 1924; Bendixen 1973.

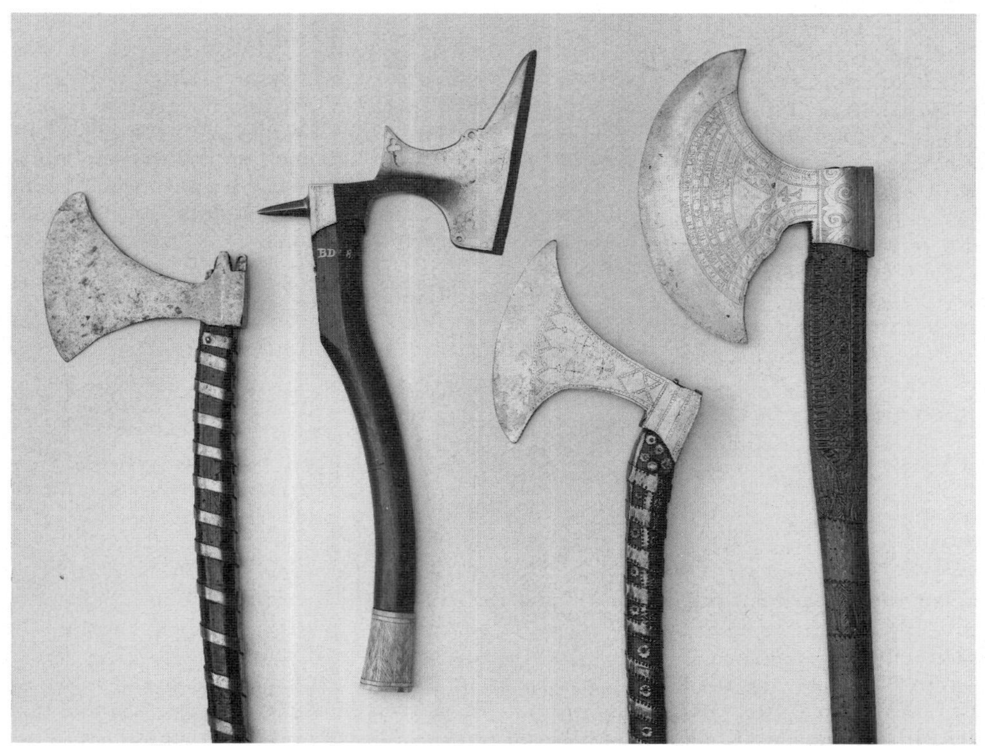

*984*

988

991a

989

988

## Dalere (coins) of Norwegian silver 1624-1648

Den kgl. Mønt- og Medaillesamling
The discovery of the large silver deposit at Kongsberg in 1623 gave the King his own silver for coining. It was used both for dalere and in alloy with copper for small coins. The first dalere of the Kongsberg silver were minted in Copenhagen, from 1628 at the newly established mint in Christiania (Oslo). The mint was not moved to Kongsberg until 1686.
*Literature:* Wilke 1919; Rønning 1986.

990

## Selection of gold coins and "brilledukater" (spectacle ducats)

Den kgl. Mønt- og Medaillesamling
Gold coins came to Denmark through the Sound dues (cf. cat. 763). Few Danish gold coins were minted, but those that were made were attractive types. Christian IV stressed that his coins, whether gold or silver, were to be lovely to look at. The minor amounts of gold in some of the silver veins in Kongsberg interested Christian IV so much that he, together with Caspar Herbach, got it extracted and thereafter minted into ducats. The spectacles on the reverse and the inscription: "Vide mira domi" (See the wonders here at home!, or: See the wonders of the Lord!) was to emphasize that the King had been right in that it could be done. The veins of gold were, however, all too small to be of any significance. The spectacle ducats are dated 1647.
*Literature:* Wilcke 1924 92-93.

991

## Special trading coins of silver

Den kgl. Mønt- og Medaillesamling
Special coins were minted for foreign trade, and their value and appearance corresponded to foreign trading coins which were internationally recognized.
a) *Løvedaleren* (the Lion daler) of 1608 imitated a Dutch coin, but the lion was Norwegian. b) *Denninge* imitated the small Russian dengi. Coined for use in Lappland by the Petsoriske Company in 1619. c) *Piastren* imitated the Spanish ones in weight and value. 20,000 were minted for the use of the East Indian Company in 1624. d) *Kronemønt.* These spectacular Kroner, coined from 1618 on, were intended for use in the East Indian trade. They

were not, however, up to standard alloy and had to be devalued. Common in domestic circulation, especially the lower face values.
*Literature:* Wilke 1919; Hede 1978 no. 65, 104, 169, 66, 105f. Bendixen 1976 69-70.

992

## Selection of foreign silver dalere

Den kgl. Mønt- og Medaillesamling
Dutch, German, Austrian, Polish and other dalere came into Denmark, especially as payment for oxen. These coins circulated as means of payment alongside the domestic coins and are found in great numbers in treasure hoards. Many were however melted down and coined into speculative mintings.
*Literature:* Bendixen 1973.

993

## Norwegian silver tankard

Mark for Bernt Platt, Christiania 1647
Chased and cast silver. H. 12.5 cm., Diam. 11.5 cm
The National Museum, Second Dep't., D686
The tankard has the wide shape, which along with spherical feet, became fashionable in the 1640's. It may be made of silver from Kongsberg. In the lid are engraved the arms of the Juel family and Peder Juel Erichsen's name and the year 1647 written in runes.
*Provenance:* Purchased in 1871 from a farmer in Stoustrup, Ringkøbing county.
*Literature:* Olrik 1909 74 no. 35.

994

## Stove plate

Norwegian, presumably from Fossum Jernværk, 1630
Cast iron. 82×70.5 cm
The National Museum, Second Dep't., D1419
Bas relief of the Creation of Eve. In the section under the relief the matrimonial arms and initials of Ove Giedde and Dorte Urne and the year 1630.
*Provenance:* Purchased in 1879 from the school teacher in Ramten near Grenå.
*Literature:* Fett 1905; Olrik 1912.

995

## Three plates from a stove

Fossum Jernværk, Norway, 1630-40
Cast iron; side plates 70.5×55.5 cm., end plates 70.5×32 cm
The National Museum, Second Dep't., D7126
The side plates have a relief of the meeting of Esau and Jacob (Gen. 33) above two quadruple coats of arms with Eiler Urne's and Jytte Gyldenstierne's four ancestral arms respectively. He was lensmand (noble lord-lieutenant) of Bratskov len – where Fossum lies – from 1620 to 1640. The end plate bears the Norwegian lion in a Baroque cartouche above Christian IV's crowned name and motto: RFP. Identical stoves are found in among other places in Hjørring, Aalborg and Antwerp.
*Provenance:* Purchased 1909 from a farmer on Læsø.
*Literature:* Fett 1905; Olrik 1912.

996

## Oventile with a portrait of the King, c. 1600

Black glazed tile, 28.5×15.8×5 cm
The National Museum, Second Dep't., D7455
Under an egg and dart ornamented arcade borne by fluted columns, a bust of the young Christian IV is depicted in relief. The King wears a high crowned hat with feathers, a ruff and a jacket with quilted sleeves; in his left hand he holds a glove and on his shoulders is a gold chain. Below, between the pedastals of the columns, an inscription: CHRISTIANUS IIII / KONING IN DENM" (Christian IIII/ king of Denm[ark]).
*Provenance:* Presumed to have come from the upper part of a "jernkakkelovn" (iron stove) at Koldinghus castle. Museet på Koldinghus, inv.no. 2454; 1910 exchanged to the National Museum for a tile from the same form. This fragment (inv.no. Dk5745), which was found at Skodborghus earthworks near Kongeåen, was in 1904 exchanged from Randers Museum, where it had had inv.no. 8488.
*Literature:* Liebgott 1972 33f.

996

*Willem Panneels: Marsyas. (1628/30). Black chalk, pen, black ink, red chalk on greyish brown paper. 210/214×401/403*

# Den kongelige Kobberstiksamling

## *Rubens Cantoor*
## *Selected Drawings by Willem Panneels*

If one considers how difficult it can often be to conjure up a clear and detailed memory of incidents one has experienced, even if they took place only a few weeks or days ago, it may well seem rash – not to say foolish – to attempt to recreate the totality of a strange pattern which was laid out many hundred years ago and is now known only in fragmentary form. A jigsaw puzzle with many pieces missing.

The exercise is not made easier by the fact that from the beginning a conscious attempt was made to envelop this whole affair in a thick veil of mist. That was, however, only an attempt. Even if it will never be possible to make a complete reconstruction of all details, there are elements involved which can be used to form the basis of a trustworthy theory of what the whole must have been.

But what is the subject of the puzzle? In brief, roughly 500 drawings from the Netherlands. They were made during the time of Christian IV and seem to have reached Denmark already then. This would have been in no way exceptional. Denmark had no national art of significance, and a lively import trade in both art and artists from the south therefore flourished. The drawings are not thematically unusual, either. In tune with the custom of the time they take their subjects from the Bible, mythology or history. There are also copies of sculptures from antiquity, anatomical drawings and many others of which the majority can directly be connected with Rubens, which, understandably enough, resulted for a long time in the drawings being attributed to him. No, the remarkable feature consists of the way many of these drawings are provided with a code, for the purpose, self-evidently, of keeping something withheld which the originator for all the world did not want to share with others.

And what could that have been? Since the publication by the Danish Professor, Vilhelm Thomsen, of his deciphering of the code in 1919 it has been possible – sometimes with difficulty – to read through the Flemish inscriptions, and the answer is rather disappointing, if one expected intimate confidences or revelations of a sensational nature. The texts contain only one simple personal admission. From an art-historical view-point, however, it is one which must be considered exceptionally useful and interesting.

The admission's constant refrain is in fact that this and that "I have taken from Rubens Cantoor". This refers to a large chest of drawers, a kind of desk, which must have stood in Rubens' home in Antwerp, and in which, according to the evidence of the inscriptions, he kepts drawings and smaller oil sketches. This secretly confessing "I" must have waited for unobserved moments when he could copy them on the sly. As a rule he seems quite satisfied with the result. He especially fastened upon whether the contours were successful, but the notes also contain information about motif and technique used.

If not before, then certainly after the deciphering of the code, any thought of the drawings being the work of Rubens himself had to be definitively abandoned. The outstanding question then was who this artist could be, who for evident reasons tried to hide his identity behind these illegible scrawls. If he had not been carried away by his bureaucratic habits he would no doubt have been able to preserve his anonymity. But pedantry has its price, especially if it is not carried through with sufficient care. One single time (cf. fig. 4 and text to fig. 3) he made a revealing mistake – he let his usual handwriting show in the code inscriptions. The handwriting moreover appears on several drawings from Rubens Cantoor (cf. fig. 5), and as the most damning evidence, on Willem Panneels' preparatory drawing (fig. 1) for the etching "Cursus Mundi" (fig. 2); Gustav Falck (1) was therefore able, a long time ago, to identify the copyist incontrovertibly as this artist. About 300 years had thus passed before it was revealed that Panneels had grossly abused the confidence Rubens had placed in him when Rubens entrusted him with the custody of his house and "all its contents", while he was travelling on one of his many diplomatic missions to Spain or England.

Even if we now know who the copyist was, we know very little about him. He could well have been born in

*Continued on p. 293*

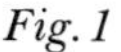
Fig. 1

Fig. 2

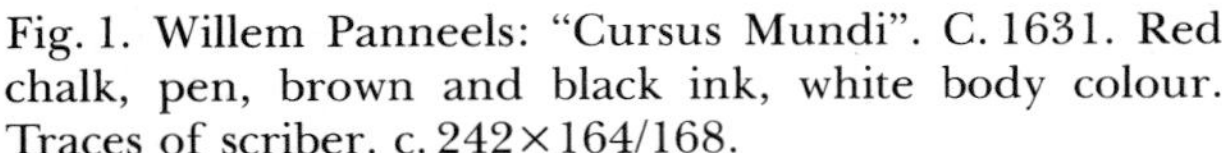

Fig. 1. Willem Panneels: "Cursus Mundi". C. 1631. Red chalk, pen, brown and black ink, white body colour. Traces of scriber. c. 242×164/168.

This allegorical presentation of life which, like a candle in a candle-stick, peters out gradually while new life is lit from the still-fluttering flame, is just as simple in its content as it is coarse in its form. An almost desperate eagerness to make the drawing successful has achieved the opposite result: a somewhat rough execution, where the many layers of correction lines and shadings to a great extent contribute to accentuating the faults instead of hiding them. But if for no other reason the drawing is at least interesting because it is a main key to the otherwise well-concealed secrets of an artist's dubious activities in the second part of the 1620s. If one compares this work with many stylistically closely related drawings in "Rubens Cantoor", there can be no doubt that they are made by the same man. He preferred, with good reason, to stay anonymous. A recurring, now deciphered, code actually reveals the drawings were surreptitiously copied from Rubens' works. The Latin inscriptions on figs. 1 and 2 reveal the copyist however: Willem Panneels.

Fig. 2. Willem Panneels: "Cursus Mundi". 1631. Etching. c. 242×164/168 (slightly trimmed).

The majority of the 36 etchings which are registered under Panneels' name are modelled on paintings or drawings by Rubens. For Panneels, Rubens' art was always the model, both literally and figuratively. Probably assuming that it would do no harm, in a few of the cases where he used his own design, as in this case here, Panneels mentioned in the Latin text that he was a former pupil of the outstanding painter P. P. Rubens. It is not always otherwise evident. Where he began his graphic work is not known, but the inscriptions on all dated etchings state that they were printed during the period 1630-32, in different places in Germany – the earliest in Cologne, the town of Rubens' childhood. It was probably not merely nostalgia which brought this about. As early as 1619, in order to prevent plagiarism and cheap imitations, Rubens had secured the graphic rights to his work in the Netherlands and France. In Germany, however, one could freely spread acquaintance with his work.

*Fig. 3*

Fig. 3. Willem Panneels: Study of an ancient statue (1628/30). Black and red chalk. 330/332×169/174.
The statue is drawn in outline strokes which are in some places insistent, and in others almost invisibly light. The forms have not been shaded to stand out from the surface of the white paper. At the bottom left is written "Een Van de Griechse Armafrodita" ("One of the Greek hermaphrodites"). Then the comprehensible Flemish changes into code, which when transcribed reads: "desehebbeick / oockgehalt vancantoor vanrubbens" ("This I also took from Rubens' cantoor"). This is the only example in the stock of the Copenhagen Print Room where the artist's ordinary handwriting is found together with the code. This hybrid inscription is therefore one of the keys to the identification of the artist.

Fig. 4. Detail of fig. 3. The inscription with the artist's ordinary handwriting and the code are reproduced in full scale.

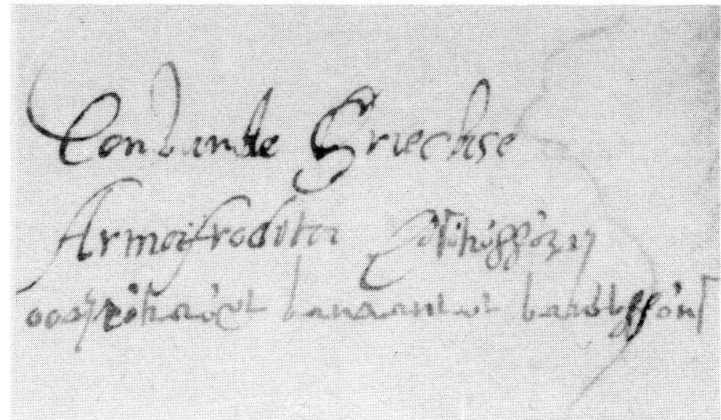

*Fig. 4*

Antwerp around 1600; from 1624-30 he was an apprentice of Rubens. For the next couple of years he stayed in different places in Germany: in 1630 in Cologne, in 1630-31 in Frankfurt-am-Main, and in the latter year also in Baden; then finally, in 1632, in Strasbourg. All this is evident from inscriptions on some of his etchings. After that all traces are lost. Did he die during the Thirty Years' War? Or did he, like many other artists from the Netherlands, travel north, to Denmark?

*Jan Garff*

1. »En Rubenselevs Tegninger«. Kunstmuseets Aarsskrift 1918. Copenhagen 1919, pp. 64-77, ill.

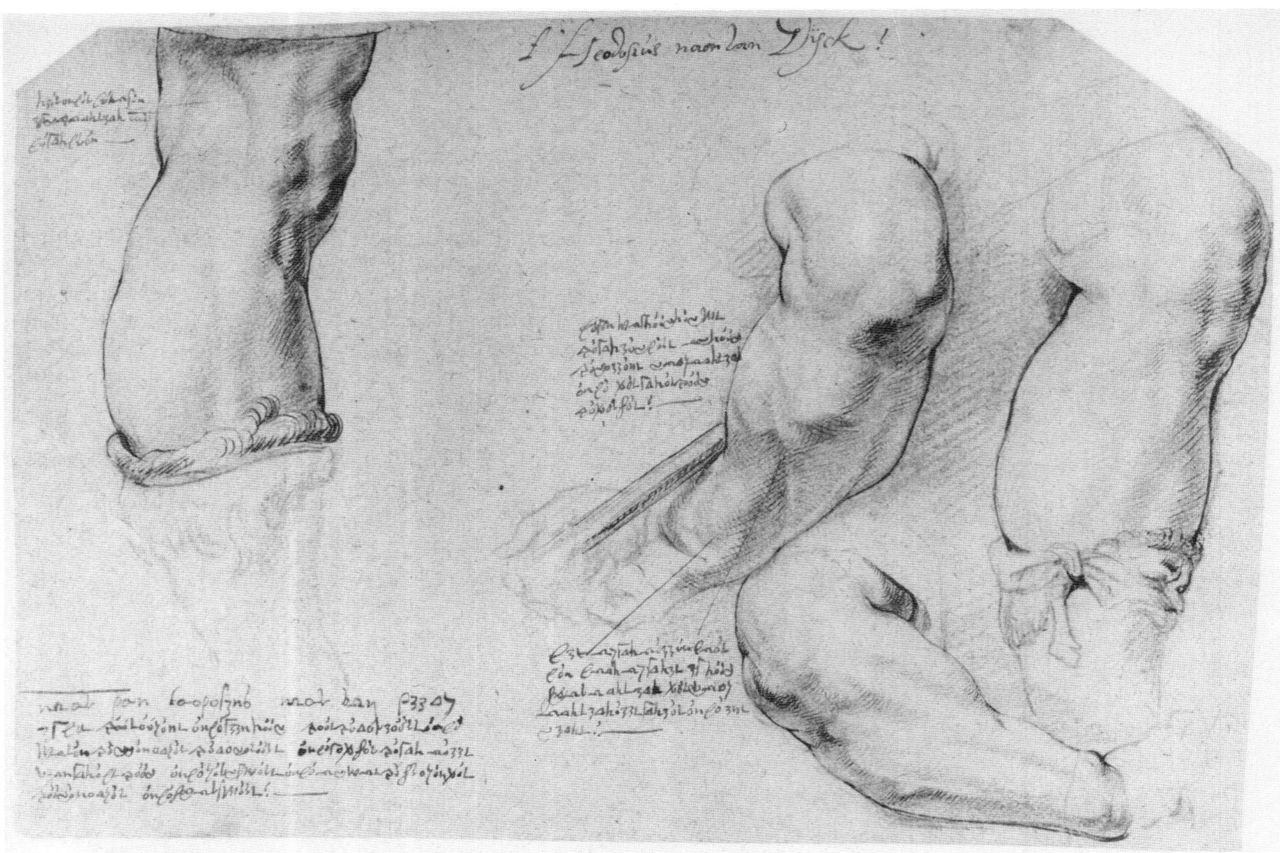

*Fig. 5*

Fig. 5. Willem Panneels: Studies of arms and legs from Anthony van Dyck's painting "Emperor Theodosius the Great and St Ambrose" (1618/20). (1628/30). Black and white chalk, pen, brown and black ink. 231/235 ×335/344 (the upper corners diagonally trimmed).

As is evident from the inscription at the top, the study-sheet's various disconnected parts of the body were taken from "t'Theodosius naer Van Dijck!". This is in all probability a reference to the large painting, now in the Kunsthistorisches Museum in Vienna. The many colour indications in code show that the copyist had worked from a painted original.

The inscription in the lower left corner is significant in a literal sense: it shows two variants of the secret signs. The first line represents the first phase. In contrast to the easy flow of the following lines, the code here seems hesitant and clumsy. In addition there appear signs for d,e,s and t in forms which were later abandoned.

Fig. 6. Willem Panneels: Pythagoras of Samos (1628/30). Black, red and white chalk, white body colour, pen, brown and black ink. 335/340×245/269 (the corners on the left rounded, the upper right corner diagonally trimmed).

The inscription below on the left matter-of-factly states "pitagoras desen/omtreck is goet" ("Pythagoras, whose outline is good"). Observations of this type can frequently be encountered in the deciphered code.

In technical respects the making of the drawing followed a well-known sequence: first slight indications, in black chalk, of points, lines and surfaces, then adjustments and a further development of figures and forms, and then red chalk and white body colour to accentuate the shaded and light areas; then with the pen the final determination of the outline, which as a rule left the artist well satisfied.

*Fig. 6*

*Fig. 7*

Fig. 8. Willem Panneels: Drunken Silenus (after P. P. Rubens) (1632). Etching. 140×152.

To attribute to Rubens all the honour and responsibility for the design of the etching, as the publisher Franciscus van den Wyngaerde does in the Latin inscription on the state, is gallantry conditioned by commercialism. If one compares the print with the drawing (fig. 7) which Panneels made from Rubens' original, a direct link can hardly be denied. So the cramped, almost square picture-area, which allows the actors scant space to move, should doubtless be seen as Panneels' own, somewhat dubious contribution to a concise edition of the original. According to the information on the first state, the etching was produced in 1632 in Strasbourg by Willem Panneels, a former pupil of Rubens. Yes, indeed a former pupil.

*Fig. 8*

Fig. 7. Willem Panneels: Drunken Silenus (1628/30). Pen, brown ink (with smudges of black chalk). 206/210×c. 304.

In addition to two painted versions in London (Courtauld Institute Galleries) and Paris (Louvre), until 1903 there was a third to be found in a private collection in Paris, a grisaille, which has since vanished without trace and is now only known by a photographic reproduction. It is this picture which Panneels' drawing most closely resembles – so closely, in fact, that it could be tempting to identify the grisaille with "the little Silenus", which according to the note in code "is sketched in white and black on a wooden panel and not yet painted". The possibility of one of the other versions being the model for Panneels' copy has to be excluded – if only for the reason that in both cases there are fewer figures. In the lost original (?) there were fourteen figures, compared with the twelve in the drawing. The missing two, the nymph and the satyr, who in the other representations form the demoniacally pirouetting vanguard of the bacchanal, are preserved in a detached fragment, probably once the left-hand part of the drawing illustrated.

Fig. 9. Willem Panneels: Two studies of the Head of Laocoön (1628/30). Black and red chalk, pen, brown ink, brush, brownish wash. 173/177×274/276.

Laocoön is an ancient sculpture representing the priest Laocoön and his sons' doomed struggle against two sea-serpents. It was found in Rome in 1506 and installed in the Belvedere in the Vatican, where it still stood in Rubens' time. The Laocoön group is depicted in its entirety or in detail in six drawings by Rubens and in twice as many by Panneels. Only three of those by Rubens are known today, which does not lessen the interest of Panneels' copies. The drawing illustrated here is in fact an example of a copy of a no-longer-known original. The code states the identity of the two heads, and that they were taken from the cantoor. The Flemish inscription below does not show the same attention to detail, but limits itself to the banal observation that the subject is a man's head. The second-rate nature of the information reveals that it must have been added by a second (and later) hand.

*Fig. 9*

*Fig. 10*

*Fig. 11*

Fig. 10. Willem Panneels: Anatomical study: Man walking, back view. (1628/30). Red and black chalk. c. 279×159/163.

The inscription beneath contains, in deciphered code, just the artist's constant refrain "ditheb ick oockvantcantoorgehaelt", which is transcribed "This I also took from the cantoor" (i.e. Rubens Cantoor).

The drawing is typical of Panneels' work as a copyist. In his figure-studies he focuses his attention very often on the body alone, the torso, its linear framework and its corporal substance. And just as in this example, the head, hands and feet are usually only suggested, more or less elegantly exhaled.

Fig. 11. Peter Paul Rubens (?): Anatomical studies: Three nude Warriors in Combat (1605/10 (?)). Black chalk. 291×200. Sold at auction 6 July 1987 at Christie's, London.

By a strange turn of fate recently eleven anatomical sketches, all attributed to Rubens, were "re-discovered". Of these no less than nine could directly be linked to Panneels' copies in the Copenhagen Print Room (cf. fig. 10), which was taken as proof of the trustworthiness of the attribution. It cannot, however, be excluded that the drawings were the work of another hand – perhaps that of Paulus Pontius, who produced engravings from some of them and from other related studies. That Panneels in code repeatedly acknowledged that he took his subjects from Rubens Cantoor is not the same as saying that Rubens was the originator of them. Among Rubens' possessions works by other artists were also to be found, e.g. Van Dyck (cf. fig. 5).

The commentaries to the drawings and the print by Willem Panneels on the preceding pages were written by Eva de la Fuente Pedersen (figs. 3, 4 and 9) and Jan Garff, who are also responsible for the exhibtion 'Rubens Cantoor – a selection of drawings by Willem Panneels' to be held at Den kongelige Kobberstiksamling, Statens Museum for Kunst, Department of Prints and Drawings at the Royal Museum of Fine Arts from 30th March – 25th September 1988 to mark the Christian IV commemoration year.

Simultaneously with the opening of the exhibition, a complete catalogue of the original Rubens Cantoor with all the Panneels drawings will be published. Later additions, including original drawings by Rubens, Van Dyck, and others, will not however be published on this occasion.

The catalogue will be issued in two volumes, consisting of i) an introduction by Jan Garff (in English and Danish), a complete catalogue of the drawings by Eva de la Fuente Pedersen and Jan Garff, a selected bibliography and various registers, and ii) illustrations of the c. 300 drawings in the catalogue.

*1121*

# Statens Museum for Kunst

## *The Age of Christian IV*
## *Art Centres and Artists in Northern Europe 1588-1648*

"The Fall of the Titans" (cat. 1016) a large painting by Cornelis Cornelisz. van Haarlem, (1562-1638), was bought by Christian IV in 1621 and is one of the few purchases of contemporary art made by the King that can be identified with any degree of certainty in the present-day collection at the Statens Museum for Kunst (The Royal Museum of Fine Arts). The work must have made a considerable impression when it was first presented at Copenhagen Castle, with its abundance of muscular male nudes, its bold foreshortenings, its wealth of figure postures and its prodigious perspective. And it must have furnished food for thought for an artist such as the Danish Reinhold Timm (d. 1639) who, in his "Children of the Sun", dated 1622, (Statens Museum for Kunst, inv.no. 1171) one of the paintings executed for the decoration of the "Long Hall" at Rosenborg Castle, had at that time been faced with problems similar to those Cornelis had solved with such *bravura.*

After a short stay in France as a very young artist, Cornelis was active in his native Haarlem from around 1582 onwards. Here he was befriended by two other artists, Hendrick Goltzius (1558-1617), who was about his own age and had come from Germany in 1577, and the somewhat older Carel van Mander (1548-1606), who had emigrated to Haarlem in 1583 from the southern Netherlands due to unrest there. Between them they created a new style of figure painting, the so-called Haarlem Mannerism, which made a tremendous breakthrough in the mid-1580s and quickly spread to Amsterdam and Utrecht via artists like Abraham Bloemaert (cat. 1002 and 1003) and Joachim Wtewael (cat. 1125). It was based on a deep inspiration from the works of Bartholomäus Spranger (1546-1611), a painter from Antwerp whom van Mander had got to know in Rome in the early 1570s and who was now Court Painter to the Emperor Rudolf II in Prague. "The Titanomachy", painted by Cornelis in the late 1580s, is a thoroughly characteristic example of this new style and one of Cornelis' most important works from this early and hectic period.

After Hendrick Goltzius' period in Italy 1590-91, however, the style became more moderate and continued to be so well into the 17th century. Hendrick Goltzius was a brilliant copper engraver and his prints were well-known in Denmark during the reign of Christian IV. In 1600, however, he gave up engraving in favour of painting (cat. 1031). Van Mander was primarily an art theorist and art historian – his renowned *Het Schilder-Boeck* (Painters' Book), published in 1604, is one of the principal sources in Dutch art history. His work as a painter is less well-known, in spite of the fact that he was, an excellent landscape painter (cat. 1059). The theoretical basis for landscape painting was explained in his poem *Grondt der Edel Vry Schilderconst* (Principles of the Noble Art of Painting), which appeared as a paragraph in his *Schilder-Boeck.* Works by both Goltzius and van Mander were included in offers of paintings made to Christian IV about 1621 by Frans Bastiaensz. and the Cavalier Theodor Rodenburgh, but it is not known whether the King bought them or not.

When this wave of Late Mannerism had receded, Haarlem still retained her position as one of Holland's leading art centres, but now also on other fronts such as landscape painting (cat. 1078, 1097-1099), genre painting (cat. 1034 and 1035) and still life painting (cat. 1006 and 1014). Esaias van de Velde played a significant role in this early development and achieved great importance in both the realistic landscape and the "Garden Party" genre (the so-called "Geselschapje" or "Buitenpartij") derived from Flemish prototypes (cat. 1103). Where still life painting is concerned, the 1630s and the 1640s saw Haarlem as the centre of the classic monochromatic breakfast piece. It is doubtful whether this aspect of Haarlem art was of any interest to the Danish Court, however.

If we compare the acquisitions of paintings made by

the King's agent Dr. Jonas Charisius in the Netherlands 1607-08 (*Nystrøm* 1909, 225 ff.) and other early purchases with one of the very early decorative works executed for the King, viz. the series of paintings set into the panelling of the so-called "Winter Room" at Rosenborg Castle in ca. 1615, and the purchases one can deduce from the inventory of Frederiksborg Castle 1636/1650 (Petersen 1866-67, 118 ff.), it seems likely that what captured the Danish interest was Antwerp, the art centre of the Spanish-Catholic Netherlands and one of the main art centres of 16th and 17th Century Europe. Contemporary Flemish landscape painting seems to have been held in especial esteem. This applies to both the romantic-fantastic mountain scenes characteristic of Joos de Momper (cat. 1062-1065) and the Flemish woodscapes as exemplified by Keirincx (cat. 1046) and Jasper van der Lanen (cat. 1057). Hunting *motifs* were also very popular (cat. 1027 and 1036). An offshoot of this Flemish landscape painting had taken root in Germany, in Frankenthal, south of Frankfurt. Many Flemish members of the Reform church, among them a number of artists, had fled from Antwerp in 1585, when it was again overrun by the Spaniards, and had sought refuge in this little town in the Palatinate which since 1562 had been decreed a refuge for them by Friederich III Elector Palatine (1515-76). During the 1580s, the town became the centre of an artists' colony and a school of landscape painters, the socalled Frankenthal school, that created a new style in landscape painting (cat. 1060, 1085 and 1068), and whose leading spirit was Gillis van Coninxloo (in Frankenthal 1587-95). Coninxloo (1544-1607) moved to Amsterdam in 1595 where, according to van Mander, his landscape style created a furore and everyone started to paint trees the way he did. When he died early in 1607 the sale of his estate which took place from March 1st to 7th, including his paintings and drawings became a draw for Amsterdam's artists. If the text has been interpreted correctly, it looks as though Jonas Charisius bought some pictures from Coninxloo's widow in 1607 (*Nystrøm* 1909, 227) but it is doubtful whether this was in connection with the auction. Antwerp, however, was not just a centre of landscape painting; it was, in fact, the centre of figure painting *par excellence.* There abounded the learned allegory (cat. 1043) and pictures from classic mythology (cat. 1042, 1044 and 1045) alongside religious *motifs.* It can well be that Jordanes' "Aeneas' Apotheosis" (cat. 1044) from around 1617 dates back to the collections from Christian IV's time; the large Rubens picture (cat. 1081) and Jordaens' mythology (cat. 1045) were added to the King's collection very late in his life. However, both genre painting (cat. 1056 and 1078) and still life painting (cat. 1086) were represented in Antwerp so it is quite possible that a great many Flemish paintings of this type are among the paintings described in the Frederiksborg inventory (cf.cat. 1103).

## II

It would probably be wrong to assume that King Christian IV's attitude to, and collecting of, contemporary European paintings and sculpture, which as far as the King was concerned meant almost exclusively works from the Netherlands and the German speaking countries, was based on a specially refined artistic taste or special aesthetic interest. It seems that, particularly in the early stages, what was decisive was quantity: the King could never resist the temptation of buying crates of unspecified paintings at low cost. Later on he selected pictures from ranges presented to him from time to time by travelling connoisseurs and art dealers, and the quality improved. In truth, the King was never an art collector proper, in the way Emperor Rudolf II was, for instance. His attitude to art was mainly functional, with the result that better results were achieved when it was a question of specific decorative needs for new royal buildings, and professional and artistic advice was at hand, and not simply the mere filling of Palace rooms with paintings as quickly as possible.

Christian IV was well aware that there were in fact no sufficiently qualified local artists to fill these needs, and since he could not attract artists of European standards to Denmark, he despatched his trusted advisors abroad to order works from the best artists in Northern Europe. This procedure was followed with remarkable artistic results in the case of three of the most important decorative projects undertaken by Christian IV, namely the Neptune Fountain at Frederiksborg Castle, the King's private oratory in the church there, and the extensive series of paintings depicting the deeds of the Danish Kings to be hung in Kronborg Castle. Christian IV may not have been a discriminating art collector of note personally, but he had a certain stature when it came to ensuring the art needed from abroad for domestic adornment. For the above-mentioned fountain, the King's trusted art agent was mintmaster Nicolaus Schwabe (ca. 1570-1629), for the oratory it was the Dutch painter Pieter Isaacsz. (1569-1625), and for the series of paintings for Kronborg Castle it was the Dutch engraver Simon de Pas (1593?-1647).

When it came to the embellishment of the forecourt of his newly built Frederiksborg Castle with a magnificent fountain adorned with bronze figures, Christian IV well knew that the right "Bossierer" (sculptor-modeller) and the right bronze casters for this work would have to be sought in south Germany or in Austria. His father, Frederik II (1559-1588) had earlier – in the beginning of the 1580s – commissioned the Neptune Fountain for Kronborg Castle from Georg Labenwolff's bronze workshop in Nürnberg. (The fountain was carried off by the Swedes in 1659 and subsequently melted down completely, all except 3 figures which are now in the Nationalmuseum in Stockholm). Mintmaster Nicolaus Schwabe was thus sent by the King on 16th April 1614, not this time to Nürnberg but to Augsburg and Innsbruck. It seems likely that the King had heard of the magnificent fountains in bronze that had been erected in Augsburg some years previously. But the reason why it was the sculptor Hans Reichle (1570-1642) of all sculptors to whom the King wished to entrust this work – as it clearly appears from the careful notes and accounts kept by Schwabe on this as well as on subsequent trips – is unknown. Reichle, who had worked in Giambologna's studio in Florence during the late 1580s and been active in Brixen (Bressanone) in southern Tyrol from 1607, was certainly an eminent sculptor in bronze, but had apparently not up till then had any experience where fountains were concerned in his own work. Seveal years prior to Schwabe's mission, however, Reichle had worked in Augsburg and had there carried out some of his greatest works in bronze (the crucifixion-altar in St. Ulrich and Afra completed 1605, and the St. Michael group on the facade of the "Zeughaus", completed 1607), and this may have given the impression that he had also had some connection with the fountains there.

At any rate, south Germany, Böhmen and Tyrol made up the centre of bronze sculpture north of the Alps, and Schwabe's travels took him to the leading towns within this field: Nürnberg where Benedikt Wurzelbauer (cat. 1127) at that time had taken over Labenwolff's workshop and had embellished the square in front of the Church of St. Lorenz with his "Tugendbrunnen" (1583-89); Augsburg, with Hubert Gerhard's Augustus Fountain (1589-94) (cat. 1030) and Adrian de Vries' two splendid fountains, the Mercury Fountain (1596-99) and the Hercules Fountain (1597-1602); and Innsbruck, where Caspar Gras (cat. 1032) worked for Archduke Maximilian III of Austria and had just taken over the workshop from Gerhard, who had moved to Munich (the only important centre of German bronze sculpture not visited by Schwabe). On his first visit to Brixen, Schwabe did not manage to contact Reichle and he searched for him right down to Venice. On the way home, however, he did meet him. Reichle accepted the commission and promised to come to Denmark which, however, he never did, and a year later saw Schwabe again travelling south, departing on 12th May. He had kept his eyes open on his 1614 trip and this time he made a change in course, going directly to Prague via Dresden with instructions from the King to engage the services of Adrian de Vries for the fountain. On his arrival in Prague on 4th June, Schwabe found that Adrian de Vries was not there. But the Master was worth waiting for and 10 days later Schwabe had de Vries' acceptance of the commission. Like Reichle the year before, de Vries too promised to come to Copenhagen but like Reichle he never did. On the other hand he did deliver his sculptures on time (cat. 1109-1119). The indefatigable Schwabe had served his King well. He had managed to secure the greatest bronze sculptor north of the Alps for the work. Originally the fountain was to have cost the King 5000 *Rigsdaler,* but in the end it cost him twice that sum. In return he got what must have been one of the finest fountains in northern Europe.

During the reign of Rudolf II (Emperor 1576-1612), who at that time was one of the greatest art collectors and patrons, Prague became an art centre with a reputation throughout Europe. Attached to the Imperial Court were a number of Netherlandish artists most of whom had been trained in Italy; names such as Bartholomäus Spranger (cat. 1087), Hans von Aachen (cat. 997), Joseph Heintz the elder (1564-1609) and Matthäus Gundelach (cat. 1033) for the painters and, for sculpture, Adrian de Vries (cat. 1107 and 1108) who was the Emperor's court sculptor from 1601 till the latter's death. These artists were a source of inspiration to one another, and in an exaggerated fin-de-siècle atmosphere, and with the Emperor's personal tastes as a basis, they created a strongly artificial style that bore the stamp of both of intellectualism and eroticism, and which represents a pinnacle in European Late Mannerism. Within the artistic image of the Prague school there were also other more naturalistic trends such as for instance are reflected in landscape paintings by Pieter Stevens and Roelandt Savery (cat. 1083 and 1088).

When Schwabe visited Prague three years after the Emperor's death, the Court had already moved to Vienna and Rudolf II's artists' colony had more or less been disbanded.

The most important art centre in south Germany along with Munich was Augsburg. It was situated on the road to Italy and experienced a tremendous artistic flourishing under the Fugger patronage and lasted through the first third of the 17th century. It was there that Hubert Gerhard (cat. 1030) and Adrian de Vries (cat. 1106) had their first triumphs, and painters like Johan Rottenhammer (cat. 1080) and Johan König (cat. 1055) were active. Before he became Court Painter in Prague, Hans von Aachen worked in Augsburg and it was also there that Matthäus Gundelach settled when he left Prague in 1615. And finally it was Augsburg during the 1620s that was able to include Georg Petel (cat. 1073-1075) in her list of famous artists. His bust of Gustav II

Adolf (cat. 1075) was cast in the same bronze workshop (Neidhardt) as the de Vries Augsburg-sculptures 30 years earlier.

## III

Whilst the King's stone mason (later master builder) Hans Steenwinckel (1587-1639) was doing his best to put the de Vries fountain together in the forecourt at Frederiksborg ("Steenwinkel is commanded to collect the well at Frederiksborg and attempt to put the said well together", as Christian IV wrote in a letter of 13th April 1620 to his chancellor Christian Friis, (cf. Friis 1872-78, 258 and *idem* 1890-1901, 215), work was in progress on building the great two-storey marble gallery in front of the castle's King's Wing, to house sculptures from Hendrick de Keyser's workshop in Amsterdam. He was the most eminent of Holland's sculptors at the time, and his principal work was the huge marble and bronze sepulchral monument (1614-23) for William the Silent of Orange in Nieuwe Kerk at Delft (cf.cat. 1105). His work also included some excellent bronze statuettes (cat. 1048 and 1049).

At the same time, indoor work was in progress on decorating Christian IV's oratory, a private chapel at the end of the castle church in the upper gallery under the great organ. Set into the panelling, which was of precious woods such as ebony and nutmeg, were to be two rows, one above the other, of paintings on copper depicting scenes from the life of Jesus and from the Parables. All the copper plates were the same height – about 103 cm – but the width varied according to where they were placed, from 56 and 58 cm to 83,91 or 94 cm sight measurements (*Danmarks Kirker* II, 3, 1970, 1878 ff).

This time the commission went to Holland. Pieter Isaacsz. had moved to Copenhagen in 1608 as the Court Painter and artistic advisor to the King, and it was he who painted the first picture in the series, as a guideline for colour and dimensions. He then went back to his former hometown Amsterdam, however, and distributed the commission to other painters belonging to the circle of the so-called "Pre-Rembrandtists": Pieter Lastman (cat. 1058), the leader of this group, who painted 3 of the pictures, Jan Pynas (1583/4-1631) who painted 2 and Adriaen van Nieulandt (cat. 1069 and 1070, who was given the largest number, namely 12. (He had been a pupil of Isaacsz. in Amsterdam in 1607 before the latter moved to Copenhagen and although he did not strictly speaking belong to the Pre-Rembrandtist group he had a strong affinity with them). Another painter, Werner van Valckert (cat. 1095) who did not belong to this group, painted 2 pictures and an as-yet-unknown painter who signed with the initials PH painted 3. Van Valckert must have been a painter to Christian IV's taste, since the King bought other works of his shortly after. Strangely enough, Jan Tengnagel (cf.cat. 1092), a painter who belonged to this group and who was a noted artist that unlike the others in the Pre-Rembrandtist circle chiefly painted New Testament themes, did not share in this commission (cf.cat. 1092). Painted in 1619-20 these pictures, alas, were lost in the fire at the castle in 1859 but are known, along with the rest of the interior decoration of the oratory, from contemporary and later descriptions and through a watercolour painting from 1858 by Heinrich Hansen (Frederiksborg).

Pieter Isaacsz.'s choice of artists seems to have been a wise one. In the first place they were all considered to be among the most significant of the new generation of Amsterdam's historical painters (Lastman, Pynas and Nieulandt are all praised in Cavalier Theodor Rodenburgh's poem from 1618, extolling Amsterdam's outstanding painters – in fact, Pieter Isaacsz. himself is also mentioned: *Roemt ... Uw Pieter Ysacx, die Uw roofden Denemercken,* "Be proud of your [i.e. Amsterdam's] Pieter Isaacsz. whom Denmark took away from you". Cf. Tümpel 1974, 17,) and in the second place Biblical subjects – although mainly Old Testament themes – made up the greater part of their repertoire. The fact that Pieter Lastman, at least, was a good Catholic apparently did not detract in this connection.

## IV

Adriaen van Nieulandt, one of the above-mentioned painters, reappeared when the King commissioned his last major decorative work, viz. the huge series of canvasses depicting the deeds of the early Danish kings, Christian IV's ancestors, to be hung in Kronborg Castle, newly rebuilt after the 1629 fire, and which were later to be published as plates in a large volume of prints. But this time it became predominantly a task for artists from Utrecht chosen on the spot between 1637 and 1639 by the King's advisor and entrepreneur, the engraver Simon de Pas, who had himself come from Utrecht in 1624, and was put in charge of the large engraving assignment. Among the artists involved were Abraham Bloemaert, father and Nestor of the Utrecht School (cat. 1005), Gerrit van Honthorst, the School's most illustrious son (who had supplied eight ceiling paintings for Kronborg Castle in 1635), Jan van Bylert (cat. 1001a and 1001b), Nicolaus Knüpfer (cat. 1051 and 1052), Simon Peter Tilmann (1601-68), Adam Willaerts (1577-1664) and Crispijn de Pas (1594/5-1670), Simon's brother. Apart from the already mentioned van Nieulandt, their numbers were augmented by other, young Amsterdam painters: Isaac Isaacsz. (ca. 1599-1688, the son of Pieter Isaacsz.), Claes Moeyaert (cat. 1061) from the group of the Pre-Rembrandtists, Salomon Koninck (cat. 1053 and 1954) from Rembrandt's circle, and finally Palamedes Palamedesz. from Delft (1607-38). Through this large commission the King got into touch with one of the most important and distinctive art centres in Holland. The character of Utrecht as an art centre was based on its Catholic strain and its close contact with Italy. After the first two decades of the 17th century, when Utrecht Mannerism had run its course, a new attitude to painting arose, inspired by Caravaggio and his Roman followers, the so-called Utrecht-Caravaggism, a style characterized by its strong *chiaroscuro,* its realism and its monumentality, and admirably suited to genre paintings with life-size figures. During the 1630s this style became more smooth and academic, the *chiaroscuro* became less intense and the palette grew lighter. One of the most important exponents of this movement was Gerrit van Honthorst. As an artist he was extremely versatile and his works ranged from the early religious paintings of his Roman period, supposedly his best work, to large genre paintings in artificial light (cat. 1039), portraits (cat. 1040), mythological representations (cat. 1041), and large dynastic allegories for the courts of England and the Hague. Honthorst mastered large groupings of figures, although this was by no means his real *forte.* However, none of his Utrecht colleagues or, for that matter, the Amsterdam painters who took part, were well equipped for the Danish commission (here we are not talking about artists like Willaerts and Palamedesz. who could have made use of their specialities – marine and battle scenes respectively). All those involved were certainly excellent artists, but they must certainly have been daunted, faced with compositions of large format portraying grandiose and dramatic subject matter, beyond their proper field and dealing with subjects they had absolutely no knowledge of. The series of pictures was never completed, and the volume of prints never saw the light of day.

It seems a rather cruel twist of fate that the extensive and decorative works which Christian IV had to go to the leading art centres in Northern Europe to get carried out have all either been lost completely, or lost to Denmark, or no longer exist in their original form. The Biblical pictures in Christian IV's oratory were lost when the chapel was destroyed in the castle fire of 1859 that also destroyed the sculptures in the marble gallery in front of the King's Wing. The bronze sculptures from Adrian de Vries' magnificent fountain were captured by Swedish troops in 1659 and carried off to Stockholm as booty, to end up as garden sculptures at Drottningholm Castle. And finally the large canvasses made for the decoration of Kronborg Castle are now dispersed in Denmark, Sweden and other countries. Fortunately, however, it is still possible to gain an impression of the artists behind all these works of art, and also other European artists whom Christian IV was in touch with over the years (e.g. David Bailly, Francois Dieussart and Adriaen van de Venne. Cat. 999, 1020, 1022 and 1100-1102).

*Olaf Koester*

Hans von Aachen

## Cologne 1552 – Prague 1615

997

*The Triumph of Time. An Allegory on Rudolf II's Regime*

Oil on copper. 55.5 ×47.6 cm. Signed: "(I?) V.ACH"

Staatsgalerie Stuttgart, inv. 2130

Painted ca. 1598 while von Aachen was Court Painter to Rudolf II, the present painting is like a paradigm of the refined art of Late Mannerism practised at the Rudolphine Court. The subject of the painting has given rise to several interpretations. It has most likely to be interpreted as an allegorical glorification of Rudolf II's regime related to the theme "Veritas filia Temporis" (Truth, the daughter of Time): abundance and wealth, art and science, and divine love will thrive in the Empire when Time triumphs over the Emperor's enemies (i.e. the Turcks). Von Aachen's painting "The Triumph of Truth" in the Alte Pinakothek in Munich (inv. 1611. Copper, 56×47, signed and dated: "HANS V.ACH.FEC. 1598") is, according to Dacosta Kaufmann, a pendant to the Stuttgart painting and encompasses a similar conception, which is closely connected with the Stuttgart picture.

*Provenance:* Bequeathed to the Staatsgalerie Stuttgart by A. Hüttenmüller, 1946.

*Literature:* Peltzer 1911-12, 132, 163 no. 53, fig. 52; Katalog Stuttgart 1962, 23, fig. 34; Dacosta Kaufmann 1978, 70ff, fig. 7; Dacosta Kaufmann 1985, 186 f. no. 1-$_{15}$, repr. p. 187.

## Jan Asselijn

Dieppe (?) ca. 1615 – Amsterdam 1652

998

*King Gustav II Adolf of Sweden at the Battle of Lützen, 16. November 1632*

Oil on panel. 70×92.6 cm. Signed and dated: "JAN.ASLEIN.fe 1632"

Statens Museum for Kunst, inv. Sp. 370

As a young artist, Asselijn executed a small number of paintings of cavalry battles, preferably those depicting Gustav Adolf's battles. According to Steland-Stief (1971), the present painting does not represent the battle of Lützen where Gustav Adolf was killed, but the victorious battle of Breitenfeld in 1631. It may well be, however, that the intention of the artist was to portray

Gustav Adolf as the great Protestant military leader and hero rather than to reproduce any particular historical battle.
*Provenance:* Gerhard Morell, sale, Copenhagen, 1773, no. 8; Schnell, Holtegaard; Treshow and Stemann. Purchased from Stemann for the Royal Danish Kunstkammer in 1781.
*Literature:* Strömbom 1932, 87 no. 259a; Cat. 1951 no. 8; Steland-Stief 1971, 21 ff, 123 cat. 6, pl. III.

## David Bailly

Leiden 1584 – Leiden 1657

999

*Vanitas still life with self portrait and portrait of a young painter*

Oil on panel. 89.5×122 cm. Signed and dated: "VANITAS VANITATUM/ ET OMNIA VANITAS/ David Bailly pinxit/ A° 1651. Colour-plate XXVII
Stedelijk Museum De Lakenhal, Leiden, inv. 1351.
A young, as yet unidentified, painter with maulstick in hand and palette hanging on the wall behind him, is sitting at a table holding in his left hand an oval portrait of an elderly man. Behind this there is a small, similarly oval portrait of a young woman, and another woman's portrait can be seen as a shadow on the wall behind the tall flute-glass. The portrait of the elderly man can be identified as a self portrait of Bailly from about 1642, but the two women are unknown. On the wall there also hangs a drawing of an old man and a drawing of Frans Hals' "Lute Player", both of which are likewise works by Bailly. On the table there are a number of objects and works of art, most of them symbolizing the frailty and

*997*

brevity of human life and earthly transience. The statuette of St. Sebastian, a symbol of Christ's passion, however, possibly refers to the Christian hope of ressurrection. Thematically the picture has been most deliberately composed, and its various elements, individually and inter-relationally, are rich in symbolic meaning. This has given rise to various interpretations. By including the portraits and the works of art and not least his self-portrait in this Vanitas context, Bailly provides his picture with a further dimension which carries both a wish to immortalize himself, his world and his works and yet at the same time contains the merciless tidings that the world of art is as transient and ephemeral as the soap bubbles floating above the table.
*Provenance:* A. Dumont, Cambrai; Mlle M. de Coussemaker, Bailleul; sale Palais Galliera, Paris 3.12.1966, no. 14. Purchased by the museum, 1967, with the support of Vereniging Rembrandt Stichting, Openbaar Kunstbezit and Vereniging van Belangstellenden in de Lakenhal.
*Literature:* Boström 1949, 99 ff fig. 1; Bruyn 1951, 216 ff repr. fig. 15; Wurfbain 1969, pp. 7a-7b; Popper-Voskkuil 1973, 58 ff repr. p. 61 (colour); Catalogus Stedelijk Museum, Leiden 1983, 51 f (bibliography); Alpers 1983, 103 ff, fig. 57.

## Hendrick van Balen I

Antwerp(?) ca. 1574/75 – Antwerp 1632

1000
*The Feast of the Gods. The Wedding of Peleus and Thetis*
Oil on copper. 35×46.4 cm
Statens Museum for Kunst, inv. Sp. 225
The principal source for this *motif* from the classical mythology is Catullus' *Carmina* LXIV. The picture was formerly attributed to van Balen. Cat. 1951, however, doubts this attribution. But as Jost pointed out, there is no reason to doubt its authenticity. The landscape and accessories stem from the hand of Jan Brueghel the Elder. The Feasts of the Gods can be considered as forerunners of the open air banquets that became such a popular theme in Dutch painting of the 17th century (then known as *Geselschapje, Banketje* or *Buitenpartij*).
*Provenance:* Entered the Royal Danish collection before 1800.
*Literature:* Cat. 1951 no. 24 (repr.); Jost 1963, 99, note 70, 113, note 87; Ertz 1979, 410, 596 (under cat. 231).

## Jan van Bijlert

Utrecht 1597/98 – Utrecht 1671

1001
*Party sitting at table with pretzels*
Oil on canvas. 90.5×119 cm. Signed: "Jv. Bylert.f."
Centraal Museum, Utrecht, inv. 16463
The picture focuses on the man and the woman each holding one end of a pretzel as though they want to pull it apart. The explanation of this strange behaviour can be found in Johan de Brune's *Emblemata* from 1624. In this, a comparison is made between pulling a pretzel and the struggle between good and evil in human nature. The fragility of the pretzel and its coiled form symbolize both life's frailties and sinful humanity turning its back on heaven to bend down towards earthly pleasures. The picture is a pendant to cat. 1001a and can likewise be dated ca. 1632-35.
*Provenance:* Acquired by the Centraal Museum, Utrecht, 1970.
*Literature:* Klessman 1983, 41.
*Exhibitions:* Rijksmuseum Amsterdam, 1976, 69 ff, no. 11; Herzog Anton Ulrich-Museum, Braunschweig, 1978, 61 (repr.).

1001a
*Company at a table, eating pancakes and waffles.*
Oil on canvas. 90,3×120.6 cm. Signed: "J v Bylert. fe"
Herzog Anton Ulrich-Museum, inv. 187
As shown by Klessman (1978), the Braunschweig painting corresponds so closely to cat. 1001 that the two paintings must originally have belonged together as a pair. However, unlike the Utrecht painting, the present picture's meaning has as yet eluded any precise interpretation. On the note being read so intently by the woman on the left, there is the partially preserved text: *Geeft my een pannekoeken wt de panne ezw.* This is the first line of a ditty sung in Holland on the eve of Shrovetide. The theme in both of these pictures is thus presumably connected with Shrovetide celebrations. The two pictures have not previously been exhibited together.
*Provenance:* Cf. Klessmann 1983.
*Literature:* Hoogewerff 1965, 7, 29 no. 81, fig. 14; Herzog Anton Ulrich-Museum, Braunschweig 1978, 61 no. 7, repr. p. 60; Klessmann 1983, 41 no. 187, repr. (with bibliography).

## Abraham Bloemaert

Gorinchem 1564 – Utrecht 1651

1002
*Apollo and Diana punishing Niobe by killing her Children*
Oil on canvas. Sight measurements 203×249.5 cm. (In the course of restoration 1978-79, later extensions to the canvas at the top (50 cm), at the bottom and along the sides (5-10) were partly removed and partly concealed in the flange of the new frame)
Signed and dated: "ANNO 1·5·9·1/A. Blommaert f(c?)". (The signature is authentic and not painted on top of an older one as claimed by Delbanco, 1928)
Statens Museum for Kunst, inv. Sp. 342
The subject is from Ovid: *Metamorphoses,* VI, 146-312, especially 227 ff. According to Karel van Mander (1604), Bloemaert, during his stay in Amsterdam (1591-93), painted "a large and magnificent painting which is now in the possession of Mr. Zion Luz in Amsterdam. It de-

picts a number of life-size, naked male and female figures finely conceived and beautifully executed. It portrays the story of Niobe, i.e. how her children are being shot by Apollo and Diana". Van Mander adds that "Recently", (i.e. about 1600), "Bloemaert has completed another large painting of the same subject but with a different composition" and that this work is now in the possession of "the Emperor". From all accounts the first-mentioned of these two pictures can be identified as that now in Copenhagen whilst the later version "by den Keyser" is today unknown. It is thus a still unsolved mystery why Arend van Buchell should write in his diary in 1591 that, at Bloemaert's studio he had seen a "Niobe" that was to be sent to the Emperor, "ut Caesari mittendam" (information kindly supplied by drs. C. J. A. Wansink in a letter dated 3.9.1980), since the picture he saw must, without any doubt, have been the Copenhagen painting and not the later version which, according to van Mander, was executed for the German Emperor. But it is always possible that the Copenhagen version really was originally intended for the Emperor. The Niobe painting is the earliest-known dated work by Bloemaert and it bears excellent witness to the extent to which Bloemaert during his stay in Amsterdam was influenced by the Spranger-Mannerism as it was then developing in near-by Haarlem under the leadership of Cornelis Cornelisz. (cat. 1016).
*Provenance:* Cf. above. Listed in the inventory of the Royal Danish Kunstkammer of 1690.
*Literature:* Van Mander 1604 fol. 297 v; Cornelis de Bie 1661, 44; von Sandrart 1675/1925, 165; Ramsdohr 1792, 135; Delbanco 1928, 17, 20 ff. 73 cat. no. 1, pl. 1 fig. V, 1; Kamenskaja 1937, 145 f; Cat. 1951, no. 67; Reznicek 1961, 167 f; Vikan 1974, 5, fig. 3; van Thiel, Gods and Heroes, Washington/Detroit/Amsterdam 1980-81, 78; de Bosque 1985, 251, pl. 250 (colour).

1003
*The Suicide of Lucretia*
Oil on panel. 93.5×71.3 cm
Statens Museum for Kunst, inv. Sp. 177
Lucretia, a virtuous woman of early Rome, was raped by Sextus Tarquinius. On being thus disgraced, she took her own life by thrusting a dagger into her heart (Livius: *Ab urbe condita,* "History of Rome", I: 57-59). Attributed in Cat. 1951 to Bartholomäus Spranger (1546-1611), an attribution dating back to the inventory of the Royal Danish Kunstkammer of 1737. However, it has such close affinity to Bloemaert's work from the 1590s, both as regards colour and treatment of the landscape and drapery, that it is here attributed to him.
*Provenance:* Recorded in the Royal Danish Kunstkammer 1692.
*Literature:* Cat. 1951 no. 577a (repr.).

1004
*Young Man with a Flute*
Oil on canvas. 69×57.9 cm. Signed and dated:
"A. Bloemaert fe 1621". Colour-plate XXIX
Centraal Museum, Utrecht, inv. 6083 b

*1001a*

*1002*

*1001*

Bloemaert's flute player is the earliest-known Dutch painting of a single musician in life-size half-figure, dressed in "romantic" fancy dress. This type of picture derives from Caravaggio and his followers in Rome and made its appearance in the Caravaggesque painting of Utrecht around 1620-21. About that time, Gerrit van Honthorst and Dirck van Baburen had just returned from Rome. It is generally assumed that Bloemaert's painting must have been inspired by a now lost work by Honthorst. De Meyere (1984) has pointed out that the composition can have erotic undertones, since 17th century Holland generally considered the flute as a phallic symbol. A print of ca. 1630 by Bartholomeus Dolendo based on a composition by Lucas van Leyden of a flute player, bears the following inscription (in translation): "Voluptuous flute/ you will cool my lust/ Let me hear you play/ so that I can feel it".
*Provenance:* Purchased by the Museum from art dealers Benedict, Berlin, 1928.
*Literature:* De Meyere 1984, 28 f no. 2 (repr.); Rooker in Utrecht/Braunschweig 1986/87, 213 f. cat. 44, repr. (colour) p. 215 (with bibliography).
*Exhibitions:* Wallraf-Richartz Museum, Cologne, 1984, no. 2; Centraal Museum, Utrecht/Herzog Anton Ulrich-Museum, Braunschweig 1986/87 no. 44.

1005
*Venus and Adonis*
Oil on canvas. 134×191 cm. Signed: *A. Bloemaert fc,* and according to Spengler (1827) and cat. 1904, dated *1632.* (Traces of digits visible)
Statens Museum for Kunst, inv. Sp. 343
The source of the story of Venus and Adonis is Ovid's *Metamorphoses* (X, 524 ff and 708 ff). The actual subject of the present picture, however, where Venus tries vainly to dissuade Adonis from joining the dangerous hunt, is not described by Ovid but springs from a tradition in painting dating back to Tizian's picture from 1553-54 (now in the Prado, Madrid, no. 422), and which was brought into the 17th century by Rubens ("Venus and Adonis", ca. 1610, now in the Kunstmuseum Düsseldorf, inv. 2300), cf. Sluijter in Washington/Detroit/Amsterdam 1980-81, 56. Both Tizian's and Rubens' compositions are reflected in Bloemaert's picture.
*Provenance:* Purchased in Holland for the Royal Danish Kunstkammer, 1764.
*Literature:* Delbanco 1928, 77 no. 39; Cat. 1951 no. 68.

## Maerten Boelema de Stomme

Friesland ca. 1620 – Leeuwaarden(?) after 1664

1006
*Still life. Breakfast piece*
Oil on panel. 58×83.8 cm. Signed and dated:
"Boelema. 1642". Inscribed on the back:
"Boelema. 1642" and bearing Gottorp's seal
Statens Museum for Kunst, inv. Sp. 395
Maerten Boelema became a pupil of Willem Claesz. Heda (1593/94-1680/82) in 1642. Heda was one of Haarlem's leading still life painters and, like other of Heda's pupils' and followers' works, Boelema's painting is influenced by his teacher's preference for depicting silver, pewter and glass. Its palette of cool, greyish tones and its diagonal composition makes it a typical example of the monochrome breakfast piece (Dutch: *onbijtje* or *banketje*).
*Provenance:* From the Gottorp Coll. Recorded at Fredensborg Castle by ca. 1800. Listed in the inventory of the Royal Danish Kunstkammer of 1827.
*Literature:* Bergström 1947, 144 f, fig. 120; Cat. 1951 no. 73 (repr.); Gammelbo 1960, 50 no. 53, fig. 53; Bergström 1956/1983, 140 fig. 121; Gammelbo 1978, 217; Vroom 1980, II, 11 no. 15, I, fig. 173.

## Paulus Bor

Amersfoort ca. 1601 – Amersfoort 1669

1007
*The 12 year old Jesus in the Temple*
Oil on canvas. 115×97.3 cm. A recent restoration of the picture has brought traces of the signature: "P. Bor" to light
Centraal Museum, Utrecht, inv. 12486
This subject, taken from Luke 2, 41-50, was popular in 17th century Dutch painting, but unlike other contemporary representations of the scene, Bor's picture portrays a static, almost set calm, with all attention drawn to the small child Jesus whose reasoning gesture is confined to a thin little index finger pointing from the folded hands. The doctors are unsympathetically characterized as a bunch of imbeciles. The picture is a fine example of how Bor, who had lived and worked in Amersfoort since around 1626, was able to develop his own original interpretation of Utrecht Caravaggism. The picture should probably be dated ca. 1630-35.
*Provenance:* Purchased by the Centraal Museum, 1964.
*Literature:* Christopher Brown in exhib. cat. Washington/ Detroit/Amsterdam 1980/81, 120 repr. p. 121; Guido Jansen in exhib. cat. Utrecht/Braunschweig 1986-87, 226 ff, repr. p. 227 (with bibliography); de Meyere 1987, 508 f.

## Ambrosius Bosschaert the Elder

Antwerp 1573 – The Hague 1621

1008
*Still life. Bouquet of Flowers in a Stone Niche*
Oil on copper. 55.5×39.5 cm. Signed and dated:
"AB 1618" (AB in monogram)
Statens Museum for Kunst, inv. Sp. 211
Painted in Utrecht, which became a centre of flower painting in contemporary Holland and where Bosschaert lived from 1616-1619. It is the earliest known dated work of flowers in a stone niche by Bosschaert

and, as such, was probably inspired by Roelandt Savery who had done niche paintings with flowers much earlier on. Among the paintings offered by Frans Bastiaensz. ca. 1620 to Christian IV, there was a flower piece by Ambrosius Bosschaert, listed as no. 230: *"de groete bloempott van Ambrosius"*. It was the most expensive picture on the list.
*Provenance:* Possibly recorded at Frederiksborg Castle 1705. In 1791 transferred to the Royal Danish Kunstkammer from Hirschholm Castle where, according to Eller 1972, it had been used as a *sopraporte* since 1741 at least.
*Literature:* Cat. 1951, no. 88; Hairs 1955, 196; Gammelbo 1960, no. 26, repr.; Eller 1972, 15 f note 14, 84; Bol 1980, 29 f, 64 f cat. 33, pl. 21; Bergström 1956/1983, 64, fig. 47.

## Leonaert Bramer

Delft 1596 – Delft 1674

1009
*The Adoration of the Kings*
Oil on copper. 28×34 cm
Statens Museum for Kunst, inv. Sp. 382
The subject was developed on the basis of Matthew 2, 1-12. Back in Delft after having spent many years in Italy, Bramer executed i.al. a number of small-scale religious works based primarily on Italian sources, which through their dramatic light effects (often nocturnes), peculiar treatment of the themes and delicate brushwork bear witness to great originality. An example of this can be seen in this slightly eccentric representation of a well-known theme, which was incidentally one of his favourites. On the basis of dated works this picture may be dated in the 1630s.
*Provenance:* According to Spengler in the Royal Danish Kunstkammer before 1690.
*Literature:* Wichmann 1923, 113, cat. 79; Cat. 1951, no. 92, (repr.).

## Jan Gerritsz. van Bronchorst

Utrecht 1603 – Amsterdam 1661

1010
*Musical Company*
Oil on canvas. 149.3×192.2 cm. Signed and dated:
"J. GvBronchors ... fecit 1646"
Centraal Museum Utrecht, inv. 13081
The works of the so-called Utrecht *Caravaggisti* abound with pictures of musicians, either depicted as single-figures or as groups (cf. cat. 1039). The *motif* of musicians grouped behind a balustrade was also much in favour after van Honthorst painted his "Concert" of 1624 (now in the Louvre, Paris). In this picture, van Honthorst transferred the illusionistic *di sotto in su-perspective* from his famous ceiling painting of 1622 (now in J. Paul Getty Museum, Malibu, cf. de Meyere 1976, 7 ff) to a picture that could be hung on a wall as a chimneypiece, for instance. J. G. van Bronchorst, in particular, specialised in this new genre.
*Provenance:* Purchased by the Centraal Museum, 1961.
*Literature:* Houtzager *et.al.* 1967, 148 f repr. p. 148.
*Exhibitons:* Centraal Museum, Utrecht, 1961, cat. 15; Galerie des Beaux-Arts, Bordeaux, 1969, cat. 27.

## Jan Jansz. van Bronchorst

Utrecht 1627 – Amsterdam 1656

1011
*Young Woman*
Oil on canvas. 82×67.3 cm. Signed:
"IV Bronchorst fec" (IVB in ligature)
Centraal Museum, Utrecht, inv. 15008
This informal portrayal of a young woman posing, one might imagine, as the repentant Magdalene, has previously always been assumed to be the work of Jan Gerritsz. van Bronchorst (cf. cat. 1010), but was recently – along with the painting of "Aurora" in Wadsworth Atheneum, Hartford, Conn. which has also been attributed to Jan Gerritsz., but which, as early as 1687 had been specifically mentioned as having been painted "van de Jonge Bronchorst" – convincingly attributed to Jan Gerritsz.'s eldest son Jan, also a painter who lived in Rome in the late 1640s, returning to Holland ca. 1650 where he died at the early age of 29.
*Provenance:* Purchased by the Centraal Museum, 1966.
*Literature:* Marten Jan Bok and Guido Jansen in exhib. cat. Utrecht/Braunschweig 1986-87, 241 ff cat. 51, repr. p. 243.

## Hendrick ter Brugghen

The Hague (?) 1588 – Utrecht 1629

1012
*The Crowning with Thorns*
Oil on canvas. 207×240 cm. (During restoration of the painting in 1985-86 a later strip of ca. 10 cm edging the canvas at the bottom has been concealed behind the decorative frame). Signed and dated:
"HT Brugghen/fecit 1620"
Statens Museum for Kunst, inv.Sp. 365
The subject is taken from Matthew 27, 28-30. The painting is one of the earliest-known 3 or 4 certain works by ter Brugghen, yet it was first painted six years after he returned to Utrecht from Rome as the first of the Utrecht *Caravaggisti* bringing with him a new approach to painting derived from Caravaggio (1571-1610) and his followers in Rome. The present subject was itself a popular one among this group of painters. Caravaggio's own picture of "The Crowning with Thorns" formed part of Marchese Vincenzo Giustiniani's famous collection in Rome, and the composition is reflected in paintings of the same subject by followers such as Manfredi (1597?- ca. 1620/21) and Valentin (1594-1632). The new

Caravaggesque style also provides the basis for the present picture, the largest ter Brugghen ever painted, but most typically mixed with archaic elements in the form of *motif*-borrowing from the 16th century (Lucas van Leyden, Albrecht Dürer) so that the result is a characteristically "Gothic" Caravaggism.
*Provenance:* According to Nicolson, the picture can be identified as the *"Croninge Christi, van Terburg"* in Frederik Alewijn's inventory from 1665 and also with *"Een bespottinge Christi van"* (ter Brugghen) in the inventory of Abraham Peronneau's collection, Amsterdam 6.1.1692 (16). However, since C. de Bie (1708) gives the measurements of the Peronneau-picture as 4½×4 voet (= ca. 135×120 cm) it cannot be identical with the Copenhagen-painting and thus the first-mentioned provenance must also now be considered uncertain. Particularly since another authentic ter Brugghen painting of the same subject, a "Crowning with Thorns" dating from ca. 1622, was recently found in The Regional Art Museum in Irkutsk, USSR, (inv. 670, canvas 119×116 cm, cf. Kuznetsov and Linnik 1982, pl. 122 and 123, with text), a work that apparently with equal justification could claim this same provenance. Purchased by G. Morell in 1755 (as a G. Honthorst). Entered the Royal Danish Kunstkammer in 1775.
*Literature:* Cat. 1951 no. 105; Nicolson 1958, 4 f, 9, 58 f cat. A 18, pl. 6, 7, 10; van Thiel 1971, 101, 110, 113, fig. e, 116 note 39; L. J. Slatkes in exhib.cat. Utrecht/Braunschweig 1986/87, 49, 83 ff cat. 3, repr. p. 85 (with bibliography).

## Louis de Caulery

Cambrai? before ca. 1582 – Antwerp 1621/22

1013
*Homage to Venus*
Oil on copper. 23×18.5 cm
Statens Museum for Kunst, inv. 1978
The subject derives from Philostratos the Elder's picture descriptions, *Eikones* 2. book, 1: "Singers", in which there is a description of a painting representing young women paying tribute and singing hymns to the Venus statue. It also, however, contains elements from Ovid's calendar of Roman Feasts, *Fasti,* 4. book, 133-192, the 1st April Feast to Venus Verticordia, "the third Venus" who turned hearts from sinful love to pure love. An enlarged version (horizontal format, on panel), certainly by a different hand, is to be found set into the wooden panelling of Christian IV's Winter-Room at Rosenborg Castle from ca. 1615.
*Provenance:* Entered the Royal Danish Kunstkammer in 1785.
*Literature:* Cat. 1951 no. 873 (repr.); Legrand 1963, 83, fig. 36; Chudzikowski 1967, 30 f, fig. 5.

## Pieter Claesz.

Burgsteinfurt (Westfalen) 1596/97 – Haarlem 1661

1014
*Still Life. Breakfast piece with Fruit Basket*
Oil on canvas. 105.5×145.5 cm. Signed apocryphally: "Fr. Snijders"
Statens Museum for Kunst, inv. Sp. 210
The picture can be dated in the late 1640s and may have been painted in collaboration with Roelof Koets I (ca. 1592/93-1655), a still life painter who specialised in painting grapes and vine leaves (if so he probably painted the basket of fruit on the left). The fine standing silver salt-cellar on the table (far right) has been identified as the work of the Utrecht silversmith Franssoys Elioet (1608-42).
*Provenance:* Recorded in the Royal Danish Kunstkammer, 1775.
*Literature:* Cat. 1951 no. 117 (repr.); Gammelbo 1960, 54 no. 59, fig. 59; Misfeldt 1970, 123 f, fig. 5; Gammelbo 1978, 219.

## Pieter Codde

Amsterdam 1599 – Amsterdam 1678

1015
*Soldiers breaking in to a Peasant's Cottage*
Oil on panel, 31.5×25.5 cm. Signed and dated: "PC 1645" (PC in monogram)
Statens Museum for Kunst, inv. Sp. 434
As a genre, pictures with subjects similar to the present painting must have become so firmly established in the repertoire of assault and plundering scenes that from as early as the turn of the century a fixed system of antithetic picture pendants on these same themes had developed. Thus David Vinckboons (1576-ca. 1632) around 1609 painted a picture of a peasant being threatened by a soldier (called "Boerenverdriet", i.e. peasant's misfortune) but at the same time he provided it with a pendant in which the soldiers are running for their lives from a furious axe-brandishing peasant. (This role-reversed pendant was called "Boerenvreugd", peasant's pleasure). Both in the Rijksmuseum, Amsterdam (repr. Goosens 1954, 85 and 87; see also Czobor 1963, 151 ff).
*Provenance:* Purchased for the Royal Collection with the J. C. Bodendick collection, 1810 (Weinwich 1825, no. 115, as Cornelis Saftleven).
*Literature:* Cat. 1951 no. 121 (repr.).

## Cornelis Cornelisz. van Haarlem

Haarlem 1562 – Haarlem 1638

1016
*The Fall of the Titans*
Oil on canvas. 239×307 cm
Statens Museum for Kunst, inv. 1

When the painting reached Denmark (1621) and until a few years ago, the subject was interpreted as "The Fall of the Angels", an interpretation referring to the struggle of Archangel Michael and his angels against the dragon and its angels (Revelation 12, 7-10). Recently, however, the *motif* has been interpreted as "The Titans' Fight with the Gods", a subject taken from Ovid's *Metamorphoses.* As a result of the struggle the Titans were thrown by Zeus into the infernal regions of Tartaros. It is a picture that reflects the close connection between Cornelis van Haarlem and Hendrick Goltzius. The fallen descend from heaven in ingenious pirouettes that vary and modulate with considerable gusto the four falling Titans in Goltzius' engravings Tantalos, Ixion, Phaeton and Ikaros from 1588. The four prints are considered to have been based on Cornelis' preliminary studies for the painting and thus contribute to its dating.
*Provenance:* Identical with no. 217, "Een Vall der Engelen van Mr. Cornelis", in the list of pictures offered to Christian IV in 1621 by Frans Bastiaensz. Listed in the inventory of the Royal Danish Kunstkammer 1690.
*Literature:* Madsen 1891, 204; Beckett 1914, II, 260; Cat. 1951 no. 134; Thiel 1984, 76f.

## Adam de Coster

Mechelen (Mâlines) ca. 1586 – Antwerp 1643

1017
*Two Sculptors by Night. Double portrait of François Duquesnoy and Georg Petel*
Oil on canvas. 114×95 cm
Statens Museum for Kunst, inv. Sp. 810
There has been some doubt as to the identity of the two sculptors in the picture. However, Karl Feuchtmayr's very feasible theory that they are from left to right, Flemish-born François Duquesnoy (1594-1643; worked in Rome from 1618) and the German Georg Petel

*1016*

1017

(1601/02-1634; in Rome 1621-22), has been accepted by several authors. The picture should consequently have been painted in Rome about 1622, but it has not so far proved possible to show that de Coster was in Rome at the beginning of the 1620s. The statuette on the table (right) is a fragmented copy of the Venetian sculptor Alessandro Vittoria's (1525-1608) famous bronze statuette of St. Sebastian (cast in two versions during Vittoria's lifetime: 1566 and 1575, cf. the signed version in New York, Metropolitan Museum of Art, inv. no. 40.24). The statuette in the picture carried by Petel under his arm is a plaster cast of a St. Sebastian that exists in several bronze versions and which has been attributed to Petel himself by some authors (cat. 1076).

*Provenance:* Listed in the inventory of the Royal Danish Kunstkammer 1690.
*Literature:* Cat. 1951, no. 880 (repr.); Olsen 1961, 28, 88, pl. XLVI B; Nicolson 1961, 186 fig. 38; Müller/Schädler in exhib.cat. Petel, Munich 1964, 18 cat. B 43; Nicolson 1966, 253; Keller 1967, 170 f, fig. 4; Woeckel 1967, 469; Feuchtmayr/Schädler *et.al.* 1973, 57, 72, 187, 190 f. cat. 160, fig. 269; Freytag 1976, 201; Middeldorf 1978, 56 fig. 9; Johanna Hecht in exhib.cat. Frankfurt 1986-87, 156.

## Dirck van Delen

Heusden 1605 – Arnemuyden 1671

1018
*Conversation outside a Palace*
Oil on panel. 43.5×32 cm. Signed and dated: "D. van Delen 1636"
Statens Museum for Kunst, inv. 375
The architecture in the works of van Delen was born out of his imagination on the basis of prints in the architectural treatises of Hans Vredeman de Vries and Serlio, combined with actual details taken from contemporary buildings. The staffage figures in the pictures were often painted by other artists. This is borne out by paintings signed by both van Delen and other artists. The elegantly dressed company in front of the palace were thus painted by Anthonie Palamedesz., according to Blade.
*Provenance:* Purchased for the Royal Danish Kunstkammer 1760.
*Literature:* Cat. 1951 no. 163 (repr.); cat. Le siècle, Paris 1970-71, 155; Blade 1976, 141 f. 146 ff., 231 cat. 53; Jantzen 1979, 222 no. 115.

1019
*Elegant Company in front of a Palace*
Oil on panel. 49.5×55 cm. Signed and dated: "DVDELEN 1644"
Statens Museum for Kunst, inv. Sp. 397
As in other paintings by van Delen, the Palace buildings are imaginary, though partially based on illustrations from Serlio's architectural treatise. The result was a foretaste of what the near future would bring. The palace to the right both in concept and in structure closely resembles Jacob van Campen's classicistic Town Hall in Amsterdam, the building of which started in 1648. According to Blade, the figures are the work of David Teniers the Younger.
*Provenance:* Purchased for the Royal Danish Kunstkammer, 1759.
*Literature:* Cat. 1951 no. 165 (repr.); Blade 1976, 29 f, 118, 238, cat. 69; Jantzen 1979, 222 no. 125.

## François Dieussart

Arquinghem, near Armentier (Hainaut) ca. 1600 – London 1661

1020
*King Charles I of England*
Bust in marble. Height: 86 cm. On the front of the socle dated: "1636" and inscribed with the initials: "C.R.". On the back signed: "F. DIEUSSART VALLON FECIT"
The Duke of Norfolk, Arundel Castle, inv. 1984/75
It is possible that Charles I sat for this bust in 1636 whilst sitting for van Dyck's triple portrait (Windsor Castle). The bust was probably commissioned by Thomas Howard, Earl of Arundel, and completes a group with three other marble busts partly still in the Arundel Collection, viz. Charles Louis, Elector Palatine, nephew of Charles I

*1020* Reproduced by permission of the Duke of Norfolk, KG. Photo Courtauld Institute of Art.

(dated 1637); Rupert of Pfalz, Charles Louis' younger brother (also dated 1637), and the Earl of Arundel himself (ca. 1636), all three being the work of Dieussart (the Rupert bust now in Ashmolean Museum, Oxford). The bust of Charles I is the earliest known portrait bust by Dieussart.
*Provenance:* Thomas Howard, Earl of Arundel 1636. Mentioned by George Vertue in Norfolk House (1725-31) cf. *Walpole Society* XX, London 1931-32 "*(Vertue Note Books)* II, 66.
*Literature:* Manners 1930, 24 ff; Whinney and Millar 1956, 123 f; Whinney 1964, 38; Avery 1974, 63, 65 ff, fig. 2; Vickers 1978, 162, fig. 2.

1021
*Queeen Henrietta Maria (1609-1669), married 1624 to Charles I of England*
Bust in marble. Height: 72 cm. The pedestal of black touchstone inscribed: "HENRIETTA MARIA REGINA 1640"
Chronological Collection of the Danish Kings at Rosenborg Castle, inv. 7-125
Charles Avery (1972/73) attributes the bust to François Dieussart. It was presumably executed on the basis of the

*1022*

three portraits of the Queen by van Dyck which were to be sent to Gianlorenzo Bernini in Rome to provide a model for a bust. The three van Dyck studies of Henrietta Maria (now in Windsor Castle) were painted in 1638 but were never delivered to Bernini and the whole project, last heard of in a letter to Bernini dated June 1639, came to nothing. It must, therefore, haved seemed obvious for Dieussart to make use of the portraits as models, just as he had done some years earlier in carving the bust of Charles I (cat. 1020) from an analogous model. No doubt regarded by Christian IV as a family portrait, the bust may have been presented to the king as a gift, or perhaps commissioned by himself, possibly as a pendant to the bust of Charles I (1633) by Pierre Besnier (?), which is still today paired with the Henrietta Maria bust in the entrance hall at Rosenborg Castle. Dieussart's bust is the only known portrait bust of the Queen.
*Provenance:* Listed in the inventory of the Royal Danish Kunstkammer 1690 along with Pierre Besnier's bust of Charles I (Liisberg 1897, 141: "His [i.e. "Caroli Primi Regis Angliæ"] Queen. Bust of marble, likewise on a precious pedestal"). Transferred to Rosenborg 1871/72.
*Literature:* Millar 1972, 126 (no. 238); Avery 1974, 68 ff. 77, fig. 5.

1022
*King Christian IV*
Bust in bronze. Socle of marble. Height: 103 cm (1643)
Reproduced in colour on the cover
Rosenborg Castle, inv. 2-48
The bust was modelled in May/June 1643 during Dieussart's stay in Denmark (1643-1644), but according to tradition the actual casting was not carried out until 1650 when it took place in the cannon foundry at Glückstadt. It is a heroic and idealistic representation of the King in a toga and Roman emperor's garb with lions' heads on the shoulders and a laurel wreath on his head – the earliest portrait of a Danish king in Roman guise. According to Avery, the format of the bust itself may owe its inspiration to the bust of Gustav II Adolf (cat. 1075) done by Georg Petel some 10 years earlier. It may even be that Dieussart's bust was intended as a sort of answer to the impressive bronze bust of the Swedish arch-rival. As far as is known, Dieussart was without experience as a bronze sculptor. All the more amazing, therefore, that with this bust he was capable of creating a portrait which is not only a masterpiece among his own portrait busts but "is also one of the finest portrait sculptures of the whole seventeenth century in Northern Europe" (Avery).
*Provenance:* Listed in the inventory of the Royal Danish Kunstkammer 1673. Transferred to Christiansborg Castle 1788. Saved from the fire there 1794. Transferred to Rosenborg Castle 1867.
*Literature:* Liisberg 1917-18, 578 ff, repr. p. 579; Liisberg 1919-20, 322 ff; Thorlacius-Ussing 1924, 308 ff, repr. p. 305; Boeck 1937, 45, fig. 6; Eller 1973, 261 f, fig. 222; Avery 1974, 76, 77 ff, fig. 18; Larsson 1984, 35.

## Herman Mijnertsz. Doncker

Enkhuizen? ca. 1610 – Haarlem (?) after 1656

1023
*Battle between Cavalry and Infantry*
Oil on canvas. 83.5×130.6 cm. Signed and dated: "HD 1636" (HD in monogram)
Statens Museum for Kunst, inv. 1032
The battle scene was introduced to 17th century Dutch painting in the 1620s by Esaias van de Velde. His followers in this genre in the 1630s were Jan Martszen de Jonge (1609?-after 1647) and Palamedes Palamedesz. (1607-1638), and the landscape painter Jan Asselijn, who painted a small number of cavalry battles for a brief period in his youth (cat. 998). To the contribution to the genre by these painters can now be added the present hitherto unnoticed early work by Doncker, who otherwise mainly painted portraits and conversation pieces.
*Provenance:* Entered the Royal Danish Kunstkammer in 1785.

## Gabriel Engels

Hamburg 1592 – Hamburg 1654

1024

*Architectural Perspective. A Square with Renaissance Buildings*

Oil on canvas. 71×84.5 cm. Signed with monogram: "GE"

Statens Museum for Kunst, inv. Stroe 589

In 1973, Peter Bondesen identified a painting of an architectural perspective signed with the monogram "GE" which was set into the wall of the Privy Passage leading to the Audience House at Frederiksborg Castle as the work of Gabriel Engels from Hamburg. He was also able to show that the painting came from Gottorp (Bondesen 1973, 33 f). Without doubt, the large hitherto unnoticed collection of 10 fairly similar works belonging to the Statens Museum for Kunst (the greater part of them formerly at Fredensborg Castle) which were all formerly attributed to the obscure Hamburg painter Ellerbroeck were also painted by Gabriel Engels. Several of them are signed with the same monogram as the Frederiksborg painting and some of them also carry the Gottorp seal on the back of the canvas. Most probably they (all?) came from Gottorp, particularly since it has been documented that Engels supplied Duke Friederich III of Gottorp with paintings of architectural perspectives in the 1640s and 1650s.

*Provenance:* Probably from Gottorp (to Fredensborg Castle?) in 1759. Recorded at Fredensborg Castle 1825.

## Allart van Everdingen

Alkmaar 1621 – Amsterdam 1675

1025

*Northern Mountain Landscape with Waterfall*

Oil on canvas. 111.5×151.5 cm. Signed and dated: "ALLART: VAN / EVERDINGEN/ 1648"

Statens Museum for Kunst, inv. Sp. 515

In 1644 the young Allart van Everdingen travelled around the southern coasts of Norway – which at that time belonged to the double-monarchy of Denmark-Norway – drawing landscapes. He was in Risör and Langesund and reached as far as the west coast of Sweden – to Gothenburg, Götaälven and Bohuslän. According to some sources, he had been shipwrecked on the coast of Norway but this may merely be surmise. Back in Haarlem in 1645 and later, when in 1652 he had moved to Amsterdam, he utilized his Norwegian experience by painting a number of Scandinavian landscapes, the exotic character of which greatly influenced Dutch landscape painting during the 1650s and 1660s.

*1024*

*Provenance:* Purchased in Holland for the Royal Danish Kunstkammer in 1761.
*Literature:* Granberg 1902, 52 no. 9; Cat. 1951 no. 211 (repr.); Stechow 1966, 144; Davies 1978, 123 f, 326 no. 30, fig. 100.

## Flemish Artist

The 1620s

1026
*A Lute Player*
Oil on canvas. 96.5.×73.5 cm
Statens Museum for Kunst, inv. Stroe 496
Previously attributed to Caravaggio and Hendrick ter Brugghen, the present picture is related to the half-length single figures of musicians and singers that were popular in the 1620s among the Utrecht-Caravaggisti, e.g. Hendrick ter Brugghen, Gerrit van Honthorst and Dirck van Baburen (1595-1624). This picture, however, appears to be Flemish rather than Dutch.
*Provenance:* Recorded at Fredensborg Castle by the beginning of the 19th century.
*Literature:* Cat. 1951 no. 879a (repr.).

## Jacques Foucquier (Attributed to)

Antwerp (?) ca. 1590 – Paris ca. 1659

1027
*Hunters in a landscape*
Oil on copper. 49×71 cm
Statens Museum for Kunst, inv. Sp. 202
Attributed to Jan Wildens in Cat. 1951 the picture has in older museum catalogues been attributed to David Vinckboons as well as to Jacques Foucquier. The latter attribution is confirmed by comparison with a signed and dated work by Foucquier (1622) which was formerly in the Wallraf-Richartz-Museum in Cologne (Stechow 1948, 422, fig. 2) and afterwards in the collection of Heinz Kister, Kreuzlingen. In the Royal Kunstkammer the present picture at one time had a pendant, a winter landscape, which was lost in the 1884 fire at Christiansborg Castle.
*Provenance:* Riding Master Schæffer. Entered the Royal Danish Kunstkammer, 1812.
*Literature:* Madsen 1926, 70f; Cat. 1951 no. 816 (repr.).

## Frans Francken the Younger (II)

Antwerp 1581 – Antwerp 1642

1028
*Apelles painting Campaspe*
Oil on panel, 72.5×60.5 cm. [The reverse of the panel bears the Antwerp city brand and the incised initials of the panel maker]
Statens Museum for Kunst, inv. Sp. 179
The picture consists of a central scene surrounded by 8 smaller rectangular compartments. The scene in the centre depicts Apelles painting Campaspe in the presence of Alexander the Great (in Cat. 1951 wrongly described as "Apelles painting Roxane"). Alexander had his favourite mistress painted in the nude by his court painter Apelles, the famous artist of ancient Greece. On discovering that Apelles while doing so had fallen in love with his model, Alexander made him a present of her. The surrounding compartments illustrate events in the life of Alexander. The story of Alexander and Apelles (Plinius Secundus the Elder "Naturalis Historia" XXXV, chapter 36) was undoubtedly considered by contemporary artists as antiquity's testimony to the ideal relationship between princely patron and artist. Alexander was the powerful and noble protector of the arts and the celebrated artist Apelles was his highly esteemed equal and friend. On the basis of style the painting can be dated to the 1620s.
*Provenance:* Christian Count Danneskiold Samsøe 1731. Purchased for the Royal Danish Kunstkammer in 1732.
*Literature:* Cat. 1951 no. 227.

## Hieronymus Francken (II) (Attributed to)

Antwerp 1578 – Antwerp 1623

1029
*The Parable of the Wise and Foolish Virgins*
Oil on panel. 52×72 cm [The reverse of the panel bears the Antwerp city brand and the incised initials of the panel maker]
Statens Museum for Kunst, inv. 3013
The subject is based on the Parable of the Ten Virgins (Matthew 25, 1-13). The five foolish virgins are depicted as elegantly clothed women lightheartedly whiling away the time. References to eroticism are to be found in the amorous mythological scene of the painting which hangs on the wall and – more indirectly – in the oysters and parsnips laid out in the foreground. Close to the five wise virgins in the background an altar with Christ on the cross and a picture of the Last Judgment can be seen. Thus the moralizing intent of the painting is obvious.
*Provenance:* Recorded at Fredensborg Castle in 1848.
*Literature:* Cat. 1951 no. 874.

## Hubert Gerhard

Amsterdam (?) ca. 1550 – Munich 1622/23

1030
*Mars, Venus and Cupid*
Bronze group. Height: 41.4 cm
Kunsthistorisches Museum, Sammlung für Plastik und Kunstgewerbe, Vienna, inv. P.5848
Mars embraces Venus with both hands on her shoulders, and has laid his left leg over her right thigh as if to keep her legs apart (a pose which was frequently used as a metaphor for sexual activity in 16th and 17th century paintings and sculpture, cf. Steinberg 1968, 343 ff; cf. also cat. 1042). In her upraised hand Venus holds a flam-

ing heart, the symbol of love. The group is a reduced variant of the very large group in bronze which Gerhard carried out for Hans Fugger, 1585-90, for a monumental fountain in the courtyard of the latter's Schloss Kirchheim an der Mindel and which has been in the Bayerisches Nationalmuseum in Munich since 1871. The elegant proportions of the Vienna-group, its complex linear interplay and exquisite modelling, and also its evident reminiscences of paintings by Bartholomäus Spranger, undoubtedly originate in the sophisticated art of Rudolf II's court in Prague.
*Provenance:* Possibly in the possession of Rudolf II in Prague but not included in his inventory of 1607-11; in the collection of Emperor Matthias at Hofburg in Vienna 1619 (for later provenance, see Leithe-Jasper 1986). Since 1891 in the Kunsthistorisches Museum.
*Literature:* Leithe-Jasper 1986, 264, cat. 72, repr. p. 265 (with full bibliography).

## Hendrick Goltzius

Mühlbrecht 1558 – Haarlem 1617

1031
*The Death of Adonis*
Oil on canvas. 76.5×86.5 cm. Signed and dated:
"HG 1603"
Rijksmuseum, Amsterdam. inv. A 1284
The earlier, Spranger-inspired Mannerism in Goltzius' work changed after his stay in Italy 1590/91. The present picture, which is one of Goltzius' earliest paintings, is an example of the newly adopted classicism. Gone are the almost over-exaggerated curves and ecstatic dynamic of Mannerism. In its place one is confronted with a relaxed human figure with a noticeable de-sensualisation that almost symbolically illustrates the death of Adonis. Adonis, the lover of Venus, was slain by a wild boar while out hunting, cf. cat. 1005. The figure of Adonis probably took its inspiration from Mantegna's "The dead Christ" which was similarly depicted in severe foreshortening.
*Provenance:* Sale, Verloren van Themaat, 1885, no. 136.
*Literature:* Hirschmann 1916, 46 ff, 73 no. 4; Reznicek 1960, 38 note 14; Reznicek 1961, cat. no. zw 8; P. J. J. van Thiel 1976, 244.

## Caspar Gras

Probably Mergentheim ca. 1585 – Schwaz 1674

1032
*Archduke Leopold Wilhelm (1614-62) on horseback*
Bronze group. Gilt. Height: 36 cm
Statens Museum for Kunst, inv. 5501
The present group belongs to a series of eight equestrian statuettes, all of which appear to represent Habsburgs. In each statuette, the horse has been cast from the same model, but the riders are different and their extremities, heads and accessories are all cast separately and the heads are detachable. The present statuette is the only gilt one. The attribution of the statuettes to Caspar Gras has a long tradition, dating back to the 18th century, and is now fairly generally accepted.
*Provenance:* Entered the Royal Danish Kunstkammer before 1775.
*Literature:* Olsen 1980, I, 56 f, II, fig. 148; Leithe-Jasper 1986, 246 ff (with full bibliography).

## Matthäus Gundelach

Hessen (Kassel?) ca. 1566 – Augsburg 1653/54

1033
*Cupid and Psyche*
Oil on copper. 33×45 cm. Signed and dated:
»M. Gundelach F. 1613«
Augsburg, Schaezler-Palais, inv. L 724
The picture was painted in Prague where Gundelach worked from 1593 to 1615, from 1st November 1609 as court painter to Emperor Rudolf II. The subject is from Apuleius: *Metamorphoses* V, 22, 4-6. The legend of Psyche was a favoured theme at the Emperor's court (cf. e.g. Adrian de Vries' two large bronze groups from the early 1590s, now in the Louvre and the Nationalmuseum, Stockholm, respectively). Gundelach's picture, too, in its composition – with the ingeniously intertwined figures – and in its distinctly erotic character, is typical of Rudolphine art. The picture was painted in the year following the death of Rudolf and may well have been painted for his brother Matthias, who succeeded him.
*Provenance:* Possibly identical with "Ein buhlschaft, Cupido mit Psiche von Gundelach" which figured on the list, dated 30th March 1623, of paintings sold from the Prager Kunstkammer to the jeweller, Daniel de Briers in Frankfurt. Zweibrücken Galerie until 1779.
*Literature:* Bender 1981, 32, 101 f, 168 cat. GA5; cat. Augsburg, 2. edit. 1984, 101; Dacosta Kaufmann 1985, 222 cat. no. 5-$_5$, repr.

## Dirck Hals

Haarlem 1591 – Haarlem 1656

1034
*Merry Company*
Oil on panel. 50×63.5 cm. Signed and dated:
"DHALS ANf 162(4?)" [DH in ligature]
Statens Museum for Kunst, inv. Sp. 223
During the 1610s a particular type of genre painting emerged in Haarlem – the Merry Companies – which developed from *motifs* with allegorical and religous overtones (The Prodigal Son, for instance) towards a more direct, everyday content.
*Provenance:* Acquired for the Royal Danish Kunstkammer, 1758 (?).
*Literature:* Cat. 1951 no. 287; Judson 1959, 59 f.

1035
*A Ball*
Oil on panel. 55.5×84 cm. Signed and dated: "DHALS 16(37?)"
Statens Museum for Kunst, inv. 639
Cf. cat. 1034
*Provenance:* Purchased for the Royal Danish Kunstkammer at the sale of C. A. Plessen's estate, 1758.
*Literature:* Cat. 1951 no. 288.

## Willem van Herp (Attributed to)

Antwerp ca. 1614 – Antwerp 1677

1036
*Landscape with Atalanta and Meleager hunting the Calydonian Boar*
Oil on copper. 40.7×53.6 cm
Statens Museum for Kunst, inv. 7209
The story of Atalanta and Meleager is taken from Ovid's *Metamorphoses* VIII, 271-424, but the *motif* can also be found in the description of one of the pictures ("Meleager") in Philostratos the Younger's *Eikones* (Imagines), 15. Cf. also the description of a boarhunt picture "The Hunters" in Philostratos the Elder's *Eikones* I, 28. Atalanta has just pierced the boar behind the ear with his arrow and Meleager approaches with his spear. The two riders on "snow-white horses" are Castor and Pollux, the Dioscuri who also took part in the hunt. The painting is clearly by the same hand as a landscape with the Calydonian boarhunt now in Musée Hyacinthe-Rigaud, Perpignan, (inv. 840-2-4), attributed to Willem van Herp by Lacambre (Le siècle de Rubens, Paris 1977-78, cat. 58). The present picture is both in *motif* and composition based on a Rubens painting from the 1630s.
*Provenance:* Holsteinborg. Presumably Chancellor, Count Ulrich Adolph Holstein (1664-1737). Purchased from Holsteinborg, 1983. Gift to the museum from Kunstmuseets Venner.

## Pauwels van Hillegaert (Attributed to)

Amsterdam 1595/96 – Amsterdam 1640

1037
*Disbanding of the Mercenary Troops on the Neude, Utrecht, July 31st, 1618*
Oil on panel. 41×72 cm
Statens Museum for Kunst, inv. 2088
The painting depicts a contemporary event in Dutch history. During the internal politico-religious disputes between the orthodox Calvinists and the more liberal Remonstrants, town militia units ("waard-gelders") were formed. These were looked upon as a threat by Prince Maurits, the Commander-in-chief of the army, however. He succeeded in disarming and disbanding the Utrecht militia and this gave rise to a general disbanding of the militia throughout the country. Several representations of this event exist, both by van Hillegaert himself and by the Utrecht painter Joost Cornelisz. Drochsloot (1586-1666). The present painting, however, is the only one showing the tower of the Utrecht cathedral in the background.
*Provenance:* Transferred from Fredensborg Castle to the museum in 1909.

## Dutch (?)

1st half of the 17th century

1038
*"Incostanza". An Allegory of Fickleness*
Oil on canvas. 106.5×82 cm. Inscribed on ribbon top left: "INCOSTANZA"
Statens Museum for Kunst, inv. Stroe 387
The woman is a personification of fickleness, based on Cesare Ripa's *Iconologia,* a manual of allegorical figures which appeared for the first time in an illustrated edition in Italy, 1603 (first published in 1593) and was later translated into other languages, including Dutch in 1644. The woman is surrounded by symbols, all of which signify "Incostanza". The picture bears witness to the influence of Utrecht-Caravaggism. It seems to be related to works by certain of the Dutch artists who worked on the decorations of Huis ten Bosch.
*Provenance:* Entered the Royal Danish Kunstkammer before 1775.
*Literature:* Tervarent 1949, 224 f, repr. p. 225.

## Gerrit van Honthorst

Utrecht 1592 – Utrecht 1656

1039
*Musical Company. The Evening Concert*
Oil on canvas. 117×146 cm. [Since the restoration of the painting in 1986, a strip of c. 10 cm added to the top of the original canvas at a later date, has been concealed behind the frame]. Signed and dated:
"G. Honthorst. fe. 1623". Colour-plate XXV
Statens Museum for Kunst, inv. Sp. 378
During his long stay in Rome (1610/15-1620) van Honthorst mainly painted religious subjects (he was, incidentally, a Catholic), but in the last year in Italy he executed (ca. 1619-20) for the Archduke of Toscana a so-called "Cena di Buffonarie" (The Merrymakers' Supper), a large painting of a merry company of men and women around a table by candlelight (now in the Galleria degli Uffizi, Florence). On his return to Utrecht, notably during the first 4-5 years, he painted a number of similar pictures in which the figures were, however, gradually reduced in numbers. He thus transferred this new type of genre picture to Holland where it gained great importance. One of the pictures, an "Allegory" in Staatsgalerie Schleissheim (no. 391), is dated the same year as the present picture.
*Provenance:* Purchased for the Royal Danish Kunstkammer from the estate of the artist Magnus Berg, 1739.

*Literature:* Cat. 1951 no. 321 (repr.); Judson 1959, 67 69 f 75 129 248 cat. 197, fig. 25; Braun 1966, 175 f cat. 45; Nicolson 1979, 59; Judson in exhib.cat. Utrecht/ Braunschweig 1986-87, 58, 60, fig. 55.

1040
*Amalia van Solms 1604-1675*
Oil on canvas. 75×62.5 cm. Signed and dated:
"G. Honthorst. fe.1632" [GH in ligature]
Centraal Museum, Utrecht, inv. 21659
Towards the end of the 1620s van Honthorst enjoyed a high reputation in Europe and there is much to indicate that he was celebrated especially as a portrait painter. The present portrait of Amalia van Solms in Arcadian costume is a fine example of how captivating his elegant and idealizing portrait style could be. The character of this courtly style can be gauged by comparison with the profile portrait of Amalia van Solms painted that same year by Rembrandt (now in the Musée Jacquemart-André, Paris). It was Amalia van Solms who had the famous – and still preserved – domed room, *Oranjezaal*, of the Huis ten Bosch palace near The Hague, decorated in 1648-52 in memory of her late husband Frederick Hendrik of Orange. The decorations consisted of dynastic and allegorical pictures carried out by Flemish and Dutch artists. Also van Honthorst contributed to the decorations.
*Provenance:* Possibly Elizabeth of Bohemia ("The Winter Queen"); the Earls of Craven, Combe Abbey, 17th cent.; sale, Sotheby's, London, 27. November 1968, no. 50. Purchased by the museum in 1968.
*Literature:* J. Bruyn *et al.* 1986, 254, fig. 6.

1041
*Diana with her Nymphs*
Oil on canvas. 199×269 cm. Signed and dated:
"G. Honthorst fecit 1650"
Statens Museum for Kunst, inv. Sp. 379
According to L. C. Sander (1792) the picture was commissioned by Christian IV from the artist to serve as a pendant to "another large Netherlandish painting". Given the contacts which the King had with van Honthorst (the decorations of Kronborg Castle) this is not unlikely. However, it can only be traced back to 1690, when it is documented in the Royal Kunstkammer. It was not until after he started working for the stadtholder Frederick Hendrik (1584-1647) that van Honthorst began seriously to take up mythological subjects, and at the court of The Hague the Diana-myth was a favourite theme. For instance, a complete room, the *Dianazaal,* in the palace of Honselaarsdijk was decorated with scenes from the Diana-myth (late 1630s) and in the inventories of the House of Orange several pictures with Diana scenes are listed, including some by van Honthorst. The present painting can perhaps be considered an offshoot of the Dutch Diana-cult.
*Provenance:* Listed in the inventory of the Royal Danish Kunstkammer, 1690.
*Literature:* Hauber 1777, 120; Sander, Deutsches Magazin, 1792, 534 f; Ramdohr 1792, 111; Cat. 1951 no. 322; Judson 1959, 186 cat. 82; Braun 1966, 302 f cat. W 36.

## Abraham Janssens

Antwerp ca. 1573/75 – Antwerp 1632

1042
*Hercules kicking Faunus out of Omfale's bed*
Oil on canvas. 150×190 cm. Signed and dated:
"ABJ 1607" [ABJ in monogram]
Statens Museum for Kunst, inv. Sp. 344
The painting depicts a humorous-erotic event from Ovid's calendar of Roman Feasts *Fasti,* 2. book, 305-358 (15. February, the Feast of Lupercalia): Faunus is eager to realize his love for Omfale and steals at midnight into the grotto where Hercules and Omfale lie asleep – after having exchanged clothes! In the dark, Faunus has to feel his way and, when he touches the soft, delicate texture of Omfale's clothing — unfortunately now being worn by Hercules – he climbs into the wrong bed. He is immediately kicked out by Hercules and the ensuing noise awakens everyone. Servants rush in with torches and the unfortunate, complaining Faunus is exposed. The picture was formerly attributed to Abraham Bloemaert. The attribution to Janssens has been disputed but is now accepted by most scholars.
*Provenance:* Count Danneskiold Samsøe before 1731. Purchased for the Royal Danish Kunstkammer, 1732.
*Literature:* Cat. 1951 no. 347; Delbanco 1928, 44 f, 78 no. 8, pl. 9, fig. XXII; Brockhagen 1963, 37 (under no. 153); Müller Hofstede 1971, 212 f, 232, 245, 246 f, fig. 19

## Jacob (Jacques) Jordaens

Antwerp 1593 – Antwerp 1678

1043
*Allegory on Science. Minerva and Cronus protect Science against Envy and Ignorance*
Oil on canvas. 117×164 cm. Signed:
"I.IORDAENS. FECIT."
Private Collection. (On permanent loan to the Statens Museum for Kunst)
At a table in the centre of the picture sits Geometry (?), a grey-bearded man bent over a globe, measuring with a pair of dividers, attentively watched by a young woman standing beside him. Above them is *Fama,* blowing a trumpet and holding a laurel wreath. Below them is *Mercury's* attribute, the cock, symbolizing vigilance. On the right, *Minerva* defeats Ignorance and rebuffs *Invidia* (Envy) with her shield. Standing with her foot resting on a ball on the left, *Fortuna* spreads a rain of golden chains, insignia and coins around her. In front sits *Cronus-Saturnus,* "Father Time", on a golden chariot drawn by putti. Taken as a whole the picture perhaps symbolizes the

good regime. In colour and style it is a very characteristic work by Jordaens of about 1617.
*Provenance:* Galerie van Diemen & Co., Berlin 1931. According to van Puyvelde, 1953, formerly in private collections in Riga and Moscow. Private Collection, Denmark, 1931.
*Literature:* N.v.H. in *Pantheon,* VIII, 1931, 296, repr. p. 297; d'Hulst 1953, 119 f, fig. 15; d'Hulst: "Zeichnungen", 1953, 214; van Puyvelde 1953, 85, 203, repr. p. 59; d'Hulst 1974, II, 481 under cat. 82; d'Hulst 1982, 74 f, fig. 42; d'Hulst 1983, 114 f, fig. 2.

1044
*The Apotheosis of Aeneas*
Oil on canvas. 212.5×236 cm
Statens Museum for Kunst, inv. 1310a
The painting was formerly attributed to the Dutch-Flemish painter Isaac Isaacsz. (1599-1665) (including Cat. 1951). The attribution to Jordaens is due to H. Q. van Regteren Altena and has been generally accepted. It is a characteristic early work which stylistically is closely related to paintings such as the signed and 1617 dated "The Daughters of Cecrops" in the Koninklijk Museum voor Schone Kunsten, Antwerp, (inv. 842, d'Hulst 1982, fig. 49), the signed "Allegory on Fertility" in the Alte Pinakothek, Munich, (inv. 10411, *op.cit.,* fig. 44) and the signed "Allegory", cat. 1043. As pointed out by d'Hulst, 1952, the subject of the picture – which formerly was wrongly called "A Goddess Carrying a Drowned Man towards Heaven" – is taken from Ovid's *Metamorphoses,* XIV, 581-609, where it is told how Aeneas became a god, an unusual subject in Flemish painting.
*Provenance:* Entered the Royal Danish Kunstkammer before 1737.
*Literature:* Cat. 1951 no. 344 (repr.); d'Hulst 1952, 23 f fig. 5; d'Hulst 1953, 104 ff, fig. 8; d'Hulst "Zeichnungen" 1953, 210; d'Hulst 1956, 27, 33 ff, 37, 46, 63, 217 fig. 6; d'Hulst 1967, 74, 84 f; d'Hulst 1982, 76, 220 fig. 43.

*1043*

1045

*Achelous is defeated by Hercules. Allegory on Fruitfulness. (The Origin of Cornucopia)*

Oil on canvas. 245×311 cm. Signed and dated: "J. JOR. fe 1649"

Statens Museum for Kunst, inv. Sp. 233.

The story is taken from Ovid's *Metamorphoses* IX, 1-100 (the subject cf. particularly 80-88). At the period in question, the moralistic interpretation or reinterpretation of classical mythology and ancient history was particularly widespread. Karel van Mander, the painter and art theorist from Haarlem, considered this aspect to be so important for artists that he devoted a whole section of his famous *Schilder-Boeck* (Haarlem 1604) to an "Interpretation of the Metamorphoses by Ovid" *(Wtlegginghe op den Metamorphosis Pub. Ouidii Nasonis)*. And, according to d'Hulst, many of Jordaens' mythological themes are to be understood in this way. The moral of this particular Ovidian tale, according to van Mander, is that wealth gives rise to power and strength.

*Provenance:* Delivered from Holland to Frederik III of Denmark in 1652 or the beginning of 1653. Listed in the inventory of the Royal Danish Kunstkammer, 1690.

*Literature:* Rooses 1908, 150, 278 catalogue, repr. p. 149; Hertz 1924, 364, repr. p. 361; Held 1939, 28 ff fig. 29; d'Hulst 1952, 23; d'Hulst 1956, 218 f, 249, 375 under cat. 131, 416 under cat. 239; Jaffé 1968-69, 57, 182 under cat. 189, 183 under cat. 190; d'Hulst 1974, I, 83, 215 under cat. A 121, 319 under cat. A 242, 321 under cat. A 244, 322 under cat. A 245, 325 under cat. A 250; d'Hulst 1982, 216.

## Alexander Keirincx

Antwerp 1600 – Amsterdam 1652

1046

*Wooded Landscape*

Oil on panel. 89.5×122 cm. Signed and dated: "A. Keirincx fec A° 1630"

Statens Museum for Kunst, inv. Sp. 375

This painting is one of the most important of Keirincx's landscapes from the period around 1630, the most characteristic period of his career. A hunt is taking place in the background but the rather empty woodland path in the foreground gives the impression that the picture was intended to have staffage figures which, however, were never painted in. A closely related wooded landscape, signed and likewise dated 1630, belongs to the Koninklijk Museum voor Schone Kunsten, Antwerp (no. 902).

*Provenance:* Entered the Royal Danish Kunstkammer 1756.

*Literature:* Sthyr 1929, 8, repr p. 28; Cat. 1951 no. 359 (repr.); Petit Palais, Paris 1970-71, 118 f (under no. 123); Keyes 1978, 294 f, fig. 5.

*1047*

## Leonhard Kern

Forchtenberg (Hohenlohe) 1588 – Schwäbisch Hall 1662

1047

*Scene from the Thirty Years War. A Soldier killing a Woman*

Alabaster group. Height: 34.3 cm

Kunsthistorisches Museum, Vienna, inv. Pl. 4363

The ravaging and plundering mercenaries' maltreatment of the people in the troubled Europe of the time is well represented in contemporary painting, but for obvious reasons not in sculpture. A grim genre scene perpetuated in a statuette group is therefore something of a rarity. The tentative, hitherto unpublished attribution to Leonhard Kern is due to Dr. Manfred Leithe-Jasper, who dates the group around 1640.

*Provenance:* Listed in the Inventory of Archduke Leopold Wilhelm's Collection in Vienna 1659, fol. 449' no. 141: *Ein nackhentes Weibespildt, welche von einem Soldaten hinderwerts mit einem Degen durchstochen wirdt* (Berger 1883, p. CLXX).

*1048*

## Hendrick de Keyser

Utrecht 1565 – Amsterdam 1621

1048
*Mercury*
Bronze statuette. Height: 32.3 cm. Signed and dated: "HDK 1611". [HDK in monogram]
Rijksmuseum, Amsterdam, inv. R.B.K. 1959-61
The messenger of the Gods and of Jupiter in particular, the God of Trade, but also the God of Thieves, is portrayed here as an athletic youth. This is the only known signed bronze statuette by de Keyser. Although it was known that de Keyser had also done small bronzes, it was only after the discovery of the Mercury in 1959 that it became possible to attribute a few other statuettes to him.
*Provenance:* Probably to be identified with the Mercury listed in the will of the sculptor's widow, Barbara van Wilder, in 1621. Three years later a mould for the figure is listed in the inventory of the silversmith Thomas Cruse in Delft: "Noch ein form van Mercuryus van de Keyser". Acquired by the Rijksmuseum in 1959.
*Literature:* "Leeuwenberg (& Halsema-Kubes) 1973, 181 f, no. 225 (repr.); Avery 1973, 7 ff, fig. 6, 7 (signature).
*Exhibitions:* National Gallery, London, 1976 no. 155.

1049
*Orpheus and Cerberus*
Bronze statuette. Height: 35.8 cm
Victoria & Albert Museum, London, inv. A 5-1972
Cerberus, the ferocious three-headed dog, guarded the entrance to Hades and also figures in the legend of Orpheus in the Underworld (Ovid, *Metamorphoses,* X, 11-85). Attributed to de Keyser by Avery with reference to the signed Mercury statuette (cat. 1048).
*Provenance:* A figure by de Keyser corresponding to the above is listed in an inventory, dated 23th October 1624, of the studio-props of the silversmith Thomas Cruse in Delft (no. 14).
*Literature:* Avery 1973, 3 ff, fig. 10, 11, 13 and 15.
*Exhibitions:* National Gallery, London, 1976 no. 156 (repr.).

1050
*Weeping Child*
Bust in reddish marble. Height: 27 cm
Statens Museum for Kunst, inv. 5515
Attributed to Hendrick de Keyser by Olsen, with reference to its close stylistic relationship to the weeping *putti* that crown the Tomb of William the Silent in Nieuwe Kerk in Delft, executed by Hendrick de Keyser 1614-21. As pointed out by Olsen, the present bust or one very similar is depicted, together with a pendant, in the painting by Willem van Haecht (1593-1637), dated 1628, of Cornelis van der Geest's picture gallery (detail repr. Weihrauch 1967, fig. 556) now in the Collection S. van Berg, New York.
*Provenance:* Recorded in the Royal Danish Kunstkammer, 1775.
*Literature:* Olsen 1980, I, 75 f, II pl. 155.

## Nicolaus Knüpfer

Leipzig (?) ca. 1603 – Utrecht 1655

1051
*"Il Contento". Mercury abducting the Goddes Contento from the Earth*
Oil on panel. 57.5×42.5 cm. Signed: "NKnüpfer" [N and K in ligature]
Statens Museum for Kunst, inv. Sp. 750
Knüpfer painted two other versions of this theme. Both are based on Adam Elsheimer's (1578-1610) famous "Il Contento" from ca. 1607, now in the National Gallery of Scotland, Edinburgh (inv. 2312). One belongs to the Bayerische Staatsgemäldesammlungen in Munich (inv. 177). The other is in the Staatliches Museum in Schwerin (inv. 2143). The Schwerin picture, which is signed and dated 1651, is considered to be one of Knüpfer's principal works. The present painting is a simplified version of that picture. Stylistically, too, it is re-

lated to the Schwerin picture and can therefore be dated ca. 1651. The source of the theme, as shown by Kuznetsow (1964), is a legend told in Mateo Aléman's picaresque novel *Vida y hechos del picaro Guzmán de Alfarache, ataloya de la vida humana* (1599), I, book I, chapter 7.
*Provenance:* Acquired for the Royal Danish Kunstkammer, 1760.
*Literature:* Cat. 1951 no. 366 (repr.); Renckens 1950, 75; Kuznetsow 1964 (Trudy), 199, 217 no. 90; Kuznetsow 1974, 195, cat. 90, cf. cat. 91-92.

1052
*Paulus the Apostle defending himself at the Trial in Caesarea*
Oil on panel. 48.5×65 cm. Signed: "NKnüpfer" [N and K in ligature]
Statens Museum for Kunst, inv. Sp. 749
The subject is from the Acts, 26. Paulus, in chains, is interrogated by Festus. Listening to them are Herodes Agrippa, sitting in the left foreground wearing a sumptuous mantle interwoven with the initials "AG", and Bernice, very décolletée (she was believed to be the mistress of Emperor Titus!). The stagelike composition of the painting (staircase, podium) makes it a very characteristic work of Knüpfer of about 1650.
*Provenance:* Acquired for the Royal Danish Kunstkammer, 1761.
*Literature:* Renckens 1950, 75; Cat. 1951 no. 365 (repr.); Kuznetsow 1964 (Trudy), 214 no. 63; Kuznetsow 1974, 190, cat. 63.

## Salomon Koninck

Amsterdam 1609 – Amsterdam 1656

1053
*An old Miser counting his Money*
Oil on panel. 67.5×51 cm. Dated: "A 1635"
Statens Museum for Kunst, inv. Stroe 270
The Gold Weigher and the Old Man counting his Money were among Koninck's favoured subjects. They were themes which have a long tradition in Netherlandish art, dating back to Quentin Metsy's picture of "The Money Changer" from 1514 in the Louvre, Paris (inv. 1444). Actually they are allegories on avarice and greed, Vanitas pictures with a moralizing meaning.
*Provenance:* Recorded at Fredensborg Castle 1799.
*Literature:* Cat. 1951 no. 747 (as Adriaen Verdoel?); Sumowski III 1986, 1645, cat. 1104, repr. p. 1678 (with literature).

1054
*Esther reading Haman's decree of the extermination of the Jews*
Oil on panel. 75×57 cm
Statens Museum for Kunst, inv. Sp. 419
The subject was formerly interpreted as "Bathseba reading David's letter", but is now assumed to be taken from the Book of Esther (4, 8) which enjoyed great popularity among artists in the circle of Rembrandt. Koninck took great interest in rendering jewellery and precious fabrics

*1055*

like velvet, silk, satin and brocade. Although never a pupil of Rembrandt, he was greatly influenced by his works – in the present picture especially Rembrandt's works of the early 1630s. According to Sumowski (1986) the present picture can be dated in the mid-1630s.
*Provenance:* Passed from the estate of Princess Charlotte Amalie to the Royal Danish Kunstkammer in 1783.
*Literature:* Van Ramdohr 1792, 919; Cat. 1951 no. 371 (repr.); Sumowski III 1986, 1627, 1641 (with literature).

## Johann König

Nürnberg 1586 – Nürnberg 1642

1055
*The Brazen Serpent*
Oil on copper. 54×76 cm. Signed: "Joh: König·fe·"
Statens Museum for Kunst, inv. Sp. 369
The subject is from Exodus 21, 4-9. This painting – a very characteristic example of König's miniature-like and many-coloured style – is a compilation of Venetian figure *motifs* mainly derived from Tintoretto: thus the figure of a man lying in the foreground has been drawn almost *verbatim* from Tintoretto's "St. Mark rescuing a slave" of 1548 (now in the Galleria dell'Accademia, Venice). The figure of Moses also derives from Tintoretto. The style of the figures and the landscape is, however, clearly indebted to Elsheimer. It would be tempting to connect König's "The Brazen Serpent" with the picture of "Die Wusten Moise", which Christian IV's mintmaster, Nicolaus Schwabe, purchased in Germany in 1615 on his way home from Prague.
*Provenance:* Recorded at Fredensborg Castle in 1799.
*Literature:* Cat. 1951 no. 374.

## Christoph van der Lamen

Antwerp or Brussels, resp. 1606/07 or ca. 1614 – Antwerp 1651/52.

1056
*Dancing party in an interior*
Oil on panel. 72×105 cm
Statens Museum for Kunst, inv. Sp. 181
The attribution to van der Lamen is confirmed by comparison with his – incidentally rather rare – paintings, cf. the painting of "The Prodigal Son feasting with harlots" in the Louvre, Paris (inv. 20384, panel, 71.5×104 cm), to which the present picture is related stylistically as well as in theme. The likewise very small number of known dated works by his hand are all from the 1640s. The large chimneypiece in the background represents Jesus appearing to the disciples at the Sea of Tiberias according to John 21, 1-8 (Peter's Second Draught of Fishes). Its prominent placing is to be taken as a Christian memento and the picture thus takes on a moralizing meaning.
*Provenance:* Consul Hans West Coll. (no. 91). Purchased for the Royal Collection in 1809 with the Hans West Collection.
*Literature:* Cat. 1951 no. 378; Legrand 1963, 86.

## Jasper van der Lanen

Antwerp? ca. 1590/95 – Antwerp? after Sept. 1626

1057
*Wooded landscape with Judah and Tamar*
Oil on panel. 79.5×115 cm. Signed:
"Jasper·vander·Lanen·Inuentor"
Statens Museum for Kunst, inv. 4456
From its style, the picture is closely related to the Coninxloo-Govaerts school of Flemish forest-landscape painting of the early 17th century. Characteristically enough, this picture was formerly attributed to G. van Coninxloo, but subsequently, when it was being cleaned in 1959, the full and authentic signature of van der Lanen was uncovered. The figures are undoubtedly the work of Frans Francken II (1581-1642). The subject can be identified as the story of Judah and Tamar from Genesis 38, 12-19.
*Provenance:* Bought by the museum from Foreign Minister Gustav Rasmussen, 1946.
*Literature:* Cat. 1951 no. 129a (repr.); Rubow 1965, 117 ff, fig. 1 and fig. 2 (signature); W. Bernt (4th edit.) II 1980, p. 30.

## Pieter Lastman

Amsterdam ca. 1583 – Amsterdam 1633

1058
*The Angel Rafael takes leave of Old Tobit and his son Tobias*
Oil on panel. 62×93 cm. Signed and dated:
"PLastman fecit A° 1618" [P and L in monogram]
Statens Museum for Kunst, inv. 3922
The subject is taken from the Book of Tobit (ch. 12), one of the Old Testament Apocrypha. On his return to his old father Tobit after a long journey, Tobias offers his faithful travelling companion half of the wealth he has brought home. But the travelling companion reveals himself as the Angel Rafael. Among the treasures on the ground in front of Tobias a very characteristic ewer can be seen on a silver dish to the right. This ewer has been identified with the still existing silvergilt ewer made in 1614 by the Utrecht-silversmith Adam van Vianen (ca. 1569-1627) for the Guild of the Silversmiths in Amsterdam, now in the Rijksmuseum, Amsterdam (inv. TM 409). The ewer was famous and can be found depicted in works by several painters of Amsterdam at that time. Lastman belonged to the group of so-called Pre-Rembrandtists (cf. no. 1061). The picture is almost contemporary with the paintings on copper which Lastman painted as his part of the decorations for Christian IV's oratory in the church of Frederiksborg Castle (destroyed by fire, 1859).
*Provenance:* According to Freise (1911): Sale, Jan Wub-

bel, Amsterdam, 16. July 1792, no. 196 (bought by Yver). Sale, Rudolph Saabye, Copenhagen, 1819, no. 21 (bought by Count Moltke). Bought at the Moltke sale, 1.-2. June 1931, no. 69, by the New Carlsberg Foundation. Gift from the New Carlsberg Foundation to the museum, 1932.
*Literature:* Høyen/Madsen 1900, 21 cat. 31; Freise 1911, 47 f, no. 42, 92, 94, 104 f, pl. VI fig. 18; Cat. 1951 no. 382 (repr.); Duyvené de Wit-Klinkhamer 1966, 86, 88, repr. p. 88 fig. 9 (detail); Chr. Tümpel in exhibit. cat. Sacramento 1974, 135, 139, repr. p. 134, fig. 89.

## Karel van Mander

Meulebeke 1548 – Amsterdam 1606

1059
*Landscape with St. John the Baptist preaching and baptizing*
Oil on panel. 77×106 cm. Signed and dated:
"KvM 1597" [KvM in monogram]
Niedersächsisches Landesmuseum, Hannover, inv. PAM 907.
The story of the preaching and baptizing of John the Baptist is to be found in all four Gospels of the New Testament (e.g. Mark 1, 1-8). The river landscape reflects Karel van Mander's perception of painting as a subjective art form that springs from the artist's imagination and not from nature itself. The detail is borrowed from nature for inclusion in compositons arranged according to the artist's own inspiration. The ideal of nature was to be obtained through the impression as a whole and not through direct imitation of nature as is the case in realistic landscape painting.
*Provenance:* Acquired by the museum in 1928.
*Literature:* Valentiner 1930, 58 ff, 83 f no. G.11, 130 pl. XXXI, fig. 38; von der Osten 1954, 84 (cat. 172); Franz 1969, I, 290 f, pl. 40; Miedema 1973, 552 fig. 71.
*Exhibitions:* Rijksmuseum, Amsterdam, 1955, no. 80.

## Anton Mirou

Antwerp (?) before 1586 – Frankenthal (?) after 1653 or 1661

1060
*Village on the fringe of a wood*
Oil on copper. 25.5×37.5 cm. Signed: "A.Mirou f"
Statens Museum for Kunst, inv. Sp. 222
The picture belongs to a group of early works, mainly village landscapes, which all have some characteristics in common, and are dated between 1604 and 1611.
*Provenance:* Collection of J. C. Bodendick, Copenhagen (Weinwich 1825, no. 16). Purchased for the Royal Collection with the Bodendick Collection, 1810.
*Literature:* Cat. 1951 no. 463 (repr.).

## Claes Moeyart

Durgerdam 1590/91 – Amsterdam 1655

1061
*God appears to Abraham in Sikem*
Oil on canvas. 102×168 cm. Signed and dated:
"CL Moeya.rt f. 1628"
Rijksdienst Beeldende Kunst, The Hague, inv. NK. 3401. On permanent loan to the Rijksmuseum Het Catharijneconvent, Utrecht
The subject is from Genesis 12, 6-7. Among the so-called "Pre-Rembrandtists", a group of artists working in Amsterdam in the early 17th century and who in the years before Rembrandt renewed Dutch history painting, there was a predilection for biblical subjects and in particular subjects from the Old Testament. This also applied to Moeyaert, whose paintings of scenes from the Old Testament, often rich in figures, constitute his most significant artistic achievement. The popularity of Old Testament themes was probably due to the fact that members of the Reformed Church in Holland at that time – not least because of the long struggle for liberation from the domination of Catholic Spain – identified themselves with the Chosen People of Israel in the Old Testament. The present painting by Moeyeart is perhaps one of the most direct examples of this, since several of the figures are probably portraits.
*Provenance:* Private collections in Düsseldorf and Amsterdam; Musée des Beaux-Arts, Louvain; Musée des Beaux-Arts, Bruxelles.
*Literature:* Tümpel 1974, 142 note 248, 247 f cat. 5, fig. 207 (with bibliography); Tümpel, exhib.cat. Sacramento 1974, 143 f.

## Joos de Momper the Yonger (II)

Antwerp 1564 – Antwerp 1634/35

1062
*Rocky Landscape*
Oil on panel. 44×73 cm
Statens Museum for Kunst, inv. Sp. 214
This picture belongs to a small, well-defined group of closely related paintings – some of the most beautiful in Momper's oeuvre. To this group can be added two landscapes set into the panelling of Christian IV's Winter Room of ca. 1615 at Rosenborg Castle, one a mountain landscape with travellers and the other a mountain landscape with Venus and Adonis. These two landscapes are among the few autograph works by de Momper in the Winter Room. The staffage figures are by Jan Brueghel the Elder (1568-1625).
*Provenance:* Purchased for the Royal Danish Kunstkammer, 1744.
*Literature:* Cat. 1951 no. 474 (repr.); Koester 1966, 8, fig. VII; Ertz 1986, 85 no. 24, 147, 470 cat. 54, repr. 130.

1063
*Winter Landscape*
Oil on panel. 37.5×98.5 cm
Statens Museum for Kunst, inv. 1528

The three landscapes, cat. 1064, 1065 and the present one, together form a series or part of a series. They are characteristic examples of the oblong, narrow landscapes frequently mentioned in inventories from the 17th century, and whose special horizontal format was determined by the use to which they were put: they were probably placed as a frieze high up on the wall above a moulding, analogous with the description in, e.g., Philip Valckenisse's inventory of 1614 (Denucé 1932, 20). The figures in all three pictures are the work of Jan Brueghel the Elder (1568-1625).

*Provenance:* Transferred to the Royal Danish Kunstkammer from Frederiksberg Castle, 1787.

*Literature:* Cat. 1951 no. 475 (repr.); Koester 1966, 29, 49 note 21, fig. XXVI; Ertz 1979, 625 no. 417; Ertz 1986, 21, 65, 86 no. 56, 247, 617 cat. 556, repr. 277.

*1067*

1064
*Mountain Landscape with a River*
Oil on panel. 37.5×98.5 cm
Statens Museum for Kunst, inv. Sp. 216
See cat. 1063
*Provenance:* Cf. cat. 1063.
*Literature:* Cat. 1951 no. 477 (repr.); Koester 1966, 13, 49 note 21, fig. III; Ertz 1986, 21, 65, 84 no. 12, 616 cat. 554, repr. 554.

1065
*Mountain Landscape with a Lake*
Oil on panel. 37.5×98.5 cm
Statens Museum for Kunst, inv. Sp. 215
See cat. 1963
*Provenance:* Cf. cat. 1063.
*Literature:* Cat. 1951 no. 476 (repr.); Koester 1966, 49 note 21, fig. IV; Ertz, 1979, 625 no. 419; Ertz 1986, 21, 65, 160, 617, cat. 555, repr. 153.

## Monogrammist IVDS

Antwerp about 1600

1066
*Rocky Landscape with a River and a Waterfall*
Oil on panel. 95.5.×153.5 cm. [The reverse of the panel bears the Antwerp city band and the incised initials of the panel maker]
Statens Museum for Kunst, inv. 6187
This typical, late-Mannerist, Flemish landscape has alternately been attributed to Roelant Savery (cf. cat. 1083), Kerstiaen de Keuninck (ca. 1560-1632/35) and Tobias Verhaecht (1561-1631). However, in 1962 it was shown that it must be by the same hand as a landscape signed with an IVDS monogram, at that time in the art trade in Vienna. Three other landscapes have subsequently been added to the list, but the artist behind the monogram has not yet been identified.
*Provenance:* Purchased from a dealer in The Hague, 1959. Presented to the museum by the New Carlsberg Foundation.
*Literature:* Herbst 1962, 10, repr.; Rubow 1965, 119 ff, fig. 4.
*Exhibitions:* Museum voor Schone Kunsten, Gent, 1960/Breda, 1961, cat. 39.

## Daniel Mytens (attributed to)

Delft ca. 1590 – The Hague 1647

1067
*Charles I of England (1600-49) when Prince of Wales*
Oil on canvas (not on paper as stated in Cat. 1951), 219.5×174.5 cm
Statens Museum for Kunst, inv. Sp. 184
The Prince is wearing a red ermine-lined cloak and the insignia of the Order of the Garter with its motto HONI SOIT QVI MAL Y PENSE. The back of the canopy, the top and the pelmet of the canopy are embroidered with a number of coats-of-arms showing the English leopards, the Scottish lion and the French fleur-de-lis and various other emblems. On the table to the right there is a reading desk whose side bears the initials *CP* (i.e. *Carolus Prince*); there is also a ground-plan of a fortification and a case containing an open watchcase. Until now this picture has been catalogued as Paul van Somer (Cat. 1951), an attribution which goes back to Spengler (1827) and which subsequently was generally accepted. However, the portrait seems to differ somewhat from van Somer's style and to be slightly above his capacity. On the other hand it is very close in style to Daniel Mytens, cf. the broad areas of light and shade in the firmly structured face and the finely modelled hands. The very type of portait, moreover, is actually the same as that in the portrait of the diplomat and connoisseur Thomas Howard, 2nd Earl of Arundel, with which Mytens introduced himself to England in 1618. The earliest-dated full-length portrait of Prince Charles by Mytens dates from October 1623. In this, the Prince has grown a small moustache, not to be seen in the present picture, which gives October 1623 as a safe *terminus ante quem* for the present portrait. On the basis of its style and the relative age of the Prince, it can be dated c. 1619-20. Just about 1620 Mytens came into contact for the first time with the English court, where he enjoyed considerable favour, particularly from Prince Charles. The portrait could thus well be both Mytens' first large commission for the English court and his earliest known full-length portrait of the Prince. The architectural perspective in the background of the picture – as has been pointed out earlier – is undoubtedly the work of the architectural painter, Hendrick van Steenwyck the Younger, as are also the figures in the background. Van Steenwyck arrived in London in November 1617 and he, too, became a protegé of Prince Charles. It was then *en vogue* at the court of the Stuarts to be portrayed against an architectural background. This put van Steenwyck in touch with *i.a.* Mytens, cf. the signed and 1627 dated full-length portrait of Charles I in the Galleria Sabauda in Turin (no. 395). In this case the architecture is separately signed and dated (1626) by van Steenwyck. The throne, its canopy, the table cloth and other accessories in the present portrait are probably the work of a third artist.
*Provenance:* The portrait must without doubt have come to Denmark as a gift to Christian IV from his English relatives. According to Povl Eller it is recorded at Frederiksborg Castle in 1677 and it may also be identified with "Prinndtzen Aff Engeland hanss Countrafey wdi Enn forgylt Ramme", listed in the inventory of 1650 (1636). Transferred from Frederiksborg to the Royal Picture Callery at Christiansborg, 1827.
*Literature:* Toynbee 1939, 122 f, repr. p. 120 fig. D; *idem* 21, pl. III fig. D (detail); Cat. 1951 no. 673 (repr.); Saxl & Wittkower 1948/1969, no. 43.7.

## Netherlandish Artist, about 1600

1068
*Wooded Landscape with Abraham banishing Hagar and Ismael*
Oil on copper. 44×61 cm
Statens Museum for Kunst, inv. Sp. 201
Compositionally and as regards the landscape setting, this painting is based on Hieronymus Cock's (master 1546 – died 1570) famous etching of a wooded landscape with "The Temptation in the Wilderness", an etching which – as recent research shows – in the first place was based on a prototype by Pieter Bruegel the Elder (drawing from 1554 in Prague, cf. Arndt 1966, 207 ff, repr. p. 206, Cock's etching repr. fig. 2), and in the second place, was of great importance to the genesis of the Netherlandish forest landscape painting in the second half of the 16th and the beginning of the 17th century. Stylistically this picture has a certain kinship with Vinckboons' early Coninxloo-inspired woodeded landscapes, but a former attribution to Vinckboons is open to doubt. The story of Hagar is related in Genesis 16, 1-16 and 21, 9-21.
*Provenance:* Purchased for the Royal Danish Kunstkammer 1744/47.
*Literature:* Coninckx 1908, 33; Cat. 1951 no. 775 (repr.); Goosens 1954, 146.

## Adriaen van Nieulandt

Antwerp 1587 – Amsterdam 1658

1069
*Abraham feeds the three Angels*
Oil on panel. 62×79 cm. Signed and dated:
"Adriaen v. Nieuland 1651". Colour-plate XXVII
Niedersächsisches Landesmuseum, inv. PAM 907
The subject is from Genesis 18, 1-15. Van Nieulandt's proper sphere was the mythological or biblical scene with a multitude of figures in the open air and in which the landscape took a fairly prominent place. In this respect he is related to the so-called "Pre-Rembrandtists". The major part of his known works of this kind originates, judging from their dates, in the 1640s and 1650s. These paintings often provoke a somewhat chaotic impression (cf. cat. 1070), and some of his small-scale works are thus with their simpler compositon and sparse figures more successfull, as the present picture in Hannover for instance, which certainly might convey some idea of the character of the biblical scenes which he painted some 30 years earlier for Christian IV's oratory in the chapel of Frederiksborg Castle (burnt down 1859).
*Provenance:* Probably Bicker van Zwieten Coll., The Hague, 2nd half of 17th century. Since 1857 in Royal Hanoverian possession. Acquired for the Landesgalerie, 1925.
*Literature:* Van der Osten 1954, 113, cat. 253.

1070
*Christ's Entry into Jerusalem*
Oil on panel. 85.5×114 cm. Signed and dated:
"Adriaen van Nieulandt/Fecit A° 1655"
Statens Museum for Kunst, inv. Sp. 256.
The story of Jesus' entry into Jerusalem is told with slight variations in all four Gospels.
*Provenance:* Purchased in Holland for the Royal Danish Kunstkammer, 1759.
*Literature:* Cat. 1951 no. 513.

## Isaac Oliver

Rouen (?) ca. 1560/65 – London 1617

1071
*A Party in the Open Air. Allegory on Conjugal Love*
Miniature. Gouache and water colour on vellum stuck onto card, 11.3×17 cm. Signed with monogram: "IO in"
Colour-plate III
Statens Museum for Kunst, inv. 6938
On the bank of a brook in a wooded mountain landscape, two groups of people meet. On the left, a distinguished gentleman and a woman, dressed in comely, dark costumes, accompanied by two similarly clad women. On the right, a merry company of men and women, some of them making music. The women are dressed in gaudy, gold-embroidered dresses, with generous *décolletage.* The contrast between the way the two groups are dressed and how they behave provides the clue to the picture, which can be interpreted as a moralizing allegory of Protestant observance of Christian conjugal love, as represented by the decorous group, left, as opposed to the sensual, i.e. deluded and corrupt love on the right. Here the lover sprawls voluptuously like "The Prodigal Son" among the harlots. Youth, wealth and beauty are as transient as the music of the flute or lute, and death lurks around the corner (cf. the gallows and the wheel in sharp silhouette in the background left). Our chaste couple, however, again appearing on the extreme left, have now taken up the narrow, stoney path of virtue which leads them to the church on top of the rock. The miniature may have been painted in connection with a wedding. The landscape, which is an exceptionally prominent feature in the picture, is indebted to works from the 1580s by the Flemish/Dutch landscape and miniature painter Hans Bol. And the group of figures in the foreground and the hunting scenes in the background are based on contemporary prints by P. Thuys and Stradanus respectively, as pointed out by Finsten. In Oliver's oeuvre, the miniature – which can be dated ca. 1590-95 – is unique of its kind.
*Provenance:* Possibly identical with a miniature recorded 1622 in the lawyer Backer's collection in Leyden. Geheimearkivar Chr. Eberhard Voss sale, Copenhagen, 23.5.1791, no. 43 (probably bought by Count Holstein, Ledreborg). Holstein family inheritance at Ledreborg. Purchased by the museum with support from the New Carlsberg Foundation from the estate of Countess

Louise Christina Holstein, née Countess Hamilton, 1976.
*Literature:* Lorenzen 1939, 122, repr. p. 121; Colding and Andersen 1950, 326 f, fig. 23 and 25 (detail of signature); Andersen 1952, 80 ff, repr. p. 80 (colour-pl.); Colding 1953, 104, fig. 114; Colding 1977, 108 ff, repr. fig. 1 (colour), p. 110 (detail); Finsten 1981, I, 100, 102 ff, II, 22 ff cat. 14, fig. 14; Strong 1983, 155, fig. 197.

## Anthonie Palamedesz.

Delft 1601 – Amsterdam 1673

1072
*Soldiers in a Guardroom*
Oil on panel, 45×64 cm. Signed: "A. Palamedes"
Statens Museum for Kunst, inv. Sp. 411
Anthonie Palamedesz. painted a number of guardroom pictures *(coortegardjes),* especially in the late 1640s and the early 1650s. The present picture may thus be dated in the late 1640s (cf. e.g., a "Guardroom", dated 1647, in the Rijksmuseum in Amsterdam, inv. A 3024). The soldiers are shown in a cellar-like room, arming themselves. Standing in the center foreground is a fully-equipped pikeman with his back to the onlooker. This figure as well as the soldier putting on his boots and other details recur in a similar, signed, picture by Palamedesz., formerly in the Galerie Liechtenstein, Vienna.
*Provenance:* Acquired for the Royal Danish Kunstkammer, 1744.
*Literature:* Cat. 1951 no. 531 (repr.).

## Georg Petel

Weilheim 1601/02 – Augsburg 1634

1073
*Salt-cellar with a Relief of the Triumph of the Sea-Born Venus*
Salt-cellar. Ivory and gilt silver. Height: 43.8 cm. The cylindrical ivory foot carved in one piece. Diameter at the bottom: 14-12.5 cm, at the top: 13-12.5 cm. Signed in the mouth of the dolphin: "J·P·F·" (= Jörg Petle Fecit)
Colour-plate XXVIII.
Royal Collection, Stockholm, inv. SS 143
The silver-gilt salt-cellar itself is in the shape of a shell, resting on a slightly conical cylinder of ivory, carved in high-relief, in part almost sculptured in the round. The relief shows the sea-born Venus, accompanied by a Triton and three Nereids (sea-nymphs). The garlands carried by the floating *putti* were originally studded with shells, coral branches and pearls, and the string being held aloft in Venus' right hand was originally studded with tiny pearls. The bottom of the salt cellar bears three stamps: a crowned hand, the stamp of authorization of the town of Antwerp, a crowned R, which is the letter signifying the year of the Deanship 1627/28, and the maker's mark IHK (in ligature), presumably referring to the Antwerp silversmith Jan Herck. Thus the salt-cellar must have been carved by Petel during his (third?) stay in Antwerp with Rubens in the first half of 1628, at the same time that he was carving the Frederiksborg crucifix. It is furthermore to be identified with certainty as the salt-cellar listed in Rubens' estate as follows: "Une salière d'yvoire, représentant une trouppe des Nymphes marines et Tritons, avec des petits anges qui attachent des festons, aussi de l'invention de Mons. Rubens". The information in the inventory that the salt cellar was the "invention" of Rubens is confirmed by two sketches of Rubens that show successive stages of preparatory studies for the relief, viz. a grisaille-sketch now in Lady Anne Bentnick's Collection, Welbeck Woodhouse, Notts., and a pen drawing in the British Museum, London. The salt-cellar was among the "raritées moderne d'ivoire chez Rubens" which Michel Le Blon (1587-1656), bought for Queen Christina of Sweden from Rubens' estate in 1649. The Queen presented it to her chancellor, Count Magnus Gabriel de la Gardie (1622-86) before 1652/53, by which date it is recorded in the inventory of his collection. From a note made in a checking of his collection in 1655, de la Gardie had, however, returned the gift to the Queen 1654 (cf. Lutteman 1977, 137). It subsequently passed into the possession of Queen Hedvig Eleonora and is recorded at Ulriksdal Castle in 1744. In 1822 it was removed to Stockholm and in the 1930s was transferred to the Royal Collection at Stockholm Castle. In the Print Room, Statens Museum for Kunst, there are amongst the drawings from the so-called "Rubens Cantoor" three black chalk drawings (by Willem Panneels?) after the ivory carving of the salt-cellar.
*Provenance:* See above.
*Literature:* Feuchtmayr/Schädler 1973, 75, 77, 98 ff cat. 14 fig. 51-56 (with bibliography); Lutteman 1977, 131 ff, fig. 107, 110, colourpl. at p. 136; Held 1980, I, 351 ff; Schädler 1985, 34 f, repr. pp. 45, 46, 47.
*Exhibitions:* Bayerisches Nationalmuseum, München 1964, no. 37; Nationalmuseum, Stockholm 1966, no. 1237.

1074
*Christ on the Cross (Leonora Christina's Crucifix)*
Ivory, sculpture in the round, carved in one piece. Corpus. Height: 68 cm, width: 15.5. cm; T-formed ebony: cross, carved rock base with yellow mica. Height: 83.5 cm
Frederiksborg inv. B 3959
The Crucifix is presumably identical with a crucifix which belonged to Leonora Christina in the 17th century and which, according to an entry in her will of the 4th September 1692, she had given away during her declining years at Maribo Kloster. ("The Crucifix of ivory, which for some time hung on the wall in my bedroom is not entered in the list, for I have given it away"). Before it came to the Frederiksborg Museum in 1951 it was in the sacristy of the Carmelite Church of St. Joseph in Vienna, where it has been deposited in 1780 by Maria Elisabeth Lobkowitz, widow of the Austrian Foreign

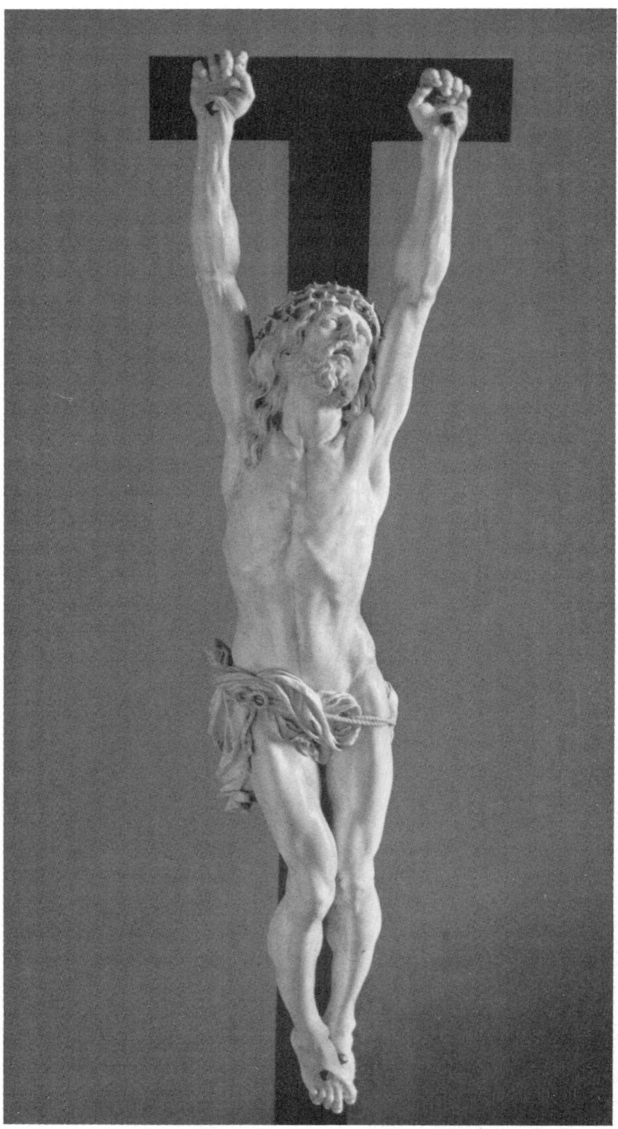

*1074*

Minister Corfitz Anton Graf Ulfeldt, a grandson of Leonora Christina. The Crucifix was apparently taken to Austria by her expatriated children. The Crucifix was formerly attributed to François Duquesnoy, but in the 1950s it was claimed both by Erich Bachmann and Kurt Feuchmayr to be an authentic work by Petel. Feuchtmayr believes that the Crucifix was acquired by Leonora Christina during her stay with her husband, the Danish chancellor Count Corfitz Ulfeldt, in the Netherlands in 1646-47, or that it was presented to her by Queen Christina of Sweden, who purchased a number of ivories from Flanders in 1649 (cf. cat. 1073). And on the basis of the presumed provenance of the Crucifix and of its style, which is closely related to the salt-cellar (cat. 1073) that Petel made for Rubens in Antwerp in 1628, Feuchtmayr identifies it as the Crucifix listed in the inventory of Rubens' estate, 1640 ("Nostre Seigneur à la croix fait d'yvoir de l'invention de feu monsieur Rubens"). This again is probably identical with the large ivory crucifix which Petel, according to Joachim von Sandrart, carved for Rubens during his stay in Antwerp in 1628. The immediate model for the Frederiksborg Crucifix is the representation of Christ on the Cross, through which Rubens had created a new type of picture in European Baroque painting about 1610. Christ is depicted here nailed to the cross with his arms in an almost vertical position as opposed to the earlier tradition in which the arms of Christ were spread out horizontally: the lonely crucifix with Christ hanging on the Cross in agony, alone between heaven and earth, cf. Rubens' picture in Greenville, the most authentic of several versions (Hubala 1967, 13 fig. 5).

*Provenance:* Presented to the museum by the Republic of Austria and the Catholic Church in Austria in 1951 (see also above).

*Literature:* Andrup 1952, 117 fig. 3 and 4; Bachmann 1964, 37 ff, pl. II; Hubala 1970, 300, pl. 346; Feuchtmayr/Schädler 1973, 77 f, 95 ff cat. 13, fig. 38-40, 45, 49 (with bibliography); Schädler 1985, 34, repr. p. 38 and 39.

1075

*Gustav II Adolf*

Bust in bronze (traces of original gilding). Height: 65.2 cm

Kungl. Husgerådskammaren (Royal Collection), Stockholm, inv. 64.

The bust was undoubtedly executed during Gustav Adolf's sojourn in Augsburg in May-June 1632. A version belonging to the Nationalmuseum, Stockholm, has been cast from the same model as the Husgerådskammaren bust and bears the inscription on the edge of the shoulder: GEORG:PETEL:AD: VIVI SCVLP: 1632/CHRISTOF·NEIDHARDT·IN AVGSPVRG: GOS· MICH: 1643:". The version in the Husgerådskammaren which however is not signed was formerly believed to be a replica of the bust in the Nationalmuseum but Feuchtmayr has pointed out that the opposite is more likely to be the case, since the Husgerådskammaren bust as regards the delicacy and precision of the execution is superior to the version in the Nationalmuseum. Presumably the bust in the Husgerådskammaren is identical with the bronze-casting made by Wolfgang II Neidhardt in 1632. A further version of the bust, now lost, was acquired from the Neidhardt bronzecasters by the city of Augsburg, which subsequently presented it to King Ferdinand III. A replica datable towards 1650, cast from a somewhat altered model, is in the Staatliche Kunstsammlungen, Dresden. It is possible that Christian IV had the bust of Gustav Adolf in mind when some 10 years later he commissioned a bronze bust of himself by François Dieussart (cat. 1022).

*1075*

*Provenance:* Probably listed in the Christina inventory 1652 (Granberg 1896, Appendix II).
*Literature:* Feuchtmayr/Schädler 1973, 65 ff, 76, 81, 125 ff cat. 34 figs. 130-133 (with bibliography); Schädler 1985, 82, 92, repr. p. 83.
*Exhibitions:* Bayerisches Nationalmuseum, München 1964, no. 59.

1076
*St. Sebastian*
Statuette in bronze. Height: 54.5 cm
The Victoria & Albert Museum, London, inv. A.28-1956
This statuette, which strongly alludes to contemporary representations of the "Deposition" is known in about 10 versions. In the St. Sebastian in the Fürstliche Sammlung Liechtenstein, Vaduz, which is the earliest documented example (1658) and in the present version, St. Sebastian,

*1076*

as a deviation from the conventional iconography, is represented entirely naked and without marks of wounds from the arrows. In the other versions – with the exception of one – he wears a loincloth and has wounds on his body. The attribution to Georg Petel is due to Middeldorf, who considers it to be one of Georg Petel's early works from his sojourn in Italy (ca. 1621/22). The attribution of the figure, however, is still a much-debated question. Recently, Hecht put forward the theory that the composition might derive from a picture by Adam Elsheimer (1578-1610) – a St. Sebastian now lost but known from copies. On this basis she dates the figure (the Liechtenstein version) to the first quarter of the 17th century. It is a plaster-cast of this St. Sebastian figure (the version with loincloth), that the young Georg Petel (?) carries in his hand in cat. 1017.
*Provenance:* Dr. W. L. Hildburgh's collection. Bequeathed to the Victoria & Albert Museum, 1955.
*Literature:* Middeldorf 1978, 48 ff (prototype/with earlier literature); Johanne Hecht in exhib.cat. New York/Liechtenstein 1985/86, 78 under no. 48 and in exhib.cat. Frankfurt am Main 1986/87, 155 under no. 7 (with full bibliography).

## Willem de Poorter

Haarlem 1608 – Haarlem after 1648

1077
*Allegory on Peace. Pax being crowned by Minerva*
Oil on panel. 59×74 cm. Signed and dated: "W.D.P. 1643".
Statens Museum for Kunst, inv. Sp. 460
As shown by Lossky, de Poorter's composition was inspired by a painting, dated 1641, of an analogous theme by the Rotterdam painter Hendrick Martensz. Sorgh (ca. 1611-1670), now in the Chateau d'Azay-Ferron. In Lossky's opinion, the picture by Sorgh can be connected with the initial steps to peace negotiations in the Thirty Years War taken at the meeting in Regensburg 1640-41. A comparable background for de Poorter's picture could thus have been the peace conference in Münster and Osnabrück in 1643.
*Provenance:* Acquired for the Royal Danish Kunstkammer from the estate of the artist Magnus Berg, 1739.
*Literature:* Cat. 1951 no. 552 (repr.); Lossky 1956, 19, fig. 8: exhib.cat. Petit Palais, Paris 1970-71, 206.

## Pieter Post

Haarlem 1608 – The Hague 1669

1078
*Landscape with Riders on a Sandy Road.* Ca. 1630
Oil on panel. 40.5×71.5 cm
Statens Museum for Kunst, inv. 3359a
The present picture was originally attributed to Esaias van de Velde, but was later attributed to the painter and architect Pieter Post of whose paintings very few are known to exist. The grey/green colour harmonies reflect a close relationship with landscape painting in Haarlem.
*Provenance:* Bequeathed in 1917 by Miss Louise von Buchwald.
*Literature:* Styhr 1929, 11, 36; Cat. 1951 no. 739 (Esaias van de Velde); Bengtsson 1952, 73; Gudlaugsson 1954, 11, 60, 62.

## Theodor Rombouts

Antwerp 1597 – Antwerp 1637

1079
*Card and Backgammon Players. Fight over Cards*
Oil on canvas. 150×241 cm
Statens Museum for Kunst, inv. Sp. 92
The painting is related to – and undoubtedly more or less contemporary with – the pictures of card and trictrac players, musicians, smokers, gypsies and soldiers which are assumed to have been originally inspired by Caravaggio's picture "I Bari" ("The Cardsharpers") from ca. 1594. The genre was popular among Caravaggio's followers in Rome during the period ca. 1610-20. Rombouts was in Rome 1616-25, but none of his known

works are with certainty datable to that period. The present attribution, which is due to Voss, has therefore been a matter of dispute.
*Provenance:* Listed in the inventory of the Royal Danish Kunstkammer of 1690.
*Literature:* Voss 1924, 474 f, repr. p. 138; Hertz 1924, 363, repr. p. 364; von Schneider 1933; Swane 1934, 87 f; Isarlo 1941, 212; Longhi 1943, 46 note 38; Bodart 1970, I, 63 f, II, fig. 16; Volpe 1972, 71, pl. 21; Nicolson 1979, 84.

## Johann Rottenhammer

Munich 1564 – Augsburg 1625

1080
*The Marriage at Cana*
Oil on copper. 37×56 cm. Signed and dated (undistinctly): "16...6 H(?) (or R) ...F (1606)"
Barockgalerie Augsburg/Schaezler-Palais, inv. L758
The subject is taken from John 1, 1 ff. Probably identical with a picture recorded in the Signori Muselli Collection in Verona 1648, and thus probably painted in Venice just before Rottenhammer moved to Augsburg after his long stay in Italy. In Nürnberg in 1615, Nicolaus Schwabe, the mintmaster to Christian IV, bought a painting by Rottenhammer which has, somewhat questionably, been identified with the large canvas of "The Brazen Serpent" in the church at Frederiksborg Castle.
*Provenance:* See above. Acquired for the Düsseldorfer Galerie by the Elector Palatine Johann Wilhelm (1658-1716) for 3000 guilders. Mannheimer Galerie, 1730.
*Literature:* Cat. Augsburg 2. ed. 1984, 204 f, fig. 4 (with bibliography).

## Peter Paul Rubens

Siegen 1577 – Antwerp 1640

1081
*The Judgement of Solomon*
Oil on canvas. 234×303 cm. Colour-plate XXVI
Statens Museum for Kunst, inv. Sp. 185
The subject is from 1. Kings 3, 16-28. According to the inscription around the coat of arms of the Rantzau family in the bottom right-hand corner, the painting was a gift to the Danish king, (Christian IV?), from Josias Rantzau: "Mons: Josias Comte de Ransav. Mar.al. De France me la donné". A painting of the Judgement of Solomon was an apt gift with which to honour the justice and good judgement of one's king. Josias Rantzau (1609-50) had some connection with Christian IV's army during the Thirty Years War in Germany. From 1635 till his death he served with the French. He was appointed a Marshal of France in 1645 and became Governor of Dunkirk till 1649. Since the inscription titulates Rantzau as Marshal of France, the gift was in all likelihood presented after 1645. How the picture came into the possession of Rantzau is not known, but it may well have decorated a courtroom in some town hall. Its date of arrival in Denmark is also somewhat uncertain. A "Judgement of Solomon" in the Queen Mother's bedchamber, mentioned in the Frederiksborg inventory 1650, may refer not to Rantzau's gift but to a painting of the same *motif* by Cornelis van der Voort, bought in 1608. On the basis of other works by Rubens and his workshop, including the related "The Continence of Scipio" (ca. 1618-20), which is known only from an oil sketch since the painting itself – which belonged to Queen Christina – was burnt in 1836, the present picture can be dated about 1620.
*Provenance:* Listed in the inventory of the Royal Danish Kunstkammer, 1690.
*Literature:* Rooses I 1886, 150 ff.; Madsen 1896, 482 ff.; Rooses 1903, 276, 278f; Beckett 1914, 259; Wanscher 1915, 152 ff; Cat. 1951 no. 609 (repr.); Held 1980 I, 385 f., II pl. 278.

## Pieter Jansz. Saenredam

Assendelft 1597 – Haarlem 1665

1082
*Christ Driving the Traders from the Temple*
Oil on panel. 46×32.9 cm. Dated: "1636"
Statens Museum for Kunst, inv. 6665
The *motif* is from John 2, 13-25. The religious struggle between Catholics and Protestants kept the theme alive throughout the 16th and 17th centuries. Here the theme is made more poignant by making use of the congregation's own surroundings. The Haarlem painter changed the temple into the town's most important church, St. Bavo. Brouwer's chapel in the south chancel became the stage where the clear light of day actively contributes to the purification. The symbolism is strengthened by giving the architecture an antique character so that the whole atmosphere is brought closer to the actual event. The Gothic arches in the entrance to the chapel are Romanesquely rounded and the half pillar in the foreground has been changed from a delicate Gothic column on a high pedestal to a heavy pillar with smooth classical lines.
*Provenance:* Bought 1971 with grant from the New Carlsberg Foundation.
*Literature:* Cat. Saenredam, Paris 1970, 26 no. 56, pl. 50; Liedtke 1975/76, 145 note 1; Liedtke 1976, 127 f.

## Roelandt Savery

Courtrai (Kortrijk) 1576 (or 1577/78) – Utrecht 1639

1083
*Mountain Landscape with Woodcutters*
Oil on panel. 26×35 cm. Traces of signature?: "S..(?)"
Statens Museum for Kunst Sp. 183
A closely related landscape, signed and dated 1610, is to be found in the Kunsthistorisches Museum in Vienna. It portrays the same landscape, with slight variations, but the staffage figures have been somewhat changed. The

present picture can be dated to the same time as the Vienna landscape and is thus one of Savery's early landscape paintings from his first years at the Court of Prague.
*Provenance:* Acquired for the Royal Danish Kunstkammer in 1739 or 1747.
*Literature:* Erasmus 1908 72 cat. 32; Cat. 1951 no. 645 (repr.); cat. Musée des Beaux-Arts Ghent 1954 18; Dacosta Kaufmann 1986 270 no. 19-49.

1084
*Still Life. Bouquet of Flowers in a Stone Niche. Vanitas*
Oil on copper, 27.5×16.5 cm. Signed and dated:
"·ROELANDT·SAVERY·FE·1620"
Statens Museum for Kunst, inv. 1520
The approximately twenty-five known flower pieces by Savery represent a limited but important part of his production, inasmuch as they place him among the most significant flower painters of the early 17th century and a pioneer in the genre. There can be no doubt that the present picture, with its symbolic content, was intended to convey a Vanitas theme.
*Provenance:* Transferred to the Museum from Rosenborg, 1896.
*Literature:* Erasmus 1908, 49, 96 cat. 85; Cat. 1951 no. 644 (repr.); Hairs 1955, 96, 231 (catalogue); Bergström 1956/1983, 91 fig. 82; Gammelbo 1960, 30 no. 29, repr. p. 31; Segal 1982, 335 note 14.

## Pieter Schoubroeck

Hessheim ca. 1570 – Frankenthal 1607/08

1085
*Village in the Hills*
Oil on copper. 25×36 cm. Signed and dated:
"P. SCHAVBRVCK 1597" [A and V in ligature]
Statens Museum for Kunst, inv. Sp. 182
An. Zwollo has suggested that the signature on this picture could be apocryphal and that the painting actually should be considered as a work of Pieter Stevens. An examination of the signature, however, has unequivocally confirmed its authenticity. It cannot be denied, however, that the picture has indeed a certain affinity with contemporary works by Pieter Stevens. Apparently it is the earliest known painting by Schoubroeck.
*Provenance:* Collection of J. C. Bodendick, Copenhagen (Weinwich 1825 no. 16). Purchased for the Royal Collection with the Bodendick Collection, 1810.
*Literature:* Plietzsch 1910, 79, 97 cat. 11, 102; Cat. 1951 no. 655; Zwollo 1968, 154 f, fig. 204.

## Frans Snyders

Antwerp 1579 – Antwerp 1657

1086
*Still Life. Kitchen Scene with Scullery Man*
Oil on canvas. 123.2×239.7 cm. Signed: "F.Snijders. fecit". [The canvas has been cut at the top and at the bottom, reducing the original height by some 20 cm]
Statens Museum for Kunst, inv. Sp. 208
This painting represents a type of picture which Snyders first developed in a kitchen scene dated 1613, formerly in Munich, art dealer Julius Böhler (canvas, 125×204.5 cm, signed: "F. Snyders fecit 1613"), and which in its main features is possibly based on Rubens' sketch from 1609-10 of "Filopoemen" in the Louvre, Paris (inv. 2124). The present picture bears some relation to Snyders' signed "Kitchen Scene" in the Alte Pinakothek, Munich (inv. 198), which can be dated ca. 1615-20. The figure was certainly executed by Snyders himself. Among the pictures offered to Christian IV by Frans Bastiaensz. about 1620, there was "en groete doeck van Snijders met 1 swinscop" (listed as no. 211). It was the third most expensive picture on the list.
*Provenance:* Poul Løvenørn (1686-1740), from whose estate it was bought by J. S. Wahl. Acquired for the Royal Danish Kunstkammer from Wahl, 1755 (1762).
*Literature:* Cat. 1951 no. 669 (repr.); Robels 1969, 63; Greindl 1983, 75, 374 cat. 26.

## Bartholomäus Spranger

Antwerp 1546 – Prague 1611

1087
*Jael kills Sisera*
Oil on panel. 70.5×73 cm
Statens Museum for Kunst, inv. 3089
Jael killed the commander of the Canaanite army by driving a tent peg into his temple. (Judges 4, 12-22). The painting is dated by Oberhuber ca. 1610 (according to Dacosta Kaufmann). The panel on which it is painted is unusually thick and appears to have been originally intended for some other use, e.g. a door panel. According to Dacosta Kaufmann the picture should be identical with no. 851 "Ein weib, die einen nagl im kopf schlegt vom Spranger (orig)", listed in the inventory of 1621 of the Prague Kunstkammer, a painting which, he believes, was taken from Prague to Sweden in 1648. However, this is by no means certain, as it cannot be proved that the picture was ever part of Queen Christina's or any other Swedish collection.
*Provenance:* Recorded in the Royal Danish Kunstkammer in 1692.
*Literature:* Oberhuber 1958; Dacosta Kaufmann 1985, 312 no. 20-83, repr. p. 312.

## Pieter Stevens

Mâlines (Mechelen)? ca. 1567 – Prague(?) after 1624

1088
*Rocky Landscape with a Goat Hunt*
Oil on panel. 53×71.5 cm

Statens Museum for Kunst, inv. 4879
Attributed to Pieter Stevens by Jørn Rubow, an attribution subsequently accepted by Frits Lugt and Zwollo. A drawing in the Graphische Sammlung Albertina, Vienna, of the picture's left side with the prominent *arco naturale,* has been published by Zwollo.
*Provenance:* Private Coll., England. Purchased from a dealer in London, 1955. Presented to the museum by Dansk Kunstmuseumsforening.
*Literature:* Grossmann 1954, 51, fig. 22; *idem* 1955, 336; Sterling 1959, 277, note 4; Rubow 1963, 110, 153, repr. p. 112; Zwollo 1968, 155 f, 162, fig. 207; Dacosta Kaufmann 1985, 318, no. $21\text{-}_{25}$, repr.

## Matthias Stom

Amersfoort? ca. 1600 – Sicily(?) after 1649

1089
*An Old Woman and a Youth by Lamplight*
Oil on panel. 115×101 cm
Statens Museum for Kunst, inv. Sp. 152
Attributed to Pietro della Vecchia when purchased in 1763, later to Honthorst and subsequently by J. Sthyr to Stom(er)?, an attribution which was accepted by Pauwels. According to Nicolson, the painting can be dated on stylistic grounds to Stom's late Sicilian period in the 1640s. The same couple, but represented as younger persons, are found in a similar painting by Stom, now in the City Art Museum, Birmingham, and can be dated, according to Nicolson, to Stom's Neapolitan period in the 1630s.
*Provenance:* Acquired for the Royal Danish Kunstkammer in 1763.
*Literature:* Cat. 1951 no. 684 (repr.); Pauwels 1953, 174, 187 fig. 68; Olsen 1961, 90, pl. Lb; Nicolson 1977, 245, cat. 136; Nicolson 1979, 96.

## Maerten Stoop

Rotterdam? 1618 – Utrecht 1647

1090
*Plundering of a Manor House*
Oil on panel. 48×60 cm. Signed: "M. Stoop"
Statens Museum for Kunst, inv. Sp. 627
Both in its diagonal composition, its figure types and its treatment of light, this painting is clearly influenced by Nicolaus Knüpfer (se cat. 1052) who worked in Utrecht at the same time as Stoop. Since Stoop died before he was 30, his oeuvre is rather limited. The present painting is one of about a dozen known to be signed by him.
*Provenance:* The Collection of the Dukes of Gottorp (the back of the panel bears the seal of Gottorp). Entered the Royal Collection in the mid-18th century.
*Literature:* Swillens 1934, 175, 176 fig. 11.

## Johannes van Swinderen (attributed to)

1594-1636. Active in Zutphen

1091
*Card Players*
Oil on canvas. 163×229 cm
Statens Museum for Kunst, inv. Sp. 694
The former attribution of the painting to Valentin de Boulogne (1591-1632), an attribution dating back to the first half of the 18th century, was upheld right up to the 1950s. Subsequently it was ascribed to the Dutch painter Gysbert van der Kuyl. The attribution to van Swinderen, who worked in the little Dutch town of Zutphen, is due to Leonard J. Slatkes. The subject of the painting and its characteristic Caravaggesque features would seem to indicate that van Swinderen had some connection with contemporary painting in Utrecht and possibly knew about French or French-Flemish *Caravaggisti.* Slatkes dates the painting to the early 1630s.
*Provenance:* Joshua van Belle sale, Rotterdam, 6. Sept. 1730, no. 19. Sale 11. July 1763, The Hague, no. 9. Acquired for the Royal Danish Kunstkammer in 1763.
*Literature:* Cat. 1951 no. 729; Longhi 1958, 62; Waddingham 1960, 48 f, fig. 28; Brejon de Lavergnée & Cuzin in exhib.cat. Grand Palais, Paris 1974, 102; Sluijter 1977, 191 cat. C 2; Slatkes 1983, 248, fig. 4.

## Jan Tengnagel

Amsterdam 1584/85 – Amsterdam 1635

1092
*The Raising of Lazarus*
Oil on panel. 90×139 cm. Signed and dated:
"JTengnagel: fecit: A°. 1615:". [J and T in ligature]
Statens Museum for Kunst, inv. 4461
The subject is from John II, 1-44. Tengnagel came at an early stage under the influence of Pieter Lastman (ca. 1583-1633) and, like him, belongs to the group of the so-called pre-Rembrandtists. However, he differs somewhat from the others in the group by the strongly emotional gestures often seen in his figures. The massive, firmly-modelled figures in the present work fill the picture surface from bottom to top, and are typical of Tengnagel's paintings from that time.
*Provenance:* Presented to the museum by Foreign Minister Gustav Rasmussen, 1946.
*Literature:* Swane 1950, 130; Cat. 1951 no. 694 a (repr.); A. Tümpel 1974, 64, fig. 91; A. Tümpel, Sacramento 1974, 22; A. Tümpel in Washington/Detroit/Amsterdam 1980-81, 125, fig. 4.

## Moyeses van Uyttenbroeck

The Hague ca. 1600 – The Hague ca. 1647

1094
*Moonlight Landscape with a Mythological(?) Subject*
Oil on panel. 41.3×66.2 cm. Signed and dated:

"M.van Wtenbro.c 1625" (?) [the last two digits of the date are unclear]
Statens Museum for Kunst, inv. Sp. 373
This nocturne, an early work by the artist, was undoubtedly inspired by Adam Elsheimer's (1578-1610) nocturnal landscape with "The Flight into Egypt", dated 1609, now in the Alte Pinakothek, Munich. Like Elsheimer's picture, Uyttenbroeck's work explores the light effects from bonfires and torches under the moonlit sky. The subject is most likely mythological (Ovid?).
*Provenance:* Transferred from Rosenborg to the Royal Kunstkammer, 1793.
*Literature:* Cat. 1951 no. 722 (repr.); Weisner 1964, 222 cat. 30.

## Werner van den Valckert

The Hague? ca. 1580 – Amsterdam ca. 1627

1095
*Family group as Caritas, with self-portrait, and John the Baptist preaching*
Oil on panel. 162×125.5 cm. Signed and dated on the sheet of paper, top left: "Ick [Werner van den Valckert] heb dit [vooltooid] uit Iaer ons heeren 1623 [the 10th] September Amstelredam". [I, W.v.d.V., completed this work in the year of our Lord 1623 on September the 10th in Amsterdam]. Cut down along the right edge by about 49 cm
Rijksdienst Beeldende Kunst, The Hague, inv. NK 1785. On permanent loan to the Rijksmuseum Het Catharijneconvent, Utrecht
The painting, described by Houbraken as far back as 1719, is a so-called *portrait historié,* i.e. a portrait in which the sitters are shown as figures from the Bible or from classical mythology, or as allegorical figures. The woman in the centre, surrounded by her five children, is represented as Caritas, the symbol of Christian love (Charity). As such she personifies the particular part of John the Baptist's sermon containing the admonition to love one's neighbour (Luke 3, 11). This is why John the Baptist is seen preaching in the background right. According to Paul the Apostle (1 Corinthians 13, 13), Charity is the foremost of the three Christian virtues (Faith, Hope and Charity) and it is thus probable that the man standing just behind the mother represents Paul pointing to the famous passage in the Bible. Obviously the figure is a portrait, but his relationship with the family is unknown to us. The man to the left of Paul, however, is undoubtedly the woman's husband. His right hand rests familiarly on her shoulder as he points with the left towards Paul as though to show that the true source of love is God's word, the Bible. The family portrait can, in this way, be seen as an allegory on the ideal Christian marriage. At the top, left van den Valckert portrays himself as the Evangelist St. Luke.
*Provenance:* J.v.d.Veen sale, Amsterdam, 14.4.1851, no. 157; Sale, Amsterdam 7.9.1853, no. 86; Art Trade, Brussels 1939; Collections of W. Peech, Amsterdam, and Dr. Keulens, Anderlecht.
*Literature:* Houbraken 1719, 170; van Thiel 1983, 163 ff, 182 f, fig. 41; Koers 1986, 5 ff, repr. p. 6.
*Exhibitions:* The Dutch World of Painting, Vancouver 1986 no. 27.

## Esaias van de Velde

Amsterdam 1587 – The Hague 1630

1096
*Village looted at night*
Oil on panel. 35×39,5 cm. Signed and dated:
"E.V. VEL/DE Y 3./1620"
Statens Museum for Kunst, inv. 3923
During the 1620s van de Velde painted a number of pictures of cavalry and infantry skirmishes, ambushes, carriage hold-ups, maraudings, plunderings etc., an important part of his oeuvre but relatively little known. The Eighty Years War between Spain and Holland (the Twelve Years Truce ended in 1621) must have provided plenty of raw material for this world of *motifs,* which just at that very time developed in a new separate genre, in which the works of van de Velde were to break new ground in the Northern Netherlands.
*Provenance:* Collection of Count Moltke, Copenhagen, 1756; Count Moltke sale, Copenhagen, 1-2. June 1931, no. 135. Bought by the New Carlsberg Foundation. Presented to the museum by the New Carlsberg Foundation, 1932.
*Literature:* Morell 1756, cat. 130; Cat. 1951 no. 735 (repr.); Bengtsson 1952, 68, repr.; Stechow 1966, 175, fig. 347; Keyes 1984, 38, 110, 131 cat. 46, pl. 300, col. pl. XI.

1097
*Landscape with a ruin*
Oil on panel. 10.5×18 cm. Signed and dated:
"E.V. VELDE·/1627"
Statens Museum for Kunst, inv. 1970
The years in Haarlem, 1610-1618, were the start of van de Velde's career as a landscape painter. With his light poetic touch he was able to grasp the moods and atmosphere of nature and bring about a radical change in landscape painting. Pendant to cat. 1098.
*Provenance:* Purchased for the Royal Danish Kunstkammer at the Jacob Snel sale in The Hague, 1763.
*Literature:* Hoet/Terwesten 1770, 340; Sthyr 1934, 187; Cat. 1951 no. 736; Bengtsson 1952, 73; Keyes 1984, 150 cat. 113.

1098
*Hilly Landscape*
Oil on panel. 10.5.×18 cm. Signed and dated:
"E.V. VELDE·1627"
Statens Museum for Kunst, inv. 1971
While living in Haarlem, van de Velde specialized in

*motifs* of local Dutch scenes. After his move to the Hague, these *motifs* underwent a subtle change. Landscapes painted with the same inspired naturalism as before now also contained elements of pure wonder, as in this peaceful, arcadian landscape with the shepherd tending his flock at the foot of an overgrown ancient ruin, and its pendant (cat. 1097) whose hilly landscape is topped by a medieval building of gigantic dimensions.
*Provenance:* Purchased for the Royal Danish Kunstkammer at the Jacob Snel sale in The Hague, 1763.
*Literature:* Hoet/Terwesten 1770, 340; Sthyr 1934, 187; Cat. 1951 no. 737; Keyes 1984, 60, 163, cat. 166.

1099
*Castle on the Rock*
Oil on panel. 15×22 cm. Signed and dated:
"E·V: VELDE/1630"
Statens Museum for Kunst, inv. 3135
Imaginary landscapes became very fashionable in the 1620s and were painted by van de Velde until his death. The present picture was painted during his last year and reflects a development towards a wildness in nature that is a forerunner of Everdingen's nordic landscapes (cf. cat. 1025).
*Provenance:* Purchased by the museum at the Dr. and Mrs. C. L. Lund sale, 1911.
*Literature:* Cat. 1951 no. 738; Keyes 1984, 66, 163 cat. 167.

## Adriaen Pietersz. van de Venne

Delft 1589 – The Hague 1662

1100
*Hoe dienen wij bij een (An Owl Couple on Skates)*
Oil on panel. 26.5×18 cm
Statens Museum for Kunst, inv. 1897
A banderole across the top of the picture is inscribed: *Hoe dienen wij bij een* (How well we go together). Originally the painting formed part of a set comprising four similar pictures depicting animal couples dressed in human clothes. All of them were recorded at Gottorp Castle in 1710. Apparently the present picture is the only one surviving. Of the four others, three are known through engravings by Christian Rothgiesser. It may well be that the present picture was intended as a political satire. The owl in woman's clothing, left, is wearing round her neck "The Golden Fleece" – in shape of a mouse! (Isabella Clara Eugenia?).
*Provenance:* At Gottorp 1710 and probably earlier. Entered the Royal Collection presumably 1759. Transferred from Fredensborg to the museum in 1905.
*Literature:* Cat. 1951 no. 743 (repr.); Schlee in exhib.cat. Kiel 1965 148, no. 374, 270 f, repr. p. 269.

1101
*Arme Weelde (Poor Luxury)*
Oil on panel. 33×60 cm. Signed and dated:
"Ad V. Venne". Inscribed on a banderole bottom right:
"Arme Weelde"
Museum Boymans-van Beuningen, Rotterdam, inv. 1896
When he had moved from Middelbourg to The Hague in 1625, Adriaen van de Venne – who in 1643 executed the painting of Christian IV as mediator in the Thirty Years War (cat. 199) – produced to an increasing extent paintings depicting low-life scenes. As a rule these had a satirical-moralizing intent and carried a painted banderole inscribed with a word, a phrase or a pun that served both as the title of the picture and as an underlining of its literary or emblematic character. The painting is in monochrome, as are all de Venne's other pictures in this genre. No other painter of his time kept so strictly to the monochrome picture.
*Provenance:* Presented to the museum by August Coster, Brussels, 1886.
*Literature:* Bol 1968, 131 no. 10, 135 fig. 18, 142; von Bogendorf-Rupprath and Robinson in Philadelphia/London/Berlin 1984, 332 ff, cat. 114, pl. 26 (with bibliography).

1102
*Street Singers*
Oil on panel. 41.5×55 cm. Remains of signature:
"Ap(?) ..."
Statens Museum for Kunst, inv. 1418
The picture, a *brunaille,* is one of van de Venne's few genre scenes that does not convey an obvious satirical message but merely depicts what appears to be a realistic street scene.
*Provenance:* According to Cat. 1922 (no. 207) this was one of the paintings seized from lord lieutenant Kaj Lykke (ca. 1625-1699) after his escape to Sweden in 1661. On the back is a seal with the initials "CL", for Caj Lykke (?).
*Literature:* Cat. 1951 no. 742 (repr.); Bol 1958, 146, note 53 no. 2; Schlee in exhib.cat. Kiel 1965, 148 no. 373.

## David Vinckboons

Mechelen (Mâlines) 1576 – Amsterdam 1632/33

1103
*Banquet in a Park (The Prodigal Son among the Harlots?)*
Oil on panel. 51×81.5 cm
Statens Museum for Kunst, inv. Sp. 175
This picture, in the opinion of Goossens, is "a faithful copy" after Vinckboons. In all probability, however, it is an autograph replica from about 1619 (cf. the signed and dated "Merry Company", in 1966 in the art trade, Cologne, see Goossens 1966, 87 ff, fig. 9) of a composition from before 1614. (The composition is reflected in Esaias van de Velde's signed "Party in a Garden", dated 1614, in the Mauritshuis, The Hague). As a type of pic-

*1106*

ture, the present painting comes within the category of genre painting described at that time as *Buitenpartij* (outdoor scene), *Geselschapje* (party) and *Banketje* (banquet). Its theme, too, is based on 16th century representations of "The Prodigal Son among the Harlots", amorous couples in love gardens, "The Five Senses" and the popular "Feasts of the Gods" (cf. cat. 1000). Although its moralizing aspect is not particularly obvious, the picture may well represent "The Prodigal Son". In the inventory of 1650 (1636) of Frederiksborg Castle is listed "j. Støcke met Affmerche Nogle Caualere med Fruentimmer Bancheterer Och Musicerer wdi En Haffve", furthermore "J. Støcke met bemerchelse, huorledis den forloren søn Bancheter" and "j. Støcke met Affmerche om It giestebud I een Lyst Haffve". The present picture may be identical with one of these three pictures, most likely with the first.
*Provenance:* First recorded in the Royal Collection in 1799 (but see above).
*Literature:* Coninckx 1908, 33; Cat. 1951 no. 776 (repr.); Goossens 1954, 95 f, 100, 146, fig. 51.

1104
*Distributing Bread to the Poor*
Oil on panel. 27/27.5×40 cm
Statens Museum for Kunst, inv. 1880
The present picture is probably a satirical-moralizing illustration of one of the Six Works of Mercy which Jesus speaks of in his Sermon on the Last Day (Matthew 25, 31-46), viz. that of giving food to the hungry. The sculpture group above the gateway on the right, of St. Martin of Tours giving half of his cloak to the naked beggar, likewise illustrates one of the Works of Mercy. Vinckboons' composition exists in several autograph versions, one of which is in the Nationalmuseum, Stockholm (no. 679).
*Provenance:* In the Royal Collection before 1799.
*Literature:* Coninckx 1908, 33 f; Cat. 1951 no. 777 (repr.); Goossens 1954, 102, 141 (catalogue), fig. 54; Legrand 1963, 123.

## Hendrick van Vliet

Delft 1611/12 – Delft 1675

1105
*Nieuwe Kerk in Delft with the Tomb of William the Silent*
Oil on canvas. 105×87 cm Signed and dated:
"H van Vliet 1659"
Davids Samling, Copenhagen, inv. B 446
The tomb of William the Silent of Orange, Liberator of the Netherlands, was begun in 1614 by Hendrick de Keyser and completed by his son Peter in 1623. The monument was looked upon as a national shrine and soon became a popular *motif* in architectural painting which notably flourished in Delft in the 1650s.
*Provenance:* The Duke of Leuchtenberg's collection 1845; Nordiska Kompagniet, Stockholm 1917; C. L. David 1936.
*Literature:* Zahle 1948, 214, repr. p. 215; Jantzen 1979, 105, 237 no. 53; Liedtke 1982, 109 no. 105.

## Adrian de Vries

The Hague ca. 1545 – Prague 1626

1106
*Sitting Youth with Shell. Figure for a Fountain*
Bronze. Height: 60 cm
Städtische Kunstsammlungen Augsburg (Maximilianmuseum), inv. 1162
The figure was originally set in the middle of a water basin at the water tower at the Roter Tor in Augsburg. It served as a fountain figure and water poured into the basin from the shell the youth holds in his arms. The sculpture is probably identical with the "Figura della tura" included in a final bill, dated 18th April 1602, which de Vries sent to the municipal authorities in Augsburg and for which he charged 250 florins. It is closely related to the so-called "Triton" busts on his large Hercules Fountain in Augsburg (1597-1602).
*Provenance:* Until 1894 at the water tower of the Roter Tor in Augsburg.
*Literature:* Buchwald 1899, 31 f; von Strohmer 1950, 105 no. 5; Weihrauch 1967, 356; Larsson 1967, 29, 118 no. 4, fig. 58; exhib. Augsburg 1980, cat. 578, repr. p. 203; Müller 1982, 49 no. 13, repr. p. 18.

1107
*Bacchus and Ariadne*
Relief in bronze. 52.5×42 cm
Rijksmuseum Amsterdam, inv. R.B.K. 14692
The story of Ariadne is related in Ovid's *Metamorphoses,* VIII, 166 ff, but the very subject of the sleeping Ariadne found by Bacchus is described in Philostratos the Elder's *Eikones (Imagines),* I, 15. The present relief was done while de Vries was Court Sculptor in Prague. Stylistically, it is related to the large relief in Windsor Castle, dated 1609, (cat. 1108) and according to Larsson can thus be dated ca. 1610. The composition is reminiscent of Egidius Sadler's engraving of "Amor and Psyche" after a composition by Bartholomäus Spranger.
*Provenance:* Presented to the Rijksmuseum in 1935.
*Literature:* Neurdenburg 1948, 70 fig. 48; Strohmer 1950, 119 no. 58, repr. p. 129; Larsson 1967, 51, 118 no. 1, repr. fig. 97; Leuwenberg/Halsema-Kubes 1973, 171, cat. 205, repr. p. 170.
*Exhibitions:* Rijksmuseum, Amsterdam 1955, no. 382.

1108
*Emperor Rudolf II introduces the Visual and Liberal Arts into Bohemia. An Allegory*
Relief in bronze. 59.5×84 cm. Signed and dated: "ADRIANVS FRIES HAGIENSIS FE 1609"
H. M. Queen Elizabeth II, Windsor Castle

This relief is described in the inventory of 1607-11 of Rudolf II's Kunstkammer in Prague as "der röm. kayser RVD:II[c] zu pferd und folgen ihme die siben freyen künst nach, die presentiert er un das[d] laster ligt ihm under den füssen zu boden" and in the inventory of 1621 it is added that the Emperor is represented "wie er die sieben freie künst in Böhemb führt". In the centre of the composition Rudolf II is portrayed on horseback dressed as a Roman Emperor. He is turning towards three naked women who, in the shape of the three Graces, personify the Visual Arts, Painting, Architecture and Sculpture. They are followed by three robed women, personifications of three of the seven "liberal arts", i.e. Poetry, Music and Astronomy. Philosophy, which contrary to traditional iconography is here personified by a man, brings the total number of persons up to the magical figure of seven. The relief is meant to be a glorification of the Emperor as protector and patron of the arts and sciences, but apparently with the particular aspect that the visual arts here are on a par with the "liberal arts". They are even elevated to the front row where it is in fact Pictura (personifying the art of painting) who receives a favour from the hand of the Emperor. Since the Renaissance there had been a strong feeling, particularly among the artists themselves, that the visual arts should disassociate themselves from their traditional connection with artisan's work and be raised

*1103*

*1108* Copyright Reserved to Her Majesty Queen Elizabeth II. Photo Courtauld Institute of Art.

to the status of the liberal arts. This new appreciation of the role of the artist, which orginated in Italy, had its breakthrough north of the Alps in the 1590s, particulary in Rudolf II's Prague. Here the Emperor issued his famous Imperial Decree of the 17th April 1595, in which he declared that from that day on the art of painting should no longer be called or considered a trade, but should be counted among the liberal arts. On the basis of this, the relief can be regarded as an art-philosophical manifesto and as the spiritual testament of the Emperor.

*Provenance:* Listed in the inventory of Rudolf II's Kunstkammer in Prague, 1607-11, fol. 323, no. 1983. Subsequent inventories, 1619, fol. 7v, 1612 no. 689. Königsmarck-inventory 1648 B no. 32 (Granberg 1896, Appendix I). Kristina-inventory 1652, no. 6 (Granberg 1896, Appendix II). Nic. Tessin the Younger? Gustavus Brander, London.

*Literature:* Buchwald 1899, 48 ff, 100 no. 9, pl. III; Strohmer 1950, 106, no. 19; Larsson 1967, 49 f, 100, 102, fig. 94.

*Exhibitions:* Nationalmuseum, Stockholm 1966, cat. 1330.

## The Neptune Fountain for Frederiksborg Castle

In May 1615, Christian IV sent his mintmaster Nicolaus Schwabe to Prague where on 14th June he made an arrangement with Adrian de Vries whereby the sculptor agreed to model and cast a number of bronze sculptures for a fountain and to supply a complete design for the fountain, including the measurements for the basin and the centre pillar, both of which were to be carved from black marble in the Frisian town of Emden. An iconographic programme for the fountain was presumably submitted to de Vries by Schwabe at that time. By the time Schwabe returned to Prague, in October 1616, (the final contract was not signed by de Vries until October 26th 1616), four large figures had been cast and three other figures were nearing completion, although it is not known which. All 16 sculptures were probably completed by the end of 1618 and the fountain itself was installed in the outer court of Frederiksborg Castle in 1622. However, during the Danish-Swedish war 1658-60 the castle was looted by Swedish troops and the sculptures were carried off to Stockholm as booty. Around 1690 they were installed in the park of Drottningholm together with a number of other de Vries sculptures which the Swedes had similarly removed from Prague in 1648 during the Thirty Years' War. The remains of the fountain were pulled down in 1685 and disappeared without trace except for a fragment of the basin which was found in 1860. The foundations of the fountain were similarly found during excavations on the site. In 1884, fifteen of the Frederiksborg sculptures, i.e. all but one that must be assumed lost, were identified by John Böttiger at Drottningholm. With copies cast from these figures a reconstruction of the fountain was put up at Frederiksborg in 1888 on the very spot where the original fountain stood. It differs considerably from the original, however.

The main source for a reconstruction of the fountain in its original form is the description of the castle, *Kurze und eigentliche Beschreibung Des fürtreffliche und weit berühmten Königlichen Hauses Friederichsburg,* by the then Palace Steward Johann Adam Berg, published in 1646. The basin itself was hexagonal, a good 10 m. in diameter and about 104 cm. in height. It was made of polished black Theux-marble. On every other corner sat the Triton figures described beautifully by Berg as "drey grosse Bilder, derer Adern und Sehnen nicht allein können gesehen, sondern auch begriffen und getastet werden", and on the remaining three corners there were groups that each had a lion and an accompanying figure, (Mercury, Fama and Victoria/Pax). In the centre of the basin stood an almost 4 m. tall triangular pillar on the pedestal cornice of which were female figures at each corner riding dolphins and bearing fertility symbols, and on each side, on the approximate level of the female figures, three *putti* with animals. Higher up the pillar there were three river gods with water jugs, and the top cornice was decorated with ornaments of fruit. On the top of the pillar stood Neptune, representing Christian IV as Ruler of the Seas. The fountain is a Victory Monument (following the termination of the Kalmar War in 1613) as well as a glorification of Christian IV as the Good Ruler. Under his courageous and vigilant protection, wealth and happiness thrive throughout his country. The design of the fountain is indebted to Hubert Gerhard's Augustus Fountain in Augsburg (1587-94) though it is primarily based on de Vries' own good ten years older Hercules Fountain in the same town. Both of these magnificent fountains had, of course, been seen by Nicolaus Schwabe in Augsburg during his travels to south Germany 1614 and 1615. Stylistically, the de Vries bronze figures for the Frederiksborg fountain are excellent examples of the late pictorial figure-style developed by him from about 1610 and which seems to perpetuate in bronze the softness and sketchiness of the original modelling.

*Provenance:* Swedish booty 1658-60. At Drottningholm from ca. 1690. Drottningholm inventories 1726, 1744, 1777 and 1867.

*Literature:* Böttiger 1884; Buchwald 1899; Strohmer 1950; Larsson 1967, 67 ff, 119 f no. 14 a-q; Eller 1973, 121 ff; Lichtenberg 1975, 15 ff; Larsson 1984, 69 ff.

*1110*

1110
*Neptune*
Statue in bronze. Height: 206 cm. Signed and dated: "ADRIANVS FRIES HAGIENSIS BATAVVS FE 1617".
Statens konstmuseer, Stockholm inv. Drh Sk 49
The figure of Neptune is clearly inspired by Giambologna's Neptune Fountain in Bologna (1563-67), but the influence of the model is worked up to a figure which certainly maintains its independence of the prototype. The pedestal, which is triangular with flattened corners, is decorated with three lions' heads in high relief, and in bas-relief, three emblematic animal figures: a griffin, a lion and a crane; the crane has a stone clutched in its raised claw. The three lions' heads functioning as water spouts refer to the Danish coat of arms, whilst the animal figures symbolize, respectively, vigilance and courage, strength and perseverance, and readiness and attention. According to a fable told by Aristoteles *(Historia Animalium* 9:10), if the crane fell asleep it would drop the stone held in its claw and thus awake immediately. It symbolizes, therefore, Vigilantia, a virtue particularly connected with monarchs. Neptune is the only one of the fountain-sculptures which is dated. Larsson 1967 cat. 14 a.

1111
*River God with a Water Jug*
Statuette in bronze. Height: 82 cm
Statens konstmuseer, Stockholm, inv. Drh Sk 142
The two River Gods, (cat. 1111 and 1112) both of whom rest a large water jug against a tree stump in front of them, originally stood, together with a third and similar figure, on consoles, but hardly in niches, some way up the sides of the fountain's centre pillar, from where they poured water into the basin. As they are clearly differentiated as regards age it may be that they represent the Three Ages of Man. Larsson 1967 cat. 14 q.

1112
*River God with an Oar and a Water Jug*
Statuette in bronze. Height: 83 cm
Statens konstmuseer, Stockholm inv. Drh Sk 59.
See cat. 1111. Larsson 1967 cat. 14 o.

1113
*Sitting Putto with a Goose*
Bronze group. Height: 46 cm. Length: 75 cm
Statens konstmuseer, Stockholm, inv. Drh Sk 61
Together with very similar group, a putto probably with a dog, now lost, the two groups, cat. 1113 and cat. 1114, were placed on a cornice on the triangular centre pillar, distributed between the three naiads, sitting at the corners of the pillar. On both figures the plinth is decorated with leaves and flowers in *bas-relief*. Larsson 1967 cat. 14 l.
*Exhibitions:* Triomphe du maniérisme, Amsterdam 1955, no. 389.

*1114*

1114
*Sitting Putto with a Snake*
Bronze group. Height: 48 cm. Length: 79 cm
Statens konstmuseer, Stockholm, inv. Drh Sk 60
See cat. 1113. Larsson 1967 cat. 14 m.
*Exhibitions:* Triomphe du maniérisme, Amsterdam 1955, no. 390.

1115
*Naiad on a Dolphin. "Ceres"*
Bronze group. Height: 142 cm. Remains of signature: "..FE.". Crowned coat of arms with three lions *rampant* (the Danish coat of arms) incised on one of the fins of the dolphin
Statens konstmuseer, Stockholm, inv. Drh Sk 50
The Naiad is here represented as a personification of the Fertility of the Earth: the figure of a naked woman, sitting on the upturned tail of the dolphin with a sheaf in one hand and a sickle in the other and wearing a wreath made of ears of corn on her head. The Naiad was placed low down on a corner of the fountain's centre pillar, on a cornice close to the water basin. On the other corners there were two similar naiads on dolphins positioned in the same way – one with a conch in her hand and a diadem of birds' wings in her hair: "Venus", the other with a bunch af grapes in her hand and vine leaves in her hair. (The water spouted from the nostrils and mouth of the dolphin). The naiads are closely related to the naiads on de Vries' own Hercules Fountain in Augsburg (completed 1602). Larsson 1967 cat. 14 c.

1116
*Victoria ("Pax") with a Lion*
Bronze group. Height: 100 cm
Statens konstmuseer, Stockholm, inv. Drh Sk 58
The present figure was formerly considered to repre-

sent Pax (Peace) but Larsson has very convincingly pointed out that it is more likely to be Victoria, a representation of Victory, even though it is a deviation from the conventional iconography, according to which Victoria is a woman. Here the figure of Victory is represented as a young naked youth holding in his outstreched right hand a laurel wreath over the lion's head, and in his left hand a palm branch. Larsson has shown that the composition is based on an antique marble sculpture of Victoria now in the Uffizi, Florence. The narrow plinth under each one of the three groups (cat. 1116-1118) forms an obtuse angle which fits the cranked corners of the basin where they were placed. The lions had their heads turned in towards the basin of the fountain and the water was spouted through a pipe in their mouths. These three crowned lions are, of course, the lions of the Danish coat of arms. Traces of broken-off parts on their heads seem to indicate that originally they all also had a Christian IV monogram, C4, attached between the crowns (or the laurel wreath) and their head, just as described by Berg in the case of Mercury. The message conveyed by the three allegories may thus be interpreted as Mercury bringing news of the Danish King Christian IV's victory and fame. Larsson 1967 cat. 14 i.

*1117*

*1115*

1117
*Mercury with a Lion*
Bronze group. Height: 105 cm
Statens konstmuseer, Stockholm inv. Drh Sk 57
Mercury, the Messenger of the Gods, is depicted as a running figure with winged helmet *(petasos)* and winged heels. With his outstretched right hand he holds a crown over the lion's head, and with his left hand his staff *(caduceus)* over its back. The immediate source of the composition is Giovanni Bologna's famous "Flying Mercury" from the 1560s. See also cat. 1116. Larsson 1967 cat. 14 k.

1118
*Fama with a Lion*
Bronze group. Height: 119 cm
Statens konstmuseer, Stockholm, inv. Drh Sk 56
Fama, the Goddess of Reputation is depicted as a naked gracile winged woman. She is blowing a long trumpet, and in her outstreched left hand she holds a crown and a short trumpet over the head of the lion. In bas-relief on the plinth there is a crane with a stone in its uplifted claw, an emblematic symbol of vigilance, *Vigilantia* (cf. cat. 1110). See also cat. 1116. Larsson 1967 cat. 14 h.

*1118*

1119
*Triton*
Statue in bronze. Height: 165 cm
Statens konstmuseer, Stockholm, inv. Drh Sk 55
Together with a third Triton (inv. Drh Sk 161, since 1977 on permanent loan to the Rijksmuseum, Amsterdam, not exhibited at the present exhibition, but the best preserved), the two Tritons, cat. 1119 and 1120, were positioned sitting with their legs over the edge of the fountain basin on three of its corners, either on the coping of the basin itself – as proposed by de Lichtenberg in her plausible reconstruction – or on heightened corners corresponding to Berg's description, which says that they were placed on "Marmorn Postamenten". According to Larsson, the placing of the figures was inspired by Bartholomeo Ammanati's Neptune Fountain on the Piazza della Signoria in Florence (1553-65). However, Hubert Gerhard's Augustus Fountain in Augsburg (1587-1594) also has figures similarly placed. The Tritons stretch upwards in an energetic, spiral movement, and blow into a large conch-shell from which a high jet of water is ejected. One leg is pulled up and the other hangs down, a pose often used and varied by de Vries in his sculptures, cf. for instance cat. 1121. Two of the Tritons hold the shell in the upraised right hand, the third holds it in both hands. They are without doubt derived from the Triton composition of Giambologna from the 1560s which has been transmitted in a bronze statuette in the Metropolitan Museum of Art, New York (cfr. Leithe-Jasper 1986, 222). Larsson 1967 cat. 14 f.

1120
*Triton*
Statue in bronze. Height: 157 cm.
Statens konstmuseer, Stockholm, inv. Drh Sk 54.
Larsson 1967 cat. 14 e.

1121
*Lazarus*
Statuette in bronze. Gilt. Height: 65 cm. Signed and dated:
"ADRIANVS FRIES HAGIENSIS BATAVVS FECIT·1615". Frontispiece p. 300
Statens Museum for Kunst, inv. 5493
The subject is taken from the Parable of Dives and Lazarus, Luke 16, 19 ff. Lazarus, a poor man whose body is covered with sores, is seated outside the rich man's gate where dogs come to him and lick his ulcers. The soft, sketchy treatment of the form and surface makes it a characteristic example of de Vries' late "impressionist" style, cf. e.g. the large bronze sculpture of St. Sebastian in the Fürstliche Sammlung Liechtenstein, Vaduz. The statuette may have been presented to Christian IV by the artist when the King commissioned the fountain sculptures for Frederiksborg Castle, but it is also possible that Nicolaus Schwabe bought it in Prague in 1615 (cf. introduction).
*Provenance:* See above. First listed in the Royal Danish Kunstkammer, 1749.
*Literature:* Strohmer 1950, 109 no. 26; Weihrauch 1967, 358; Larsson 1967, 73, 121 no. 26, fig. 149; Olsen 1980, I, 141 f, II fig. 147.

1122
*Cain killing Abel*
Bronze group. Gilt. Height: 70 cm. Signed and dated:
"ADRIANVS·FRIES HAGIENSIS BATAVS FECIT · 1622"
Statens Museum for Kunst, inv. 5492
The subject has also been described as Samson slaying a Philistine but is undoubtedly Cain and Abel (Genesis 4, 8). The group is a slightly varied replica of a signed version, dated 1612, in the National Gallery of Scotland, Edinburgh, which possibly comes from the Kunstkammer in Prague. The composition derives from Giovanni Bologna's (1529-1608) large marble group of Samson slaying a Philistine (ca. 1568) from Francesco de Medici's casino, now in the Victoria & Albert Museum, London. Possibly the statuette was originally intended for Count Ernst of Schaumburg-Lippe (1569-1622) in Bückeburg, but was still unfinished at the time of his death, cf. "Un gruppo di Cain et Abel di 2 piedi di bronzo", listed among other unfinished sculptures in a letter dated 11th March 1621 written by de Vries to the Count. Probably presented to Christian IV by the artist in connection with

the last payment for the Frederiksborg sculptures.
*Provenance:* The same as for cat. 1121.
*Literature:* Strohmer 1950, 112, no. 32, repr. p. 111; Weihrauch 1967, 358; Larsson 1967, 57, 74, 87, 121 no. 27, fig. 147; Olsen 1980, I, 140 f, II, fig. 145.

1123
*Laocoön*
Statuette in bronze. Gilt. Height: 63 cm. (Mounted on a partially gilt, wooden pedestal in the form of a rock).
Statens Museum for Kunst, inv. 5494
This statuette is a slightly altered, reduced copy of the figure of Laocoön in the famous late-Hellenistic group in Museo del Vaticano, Rome, depicting Laocoön and his sons being killed by two snakes (Virgil, *Aeneid,* 2. book). Unlike the two other de Vries statuettes (cat. 1121 and 1122) this one is not signed and it is doubtful whether it belongs together with them. Its attribution to de Vries dates back to Lange (1896) and has been accepted by Buchwald, Brinckmann, von Strohmer and Weihrauch, but not by Larsson. In the handling of the form it is closer to the Cain and Abel statuette than to the Lazarus.
*Provenance:* First recorded in the Royal Danish Kunstkammer in 1776.
*Literature:* Lange 1886, no. 311; Brinckmann 1923, 18, 39; von Strohmer 1950, 120 no. 61; Weihrauch 1967, 358; Larsson 1967, 126 no. 20; Olsen 1980, I, 142, II, fig. 147.

1124
*A Rearing Horse*
Statuette in bronze. Height: 95.5 cm. Signed and dated: "ADRIANVS FRIES HAGIENSIS BATAVVS FECIT 1622"
Statens konstmuseer, Stockholm, inv. Drh Sk 62
The rearing horse was in all probability originally made for Count Ernst von Schaumburg-Lippe and is probably identical with the "cavallo che salta", mentioned in a list of unfinished bronzes in a letter dated 11th March 1621 from de Vries to the Count, (cf. cat 1122), but which, after the latter's death, was presented by the artist to Prince Albrecht von Wallenstein in Prague. This assumes that it is the same statuette which de Vries mentions in a letter dated 26th August 1626. It corresponds very closely to de Vries' equestrian statuette of Duke Heinrich Julius von Braunschweig from c. 1607/11 (formerly in the Herzog Anton Ulrich-Museum, Braunschweig, but lost since 1945), and there has consequently been a general acceptance of the date to about the same time, presuming that the year 1622 was a later addition. The earlier dating, however, has been rejected by Larsson. (Yet it is a strange coincidence that precisely the date 1622, found on the Cain and Abel group (cat. 1122) might also from its character, be a later addition).
*Provenance:* Possibly Prince Albrecht von Waldstein, Prague, and later among the sculptures carried off from Prague by the Swedes in 1648. At Drottningholm probably since ca. 1690, Drottningholm-inventories 1726, 1744, 1777, 1867.
*Literature:* Böttiger 1884, 31 f, 53 pl. III A; Buchwald 81 f, 102; Strohmer 1950, 112 no. 35, fig. 49; Larsson 1967, 86, 120 no. 16, fig. 175; Larsson 1984, 30 ff no. 12.
*Exhibitions:* Rijksmuseum, Amsterdam 1955, no. 387; Nationalmuseum, Stockholm 1965, no. 1331; Nationalmuseum, Stockholm 1984-85, no. 47.

*1120*

1122

## Abraham Willaerts

Utrecht c. 1603 – Utrecht 1669

1125
*Coastal Battle between the Spanish and Dutch Fleets*
Oil on canvas. 163.5×243 cm. Signed and dated; "WILLAERTS F./1641"
Statens Museum for Kunst, inv. Sp. 441
This seascape, the Museum's earliest dated marine painting, was originally acquired as a work of Adam Willaerts, but it has since been attributed to his son, Abraham Willaerts (cat. 1951). Its subject is one of the numerous battles between the Spanish and Dutch fleets.
*Provenance:* Acquired for The Royal Danish Kunstkammer 1755.
*Literature:* Spengler 1827 282; Cat. 1951 no. 817 (repr.); Bol 1973 330 note 180 and note 183.

## Joachim Wtewael

Utrecht 1566 – Utrecht 1638

1126
*John the Baptist Preaching in the Forest*
Oil on panel. 86×145 cm. Signed and dated: "Jo wte wael fecit An° 1618"
Statens Museum for Kunst, imv. Sp. 346
The account of John the Baptist's sermon appears in all four gospels in the New Testament (Luke 3. 1-21, for example). It was a favourite subject with Dutch painters around 1600, probably prompted by the many open-air services performed by the Reformed congregations, for whom the sermon was indeed the essence of the service.
*Provenance:* To the Royal Collections 1760.
*Literature:* Lindemann 1929 60 ff. 245 250 cat. XIII pl. X; Cat. 1951 no. 815; Lowenthal 1975 (1982) 84 301 ff. cat. A-59 pl. XXI; Lowenthal 1986 50 144 f. cat. A-79 pl. 110 and col. pl. XXI.

## Peter Wtewael

Utrecht 1596 – Utrecht 1660

1127
*Caritas*
Oil on panel. 83×62 cm. Signed and dated: "P wte wael fecit A° 1628"
Private Collection
The painting is presumably an allegory of pure non-sensual love *(liefde* as opposed to *minne)* personified by the figure of Caritas (Charity). Peter Wtewael painted several different versions of this *motif.*
*Provenance:* Johan Pater and Antoinetta Pater-Wtewael, Utrecht 1655; Johan van Nellesteyn and Hillegonda Pater, Utrecht 1669 (1671?); Auctioned by Winkel and Magnussen 1955; the Art Trade.
*Literature:* Gammelbo 1966 75 f. pl. XXXIV; Lowenthal 1974 458 462, fig. 48 and fig. 54 (signature); Lowenthal 1986 69 note 1 cat. D-21 pl. 183.

## Benedikt Wurzelbauer (attributed to)

Nürnberg 1548 – Nürnberg 1620

1128
*Pero (?)*
Statuette in bronze. Height: 30.5 cm
Herzog Anton Ulrich-Museum, Braunschweig, inv. Bro. 171
The fable of Cimon and Pero dates from Antiquity (Valerius Maximus: *De Factis Dictisque Memorabilibus* V, 4). The ageing Cimon languishing in prison was kept alive by his daughter Pero, who breast-fed him during her visits to the prison cell. The subject is usually called "Caritas Romana". The statuette was presumably conceived as a fountain figure, possibly for a table fountain, with a stream of water coming out of the woman's breast.
*Provenance:* Mentioned for the first time in 1753 in the first inventory of the Ducal Collection in Braunschweig.
*Literature:* Kat. Europäische Kleinplastik, Lübeck 1976 29 no. 38 repr. fig. 15 (with bibliography).
*Exhibitions:* Rijksmuseum Amsterdam 1955, no. 396; Herzog Anton Ulrich-Museum, Braunschweig 1975, no. 147.

*1247*

# Tøjhusmuseet

## *Christian IV: Defender of Crown and Faith*

There is no doubt that Christian IV liked to see himself as a warrior. This was in accordance not only with the ideals of the time, but also with the duties of the monarch as set out in the constitution. War indeed figured largely in his life. Europe was harassed by strife, and he himself was involved in three wars: the Kalmar War, 1611-13, the Emperor's War, 1625-29, and the Torstensson War, 1643-45. He was permanently involved in the aspects of state life related to the armed forces of the country, and his wishes were decisive in the development of these. He was in the true sense of the term the warlord of his country.

*

By the time of his coronation, with full festivities, on 29th August 1596, Christian IV was well prepared for his responsibilities as king. He had been carefully educated. As tutor in general subjects he had had the very capable Hans Mikkelsen, who gave the Prince a solid background in languages, mathematics, physics and drawing. His education in physical skills such as dancing, fencing and riding had been entrusted to the former royal servant Lucas Mutzil. Both teachers must have been satisfied with the achievements of their pupil. But that was not all. Frederik II (who died in 1588) had awakened in his son a deep-seated military interest by having two comprehensive books on war written especially for him, and he opened his son's eyes to the attractions of life at sea by letting him try his hand at seafaring from an early age. No Danish king has ever know more about shipbuilding, sailing and navigation than Christian. And no other king led troops in the field as he did.

*

Christian IV's first and very far-sighted military effort was the construction of the Armoury complex just south of Copenhagen Castle (1598-1610). It was an impressive complex, even by European standards. To the west was the 160 m long Tøjhus building (Armoury). To the east, parallel, the equally long Proviantgård (Provision-house). To the south was a low galley-house which adjoined the Provision-house, and a Sulphur-house which adjoined the Armoury. Between these two low buildings a canal was dug which led into a square harbour basin (78.5×78.5 m) between the two long buildings. Here the navy's ships could be fitted out and could take in supplies without being watched by curious strangers.

For the protection of the capital, the Armoury complex and the harbour, Christian IV in the years 1607-1623 modernised his father's defence works around the town. The deteriorating walls were covered on the outside by earth ramparts which could better resist gunfire, and the old towers were replaced by protruding bastions, which provided stands for the guns of the defence. South of Copenhagen a new fortified town was constructed: Christianshavn (1618-25), which effectively protected the harbour from the south. Several years later Christian IV extended the rampart system of Copenhagen from Nørreport (North gate) to the Saint Anna redoubt (the forerunner of the citadel). This work was scarcely finished at the King's death in 1649.

The country's defences profited to a high degree from Christian IV's enormous enthusiasm for building. He expended great energy and vast amounts of money on defence constructions. Before the Kalmar War he focused particularly on strengthening eastern Denmark and Norway against growing Swedish aggression. To counter threats to Kalmar the small fortress-town of Christianopel (1599-1611) was founded. Halmstad (1598-1605) was reinforced to counter the central castle of Jönköping, while Varberg to the south (modernised c. 1600) and Bohus to the north (1594-1604) were meant to neutralize Elfsborg. Christianstad was built later (1614-1618). Furthermore the hinterland was secured by fortifications around Malmø (1588-1611), Laholm (1609-15) and Akershus.

After the Peace of Knærød in 1613 Swedish interest was directed towards the east and Christian IV's towards the south. But when Christian IV founded the fortified town of Glückstadt (1615-25) at the River Elbe, in his German fief the Duchy of Holstein, it was more for reasons of trade than for defence purposes. Nevertheless the town's well-constructed modern system of fortifications was of great use during Christian IV's two following wars. Although Denmark for many years after the Emperor's War (1625-1629) witnessed armies fighting

*1238*

on the very doorstep, very few defence constructions were begun. To some extent Christian IV was responsible for this, but the Rigsråd (Council of the Realm) was also to blame. Unity was lacking. The King, however, succeeded in carrying out Axel Urup's fortification plans at Kielerfjord, known as Christianspris, during the years 1631-43. Shortly after, this stronghold was taken by the Swedes, on 18th December 1643. The fortress was in fact manned only by a peace-time force when the Swedes, totally without warning, crossed the border.

It is well-known that Christian IV, as did most leaders in Europe at that time, preferred mercenaries to conscripted peasant soldiers for several reasons. The enthusiasm of conscripts was normally low, since they were naturally more interested in tilling the land than in fighting. But more important, perhaps, was the time required to learn the necessary military skills; conscripts would turn up, for instance, with no training in the use of arms or fighting tactics, whereas the hired men would already have mastered these skills. It was probably not without significance that the King would have a freer hand in directing hired troops than conscripts. This was no doubt the reason for the unwillingness of the Rigsråd to grant Christian IV money for his preferred hired troops.

This did not mean that Christian IV disregarded the need for an organised peace-time force. At least it could be useful in providing labour for the construction of fortresses, and in case of outbreak of war it could replace those sent to war as man-power for the fortifications. Finally, the conscripts could of course be trained to become proper soldiers if they stayed on long enough under the banner, as the King had seen was the practice in Sweden. There is therefore no reason to believe that the decision to create a militia was forced through by the Rigsråd against the will of Christian IV. The arrangement was probably worked out between them and was not, as was usual in such cases, the result of Christian IV's initiative.

The so-called militia was established in 1614 to secure the country and the people against surprise attack from outside. In such situations the country would normally be without "trained and trustworthy soldiers on foot". Furthermore, by this means one could avoid "that strange and foreign people at a great cost and for small reason should be hired and brought into the country", as the King described it. At first this conscription was only imposed on the yeomanry, who had to present a man from each farm. If the full strength of 4,000 men could no be reached in this way the King's wealthier tenants had to be included in the arrangement. All the farms in question were relieved of all burdens to the state, such as ordinary taxes and other duties and levies. This conspicuously inequitable arrangement of the defence system was made more equitable in 1621, when all the peasants of the Crown and the Church were incorporated into it. It was typical that the peasants of the nobility were exempt. A recruiting area comprised nine farm, and each area had to provide a suitable, preferably unmarried, young man for military service, which consisted of basic drill on a few Sundays during the summer, in suitable places, most often behind the local church. In some years larger groups of soldiers were kept around the fortresses, but in this case following a royal order they were more often used as workers and not trained as soldiers.

*

Christian IV became especially attached to the navy. It was in a sense his own source of power, to a large extent financed out of his own coffers. He was therefore very active in the development of Copenhagen into an extensive and secure base for the navy.

To this end, he developed just to the east of the earlier-mentioned Tøjhus (Armoury) complex, a thriving concern on Bremerholm (Gammelholm) for the navy's benefit. He built a large new anchor-smithy, with a hammer that was worked by an ox-trea. The old smithy was converted in 1619 into the present-day Holmens Church. Not far away from the smithy was the 900 ft long Reberbane (Ropewalk); during Christian IV's reign this became busier than ever before. The demand for ropes of all dimensions increased as a result of the growth of the navy.

The ship-building also took place on Bremerholm. As early as 1611 there were three open docks facing the water. These may look rather modest in the etching by Campen; nevertheless, many big naval ships were built there. But is must at once be added that there were other dockyards in the King's domains, e.g. at Akershus, Nakskov, Flensborg and Neustadt. Here skilled English and Scottish master ship-builders worked, mostly called in by the King.

The results of Christian IV's naval building were impressive. In 1596 he had taken over 22 ships from the Regency, with a total gun-carrying capacity of 588 guns. According to a reconstructed naval list from 1648, the King by the time of his death had at his disposal 41 ships with in all 1067 guns, and that was despite the major losses suffered by the navy at the Battle of Fehmern Bælt on 13th October 1644, when no less than 3 capitalships and 9 frigates, with a total of 394 guns, were lost. To the 41 actual men of war should be added the so-called defence-ships, i.e. solidly-built private merchant ships fitted out to carry guns. Their owners received various privileges from the King, such as reduced customs duty on merchandise imported on board these ships. This Royal initiative was best received in Copenhagen and Bergen. Christian IV, however, also thought of the steadily growing naval manpower. In 1615 it consisted of 1,500 men, which of course created great housing problems. After several makeshift measures the King thought out a very bold plan. He simply decided to build a whole new town for the permanent staff of Holmen (the Naval Dockyard). During the years 1631-39 he built outside the old Østervold (present-day Gothersgade) more than 600 dwellings in low one-storey rows, which bear some resemblance to modern terraced houses. It was a brilliant solution to a difficult social problem.

*

Weapons are the prerequisite of military power. As a true mercantilist, Christian IV sought to promote his own weapon-production. For economic reasons he was especially interested in starting up domestic casting of the expensive brass cannons. The casting mainly took place in Copenhagen. Until 1610 casting was carried out in St. Clara Church, which was turned into a gun foundry as early as 1586. After that production was moved to a new and more suitable building in present-day Pilestræde. But Christian IV also had a productive foundry at Kronborg, established c. 1600, from which several pieces have been preserved. Later there was added to these the very effective gun foundry set up by private persons in Glückstadt after the German War. The cheaper iron guns and iron cannon balls were in lesser quantities cast in Norway but were mainly imported from Sweden and the Netherlands.

Christian IV showed great personal interest in his artillery and he was often present at the trial firing of new consignments of guns. He also put his personal mark on the production of guns by trying to systematize it; numerous series of guns were made in the same shape, length, calibre and weight. This had advantages with regard to both production and tactics. A typical series is e.g. the 100 "Old Kings", cast 1603-07. Other similar series had picturesque names such as "Dragons" or "Nettle-leaves", often named after the decoration on the barrel. It can be seen that, all in all, Danish production of guns had reached sizeable proportions from the information that during the reign of Christian IV no fewer than 1360 guns were cast in Copenhagen and Kronborg.

As regards hand-weapons the situation was somewhat different. Not that Christian IV was uninterested in Danish handgun-, sword- and armour-making, but in Denmark these activities had not developed beyond the stage of journeyman. The most comprehensive production of Danish hand-weapons came from Elsinore; a work-shop there delivered a long series of identical wheel-lock rifles for the King's life-guards. 40 of these rifles are still preserved. In the same way a reasonably large production of armour went on in Elsinore and Copenhagen. But the Danish production of hand-weapons was mainly directed towards the private market.

Gunpowder was also to some degree produced in Christian IV's Denmark. The King attached great importance to the supervision by the feudal nobility of the production of salpetre, which the royal estates had a duty to sustain. Of the other ingredients for making gunpowder, sulphur was imported from Iceland and charcoal was delivered from the forests of north Sealand and elsewhere. Several powder-mills were built along the Mølleå (Mill River) in Christian IV's time, i.e. at Brede, Lyngby and Ørholm, but in spite of royal support and enthusiasm domestic production did not show impressive results. By far the greater part of the gunpowder still had to be imported from abroad.

*

Christian IV is perhaps best known and admired for his never-faltering courage on the battle-field. An important part of the story of Christian IV as war-lord must therefore deal with his activities as a commander in the field.

After years of fruitless border meetings between the Danish and Swedish councils, Christian IV's patience ran out, and he decided to use force to end the unacceptable provocations of the Swedish King (Carl IX) in northern Norway and the Baltic. On 9th February 1611 he forced the reluctant Council of the Realm to accept war. On 4th April the same year he signed the Declaration of War against Sweden.

The King's strategic plan was simple, evident, and in principle sound. It consisted of action from two directions: from Christianopel towards the Swedish key-stronghold, the Castle of Kalmar, and from Halmstad towards the central Swedish assembly-point of Jönköping. But already here in his first campaign he revealed a fatal weakness in judging his opponent's strengths and capabilities. Kalmar resisted longer than expected; the castle held out against the Danish siege from 3rd May until 3rd August 1611. As a result, Carl IX unexpectedly managed to muster such a large army at Ryssby, c. 15 km north of Kalmar, that Christian IV had to summon his army from Halmstad for assistance. Even then it was only by the skin of their nose that the Danes avoided a catastrophe in the battle for the Danish camp on 17th July 1611. Christian IV showed both breadth of vision and courage in the thick of the battle, but his strategy for the year 1611 had been blighted in spite of the fact that the castle fell to him in the end.

The plan for the war-year of 1612 naturally had to be adapted to meet the new situation. The Kalmar army had now first of all to secure its hinterland by bringing Øland under Danish control, while an army repositioned at Halmstad was to capture the castles of Elfsborg and Guldborg at the mouth of the Göta River. Next there would be a pincer-attack on Jönköping. Christian IV led the attack on Elfsborg, and was successful. The castle surrendered on 24th May, and Guldborg followed on 1st June. Slower progress was made at Kalmar, where the main stronghold of Øland, Borgholm, fell on 12th June, while the situation on the island was not absolutely secure until fully a week later. Then the way was clear for the intended drive towards the central Swedish stronghold. But it was not to be. Christian IV had intended to use the waiting time to secure what was to be his left flank by a thrust into the north of Väster Götland, up to Lidköping. Because of this, for most of June he became involved in long-drawn-out skirmishes, in which the Swedish resistance was led by the recently-deceased King Carl IX's young son, Gustavus Adolphus; this seriously impaired the strength of the Danish army. Then Gert Rantzau's Kalmar army ran into all sorts of difficulties after striking camp at the end of June. Lack of money, supply failures, guerrilla attacks and the menace of a Swedish attack under Gustavus Adolphus' leadership demoralized the army to the point where Rantzau, in the second week of July, had to turn back at Vimmerby, about 120 km east of Jönköping. This totally ruined Christian IV's plan of campaign, since the cavalry which he himself was leading on to Jönköping in support of Rantzau completely lacked the strength to penetrate Swedish defences. Much the same could reasonably be said of the naval demonstration which he personally carried out at Stockholm in the period 31st August to 8th September. It was not without a certain psychological effect, however.

The peace treaty was concluded at Knærød on 20th January 1613. Since Denmark had two decisive Swedish fortresses in hand and had demonstrated her mastery of the sea, the issues of conflict were settled to Danish advantage. Denmark had distinguished herself for the last time as the leading power in the Nordic area.

*

In the middle of the 1620s, the Thirty Years' War (1618-48) drew nearer to Northern Germany, and Tilly's formidable shape loomed larger. Since Christian IV, as Duke of Holstein, was a member of the Lower Saxon circle (Holstein, Mecklenburg, the archdiocese of Bremen, Braunschweig-Lüneburg and the archdiocese of Magdeburg), this constituted in many respects a threat to his interests. The whole circle, and Holstein with it, was afraid of the Catholic reaction; but this fear was particularly strong for the previously ecclesiastical domains, the archdiocese of Bremen and the diocese of Schwerin, which Christian IV, with great difficulty and a cost of many sacrifices, had managed to reserve for his sons Frederik and Ulrik. As a means of supporting the two Princes, feelings of Protestant solidarity, pledges of alliance from England and the Netherlands, and, not least, fear of Swedish intervention in Germany, drew him towards involvement in the war. Christian IV on 2nd May 1625, finally allowed himself to be chosen as Colonel-in-Chief of the Lower Saxony forces (the highest officer responsible for the defence of the Circle). The Danish Rigsråd warned the King in no uncertain terms against taking such a step, but Christian IV, armed with faith and hope, dismissed this advice. The treaty between England and the Netherlands came into force on 29th November 1625. Christian IV was thereupon drawn into the ruinous European maelstrom. He pushed across the Elbe with his army of mercenaries on 7th June. The war had started.

In the first year of the war, 1625, Christian IV attempted, as colonel of the allied forces, to carry out his defence-responsibilities. He therefore mainly held back behind the River Weser, the western boundary of the Lower Saxon Circle territory. Both he and Tilly used the time to call up further reinforcements of mercenaries.

For Christian IV it was a matter of grave concern that a new army might turn up on the enemy side. The Emperor had in fact decided to set up his own army under Wallenstein, and thus become less dependent on the power of the Catholic League under Tilly. Christian IV's treaty with England and the Netherlands was seen as a counter-move against this new threat, which seemed to indicate that Christian IV had taken upon himself too large a task.

In the spring of 1626 Christian IV therefore found himself confronting two hostile armies, each of a scale compared with his own. Awkward though this situation was, he nevertheless confronted it in a masterly way. On 20th June he sent one of his sub-commanders, the daring Count Ernst of Mansfeld, to the east, around Wallenstein's troops at Dessau, south of Magdeburg and into the Emperor's Silesia. From there he was to proceed to Hungary and join up with the Emperor's enemy, the Prince of Siebenbürgen, Betlen Gabor. The plan was totally succesful, in that Wallenstein, on the Emperor's account, had to chase after Mansfeld with the majority of his army. The pressure on Christian IV was decisively slackened, and naturally he took advantage of it.

In the summer of 1626 Christian IV with his main forces took up position at Wolfenbüttel, just north of the Harz Mountains. Separated from him by the mountainous Harz countryside, Tilly was positioned to the west, near Göttingen, to which he was laying siege; the small force left behind by Wallenstein to the east, near Dessau. Christian IV decided to attack Tilly, if possible before Göttingen fell and in any event before the two armies could unite. On 5th August he besieged the strong county-hall in Lutter am Barenberg, but he did not move further south until 11th August. By then, however, Göttingen had already surrendered, on 1st August, and all Tilly's troops were therefore available again. This delay proved fatal to Christian IV's plans. Tilly even had time to call up Wallenstein's reserve troops, so that from 12th August onwards he had considerable advantage over Christian IV in terms of numbers, as well as his greater experience. From 14th-17th August he pressed Christian IV north until at Lutter am Barenberg the Danes were forced to do battle. The result was a crushing defeat for the King. It is assumed that during the fight Christian IV had transferred command to General Fuchs in some confusion; in any event, the Danish leadership failed completely, so that not even Christian IV's personal bravery could affect the outcome. He had undeniably suffered major losses of men, material and morale. The war was *de facto* lost for Christian IV.

It was not until 1627, however, that the misfortunes spilled over into Christian IV's own territories – but when they did they arrived in double force. From the south, Tilly crossed the Elbe at Blekede on 24th-25th July, and from the east, Wallenstein reached Denmark in late August. Before the end of October all of the Jutland peninsula, except for the fortresses of Glückstadt and Krempe, was occupied – a situation which lasted almost unchanged until the Treaty on Lübeck on 12th May 1629.

In spite of claims that Danish troops had already plundered Jutland, Wallenstein found "almost every house filled with God's blessings". He did not find unbroken peace there in his "fat quarters", however. Apart from building up an effective coastal defence of the islands, in 1628 Christian IV was also immensely energetic in harassing the enemy by raids across the sea. He thus supported the besieged fortifications, and operated for a long time on the east coast of Holstein with Fehmern as a base. Most important, however, was his involvement in Stralsund. Here he crossed the European plans of the House of Habsburg which consisted of establishing Spanish-Austrian supremacy in the North Sea and the Baltic. Stralsund refused to surrender to Wallenstein and called for Christian IV's assistance. On 9th July 1628 the Danish Colonel Henrik Holck arrived with 1000 men to the rescue of the beleaguered town. At the same time Christian IV himself went into action off the nearby coast with a relatively large force, which continued operations there until the middle of August. Denmark and Sweden even launched a cooperative venture for the defence of Stralsund. A meeting between the two Nordic Kings in the vicarage of Ulvsbäck on 22nd-25th February 1629 did not lead to more comprehensive combined efforts, but the meeting made their enemies uneasy, since at the same time they were hard-pressed by Danish troops in North Friesland. Under these conditions Wallenstein's far-reaching plans concerning the Baltic had to be abandoned, and the Emperor recognized that he had to accept the Treaty of Lübeck on 12th May 1629. As a result of this Christian IV escaped from the war without losses of land, but he had to refrain from any interference in relations within the German Empire and he had to give up the dioceses of the two Princes. He had actually got off surprisingly lightly; that he had not lost more was to a high degree due to the King's intractable obstinacy and to his inexhaustible energy.

*

During the long period between the Emperor's War and the Torstensson War, i.e. from summer 1629 until December 1643, Christian IV's diplomacy was mainly occupied with obstructing Swedish attempts to acquire possessions on the north German coast (e.g. Pomerania and the arch-diocese of Bremen) as part of a future peace treaty. The situation became more tense as the

Peace Congress began to convene during the summer of 1643 in Münster and Osnabrück. Sweden now decided to obstruct Christian IV's influence during the peace negotiations. A surprise attack was planned in order to achieve this.

Without a declaration of war, the Swedish Field Marshal, Lennart Torstensson, thrust into Holstein on 12th December 1643. Before the end of January 1644 all of Jutland was occupied. Resistance was out of the question. The Danish army was scattered in winter quarters, making any coherent retaliation impossible, and the land militia turned out to be just as ineffective as in 1627. In the following month Field Marshal Gustav Horn attacked Skåne from the north, and here he quickly conquered several fortified towns of strategic importance. He could not, however, take Malmø. There the campaign stopped. Christian IV's decisive hour had come.

In spite of his 67 years, Christian IV demonstrated amazing energy in 1644. First, on Funen, the coastal defence had to be set up and the soldiers's quarters organized. This was all arranged by the end of February, when the King travelled to Copenhagen. He then intended to launch a combined land and sea attack on Göteborg. The fitting out of the navy took some time, but on 5th April the Danish ships with Christian IV on board the *Trefoldighed* arrived at Elfsborg. Here his troops immediately started to construct a fortification for the closing of the port. Messages that a Swedish auxiliary fleet, hired in the Netherlands, was now positioned at the Frisian Islands made Christian IV leave Göteborg on 30th April. He met his enemies at Listerdyb, between Rømø and Sild, off the west coast of Jutland, and here he damaged their ships so badly on 16th and 17th May that they could only start to limp homeward on 24th May. The danger that Torstensson, with the help of the Dutch ships, might try to land on the Danish Islands was happily averted.

For a short interval thereafter there was peace in Danish waters – but not for long. The Swedish main fleet left Stockholm on 1st June, and on 29th-30th June the seaborne Swedish troops occupied Fehmern. The Danish navy set out from Copenhagen on 26th June, again led by Christian IV on the *Trefoldighed.* The famous Battle of Kolberger Heide, in the southern Baltic, was fought on 1st July. The Danish navy held the sea while the Swedish navy sought protection at Christianspris in the Kielerfjord. A Danish attempt to shoot the Swedish navy to pieces from a battery placed at Labö on the south side of the fjord did not succeed. The Swedish Admiral, Clas Fleming, however, was killed. His successor was Carl Gustav Wrangel. In spite of his wounds, Christian IV remained off the coast; he delegated the surveillance of the fjord estuary to the old Admiral Peter Galt. Because of negligence on the latter's part the Swedish navy on 1st August slipped out of the trap. This cost Galt his life. The Swedish navy got back to Stockholm on 5th August.

On Christian IV's homeward journey to Copenhagen something very unexpected happened. As he sailed north through the Sound, on 10th August, he met a new Swedish auxiliary fleet from the Netherlands, outside Dragør. What was worse, the King did not manage to engage the enemy, and the Dutch ships escaped to Kalmar. The King assumed, however, that the damaged Swedish naval force would not put to sea again that year – an assumption he believed to be confirmed by a letter he had intercepted – and he therefore saw no reason to keep his entire navy in the Baltic. The fleet was consequently laid up for the winter, and only a frigate-squadron of 15 ships was kept under sail. This was fatal error of judgement. On 13th October a Swedish-Dutch fleet of more than twice that size met the Danes in Fehmern Bælt. The outcome could only be a stinging defeat for the Danes. Only 3 Danish ships escaped. Admiral Pros Mund and many others fell. Two admirals and about 1000 men were taken prisoner. This was Carl Gustav Wrangel's second victory over the Danes, but he abstained from any attempt to invade the Danish Islands.

Nevertheless, the catastrophe of Fehmern Bælt had a devastating effect on Chrstian IV's succesfully initiated campaign in Skåne. He had decided to make at strenuous effort to drive Field Marshal Horn out of there. Together with Lord High Constable Anders Bille the King had pressed Horn from Malmø towards Lund, but at the news of Pros Mund's fate the offensive had to be cancelled and the army transferred back to the islands, which were now threatened by fears of Swedish invasion.

This marked the end of Danish offensive initiatives, and peace negotiations were unavoidable. In December it was agreed that the two parties should meet at Brømsebro on 8th February 1645. After hard negotiations, on 13th August 1645 Christian IV had to accept humiliating peace conditions. He was forced to cede the islands of Gotland and Øsel in the Baltic, and the Norwegian provinces of Härjedalen and Jämtland. In addition the Danish province of Halland was given up for a period of 30 years. Denmark had not had to accept peace conditions as hard as this for centuries. Because of this it became evident that Sweden was now the leading power of the North. Perhaps it was fortunate that Christian IV did not live to experience the Treaty of Westphalia in 1648. He thus avoided seeing his nightmare come true: Sweden as ruler of Pomerania and Bremen.

*

It is not words, but deeds and results that give character to a life's work. It should be clear from this presentation of Christian IV's achievements in the military field that he was an extraordinary man. There was hardly any aspect of this field that did not engage his attention, and he dealt with the whole range of topics with the skill of a professional. In most military matters he was totally up-to-date; he seems, however, not to have been an innovator in the art of war, in the style of Gustavus Adolphus. There is no doubt that he over-estimated his abilities as a commander in battle, thus several times making grandiose campaign plans which presumed the existence of resources greater than those at his disposal. He nevertheless possessed a sound strategic insight. On the battle-field he was brave and resolute, but in the initial phases of battle he was often hesitant and indecisive. His self-confidence made it difficult for him to cooperate with others and listen to good advice. His basic political and military theory, that Sweden posed the main threat to his kingdom, was right, however; this was abundantly demonstrated in his own time. Unfortunately it was beyond his reach to solve this problem. He did not manage, for instance, to persuade the Rigsråd and the nobility of the value of major military efforts at the decisive moments, as Gustavus Adolphus did. The King alone was not to blame for this. He had to deal with a privileged class of nobility, the majority of which had forgotten its elementary duties in respect of the defence of the realm and was more attracted by domestic life than by the discomforts and dangers of life in the field. This was a most unfortunate state of affairs in perhaps the most belligerent century in Europe's history.

The life of Christian IV ended as a tragedy, both for him and for his kingdom. But many memories of his versatile endeavours on his country's behalf live on and have secured his image as a King of undeniably European stature.

*Finn Askgaard*

1128

## Christian IV

Artist unknown. Søværnets Modelkammer at Nyholm (Collection of models in the possession of the Royal Navy), about 1860
Oak. L. 240 cm, d. 80 cm, br. 80 cm
Søværnets historiske Modelsamling
Copy of Thorvaldsen's bronze statue which was executed in 1840 and erected in Roskilde Cathedral. With the disappearence of the wooden vessels, the wood-carvers working at the Royal Dockyard lost their jobs. According to tradition, this figure was executed as a "pastime occupation" to be erected in the "Modelkammer". The pedestal is inscribed "R.F.P.", Regna Firmat Pietas (Piety strengthens the Realms) which was the King's motto.
*Provenance:* To Søværnets historiske Samling c. 1870.
*Literature:* Katalog over Den historiske Modelsamling 1896 117 no. 247.

*Cuirassier on horseback and his armour. Engraving from Walhausen: Kriegskunst zu Pferdt. Frankfurt a.M. 1616*

1129

## Copy of Frederik II's Armour

Berlin 1880
Iron
Frederiksborg no. B 392e.
The armour consists of: backplate, breastplate, neck-guard with pauldrons, gauntlets, and helmet with visor. Executed for the Frederiksborg Museum after the original in Vienna. The original is in the collection of the so-called "Heltekammer" (Chamber of Heroes). This collection was founded by Ferdinand of Austria in 1583.

1130

## Frederik II

Oil on canvas. 211×120 cm
Frederiksborg R 1. (Deposited at Kronborg)
Full-length *en face*. The King is depicted as war lord in armour and brassards. The baton is held against his right hip. On the table beside the figure a twelve-pointed crown.

*Provenance:* Until the fire in 1859 the picture was at Frederiksborg.
*Literature:* Heiberg 1984.

1131

## The Battle of Ditmarsken, 22nd May-20th June 1559

Plaster cast executed after a relif on the sarcophagus of Frederik II in Roskilde Cathedral by Gert van Egen (?-1590-1611-?), 1594/98. (1940/45)
44.7×116 cm
Frederiksborg A 6696
Christian III died on New Year's Day 1559 and Frederik II (1534-1588) succeeded to the Throne. The peasantry of Ditmarsken had been under the Archbishop of Bremen since time immemoiral. Nevertheless, the German Emperor had granted enfeoffments of the area to Holstein princes, and these rights had to be enforced. Frederik II supported the princes and a large powerful army was mustered. The border was crossed on 22nd May 1559 and the people of Ditmarsken soon had to surrender. A cartouche is inscribed: "DITMARSCHE/GESCHACH. 1559". There is no doubt that this victory encouraged the young Prince to military ambition.

1132

## The Siege of Elfsborg 22nd August-4th September 1563

Plaster cast executed after a relief on the sarcophagus of Frederik II in Roskilde Cathedral by Gert van Egen (?-1590-1611-?). 1594/98. (1937/38)
45×118 cm
Frederiksborg A 5749
The relief portrays the Danish siege of Elfsborg (22nd August-4th September 1563), an incident from the Northern Seven Years' War (1563-1570). A cartouche is inscribed: "ELFSBORCH/GESCHACH 1563". The prototype for this relief is an engraving in Gasp. Ens, rerum Danicarum Friderico II ... Historia, 1593.
*Literature:* Otto Smith 1927 189f.

1133

## The Attack on Varberg 1569

Plater cast after a relief on the sarcophagus of Frederik II in Roskilde Cathedral by Gert van Egen (?-1590-1611-?). 1594/98. (1940/45)
45×117.5 cm
Frederiksborg A 6695
The attack on Varberg and the subsequent capture of the fortress on 13th and 14th November 1559 occured during the Northern Seven Years' War (1563-1570). The relief shows the location of the fortress facing the sea behind a wide moat and a rampart which is trimmed with gabions and guns. In the foreground on the right of the fortress is Frederik II's army. In the prominent foreground a camp of tents. Cartouche inscribed: "WARBERG/GESCHACH 1569". The four military subjects on the sarcophagus represent important aspects of the King's interests. They are also extremely interesting from the point of view of military history.

1134

## Cuirassiers' Armour

Denmark about 1620
Weight: c. 32 kg apiece
Tøjhusmuseet
Each cuirass consists of a closed helmet, gorget, backplate, breastplate, tassets, taces and arm defence. Heavy cavalry from the time of the Thirty Years' War (1618-48)
*Provenance:* The Copenhagen Arsenal stock.

*1133*

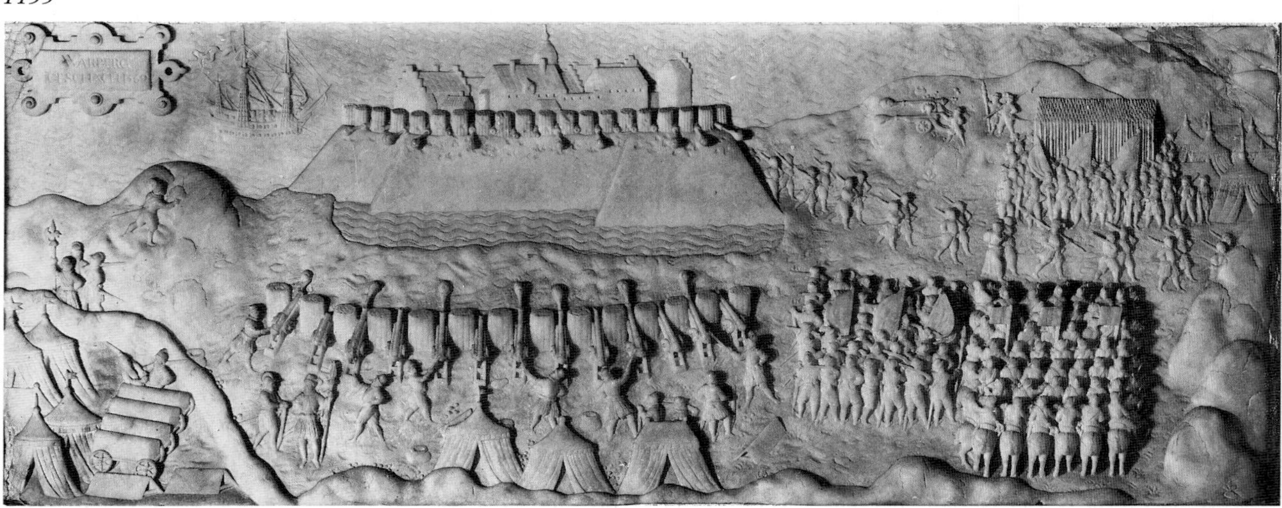

1135

## Denmark 1585

Engraving. 42.1×53.0 cm
Det kongelige Bibliotek, Kort- og billedsamlingen, 1111-0-1585/1
The engraved map is a separate sheet in Georg Braun and Franz Hogenberg, Civitates orbis terranum (etc.) 1588. The map shows the young Christian IV's conception of his kingdom.

1137

## Elsinore with Kronborg Castle and environs including a perspective of Kronborg

Unsigned. Undated (1587/88)
Engraving (illuminated). 42.5×53.3 cm
Det kongelige Bibliotek, Kort- og billedsamlingen.
The map is printed on a sheet in Georg Braun and Franz Hogenberg, (Civitatis orbis terrarum (etc.) 1588) Vrbivm præcipvarvm totivs Mvndi, vol. IV no. 26, Cologne 1617.

1138

## Drawing. Artillery on the march

Joachim Arentsehe, Copenhagen 1578
Watercolour. 30.7×62 cm
Det kgl. Bibliotek, Danske Samlinger, cat. 27-41 fol.
The watercolour was published in a work on military history which was printed at the request of Frederik II for his son, the later Christian IV, whose manuscript notes lend it its particular character. The book is beautifully illustrated with the writer's own drawings. Oddly enough, only one copy of the book was printed, probably to avoid compromising the military information it held. The watercolour is a depiction of a besieging army on the march. Guns and gun carriages were transported on separate wagons along with various ordance equipment etc. For the transportation of a single gun, a team of 8-12 horses was needed, in some cases even more if the artillery was heavy, due to the bad conditions of the roads at that time and the considerable weight of the ordnance.
*Provenance:* Joachim Arentsehe, Ein Buch zusammengezogen aus vielen Probierten Künsten und Erfahrungen wie ein Zeughauss sampt aller Munition anheimische gehalten werden soll ... Koppenhagen, Lorentz Benedicht.
*Literature:* Madsen 136ff.

1139

## A Single Combat

Unsigned, undated (the early 17th century)
Paper, pen and ink. 20.8×17.2 cm (the sheet is displayed folded up)

Rigsarkivet, A2: Kongehusets arkiv: Christian IV
This sheet is enclosed in Christian IV's exercise book (1583-1591) but it was probably sketched at a later date. It is uncertain whether the King himself is the master of it. The sheet is inscribed: "MM/MUNUS/MANUS/MINUS/MAROR". The fact that the sheet exists may be seen as an indication that the King took an interest in military subjects from an early age.

1140

## Drawing of a naval action between a Danish and a Swedish Warship

Rudolph v. Deventer, Copenhagen c. 1585
Watercolour and pen. 31.5×82.5 cm
Det kgl. Bibliotek, Ny kgl. Samlinger 101.2°
This drawing is one of the illustrations in a work on the manufacturing of ammunition and the use of artillery. The work corresponds with various German books on the subject and is almost identical with cat. 1142, although the illustrations and their place in the books may sometimes differ. This drawing depicts a Swedish and a Danish warship in action about 1570. The artist is obviously on the side of Denmark as all the Danish shots seem to hit while the Swedish ones miss. Both parties use round shot, chain shot, and explosive shells, the same as were used in battles ashore. The display of the flags is interesting. The Danish vessel flies the Dannebrog and the Swedish ship both a blue and yellow "bolsan" (the national symbol), a blue and red "bolsan" with three golden crowns, and big flags with blue and white stripes which may well be admiral's flags.
*Provenance:* Rudolp v. Deventer, Bericht vom Pulver und Feuerwerken. The book is dedicated to Frederik II.
*Literature:* Mejborg

1141

## Christopher Suencke

Simon de Pas (c. 1595-1647). 1635
Engraving. 25.2×19.0 cm
Den kongelige Kobberstiksamling, 700 no. 54.
Christopher Suencke (-1618-1649--) was the "tøjmester" Master of ordnance of the Copenhagen Arsenal from 1618, and from 1625-27 he served as the King's trusted "felttøjmester" (Master of field ordnance) in Northern Germany. The portrait is set in an oval frame surrounded with trophies, and Mars and Minerva.

1142

## Drawing of a scene from af fictitious siege, c. 1570

Rudol v. Deventer, Copenhagen 1585
Watercolour. 32.8×79 cm
Det kongelige Bibliotek, Thott 273, 2°
The drawing depicts the siege of a city which is surrounded by a city wall with bastions and roundels armed with heavy artillery. Outside the city, a besieging army

has dug shelter trenches for the infantry and placed heavy artillery, cannons as well as mortars, for the bombardment of the city. Part of the drawing shows a sortie through the city gate with the object of destroying and delaying the enemy's siege works. Incendiary and explosive shells are being fired into the city and their blazing tails can be seen on their way to the target. Since 1550, many new types of munition for use with mortars during a siege had appeared.
*Provenance:* Rudolf v. Deventer, K. M. Argkaley-mester, Kunstbuch von allerhand Kunsten der Argkerley, Geschütz und Feuerwerk zu Wasser und zu Land, "ab autore dedicatus Chr. Walkendorf 1585. Delineationes coloribres inducto. Fecti 1607.
*Literature:* Madsen 143f. Schmidtchen 102ff.

1143

## Account settled between the Copenhagen Arsenal and Claus von Dam. 1649

Paper, pen ink
Rigskarkivet, Rentekammeret.
Afregninger. XIII 20-30, 216-278
This account settled with the cannon founder Claus von Dam (? – 1655) includes a hanging mortar, which was cast for Anders Bille (1600-1657), Lord High Constable in 1647. The same mortar was brought to the fortress of Marstrand in 1653 and on the ceding of Bohus len in 1658 it was taken aboard the warship the *Snarensvend.* The ship sank south of Kronborg in the summer of 1658. In 1984 the hanging mortar was discovered near the wreck by amateur divers. The mortar is exhibited as cat. 1309. The account settled with Christopher Suencke (-1618-1649-) is dated and signed: "... Tyghusett dend 29 Novemb: Ao 1649/Christoffer/Schwenk/Under Hands/Eyen Hand«.
*Literture:* Frantzen 26f.

1144

## Model of a brass cannon in carriage

Unknown modeller, modelkammeret at Christiansborg, before 1785
Brass, wood, H. 17 cm, l. 58.3 cm, b. 22.5 cm, w. 5.7 kg
Tøjhusmuseet A/M 8
Model of a brass cannon in carriage with outward spiral-turned barrel. Painted black gun- carriage with adjusting mechanism. This model shows a muzzle-loader from Frederik II's time and is a typical example of the armaments taken over by Christian IV. Cannons have always been regarded as 'individuals', and this was often emphasized by each one's handsome and characteristic appearance. In the field, however, a more uniform, standardized cannon was called for, and it is Christian IV's merit that he took steps to systematize artillery production through the casting of large series of identical cannons.
*Provenance:* Transferred to Artilleriets Modelsamling from Modelkammeret at Christiansborg, according to kgl.res. af 31.3.1785.
*Literature:* Separate exhibition 1947, models no. 57. Separate exhibition 1972, Models.

1145

## Artillery instruments in a dagger sheath

Italy c. 1590. Colour-plate XIV
L. of sheath 28.5 cm, d. 4,9 cm, w. 0,43 kg. Awl 25.8 cm
Tøjhusmuseet no. C 228/1942
Dagger sheath of leather with gilt locket and chape. Inside, artillery instruments consisting of six different measuring rules, awl, probe and gimlet.
*Provenance:* Bought in 1930.

1146

## 'Inspection and trial firing at Tøjhuset'

Manuscript by Jon Olafsson, Iceland c. 1660
Det Kongelige Bibliotek 2076b
The manuscript is in three volumes, the first of which deals with Jon Olafsson's life until his journey to India. The second describes his experiences in the Danish East India colonies, and the third concerns his later fortunes in Iceland. Jon Olofsson's observations are in the main historically accurate and include many first-rate incidents about conditions at the Arsenal at the time of Christian IV. Pages 56-77 describe the inspection and trial-firing of newly-cast brass cannons at Tøjhuset, and bear witness to Christian IV's great interest in and knowledge of artillery.
*Literature:* Julius Clausen and Rist. Memoirs and Letters I 1966 63-66.

1150

## Calibre Rule in Rattan Cane

Artist unknown, c. 1588-1648
Rattan cane, silver, brass. L. 134 cm
Tøjhusmuseet, no. 1877/D 89
The hollow rattan cane is adorned with a silver knob at the top. A number of silver rings are attached to the rule at intervals of 3,6,9 and 12 inches from the knob on which four figures are outlined which may be a depiction of the breechpiece of a cannon, and with the numbers: 3,6,9 and 12. The calibre rule itself is 28 cm long. A length of about 15 cm is missing. It has four sides with graduations for iron, stone and lead bullets and for inches measured by the so-called Nürnberger calibre measure. All in all this instrument can have been a handy measuring tool not only to estimate the calibre of artillery and ammunition but also in general for measuring length. The rattan cane may have contained other instruments as well.
*Provenance:* Den historiske Våbensamling 1877
*Literature:* Blom II 14.

1151

## Model of a Brass Cannon in Carriage c. 1640

Model unknown, c. 1670
Brass and wood. H. 22 cm, l. 57.5 cm, w. 29.5 cm, w. 5.4 kg
Tøjhusmuseet no. A/M 5
Model of a typical piece of field artillery from Christian IV's time. The beehive-shaped cascabel has ornamental rings, the breech is cornice-moulded with clusters of grapes. The cannon has a single base and first reinforce ring, two second reinforce rings, a muzzle astragal and fillets and a tulip-shaped muzzle. The second reinforce has two low trunnions and two dolphin handles. The gun lies in a red-painted field carriage with painted yellow iron fittings, two wooden axels each with two eight-spoked wheels and four linchpins. The red and yellow colours of Oldenborg were always used for painting artillery equipment during the years 1550-1820.
*Provenance:* The model was presented to the Nationalmuseet c. 1898 and transferred to Hærens tekniske Korps modelsamling. From there to Tøjhusmuseet.
*Literature:* Separate exhibition 1947, Models, cat. 58. Separate exhibition 1972.

1152

## Artillery ammunition round shot

Maker unknown, c. 1570
Iron and lead. 6.4 cm in diameter, w. 0.875 kg
Tøjhusmuseet, no. A 967
Two-pound round shot made of cut up iron with a leaden shell.
*Provenance:* Caught in a fishing trawl west of Bornholm about 500 metres south of Helligpeder in 1886 where a warship was stranded during the Seven Years' War. To Tøjhusmueet 1887.
*Tøjhusmuseet:* Laboratoriets historiske Samling 1903.

1153

## Artillery ammunition-Round shot of stone

Maker unknown. 16th century
Sandstone. 7.2 cm in diameter, w. 0.510 kg
Tøjhusmuseet, no. A 961.
One-pound round shot made of sandstone.
*Provenance:* Tøjhusmuseet: Laboratoriets historiske Samling 1903.

1154

## Head of a Deer

Rosenborg 1. 135
Head of the deer which is traditionally supposed to have woken the Danish army outside Kalmar on 17th July 1611, thereby saving the soldiers from being surprised by the enemy.
*Provenance:* The Rosenborg Inventory of 1737.

1155

## Christian IV on horseback

Unsigned, undated
Oil on panel. 59.2×55.4 cm
Rosenborg no. 7-371
Equestrian portrait of the King from the side, his head *en face* to the right. He is wearing armour and holds the baton of command in his right hand. In the background a landscape showing Kalmar Castle where two armies meet. The rendering of the Castle is based on a medal which was struck in 1613 to celebrate the victory over Sweden in the same year.
*Provenance:* Purchased in 1843.
*Literature:* DMP II 79. Eller 1971 151.

1156

## Study of the Siege of Kalmar

Unsigned. 1611
Paper, pen. 58.0×78.3 cm
Kungl. Krigsarkivet, Sveriges krig, 1.33
The struggle between Denmark and Sweden for the sovereignty of the North continued under Christian IV. A declaration of war on Sweden of 4th April 1611 marked the beginning of the Kalmar War (1611-1613). On 1st May, Christian IV crossed the Swedish frontier, and a few days later he had got as far as Kalmar. After a three weeks' siege, the city was stormed on 26th and 27th May. The fortunes of battle fluctuated, but the result was a temporary Danish victory. This sheet is a depiction of a scene from the siege of Kalmar. Inscribed: "Calmars Belägringh ... den 3 Junij 1611".

1157

## Karl IX, King of Sweden 1604-11

17th century copy. Artist unknow. Undated
Oil on canvas. 70×57 cm
Gripsholm 1783
Karl IX (1550-1611), Regent of Sweden (1599-1604), King of Sweden (1604-1611) in half length *en face.* Inscribed in the upper right corner of canvas: "Carolvs R.S."
*Provenance:* Carl XIII's samling på Rosersberg. To Gripsholm 1901.

1158

## Gustavus II Adolphus, King of Sweden 1611-1632

Paul Pontius (1603-1658) after Ant. van Dyck (1599-1641). Undated
Engraving. 24.4×17.6 cm
Den kongelige Kobberstiksamling, 305 no. 10a
*Literature:* Fr. Wibiral 1877 51.

1159

## Wheel-lock Rifle

Jørgen Dressler, Elsinore 1611
Total 121.7 cm, barrel 96,8 cm, cal. 15,8 mm, w. 3.54 kg
Tøjhusmuseet, no. B 357
Wheel-lock rifle of military type made in Denmark. The number of rifles preserved – about forty – indicate that the rifle must have been mass-produced in the years between 1611 and 1622.
Barrel stamp: Støckel 1101 and 3138. Date on barrel: 1611.
*Provenance:* Rustkammerbeholdningen (Arsenal Stock). Tøjhuset inv. 1877.204.
*Literature:* Hoff 1951 34 201.

1160

## Matchlock Musket

Amsterdam, c. 1610
Total l. 138.1 cm, barrel 100.2 cm, cal. 19 mm, w. 4.14 kg
Tøjhusmuseet inv. B.396
Matchlock musket of a type which was commonly used in the Danish army in the early 17th century. Barrel stamps: Støckel 5353 and 6039. Large numbers of muskets of this type were imported to be used in the Danish-Swedish war, the Kalmar War (1611-1613).
*Provenance:* Det kongelige partikulære Rustkammer, inv. 1775. No. 255/p. 93.
*Literature:* Smith 1938 82.

1161

## Cutlass

Clemens Horn, Solingen about 1600
Total l. 90.1 cm, blade l. 73,9 cm, blade b. 3,9 cm, w. 0,88 kg
Tøjhusmuseet, no.C. 143/42
Hilt of gilt iron. S-shaped quillons and two finger guards. Oval pommel. Straight, double-edged, flat blade with tapering point.
The blade is stamped: "CLEMENS HORN" and "ME FECIT SOLINGEN".
*Provenance:* Copenhagen Arsenal stock. Probably a present from Maurice of Orange.
*Literature:* Adam von Breen, Neuwe Nassauwische Waffenhandlung, The Hague 1618.

1162

## Musketeer's Rapier with Scabbard

DE HORTUNO EN TOLEDO c. 1620
Total l. 113.7 cm, blade l. 96.5 cm, blade b. 4 cm, w. 1.41 kg
Tøjhusmusset, no. C130/1942
Hilt of tin-plated iron, S-shaped quillons. Two openwork shell guards. Oval pommel. Straight, double-edged, flat blade with tapering point. The blade is stamped: DE HORTUNO EN TOLEDO and O BONE JESU ADJUBA ME
*Provenance:* Det kongelige partikulære Rustkammer.

1163

## Matchlock Caliver

Suhl, Germany c. 1610
Total l. 133.8 cm, barrel 98.0 cm. cal. 18.7 mm, w. 3.91 kg
Livrustkammaren, no. 3121
Typical light musket from the early 17th century. Such light muskets could be used without a fork stick (musket fork), but as they would have to be used with less loading than the heavier muskets they had less penetration.
*Provenance:* Livrustkammaren inv. 1868. Originally in the Collection of Karl XV.

1164

## Matchlock Musket

Jönköping, Sweden 1600-1625
Total l. 153,0 cm, barrel 116.2 cm. cal. 18 mm, w. 5.44 kg
Livrustkammaren, no. 3117
Heavy musket. Early 17th century. Fork sticks (musket forks) were currently when firing these heavy muskets.
*Provenance:* Livrustkammaren, inv. 1867 no. 1234. Acquired from the Oxenstiernske Rustkammer on Tidø.
Alm 1933 166 f. Same 1953 96.

1165

## Musket Fork

Sweden? Early 17th century
L. 155 cm, w. 380 g
Livrustkammaren no. 24557
*Provenance:* To the Livrustkammeret 1862 from the Collections of Friherre G. A. Fleetwood.

1166

## Musketeer's Bandolier

Sweden, late 16th century
Bandolier 122 cm. Powder flask 6.1 cm
Skoklosters Slott no. 7226
Bandoliers were used by musketeers for the transportation of ready-apportioned charges of powder. The small wooden flasks, contained propelling charge for one shot. These flasks were called "patroner" (cartridge) – hence the word which today is used for the unit which includes case, percussion cap, charge and projectile.
*Provenance:* Skokloster inv. 1710.
*Literature:* Supplement til katalog for Gustaf II Adolf udstillingen 1932. No. 48.

1167

## Pair of Wheel-Lock Pistols

Germany 1603
Total l. 84 cm, barrel 62 cm, cal. 8.8 mm, w. 1.7 kg
Livrustkammaren, no. 11121-22
Dress pistol of a type which was predominant in Central and Western Europe in the early 17th century. The butt is still rather straight and the pistols have very long barrels in order to make the most of the slowly burning powder. On the comb of the butt a gilt silver plate inscribed: "VERBUM DOMINI MANET IN AETERNUM ANNO 1603".
*Provenance:* Livrustkammaren 1654:113 b 1.
*Literature:* Hoff 1969 I 122. Alm 1933 114.

1177

## Rapier

Solingen c. 1620
Total l. 117.9 cm, blade l. 92.7 cm. Max. width of blade 3.9 cm. w. 1.7 kg
Livrustkammaren no. 10.565
Hilt of silvered steel. The grip is bound with fine gilt brass wire. Straight, double-edged blade. Stamped "ANDONA" and "FERARA".
*Provenance:* Presented to Gustavus II Adolphus by Erik Larsson von der Linde.

1178

## Pair of Wheel-Lock Pistols

Nuremberg. Germany c. 1600
Total l. 78.4 cm, barrel 61.5 cm, cal. 9.9 mm, w. 1.79 kg
Tøjhusmuseet, no. B 286/87
Due to the extremely long barrels, the pistols can be dated to about 1600. The shape of the stock and the lock are, however, atypical and show traces of an earlier tradition. Lock stamps: Stöckel 1595 and 2551. Instead of the butt ball the grips have an S-shaped neck ending as hand support. The lock plate is rhomboid with the downward point placed exactly under the wheel.
*Provenance:* Det kongelige partikulære Rustkammer inv. 1775. No. 196/p. 404.
*Literature:* Hoff 1969 136 ff.

1179

## Wheel-Lock Rifle

Georg Gessler, Dresden 1614
Total l. 137.4 cm, barrel 98.4 cm, cal. 19.6 mm, w. 5.74 kg
Tøjhusmusset, no B 205
The barrel is octagonal and has 10 grooves. The wheel cover is made of brass which is typical of the Saxon area. The musket-like stock is possibly Danish. Barrel stamps: Stöckel 2598 and 4972. Barrel is dated 1614.
*Provenance:* Det kongelige partikulære Rustkammer inv. 1775 No. 409/p. 257.
*Literature:* Hoff 1951 28. Smith 1938 177.

1180

## Christian IV's Stirrups

C. 1600
Coppergilt. H. 17.3 cm. W. 12.0 cm
Livrustkammaren, No. 18502-18503
Richly ornamented stirrups with quartered baseplates. The overall decoration is that of a pelican feeding its young from a wound in its own chest. There is also a depiction of a lion holding an orb between its forepaws.
*Provenance:* Deposited at Statens Historiska Museum in 1758 by Niels Wessman, Scania.

1181

## Carl IX's Rapier and Scabbard

Blade by Clemens Horn, Solingen. Hilt by Johan Pederson, Stockholm
Total l. 114.4 cm, length of blade 92.7 cm, max width of blade 3.8 cm. w. 1.5 kg
Livrustkammaren, 7905/7906
Rapier with silver hilt, oblong pommel, and S-shaped quillons. The grip is bound with silver wire. Straight double-edged blade with rhomboidshaped section and tapering point.
*Provenance:* Stored in Strängnas Cathedral along with the armour of Carl IX.
*Literature:* Cederström – Malmborg 1930. Seitz 1965.

1182

## Gustavus II Adolphus' Rapier

Blade by Jacob Brach/ Solingen c. 1600
Total l. 109.7 cm, length of blade: 88.2 cm, width of blade: 3.5 cm. w. 1.74 kg
Livrustkammaren, No. 10584
Hilt of open-work steel. Incised foliage of silver. Straight, double-edged blade with tapering point. The ricasso bears the stamp of Jacob Brach.
*Provenance:* From Ridderholmskyrkan. Referred to as the rapier "most frequently used by His Late Majesty".
*Literature:* Cederström – Malmborg 1930.

1183

## Draft or Copy of Christian IV's Declaration of War (1611)

Rigsarkivet, TKUA, Sverig A. I, 1588, 1591-1624
In 17th century Northern Europe, it was the custom to open war by a declaration. This had to be in writing in an open letter which would be delivered by two nobleman. It could also be done *viva voce,* if the adversary was willing to accept it in this manner. The declaration of war sent by Christian IV to Carl IX of Sweden begins: "Wÿ Christian den Fierde ... güds Naade, Dan=/marcks Norgrig Wendis oc Go..tis Konning, Hertug till Slesvig Holsten Stormarn oc Ditmarsken, graffen till/ Oldenburg oc Delmenhorst tilbiuede oc Kundiøre/ den Stormægtige

høigborne Fürste her Carl den/ Nÿende Sueigis Go..tis (?) oc Wendis Konning oc Woris Naboe (etc.)". The original Declaration is dated 4th April 1611.

1184

## Instructions for the Danish Infantry 1611

Rigsarkivet. Danske Kancelli, B. 165b
Instructions (operational orders) for the Danish infantry are dated 10th April 1611. Signed and dated: "Giffvedt paa Wort Slott/ Kiøpenhaffen dend 4. Aprilis Anno 1611/ Christian". The instructions were printed by Heinrich Waldkirch, Copenhagen 1612.
*Literature:* Secher III 198/94 no. 344.

1185

## Captain's Commission 1611

Rigsarkiver, TKIA A 46
Anybody who was appointed captain, civil servant or the like, would receive a "commission", a notification in writing stating his rights and duties. This captain's commision is dated 10th February and begins: "Insetz von GOTTES gna=/den CHRISTIAN des Vierdten, zu Dennemarcken, Norwegen, der Wenden/ und Gotten Königs, Herzogen zu Schless=/wig, Holstein, Stormarn und der Dithmarschen,/Grauen zu Oldenburg und Delmenhorst" and "Bestallung/ Worauf Wir unsern Rittmester N:N: auff N. Pferde, bestellet und angenom=/men etc.".

1186

## Peace Treaty between Denmark and Sweden concluded at Knærød 20th January 1613

Rigsarkivet, Kongehuset E. Forholdet til udlandet, Sverige 1537-1699
The Kalmar War (1611-1613) ended with the conclusion of peace at Knærød 20th January 1613. The treaty was signed by the four Danish negotiators. It includes the text of the *quid pro quo* which Christian IV and the Danish Council of the Realm were to give Sweden, viz. the return of Elfsborg Castle and the county of Elfsborg as soon as the indemnity of one million rdl. had been paid. Dated and signed: "Datum Knærød thend 20. dag. Januarii anno 1613/ Christian Friis/ egen hand Manderup Parsberg/ egen handt Axel Brahe/ egen hand// Eske Brock/ egen handt".
*Literature:* DN III 1916 no. 17.

1187

## Matchlock Musket

Suhl, Germany c. 1600
Total l. 152.9 cm, barrel 116.0 cm, cal. 18 mm, w. 4.01 kg
Tøjhusmuseet, no. B.393
Military matchlock musket of a type which was in frequent use in the Danish army in the early 17th century. Suhl and Holland were the main contractors of firearms to Denmark in that period. Barrel stamps: Støckel 1677 and 5411. Lock stamps: Støckel 1733.
*Provenance:* Tøjhusmuseet inv. 1903. No. 177a

1188

## Musket Fork

Germany, late 16th century
Total L. 120.7 cm, w. 0.51 kg
Tøjhusmuseet, no. B.93.
Due to the weightiness of the old muskets, a musket fork was used to support the weapon during use.
*Provenance:* Tøjhusmuseet. Catalogue 1877, no. D54.

1189

## Pair of Wheel-Lock Pistols

Ausburg, Germany c. 1610
Total l. 78.2 cm, barrel 54.3 cm, cal. 11.9 mm, w. 1,41 kg
Tøjhusmuseet, no. B. 304/05
Wheel-lock pistols with German-type locks. This type of lock, which was used for pistols as well as rifles, is charactised by the large angular lock plate which often has brass decorations. The Western European type, however, is characterized by a smaller and more elegant lock plate, which was not made any larger than technical demands required. In the early 17th century the barrels tended to be shorter, while the charactistic butt ball of the 16th century is about to disappear.
*Provenance:* Rendsborg Rustkammer. Tøjhusmuseet, Catalogue 1877, no. 1435.

1190

## Musketeer's Bandolier

Denmark c. 1625
Bandolier: 130 cm. Powder Flasks: 8.0-9.5 cm
Tøjhusmuseet, no. B. 174:2
Bandoliers were used by musketeers for the transportation of ready-apportioned charges of powder. There is a total of six powder flasks on this bandolier.
*Provenance:* Tøjhusmuseet. Catalogue 1877, no. D.19.

1191

## Powder Horn Carrier (Flask Leather) with Bullet Purse

Denmark c. 1600
Total: 31.3 cm, w. 329 g
Tøjhusmuseet no. B. 199:1.
By means of a hook it was possible to fasten a priming horn to the bottom of the flask leather. The purse was used by the rifleman for keeping his bullets. Flask leathers of this type can be seen on contemporary drawings by de Geyn and Wallhausen.
*Provenance:* Tøjhusmuseet, inv. 1941 no. B 199:1.

1192

## Powder Horn Carrier (Flask Leather) with Bullet Purse

Germany? c. 1600
Total: 40.5 cm
Tøjhusmuseet no. B. 241:1
Apart from the bandolier, which carried the flasks of powder for the propelling charge, the musketeer also carried a priming horn and a bullet purse. By fastening a hook through the brass mountings under the bullet purse, it was possible to attach the priming horn to the flask leather.
*Provenance:* Tøjhusmuseet inv. 1941 no. b. 1032.

1193

## Pikeman's Rapier

Southern Germany c. 1600
Total l. 118.9 cm, length of blade: 103.8 cm, width of blade: 2 cm, w. 1.22 kg
Tøjhusmuseet, no. C 90/1942
Hilt of black iron. Open knuckle guard, quillons, and finger guards. Double-edged blade with tapering point.
*Provenance:* Acquired from the Armémuseet in Munich in 1934. Bavarian Arsenal stock.

1194

## Musketeer's Rapier

Tøjhusmuseet
Weilm Klein, Germany 1588
Total 1. 114 cm, length of blade 96.5 cm, width of blade 3.7 cm, w. 1.34 kg
Tøjhusmuseet no. C 161/1942
Hilt of tinned iron. S-shaped quillons. Side guards, finger guards, and section guards. Oval pommel. Straight doubled-edged flat blade with tapering point. The ricasso is stamped with the mark of Weilm Klein and the year 1588.
*Provenance:* Det kongelige particulære Rustkammer.

1195

## Cavalry Rapier

Germany c. 1600
Total l. 101.7 cm, length of blade 84.3 cm, width of blade 5.5 cm, w. 1.59 kg
Tøjhusmuseet no. C 182/1942
Blued open bow hilt with curved quillons and side guards, finger guards, section guards, and oval pommel. Straight double-edged blade with tapering point. Blade of rhomboid section.
*Provenance:* Acquired from Leyden's Collection.
*Literature:* Seitz 1965 62.

1196

## Half Pike

Denmark c. 1600
Ash wood/ iron. L. originally 4.5 m
Tøjhusmuseet
Shaft of ash wood with chape and rhomboid spearhead. Iron band reaching from point to 75 cm of shaft.
*Provenance:* The Copenhagen Arsenal stock.

1197

## Maurice of Orange. Dutch Captain-general, 1584-1625

Willem Jacobsz. Delft (1580-1641) after Michiel Jansz. van Miereveld (1567-1641). 1625
Engraving. 44.2×31.5 cm
Den kongelige Kobberstiksamling, 240 no. 40
Maurice of Orange was the son of Vilhelm of Orange, who revolted against the Spanish supremacy of the Dutch provinces. After the murder of his father in 1584, the seventeen-year-old Maurice was elected Regent and Commander-in-Chief of the Netherland army. He continued the struggle against the Spaniards and eventually became one of the best strategists of his time. His thoughts and strategies influenced and were studied by several of the commanders of the Thirty Years' War. His ideas are embodied in the works of J. de Geyn and J.J. van Wallhausen.
*Literature:* Franken 1872 no. 58.

1198

## Round Shield

Holland c. 1600
Diameter: 69 cm. Weight: 3.0 kilo
Tøjhusmuseet no. D 204
Wooden round shield, covered with canvas, plaster, and leather. The leather is painted and gilted. Leather strap on the inside. Maurice of Orange experimented with shields for the infantry, taking Roman soldiers as his models.
*Provenance:* The Copenhagen Arsenal stock. Probably part of a present from Maurice of Orange.
*Literature:* Adam von Breen, Neuwe Nassauwische Waffenhandlung, the Hague 1618.

1199

## Pavis

Holland c. 1600
H. 94.0 cm, width 65.4 cm, w. 4,2 kg
Colour-plate XIII
Tøjhusmuseet, no. D. 206
Wooden pavis covered with canvas, plaster, and leather. The leather is painted and gilted. Leather straps on the inside.

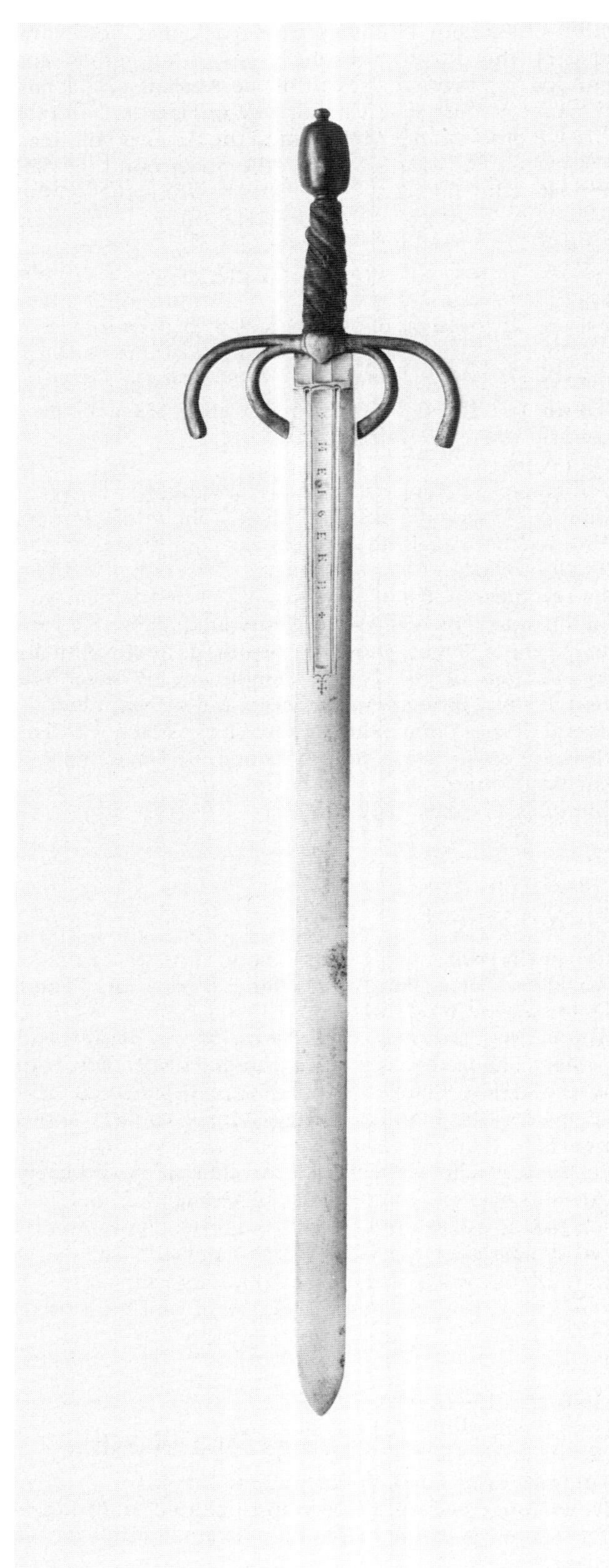

*Provenance:* The Copenhagen Arsenal stock. Probably a part of a present from Maurice of Orange.
*Literature:* Adam von Breen, Neuwe Nassauwische Waffenhandlung. The Hague 1618.

1200

## Cutlass

Weilm Klein c. 1600
Total l. 84.7 cm, length of blade 69 cm, largest width of blade 4.3 cm, w. 0.85 kg
Tøjhusmuseet, no. C. 139/1942
Tempered iron hilt with curved quillons and finger guards. Oval pommel. Straight double-edged flat blade with tapering point. The blade is stamped Weilm Klein and his mark.
*Provenance:* The Copenhagen Arsenal stock. Probably part of a present from Maurice of Orange.
*Literature:* Adam von Breen, Neuwe Nassauwische Waffenhandlung, The Hague 1618.

1201

## Swedish and Imperial Armies drawn up in battle order at Lützen, 6th November 1632

Theatrum Europæum II, Frankfurt 1637. Engraving by Mathäus Merian (1593-1650)
31.5×37.0 cm
Det kongelige Bibliotek, Kort- og billedsamlingen
In June 1630 Gustavus II Adolphus landed in Northern Germany. He forced his way forward victoriously. On 7th September 1631 he defeated Tilly at Breitenfeldt. He was overtaken by destiny at Lützen on 6th November 1632. He was killed in action fighting the Imperial troops. This sheet depicts the two armies drawn up in battle order. Inscribed with a Latin text and: "Delineation/Der Schwedischen/ und Keyserlischen Slacht=/ordnund den 6. Novemb: 1632 / beÿ Lützen gehalten", "Matthæus Merian sculpsit". This engraving has been executed after a drawing made by a participant in the battle: Olof Hansson Ornehufvud, Swedish engineer and later on "generalkvartermester" (quartermaster-general). The drawing justly accentuates the flat articulated Swedish infantry formation as distinct from the big, square Imperial formations, which were complicated to move but strong in defence.

1202

## Order of Battle

Erik Dahlbergh 1687
Paper and pen. 28.5×45.5 cm
Kungl. Krigsarkivet, Stockholm, Ordre de bataille 1600-1679, Stockholm 1687

*1200*

Order of battle or *Ordre de bataille* is a schematic disposition of the constituent parts of the army. The order was adapted to the different situations.
Inscribed: "Stockholm 1687"

1203

## Scenes from the Thirty Years' War 1633

Israel (1592-1635) after Jacques Callot
Etchings
Den kgl. Kobberstiksamling 151
a: Soldiers enlisting 9.9×20.4 cm, no. 191
b: Scene of a battle 9.2×19.6 cm, no. 192
c: The plundering of a farm 9.9×19.4 cm, no. 194.
d: The assault on a wagon. 9.5×20 cm, no. 195
e: An execution by shooting 9.7×19.4 cm, no. 201
f: A breaking on the wheel 9.0×19.4 cm, no. 203
Cat. nos. a-f originate from a series by Jacques Callot, "Les Miseres et les Mal-heur de la Guerre", published in Paris 1633. Callot was the first "modern" artist to deheroize war. Instead of glorifying it, he chose to display its horrors: the more or less compulsory enlistments, the executions, torture, assault, and plundering which were part of everyday life, also for the civilian population. On the edge of the plate of each sheet is a stanza written by Abt Michel de Marolles.
*Literature:* Meaume 1860 577 II. Lieure 1925 1352. Scröder 1344 (with references).

1204

## The Warship *Trekroner*

Probably Jan Dirichs van Campen (-1602-1618-) after Christian Møller.
Engraving. 57.1×66.5 cm
Den kongelige Kobberstiksamling, skuffe 7 no. 1
The *Trekroner* was built in Flensborg in 1601 by a Scotsman, David Balfour, and it was used for Christian IV's journey to England in 1606. Inscribed: "AD DIVUM CHRISSTIANUM:IV. SEPTEMTRION IS REGEM POTENTISSIMUM" and a poem in Latin. Inscribed: "Christian Møller/Inuentit delincuit/I.D.S.".
*Literature:* Styhr 1943 60. Landström 15ff.

1205

## Prospect of Copenhagen seen from the south

Jan Dirichs van Campen (?-1602-1618-?) after Johan Classzen van Wijk (? – at the latest 1613) 1611
Engraving, size of plate: 27.5×92.5 cm
Private collection
Bird's-eye view of Copenhagen seen from a high-lying spot above Amager. In the foreground the harbour entrance and behind that in the left of the picture the Arsenal Harbour between the Arsenal, built in 1598-1604, and the Proviantgården (Provision Yard) from 1602-1606; both buildings were part of a new naval arsenal, the purpose of which was to strengthen and enlarge the navy. To the left of the Arsenal a brick bastion on the spot where Christian IV was later to build the Brew-House. Immediately behind the Arsenal buildings, the old Copenhagen Castle. In the background the City with its churches and towers. In the front the smithy, which was later to become Holmens Kirke. Inscription: "HAFNIA METROPOLIS ET PORTVS CELEBERRIMVS DANIÆ", S.K.M. pictor Iohanes van Wijk/pinxit et excudebat/Iohan Dircksen scul.", "C.S.L./ Anno 1.6.1.1". The bottom of the picture is inscribed with a Latin stanza, and has the crowned compound monograms of Christian IV and Queen Anne Catherine in cartouche.
*Literature:* Vilh. Lorenzen 1937 63.

1206

## Ove Giedde (1594-1661), Admiral of the Realm

Albert Haelwegh
Engraving. 51.4×38.5 cm
Den kongelige Kobberstiksamling, 905 no. 29
Portrait set in an oval frame supported by Minerva and Mars. Above the frame the family coat of arms. The portrait is an allegorical commemorative print.

1207

## Houses at Nyboder

Unsigned, undated (c. 1770)
Watercolour. 40.0×51.4 cm
Rigsarkivet
Elevations, plans, and sections of a four-family house, which was probably projected about 1770, and an older slightly modernized two-family house, respectively, both at Nyboder. The oldest part of Nyboder was built c. 1631-1641 to provide housing for the permanent staff of the Royal Dockyard. The houses built by Christian IV were single-storied and accomodated one, later two families. Under successive kings, two-storied houses were added, which were projected to accomodate four families. This drawing depicts the old type as well as the more recent one. Inscribed: "Tegningen af de ny 2 Etage-Huuse i/Nÿeboder til 4re familier", "Tegningen af et gammelt 1. Etage=Huus/ til 2de Familier". The dating of this drawing is attributed to the inscriptions by the archivist on the back of the sheet, all of which have been dated 1771.

1208

## Constructional Drawings for a Warship

Unsigned, undated (probably about 1640)
Paper on pasteboard, pen and ink. 44.2×56.1 and 43.2×57.2 cm
Rigsarkivet SKTS, E 2 and E 3.

Sketches of side- and half-breadth plans for a larger warship. The uppermost and the lowest batteries have nine gun ports each, while the quarterdeck and the forecastle have six. These drawings may have been executed by David Balfour, the Scottish naval architect who was called in by Christian IV. However, it has not been possible to demonstrate a connection between any known ships and these drawings.
*Literature:* Lind 1890 315ff. Bjerg and Erichsen 1980 11.

1209

## Brass Gun

Gun founder unknown, Copenhagen or Elsinore c. 1610-48
Bronze, cat. L. 152 cm, cal. 5 cm, length of calibre 30, w. 80 kg
Tøjhusmuseet no. A 86
One pounder bronze gun, a so-called "falcon". On the breech-piece a crowned "C4". By no means all of the more than 345 one-pounder cannons which are known to us from the accounts can be identified. This holds true for this piece of ordnance as well, as it carries neither the name of the founder, the year of the casting, nor a stamp indicating the weight. The gun was found in 1888 during dredging operations in the harbour of Copenhagen, and may have come from the warship the *Trefoldighed,* which was burnt out in the harbour in 1676, after which it remained there as a wreck. The "falcons" were weapons for fighting at close quarters, and were used on board small-sized ships or placed in a rowlock (fork) on the rails of larger warships.
*Provenance:* Den historiske Våbensamling 1888.
*Literature:* Blom I 230ff. Blom II 67 ff.

1210

## Artillery ammunition – Chain Shot

Founder unknown
Iron, forged and cat. L. 58.2 cm, diam. 10.4 cm, w. 4.45 kg
Tøjhusmuseet, no. A 1001
Eight-pound chain shot. One half of the ball is well-preserved with a groove in the circumference and three dents. On the other half much has come off, so that the groove is no longer visible and only the remainder of two of the knobs can been seen clearly. Chain shot was used at sea against the rigging of an enemy ship.
*Provenance:* Tøjhusmuseet. Laboratoriets historiske Samling 1903.

1211

## Artillery ammunition – Bar Shot

Founder unknown, 17th century
Iron, cast. L. 16.6 cm, diam. 6.9 cm, w. 1.69 kg
Tøjhusmuseet, no. A.993
Three-pound bar-short used to destroy the rigging of an enemy ship.
*Provenance:* Tøjhusmuseet. Laboratoriets historiske Samling 1903.

1212

## Brass Calibre Rule 1605

Christoph Treschler Mecanicus 1605, Dresden Brass.
L. 42.0 cm, br. 0.06 cm, d. 50 cm, w. 110 g
Tøjhusmuseet, no. a 66
Calibre rule made of brass with traces of gilt. At the top a double head, Janus?
Inscribed: "CTM 1605". "EISEN KUGEL", "STEIN KUGEL", "BLEY KUGEL", "ZOL" and "PFUNT". The calibre gauge has four sides with graduations for iron, stone, and lead bullets and for inches measured according to the so-called Nürnberger calibre measure, which was used in this country until the 1680s. But in other countries, especially in Germany, it was in use until the middle of the 19th century. By using the scales on the calibre gauge, the gunner was able to estimate the calibre of guns and ammunition and thereby make sure that the right projectiles were used.
*Provenance:* Tøjhusmuseet 1942
*Literature:* Blom II no. 14.

1212a

## Rapier belonging to Admiral of the Realm

Ove Giedde
Germany c. 1640. Blade inscribed (S)AHAGUM and unicorn mark
Total l. 101 cm, length of blade 86.5 cm, largest width of blade 2.5 cm
Roskilde Domkirke
Straight double-edged blade with tapering point. 16.5 cm long fuller. Cross-formed grip with button and small downward curving shell guard in mussel-shell form.
*Provenance:* Admiral Ove Giedde's coffin in Roskilde Domkirke.
*Literature:* Bruhn 1949-51 5-38

1213

## Ship's Lantern

Denmark c. 1640
Brass lantern on a wooden pole painted black
H. 142.0 cm, br. 19.0 cm
Rosenborg F.a. 1.64
Brass lantern with turncap. On the side C4. Traditionally used by Christian IV on board the navy's ships.
*Provenance:* Rosenborg inv. 1737.

1214

## Model of the warship *Wasa*

Sixten Ostelius, cabinetmaker and maker of models, Norrköping Sweden 1980
Birch, mock orange "abache", hand-built. L. 140 cm. h. 105 cm, scale 1:50
Statens sjöhistoriska Museum, Wasavarvet
The *Wasa* was a warship built in Stockholm and launched in 1626. While it was navigating out of the harbour in 1628 it capsized, probably as a result of being loaded and built incorrectly; for one thing, the height from the waterline to the gun ports of the lowest battery was insufficient, causing it to suddenly keel over and take in water through the open ports. Discovered in 1956 and raised in 1961. Data: Displacement 1200 tons, total length 61 m, over the stems: 47.5 m, max.width: 11.3 m, total height: 52.2 m, draught: 4.8 m
Armament: 48 pieces of 24 pounders on gun decks. 8 pieces of 3 pounders on quarterdeck and forecastle. 2 pieces of one pounders on quarterdeck and forecastle, 6 storm cannons.
*Provenance:* Purchased by Statens sjöhistoriska Museum 1981 to be exhibited at the Wasavarvet.
*Literature:* Landström 1980.

1215

## Prospect of Stockholm seen from the ramparts of the Citadel

Willem Swidde (1660/61/1697)
Engraving, size of plate: 24.2×77.8 cm
Kunstakademiets Bibliotek
This page in Suecia Antiqua et Hodierna (1716), a work which was principally collected and partly executed by Erik Dahlbergh (1625-1703), is a depiction of Stockholm within the ramparts of the Citadel. In the foreground a part of the harbour with the numerous ships; behind this, the City with the Royal Palace and churches are seen in silhouette. The print is inscribed: "STOKHOLMIA Orientem versus" and: "W. Swidde Sculp. Holmiæ A. 1692".

1216

## Matchlock Gun with Copper Barrel

Holland c. 1625
Total 147 cm, barrel 106.5 cm, cal. 34.1 mm, w. 5.30 kg
Skoklosters slott, no. 5848
So-called blunderbuss to be used for defence at close range on board Dutch warships. The loading was a number of small lead bullets and the effect was like that of a very powerful shotgun.
*Provenance:* Skokloster inv. 1710.
*Literature:* Alm 1933 195.

1217

## Prospects of Copenhagen

Artist unknown 1587
Engraving, illuminated. 40.9×52.4 cm
Det kongelige Bibliotek, Kort- og billedsamlingen, Kbhvn.s alm. prospekter indtil 1600, fol. 1911, 10396
This print is a separate sheet taken out of Georg Braun and Franz Hogenberg, Civitatis orbis terrarum Vol. IV, probably the Cologneedition 1588, Plate no. 28. The print shows two prospects of Copenhagen. One depicts the city from the west showing City walls and towers. The following buildings can be identified; Copenhagen Castle, Vor Frue Church, Helliggejst Church, St. Nicolai Church, the King's Smithy (later to become Holmens Church). On the other print the City is seen from the harbour entrance towards the Slotsholmens (Castle island) with Copenhagen Castle and the churches of the city. Inscribed in cartouche: "Hafnia" and "Kopenhagen", "Hafnia vulgo Kopenhagen Vrbs Daniæ primaria qua fe terra marique conspiciendam exhibet Anno Salutis M.D. LXXXVII". This print shows the old fortification works of Copenhagen with brickwork and towers.

1218

## Christian IV as fortification engineer before Copenhagen

Artist unknown. Undated (1638-1640 ?)
Oil on panel. 24.7×34.5 cm
Private collection
The picture depicts the King on horseback in the area where Østervold (the east rampart) had been projected to continue in a curve to the Citadel, thereby protecting a newly-projected part of the city where Rosenborg was to be built. The Castle is visible in the background. This may well be the project which the King is seen explaining to a gentleman, who listens respectfully, hat and drawing in hand. The *motif* is known from the much larger painting at Rosenborg, which may be a copy of an as yet unknown picture . The representation of the King is of a type from about 1638-1640, but could also be much later. The standing gentleman is generally believed to be a fortifications engineer or an inspector of earthworks. The picture underlines Christian IV's personal interest in the enlargement of the city's fortification.
*Provenance:* Acquired from a Copenhagen secondhand dealer c. 1950.
*Literature:* Gamrath 1980 31. Lorenzen 1937 15f. Eller 1971 141 f.

1219

## Prospect of Copenhagen during the Swedish Siege 1658

Albert Haelwegh
Engraving. 31.0×40.4 cm
Den kongelige Kobberstiksamling, 904 nos. 16 and 17.

1218

Title of the print: "ABBILDUNG DER KÖNIGL. DANNEM: RESIDENTZ=VND HAUPT.STADT WIE/ AUC WELTBERUMTEN FESTUNG COPENHAGEN. WELCHER GESTALT DIESELBE VOM/ SCHWEDISCHEN KÖNIGE CARL GUSTAV A° 1658 DEN 12 AUGUSTI IST BELAGERT WORDEN". This print depicts very broadly the Copenhagen fortification works of Christian IV as they looked at the time of his death.
*Literature:* Sthyr no. 201.

1220

## Plan of Christianopel

Unsigned, undated (probably c. 1660)
Paper, pen, and watercolour. 74.5×82.0 cm
Kungl. Krigsarkivet, Stads- og Fæstningsplaner no. 2a, Kristianopel.
Three small towns in Blekinge (Elleholm Lyckå, and Avaskär) had to be abolished and their charters annulled when the construction of Christianopel was begun in 1599. The engineer in charge was Hans van Steenwinckel (c. 1545-1601), and, after his death, Hans Grabow. The King's instructions, however, were followed very closely. The condition of the ground made a polygonal form impossible. Instead the fortress was given a symmetrical parallel shape with four bastions. To the extreme disappointment of Christian IV, Christianopel was taken by surprise and burnt to the ground by a lightning attack in 1611 during the Kalmar War. The Swedish troops were commanded by Gustavus Adolphus (son of Carl IX), who, however, did not manage to hold the fortress. Inscribed: "Plan aff Christianopel og dess Situation".
*Literature:* Lorenzen 1937 150ff. Jagd 1986 164ff.

1221.

## Plans of Halmstad and Kristianstad

Erik Dahlberg (1625-1703). (1648)
Paper and pen. 31.0×48.9 cm
Kungl. Krigsarkivet, Stockholm, Fol. 44, Erik Dahlberg, Handritade kartverk, no. 21.
Erik Dahlbergh's "handritade kartverk" (handwritten

work of maps) open on a sheet showing plans of Halmstad and Christianstad. In the 16th century, Halmstad was an enterprising commercial centre. In 1619 the city was destroyed by fire and Christian IV took the opportunity to effect a completely new town plan in connection with the fortress. Work began in 1620 with Abraham de la Haye, a Dutch engineer, in charge. After the Kalmar War (1611-1613), Christian IV decided to build a new fortified city in Allö on Helgeå River called Kristianstad. Inscribed: "Halmstadh – Christianstadh".
*Literature:* Lorenzen 1937 160ff, 186. Jagd 1986 165, 169ff.

1222

## Plan of Kristianstad

Peter Jacob Wilster (1661-1725)?. 1680
Paper, pen ink and watercolour. C. 33.2×50.3 cm
Tøjhusmuseet, reg. U-349
The Kalmar War had demonstrated that unprotected towns could far too easily become the prey of the Swedish troops. The city of Vä, for one, was destroyed in 1612. The town was not rebuilt. Instead it was decided to build a fortified town in Allön on Helgeå, namely Kristianstad. The construction began in 1614, and in the same year Vä's charter was annulled. The condition of the ground at and around Allö was very like that of the marshland areas, and a Dutch expert within that sphere, the engineer Johan Semp, was commissioned to supervise the construction work. The King took lively interest in the project and often came to inspect it. This plan was probably ordered by Ulrich Frederik Gyldenløve (1638-1702), Governor of Norway 1664-1699, who initiated a systematic surveying of Danish/Norwegian fortresses. Inscribed on the reverse: "Christianstad d 14 octb (?) Anno 80/PJ (?) Wilster".
*Provenance:* Artilleriets Tegnearkiv 1928, Tøjhusmuseet.
*Literature:* Lorenzen 1937 160ff.

1223

## The Fortress of Bohus

Unsigned, undated (the 1680s)
Watercolour. 16.2×34.3 cm. Colour plate XIII
Tøjhusmuseet, reg. Y-362
The fortress of Bohus on Kungelven near the mouth of the Götaelven goes back to the 14th century. As a frontier fortress, it was of major strategic importance throughout the ages. The fortress was frequently rebuilt; in the 1590s it was renovated by Christian IV, and it was futher enlarged under Swedish sovereignty. Here the fortress is displayed as it looked in the 1680s, before Dahlbergh's renovation. Inscribed: "BAHUS"
*Provenance:* Artilleriets Tegnearkiv 1928, Tøjhusmuseet.

1224

## Axel Urup (1601-1671), Councillor of the Realm, Engineer

Albert Haelwegh probably after Abraham Wuchters. Undated (c. 1657).
Engraving. 33.1×22.0 cm
Den kongelige Kobberstiksamling, 903 no. 49.
Axel Urup was a Danish Councillor of the Realm, officer, and engineer. He was in charge of the construction of Christianspris on the Kielerfjord 1631-1638, where he was later to become Governor. In 1643 he was taken prisoner while defending Christianspris. In 1651 he completed the rebuilding of the Copenhagen Arsenal after the disastrous fire of 1647. This engraving is part of a series of depictions of councillors of the Realm.
*Literature:* Styhr 186. Lorenzen 1953 6. Klint 1975 116.

1225

## Wheelbarrow found in Christian IV's rampart

Denmark c. 1640
Wood. L. 123 cm, br. of lead 90 cm, wheel diam. 32 cm
Nationalmuseet.
Wheelbarrow found in the earth. Barrow consisting of a wooden frame with three stocks. At the bottom two sideboards and a wheel with eight spokes.
*Provenance:* Found during the excavations of Christian IV's rampart.

1226

## Plan of Copenhagen

Heinrich Thome (? -1624-1635) 1624
Paper, pen, and watercolour. 36.7×57.5 cm
Kungl. Krigsarkivet, Stockholm, Utländska kartor, Stads- og fästningsplaner, no. 1.
The work on the enlargement and renovation of the fortification of Copenhagen, which had been initiated by Christian IV, went on during the greater part of his reign. About 1600 it became evident that without a system of bastions, the fortification of the City would be hopelessly out of date. Step by step, a modernization-project was carried out, which included an extention of the naval arsenal, defensive works on the landward side, the foundation of Christianshavn, the projecting of the Citadel, and a new line of ramparts on the north. This plan, which is probably a spy's map, displays the situation as it looked in 1624. Inscribed: "Ano 1624/ gemacht von/ Heinrich Thome/ ingenieur".
*Literature:* Lorenzen 1937 63ff. Jagd 1986 74ff.

*1234*

1227

## Danish Cavalry Standard

The early 17th century
Silk damask with embroidery. 67×79 cm
Tøjhusmuseet, no. Fa.2
The cloth is made of yellow floral silk damask with a 4 cm yellow silk fringe. Embroidered inscription in letters of red silk damask: "DEN FALSK ER FAAR VIST SIN STRAF". In the upper corner by the pole the national emblem 26×26 cm in yellow and red damask appliqué. It seems that during Christian IV's participation in the Thirty Years' War, he ordered that the regiments which took part – including those recruited from abroad – should provide their standards with a small national emblem in the upper corners. In 1628 this was introduced for all Danish regiments.
*Provenance:* Tøjhusmuseet's historical collection of flags.
*Literature:* Bruhn 1949 85.

1228

## Standard

Denmark c. 1625
Cloth: 59×53 cm, pole: c. 3m
Rosenborg L.e. 6214.
The cloth is made of silk damask. It is divided into four fields, of which two are red and two yellow. In the upper field a white cross. In the middle of the standard Christian IV's crowned monogram encircled by the letters R F P, and in a circle: NON ME IMPUNE LACESSES. The cloth is edged with a narrow silk fringe.
*Provenance:* Rosenborg.

1229

## Muster Roll for the Citizens of Copenhagen 1588

Rigsarkivet. Danske Kancelli B. 97
The muster roll gave the authorities a general idea of the forces available and their various arms. In the case of Copenhagen, this registration was carried out districtwise: Øster kvarter, Strandkvarter, Snarens kvarter, etc. After each name, the function and accoutrement of the owner is stated. The muster roll opens on the summing up of personel living in Øster kvarter. The role of the civic guard was to defend the City, not to serve in the field.

1230

## War Ordinance for the Cavalry and Laws of Chivalry (1611)

Rigsarkivet. Danske Kancelli, B. I 2f, 165b
The present ordinance or statute falls into two paragraphs, namely the cavalry law proper and the laws of chivalry. The ordinance laid down the rules for the relations between members of the cavalry and their relations with the enemy.
*Literature:* Secher III 1891/94 349.

1231

## Draft of a War Ordinance for the Danish Infantry in Zealand, Jutland, and Funen 1621

Rigsarkivet. Danske Kancelli B 55
At a meeting of the council of the Realm held in March 1620, Christian IV made a proposal for the modernization of the "Landeværn" (military defence), which had been established 1614-15, to which proposal the Council replied in a declaration. As the King wanted a simplification of the war ordinance, the Lord Lieutenants of Scania were called upon to work out a survey of the peasants living in the parishes and districts within their jurisdiction. Consequently a new war ordinance for Scania, Halland, and Blekinge appeared on 14th September, probably by way of experiment. On 12th April 1621 a missive was sent to the other provinces. The peasants were divided into recruiting areas of 9 farms, each of which was to furnish one soldier chosen among their farm hands. His legal status was defined according to the war ordinance.
*Literature:* Secher III 1891/94 645ff.

1232

## Christian IV's Decree of Noblemen's Military Service of 1st April 1625

Det kongelige Bibliotek, Forordningssamlingen u. nr. 8°. This decree lays down the regulations for noblemen and lord lieutenants of the counties as to the number of armed soldiers and horses each of them had to furnish. The actual number of men and horses would depend on the size of the estate; from time to time, half a horse is mentioned, where two smaller estates would agree to equip one horse between them. The roll call took place every year.

1233

## Marquart Rantzau's Commission as Commander in Chief of an Infantry Regiment 1638

Rigsarkivet, TKIA, A. the period before 1660 no. 46
Anybody who was appointed officer, civil servant or the like would receive a "commission", a notification in writing which stated his rights and duties. Marquart Rantzau (c. 1590-1640) participated in the Kalmar War, and in 1625 he was appointed captain of the infantry. In 1637 he obtained permission to enlist a regiment of infantry and in 1638 he got his commission. It begins: "Wir CHRISTIAN der Vierdte von Gottes/gnaden zu Dennemarck Norwegen der Wenden und Gots König etc". It is inscribed: "Königl. bestallung Auff/ Ein Regiment zu fuss/Glücksburg den/21 April A 1638" and signed: "Glücksburg d 21 Aprilis an 1638/ Christian".

1234

## Danish Cavalry Standard

Reign of Christian IV
Silk damask with embroidery
50×56 cm
Tøjhusmuseet, no. Fa. 1
The cloth is of light yellow silk damask with a yellow silk fringe. In the middle a green laurel wreath divided by four red roses in appliqué. Within the wreath, in silver thread embroidery, a bowed arm in armor, which corresponds to Christian IV's order of chivalry, the "Armoured Sword-Arm", holding a short straight blade on which there is a skull, likewise in silver, with eye sockets and nasal meatus in black silk. In the upper corner by the pole, the national emblem 13×13 cm. Inscribed at the bottom:"ÆRE OD(E)R DO(DT)". The name of the standard-bearer is unknown.
*Provenance:* Tøjhusmuseet's Historical Collection of Flags.
*Literature:* Bruhn 1949 87.

1235

## Flag Design, Danish Standard

Artist unknown c. 1600
Watercolour with gold. 27×35 cm
Det kongelige Bibliotek, Thott fol. 832 and supplement.
Danish standard upon which the middle section is divided by the Cross of Dannebrog and the joint monogram of Christian IV and Queen Anne Catherine, compounded of C4 and AK. Among the arms that surround the monogram – apart from the emblems of the national coat of arms – is the black and white checkered arms of the Hohenzollers (the Queen's family arms), which had been given a prominent place in the order of precedence. Around 1600 the Danish standards seem to have had complicated patterns in red and yellow. They all carry the national coat of arms or sections of these. In the latter case, they are displayed either in small escutcheons or fitted into small square sections in the cloth pattern.
*Literature:* Kannik 108-114.

1236

## Pikemen's Armour

Denmark c. 1620
Weight: c. 8 kg apiece
Tøjhusmuseet
Each armour consists of helmet, gorget, backplate, and breastplate with short tassets.
*Provenance:* Transferred from Copenhagen Armoury stocks.

1237

## Pikes

Denmark c. 1600
L. 3.96 m, w. 1.71 kg, length of plates: 65 cm, point: 13 cm
Tøjhusmuseet
Iron-mounted pikes of ash wood with armour-piercing point in the shape of a leaf.
*Provenance:* Transferred from Copenhagen Armoury stocks.

1238

## Soldier armed with caliver

Jacob de Geyn 1608
Illuminated engraving. Size of plate. 24.5×17.5 cm
Det kgl. Bibliotek, cat. 27-75
Engraving from the well-known magnificent edition by J. de Geyn, which was published in many languages. The book is illustrative of the new tactical doctrines of the Dutch Captain-general, Maurice of Orange, who makes a distinction between two kinds of soldiers armed with guns: the caliverman, who is armed with a light gun, match, rapier and powder flask etc, and the musketeer, armed with a heavy musket, musket fork, match, and

*1241*

priming flask in addition to the characteristic bandolier with small powder measures, which was carried over the left shoulder. De Geyn also depicts another important infantry-type, the pikeman, who worked with the abovementioned soldiers.
*Provenance:* Jacob de Geyn: Waffenhandlung von der Rören, Musquetten undt Spiessen. The Hague 1608.
*Literature:* Askgaard 1971 7-71.

1239

## Book of Engravings and Texts: Danish Commands to be used for operating arms Jacob de Geyn 1608

Engraving. Size of plate: 25.5×17.5 cm, fol.
Det kongelige Garnisonsbibliotek
Jacob de Geyn's work was first published in 1607. Then came the 1608 edition in Danish and four other languages. Later on more editions followed. The book remained valid throughout the 17th century and laid the foundation for all other works on the subject of the infantry's use of arms. The work falls into three parts containing large folio drawings of the different operations. The exact reproduction of each singular movement shows the importance that was attached to accuracy in every move. The text is made up of short but adequate explanations that also include different words of command. Cf.cat. 1238.
*Provenance:* Jacob de Geyn. Wapenhandelinghe van Roers, Musquetten ende Spiessen. Amsterdam 1608.

1240

## Engraving of a Battle Scene

Diago Ufano, Frankfurt 1614
Engraving. Size of plate 20–30 cm
Det kongelige Garnisonsbibliotek
Ufano's book is by far the most outstanding work on artillery from the early 17th century. Ufano was a Spanish officer. He was present during the siege of Ostende and completed his work in 1612, while he was serving in Antwerp as Chief of the Artillery. Immediately after its appearance, the book was translated into German by de Bry (Frankfurt 1614), a citizen of Oppenheim and a man of enterprise, who in the same year published a translation into French with engravings that were derived from the German translation. The book falls into three parts. The first part describes the ordnance, then follow questions of a theoretical and practial nature concerning the

artillery, and finally a section on the men's duties in connection with the use of arms.
*Provenance:* Diego Ufano: Artilleri. C'est a dire Vraye instruction de l'artilleriet et de toutes ses appartenances. Franckfort, Egenolf Emmel. 1614 Folio. Translated into the French by Iean Theodore de Bry 164+5 p. With illustrations in genuine parchment.

1241
## Kettledrums for the Artillery
Denmark c. 1634
Copper plates. Diam. 110 cm, depth: 72 cm, w. 8 kg
Tøjhusmuseet mus no. m. 652: 1 & 652: 2
Each kettledrum is made up of four copper plates which constitute a truncated cone. This cone is fixed to a big curved circular plate with a 2.2 cm hole in the middle.
*Provenance:* Armoury Accounts 1657.
*Literature:* Askgaard 1962-64 206f

1242
## Cavalry Armour c. 1600-1620
Germany c. 1600
Burnished armour, w. 24 kg
Tøjhusmuseet D. 40
Armour consisting of back, breastplate, gorget, arm-braces, and tassets.
*Provenance:* Transferred from Copenhagen Armoury stocks.

1243
## Christian IV
Artist unknown. Inscribed "Christianus Daniæ Rex 1604"
Oil on canvas. 221×148.5 cm
Frederiksborg A 2776
The King is depicted in full-length standing *en face.* His hair is brushed back with a small pigtail on the right. He is wearing armour edged with narrow gold selvages, buckskin breeches and long boots with spurs. On a table on the King's left, the crown and the orb. This is one of the very few renderings know to us of Christian IV from around the turn of the century.
*Provenance:* Came originally from England. Acquired by the Museum of National History at Frederiksborg Castle at Etatsråd Glückstadt's Sale 1923 Auc. no. 28.8 1923, cat. 1448.
*Literature:* Wittelsbach und Bayern, cat. II/2 no. 576.

1244
## Christian IV
Plaster figure after a bust in the Rosenborg collection by Francois Dieussart (?-1622-1631-1661?) 1643/44
H. 102 cm, br. 72 cm, d. 55 cm
Frederiksborg A 2919

*1245*

The original bust is placed on a relatively high pedestal. The King wears an Emperor's costume with a laurel wreath round his head, antique armour, and a drapery over his shoulder. The pigtail in depicted on the left. There is no doubt that Christian IV wanted to be represented as the powerful peacemaker in the years immediately before 1643.

1245
## Christian IV's Cavalry Armour
Jacob Gering, Copenhagen 1642
Weight: 24.87 kg
Tøjhusmuseet, no. D 49
Blued and gilt armour, covered with velvet. Consisting of bullet-proof helmet, bulletproof breastplate, back-plate, diminutive tassets, loin-guards, pauldrons, and a very characteristic gorget. It is possible that this advanced piece of reduced cavalry armour was sent to Karel van Mander to serve as model for the armour in his large equestrian portrait of the King.
*Provenance:* Copenhagen Armoury stocks.
*Literature:* Askgaard 1962-64 193

*1249*

1246

## Pair of Wheel-Lock Pistols

Jørgen Dressler, Elsinore 1619
Total: 69.5 cm, barrel 49.3 cm, cal. 14.2 mm, w. 1.78 kg
Tøjhusmuseet, no. B. 350/51
These pistols belonged to Christian IV. Jørgen Dressler also furnished the State with a considerable number of military type wheel-lock rifles. Barrels stamped: Støckel 1100 and 1101. These may well be the pistols displayed in Karel van Mander's large equestrian portrait of the King.
*Provenance:* Det kongelige partikulære Rustkammer inv. 1775 no. 193/p. 403.
*Literature:* Hoff 1951 38, 201.

1247

## Christian IV's Sword

Petther Wersberg / Solingen c. 1620
Total l. 110 cm, l. of blade 87.2 cm, br. of blade 5.3 cm, w. 1.625 kg. Frontispiece p. 350
Tøjhusmuseet no. C. 159/42
Hilt of gilt iron. S-shaped quillons mounted with two kidney-shaped pierced shell guards. Oval channelled pommel. Straight double-edged blade with tapering point. Length of ricasso 5.3 cm. Inscribed on both sides of blade "PETTHER WERSBERG" and his stamp. This sword can be identified as the one in Karel van Mander's large equestrian portrait of the King.
*Provenance:* Det kongelige partikulære Rustkammer.

1248

## Portrait of Christian IV on Horseback

Karel van Mander (1609-1670) and Morten van Steenwinckel (1595-1646). c. 1642
Oil on canvas. 75.3×58 cm
Rosenborg no. 7-374
This picture is a preliminary study for the large equestrian portrait now at Frederiksborg. The King is portrayed on horseback in full length from the side, his head to the right front. In the background, a cavalry skirmish and a burning town. Christian IV was obviously eager to demonstrate his military capability in spite of his age (c. 65).
*Provenance:* Probably Johan Conrad Sprengler. To Christian VIII, then transferred to his Queen, Caroline Amalie; from her estate to Rosenborg 1881/82.
*Literature:* DMP II. Eller 1971 156f.

1249

## Christian IV

1616
Bust of gilt sandstone c. 1 m high, w. 125 kg
Tøjhusmuseet
Originally placed at Vesterport. It was taken down when Copenhagen was besieged by Carl X Gustav.
*Provenance:* Mentioned in the Royal Danish Kunstkammer inventory 1674 ($23^a$, 15). To the Copenhagen Arsenal 1825.
*Literature:* Smith 1926.

1250

## Curassier's Armour

Germany 1640
Weight: 31.7 kg
Tøjhusmuseet D. 47.
Blued and gilt armour edged with red velvet, lobster-tailed helmet. This piece is a very late example of bullet-proof curassier's armour in a beautiful princely version.
*Provenance:* Rendsborg Armory. Transferred to Copenhagen Arsenal 1852. Originally in Det Gottorpske Rustkammer, which was taken when the fortress of Tønning fell into enemy hands on 7th February 1714.
*Literature:* Askgaard 1962 72.

1251

## Wheel-Lock Gun

Denmark 1593
Total: 135.5 cm, barrel 108.0 cm, cal. 18.3 mm, w. 6.38 kg
Skoklosters Slott no. 6091
German type wheel-lock gun. The owner, S. Rosenkrantz, is probably Sophie Rosenkrantz née Brahe who married Councillor of the Realm Holger Rosenkrantz. The gun was probably booty from the Danish-Swedish

wars 1657-60. Barrel dated 1593. Wax seal with the Rosenkrantz arms and S RK. Many private Danish arms ended in C. G. Wrangel's Collection at Skoklosters slott, most of them probably as spoils of war.
*Provenance:* Skokloster inv. 1710.
*Literature:* Hoff 1951 63ff.

1252
## Wheel-Lock gun
Jørgen Dressler, Elsinore 1615
Total: 136 cm, barrel 108 cm, cal. 18.8 mm, w. 5.74 kg
Skoklosters Slott no. 5947
Typical German-type wheel-lock gun with short straight butt without a shoulder support. Cheekpiece, fore-end and trigger guard are covered with leather. Barrel stamped Stöckel 1100 or 1101, 1102-04. Barrel inscribed: "MOGENS ARENFELDT". Barrel dated 1615.
*Provenance:* Skokloster inv. 1710. In the possession of Mogens Arenfeldt (1603-1671), "hofjunker" to Christian IV 1624-1625.
*Literature:* Hoff 1951 34f.

1253
## Wheel-Lock Gun
Bernt Wegener?, Copenhagen 1619
Total: 136.2 cm, barrel 105.8 cm, cal. 18.5 mm, w. 5.59 kg
Tøjhusmuseet no. B. 190
Danish type wheel-lock gun with smooth, trough-shaped trigger guard and hartshorn mountings. Barrel stamped Støckel 2115 and 2310.
*Provenance:* Det kongelige partikulær Rustkammer inv. 1775 no. 508/p. 299.
*Literature:* Smith 1938 201. Hoff 1951 55, 66, 210.

*1254*

1254
## Wheel-Lock Gun
Søren Rasmussen, Ålborg 1636
Total: 121.5 cm, barrel 95.4 cm, cal. 21.8 mm, w. 5.69 kg
Tøjhusmuseet no. B. 196
Wheel-lock gun belonging to Christoffer Lindenov (1612-1679), who was the Admiral of the Royal Dockyard 1645-1657. According to an inscription on the mounted silver plate, the owner killed two roebucks with one shot from this gun on 5th August 1652. Barrel stamped Støckel 4532. Date on barrel 1636.
*Provenance:* Det kongelige Partikulære Rustkammer 1775 no. 360/p. 237.
*Literature:* Smith 1938 167. Hoff 1951 48 f, 196f.

1255
## Wheel-Lock Gun
Isach Lampe, Odense 1637
Total: 126.5 cm, barrel 97.2 cm, cal. 20.8 mm, w. 6.09 kg
Tøjhusmuseet no. B. 171.
This gun belonged to Henning Valkendorf (1595-1658). He was Lord Lieutenant of Funen and during the war with the Emperor (1625-29) he was one of the three "generalkrigskommisærer" of Funen. Barrel dated 1637. Stamped on barrel Støckel 3444.
*Provenance:* Det kongelige partikulære Rustkammer inv. 1775 no. 503/p. 297.
*Literature:* Smith 1938 200. Hoff 1951 60, 236.

1256
## Wheel-Lock Rifle
Andreas Neidhardt, Nykøbing F. 1642
Total: 146.2 cm, barrel 114.8 cm, cal. 17.8 mm, w. 6.61 kg
Tøjhusmuseet no. B. 160
This rifle belonged to the Prince Elect Christian "5", who died in 1647. He was very interested in arms and owned a large collection. This rifle has especially deep grooves to be used for firing very big shot. Wheel-lock with inside wheel and box-shaped cock. Barrel dated 1642. Lock and barrel stamped with a crowned C5. Barrel stamped Støckel 1934.
*Provenance:* Det kongelige partikulære Rustkammer inv. 1775 no. 379/p. 245.
*Literature:* Smith 1938 171. Hoff 1951 45 f, 204.

1257
## Wheel-lock magazine rifle
Peter Kalthoff, Flensburg 1645
L. 132.2 cm, barrel 99.2 cm, cal. 9.8 mm, w. 2.73 kg
Tøjhusmuseet no. B. 180
The clumsy loading procedure for muzzle loaders led to early experiments with repeater weapons. This is a repeater, with built-in powder and bullet magazine. By

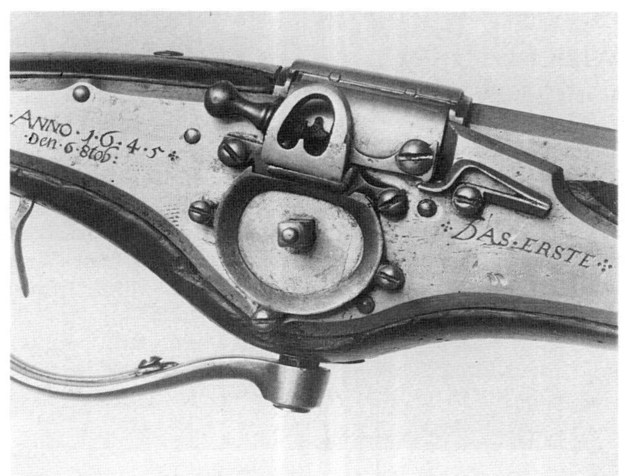


*1257*

means of an ingenious mechanical device, the weapon could be loaded by turning the trigger guard forward and backwards. Lock plate inscription 'Anno 1645. Den 6. Otob' and 'DAS ERSTE'.
*Provenance:* Det kongelige partikulære Rustkammer inventar 1775. No. 262/p. 203
*Literature:* Smith 1938 146. Hoff 1951 89, 102, 105, 120, 214. Ibid. 1969 271.

1258

## Cavalry Armour

Jacob Gering, Copenhagen 1642?
W. 18.95 kg
Tøjhusmuseet no. D.48
Smooth cavalry armour with lobster-tail helmet and collar.
*Provenance:* Transferred from Copenhagen Armoury stocks.
*Literature:* Askgaard 1962-64 187.

1259

## Ceremonial Sword

David Kohl 1648, Broby, Funen
L. 123.O cm, blade 96.3 cm., br. 5.0 cm
Rosenborg no. 23
Hilt of steel with cross-formed quillons mounted with two velvet-lined leather flaps studded with 35 leaden studs. Straight double-edged blade with rounded point. On the blade: 'FECIT IN BRO/BY FYN 1648/DAVID KOHL' and Christian IV's coat of arms and motto. On the other side: 'CONCORDIA RES/PARVÆ CRESCUNT/DISCORDIA MAGNÆ DILABUNTUR'.
*Provenance:* Mentioned for the first time in Rosenborg inventory 1718.
*Literature:* Boesen, Hoff and Schepelern 1956 no. 23.

1260

## Prince Christian, the Prince Elect's Broadsword

Willum Hermansen c. 1625, Elsinore
L. 112.5 cm, blade 92.0 cm, br. 3.1 cm, w. 1.22 kg
Tøjhusmuseet, no. C125/1942
Iron, silvered and gilted hilt with S-shaped quillons. The knuckle guard is screwed to the pierced pommel. Shell guards. On the inner shell guard a crowned C5. Straight double-edged blade with tapering point. Inscribed with a cryptic text and a wolf mark.
*Provenance:* Det kongelige partikulære Rustkammer.
*Literature:* K. S. Nielsen 1985 87.

1261

## Cutlass

Clemens Meigen ca. 1600, Solingen
L. 84.8 cm, blade 69.0 cm, br. 3.7 cm, w. 0.7 kg
Tøjhusmuseet, no. C 133/1942
Tarnished iron hilt with downward curving quillons and finger guards. Oval pommel. Straight double-edged flat blade with tapering point. On the blade stamped CLEMENS/MEIGEN.
*Provenance:* Transferred from Copenhagen Armoury stocks. Probably part of a gift from Maurice af Orange.
*Literature:* Adam von Breen: Neuwe Nassauwische Waffenhandlung, The Hague 1618.

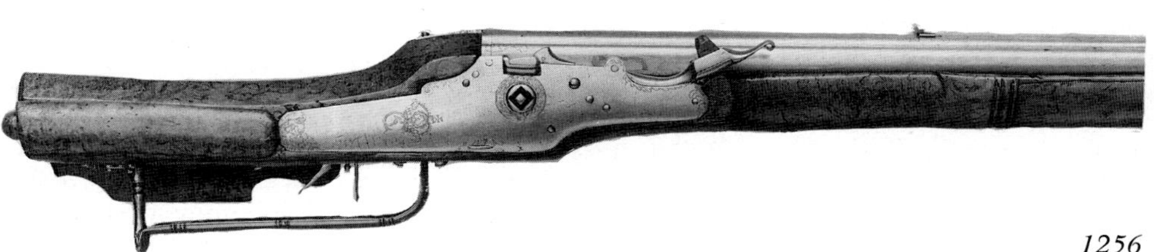

*1256*

1262

## Spring-lock carbine with priming magazine

Denmark?/Holland? c. 1645
L. 97.1 cm, barrel 65.2 cm, cal. 13.5 mm, w. 1.98 kg
Tøjhusmuseet, no. B 387
The trigger is cocked by turning the trigger guard, thereby leading the priming into the pan and reducing the loading time. A simplified version of the Kalthoff system.
*Provenance:* Det kongelige partikulære Rustkammer inv. 1775 no. 284/p. 103
*Literature:* Smith 1938 88.

1263

## Wheel-lock pistol

Kjeld Holdensen the elder, Ålborg c. 1640
L. 54.0 cm barrel 35.2 cm, cal. 15.8 mm, w. 1.43 kg
Tøjhusmuseet no. B 423:1
The oldest preserved Danish made wheel-lock pistol. Stamped on the barrel 'Stöckel 3697'.
*Literature:* Hoff 1951 52.

1264

## A pair of flint-lock pistols with priming magazine

Denmark?/Holland? c. 1645
L. 71.8 cm, barrel 53.1 cm, cal. 13.7 mm, w. 1.11 kg
Tøjhusmuseet no.B. 177/78
The built-in priming magazine serves to make loading easier and speedier. The construction is thought to be connected with the Kalthoff production.
*Provenance:* Tøjhusmuseet, cat. 1877, no. 1450.
*Literature:* Hoff 1951 96.

1265

## Partisan blade M. 1648

Brobyværk 1649
Etched iron. Blade l. 51 cm, br. 19.6 cm, point 35 cm
Tøjhusmuseet stocks
Partisan with Danish coat of arms. The blade is marked 'Broby in Fyn 1649'.
*Provenance:* From Tøjhusmuseet stocks.
*Literature:* Askgaard 1969.

1266

## Prince Christian, the Prince Elect

Albert Haelwegh, after Karel van Mander
Engraving. 41.4×29.6 cm
Den kongelige Kobberstiksamling, 901, no. 10.
*Literature:* Sthyr no. 7.

1267

## Frederik III

Albert Haelwegh, after Abraham Wuchters. Undated (1648)
Engraving. 54.5×40.6 cm
The Royal Collection of Engravings, 902 no. 12
The portrait of Frederik II (b. 1609), ruled 1648-1670, was probably commissioned on the occasion of his succession to the throne. Inscription: 'REGVM PHOENICI FRIDERIC III' and an Ode by Otto Sperling.
*Literature:* Sthyr 1965, no. 129.

1268

## Wheel-lock rifle

Hans Nulte, Danzig ca. 1625
L. 152.8 cm, barrel 116.0 cm, cal. 19.6 mm, w. 8.45 kg
Tøjhusmuseet no. B. 267
Self-cocking wheel-lock rifle; the mainspring is cocked when the hammer is turned. Lock-plate engraved with prospect of Danzig. On the inner side of the lock plate another prospect of the town. Barrel stamped 'Stöckel 3018' On the lock 'DANTZICK'.
*Provenance:* Det kongelige partikulære Rustkammer inventary 1775 no. 349/p. 233.
*Literature:* Smith 1938 164.

1269

## Christian von Pentz, 1600-1651, Christian IV's son-in-law, Governor of Glückstadt

Probably done in 1640 by Direck Diricksen 1613-1653
Engraving. 41.0×32.7 cm
Det kongelige Bibliotek, map and picture collection 1961 412/62
Christian von Pentz (1600-1651), one of Christian IV's sons-in-law, was a German Count of the Empire and Danish Governor of Glückstadt. He played an important political role in the 30 Years' War. Inscription: 'Christian Pentz Comte de L'Empire, Consaillier du Roÿ,/Cheuallier de L'ordre, Gouverneur de Glucstat et de paÿ circonvoysins, Colonel'. Signed: 'Direck Diricksen Hamb: Fecit'.
There is hardly any doubt that Pentz influenced Christian IV towards a pro-Imperial policy in the period up to 1643.
*Provenance:* Accession: Det kongelige Bibliotek 1961

1270

## Cavalry standard, Danish

First half of the 17th century
Silk damask with embroidery. 53×58 cm
Tøjhusmuseet no. Fa.3
The flag is of red silk damask with red and yellow silk fringes. Embroidered with yellow silk and silver thread within a wreath, the crowned lion of Norway stands on a

*1275*

halbard with a curved shaft. Beneath, the words 'NORSKE LØWE' worked in silver thread. Under the wreath, the motto 'ANIMOSIS ARMA PARATA' (The gallant have ready weapons) in silver letters. In the upper corner by the pole the national emblem 15×16 cm in red silk damask appliqué. As a standard with this inscription and marking was taken by the Swedes at Frederiksodde in 1657 from The Lord High Constable Anders Bille's Lifeguard Dragoon Regiment, this standard is also thought to originate from this regiment.
*Provenance:* Tøjhusmuseet's Historical Collection of Flags.
*Literature:* Bruhn 1949 85 fol.

1271

## Ernst af Mansfeld 1580-1626, officer

Robert van Voerst (1597-c.1636) after Ant.van Dyck
Engraving. 24.6×18 cm
Den kongelige Kobberstiksamling, 340 no. 5
From 1625-26 the brave but unruly Mansfeld was in Dutch-Danish service. With utmost competence he led the significant thrust towards the Imperial hereditary kingdoms, drawing Wallenstein's main force away from North Germany in 1626.
*Literature:* Wibiral 1877 187.

1272

## Johan Philip Fuchs 1626, officer in Danish service

Gottfr. Muller
Engraving. 18.4×12.2 cm
Det Kongelige Bibliotek, collection of maps and pictures
Johan Philip Fuchs von Bimback was a Danish infantry general appointed by Christian IV, who held him responsible for the fatal defeat at Lutter am Barenberg, where Fuchs was killed.
*Literature:* Westergaard, no. 3438.

1273

## Wetzel Rothkirch 1597-1655, master constabel

Albert Haelwegh, after Abraham Wuchters. Undated (1656)
Engraving. 42.1×33.2 cm
Den kongelige Kobberstiksamling, inv. 11331
The portrait is in an oval frame with medaillons on each side denoting 'Tolmoedighed', 'Sorrig', 'Siigdom', 'Døeden', 'Troen', 'Rætfærdighed', 'Mandhaftighed', and 'Forsictighed'.
Under the portrait a pall with 'ligvers' (elegiac verses). The engraving was used in Erick Erickszøn Pontoppidan's funeral oration, 1656. W. Rothkirch became known when during the retreat from Lutter am Barenberg he gave his horse to Christian IV, whose horse was shot under him. The devoted Rothkirch thus became Tilly's prisoner.
*Literature:* Sthyr, no. 190.

1274

## Ferdinand II, German Emperor 1619-37

P. van Sompet 1644, after Peter Claesz Soutmann, (c. 1580-1657) 1644
Engraving. 50.2×40.2 cm
Det kongelige Bibliotek, Kort- og billedsamlingen
Ferdinand II personally ratified the peace treaty with Christian IV in 1629. The print has a long Latin inscription with the Emperor's titles and glorifications.

1275

## Portraits of three Imperial officers

Unknown artist 1627-29
Wooden panelling on an altar table
Henne Church, Jutland
In two front panels and one side panel, half-length portraits of three named cavalry officers. The portraits are only faintly visible in a dark outline through a light reddish over-coating which covers the whole altar table. The officers are General Octavius Piccolomini, Her Ohr

Rohr and Her Johan de Wehrt. Their names are handwritten.
*Provenance:* Paintings presumably originate from Henegård, the panelling of which was used to restore the altar in 1725.

1276

## Johan Tscerclaes Tilly 1559-1623, Commander-in-Chief for the Catholic League

Pieter de Jode, after Ant. van Dyck
Engraving. 26.9×20.9 cm
Det kongelige Bibliotek, collection of maps and pictures. (Cf. catalogue no. 173).

1277

## Wallenstein 1583-1634, Imperial Fieldmarshal

Pieter de Jode, after Ant van Dyck. Undated
Engraving. 26.2×18.6 cm
Den kongelige Kobberstiksamling, 271 no. 72
Albrecht Eusebius Wenzel von Wallenstein (Waldstein) (1583-1634) pictured here in half-length portrait dressed in a cuirass and holding his fieldmarshal's baton in his right hand. He was Imperial general and fieldmarshal and a controversial figure, hated by his foes and unpopular with his allies. In 1628 he attempted to occupy the Baltic towns but was halted at Stralsund. He occupied Jutland from 1627-29. In 1630 he was removed from command by the Emperor, but reinstated 2 years later, after which he fought against the Swedes in the Battle of Lützen. He was assassinated in 1634. (Cf. catalogue no. 171).
*Literature:* Wibiral 1877, no. 40 III.

1278

## Portrait of Ottavio Piccolomini

Unknown artist. Undated
Oil on canvas. 92×72 cm
Nationalmuseum, Stockholm, inv. 765
Ottavio Piccolomini (1599-1656), Duke of Amalfi, Imperial German Fieldmarshal and Count of the Empire. He took part in the 30 Years' War and from 1627 served under Wallenstein, taking part in the occupation of Jutland (1627-28) when still a regimental colonel.
The portrait appeared in the catalogue of an exhibition in Munich held in 1980, ascribed to Justus Sustermanns (1597-1681) and dated in the 1600s.
*Provenance:* N. Byström's Collection 1851, transferred 1861 to the Kungl. Museum.
*Exhibitions:* Bruges 1962, La Toison d'or, no. 206. Munich 1980. Wittelsbach and Bavaria II/1 no. 713.

1279

## Cavalry Sword

Blade by Alonzo Luis de Sahagon Toledo, hilt from Solingen (?) c. 1600
L. 122.8 cm, blade l. 101.8 cm, br. 2.5 cm, w. 1.1 kg
Livrustkammaren, no. 10583
Officer's sword. Double-edged, flamed blade with tapering point. Blade rhomboidal in section.
*Provenance:* From Gustav II Adolf's Armoury.
*Literature:* Cederström and Malmborg 1930. Seitz 1955 and I 1965.

1280

## Cavalry Sword of the so-called Pappenheimer type

Holland, c. 1620
Iron hilt. Blade l. 94.6 cm. Total l. 103 cm, max.br. 2.6 cm
Tøjhusmuseet C. 210/1942
Iron hilt with knuckle guard, quillons and sharply upward-curving shell. The blade is straight, double-edged with tapering point.
*Provenance:* Acquired 1939.

1281

## Map of the area around Nienburg by the Weser

Unsigned, undated (1625)
Paper, pen, ink, water colour. 38.5×32.6 cm
Rigsarkivet TKIA, the period up to 1660, no. 96 I
When Christian IV started his German campaign in June, 1625, Johan Philip Fuchs commanded the infantry. The King advanced unhindered to Hamelin. Not until 18th July was Tilly given permission to advance. He crossed the Weser but was halted at Nienburg. The map shows the positions here. Signs indicate plundered villages and cavalry billets. The paper was found in a communication from General Fuchs dated 26th November 1625, with the words: 'Da solcher – Streich stehen, seindt ausgeplinterte Ort, /Da+ stehen, ligt angemusterte Reiterrey'.

1282

## Christian IV's note-calendar from 1614 and 1625

Rigsarkivet A2: Kongehusets arkiv
The calendars contain handwritten notes reminiscent of diary entries. The calendar for 1614 in inscribed on the leather binding '1614' and a crowned C4.
Both calendars were printed by Henrich Waldkirch in Copenhagen.

1283

## Sketch map of the situation at the Elbe, 1626

Unsigned, undated
Paper, pen, ink. 41.0×33.2 cm (20.2×33.2 cm)
Rigsarkivet TKIA, A no. 96, enclosure in J. P. Fuchs communication dated 18.6.1626
On the map, indication of infantry billets. Johan Philip Fuchs von Birnback (?-1626) was General of the Danish infantry. He fell in the Battle of Lutter am Barenberg on 17th August 1626. The map was found in a communication from General Fuchs, dated 18th June 1626, that is, a month before the battle.
This and the previous map are rare examples of sketch maps in contemporary signals.

1284

## One pound round shot

Unknown, before 1625
Iron, cast. Diam. 5.0 cm, w. 575 gr
Tøjhusmuseet, no. a 823
One pound round shot of cast iron from the battle field by Lutter am Barenberg.
*Provenance:* Found on the battlefield in later years and presented to Tøjhusmuseet on 5th April 1964.

1285

## A Pair of Wheel-lock Pistols

Reinert Pasquier, Elsinore 1628
Total L. 60.5 cm, barrel 42 cm, cal. 14.2 mm
Skoklosters Slott, no. 5784/85
This type of pistol came originally from Holland, and was characterized by the convex lock-plate pointed at the back. The butt is curved, with only a suggestion of a butt knob. A very popular type in Western and Northern Europe 1620-40. These pistols belonged to Wenzel Rotkirch (cat. 1273).
*Provenance:* Skokloster inventar 1710.
*Literature:* Hoff 1951, 39 201 fol.

1286

## Gustav II Adolf's Rapier

Holland/Germany. C. 1620
Hilt of steel, silver-plated with remains of gilding. Pierced pommel. Knuckle guard, quillons and ring guard with shell guard. Straight, double-edged blade with tapering point. On the blade: 'SOLI DEO GLORIA / FIDE SED CUI VIDE and SPES MEA EST DEO / VINCERE AUT MORI'.
*Provenance:* Rosenborg inv. 1718.
*Literature:* Boesen, Hoff and Schepelern 1956 pl. 12. no. 20.

1287

## Duke Ulrik's Rapier c. 1620

Holland/Spain c. 1620. Ivan Martinez Toledo
Hilt of silver-plated steel. L. 109.5 cm, blade 92 cm br. 4.0 cm
Rosenborg 7.160
Rapier with grip wound with silver wires and bands. S-shaped quillons, two finger guards and kidney-shaped shell guard. The blade is straight, double-edged and with tapering point. Blade marked: 'IVAN MARTINEZ EN TOLEDO / ESPADERO DEL REI'.
*Provenance:* From the Kunstkammer.
*Literature:* Boesen, Hoff and Schepelern 1956. Pl. 12, 2 no. 19.

1288

## Situation from the Imperial siege of Stralsund 1628

Claes Jansz Visscher the younger, 1586-1652
Engraving. 48.0×52.8 cm
Det kongelige Bibliotek, collection of maps and pictures, Müller's Pinakotek, Vol. 7, pl. 11, I.
The map shows a situation from Wallenstein's siege of Stralsund, part of efforts to wrest command of the Baltic from Christian IV. Through the intervention of Christian IV and Gustav II Adolf of Sweden, the siege was raised and Wallenstein had to retreat.
The map is inscribed: 'STRALSUND BELEGERT/ door Albert bý der G. G. Herzog von Friedland, gene=/rael van Keÿserlyke M[ts] velt-Legher; doch sonder/ver-overinge verlaten den 19[en] Julÿ Anno 1628' and 'Augustissimo Potentio./ CHRISTIANO/QUARTO/DANIÆ, NOWEGIO/, vandalorum. Gotthorum=/q3 Regi, Schlesvici, Hol=/satæ, Stormariæ, Dith=/marsiæ et Delmenhorst/comiti/Amoris ergo defect/ Nicolaus a Wassenaer/Asterod. Medicus', and 'C/Visscher'. In applied print futher information. Scale: 10 roder= 7.5 mm.

1289

## Painting of a flag design (Imperial?)

Unknown artist, possibly c. 1600
Water colour with gold. 27.5×37.0 cm
Det Kongelige Bibliotek, Thott fol. 832 + append
In the middle of the water colour is a black, two-headed, haloed eagle with golden beak and claws. The crowns are golden and varicoloured. The escutcheon on the eagle's breast is made up of the Austrian-Habsburg coat of arms, which came into use under the Emperor Rudolf II (1575-1612). The wreath around the eagle is green, with the following arms above, from top nearest the pole: Sicily, Aragon (?), Granada (?) (silver with black lion), the Tyrol, Dalmatia, Corinthia, Hungary, Salzburg, Styria, Austria and Croatia. The 'torches' at the corners are golden with reddish-yellow flames, the border is reddish-purple acanthus leaves and the leaves at

the corners are yellow in light blue frames. Belonged to an unknown unit.
*Literature:* Kannik 109 110 129 132.

1290

## Cavalry Standard from the Holy Roman Empire

Probably from the 30 Years' War
Silk damask, painted. c. 63.0×67.0 cm. Colour-plate XIII
Tøjhusmuseet, no. Fb 1
Pale yellow silk damask cloth, upon which painted two crossed straight swords with golden hilts piercing a ring of thorns. In each of the four triangles between the swords are five painted golden flames. Above and below the inscription 'PRO CHRISTO/ 'ET ECCLESIA'. In the upper left hand corner are the remnants of a later national emblem in *appliqué*. 14×13 cm
With its Catholic inscription, the standard can hardly have been made for a Danish unit. It must have been captured from an Imperial cavalry unit and subsequently given to a Danish unit after being provided with the national emblem, introduced by Christian IV in 1628.
*Provenance:* Tøjhusmueet's historical collection of flags.
*Literature:* Bruhn 88 fol.

1291

## Wheel-lock Pistol

Germany, Suhl c. 1625
Total L. 61.6 cm, barrel 39.7 cm. cal. 14.9 mm, w. 1.335 kg
Typical cavalry pistol from the time of the 30 Years' War. The Western European lock type and shape of butt, developed in Holland, had now reached Germany and replaced the larger and clumsier German wheel-lock.
*Provenance:* Tøjhusmuseet inv. 1941. No. B 412:2

1292

## Perspective of Christian IV's Christiansborg c. 1746

Louis-Augustin Le Clerc (c. 1688-1771)
Paper, pen, brush and ink. 53.0×72.5 cm
Den Kongelige Kobberstiksamling, drawer 19 no. 3
The view of Christiansborg and its surroundings is seen from Nybrogade. We are looking over the chapel, the carriage houses and stables on to the riding ground. Beyond it, in the middle of the picture, is the building now called the theatre wing. At one time it housed the Kongelige Partikulære Rustkammer.
*Literature:* Elling 1958, 59. Voss 1971, 141. Christiansborg Slot, 1975, I, fig. 246 and 248. Hjort Nielsen 1979, 33.
*Exhibitions:* London 28th October 1948, 2.1. 1949, ex. cat. Copenhagen's City Museum 1974 no. 58.

1293

## Wheel and Match-Lock Gun

Brunswick, Germany c. 1570
Total L. 131.0 cm, barrel 104.0 cm, cal. 14.7 mm, w. 5.96 kg
Tøjhusmuseet, no. B 70
This type of covering of sheet brass gilt is found on a small group of weapons produced in Brunswick c. 1570. This one belonged to Duke Heinrich Julius of Brunswick, 1564-1613.
On the butt plate the Braunschweig-Lüneburg coat of arms. On the barrel and stock a cryptogram: 'JESUS HILF ZUR SELIGKEIT'. On the stock: 'ALLIIS INSERVIENDO CENSUUR'.
Probably a gift to Christian IV from his brother-in-law, Duke Heinrich Julius.
*Provenance:* Det Kongelige Partikulære Rustkammer-inventar 1775, No. 528/p. 307.
*Literature:* Smith 1938 206 Hoff 1969 II 81 fol.

1294

## Revolving Rifle with Snaphaunce

Wolf Stolper, Nuremburg, Germany 1597
L. 104.6 cm, barrel 70.2 cm, cal. 10.6 mm, w. 3.00 kg
Tøjhusmuseet, no. B 294
The many attempts to increase firing speed led to a number of different types of construction. One of the more successful was the revolving rifle. This rifle's cylinder has 8 chambers. The dated butt plate is now lost.
Lock stamp: Stöckel 5881
Stock stamp: Stöckel 2357
*Provenance:* Det Kongelige Partikulære Rustkammer-inventar 1775, No. 344/p. 232.
*Literature:* Smith 1938 163 pl. 12. Hoff 1969 I 184.

1295

## Wheel-Lock Rifle

E. Sadeler/A. Vischer München. Germany c. 1605
L. 109.5 cm, barrel 80.7 cm, cal. 15.2 mm, w. 3.73 kg.
Tøjhusmuseet no. B. 308
This rifle is one of a group of four almost identical weapons, named 'goddess guns' after their decoration. They are *de luxe* models of highest international quality.
Barrel stamp: Stöckel 5736
Stock stamp: Stöckel 1982
The finely engraved goddesses represent Minerva on the patchbox cover and Venus on the ramrod plate.
*Provenance:* Det Kongelige Partikulære Rustkammer inv. 1771 No. 424/p. 264.
*Literature:* Smith 1938 181.

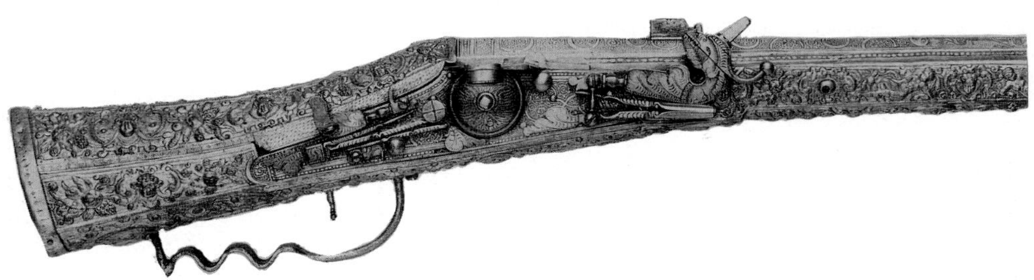

*1293*

1296

## Wheel-Lock Rifle (Tschinke)

Germany c. 1640
L. 117.3 cm, barrel 91.1 cm, cal. 7.7 mm, w. 2.45 kg
Tøjhusmuseet, no. B 334
Special type of small calibre gallery rifle with external wheel-lock. Found in the first half of the 17th century, this type of rifle was called a tschinke-gun, after the town of its origin, Teschen, now Silesia in Poland. The stock was aptly named 'hind's foot' after the shape of the butt. The stocks of these rifles were nearly always highly decorated with polychrome inlaid mother-of-pearl.
*Provenance:* Det Kongelige Partikulære Rustkammer inv. 1775, No. 450/p. 278.
*Literature:* Smith 1938 189.

1297

## Rapier

Clemens Meigen, Solingen 1600
L. 108.6 cm, blade 92.0 cm, br. 3.0 cm, w. 1.21 kg
Tøjhusmuseet no. C 169/1942
Blued hilt with gilding. S-shaped quillons with ovoid pommel. Straight, double-edged blade with tapering point. On the blade: 'CLEMENS MEIGEN', and a stamped mark on the ricasso.
*Provenance:* Det Kongelige Partikulære Rustkammer.

1298

## Rapier

Ottmar Wetter 1594 Bavaria
L. 138.0 cm, blade 109.0 cm, br. 3.1 cm, w. 1.58 kg
Tøjhusmuseet, no. C 184/1942
Deeply chiselled steel hilt, decorated with masks, figures and flowers. In the hilt a spring blade (L. 13 cm) released by a button on the ricasso. Blade straight, double-edged with tapering point. The blade is rhomboid in section.
*Provenance:* Det Kongelige Partikulære Rustkammer.
*Literature:* Haenel 1923.

1299

## Rapier belonging to Prince Christian, the Prince Elect

Willum Hermansen, Elsinore, c. 1625
L. 111.4 cm, blade 87.0 cm, br. 3.0 cm, w. 1.33 kg
Tøjhusmuseet, no. C 126/1942
Gilt iron hilt, grip with silver-plated floral decorations. The knuckle guard is screwed on to the flat, oval hollow pommel. The hilt is also equipped with a finger guard, a thumb hook and a smaller shell guard. On the thumb hook, 'C5'. Straight, double-edged blade with tapering point. Oblong mark on the ricasso.
*Provenance:* Det Kongelige Partikulære Rustkammer.
*Literature:* K. S. Nielsen 1985 87-96.

1300

## Hunting Sword

Daniel Sadeler c. 1620, Munich
L. 91.6 cm, blade l. 77.6 cm, br. 4.0 cm, w. 0.9 kg
Tøjhusmuseet, no. C 186/1942
Hilt of gilt steel, silvered grip. Open knuckle guard, downward curving quillons. The hilt decorated with floral tracery. On the grip the figure of a man. Straight single-edged blade with tapering point. On one side a flower, INTER ARMA SILENT LEGES' and an inscription 'Daniel Sadeler München', and on the other side 'IN TE DOMINI SPERAVI'.
*Provenance:* Det Kongelige Partikulære Rustkammer.

1301

## Rapier

Salomon Serger, Amsterdam, c. 1620
L. 119.3 cm, blade l. 100.0 cm, br. 2.8 cm, w. 1.13 kg
Tøjhusmuseet no. C 209/1942
Gilt openwork hilt, with medaillons on the pommel and the S-shaped quillons' finials. Shell-shaped finger-guards. Straight double-edged blade with tapering point. On the blade: 'SEBASTIAN HERNANDES'. On the ricasso 'SALOMON SERGER AMSTERDAM'.
*Provenance:* Accession Tøjhusmuset 1838.

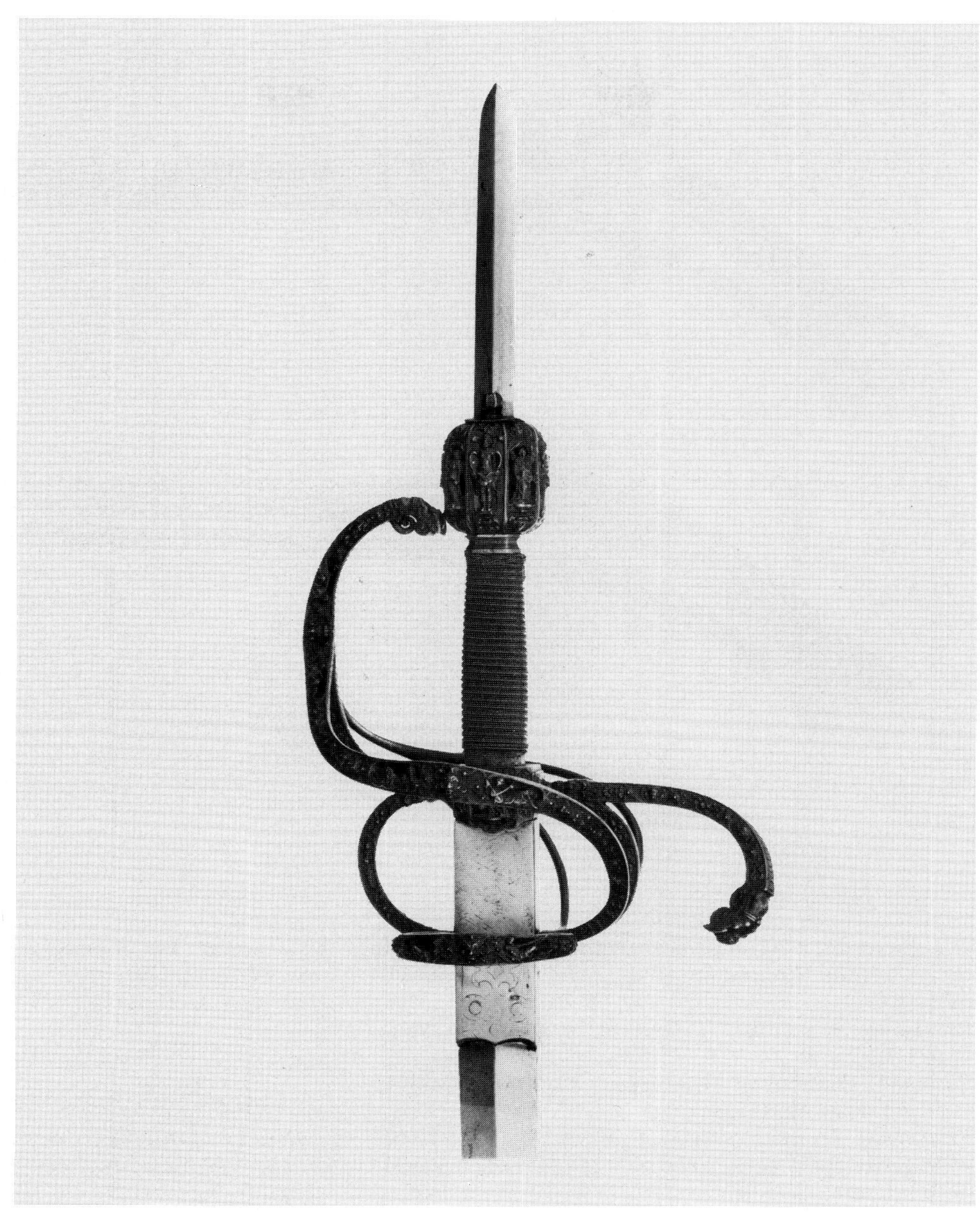

*1298*

1302

## Rapier

Denmark? c. 1600
L. 118.0 cm, blade l. 102.0 cm, br. 2.5 cm, w. 1.27 kg
Tøjhusmuseet no. C 129/1942
Steel gilt hilt sat with 14 Roman coins. The knuckle guard is mortised into the pear-shaped pommel. The hilt is made up of finger guards and cross guards. Straight double-edged blade with tapering point. On the blade, a mark and 'SAHAGUN'.
*Provenance:* Det Kongelige Partikulære Rustkammer.

1303

## Prince Christian, the Prince Elect duck-shooting at Nykøbing Palace.

By an unknown painter, the monogram AM (Adriaen Muiltjes ?) 1639
Oil painting on wood. 12.5×27.3 cm
Statens Museum for Kunst, inv. 1530
Shooting was favourite pastime of royality and the nobility. This picture depicts the Prince Elect on horseback,

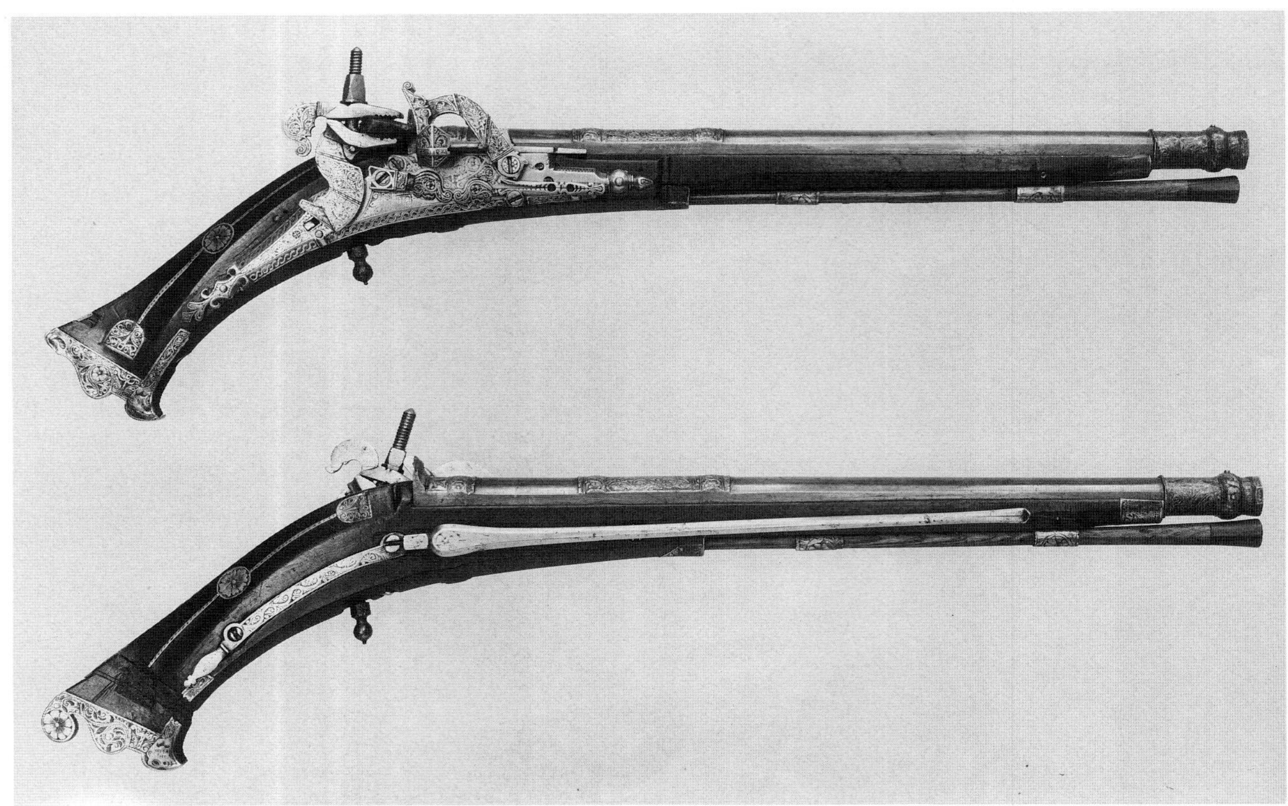

*1305*

with game and two companions, with Nykøbing Palace in the background behind the Sound. The picture is singed 'AM 1639'.
*Provenance:* Bodendick's Collection, bought 1810. Weinwick 1825 no. 36.
*Literature:* Madsen, in 'Tilskueren' 1897, 134, Andrup 1920 fol. Eller 1971 118.
*Exhibitions:* Kunstforeningen 1896 no. 74. Raadhusudstillingen Copenhagen 1901 no. 1204. Rosenborg 1948 no. 23. London, Danish Art Treasures 1948, no. 147.

1304

## A Pair of Snaphaunce pistols

Spain c. 1610
L. 72.8 cm, barrel 59.9 cm, cal. 13,9 mm, w. 1.32 kg
Tøjhusmuseet no. B 342/43
Spring-lock pistols with typical Southern European locks. The pistols were made in Ripoll, an important armaments manufacturing town in Spain. The long barrels are characteristic of European pistols of the early 17th century. The butts are curiously small. Barrel stamp: Stöckel 4973.
*Provenance:* Det Kongelige Partikulære Rustkammer inv. 1775, no. 197/p. 405.
*Literature:* Hoff 1969 I 229 fol.

1305

## A Pair of Snaphaunce pistols

James Low, Dundee(?), Scotland, 1602
L. 45,0 cm, barrel 31.2 cm, cal. 12.2 mm, w. 0.74 kg
Tøjhusmuseet no. B 345: 1-2
Scottish pistols are characteristic in that they are made with a special left and right lock for each pair. The fish-tail-shaped butt and the engraving is also a Scottish speciality. Lock stamp: Stöckel 3438. Dated on the flash-guard 1602.
*Provenance:* Oldenborgske Rustkammer inv. 1718 no. 3. Det Kongelige Partikulære Rustkammer inv. 1775 no. 207/p. 408.
*Literature:* Hoff 1969 I 212 fol.

1306

## Two Suits of Armour for Officers

Denmark c. 1620
Blued tempered, weight 23 kg
Tøjhusmuseet
Each suit of armour consists of helmet, collar, backplate, breastplate, vambraces and tassets. They are 'bullet-proof', that is, they have been tested. From various accounts we know that officers wore either burnished or tempered suits of armour.
*Provenance:* The Copenhagen Arsenal stock.

1307

## Bronze Bust of Christian IV

Copy by Jørgen Balthsar Dalhoff (1806-1840) of Bertel Thorvaldsen's original in Christian IV's Chapel in Roskilde Cathedral
Bronze, gilt and silver gilt. H.61.5 cm, br.72 cm, d.36 cm
Tøjhusmuseet
*Provenance:* Purchased from J. B. Dahlhoff 26.11.1858 for 1600 lbs. metal. Copenhagen Arsenal.

1308

## Model of the Man-of-War *Trefoldighed*

Made by late Erik Skive, Copenhagen 1985-87
Pear wood. H. 198 cm, L. 208 cm, br. 37 cm. scale 1:30
Tøjhusmuseet no. Q/M 10
The *Trefoldighed* was a three-masted man-of-war with 2 gun decks, built in Neustadt and launched in 1642. It was fitted out in 1644, and in the same year Christian IV decided that the stern was to be decorated with scenes of the Baptism of Christ. The *Trefoldighed* was Christian IV's flagship at the battle of Listerdyb on May 16th 1644, and at the battle of Kolberger Heide on July 1st the same

*1308*

year. It was rebuilt in 1657 and taken out of naval service the year after. Displacement c. 1000 tons, length 71 alen (1 alen = c. 2 ft), breadth 18 alen and depth 8 alen. The crews numbered 300-350, depending on the type of equipment and the engagement. Guns: 4 36-pounders and 18 24-pounders on the lower gun deck and 22 12-pounders cannons on the upper gun deck.
*Provenance:* Gift from Mr. Erik Skive in 1987.
*Literature:* Lind 1890 315-43 and 409-52.

1309

## 30 pounder brass mortar

Founder Claus van Dam, Copenhagen 1647
Brass, cast. L. 75.0 cm, cal. 220 mm = 30 pd.stone, w. 307 kg
Tøjhusmuseet no. a 1131
While examining the wreck of the Danish man of war *Snarensvend,* which sank just south of Kronborg in the summer of 1658, sports divers from the 'Aquanaut' club found this mortar in 1984. It is a brass hanging mortar, cast for the Danish High Constable, Anders Bille in 1647, presumably to comply with the wishes of Christian IV regarding the defence of the realm. In 1653 the mortar was taken to the fortress of Marstrand, and after the ceding of Bohus Len in 1658 as a result of the Treaty of Roskilde, some of the ordnance stocks from the deserted defences in the province were taken aboard the *Snarensvend.*
*Provenance:* Accession Tøjhusmuseet 1984.
*Literature:* Frantzen 1986 13-27

1310

## 8 pounder brass cannon

Gun founder Rolf Borchardtsen, Copenhagen 1623
Brass, cast. L. 202 cm, cal. 11.2 cm, cal. l. 18 cm, w. 808 kg
Tøjhusmuseet no. A 83
8 pounder brass cannon (metal cannon), called 'Dragon' after the dragon figure on the chase. The cannon, like all Christian IV's brass 8 pounders, has a conical muzzle, astragal and fillets and double base rings. It differs from the other cannons in that instead of having a knob, or button, at the back, it has a dolphin-shaped handle like the dolphin handles on the second reinforce. Stamped on the muzzle moulding, 'RUDOLF BORCHART GOSS MICH ANNO MDCXXIII'. On the first reinforce, Christian IV's monogram.
*Provenance:* In 1710 the cannon was aboard the navl vessel *Dannebrog* on October 4th when it exploded during the Battle of Køge Bugt against the Swedes. It was salvaged in 1873-74, after which it became part of Den Historiske Våbensamling in July 1874.
*Literature:* Blom II 59-62 no. 62.

*1309*

1311

## Brass saluting cannon in carriage

Unknown origin, c. 1650
Cannon cast in brass, carriage of wood. L. 67.5 cm, cal. 35.7 mm
Skoklosters Slott no. 10270 (cannon) and 10271 (carriage). Saluting cannon with trunnions and dolphin handles. Behind the muzzle moulding, foliage. Profiled rings and decorative foliage on each side of the handles. On the vent field, profiled rings on each side of the vent, foliage and the Wrangel Family coat of arms with helmet, and crown and crest in the form of a three-armed beam between two wings.
*Provenance:* Belonged to Carl Gustav Wrangel, Skokloster Slott.

1312

## 30 pounder cast iron foot mortar

Unknown, probably Westphalian (Sauerlandish( c. 1604-10
Iron, cast, bore l. 59 cm, cal. 23.5 cm, cal. l. 2.5 cm, w. 295 kg
Tøjhusmuseet no. A95
This cast-iron mortar of 30 pound stone is cast with a fixed elevation (8o°) in one with a square bed, and is the only cast-iron mortar from Christian IV's time which is preserved. Its range can hardly have been more than 600 m. This mortar illustrates the efforts of Christian IV expended on accumulating inexpensive cast-iron ordnance for the fortresses of the realm and to the navy, both by encouraging production of cast-iron round shot and small cannons in Norway, and by overseas purchases. Mortars were few at the start of Christian IV's reign, but his great interest in artillery led to a considerable exten-

sion of his mortar force. At this death they existed in fairly large numbers.
*Provenance:* Accession: Den Historiske Våbensamling 1845. Cat. 1877 p. 17.
*Literature:* Blom I 253 fol. Blom II 249 fol.

1313

## 2 pounder cannon in carriage (leather cannon)

Unknown origin, possibly Swedish c. 1630
Copper, iron, cordage and leather. Bore l. 105.6 cm, cal. 66 mm w. 45.5 kg
Tøjhusmuseet no. A104
The leather cannon consists of a 5 mm thick inner tube which in turn consists of an inner copper tube and an outer iron tube. Round it is a layer of iron rings wound with cordage and encased in leather. The carriage appears to be original. In the 1620s, experiments were carried out in several countries to develop light cannon which could accompany infantry as close support, something the existing heavy field artillery was unable to do. Christian IV also conducted experiments with leather cannons. They proved untenable everywhere and were soon replaced by light brass cannon, the so-called regimental pieces, first introduced in Sweden.
*Provenance:* Accession 1856 in exchange with the Armoury in Hamburg.
*Literature:* Meyerson 1938.

1314

## 4 pounder Brass Cannon

Gun founder Hans Kemmer, Elsinore 1623-25
Brass, cast, bore 1. 53 cm, cal. 8.70 cm, cal.l. 17½, w. 348 kg
Tøjhusmuseet no. A85
This 4 pounder brass cannon is the 50th of a series of 59 cannons referred to in the armoury accounts as 'clipped nettleleaf', after the heraldic Holstein nettle cast on the chase of all the 4 pounder cannons of brass from Christian IV and Frederik III's time. A characteristic of this

*1313*

series is the handle at the back in the form of a dolphin instead of the usual knob or button. The cannon was found in 1893 during the dredging of the entrance to Ebeltoft harbour. It was possibly aboard the Dutch frigate *Wapen van Enckhuysen,* which blew up during an engagement with Swedish ships on July 23 rd 1659.
*Provenance:* Accession Den Historiske Våbensamling 1893.
*Literature:* Blom I 226 fol. Blom II 64 fol. Askgaard 390-91.

1315

## 1 pounder Brass Cannon

Claus v Dam, Copenhagen, c. 1640
Brass, cast. L. 76 cm, cal. 5.5 cm, cal.l. 14, w. 71 kg
Tøjhusmuseet no. A 88
1 pounder brass cannon, so-called 'Falconet', with the gun founder's mark stamped on the chase (C.v.D) and on the first reinforce the arms of the Rosenkrantz family. The handles have been chiselled away, indicating that the cannon was used at sea. As Royal Gun Founder in Copenhagen from 1638-1655, Claus V. Dam made many hundred guns for the King, of which about 120 were 1 pounders. It is also known, however, that he made guns for private supply. This production was for the nobility, and continued throughout Christian IV's reign and was especially widespread in his last years, we are told, probably as part of the defence of the realm. Cf. A. Bille's mortar from 1647.
*Provenance:* Catalogue 1877, p. 14 no. 41.
*Literature:* Blom II 71 fol.

1316

## 15 cut Pulley with Brass Blocks

Borchart Geelgiesser, Copenhagen 1609
Brass and wood. 1st block h. 38 cm, b. 18 cm, d. 12 cm, w. 28 kg. 2nd block h. 40 cm, b. 13 cm, d. 14 cm, w. 28 kg
Tøjhusmuseet no. A98
15 cut pulley with metal blocks with two hauling parts. Both blocks have a large eyelet with swivel. The upper block has a crowned 'C4' and the date 1609, and the inscription 'BORCHARD GEELGIESSER G.M.' (goss mich). The lower block has a crowned 'C4'. Pulleys of this type were used to bring the barrel of a cannon into its mount.
*Provenance:* Accession 1847 from the arsenal in Rendsborg.
*Literature:* Eriksen 23.

1317

## Carl Gustav Wrangel. 1613-76, Swedish Admiral

Jeremias Falck (1620-1677) after David Klöcker (1629-1698). Undated
Engraving. 56.7×45.8 cm
The Royal Collection of Engravings, 247c no. 108

*1316*

Wrangel was both naval and army officer, not unusual at the time. He led the Swedish fleet home from Kielerfjord, hence it had fled after the Battle of Kolberger Heide on July 1st 1644. He subsequently annihilated a Danish squadron at Femern on 13th October 1644.
*Literature:* Block 1890.

1318

## The Battle of Femern, October 1644

Signed 'W:v Velde f' for Willem van de Velde (c. 1611-1693)
Painted c. 1650
Water colour. 63.0×144,0 cm
Skoklosters Slott, Bålsta, Sweden, inv. 1674
*Provenance:* Carl Gustav Wrangel's inventory Wolgast 1676.

*Literature:* Sjöhistoriska samfundet, Minneskrift, Uppsala 1944. Meyerson 1973. Probst. 1986.

1319

## Lennart Torstensson 1603-51, Swedish Rigsråd and Fieldmarshal.

Inscription: 'Fältmarskalken/Lennart Torstenson/som förde Sweriges/segrande wapan/till Donau vid Wien-,/väpnades som yng=/ling på Gripsholms/slott, under Riks=/baneret til War-/aktig, af den store/Gustaf Adolf'
Oil on canvas. 73×59 cm
Statens Konstmuseum, Slottsamling, Gripsholm, inv. 956
Lennart Torstensson (1603-1651) was Swedish Rigsråd and Fieldmarshal. He took part in the 30 Years' War and defeated Piccolomini at Breitenfeld in 1642. In 1644 he occupied Jutland. Cfr.cat. 203.
*Provenance:* Kronprins Oskar af Sverige (Oscar I), and presumably from him to Gripsholm Castle in 1822/27.
*Literature:* Sjöberg 1907 52.

1320

## Christina 1626-89, Queen of Sweden 1632-54

Jakob Henrik Elbfas' workshop. Undated (c. 1637)
Oil on canvas. 76×58 cm
Thomasgymnasiet, Strängnæs, Sweden
Christina was the daughter of Gustav II Adolf, and became Queen of Sweden in 1632 at the age of 6, although not becoming Regent until 1644. She abdicated in 1654, converted officially to the Catholic faith in 1655 at the Castle Chapel of Innsbruck and lived thereafter in Rome. As Queen of Sweden, she ratified the Peace Treaty of Brømsebro on August 13th 1645.
*Literature:* Steneberg 1955 44 pl. 7a. Malmborg 1966 236 fol.
*Exhibitions:* National Museum, Stockholm 1966, no. 46.

1321

## Clas Fleming 1592-1644, Swedish Admiral

Copy from the 18th century
Oval. Oil on canvas. 66×57 cm
Gripsholm 968
Clas Fleming led the Swedish fleet in the celebrated Battle of Kolberger Heide in 1644. He was felled by a Danish cannonball at the Kielerfjord on July 26th 1644.
*Provenance:* Gift from Count Klaes Fleming.
*Literature:* Sjöberg 1907 12

1322

## Jørgen Vind Gundestrup 1593-1644, Rigsråd and Admiral

Engraving by Simon de Pas 1645
31.4×22.9 cm
Den kongelige Kobberstiksamling, 700 no. 64
Jørgen Vind took part as commander of a squadron in the Battle of Kolberger Heide on July 1st 1644 between the naval forces of Denmark and Sweden. He was severely wounded and died shortly after.
*Literature:* Strunk 3276. Westergaard 13092.

1323

## Gustav Horn 1592-1657, Swedish Fieldmarshal

Engraving by Jeremias Falck after a painting by David Beck, 1651
Engraving. 31.6×21.6 cm
Den kongelige Kobberstiksamling, 248a no. 98
Gustav Horn was a Swedish military leader who fought Christian IV in Scania. Horn attempted unsuccessfully to take the Scanian provinces in 1644.

1324

## Christian IV

Engraving by Albert Haelwegh after a painting by van Mander
Undated (1643/44)
Engraving. 61.5×38.5 cm
Den kongelige Kobberstiksamling, 901 no. 2
The imprecise dating, 1643/44' is due to the Latin inscription by Otto Sperling, in which he describes himself as 'Botanicus Regius', from which position he was removed in 1644.
*Literature:* Sthyr no. 1 Faaborg 1264.

1325

## Hannibal Sehested 1609-66 Rigsråd, Govenor of Norway

Albert Haelwegh (?-1673) after Karel van Mander (1609-1670) 1650
Engraving. 57.3×40.1 cm
Den kongelige Kobberstiksamling, 902 no. 21
Hannibal Sehested sought to increase Norway's economic and military independence, and was to a certain extent successful. His energetic military leadership in Norway gave rise to the Norwegian war's nickname 'Hannibal's Feud'. Cfr. p. 52.
*Literature:* Sthyr 74. Westergaard 10894.

1326

## Loud-hailer

c. 1640
Brass, gilt mouthpiece. L. 168.5 cm, br. 40.5 cm, w. 4.4 kg
Skoklosters Slott no. 7134
A tradition from the 1800s has it that Carl Gustav Wrangel used this loud-hailer during the Battle of Femern on October 13th 1644.
*Provenance:* Skokloster Slott inv. 1710.
*Literature:* Svenska Flottans Historie I 1942 353.

1327

## Example of the Copenhagen Arsenals Accounts, 1644

Rigsarkivet (Public Record Office), Military accounts B. Fortifications accounts: IV C
Copenhagen Armoury accounts, no. 2 1621-51
The exhibit shows a list of arms sent to Funen at various periods in 1644. Inscribed: 'Fyen/1644 Dend 6 January ehr forskicket/ till Hans May-tt[s] i Fyen', and below: '16 Augusty ehr forskicket till her Riigens/Marsk Anders Bilde, udj Fyen', both inscriptions followed by lists of arms.

1328

## Axel Oxenstierna 1583-1654, Swedish Chancellor

Drawn in 1635 by Daniel Dumoustier (1574-1646). Inscribed: 'Illustrissimus D. D. Axelius/Oxenstiernia fait ce vendredy / 4 de may 1635 en moins / d'une demie heure devant / le naturel / par Dumouttier'. Written on the back: 'Målad vid en conference med Cardinal Richeliue'. Charcoal and pastel, mounted on canvas, 45.8×33.4 cm. Kungeliga Vitterhets Historie och Antikvitetsakademien, Stockholm.
The drawing was done during Oxenstierna's sojourn in France in 1635, when he negotiated with Cardinal Richelieu for French support against the German Emperor. Cfr. cat. 158, 201.
*Provenance:* Received as a gift in 1842 from C. E. Gyldenstolpe (whose paternal grandmother was an Oxenstierna).
*Literature:* Wrangel 1914 117 fol. Granberg 1929 64. Bjurström 1976 no. 386.

1329

## Axel Oxenstierna's rapier with scabbard

Spanish blade by Miguel Canero, Toledo, Germany c. 1600
L. 121.3 cm, blade l. 78.5 cm, blade b. 22.3 cm, w. 1.37 kg
Livrustkammaren no. 10.012 + 10.013
Guarded hilt of tempered steel with inlaid gold. Straight, double-edged blade with tapering point. Matching stirrups no. 10027.
*Provenance:* Accession Livrustkammaren in 1858 from the 'Oxenstierna Rustkammar' at Tidö.
*Literature:* Seitz 1965.

1330

## Axel Oxenstierna's Spurs

C. 1600
Steel gilt. H. 17.7 cm, b. 9.1 cm, w. 0.16 kg
Livrustkammaren, mus.no. 10029
*Provenance:* Accession Livrustkammaren in 1858 from the 'Oxenstierna Rustkammer' at Tidö.

1331

## A Pair of Flint-lock Wender Pistols belonging to Corfits Ulfeldt

Jan Kitzen, Maastricht, c. 1650
L. 73.0 cm, barrel 50.0 cm, cal. 12.9 mm, w. 1.20 kg
Skoklosters Slott no. 5620/21
The flint-lock was invented around 1610. About mid-century, a number of so-called wender guns were made, with one lock and several barrels, to increase firing speed. They had two, three or four barrels. Corfitz Ulfeldt can have purchased these pistols in Holland while travelling as an envoy in 1649.
*Provenance:* Wrangel's Wolgastinventar 1653. As Lord Chamberlain, Corfitz Ulfeldt fled to Sweden in 1651 and probably gave the pistols to Carl Gustav Wrangel.
*Literature:* Meyerson and Rangstrøm 1984 305 fol.

1332

## Rapier with Scabbard belonging to Corfitz Ulfeldt

Germany c. 1525
Iron hilt w. gold. L. 101.5 cm, blade l. 84.3 cm, blade b. 3.0 cm, w. 1.05 kg.
Skoklosters Slott no. 7247/48
Black hilt of iron with inlaid gold. Quillons in the form of a serpent winding its tail around the pommel, which is shaped like af wolf's head. The grip is of black fluted wood. Straight, double-edged blade with tapering point. On each side of the quillons there are seven gold-topped studs. The scabbard is of wood covered with black velvet. The chape is iron gilt decorated with a lion's head and a serpent.
*Provenance:* Wolgastinventaret 1653.
*Literature:* Amos Anderson's Art Gallery, Helsinki 1971 no. 49.

1333

## Lennart Torstensson's Rapier

Sebastiani, Germany c. 1645
L. 107.8 cm, blade l. 92.5 cm, blade br. 2.6 cm, w. 840 gr.
Skoklosters Slott no. 12462
Hilt of black tempered steel. Richly decorated with stamped silver thread in patterns of flowers, foliage and sprays. On the pommel and quillons cherub heads between angels' wings. Straight, double-edged blade with ricasso and tapering point. On the ricasso a stamped cross and 'SEBASTIANI'.
*Provenance:* Skokloster Slott Inv. 1793. Came from the armoury at Salsta.

1334

## Carl Gustav Wrangel's Rapier

C. 1640
L. 100.8 cm, blade l. 85 cm, blade br. 2.15 cm, w. 1.1 kg
Skoklosters Slott no. 7238
Silver hilted rapier with only one shell. Straight, double-edged blade with tapering point. On the ricasso a number of letters.
*Provenance:* Carl Gustav Wrangel's inv. Wolgast 1653.

1335

## The Swedish ratification of the Peace Treaty at Brømsebro in 1645

4.9.1645
Rigsarkivet Kongehuset E. Relations with other countries, Sweden 1537-1699
With Torstensson's thrust into Holstein in 1643, a new war broke out between the rival states of Denmark and Sweden. After French mediation, peace negotiations were conducted at Brømsebro, on the Dano-Swedish border in 1645. The opening illustrates the Swedish ratification of the peace agreement signed by Queen Christina, who had taken over the Swedish throne at her coming of age in 1644. Also depicted are 17 Swedish rigsråds.
*Literature:* DN IV 437 fol.

1336

## A Pair of Wheel-lock Pistols belonging to Anders Bille Denmark? 1642

L. 55.7 cm, barrel 35.4 cm, cal. 15.5 mm, w. 1.40 kg
Skoklosters Slott no. 12856/57
On the butt plate Anders Bille's monogram and arms, and the date 1642. The pistols are of the so-called Western European type prevalent in North West Europe from 1620-50. Barrel stamp WO in a square. The handles have only a slightly downward curve ending in an oblique line. The butt-end is reinforced by an iron ring.
*Provenance:* Skoklosterinventary 1710. The first owner was the Danish Lord High Constable Anders Bille (1600-1657).
*Literature:* Hoff 1951 79. Ibid 1969 126.

1337

## Match-lock musket

Jönköpings gevärfaktori c. 1625
L. 154.0 cm, barrel 118.5 cm, cal. 19.6 mm, w. 4.94 kg
Skokloster Slott no. 5797
The match-lock was invented early in the 1500s but was gradually replaced in Central Europe by the wheel-lock and the flint-lock. This weapon has a very characteristic feature for the period, the musket stock with a large triangular butt designed as shoulder support.
*Provenance:* Skoklosterinventary 1710
*Literature:* Alm 1953 92

1338

## Christian IV Lying in State

Copy by C. Christian Andersen after a painting in a private collection
Andersen (the 1890s)
Oil on canvas. 135×236 cm
Frederiksborg A690

1339

## Medal commemorating the Capture of Kalmar in 1611

Medal of silver gilt struck by Nicolaus Schwabe. Diam 6.1 cm
Den Kongelige Mønt- og Medaillesamling, the National Museum
The face shows Christian IV as the victorious commander in full armour with his field marshal's baton. On the reverse, with artistic licence, a combination of the events of 26th May, 1611, when Kalmar was stormed, and the 3rd August when the castle capitulated. The medal depicts in detail the siege with entrenched infantry, the besieging artillery trained on the town and its fortifications, and the final storm.
*Literature:* Galster 43.

1340

## The Fall of Elfsborg, 1612

Silver gilt medal struck by Thomas Borstorff
Diam. 5.2 cm
Den Kongelige Mønt- og Medaillesamling, National Museum
The medal was privately produced in commemoration, and designed for sale to those who were at Elfsborg, and others. On the face, the victorious Christian IV on horseback in armour and with his commander's baton. On the reverse, the Danish camp in the foreground with its four

quarters, and in the middle, the situation on May 22nd when the main fortress tower is breached. The scenery gives an excellent impression of contemporary military technique during a siege, with a fortified camp alerted against a *sortie,* shelter trenches for the infantry and besieging batteries to demolish the enemy's defences.
*Literature:* Galster 61.

1341

## The Fall of Gullberg. 1612

Silver Medal struck by Thomas Borstorff 1612
Diam. 3.7 cm
Den Kongelige Mønt- og Medaillesamling, National Museum
The face of the medal shows Christian IV in the foreground as the victorious warrior king in field uniform and with his commander's baton. Behind him is depicted the storming of a fortress that appears to be Kalmar Castle with its walls and towers. On the reverse, the Danish camp, marching troops and the besieging artillery firing on the fortress's massive defences and bastions prior to the final storm.
*Literature:* Galster 62.

1342

## Christian IV during the German Wars

Silver medal. Diam. 4.6 cm
Den Kongelige Mønt- og Medaillesamling, National Museum
The face of the medal shows Christian IV mounted, without armour. In the background a tower and two tents. Two interpretations are possible. The medal could be connected with the building of the Round Tower in about 1637, as suggested by the tower, the fact that Christian IV is not in uniform, and the enigmatic reverse with royal crown and heart. But it seems more likely to have been made in commemoration of participation in the German Wars. The rearing horse symbolizes warlike behaviour. The background scenery (the tents) could indicate a siege, although Christian IV never took part in one, and the tower could be the still existing tower in the town Lutter am Barenberg, where the King suffered the decisive defeat of the war.
*Literature:* Galster 73.

1343

## The Peace of Brømsebro, 1645

Silver medal struck by Johan Blum, Bremen 1645
Diam. 5.3 cm
Den Kongelige Mønt- og Medaillesamling, National Museum
The medal is believed to have been commissioned by Prince Frederik, Christian IV's second son, who as former Archbishop of Bremen knew the medal-maker (who could, however, have made it on his own initiative). The face has the King's portrait in high relief. The symbolism of the reverse, with its felled tree-trunk (Denmark) putting out fresh shoots under Jehovah's sun and shaded by Piety and Justice, with related legend, is not necessarily connected with the sorry peace. It is found on many contemporary coins.
*Literature:* Galster 76.

1344

## The Mailed Sword-Arm

Gold, diamonds
Rosenborg
In 1616 Christian IV conferred a new Order, 'The Mailed Sword-Arm' on a number of Danish and Holstein noblemen who had distinguished themselves in the Kalmar War. It has not been conferred since. Cf. cat.nos. 85, 179, and 563.
*Provenance:* Rosenborg.

1345

## Partisan

David Kohl Brobyværk 1648
L. 233.0 cm, blade l. 51.0 cm, blade br. 19.6 cm, w. 3.435 kg
Tøjhusmuseet, C's 358/1942
Partisan made at Brobyværk, Funen. Etched on both sides of the blade with the Royal Danish arms and 'BROBY BRVK IN FYNEN' and the date 1648.
*Provenance:* Transferred to Tøjhusmuseet from the Copenhagen Arsenal stocks in 1926.
*Literature:* Askgaard 1969.

1346

## Partisan M. 1648

David Kohl, Brobyværk 1649
L. 233.0 cm, blade l. 50.0 cm, blade br. 19.6 cm, w. 3.45 kg
Tøjhusmuseets C's 359/1942
Partisan with Royal Danish arms, marked 'Broby Bruk IN FYNN 1649'.
*Provenance:* Transferred to Tøjhusmuseet from the Copenhagen Arsenal stocks in 1926.
*Literature:* Askgaard 1969.

*Christian IV entering the Emperor's War 1625.*
*Silver medal. Diam. 5.8 cm. Den kongelige Mønt- og Medaillesamling,*
*Nationalmuseet. Cf. cat. 1344.*

*The large mural-quadrant on Uranienborg, Hven. From Johannes Blau:* Atlas Maior. *Det kgl. Bibliotek.*

# Rundetaarn / Trinitatis Kirke

## *Between Heaven and Earth*

Arranged by Det kongelige Bibliotek

Books and pictures preserved from the past are our best source of knowledge about what provided the individual person and society as a whole with spiritual substance, both in daily life and on festive occasions. But at the same time, it must be remembered, these books and pictures bear the stamp of the very narrow circle which produced them, and to whom they are addressed. This is particularly true of learned literature, most often written in Latin, where the many titles are inversely proportional to its limited circle of readers. Nevertheless books in Latin could also be read abroad. Fewer titles appeared in Danish and German, but in larger editions; these were what made the printers their profits. However, such books are often bibliographic rarities today; continual use in a population whose literacy was rising constantly simply wore them out. The messages of the books reached beyond the world of the learned, the rich and the prominent, and this was true even for Latin language works, if only indirectly.

Virtually all authors were the products of the Latin grammar schools and belonged to the world of the learned, the only place where it was possible to devote most of one's time to reading and writing. For all others, even for the king and the nobility, little time was left for reading once schooling was finished. For the latter, as for the citizen and peasant, cultural experience was primarily oral. Books may been read aloud within the domestic circle, but otherwise table conversation, domestic prayers and regular attendance at church services provided primary access to culture. General knowledge, also new ideas, slowly seeped out to all layers of society, to both men and women. Through women – especially in the lower levels of society – ideas also reached children and servants. In this way, the individual book could have an impact on the whole society.

*H. D. Schepelern*

1347

### Family portrait of the Worm family 1647

Oil on canvas. 120×250 cm
Nationalmuseet

Group picture with 31 persons. Names added later. In the upper left corner 2 coats of arms and a Latin verse by Thomas Bartholin. In the back row; "4 of the Saviour's disciples", no. 3 depicts Worm's father-in-law, Thomas Fincke, the three others may be Fincke's sons-in-law, Jørgen Fuiren, Hans R. Brochmand and Caspar Bartholin. Next is the fourth son-in-law, Ole Worm, his three wives (the two first each carrying a dead child) his two elder daughters and their spouses, bishop Jens Schielderup and professor Erik Torm. In the middle ground on the left, Christ in profile, on the right 18 children in two rows. Numbers two and three in the middle row are named as Worm's two next to youngest sons Mathias and Willum. The rest, unidentifiable, are children and grandchildren, many of whom died in infancy.

The painting shows a cross-section of a well established scholarly dynasty, and illustrates as well the period's deeply rooted Christian view of life as a progress towards death.

*Provenance:* Gift from rector Oluf Worm in Horsens 1830, the year in which the donor died. A letter which survives indicates that a change in intention meant that the painting actually should have gone to the diocesan library in Århus, but it had already been sent to the Museum of Nordic Antiquities in Copenhagen.

## Tycho Brahe: noble researcher with a royal grant

Learning in astronomy and chemistry was a rather non-traditional background for the mode of life of a nobleman. But despite the interests of the family and the prejudices of their class, the young Tycho Brahe mastered the learning of his day in these subjects through twelve years of travel and study. At that point he became known as the leading astronomer in Europe, and could naturally count on, and also received, favourable conditions under which to work as a nobleman-researcher under Frederik II.

Thus generous grants went to basic research in astronomy at a time when only large-scale investments in instruments could further developments within the discipline. And in the period 1576-97 Tycho laid the foundations for modern astronomy on his little island Hven in the Øresund.

Hven became the home of, for its time, a unique research institution. Tycho gathered here a small group of gifted and sharp-eyed assistants, uninfluenced by petty considerations of nationality, rank or prior education. According to Tycho's plans, the art of instrument making and observation technique were developed, an extensive observation and calculation program was carried out, and theoretical works were brought to completion in the form of scientific publications, in part printed on homemade paper in Uranienborg's own printshop.

*Peter Kristian Moesgaard*

1348

## Tycho Brahe

*De nova et nvllivs ævi memoria privs visa stella. Hafniæ 1573*
Det kongelige Bibliotek
The publication of this little book about the New Star in 1572 – which we today know was a supernova – made the 26 year old Tycho the most prominent astronomer in Europe. He proved unequivocally that the star was further from the Earth than the Moon, and could therefore by no means be an atmospheric phenomenon, but most likely belonged to the fixed stars in the so-called eighth sphere, beyond all the planets. This meant that on the Aristotelian heaven itself, the seat of immutability, Tycho had seen with his own eyes an unusually clear star suddenly flare up and then slowly die away.

1349

## Tycho Brahe

*Astronomiæ instavratæ progymnasmata, Pragæ Bohemiæ, 1602*
Det kongelige Bibliotek 19-119 4°
In 1588 Tycho began the printing of his major astronomical treatise on The New Star from 1572. But not until after he had died, in 1602, was the book finally readied for publication in Prague. It is a bulky book of over 800 pages, divided into three parts, the first of which presents Tycho Brahe's new theories about the sun and the moon and his revised catalogue of the stars, the second on his new star, and the third gives a thorough, critical evaluation of c. 30 other authors' writings on the new star.

1350

## Tycho Brahe

*Demvndi ætherei recentioribvs phænomenis liber secvndvs. Vranibvrgi cvm privilegio 1588*
Det kongelige Bibliotek 19-120-4°
Tycho Brahe closely observed seven comets from Hven, and he wrote this major contribution to astronomy, printed on Hven in 1588, on the first and largest of them, observed in 1577.

In this book Tycho Brahe published his own theory of the universe.

1351

## Tycho Brahe

*Oberservationes astronomicæ a Solstitio Hiberno anni 1577 ad 1581, maxima ex parte Autogr.*
Det kongelige Bibliotek, GKS 1825 4°
Tycho Brahe made his observations more precisely and with more attention to planning than any previous astronomer. His results were clearly recorded for later analysis. One of his record books is shown here, which covers the period 1577-1581.

1352

## Tycho Brahe

*Astronomiæ instauratæ mechanica. Wandesbvrgi, 1598*
Det kgl. Bibliotek 19-107 2°
In the spring of 1597 Tycho Brahe left Hven with his household, and a half year later he took up residence at Wandesburg Castle at the invitation of Henrik Rantzau. There he printed a small edition of this book, which contains illustrations and descriptions of the most important of the instruments he had developed, as well as a brief survey of his theoretical results. Together with the catalogue of over 1,000 stars (cf. no. 1353), this book was sent to a group of colleagues and princes. The leading astronomer in Europe was searching for a new employer.

1353

## Tycho Brahe

*Stellarvm octavi orbis inerrantivm accvrata restitvtio. Wandesbvrgi, 1598*
Det kongelige Bibliotek, GKS 306 2°
Among the theoretical results that Tycho Brahe himself experienced the completion of, his catalogue of stars deserves primary mention since it is the first real improvement in the field after antiquity. No astronomer before him had recognized the need to begin rethinking the theories on planetary motion based on precision in fixing the positions of the reference points, the fixed stars. The star catalogue in "Progymnasmata" (cat. 1349) covers 777 stars, and at Wandesburg Tycho Brahe expanded the coverage to 1,000 stars and had a set of copies made to send to colleagues and princes.

## The Tychonic system

Tycho had only a few and uncertain observations on which to base the choice between the traditional and the Copernican systems. But in the final analysis the theory of the earth's motion remained unreasonable to him. The idea was in conflict with several Biblical texts, and vast empty useless space between the last planet, Saturn, and the sphere of the fixed stars appeared to be an absurdity.

Tycho thus came to a compromise; around the immobile earth in the center of the universe revolve the sun and the moon, and around the sun, another mobile center, revolve the five planets then known. Tycho published this system himself in his book on the comet in 1588 (no. 1350), and from then on he argued without scruple against the Copernican system.

*P. K. M.*

1354

### Johannes Mejer

*Delineatio systematis planetarii in folio unico patenti*
Det kongelige Bibliotek, Thott 241 2°
A beautiful and thorough presentation of the Tychonic system by Johannes Mejer (1606-1674).

1355

### Nicolaus Raimari Ursus

*De astronomicus hypothesibus, sev systemate mvndano, tractatus astronomicus et cosmographicus ... Item astronomicarvm hypothesivm ... Pragae Bohemorvm apvd avtorem; absqve omni privilegio, 1597*
Universitetsbiblioteket, 2. Department
Tycho Brahe was jealous of his rights as creator of the Tychonic system. He carried on a feud with Claus Reymers Ursus for many years over Ursus' presentation as his own invention, first in "Fundamentum Astromicum" (1588) and again in the book from 1597 shown here, of a system nearly identical with Tycho's.
Ursus had been a swineherd in his youth, became an autodidact mathematician and astronomer and was employed as the court mathematician by the Emperor Rudolf II in Prague. Tycho believed that he had stolen the Tychonic system on a visit to Hven in 1584.
The 1597 book is unusually slanderous and abusive. It was privtely printed "without any rights", and after Ursus' death in 1600, Tycho got a court order to seize the remainder of the edition.

## Horoscopes, weather forecasting and almanacs

On Hven Tycho reigned supreme over his, for its time, unique research institution with its chemistry laboratory in the cellar and the astronomical observatory. He was hired to be a universal scientist; he was to deliver an annual almanac to the king, he cast horoscopes for the princes, Christian in 1577, Ulrik in 1579 and Hans in 1583, and he wrote out prescriptions and prepared medicines.

There is no doubt that Tycho had hopes that improving the foundations of astronomy would also produce a more reliable astrological practice, especially with regard to astrological meteorology, the basis for the weather forecasts in the almanacs.

When Christian IV personally assumed power in 1596 he found the scientific state within the state on Hven to be too costly. He divided the empire; astronomy was handed over to the university, to deal with chemistry he hired his "distiller" Peter Paynck (1575-1645) in 1609, who set up the "Distillery house in the gardens of Rosenborg Castle", and from 1616 on Niels Hansen Heldvad (1564-1634) was employed as the "royal court astrologer, astronomer or mathematician".

*P.K.M.*

1356

### Tycho Brahe

*Horoscopus Regis Christian IV, ad mandatum Friderici II conscriptus in insula Hwena, a Tychone Brahe Uttonide, Cal. Jul. 1577 infanti Christiano inscriptus, nebst Astrolog. Urtheil von dieses jungen Herren Nativitet.*
Det kongelige Bibliotek, GKS 1820 4°
The horoscope cast for prince Christian (IV) starts with an astronimical calculation of the positions of the planets according to the tables of Copernicus, with a few corrections based on Tycho's own observations. Next the horoscope, and tables over the relations of the planets to each other. The final section gives the astrological interpretation of the results, divided into sections by topic, childhood, course of life (with remarks on "dangerous ages"), character, morals and disposition, body build, travels, marriage, children, friends and death.
The section on marriage ends with a reservation: But as is said, this relationship depends more on the will of man than on the stars.

1357

### Elias Olai Cimber

*Diarvm astrologicvm et metheorologicvm Anni a nato Christo 1586, et de cometa qvodam rotvndo omniqve cavda destitvto, qui Anno proxime elapso mensibus Octobri et Nouembri con-*

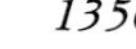

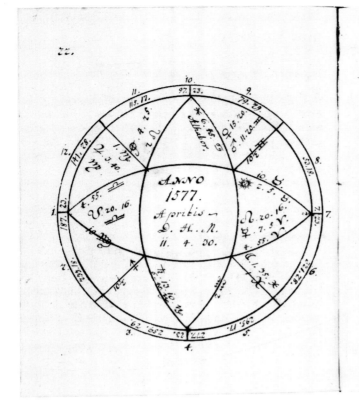

*1356*

*spiciebatur, ex obseruationibus certis desumta consideratio astrologica. Excusum in Officina Vranibvrgica (1586)*
Det kongelige Bibliotek
Elias Olsen Morsing worked as an assistant on Hven from about 1581, and in 1586 he published this work on the comets, combined with an astrological and meteorological calendar for the year 1586, which he had calculated according to Tycho's methods.

1358

## Peder Jacobsen Flemløs

*En Elementisch oc Jordisch astrologia. Om Lufftens forendring oc hues der under begribes, tagen aff de Tingest, som for øgnen sees oc forfares, oc huer Mand Letteligen kand affmercke oc tilforn wijde; Huilcken holder paa alle Aar ret oc er udi alle Land gaffnlig. Prentit paa Uraniborg Aff Hans Gashits, 1591*
Det kongelige Bibliotek 20-225 8°
Peder Jacobsen Flemløse, c. 1554-98, who came to work on Hven in 1578, was one of Tycho Brahe's most trusted assistants. This collection of weather signs by Flemløse was re-issued in 1644, 1745 and 1865.

1359

## Nicolaus Heldwaderus

*Almanach oc Practica Paa det Aar effter vor HERris JEsu Christi Naaderige fødsel MDXCI. Prentet i Kiøbenhaffn aff Mats Vingaard*
Det kongelige Bibliotek, Hielmstierne 2544 8°
Niels Hansen Heldvad was the court calendrist and published almanacs and prognostica (predictions) between 1591-1635. In his last years he had to give up predictions on "war, the navy, rising prices and plague" and merely predict the weather.

After Heldvad's death, the university received the privilege of bringing out an annual almanac, "without predictions on either the commons or other ranks or persons, wars, peace or such events". From this time astrology can be viewed as officially abolished in Denmark.
*Literature:* Gregersen: 1957.

1360

## Nicolaus Helduaderus

*Prognosticon astrologicon. Paa det Aar effter vor kiere Frelseris oc Saliggiøreris JEsu Christi Guds oc Jomfru Mariæ Søns Naaderige oc ærefulde Fødsel MDCXXII Aff den rette oc sande Astronomiske Konst beregnet tilsammenskreffuet oc publiceret. Prentet i Kiøbenhaffn hos Waldkirch, 1622*
Det kongelige Bibliotek 19-155 4°

In connection with the almanacs Heldvad issued prognostica, i.e. predictions, primarily regarding the weather, but from Heldvad these came spiced with anecdotes, sayings and proverbs. In the Prognosticon shown here for 1622, for example, the winter is claimed not to be particularly cold and harsh, but more marked by "rain, splish and splash, in which the chills will be common among the peasants. Catarrh and old cough will plague many throughout. Shoemakers and furriers will have plenty of work, since boots, shoes and warm clothing will be needed for this season".
*Literature:* Gregersen: 1957 p. 140.

## Natural philosophy after Hven

The new results from Hven, especially with regard to the refraction of light in the atmosphere, and the movement of the comets, made it unreasonable to cling rigidly to the traditional Aristotelian division between the sublunar, or earthly, and the celestial, physics and the idea of impenetrable boundaries between the spheres of the planets. Tycho's Danish heir in astronomy, Christian Sørensen Longomontanus (1562-1647), founded at the university a Tycho-Copernican scholarly tradition which accepted the daily rotation of the Earth and was supported by a corresponding physical theory on the nature of the material of the heavens and the larger celestial bodies, i.e. the Earth and heavenly bodies. The Aristotelian dividing line was thus broken down by making the Earth a heavenly body of the same sort as the planets and stars, and this was more Copernican than either the natural philosphers (physicists) or the theologians liked.

Another of Tycho's assistants, Kort Aslaksen (1564-1624), was and remained a theologian. He proposed a completely different solution, and thus laid the base for a Tycho-Aristotelian scholarly tradition in natural philosophy at the university. The co-existence of these two schools of thought does not appear to have caused any serious conflicts between Tycho's heirs in astronomy and those in natural philosophy.

*P. K. M.*

1361

### Cunradus Aslachi Bergensis

*De natura cæli triplicis libelli tres, quorum I, de cælo aëreo, II, de cælo sidero, III, de cælo perpetuo, e sacrarum litterarum et præstantium philosophorum thesauris concinnati. Sigenae Nassoviorum, 1597*
Det kongelige Bibliotek 19-131 8°
In this book "On the nature of the three-fold Heaven" Kort Aslaksen attempts to unite the Bible and traditional natural philosphy with the new natural science he had learned on Hven. Instead of making the Earth one of the celestial bodies, he preferred to transform the whole of the Heavens to a universal atmosphere, the density of which gradually diminished with distance from the surface of the Earth.

1362

### Christianus Severini Longomontanus

*Disputatio prima astronomica de præcognitis: in qua definito materice coeli adeoque loci cuncta corpora mundana majora ... Hafnia 1611*
Det kongelige Bibliotek 19-21 4°

1363

### Caspar Bartholin

*Astrologia seu de siderum natura, affectionibus et effectionibus Wittenberg, 1616*
Det kongelige Bibliotek 19-27 8°
The Tycho-Aristotelian tradition in natural philosophy founded by Kort Aslaksen set its stamp on the extensive textbook production of Caspar Bartholin (1585-1629), and again on the later cosmological dissertations of, among others, Ole Worm (1588-1654) and Jacob Finke (1592-1663).

## Astronomy at the university and the astronomical observatory

Born of peasant stock in Lomborg near Lemvig, Christian Sørensen Longomontanus (1562-1647) obtained in 1589 an apprenticeship on Hven. During a period of ten years on Hven and in Prague he was Tycho's most trusted assistant, and was himself an experienced scientist with responsibility for both programs of observation and theoretical studies. He became Tycho's Danish heir, and in 1605 started more than 40 years as professor at the university. In 1621 his chair in mathematics was raised to a special chair in astronomy, "Mathematicus Superior".

In his old age in the 1640's, Longomontanus was involved in setting up the university's observatory, or "astronomical theatre" at the top of the Round Tower, built in connection with Regenskirken (Trinitatis Church). Thus Copenhagen obtained a university observatory a generation earlier than the those founded at Paris in 1667, or Greenwich in 1675.

*P. K. M.*

1364

### Christianus Severini Longomontanus

*Astronomia Danica. Amsterdami 1640*
Det kongelige Bibliotek 19-28 2°
With this major work in astronomy, Astronomica Dani-

ca, Longomontanus obtained two objects: first, the completion of a theoretical astronomical system based on the observations done on Hven, and second, founding a tradition of high-level university teaching in astronomy. The book exerted considerable influence both abroad and in Denmark through its three editions of 1622, 1640 and 1663, and here it remained the basic astronomy text until Ole Rømer's time. Longomontanus explains all three systems carefully and leaves it to the reader to make a free choice of system.

1365

## Ambrosius Rhodius

*Typus ecclipsis solaris juxta hypotheses Astronomiæ Danicæ 1654 2^da^ Aug, ad elevationem Christianiensem 59° 42'*
Det kongelige Bibliotek, GKS 1833 4°
Ambrosius Rhodius used the Astronomica Danica when calculating the occurence of an eclipse of the sun in Christiania (Oslo), the second of August, 1654.

1366

## Christianus Severini Longomontanus

*Disputatio prima De chronolabio historico sev tempore ... in qva ... præcipue de natura variaqve definitione temporis ... Disputatio secunda De temporis speciebus nempe die, hora, septimana, anno et mense ... Disputatio tertia De temporis trium præcipuarum epocharum, nempe I, mundi conditi, II, Christi nati ... III. Olympiadis Iphiteæ ... constitutione. Cui accedit contemplatio de septem ætatibus mundi ... Hafniæ, Typis Salomonis Sartorii, 1627, 1628, 1629*
Det kongelige Bibliotek 19-168 4°
Longomontanus' three dissertations on calculation of time from the period 1627-29. In the last of these he deals with the problem of dating the creation of the world, and in this connection he draws up his scheme for the seven ages of the world. Longomontanus calculated that the world was created in the year 3967 B.C., and this calculation was the basis for the year given in our almanacs for this event all the way up to 1911.

1367

## Christianus Severini Longomontanus

*Introductio in theatrum astronomicum, quod in honorem cælestium opificis D.O.M., nec non totius orbis utilitatem, auspicio serenissimi et potentissimi Regis Daniæ et Norvegiæ Dn. Christiani Qvarti, Havniæ metropolis Daniæ modo instauratur, et tam miraculose quam operose construitur, stricte cum suis requitsitis delineata. Havniæ, Typis Sattorianis, 1639*
Det kongelige Bibliotek 19-28 4°
This "Introduction to the astronomical theatre, which ... for the glory of God and the improvement of all men ... soon will be established in Copenhagen and will be constructed just as wonderously as ingeniously" is Longomontanus' other major work in astronomy. We are taught here that astronomy must be based on both theory and practice, and the latter requires professionally produced instruments placed in a proper observatory.

1368

## Jean Baptist Morin

*Coronis astronomiæ jam a fundamentis ... restitutæ; qua respondetur ad introductionem in Theatrum Astronomicum C. Longomontani, Parisiis, 1641*
Det kongelige Bibliotek 19-28 4°
Longomontanus' Introduction to the astronomical theatre also included polemical attacks on colleagues who had not immediately accepted the improvements in methods from Hven, or Longomontanus' own synthesis of the results from the work on Hven. Several debates resulted, among them the polemic shown here between Jean Baptiste Morin (1583-1656) and Jørgen From (1605-51), who had succeeded to the astronomy professorship after Longomontanus.

1369

## Georgius Frommius

*Dissertatio Astronomica de mediis qvibusdam ad astronomiam restituendam necessariis pro Introductione in Theatrum Astronomicum ... Christiani Longomontani ... cum ... Johanne Bapt. Morino ... instituta. Hafniæ, Literis Sartorianis, 1642*
Det kongelige Bibliotek 19-28 4°
From wielded a sharp pen and characterized Morin as a mere theorist who had only a thin acquaintance with the practical side of astronomy, and believed the discipline could be reconstructed with only the use of a single quadrant. From criticized Morin's use of a telescope to determine the positions of the stars. It is clear that From was familiar with the use of the telescope and its potential, and had a pipe which enlarged roughly one hundred times.

1370

## Jean Baptiste Morin

*Defensio astronomiæ a fundamentis ... restitutæ, contra ... G. Frommii .. dissertationem astronomicam. Parisiis, 1644*
Det kongelige Bibliotek 19-28 4°
Cf. cat. 1368 and 1369.

1371

## Georgius Frommius

*Responsio ad doctissimi viri Johannis Bapt. Morini, Parisiis regii mathematum professoris Defensionem astronomiæ restitutæ. Hafniæ, Literis Viduæ Salomonis Sartorii, 1645*
Det kongelige Bibliotek 19-29 4°
Cf. cat. 1368 and 1369

1372

## Tyge Christensen

*Ars navigationis indeholdendis trende Parter, vdi huilcke findis alt, huis en Seilings Mand fornøden giøris vdi Siøfarten. København, 1642*
Det kongelige Bibliotek 27-291 4°
Astronomy is also basic knowledge for navigation. Here is a handbook in navigation written by a ship captain.

# Mathematics in the time of Christian IV

1373

## Thomas Finkii Flenspurgensis

*Geometriæ rotvndi libri XIIII. Basileæ, per Sebastianvm Henricpetri, 1583*
Det kongelige Bibliotek 18-269 4°
Thomas Fincke (1561-1656) had a long career at the university, primarily as a professor of medicine. In his youth he published the book on geometry shown here.

1374

## Georgius Frommius

*Arethmetica Danica, seu brevis ac perspicua institutio arithmeticæ vulgaris, astronomicæ, geodeticæ, in usum gymnasiorum et scholarum Daniæ as Norvegiæ Jussu Regio adornata. Hafniæ, Typis et sumptibus Melchioris Martzan, 1649*
Det kongelige Bibliotek 18-38 4°
The royal authorized textbook in arithmetic for gymnasium and grammar schools. The material covers arithmetic, extraction of square and cubic roots, as well as the rule of three. Ordinary arithmetic treats calculation with whole numbers and fractions, the "astronomical or logistic" arithmetic treats calculations with sexagesimal numbers, i.e. calculations in a base 60 number system, whereas finally the "geodetic" arithmetic is calculations with decimal numbers in the usual base 10 system. Decimals had been introduced by the Dutchman Simon Stevin (1548-1620) in a little book from 1585, "Die Thiende".

1375

## Christianus Severini Longomontanus

*Cyclometria vere et absolute in ipsa nature circuli cum rectilineo inventa, et ita qvidem, ut circino et regula exquisite tractari possit. Cui acessit introductio ad canonem trigonometriæ sub initium et finem quadrantis circuli instaurandum. Hamburg, 1627*
Det kongelige Bibliotek 18-269 4°
Longomontanus first wrote about squaring the circle in 1612, and later published several works on the subject. He himself believed that he had solved the problem of squaring the circle, which naturally was not the case, and he was rightly criticized by contemporary mathematicians, among them Paul Guldin (1577-1643), John Pell (1611-1685) and Thomas Fincke.

1376

## Hans Willumsen Lauremberg

*Logarithmus, seu canon numerorum, sinuum ac tangentium novus; cuius adminiculo operationes arithmeticæ et geometricæ per solam additionem et subtractionem perficiuntur. Leiden, 1628*
Det kongelige Bibliotek 18-65 8°
Hans Willumsen Lauremberg (1590-1658) was professor of mathematics and geography at the Academy at Sorø. In the work exhibited here he introduced logarithmic calculation to Denmark, which method had first been published by the Scots mathematician John Napier (1550-1617) in 1614. At the university the so-called "prostaphairese"-method, which had been developed on Hven by Tycho Brahe and Paul Wittich, was employed for yet a generation.

1377

## Set of terrestial and celestial globes

Willem J. Blaeu, 1622-28
D. 68 cm
Det kongelige Bibliotek
The Dutch cartographer Willem Janszoon Blaeu (1571-1638) had been an assistant to Tycho Brahe on Hven from 1595 to 1596. The pair of globes exhibited here from his famous workshop in Amsterdam is dedicated to Christian IV
*Literature:* Kejlbo 1968, p. 23.

1378

## Celestial globe

Willem J. Blaeu, 1603
D. 34 cm
Rundetårn, den historiske samling, nr. 1a
Celestial globe from Willem Janszoon Blaeu's (1571-1638) workshop in Amsterdam. Blaeu was a student of Tycho Brahe, and on the globe the stars are arranged using Tycho's own large celestial globe as a model.
*Provenance:* The globe belonged to Kammerherre Rothe and was purchased at auction at Hee in 1924.
*Literature:* Kejlbo 1968, p. 23.

1379.

## Celestial globe

Willem J. Blaeu, 1606
D. 13.5 cm
Rundetårn, den historiske samling, nr. 429
Celestial globe from Willem Janszoon Blaeu's (1571-

1638) workshop in Amsterdam. Most of the stars are placed in accordance with Tycho Brahes' new and exact mapping of the stars. The globe is dedicated to professor Adrian Metius, Paris.
*Literature:* Kejlbo 1968, p. 23.

1380
### Christianus Severini Longomontanus
Copper engraving done by Simon de Pas, 1644
Copper engraving, 13.5×11.5 cm
Rundetårn, den historiske samling nr. 175
*Literature: Westergaard 7229; Schepelern 1951, p. 45.*

1381
### Universal sun dial
Johan Soiner, Augsburg, First half of the seventeenth century
Brass, d. 7 cm
Rundetårn, den historiske samling nr. 60
Sun dial for universal use, i.e. use at different latitudes. The equator-ring is divided into half hours, and the bridge into intervals of 10 24-hour periods. The polar altitude for a series of cities is indicated.
*Provenance:* Purchased in Munich in 1922.

1382
### Sun dial in the form of a bowl
Copper engraving by Georg Brentel Lavinganus, Nürnberg, 1608
22×13 cm. Mounted in bowl in 1935
Rundetårn, den historiske samling, nr. 276
The engraving is decorated with a unicorn head and a heraldic rose, possibly the arms of the Nürnberg mathematician Caspar Uttendorfer, to whom the engraving is dedicated.

1383
### Cubic sun dial
Made c. 1590
Marble, length of the edge 20.5 cm
Rundetårn, den historiske samling, nr. 488
*Provenance:* From an old merchant house in Helsingør (Elsinore). Perhaps the gift of Tycho Brahe. Gift from director L. Brahe Christensen, Charlottenlund, 1968.

1384
### Proportional compass
C. Whitwell fecit 1597
Length of legs, 16 cm., with closed legs, width 2.5 cm
Rundetårn, den historiske samling nr. 224
Measuring, drawing and calculating instrument with a transversal scale.
*Provenance:* Gift from civil engineer T. Hansen, 1936.

1385
### Geometric quadrant
*Franc Schillem sculpsit et præscripto P. Lansb. c. 1600*
Copper engraving, glued onto wood. Radius 17.5 cm
Rundetårn, den historiske samling, nr. 305

## Geography and Cartography in the time of Christian IV

The sixteenth and seventeenth centuries were the epoch of European expansion. The discovery of America expanded the horizons of the world, and after Magellan's circumnavigation of the earth in 1519-22, colonization of the new lands began in earnest. In 1493 the Pope divided the rights to all the newly discovered lands between Spain and Portugal, but in reality these rights were unenforceable.

Christian IV was obsessed with the idea of creating Danish foreign trade supported by colonies. As early as 1599 he had personally commanded a fleet of eight ships on an expedition to the Northern Cap and the Kola peninsula. The goal was to claim sovereignty over the area and mark the boundaries to Russia, as well as exploring the most northern sections of the kingdom. A significant motive was the desire to find a route to India. This was also the background for renewed interest in Greenland. All contact with the old Nordic settlements on Greenland had little by little been lost, and the old sailing routes were forgotten. In 1605 the first of three expeditions sailed off towards Greenland, and, despite great difficulties in the icy waters, succeeded in landing on the west coast of Greenland. No traces of the Nordic settlements were found, but contact was made with the Eskimoes, and a few of them were captured and brought back home.

Christian IV was not blind to the possibilities to which a discovery of the Northwest Passage might lead. The explorations of the Englishmen John Davis and Henry Hudson in 1585 and 1610 gave reason to hope for early results, and in 1619 a Danish expedition was sent off under the command of Jens Munk. Its tragic end put a temporary stop to new attempts at exploration of the arctic regions.

The establishment of a trading colony in India was a more successful venture. In 1618 Christian IV had sent out Ove Giedde as admiral of a fleet of five ships which finally reached Ceylon in May of 1620 after many hardships. Trading stations were established for the newly created Danish East India Company both here and in Trankebar on the Coromandel Coast. After Denmark's ill-fated intervention in the Thirty Years War and the Torstensson War in 1643, Christian IV no longer took the initiative for new projects, and all other plans were dropped.

*Vivian Etting*

## The surveying of Denmark

Concurrent with the great voyages of discovery and the charting of the globe, a systematic surveying and mapping of the Danish provinces was carried out. In 1588 the oldest printed map of Denmark of directly Danish origin was published in the work "Civitates orbis terrarum". Marcus Jordan (d. 1595) from Holstein, a professor in Copenhagen, had executed the map at the order of the royal viceregent in the duchies, Henrik Rantzau. Despite its many errors, the map represented a great step forward within cartography.

Christian IV cherished considerable interest for the mapping of Denmark. In 1631 he directed Hans Wilhelmsen Lauremberg, professor of mathematics and geography at Sorø Academy, "to produce a map of Denmark by means of the mathematical arts". The project ran into difficulties, and in 1645 Christian IV gave him a serious reprimand. Two years later the king had run out of patience, and Johannes Mejer was named royal mathematician. Lauremberg did manage to get several of his maps printed in some of the large Dutch atlases.

Johannes Mejer was one of the period's most talented cartographers, but unfortunately only a few of his maps were printed. As early as 1636 he had delivered a number of maps to Duke Frederik of Gottorp, and a few years later he completed a large hand drawn volume of 63 maps of Åbenrå County. These detailed maps of villages, fields and forests are today an exceptional topographical source material. In the autum of 1642 Christian IV gave him the task of mapping the west coast of Holstein and Jutland from Glückstadt to Varde, and already three years later he had nearly completed this job. Through the years Johannes Mejer was alternately employed by the King and the duke of Gottorp, and it was through his maps of the duchies that he became known to the rest of the world. These were actually the only ones among his maps which were ever printed.

Christian IV had ordered a general map of Denmark shortly before his death, which was finished in 1650. This exceedingly correct map hung in Frederik III's study in Copenhagen Castle, but paradoxically it had no significance for the further development of cartography, since it was never printed.

*Vivian Etting*

1386

### Set of a celestial globe and a terrestial globe

Willem Janszoon Blaeu c. 1622
Cast in plaster of Paris and covered with paper. D. 68 cm
Det kongelige Bibliotek, The Map Collection
The Dutch astronomer and geographer Willem J. Blaeu (1571-1638) set up a printing and copper engraving works in Amsterdam, where many of the best astronomical and geographical works of the period were published. The production of both celestial and terrestial globes made up part of the business, and this set of globes can be dated to c. 1622, at which time a nearly identical set was made. The terrestial globe has a dedication to Christian IV, and on the celestial globe there is a small portrait of Tycho Brahe, who had been W. Blaeu's teacher during his stay on Hven towards the end of the 1590's.
*Literature:* Friis 1909.

1387

### Verdenskort fra "Atlas, Das ist / Abbildung der gantzen Welt/ mit allen darin begriffenen Ländern u. Provintzen".

Gerard Mercato and Jodocus Hondius, Amsterdam 1633
Hand coloured copper engraved map, 45×62 cm
Det kongelige Bibliotek, The Map Collection Fol. 23
This map of the world was produced by the Dutchman Henrik Hondius on the basis of an earlier map by his father, Jodocus Hondius and the cartographer Gerard Mercator. It demonstrates how far cartography had come in its understanding of the extent and shape of the continents. The four corners of the map are decorated with portrait medallions of Julius Caesar, Claudius Ptolemæus, Gerard Mercator and Jodocus Hondius. Allegorical depictions of the four elements, fire, air, earth and water, surround the projection of the globe.
*Literature:* Atlantes Neerlandici: 1969, II, p. 365; Me 37.

1388

### Measuring carriage made of wood, painted red, with (h)odometer

Seventeenth century
Tøjhusmuseet inv.nr. A 314
This carriage constructed for cartographic measurement of roads is equipped with a simple mechanism. The axle of the wheels, which is also the axle of the mechanism, transfers the revolutions to the two cam discs, which have 25 and 26 cogs respectively. The circular display dial has two graduations, the outer from 0 to 100 alen, and a complete revolution of the cam disc with the 25 cogs corresponds to 100 alen. Every time a distance of 100 alen has been covered, the 26 cog cam disc moves forward one. The odometer can thus register up to a total distance of 2600 alen.
*Provenance:* Transferred from Rosenborg 1717. Christiansborg particulære rustkammer 1775. Tøjhusmuseet 1838.
*Literature:* Bugge 1779 Pade 1976.

1390

### Odometer of gilded bronze

Unsigned, probably Thomas Rückert of Augsburg. Between 1581-1593
H. 18.5 cm, W. 9,5 cm, D. 4,2 cm
Nationalmuseet, 2. Department, Inv.nr. D144

This excellently made odometer consists of a flat lower part and a round, cylindrical upper part. It was attached to a carriage, in such a way that the lever was connected by a cord to the carriage wheel. With each revolution of the wheel, the movement was transferred through the lever to a series of cogwheels with dials for alen, kvartmil, and mil. One mil equals 12,000 alen. In addition the odometer had another function. The upper part's cogwheel pulls a narrow strip of paper across a small compass. The needle of the compass has three spikes in a row, and for every 100 alen a trigger in the lower section presses the compass needle up, so that the spikes make three holes in the paper strip. In this way measurement of rod distance could be combined with measurement of the direction in which one drove. There exist in German museums four nearly identical odometers, signed by Thomas Rückert in Augsburg, who had an imperial monopoly on the production of "artificial road measuring devices". On this odometer are engraved the letters: CVM GRA: ET PRIVIL: CAES: MA.
*Litterature:* Yde-Andersen 1952

1391

## Marcus Jordan

A map of Denmark and a map of Jutland and Funen from Abraham Ortelius, *"Theatrum orbis terrarum"*. Antwerpen 1595
Hand coloured copper engraved maps, both 35×25 cm
Det kongelige Bibliotek, The Map Collection Fol. 8
In the editions of "Theatrum orbis terrarum" from after 1595, there often are both a map of Denmark, based on Marcus Jordan's now lost map from 1552, and a much newer map by Marcus Jordan of Jutland and Funen. It is amazing that it did not bother the publisher to place two maps of Denmark with such great differences between them on adjoining page.
*Literature:* Bramsen 1952, p. 51-54, fig. 40-41, Nørlund 1942.

1392

## Marcus Jordan

Map of Denmark from *"Civitates Orbis Terrarum" IV.* G. Braun and F. Hogenberg, Køln 1588 (vol. 4)
Hand coloured copper engraving, 38×46 cm
Det kongelige Bibliotek, The Map Collection, Fol. 232,4 (latin ed.A)
This map of Denmark was produced on the orders of Henrik Rantzau, viceregent in Schleswig and Holstein. The map is therefore dedicated to the house of Rantzau, and the inscriptions praise the achievements of the family. This is the oldest printed general map of Denmark of Danish origin. Jordan's signature and the year 1585 are given on the map, which represents considerable progress within cartography. Zealand is remarkably lacking in detail in comparison to Funen and Jutland.
*Provenance:* This copy has a dedication to Frederik II and Christian IV.
*Literature:* Skovgaard 1915, Nørlund 1943, Bramsen 1952.

1393

## Hans Wilhelmsen Lauremberg

Map of Zealand from *Atlas Novus* J. Janssonius 1647
Hand coloured copper engraving, 42×50 cm
Det kongelige Bibliotek, The Map Collection Fol. 29.1. (an edition af 1649)
Lauremberg's mapping of Denmark was never completed. Although negotiations were carried on towards the end of the 1630's about printing c. 150 of the plates, the project was given up for reasons unknown. In 1645 Lauremberg received a royal reprimand, and two years later he was fired from his postion as royal mathematician and cartographer. Some of his maps, however, did appear shortly after this in Janssonius' Atlas Novus, where from the dedication to Judge Jørgen Seefeldt it is clear that the latter had arranged the connection to Holland. Lauremberg's own name does not appear on these exceeding exact maps of Zealand, Lolland and Falster.
*Literature:* N. E. Nørlund 1942, p. 48-53, Lauridsen 1887-88, p. 294-301, Bramsen 1952, p. 68-72, fig. 10.

1394

## Hans Wilhelmsen Lauremberg

Map of Jutland from Johan Blaeu *"Atlas Maior"*, Amsterdam, 1662 (partly based on map by Johs. Mejer)
Hand coloured copper engraving, 44×58 cm
Det kongelige Bibliotek, The Map Collection Fol. 36.1
Lauremberg was fired as royal mathematician in 1647 due to Christian IV's dissatisfaction with the apparent lack of progress in his work. Shortly thereafter some excellent maps of Zealand and Lolland/Falster turned up in Dutch atlases, without any doubt based on Lauremberg's work. In 1662, a few years after his death, this map of Jutland was published, which for the first time shows the well-known hump on the west coast of Jutland. This error was repeated often during the next one hundred years.
*Literature:* Bramsen 1952, p. 68-72, fig. 90, N. E. Nørlund 1942, p. 48-53, Lauridsen 1887-88, p. 294-301.

1395

## Johannes Mejer

*Grundliche Unndt Summarische Beschreibung Des gantzen Amptes Apenrade 1641*
Handwritten folio with fold-out maps and descriptions of the parishes
Det kongelige Bibliotek, NKS 2074 2°
This atlas consists of 63 maps of Åbenrå county, made in the years 1639-41. The county at that time was made up of only two herreder; Sønder Rangstrup and Rise, as

well as Varnæs birk. These surveys of each individual village are the oldest of their kind in Denmark, and present an exceptionally good picture of the nature of the Danish landscape of 350 years ago. In the village maps all the farms, houses, fields, field boundaries, meadows, forests, marshes, roads, barrows etc. are indicated, with an extensive list of the names of the peasants and the distribution of crop lands, grazing areas, marshes and moors. The maps can be divided into three groups; 1 county and 2 herred maps, 9 parish maps and 51 village maps. The land areas are given in toftroder and square roder, (1 rode = 5,61 m).
*Provenance:* Made on order for Count Frederik III of Gottorp.
*Literature:* N. E. Nørlund 1942, Lauridsen 1887-88, p. 239-402.

1396

## Johannes Mejer

General map of the kingdom of Denmark 1650
Hand drawn map on paper, 135×124 cm
Det kongelige Bibliotek, The Map Collection, kortbordet, 1100-0-1650
Christian IV ordered Johannes Mejer to prepare a general map of the Danish kingdom in the course of six years, as well as several specialized maps. Already in 1650 the general map was presented to Frederik III. This hitherto best map of Denmark was never printed and therefore did not exert any influence on the further development of cartography. Probably the map was prepared prior to the individualized maps of each of the herreder due to the king's desire for quick results. The drawing of Zealand and Jutland also suggests that Mejer made some use of Lauremberg's map.
*Provenance:* The map hung in the work room of Frederik III at the palace of Copenhagen.
*Literature:* N. E. Nørlund 1942, Lauridsen 1887-88, p. 239-402, Bramsen 1952.

1397

## Caspar Danckwerth

*Newe Landesbeschreibung der zwei Herzogthumer, Slesvig 1652*
Det kongelige Bibliotek 40-21 St.Fol.
Johannes Mejer's excellent maps of the duchies of Schleswig and Holstein were the only ones of his many maps that ever were printed. Not until about 150 years later were they replaced by more exact maps. His cooperation with Caspar Danckwerth, who wrote the text to this large work, brought with it many problems. Errors and shortcomings characterized the text, as well as a marked political tendency towards the Duke of Gottorp. Mejer had thus got himself in a difficult situation, since the Danish king had paid for his labors after he was named royal mathematician in 1647. Mejer decided to rewrite the whole book, but the large manuscript of 1100 folio pages was never printed.
Among the maps in this large work is an antiquarian/topographical reconstruction of the marsh areas in 1240, inspired by the work of Peter Sax. Mejer has drawn in many churches and parishes which had disappeared, such as he imagined that they were situated before the great floodings. Today the map represents a curious expression of the antiquarian interests of the seventeenth century.
*Literature:* N. E. Nørlund 1943, Lauridsen 1887-88, p. 239-402, Bramsen 1952.

1398

## Hans Hansøn Skonning

*Geographia Historica Orientalis, Det er: Atskillige Østerske Landis oc Øers/ met detz Folckis Beskriffuelse ... Århus 1641*
Det kongelige Bibliotek 28-71 4°
This book of 778 pages is a long winded description of a series of exotic peoples and countries, such as China, India, Egypt, Turkey, Judea, the Tartars and America, which he however confuses with India. The book is dedicated to Utte Marsvin and Mette Brahe, who had given economic support to the publication of the book.
*Literature:* Rahbek and Nyerup 1805, p. 69-83, Hubertz 1845, p. 70, 83-94, 105.

1399

## Hans Nansen

*"Compendium Cosmographicum. Det er: En kort Beskriffuelse offuer den gantske Verden ..." Kbh. 1633*
Det kongelige Bibliotek 28-39 8°
Hans Nansen particpated in his youth in several trade expeditions, among them voyages to the Kola Peninsula and Russia, and had an interest in the Icelandic Company. This geography handbook is divided into three sections; the first treats "the celestial bodies and divisions of the heavens" and has an unmistakable resemblence to the medieaval Lucidarius; the second covers "all kingdoms and countries, which are here on Earth", and here Nansen's sources are the Dutch atlases, Antoni de Herrera and others; the final section gives information relevant to navigation, courses for compasses and distances between diverse cities and countries.
The book was widely used and appeared in several enlarged editions. It was also translated into Icelandic.
*Literature:* Adils 1927.

1400

## Hans Willumsen Lauremberg

*Gromaticæ libri tres I. De Jugeratione. II. De Podismo. III. De Centuriatione, Hafnia 1639*
Det kongelige Bibliotek 18-643 4°
*Provenance:* The book is dedicated to Christian IV.
*Literature:* Daae 1884, N. E. Nørlund 1942, p. 48.

1401

## Adam Olearius (1603-1671)

*"Offt begehrte Beschreibung der Newen Orientalischen Reise" Schleswig 1647*

Det kongelige Bibliotek 28-149 2°

Count Frederik III of Gottorp had plans of establishing direct trade connections with Persia. In 1633 he sent a delegation to Moscow which had Olearius as secretary to ask for the Tsar's permission to travel through Russia. In October, 1635, the great expedition started. After travelling through Reval, Moscow, Astrakhan and the Caspian Sea the expedition finally reached Isphahan in Persia in August of 1637. In 1639 the long journey was completed. Judged from the viewpoint of trade the results were meager, but the travel account of Adam Olearius is a landmark in the history of ethnography. It contains a wealth of ethnographic, historical and archaeological observations, illustrated by maps and copper engravings. The book appeared in Dutch, French and English translations.

*Literature:* Andresen and Stephan 1928, Bobé 1948, p. 179-82, Grosse 1867.

1402

## Jens Munk

*Navigatio Septentrionalis. Det er: Relation eller Bescriffuelse / om Seiglads oc Reyse / paa denne Nordvestiske Passagie, som nu kaldis Nova Dania, København 1624*

Det kongelige Bibliotek 39-175 4°

Jens Munk's expedition to Hudson's Bay in 1619-20 to find the Northwest Passage, the so-called "Anianstræde" north of America to China, ended in tragedy. Only Jens Munk and two other sailors survived of the original 64 men on board the frigate "Enhjørningen" (The Unicorn), and the yacht "Lamprenen". The moving story of the voyage and the winter spent in Hudson's Bay was published four years later. The book has a few maps and copper engravings.

*Literature:* Gosch 1897, Lauridsen 1883, K. Birket-Smith 1929. T. Hansen and Seeberg 1965. H. Ilsøe 1974 165f.

1403

## Passport for Godske Lindenov and others, 18 April, 1605

Rigsarkivet, Kongehusets ark. D 12 Grønland, supplement

This passport with the signature of Christian IV himself was issued on the 18th of April, 1605 on the occasion of the departure of the first expedition to Greenland. The passport is issued to the nobleman Godske Lindenov, who had command of the flagship "The Red Lion" (RVBER LEO), and to his first officer, Peter Kjeldsen, and to Nikolaj Creisen. During the expedition, which was under the leadership of the English admiral John Cunningham, "The Red Lion" separated from the two other ships because of disagreements. It reached home before the others, however, bringing with it two captured Greenlanders.

1404

## Claus Christoffersen Lyschander

*Den Grønlandske Chronica* Kbh. 1608

Det kongelige Bibliotek 39-210 8°

For an historian, and later royal historian, Greenland was an obvious subject to write about on the occasion of the expeditions of 1605-1607. A chronological survey of the history of Greenland since 770 to the end of the Middle Ages, written on the basis of "old Antiquities and Documents", makes up the first part of the book. The second gives a thorough account of the the expeditions to Greenland, and here Lyschander is one of the main sources. The book is written in verse.

*Literature:* F. Gad I 1967, Kisbye Møller 1987.

1405

## Jens Bielkes relation om Grønland 1605

Det kongelige bibliotek, GKS 996 2°

This manuscript, which altogether fills 66 pages, is a thorough account of Christian IV's first expedition to Greenland in 1605. Written in verse in Danish, its sources are surely eye-witness accounts, and Jens Bielke gives detailed descriptions of the Greenlanders' mode of life, clothing etc. Together with the Greenland Chronicle by Lyschander, this manuscript forms the only source to that part of the expedition which was related to the "Red Lion".

*Provenance:* Dedicated to Christian IV.

*Literature:* Kisbye Møller 1987, p. 117-148.

1406

## Hans Poulsen Resen

*"Indicatio Grønlandie (et) vicinarum regionum, versus Septentrionem (et) Occidentem*

Det kongelige Bibliotek, The Map Collection 4100-0-1605

In excitement over the success of the first expedition to Greenland, the learned professor and later bishop of Zealand, Hans Poulsen Resen, made a large map of Greenland in 1605 decorated with small drawings of the native Greenlanders with kajaks, dogsledges, bows and arrows etc. The map was based on the Greenland map of the Icelander Sigurd Stefansson from 1590, which later was printed in Bjørn Jonsens of Skardsaae; Grønlands Beskrivelse (GKS 2881 4°).

*Provenance:* The map is dedicated to Christian IV.

*Literature:* Kornerup, I-II 1928-69, Meddelelser om Grønland, Vol. 9, 1889 (tv. 1), F. Gad 1967, p. 270, Skelton and others 1965, p. 147. Pl. XIX.

1407

## "Grønlandia" c. 1625

Hand coloured map, 53×129 cm
Det kongelige Bibliotek, The Map Collection 4100-0-1625

The map shows Greenland and the lands and seas which surround it. Of particular interest are the Nordic churches which are marked on the map, the names and locations of which were only known from medieval sources. That Christian IV showed considerable interest in the vanished Nordic settlements is known from his instructions to the Greenland expedition of 1607. The date of this map is uncertain, but nevertheless it is from *after* Jens Munk's expediton to Hudson Bay in 1619-1620, since this area is labeled "Nova Dania". "Munckes Vinterhavn" (Muncke's winter harbour) is also marked on the map.

# The Grand Tour

After the Reformation it became increasingly the custom for the Danish nobility, clergy and bourgeoisie to send their sons abroad to be educated at renowned academies and universities. There they could learn foreign languages and acquire a broader, or more thorough, education than was possible at home. This phenomenon, the tour abroad for study and acquisition of culture, culminated during the reign of Christian IV, when over 2,000 youths studied abroad, many for several years.

The German universities were often visited, not uncommonly as a first step on the way to more distant goals. When it was a question of theological studies, one of the German Protestant universities was a natural major stop, and before the academy at Sorø was founded in 1623, the Collegium Illustre at Tübingen attracted a number of youths. But western and southern Europe exerted a stronger pull, not only because of excellent universities and professors, which offered the best within the subjects of philosophy, political science and medicine, but also because French and Italian culture were the fashion, a knowledgye of which was viewed as a necessity for anyone who hoped to cut a figure as a man of the world.

Important sources for the history of these tours of study are the albums these youths carried with them, in which autographs and greetings from friends and acquaintances indicate both where they visited, and with whom they came into contact. Books with inscriptions that show they were purchased and perhaps read on the tour provide additional sources. These sorts of books form a base with which to illustrate various aspects of the cultural influences to which young Danes were subjected on their study and cultural tours.

*Harald Ilsøe*

1408

## Peter Eisenberg

*Itinerarium Galliæ et Angliæ. Reisebüchlein, Darinn Die Reise in Frankreich undt Engelland ... beschrieben ist, Leipzig 1614*
Det kongelige Bibliotek 28-100 8°

Printed travel guides became common in the beginning of the 1600's. The Dane Peter Eisenberg (d. 1615 in France) persuaded a publisher in Leipzig to publish his guide book in German while on his first trip abroad. The preface is addressed to Caspar Markdanner, the lensmand at Koldinghus, whose sons Eisenberg had agreed to direct on a trip to France.

1409

## William Davison

*Profitable Instructions. Describing what speciall Observations are to be taken by Travellers in all Nations, States and Countries, London 1633*
Det kongelige Bibliotek, Geogr. 660 8°

This travel guide was bought by the Danish nobleman Gabriel Ackeleye (1616-52) who learned English while studying in England c. 1636-40. On the flyleaf he wrote: "Gabriell Acheleye bought this boke in London for two grotes. A[nn]o 16 thirtie Nine". Later, when he had brought the book home to his estate Hjularod in Scania, he wrote across from the title page: "Gabriell Ackeleye's own hand. Julerød the 4th of October A[nn]o 1642".
*Literature:* Bøgh 1971, p. 26, 30.

1410

## Album belonging to Nicolaus Köndig (d. 1647), vicar of Moltrup

Det kongelige Bibliotek, NKS 993 8°

Before starting on travel abroad it was customary for the traveller to purchase a book with blank pages in which friends and acquaintances could record a few pleasant remarks on departure from one place to travel on to another. These albums (album amicorum) are not dissimilar to contemporary autograph books. A Danish printer attempted to satisfy demand for this article by producing albums with a title page and ornamentally framed pages.
*Literature:* Helk 1975-76, p. 40f, 78f.

1411

## Decreee on Religious Examination

*Decree that persons who are to guide youths abroad must be examined, 4th July 1616*
Det kongelige Bibliotek, 3 page pamphlet

The Danish authorities appear to have been anxious about the possiblity that youths might be influenced either by Calvinism or Catholicism while travelling abroad. Thus it was decreed that the tutor whom a nobleman paid to direct the travels of his children abroad should be subjected to a religious test by the bishop of the diocese from which the trip originated.

1412

## Travel diary of 1642 kept by Christen Jørgensen Skeel (1623-88), amtmand

Det kongelige Bibliotek, NKS 141f 8°
Christen Skeel's brief diary of a tour through the Netherlands is written on interleaves in a Dutch almanac for the year 1642. The matchbox size format made it easy to transport. Though it was probably common to keep a diary of travels, only a few have survived. Cf. however cat. 1477.

1413

## Kjeld Krabbe

*Oratio valedictoria de quæstione illa: An iuveni studioso multum sit peregrinandum, habita in concessu Witebergæ die 5 Maij Anno 1601, Wittenberg 1601*
Det kongelige Bibliotek, Hielmstierne 1400 4°
Translation of the title; Farewell speech on that well-known question of whether a young student ought to travel extensively abroad, held in a gathering at Wittenberg the 5th of May, 1601.
Commoners could attain academic credentials by defense of a thesis, but this was rarely done by students from the nobility. It was more common that the latter, like Kjeld Krabbe (1588-1612), documented the results of their studies by making a speech in Latin on a topic of their own chosing.

1414

## Certificate for Poul Andersen from Copenhagen (1586-1628), doctor

Det kongelige Bibliotek, GKS 1076 I 2°
On a printed from filled in with Poul Andersen's name, the rector of the University of Wittemberg attests on 12th of October, 1608, that Andersen has been admitted to the university.
*Literature:* Rørdam 1868-74 p. 598f.

1415

## Johann Gerhard (1582-1637) Lutheran theologian, professor at Jena

Copperplate engraving by Johann Dürr
Det kongelige Bibliotek, The Picture Collection
Johann Gerhard was greatly respected both as a theologian and as an inspirational author in the Lutheran world. In Denmark he was so highly regarded that in 1623 he was offered the position of professor of theology at the Academy at Sorø. Below at right a poem to him by the Dane Peder Winstrup (cf. the next no.).

1416

## Peder Pedersen Winstrup

Epigrammatum Libri Tres, Jena 1632
Title engraving
Det kongelige Bibliotek 53-72 8°
Peder Winstrup (1605-79) was Bishop of Lund from 1638. In the period 1630-32 he studied theology and the humanities in Jena and boarded at the house of Johann Gerhard (no. 1415), Gerhard's orthodox faith exerted a lasting influence on Winstrup; in this collection of poems Winstrup calls Gerhard the sun within the circle of the learned. The engraving on the title page expresses Winstrup's bourgeois self-esteem in the inclusion – encircling the title and the national coat of arms – of his family arms. Above left his father's arms, a bunch of grapes, to the right his mother's, Anna Eisenberg. Between these are the arms of Bishop Hans Poulsen Resen, whom his mother married in 1615; Resen was thus Winstrup's stepfather. In the lower row the Winstrup arms and the initials of Winstrup's brothers and sisters.
*Literature:* Hansson 1950, p. 42-46.

1417

## Watercolours from Jena in an album belonging to Poul Trane (d. 1650), Norwegian clergyman

Det kongelige Bibliotek, Thott 1848 4°
The idyllic scene on the left was painted at the request of a German student comrade in Jena in 1605 and probably illustrates a location in the area of the university. On the right a gentleman with a woman of easy virtue. Both motifs suggest that student life was not merely a question of keeping one's nose in a book.
*Literature:* Helk 1975-76, p. 54f, 67, 84f.

1418

## Collegium illustre in Tübingen 1618

Watercolour in an album belonging to Frans Rosenberg (1593-1658), Bishop of Ålborg
Det kongelige Bibliotek, NKS 2090h 4°, p. 194-95
The Collegium illustre in Tübingen was a school for princes and the nobility, founded by the Duke of Würtemberg to deal with the special needs of princely or noble upbringing, in particular chivralric accomplishments such as fencing and riding. The school was dedicated in 1592 and was popular with the Danish nobility until the establishment of the Academy at Sorø. As the left page indicates, the watercolour was painted at the instance of the Danish nobleman Hans Barnekow. Frans Rosenberg resided in Tübingen during 1618-21 as tutor for the nobleman Iver Krabbe.
*Literature:* Helk 1975-76, p. 40f., 82.

1419

## Lecture auditorium at the Collegium illustre in Tübingen

Copper engraving in J. C. Neyffer: *Illustrissimi Wirtembergici ... Novi Collegii ... Delineatio (1626)*
Det kongelige Bibliotek 46-164 4°

1420

## Leiden

Copper engraved prospect in Jean-François Le Petit: *Nederlantsche Republycke. Arnhem 1615*
Det kongelige Bibliotek 64-43 4°

1421

## The anatomy hall and the botanical garden at the University of Leiden

Copper engraving in *Alma et illustris Academia Leidensis, Leiden 1614*
Det kongelige Bibliotek 46-138 4°
The University of Leiden was founded in 1575 and soon became the leading university in the Nederlands. This was not only due to excellent professors and good facilities, but also clever advertising. This beautifully appointed book, which appeared in several editions, mostly consists of portraits of the professors accompanied by commendatory biographies and listings of their literary publications. Thus the reputation of the university was promoted and greater numbers sought to study there.

1422

## Christoffer Dybvad

*Decarithmia ded er Thinde-Regenskab, Leiden 1602*
Det kongelige Bibliotek 18-37 8°
The later royal mathematician Christoffer Dybvad (1572-1622) studied medicine and mathematics in Leiden beginning in 1598. On the basis of a Dutch work he prepared this little treatise, in which decimal arithmetic is explained for the first time in Danish. In his attempts to find Danish terms for mathematical concepts he was influenced by his familiarity with the Dutch terminology. For example, the term »viskunstener« on the title page, which means mathematician.
*Literature:* Hammerich 1945, p. 336-38.

1423

## Stephan Stephanius

*Breves notæ ac emendationes in ... Saxonem Grammaticum Sælandum Danum, Leiden 1627*
Det kongelige Bibliotek 35-28 8°
Professor at Sorø, Stephan Stephanius (1599-1650), is renowned for his great critical edition of Saxo, 1645. The work was begun in Leiden, where he studied Latin in the 1620's with the famous philologists Daniels Heinsius and Gerardus Johannes Vossius (nr. 1424). Both of these men are thanked in this preliminary work to the Saxo.

1424

## Gerardus Johannes Vossius (1577-1649), famous Dutch scholar, classical philologist

Copper engraving
Det kongelige Bibliotek, The Picture Collection 8°

1425

## University library in Leiden

Copper engraving in *Beschrijvinge der Stadt Leiden, Leiden 1641*
Det kongelige Bibliotek 66-288 4°
The university library was housed in an earlier church building, and from 1587 it was open to the students (this was not the case in Denmark until 1657). The books in folio format were chained to high desks, at which one stood to use them.

1426

## Library Catalogue from Leiden

*Nomenclator autorum omnium ... in Bibliotheca Academiæ Lugduno-Bataviæ. Leiden 1595*
Det kongelige Bibliotek 79 I-247 4°
The catalogue of the books in the university library in Leiden is the first printed catalogue of the collection of a public library. The arrangement is according to the shelving, and after each major section space has been left for additional entries. In this copy the additional entries are printed on separate sheets of paper which have been glued in at the relevant places, thus in actual fact this represents the "second, enlarged edition".

1427

## Catalogue from a book auction dated the 8th of October, 1646

With indication of both prices and some of the buyers
Det kongelige Bibliotek 79 II-39 4°
Numerous books in Danish private libraries of the seventeenth century were purchased on travels abroad. The Nederlands was the home of the book auction, and when the later attorney general Peder Scavenius (1623-86) was studying in Leiden in the years 1644-47, he acquired a collection of in all 144 book and auction catalogues, several of which are now unique copies. They were gathered in 5 vellum bindings and later became part of the collections of The Royal Library. As shown by the handwitten "Scanvenius" by some of the titles, he also bought at the auctions, most likely through a commission.
*Literature:* Lange 1914, p. 133-48.

1428

## René Descartes (1596-1650), philosopher and mathematician

Copper engraving by Frans van Schoten c. 1650
Det kongelige Bibliotek, The Picture Collection 8°
One of the few Danes who had a connection to the famous Descartes was Erasmus Bartholin (1625-98), later professor of mathematics. He associated with Descartes during his studies in Leiden in the years 1646-50 and published an introduction to Descartes' geometry in 1651. On the subject of this particular portrait he wrote home to Ole Worm in Denmark; "I am sending a portrait of M. Descartes; it portrays him quite exactly and lifelike, as far as I, and others who have seen him, can judge. The publisher has only made 100 prints, of which two have come into my possession ..."
*Literature:* Nordström 1957-58, p. 201-06, Schepelern, III. 1968, p. 435.

1429

## Entry by Erasmus Bartholin in an album belonging to Henrik Fuiren (1614-59), doctor

Det kongelige Bibliotek, NKS 373 8°
On the left the greeting from Erasmus Bartholin dated Leiden, 1st of August, 1646 (cf. previous no.). On the right a greeting from Poul Moth, later a Danish doctor, dated Paris, April 1639. Both greetings are in the scholarly language Latin.
*Literature:* Helk 1976-76, p. 74.

1430

## John Barrett

*An Alvearie or quadruple Dictionarie, London 1580*
Det kongelige Bibliotek 17-21 2°
Dictionaries are indispensible when learning a new language. This stately edition was bought on March 4, 1593 (1594 by the Danish calender) by the later Bishop of Odense, Hans Knudsen Vejle (1567-1629) while visiting Cambridge. The dictionary contains words in four languages; English, French, Latin and Greek.

1431

## Homage paid to Christian IV by Oxford University

*Charites Oxonienses sive lætitia Musarum in adventu Christiani IVti, Daniæ Regis, nomine Academiæ Oxoniensis*
Det kongelige Bibliotek, GKS 879 2°
A collection of handwritten poems of homage from professors, etc. at the University of Oxford. The manuscript was presented to Christian IV, when he visited his brother-in-law, James I, accompanied by a train of Danish noblemen, professors and students. The well-preserved volume is covered in green velvet, and in the middle of the binding the English arms are embossed in gold. The visit resulted in greater cultural connections between the two countries.

1432

## William Camden

*Britain or a Corographical Description of ... England, Scotland and Ireland ... translated by Philemon Holland, London 1637*
Det kongelige Bibliotek 14-153 2°
The English historian William Camden (1551-1623) produced in his famous work "Britannia" a basic historical-topographical description of England. It appeared from 1586 on in increasingly enlarged editions. Originally Camden knew little about the early Danes, but in the editions from 1590 and after he was able to cite a treatise by "Andrew Velleius", i.e. the Danish historian Anders Sørensen Vedel. And the editions from 1607 and after show that he had made the acquaintance of the Danish historian Jonas Jacobsen Venusin. This was because Venusin accompanied Christian IV to England in 1606.

1433

## Paris c. 1630

Copper engraved prospect in Nicolas Tassin: *Les plans et profils de toutes les principales villes et lieux considerables de France, Paris 1636*
Det kongelige Bibliotek 66-6 4°
Nearly every visitor to France had to see Paris, if even for only a few days. Danish students did not study at the university, and therefore entries of names in albums and dated book purchases are important sources of information on Danish visits to Paris. Cf. cat. 1434-35.

1434

## Justinian's Roman Law

*Dn. Justiniani PP.A. Institutionum iuris libri IIII. Antwerpen 1575*
Det kongelige Bibliotek 100-137 8°
This book deals with the Roman law which was then fundamental for law students, and, as noted on the flyleaf, was purchased in 1604 in Paris by Erik Stensen Brahe (d. 1631). The book is a study copy with notes on interleaved white pages.

1435

## French Nobleman

Hand coloured drawing by a French nobleman, presumably a courtier, in an album which belonged to Jacob Fincke (1592-1663), professor
Det kongelige Bibliotek, GKS 3650 8°
The drawing was made in Paris at the instance of the Danish nobleman Palle Urne (d. 1660). On the left-hand

1439

page he wrote in French: "A dieu complaire / iamais mal fere / à tous servir/ cest mon desier". Translated: "To please God / Never to do wrong / To serve all / This is my endeavor".
*Literature:* Helk 1975-76 p.48 67 74.

1436

## B. Castiglione

*Le parfait courtisan du Comte Baltasar Catillonnois, En deux langues ... De la traduction de Gabriel Chapuis, Tourangeau, Paris 1585*
Det kongelige Bibliotek Sfv. I-1227 8°
Text in Italian and French in two columns. The Italian Castiglione's portrait of the perfect courtier encompassed the ideal of the nobleman, "the consummate gentleman". The book was a classic work on breeding, which appeared in numerous editions and was commonly found in the libraries of the nobility of the day. According to a note on the flyleaf, this copy was purchased in Orléans in 1604 by the Danish nobleman Niels Friis of Faurskov (1584-1651).

1437

## Saddle horse

Copper engraving pasted into an album which belonged to Tage Thott (1580-1658), councilor of the Realm
Det kongelige Bibliotek, NKS 681 8°
The most popular university town in France with the Danes was the city of Orléans. In addition to the university, Orléans boasted a riding and fencing school at which the students from the nobility could practice knightly sports. Below the engraving, a riding master, probably Thott's own instructor, wrote a greeting to Tage Thott in 1602.
*Literature:* Helk 1974 p. 11, 13, 22f, 34f, 43.

1438

## Academic procession in Montpellier

Hand coloured drawing in an album which belonged to Ole Worm (1588-1654). Colour-plate XIV
Nationalmuseet, 2. Department
The university in Montpellier was particularly popular with medical students. Ole Worm studied here from 1609 to 1610, and a student comrade, Peter von Spreckelsen from Hamburg, arranged that the drawing be made in the album.
*Literature:* Schepelern 1961, p. 39-45.

1439

## The university in Padua

Copper engraving c. 1600
Det kongelige Bibliotek, the Picture Collection
In Italy, the university in Padua was that most commonly visited by North Europeans. Its teaching in the subjects of medicine and law was particularly famous. The transverse section shows the inner courtyard of the university; the above left the anatomy hall, where the audience sat on steeply rising benches round about the demonstration table. The engraving in this copy has been provided with the Brahe family arms, and a printed dedica-

*1441*

tion from an otherwise unknown Franciscus Alciatus in Padua to the Dane Otte Axelsen Brahe (1579-1611). He studied in Padua 1599-1601 and fell later as an officer in the Kalmar war.

1440

## S. Guazzo

*La civil conversatione del Signor Stefano Guazzo, Venezia 1589*

Det kongelige Bibliotek Filos. 4002 8°

A common handbook on good breeding, it was written in dialogue form in Italian. According to a note on the title page it was purchased in Padua in 1592 by the later lensmænd Corfits Rud (1573-1630). A note later in the book informs us that he finished reading the first section on February 13, 1593. Underlining and marginal notes in Italian and Latin show that Rud worked conscientiously on the book. On the right-hand page shown here he has written "NB" by the subject of women ("Donne")!

1441

## The Danish medical scientist Johan Rhode (1587-1659) in Padua

Drawing by J. J. Corman, 163, in Johan Rhode's album

Det kongelige Bibliotek, Thott 573 8°

The Dane Johan Rhode settled in Padua in 1622, where he was respected as a learned medical scientist and assisted uncounted numbers of Danes. His album contains c. 780 entries, of which roughly 200 stem from Danish visitors in Padua.

*Literature:* Helk 1975-76 p. 49-51, 82

1442

## Album which belonged to Henrik Fuiren 1614-59, doctor

Det kongelige Bibliotek, NKS 372 8°

Peder Juel of Hundsbæk (1623-54), later a diplomat, had taught himself to write in runes. While he was studying at Padua, he wrote, in 1644, in one of Henrik Fuiren's albums a quotation from the Greek historian Thucydides, in Italian and in runes! In the lower left is written: "Pietro Juell Cimb[er] mpp [= in his own hand]." Fuiren's other album see cat. 1429.

*Literature:* Petersen 1949, p. 88, 113. Helk 1975-76, p. 74.

1443

## Doctoral diploma given in Padua to Peder Hegerfelt (d. 1671), judge in Norway

Det kongelige Bibliotek, Thott 1934 4°

Peder Hegerfelt studied abroad from 1644-56, and like many other Danes and Norwegians he took a medical degree at Padua. The diplomas were beautifully inscribed and ornamented in accord with the price the new doctor was prepared to pay.

1444

## Siena

Engraved prospect. *Teatro della citta d'Italia. Vicenza 1616*

Det kongelige Bibliotek 63-629 4°

The university at Siena ranked next after that in Padua in popularity with the Danes who visited Italy. According to a note on the title page, this book belonged to the later lensmand, the book collecter Laurids Ulfeldt (1605-59), who resided in Siena in 1626.

1445

## The Rialto in Venice, c. 1600

Watercolour in an album which belonged to the Austrian Zacharias Plass

Det kongelige Bibliotek, Thott 1285 4°

From the university cities students made excursions to

1449

La corne dabondance il porte sur sa teste
Et la pour se vanger si qlqun le frappoit
Je men vay doncq dicy car s'il me happoit
Il me pourroit hurter (coe un boeuf) de sa creste.
Das Ceres horn so treget er
Auff seinem kopf für sein gewehr:
Ich mag hinschleichen als ein fuchs,
Das mich nit stoss der grimmig ochs.

tourist sights such as Rome, Naples, and especially Venice, to which Padua belonged.
*Literature:* Helk 1976-76, p. 68, 71, 81.

1446
## The ship of the Doge in Venice

Watercolour in an album belonging to Thomas Fuiren (1616-73), doctor
Det kongelige Bibliotek, Thott 562 8°
Thomas Fuiren had two albums. This one contains entries from his travels in Italy in the years 1639-45, during which he visited Venice in 1643. The president of Venice, the doge, had this picturesque ship named "Bucentore" at his disposal.
*Literature:* Helk 1975-76, p. 52, 67f., 74f.

1447
## Henrik Rantzau

*Reise-Buch auff Jerusalem, Cairo in Ægypten und Constantinopell, Kbhvn 1669*
Det kongelige Bibliotek 28-146 4°
Numerous Danes, especially well-to-do noblemen, made tourist trips to the Near East. Henrik Rantzau (1599-1674), later Councilor of the Realm, described his visit to Egypt in 1623, among other places, in a travel diary which he published in his old age. Here he saw the pyramids, whose chambers and tunnels are illustrated by a woodcut in the text.
*Literature:* Hermansen 1951, p. 12-16.

# The Students and the World of Elegance

In the albums of students and learned men the entries are not exclusively restricted to topics connected to the world of learning. The many allegorical love scenes and playful, or piquant, genre pictures provide a look at the polite world with which Danish students also became acquainted on their Grand Tours.

*Charlotte Christensen*

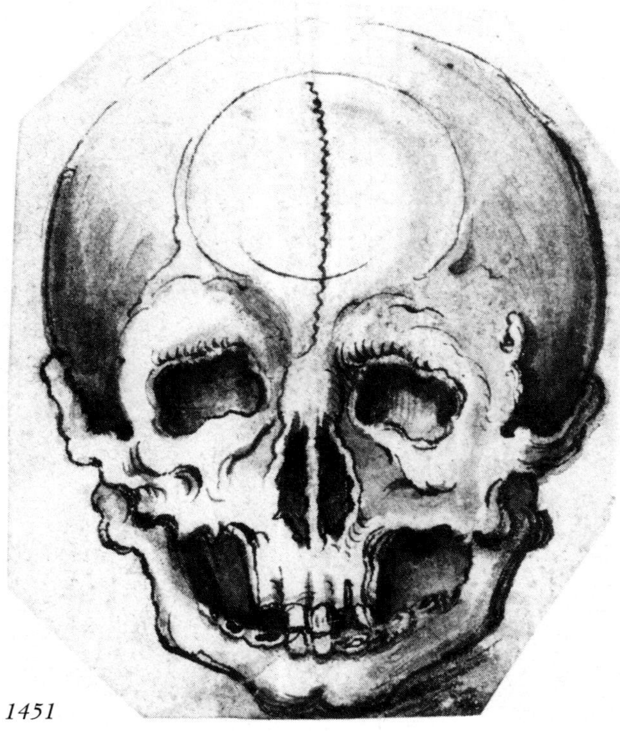

*1451*

1449

## Album belonging to Andreas Blume from Wittemberg

Det kongelige Bibliotek, Thott 403 8°
This album contains entries from many German cities. There is a drawing of a pair of lovers, Amor and a satyr and a woman, by the Hague painter Johann Hauer, signed JH and dated 1617. In the book there are also three engravings of masked figures in erotic situations.
*Provenance:* Temler, p. 366, no. 29. Thott. Det kongelige Bibliotek.
*Literature:* Helk 1975-76, p. 72 no. 9.

1450

## Album belonging to Carl Sitzinger from Augsburg

Det kongelige Bibliotek, Thott 393 8°
The album contains entries from 1590 to 1616 from Nürnberg and Augsburg, but is noteworthy primarily for its wealth of illustrations, which makes it one of the most remarkable in the Thott collection insofar as the pictures are concerned. Religious and secular allegories and subjects from classical mythology alternate in a jumbled superfluity throughout the album.
*Provenance:* Templer p. 365, no. 19 Thott. Det kongelige Bibliotek.
*Literature:* Helk 1973, p. 42, no. 60, mentioned p. 32.

1451

## Album belonging to Petru Ludovicus of Mömpelgard

Det kongelige Bibliotek, Thott 404 8°
The album contains entries from 1574 to 1580 from Padua, Venice and Tübingen. Some of these belong to the "standard repertoire" of those albums which were decorated in Italy; costume studies of civil servants or representatives of the Italian citites in their characteristic costumes; of a higher artistic quality in this album is the unsigned pen and ink drawing of a cranium p. 145 recto.
*Provenance:* Temler p. 366, no. 30, Thott, Det kongelige Bibliotek.
*Literature:* Helk 1973, pp. 40-41 no. 37, mentioned p. 31.

1452

## Album belonging to the jurist Joh. Hensen from Zell/Trier

Det kongelige Bibliotek, Thott 377 8°
The album contains entries from Trier, Speyer, Köln, Regenburg and Louvain, among other cities. In addition to many drawings of coats of arms, it contains many humorous reproductions of youthful student life. The results of student lovelife (infants) are portrayed in one picture which is rather affected; a carriage is inscribed "student goods"; when a small flap is lifted there is a swaddled infant in the carriage.
*Provenance:* Thott, Det kongelige Bibliotek
*Literature:* Helk 1975-76, p. 76 no. 61.

1453

## Album belonging to Adam Ernst Schrimpf from Graz (?)

Det kongelige Bibliotek, Thott 420 8°
The album contains 22 entries from the years 1615-23

*1454*

Das haist recht Adelich gelebt,
Wa man nach Ehr vnd Tugent strebt.
Perseus erleget den Drachen,
Erlöst dardurch Andromeden,
Welche er gleich zu eigen Nam,
Vnd Jrer Eltern Huld bekam.

Allein Gott die Ehr.

1450

1453

1457

from Graz. The illustrations are primarily coats for arms, interspersed with a few secular and antique subjects.
*Provenance:* Temler p. 366, no. 48, Thotts samling. Det kongelige Bibliotek.
*Literature:* Helk 1975-76, p. 83 no. 121.

1454

## Album for Jeronimus Pleninger from Nürnberg

Det kongelige Bibliotek, NKS 802 8°
The album contains 18 entries from the period 1612-18, from Nürnberg, Augsburg, Amsterdam and Copenhagen. Noteworthy is the sketch on p. 63, recto, of a merry party, signed by the painter Isaac Isaacsz. and dated 1618.
*Provenance:* C. E. v. Deurs; to The Royal Library 1937.
*Literature:* Helk 1975-76, p. 81 no. 104; Isaac Isaacsz.' watercolour repr. p. 69, discussed p. 68.

1455

## Album belonging to Chancellery secretary Philipp Julius Bornemann from Bückeburg

Det kongelige Bibliotek, NKS 362 8°
The album contains entries from the period 1618-23 from various German citites as well as 30 drawings of coats of arms and a few other pictures. Most of the illustrations are in the category of elegant portrayals of the life of youth. The open pages show a young couple, accompanied through an empty street at night by musicians.
*Literature:* Helk 1975-76, p. 72 no. 10.

1456

## Album belonging to Joseph Eder of Vöcklabruck

Det kongelige Bibliotek, Thott 1283 4°
This very large album with entries from Germany and Italy contains highly imaginative drawings of coats of arms.
*Provenance:* Temler p. 365, no. 6. Det kongelige Bibliotek.
*Literature:* Helk 1973, p. 39 no. 21.

1457

## Album belonging to Franz Christoph Deublinger from Speyer

Det kongelige Bibliotek, Thott 434 8°
Franz Christoph Deublinger's album belongs among the most richly illustrated albums in the collections of the Royal Library; it has a wealth of pictures, especially from the period between 1638 and 1648. Some of the illustrations are done in a non-traditional manner, for example, the "collage" of an embroidered flower, which when opened reveals a youth with a musical instrument (dated Paris, 1642). In addition the album contains humorous prospects of Paris and Charenton, loving couples, secular allegories, a few religious pictures and classical topics. Of particular art historical interest is a signed pen and ink drawing (p. 121) by Hermann Swanevelt, dated Paris, 1745.
*Provenance:* Temler p. 367, no. 68. Thotts samling. Det kongelige Bibliotek.
*Literature:* Helk, 2, p. 73 no. 21; discussed p. 68, illustration p. 61.

1458

## Album for Knight of St. Mark Anton Erich Rentsch

Det kongelige Bibliotek, Thott 432 8°
This album contains 119 entries from the period 1615 to 1647 from many areas of scholarly Europe; Leyden,

*1458*

1461

Haag, London, Paris, Italy and Germany. It has the greatest number of illustrations of the Royal Library's albums from the period of Christian IV; 49 drawings of coats of arms and 102 other pictures. Italian costume studies, allegories over the power of love and mythological subjects are especially well represented in this album.
*Provenance:* Temler p. 367, no. 66. Thotts samling. Det kongelige Bibliotek.
*Literature:* Helk 1975-76, p. 82 no. 110; discussed p. 68.

1459

## Album belonging to Joh. Christoph. Geyher von Osterberg

Det kongelige Bibliotek, Thott 1280 4°
This album is particularly plentifully supplied with professionally done drawings of coats of arms.
*Provenance:* Temler p. 365, no. 2, Thotts samling. Det kongelige Bibliotek.
*Literature:* Helk 1975-76, p. 75 no. 45, discussed p. 68.

1460

## Album belonging to Jacob (and Erasmus) Heckelsberger of Hohenburg, Austria

Det kongelige Bibliotek, Thott 1282 4°
This album contains copious illustration from Padua and Venice, from the period 1572-74, among others the popular depictions of the inhabitants of the Italian cities in their characteristic costumes.
*Provenance:* Temler p. 365, no. 5. Thotts samling. The Royal Library.
*Literature:* Helk 1975-76, p. 39 no. 28; discussed p. 31.

1461

## Album belonging to Wolfgang Dobler from Augsburg

Det kongelige Bibliotek, Thott 1286 4°
The entries in this album, all of which are from Augsburg, are from the period between 1631 and 1634. Particularly worthy of note are the many allegories on the topic of love in this album.
*Provenance:* Temler p. 365 no. 9. Thotts samling. Det kongelige Bibliotek.
*Literature:* Helk 1975-76 p. 73 no. 22; discussed p. 68.

1462

## Album belonging to Baron Stephan Haymb v. Reichenstein, from Austria

Det kongelige Bibliotek, Thott 1279 4°
This album, which contains entries from the years 1575 to 1591, is remarkable for its large collection of pencil

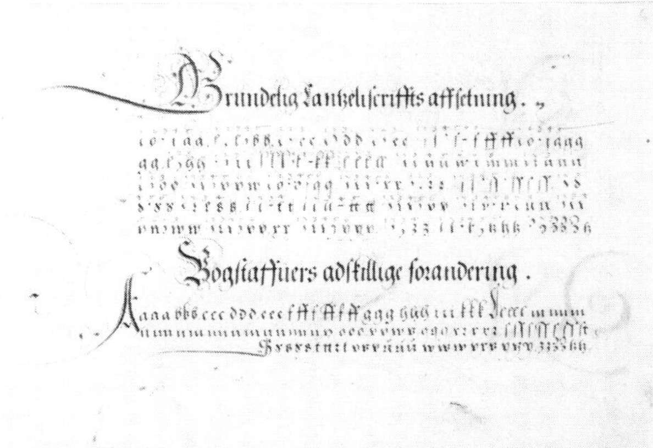

*1465*

sketches from Constantinople. These drawings portray Turkish folk life and Turkish costumes as well as architecture and a rhinoceros. Baron Haymb von Reichenstein resided in Constantinople from 1575-76.
*Provenance:* Temler p. 364, no. 1. Thotts samling, Det kongelige Bibliotek.
*Literature:* Jahrbuch d. einbandkunst, IV, Leipzig, 1937, pp. 78-88; Kyster 1938, no. 31; Helk p. 39 no. 27, discussed p. 32.

1463

## Album belonging to Ulrik, Duke of Mecklenburg (d. 1603)

Det kongelige Bibliotek, GKS 2161 4°
Virgilius Solis "Wappenbüchlein", has been used as the album, and the book contains entries from the period 1588-94 from Copenhagen and Güstrow, Noteworthy are the royal autographs; Frederik II from 1588, the Queen Dowager Sophie from 1589, Christian IV from 1588 and from 1590 both those of James VI of Scotland and his Danish wife Queen Anna.
*Literature:* Helk, 1, p. 43 no. 70.

# Education of children and youth

Examples of text books demonstrate what sort of materials were used in the education of children: from the earliest preserved Danish ABC and a writing master's "the art of writing" to aids to Latin such as the obligatory donat (a grammar book) and Stephan Stephanius' text book system. Sources preserved from the actual classroom situation are several essay notebooks, that of Christian IV from c. 1590 and Ole Borch's from c. 1640.

An innovation during Christian IV's time was the founding of the academy at Sorø for the sons of the nobility in the age group 15-19. Many of the teachers and professors called in from abroad to teach were researchers with international reputations. Physical skills such as riding and fencing were also part of the educational program, and to illustrate this two versions of an elegant work on the art of fencing have been included. They were produced by the Italian Salvator Fabris, Christian IV's fencing master from 1601 to 1607.

*Harald Ilsøe*

1464

## Abc Kbhvn. 1649

Det kongelige Bibliotek 3-435 8°
Abc's have as a rule either been worn out by use or thrown away when no longer needed, so it is pure accident that the oldest preserved fragments of an ABC in Danish are as old as 1649. These eight pages have been removed from a binding from 1650, where they had been used as filler, and were originally a pupil's catechism-ABC made up of the Lord's Prayer, the Ten Commandments and prayers. On the last page appears a rooster, the old symbol of vigilance, which also appears on the last page of a Low German ABC from 1591. Next to the rooster is the text; Fear God, work, learn/ Children, great honor you will earn!"
*Literature:* J. Nielsen 1973, p. 36-37.

1465

## Peder Trellund

*Skriffuer Konst.* [Ms.] 1590
Det kongelige Bibliotek, Thott 846 4°
A writing master from Ribe, Peder Trellund, presented Christian IV this book of specimen hands, written and drawn on parchment. From 1599 until his death in 1612

Trellund worked as a writing master in Copenhagen. The left hand page shown illustrates "A good and proper grasp of the pen" and above right hand page "Thorough marking out of the chancellery hand". Here Trellund dissects the letters into their indiviudal elements and indicates with small red numbers the course of the pen which leads to the finished letter. Below is described "The numerous changes of the letters".
*Literature:* J. Nielsen 1973, p. 18f.

1466

## Anders Olsen

*En ny Regne-Bog, Kbhvn. 1614*
Det kongelige Bibliotek 18-111 8°
Anders Olsen's arithmetic book was one of the popular arithmetic books of the period. It appeared for the first time in 1560 and the edition of 1614 was most likely the fifth edition. New editions were published in 1619 and 1622.

1467

## Donatus

*Methodus grammatices, Kbhvn 1580*
Det kongelige Bibliotek, Hielmstierne 2059 8°
A "donat" – short for the author Donatus – was the traditional textbook in Latin grammar since the Middle Ages. This copy – cut in rebinding – belonged to Christian IV while still prince. Above the title before cutting was written; "Donatus Principis Christiani". His teacher, Hans Mikkelsen, added extra specific examples with which the prince could work in numerous places in the text.
*Literature:* Molbech 1849-50, p. 274-75.

1468

## A handwritten Essay by Christian IV, c. 1584-91

Det kongelige Bibliotek, Schiøning 2 8°
Christian IV's teacher Hans Mikkelsen often used the method of setting the prince an essay in the form of a letter in Danish, which he then afterwards was required to translate into Latin. The essays were without set topics, insofar as the prince wrote about what concerned him from day to day. Here he writes to his younger brother Ulrik and warns him when they play chess, to pay attention to the game, and nothing else! The teacher has made corrections in the Latin version.
*Literature:* Molbech 1849-50, p. 274-75.

1469

## Arithmetic in Latin by an unidentified author, copied by the crown prince Christian

Det kongelige Bibliotek, NKS 72 8°
The beautiful handwriting stems undoubtably from prince Christian (V)'s school days, c. 1615-20. On the title page is a message that the book has been presented to Ole Worm in February of 1647; "... Elctus Princeps Christianus Qvintus manu sua exaratum hunc libellum D[ono] D[edit] Olao Wormio Anno MDCXLVII Mense Februarii". The binding is covered with green velvet. The pages open, 34v-35, deal with rule of three.

1471

## Ole Borch's exercise book 1641

Det kongelige Bibliotek, NKS 360 1 8°
An exercise book has been preserved from the schooling of the later famous scientist Ole Borch, at the Latin school in Ribe, written when he was about 15 years old. It contains Latin essays written in the manner of different classical authors, e.g. Cicero and Terence, and the corrections of the teacher are visible. On leaf 12 Borch drew a man, a stork and a horse, and wrote below them in Latin that man, bird and horse are the same part of speech. The sentence at the top of the page is a pædagogical maxim which Borch has written several times in the exercise book, perhaps because it was a favorite of his teacher. "Omnia conando docilis solertia vincit" can be translated: "With dogged eagerness and efforts / Comes mastery of all things«.
*Literature:* Kornerup 1947, p. 419.

1472

## Stephanus Johannis Stephanius

*Colloqviarum familiarium libri IV, Kbhvn 1634*
Det kongelige Bibliotek 47-127 8°
One of the most well-known and longest lived school texts from the time of Christian IV is "Intimate Conversations" in Latin by a professor at Sorø, Stephanus Stephanius. His aim was to follow the example of Erasmus of Rotterdam and promote understanding of Latin by introducing the pupil to simple daily situations, in which suitable and instructive topics were pædagogically discussed. The pupils could be directed to memorize the lines and act out the short scenes in the classroom. Each conversation stays within a specific subject area and its appropriate glossary (cf. next no.).

1473

## Stephanus Johannis Stephanius

*Nomenclatoris Latinodanici libri IV, Copenhagen 1645*
Det kongelige Bibliotek 47-99 8°
Stephanius' Latin dictionary follows closely his "Colloqvia", since the Latin vocabulary with its Danish translation is collected in short chapters, each of which covers a topic which corresponds to one of the conversations in Colloqvia, e.g. the topic of religion, or architecture. At the back of the book the Danish words are listed alphabetically with references to the page numbers for the Latin words. The pupil had available both a systematic and an alphabetical access.

1474

## Johann Michael Moscherosh

*En from Faders christelige Siæle-Gaffue. Copenhagen 1645*
[Translated from German]
Det kongelige Bibliotek 4-73 8°
The daily reading of the Bible, which in the ideal Christian home was carried out with the family gathered around the table, is depicted on this engraved title page of German origin. It must be noted that the children, evidently two girls, remained nicely standing in the presence of the adults. The lack of schools for girls meant that their upbringing was far more marked by the household rituals than that of boys, either by staying at home for many years or leaving early to live with relatives.

1475

## Lucas Martini

*Alle christelige oc dydige Jomfruers ærekrantz, Kbhvn. 1614*
Det kongelige Bibliotek 4-73 8°
This "Wreath of Honor", which appeared in several Danish editions, depicts the many moral and domestic virtues expected of maidens of good family. The woodcut on leaf B8 – C shows just such a maiden sitting in a garden and making a wreath. On the inside back cover is written; "This book belongs to me Kirsten Jenss daughter by right and was given to me by my dearest mother in the year 1636 the 18th of July. Kirsten Jenss daughter by her own hand".

1476

## Charter of Sorø Akademi

*Fundatz oc Anordning paa det Kongelig Adeligt Academie udi Soer, Anno MDCXXIII. Kbhvn. undated*
Det kongelige Bibliotek $34^3$-185 4°
The academy at Sorø was founded in 1623 to provide both the sons of the nobility and Christian IV's own sons an appropriately noble education under reassuring circumstances, instead of being sent abroad to school at a young age as had been the custom. Chairs were established in the relevant disciplines: history, political science, law, mathematics and modern languages, and renowned professors were hired from abroad. Riding masters and fencing masters and others gave instruction in physical skills. On the title pages is the name of the owner: Claus Wrne.

1477

## Daniel Matras

*Le petit dictionaire françois-danois. Et lidet frantzøskt oc danskt dictionarum. Kbhvn. 1628*
Det kongelige Bibliotek 47-420 8°
A first step on the road to becoming men of the world for the academy's noble students was to learn the modern languages of culture. The Frenchman Daniel Matras (1598-1689) came to the academy in 1624 as a teacher of both French and Italian. Among the aids he compiled and published are the first French dictionaries printed in Denmark.

1478

## Henrik Ernst 1603-65, professor at Sorø Academy

Copper engraving by A. Haelwegh c. 1650
Det kongelige Bibliotek, The Picture Collection
Henrik Ernst, a German born in Helmstedt, spent several periods teaching at the academy at Sorø, the last one from 1639-60 as the professor af law. As did several other foreigners, Ernst lent lustre to the academy by his literary production. He was an internationally known jurist (cf.cat. 1479, 1480, 1620), but also did significant work in philology, and published sources for Danish history.
*Literature:* Sthyr 139.

1479

## Henrik Ernst

*Methodus discendi juris civilis conscripta in usum nobilissimorum studiosorum ... Academiæ Soranæ, Sorø 1647*
Det kongelige Bibliotek, Hielmst. 757 4°
Henrik Ernst's "Methodus" is a pedagogical introduction to Roman law, a by-product of his teaching and written for his noble students. In fold-out tables he provides systematic surveys of individual parts of the Roman law.

1480

## Henrik Ernst

*Methodus discendi juris civilis et canonici*
A lecture taken down in handwriting by Corfits Rosenkrantz
Det kongelige Bibliotek, NKS 61 8°
One of Henrik Ernst's pupils, Corfits Rosenkrantz, wrote down his lectures in Latin, perhaps from dictation. Corfits Rosenkrantz (1628-53) was at Sorø Academy from 1644-48 and most likely attended the lectures before Henrik Ernst had published his "Methodus" (cf. previous no. 1479).

1481

## Hans Lauremberg

*Tes Hellados hypotyposis*
[Ms. in Greek.]
Det kongelige Bibliotek, Thott 538 2°
Hans Lauremberg originally came from Rostock, and from 1623 on was professor at Sorø Academy in mathematics and engineering. He was an expert in the fields of surveying and cartography, and made a study in

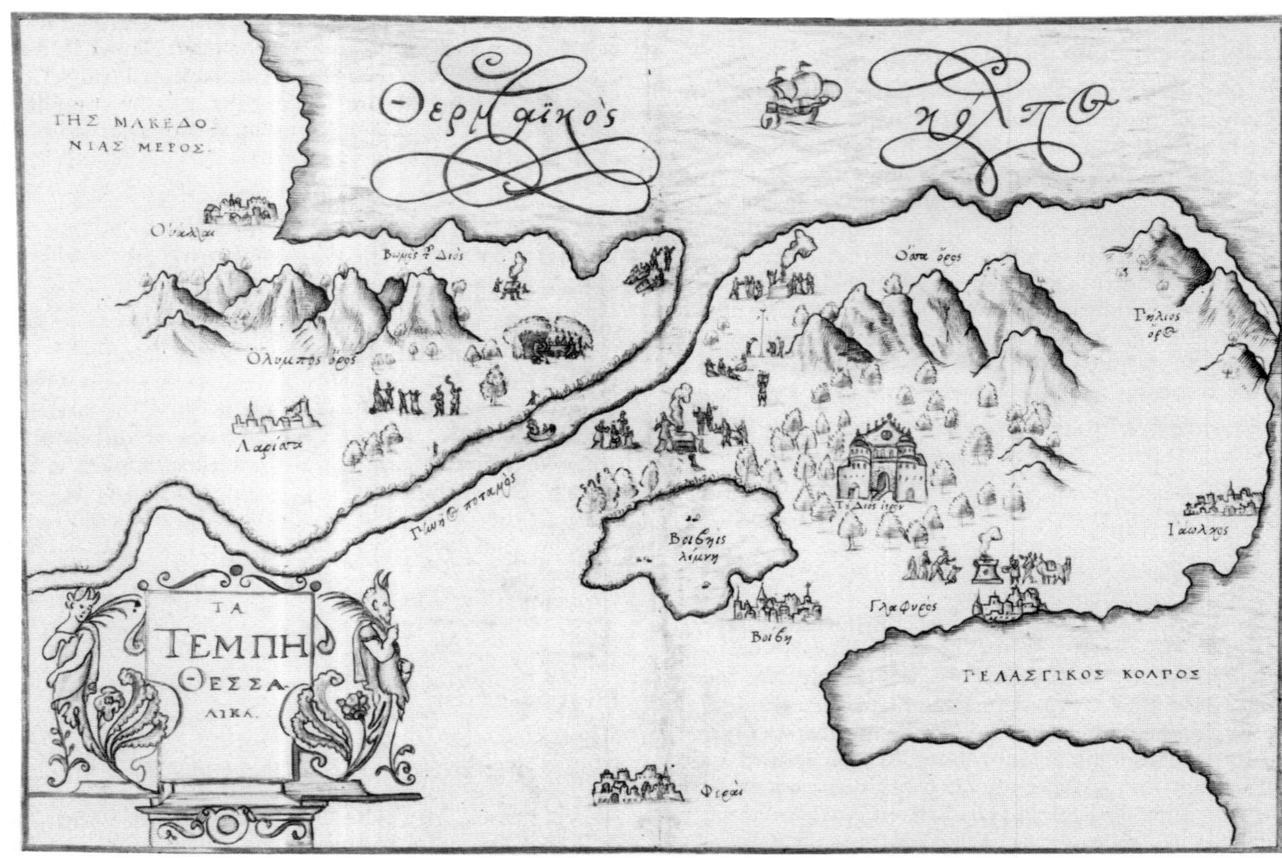


*1481*

particular of the geography and topography of ancient Greece. His "Geographical description of Hellas" is written in Greek and provided with informative map illustrations. In this handsome copy, which he prepared as a gift for his patron Holger Rosenkrantz the Learned (d. 1642), the text and map pages are of parchment and the maps are drawn with brown and gold ink. The open pages show the Vale of Tempe in Thessaly between Mt. Olympus and Mt. Ossa. The work was not published until after Lauremberg's death.

1482

## Mogens Krabbe

*Fechtbog 1656*

[Fencing book written down by Mogens Krabbe in Sorø]
Det kongelige Bibliotek, NKS 79 8°

Mogens Krabbe, who died as an officer in 1676, studied at Sorø Academy 1655-56, and on April 17, 1656, he started to copy out a fencing book, quite possibly as an aid in learning the 110 lessons in the text as he practised the fencing exercises themselves. No illustrations. Text in Danish.

1483

## Salvator Fabris

*Sientia et practica del Arme*

Ms. dated Vorde (Bremervörde) Sept, 30, 1601
Det kongelige Bibliotek, GKS 1868 I-III 4°

The art of fencing with all its finesses is illustrated in this splendid work by Christian IV's fencing master from 1601 to 1607, Salvator Fabris. The voluminous manuscript in three volumes is on parchment. It consists partly of a text in Italian, beautifully written and surrounded by varying decorative frames in gold and colours, and also of many coloured drawings of naked pairs of males, in changing fencing positions, mostly covering double pages. At the front of volume I is a drawing of the Gottorp coat of arms, in which minutely written lines of text make up the curved contours of the coat of arms. A dedication to Johan Frederik of Gottorp (1578-1634), the archbishop of Bremen and a cousin of Christian IV, follows. Fabris later worked as a fencing master in Padua.

*Provenance:* Gottorp Library.

1484
## Salvator Fabris

*De lo schermo o vero scienza d'arme, Kbhvn. 1606*
Det kongelige Bibliotek 17-327 2°
The printed edition of Fabris' fencing book must be based on a manuscript corresponding to the previous no., but this has not been investigated. The book was printed by Henrik Waldkirch and represents the high point of Danish book making in that period, e.g. it was the first book printed in Denmark to have copper engraved illustrations. The roughly 190 fencing scenes are printed in the text and were engraved by the Dutchman Jan Halbeeck and the Italian Francesco Valeggio, whereas the two portraits, of Christian IV (no. 22) and the author, were engraved by Nicolaus Andrea from Flensburg. The work was naturally dedicated to Christian IV. It received international attention and appeared in new editions in both Germany and Italy.
*Literature:* Dansk Boghaandværk gennem Tiderne 1482-1948, Copenhagen 1949, no. 37.

# History

The lack of a work on Danish history in keeping with the times had been felt since the mid-sixteenth century. Anders Sørensen Vedel started in about 1575 to prepare such a work in Danish, but did not get beyond collecting material and making excerpts and rough drafts. When it became clear that Vedel was not up to the task, a nobleman and Councilor of the Realm, Arild Huitfeldt, quickly wrote his "Danmarks Riges Krønike" (1595-1603), which, because of the independent opinions of the author and its rich documentation of sources, represents a landmark in Danish history writing. The government also desired at that time that a distinguished Latin language Danish history be produced for foreign consumption, but did not succeed until the 1630's, when the two Dutchmen, Johannes Pontanus and Johannes Meursius, were hired as royal historians. And their printed accounts only covered the years up to 1523.

The poet and historian Claus Christoffersen Lyschander, who in his fantastical "Slectebog" bridged the gap between the stories of the Bible and the earliest periods of Danish history, represents an isolated phase. After the 1620's Danish historical research concentrated on the gathering and publication of source material. Stephan Johannis Stephanius republished Saxo Grammaticus in 1644-45 accompanied by a wealth of learned notes, and Ole Worm managed among many tasks to register and investigate systematically the rune stones of Denmark, the result being his famous publication on the runes in 1643. Both this, and his illustrated treatise on the golden horns found in 1639, exited international interest.

Numerous members of the nobility, especially noble ladies, pursued private family history studies. The pride of family which motivated such studies was exhibited to the world at large in copper engravings filled with rows of family coats of arms with which it became common to decorate printed funeral sermons on nobles in the period of Christian IV. A romantic sentiment centered on the king shows up in the production of manuscripts with drawn and hand-coloured pictures of the king.

*Harald Ilsøe*

*1483*

1485
## Anders Sørensen Vedel

*En sørgelig Ligpredicken ... Frederich den Anden ... giort udi Riber Domkircke den 5. dag Junii ... Sidst effter ... følger en liden Cronologia .. Kbhvn. 1588*
Det kongelige Bibeliotek 35-181 4°
The first historical writing from the period of Christian IV concerned the life and deeds of Frederik II. Anders Sørensen Vedel (1542-1616) had worked for at long time on a history of Denmark and added a chronological survey of events during the king's lifetime (1533-88) to the printed edition of his funeral sermon on the king. This was a sample of the great chronology which, according to his plan, was to accompany his completed History of Denmark (cf.cat. 1491).

1486

## Frans Hogenberg and Simon Novellanus

*Res gestæ ... Friderici II ... ex monumento pyramidali Segeberg ab Henrico Rantzovio erecto. S.l. [1589].* Colour-plate III
Det kongelige Bibliotek 35-170 2°
In memory of Frederik II, the viceregent of the duchies of Schleswig and Holstein, Henrik Rantzau (1526-98), a man with a strong interest in history, had constructed a memorial in the style of a pyramid at Segeberg, on which the high points of the king's career were depicted. A version in copper engraving was produced in 1589, and this copy, in which the engravings are coloured and there is a Latin inscription, was given to Christian IV. The open pages show the procession at Frederik II's funeral. Immediately following the coffin come Christian IV and his brothers and sisters led by their uncle, Duke Ulrik of Mecklenburg.

1487

## Peter Lindeberg

*Historia rerum in Europa ab anno octavagesimo sexto ... gestarum narratio. Hamburg 1591*
Det kongelige Bibliotek 30[I]-165 4°
This prospect of the Jelling stone and its surroundings is the first published depiction of a Danish prehistoric monument. Henrik Rantzau took the initiative, and arranged that the engraving be included in a book by his assistant Peter Lindeberg.

1488

## Henrik Rantzau

*Cimbricæ Chersonesi ... Descriptio nova ... e penu ... Henrici Ranzovii, 1597*
Det kongelige Bibliotek, Thott 1483 4°
The major work among Henrik Rantzau's historical studies was his historical-topographical description of the peninsula of Jutland from Skagerrak to the Elbe. It only exists in later copies. A portrait of Henrik Rantzau drawn in ink on the basis of an engraving has been used as frontispiece in this copy from the eighteenth century.

1489

## Henrik Rantzau

*Cimbricæ Chersonesi ... Descriptio nova ... e penu ... Henrici Ranzovii, 1597*
Det kongelige Bibliotek, Thott 1439 4°
Henrik Rantzau's description of the peninsula of Jutland treats the customs and mores of the Cimbrians (the Jutes), and is illustrated by drawings that show the costumes of the different population groups. Copy from the eighteenth century.

1490

## Prospect of Ribe c. 1590

Copper engraving from Georg Braunius and Frans Hogenberg; Theatrum Urbium
Det kongelige Bibliotek, The Picture Collection
Through the influence of Henrik Rantzau, Denmark was especially well represented in Braunius and Hogenberg's collection of city prospects, Theatrum Urbium, vol. 5-6 (Cologne 1588-98). One of the several Danish informants was Anders Sørensen Vedel, from 1580 a resident of Ribe, who was supported by a canonry at the cathedral while he worked on his history. He supplied the text, and perhaps also the drawing for the prospect of Ribe through Niels Kaas. The domed tower just to the right of the cathedral is the tower of Vedel's own house in Ribe (the "little Uranienborg").
*Literature:* Skov 1937. p. 98-109 (with a translation of the text to Danish).

1491

## Anders Sørensen Vedel

*Kong Svend Haraldsøn Tiuve-skæg, Kbhvn. 1705*
Det kongelige Bibliotek 35-106 8°
After Vedel in 1675 had translated Saxo into Danish he struggled for a long time with the writing of a history of Denmark without completing it. Only a few fragments, the story of Svend Tveskæg (Svend Forkbeard) and a preface to the whole of the planned work, reached printed form in 1705 through one of his descendents. In the preface leaf C 2v ff., he explains the arrangement of the work in six major sections: A description of Denmark – the origins of the Danes – the customs and mores of the Danes – the history of the kings of Denmark – the generalogy of the royal family – and a complete chronological survey (cf.cat. 1485).

1492

## Anders Sørensen Vedel

Preliminary drafts for a genealogy of the Danish royal family
Det kongelige Bibliotek, NKS 2155 b 4°
In 1595 Vedel had to turn over his papers – excerpts, transcriptions and his own drafts – to the newly appointed royal historiographer Niels Krag. Much of his material has been preserved, e.g. notes on Sven Estridsen ("Great Svend") and his descendents. These were no doubt preliminary drafts for his royal genealogy, to be a part of his complete Danish history.

1493

## Anders Sørensen Vedel

*Fragmenta Historiæ Danicæ. Excerpter til dansk historie*
Det kongelige Bibliotek, Add. 120 4°
On a separate sheet with the heading "From an old scroll

coming from Soroe" ("Aff een gamle Rolle som kom aff Soer") Vedel has written some extracts from a (rolled up?) manuscript from Soroe, which no longer exists. Among the extracts is the only known (incomplete) text for a yearbook in Latin, which now is described as "Annales Sorani ad 1268".
*Literatur:* Kroman 1980 p. 78.

1494

## Arild Huitfeldt 1546-1609, Councilor and Chancellor of the Realm

Copper engraving of Albert Haelwegh
Det kongelige Bibliotek, The Picture Collection
The nobleman Arild Huitfeldt rose from secretary of the Chancellery to Councilor of the Realm and then Chancellor (Rigskansler). His strong interest in history made him support Ander Vedel Sørensen's work on a history of Denmark, and exploit his own access to the archives to establish historical collections. When Vedel's project failed of completion, Huitfeldt brought out between 1595 and 1603 his own nine volume work, Danmarks Riges Krønike, (Chronicle of the Kingdom of Denmark), the first large-scale history of Denmark since Saxo. The inclusion of the texts of many documents and the independent opinions of the author on the historical events give it a distinctive character. (cf. cat. 45).

*1494*

1495

## Arild Huitfeldt

Fragment of a manuscript on the history of Christian III
Den kongelige Bibliotek, NKS 1832 2°
The speed with which Huitfeldt was able to write his Danish chronicle was in part due to his use of practised clerks. The chancellery clerk, Claus Mortensen, wrote a fair copy of these pages of manuscript, whereupon Huitfeldt edited yet further in the text with additions and crossings out.
*Literature:* G. Ilsøe 1975.

1496

## Arild Huitfeldt

*Historiske Beskriffuelse om ... Kong Christiern den Anden. Kbhvn 1596*
Det kongelige Bibliotek 35-33 4°
Huitfeldt prefaced all nine volumes of Danmarks Riges Krønike with an address to Christian IV, in which he stressed that princes and regents can learn from history. In the first volume that appeared (1595), Christian III is described as ideal king, and in the next, Christian II is introduced as his frighteningly tyrannical opposite number. On the left-hand page: the Danish coat of arms. This copy is bound in red velvet with gilt edges; it was presented in 1643 to prince Christian (V) by the nobleman Niels Trolle.
*Literature:* H. Ilsøe 1967, p. 48-49.

1497

## Arild Huitfeldt as ambassador

Copper engraving in Johannes Pontanus: *Historische Beschrijvinghe der seer wijt beroemde Coopstadt Amsterdam. Amsterdam 1614*
Det kongelige Bibliotek 66-278 4°
During the years in which Huitfeldt published Danmarks Riges Krønike he was sent several times on diplomatic missions. This engraving (p. 177) shows how he and Christian Barnekow were hospitably treated by the city of Amsterdam on their way home from a mission to England in 1597 (the two men in seats of honor). During the banquet several newly returned North Pole explorers turned up, and greeted the Danes (cf. the ship shown on p. 176). They had been on an expedition led by Jakob van Heemskerk and Willem Barents which attempted in vain to find a sea passage to India north around Asia.

1498

## Arild Huitfeldt

*En kaart Chronologia, I* [1182-1286], *Kbhvn 1600*
Det kongelige Bibliotek 35-33 4°
In his Chronologia I Huitfeldt began a description from the point at which Saxo had stopped. As the title suggests, the treatment is strictly chronological, and events are covered year by year. Now and then the author states his personal opinion, as on p. 206 on the clergy in the Middle Ages, which because of its dependence on the Pope, "always had the same effect on kings that mustard has on the nose". On p. 207 he claims that fundamentally the state is directed by interests of state, for which reason the bishops and councilors at the election of the king in 1250 were more concerned with what was practicable than what was right or Christian duty.
*Literature:* H. Ilsøe 1967 p. 48-49.

1499

## Arngrímur Jónsson

*Apotribe virulentæ et atrocis calumniæ. Hamburg 1622*
Det kongelige Bibliotek 39-43 4⁰
Niels Krag (1550-1602) took over Anders Sørensen Vedel's papers when Krag became royal historiographer, but also collected on a large scale himself. He had a connection with the learned Icelander Arngrimur Jónsson and arranged that Jónsson received a royal mandate to collect sources for him on Iceland. In the letter from 1598 reproduced on p. 92-93 Krag thanks him for a recently received shipment of historical documents. The signatory to the letter on p. 92 is Krag's successor as royal historiographer, Jon Jacobsen Venusin (d. 1608), who in 1597 sent Huitfeldts's history of Christian II to Jónsson.

1500

## Johannes Isaacius Pontanus 1571-1639 royal Danish historiographer

Copper engraving by J. V. Velde, c. 1630
Det kongelige Bibliotek, The Picture Collection
Huitfeldt wrote in Danish and viewed his chronicle of Denmark as a preliminary to an official history of Denmark in Latin, aimed at a European audience. After several Danish historians in a row had failed to produce this work, the government engaged Dutch philologists and historians to carry out the task. The first of these was the Danish-born Dutchmann Johannes Pontanus. He was a professor in Harderwijk and had previously written a history of Amsterdam (cf.cat. 1497). From 1618 he worked on the Latin language history of Denmark in Hardewijk as royal Danish historiographer. Pontanus was brother of the painter Pieter Isaacsz.

1501

## Johannes Isaacius Pontanus

*Rerum Danicarum Historia, Amsterdam 1631*
Det kongelige Bibliotek 35-34 2°
After 13 years of work Pontanus completed the first volume of a Danish history which covered the period up to 1448. A continuation existed only in manuscript on his death. This imposing volume, which was printed in 1631, builds heavily on Saxo and Huitfeldt, and the most interesting section is actually a thorough description of the country placed at the back, pp. 637-801. Here is information on the different sections of the country, the condition of the country, the customs and mores of the Danes, spiritual and cultural life among other topics, On p. 793 the Lord's Prayer is printed in several languages for the sake of comparison with the Danish version.

1502

## Johannes Meursius 1579-1639

Copper engraving by Simon de Pas 1631
Det kongelige Bibliotek. The Picture Collection
Johannes Meursius was a professor at Leiden when the Danish government called him to be professor of history and political science at the academy in Sorø in 1624. At the same time he was to relieve Pontanus by writing the history of the Oldenburg kings. In 1630 the history of the first three Oldenburg kings appeared, actually a continuation of Pontanus' Danish history of 1631, but Meursius then continued backwards in time, and by 1638 he had finished a complete history of Denmark, covering from the beginning to 1523: "Historia Danica".
*Literature:* Schepelern 1951 42 and no. 16

1503

## Claus Christoffersen Lyschander

*Synopsis historiarum Danicarum ... De danske Kongers Slectebog, Kbhvn. 1622*
Det kongelige Bibliotek 35-34 2°
The historian and poet Claus Lyschander (1558-1624) had been entrusted with the task of writing the Latin language history of Denmark prior to both Pontanus and Meursius, but was not up to it. Instead he prepared an (unprinted) description of the country, and a highly fantastical "Slectebog" (Genealogy) in which he completely seriously traced the Danish royal family back to Adam. To support this claim he referred in part to an invented document by an earlier historian which claimed that Jutland was settled by a descendent of Noah. To make the document even more convincing, Lyschander had it printed written in runes (p. 23).

1504

## Svend Aggesen

*Svenonis Aggonis filii ... quæ extant Opuscula, Stephanus Johannis Stephanius ex vetustissimo codice mebraneo ms. Regiæ bibliothecæ Hafnienses primus publici juris fecit ... Sorø 1642*
Det kongelige Bibliotek 35-24 8°
Stephanus Johannis Stephanius (1599-1650), professor at Sorø, succeeded Meursius as royal historian and com-

pleted his unfinished work with a book about the last years of Christian III (1550-59). He was, however, primarily a philologist, educated at Leiden, and he concentrated his efforts on studying the important written sources for the early history of Denmark. As an introduction to his major work, an edition of Saxo, he published in 1641 the works of Svend Aggesen, based on a manuscript in the University Library. The book belonged to Bishop Peder Villadsen (1610-73).

1505

## Stephanus Johannis Stephanius

*Notæ uberiores in historiam Danicam Saxonis Grammatici, Sorø 1645*

Det kongelige Bibliotek 35-25 2°

Stephanius' edition of Saxo (1645) was the philological accomplishment of its day. He succeeded in correcting the traditional text, published in 1514 by Christiern Pedersen, and illuminitated it through references to Saxo's linguistic and stylistic models. An accompanying volume of notes contained much learned commentary and illustration. On p. 75 is an illustration of a reconstruction of the royal seat at Lejre described in both the legends and in Saxo. The picture is a pewter engraving borrowed from Ole Worm.

1506

## Stephanus Johannis Stephanius

Letters to Ole Worm 1641 and 1644

Det kongelige Bibliotek, GKS 3119d 4°

Stephanius wrote numerous letters in his lovely round humanist hand from Sorø to his friend, the expert in antiquitites, professor Ole Worm in Copenhagen. These two researchers in antiquities presented each other with the problems that turned up and kept each other up to date on recent developments in the scholarly world. The correspondence preserved between them from 1626-50 is a significant source for an understanding of their personalities and their works.

1507

## Ole Worm 1588-1654

Copper engraving by Simon de Pas 1626

Det kongelige Bibliotek, The Picture Collection

Ole Worm founded Nordic prehistoric studies, made the pioneer runological studies and founded the first Danish museum of any size. It was characteristic of his systematic approach to his research that in 1622 he arranged for a royal order to be sent to all Danish bishops requiring that the parish vicars answer a series of inquiries about the local prehistoric monuments and other local relics. In 1625 he succeeded in gaining economic support for himself and his staff to travel around and examine the runic monuments throughout the country.

*Literature:* Schepelern 1951, 42 no. 2, Hollstein XVI, 186 no. 126.

1508

## Ole Worm

*Fasti Danici, Kbh. 1626*

Det kongelige Bibliotek 31-93 2°

Ole Worm's first antiquarian treatise dealt with the old Danish calendar system, in particular the runic calendars, some of which were carved in wooden sticks or discs to indicate the fixed calendar days of the year. The illustrations of the items described were done in copper engraving by Simon de Pas.

*Literature:* Schepelern 1951 4ff, 42 no. 3, Hollstein XVI, 189 no. 135.

1509

## Ole Worm

*Danicorum Monumentorum Libri sex, Kbhvn 1643*

Det kongelige Bibliotek 31-159 2°

Worm's major work – a major work in all of the antiquarian literature of the seventeenth century – is the book about the Danish runic monuments and their topographical locations. As the beginning of the section on Funen shows (leaves 238-39), he introduces each section with a description of that area borrowed from Lyschander (cf. 1503). The individual monuments are commented on and reproduced in pewter or wood cuts, usually from an original drawn by Worm's assistent Jon Skonvig. Due to the primitive examination techniques and the insufficient state of knowledge of historical linguistics, the decipherings rarely fulfill present day requirements, but Worm's reading of the Rønninge rune stone corresponds more or less to today's (Danmarks Runeindskrifter no. 202); "Sorte satte denne sten efter sin broder Elev, søn af Asgot med det røde skjold«. ("Sorte raised this stone to his brother Elev, son of Asgot with the red shield").

1510

## Ole Worm

*De aureo ... cornu, Kbhvn 1641*

Det kongelige Bibliotek 30-149 2°

The famous golden horn was found in 1639 by Gallehus and presented to Christian IV, who handed it on to the crown prince Christian (V). The latter showed it in 1640 to Ole Worm, and a few months later Worm announced the find and his allegorical interpretation of the figures on the horn to the learned world. On the accompanying copper engraving above left there is a gold knob which the prince had had made in order to close the narrow end of the horn, the better to use it as a drinking horn. The Prince had allowed Worm to drink from it, but in Worm's opinion it was more likely that it was a type of wind instrument from the time of Frode Fredegod.

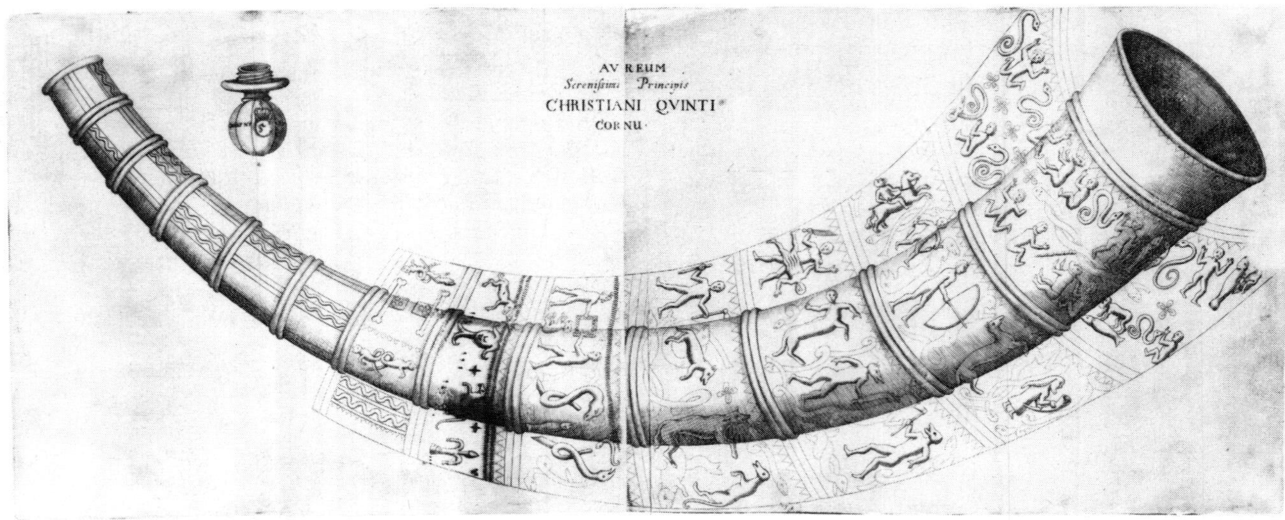


*1510*

1511

## Lisbeth Bryske

Generalogical manuscript
Det kongelige Bibliotek, GKS 1085 2°
On the sidelines of official history writing and learned studies of antiquities, the members of the nobility carried on genealogical research, usually with the goal of tracing their family line back as far as possible. Such studies were a speciality of noble ladies, and among these is Lisbeth Bryske (1585-1674), whose genealogy is typical of the genre. The information was gathered over the years, and Lisbeth Bryske left plenty of space on the pages from the beginning. [As can be seen, e.g. leaf 20, she later made an addition above the upper row of arms regarding the marriage of a Frederik Rantzau with Ida Skeel].
*Literature:* W. Christensen 1932, p. 6-13.

1512

## Armorial collected by Niels Akselsøn Juul (1634-c. 1680)

Det kongelige Bibliotek, Thott 1893 4°
On the first two leaves there are drawings of coastal profiles, the rest partly coloured drawings of coats of arms in alphabetical order. On the second leaf is written: "I have collected this armorial myself and done it during my schooling through my virtuous mother's tutoring. The paper is made of silk and was brought from the East Indies by her betrothed Niels Rosenkrantz, and was his map book on the same journey. Niels Juel Axelsøn, his own hand".

1513

## The progenitor af the Thott family

Copper engraving in Hans Mikkelsen: *En christelig Ligprædiken der ... Christian Tot til Boltingaard, hans salige Liig bleff hederligen nedersat udi S. Knuds kircke i Othense Aar 1617. Kbhvn 1620*
Det kongelige Bibliotek 46-184 4°
The nobility's pride of family left its traces in the flourishing funeral sermon literature, which by Christian IV's time generally included copper engravings with tables of coats of arms to show the illustrious lineage of the deceased's parentage. Somewhat more unusual is this engraving in a funeral sermon on Christian Tott. It is intended to illustrate that he is the twelfth in the series of Thotts, starting with a knight in armour, in repose, who is alleged to have lived c. 1085. Tott's widow was the generalogical author Sophie Below (1590-1650), and she clearly wished to honor her spouse's memory in this way.

1514

## Manuscript with a rhyme on the Danish kings, and coloured pictures of the kings

Det kongelige Bibliotek, Thott 797 2°
A patriotic and historical royal romanticism expressed itself in collections of rhymes on the Danish kings in either Danish or German, illustrated with pictures drawn of the Danish kings, and circulated in manuscript. At least twelve such manuscripts are preserved from the period c. 1590-1650. This one belonged to the persistent collector of things historical, Anne Krabbe of Stenalt (d. 1618). On leaf 23 Hamlet is shown as the Danes conceived him c. 1600.
*Literature:* Mackeprang and Flamand Christensen 1950, p. 69-71.

1515

## Manuscript with a rhyme on the Danish kings, and coloured pictures of the kings

Det kongelige Bibliotek, Thott 795 2°
The manuscript is from c. 1600 and has belonged to Lene Rud (1594-1671). On leaf 178 is a depiction of Queen Margrethe I.
*Literature:* Mackeprang and Flamand Christensen 1950, p. 67-69.

1516

## Manuscript on parchment with a German language rhyme on the Danish kings, and coloured pictures of the kings

Det kongelige Bibliotek, GKS 2427 4°
The manuscript is from c. 1600 and is of interest because the figures of the kings are copied from the woven tapestries at Kronborg, most of which later disintegrated. Among others, the Kronborg tapestry of Christoffer of Bavaria no longer exists, but here is in a copy on leaf 95.
*Literature:* Mackeprang and Flamand Christensen 1950, p. 61-63.

*1513*

# Museum Wormianum

Ole Worm (1588-1654) was a true polyhistor, who achieved much in many fields. In 1613 he became professor at Copenhagen after a tour abroad that had lasted many years, and which had made him recognize that evidence of the senses was the route to the renewal of the natural sciences. Until he became a professor of medicine in 1724, he had to participate in the teaching of Latin, Greek and Aristotle's physics, but understood how to weave in his many new observations. As professor of Greek from 1615 to 1621 he became involved in research on runes, with which he continued with for the rest of his life. His inaugural lecture in physics in 1621 dutifully praises Aristotle and tradition, but in the end emphasizes the superiority of the observations of the senses. At this same time he began his collecting, which became the other great work of his life, made known through the folio work, MUSEI WORMIANI HISTORIA, which appeared the year after his death. In the introduction he unambiguously indicates that autopsy (lit.: "seeing with one's own eyes") was far more important than verbal instruction. At that point he had already for a generation used items from his collection for demonstration purposes in his own medical teaching – apparently as the first in Europe.

The four books in the history of the museum deal with the mineral, plant, and animal worlds, and man-made items. After Worm's death the collection became a part of the Royal Kunstkammer, founded by Frederik III, which in the 1820's was dispersed into the many new specialized scientific museums, where Worm's natural objects in particular are lost among the numerous specimens.

A portion of Worm's ethnographical and other man-made items have however been identified, particularly in the collections of Nationalmuseet.

The exhibit attempts to re-establish the museum interior as shown in the large copper engraving in Worm's work on the history of the museum.

*H. D. Schepelern*

1522

## Drinking tankard

Norway, 1600's (?)
Maple. H. 21.6 cm, Diam. 12.3 cm
Nationalmuseet, 2. Department no. 6023
On the lid is carved a stylized lion between vines under a wreath of foliage and ribbon. The lid lever is carved as a lion.
*Provenance:* Acquired 1841.

*Title-engraving from Museum Wormianum 1655.*

1523

## Pair of spurs

1400's-1500's
Iron neck: 23 cm, wheel: Diam. 10.5 cm
Nationalmuseet, 2. Department no. 622 and 10002
On the straight parts of the neck are placed 9 lattice work h's, which gave these spurs the nickname "King Harald's spurs".
*Provenance:* Museum Wormianum Kunstkammeret, Kunstmuseet BDb 12.
*Literature:* Museum Wormianum 1655 p. 356. Worm Monumenta Danica p. 50. Schepelern 1971, p. 340 no. 81.

1525

## Moose hoof mounted with a cup of maple

1500's-1600's
Animal hoof and wood, ivory knobs, 74.6×8 cm
Nationalmuseet, 2. Department no number
A moose hoof mounted on a round base of wood. Above a maple goblet with a wreath of small ivory knobs.
*Provenance:* Museum Wormianum or the Gottorp Kunstkammer.
*Literature:* Museum Wormianum 1655 p. 337. Schepelern 1971, p. 174.

1526

## Drinking horn with mounting of gilded copper

1500's-1600's
Horn and metal. Diam. 16 cm, L. 76 cm
Nationalmuseet, 2. Department no. 10542

Wide, seven-lobed mouthpiece. Two rings around the horn. The tip closes with an extension tipped by many-lobed knob.
*Provenance:* Kunstkammeret. Kunstmuseet in Dronningens Tværgade BCe 8.
*Literature:* Olrik 1909, p. 18.

1527

## Drinking horn mounted in copper, 1400's

Horn and metal. Diam. 8.2 cm, L. 42.1 cm
Nationalmuseet, 2. Department no. 8
Wide mouthpiece with the names of the Three Wise Men. Two rings around the horn connected by ornamental strips. The tip closed with a metal extension crowned by a dwarf sitting on a barrel.
*Literature:* Olrik 1909, p. 23.

1528

## Sepulchral urn

Vejrum, Jutland, early bronze age, 1st millennium B. C.
Red-gray clay. H. c. 50 cm. Diam. c. 38 cm
Nationalmuseet, 2. Department no. 621
Glued-on label, with ink inscription: URNA SEPULCHRALIS WEIRUMENSIS and the circumstances of the find.
According to the protocol of the Museum of Northern Antiquities, the urn was filled with ashes when received; according to a letter to Worm of Sept. 8, 1649 there were pieces of bone and women's jewelry, "especially pieces of amber and a ring, which may have been a woman's bracelet".
*Provenance:* Found by Councilor of the Realm Mogens Høg (1593-1661). Presented to professor Steffen Hansen Stephanius at Sorø. Presented by Stephanius to Ole Worm, and added to to the Royal Kunstkammer with his collection, and at its dissolution moved to the Museum of Northern Antiquities.
*Literature:* Breve til og fra Ole Worm no. 1654; Museum Wormianum, 1655, p. 349 (with illustration, also visible on title page engraving); Museum Regium, 1696, p. 63 and 1710, 11, 3; Schepelern; Museum Wormianum 1971, p. 181 and 332-33, no. 21.

1529

## Bracelet with appendages

Roman iron age, 1st to 4th centuries
Bronze. 10,4 cm in dia., 13 cm long
Nationalmuseet, 1. Department no. 8122
Cylindrical in form, with 13 open rings mounted on the outside, cut through to allow for expansion of the bracelet, 3 exterior mounts with appendages, two of metals discs, the third like a small bell clapper.
*Provenance:* Found near Kolding, Added to Worm's collection before 1644 (Breve til og fra Ole Worm no. 1233). From Det kongelige Kunstkammer to Oldnordisk museum, now The National Museum.
*Literature:* Th. Bartholin De armillis veterum, 1647; Museum Wormianum, 1655, p. 353; Schepelern 1971, p. 336 no. 60.

1530

## Alligator mississipiensis (Daud.)

Stuffed alligator, 125×40 cm
Zoologisk Museum, CN 18
*Provenance:* North America, Odense Zoo 1,12, 1942.
*Literature:* Museum Wormianum, p. 315.

1531

## Varanus exanthematicus (Daud.)

Stuffed monitor (lizard), 95×35 cm
Zoologisk Museum. R. 4215
*Provenance:* South Africa, Copenhagen Zoo 4.5.1921.

1532

## Caretta caretta (L.)

Upper shell of a mock loggerhead turtle, 78×68 cm
Zoologisk Museum, R 2727
*Provenance:* Atlantic Ocean, Danmarks Akvarium, 87-1981.
*Literature:* Museum Wormianum p. 316.

1533

## Chelonia viridis (Schiv.)

Cranium of a green turtle, 25×14 cm
Zoologisk Museum, CN 56
*Provenance:* Tropical garden

1534

## Boidae sp

Skin of a boa constrictor, 210×10 cm
Zoologisk Museum
*Literature:* Museum Wormianum p. 263.

1535

## Pristis pristis (L.)

Snout of a sawfish, 77×20 cm
Zoologisk Museum, CN 37
*Literature:* Museum Wormianum p. 288 (ill.).

1536

## Galeorhinus galeus

Stuffed tope, 135×35 cm
Zoologisk Museum
*Literature:* Museum Wormianum p. 271-72 (ill.)

1537

### Diodon hystrix (L.)

Stuffed porcupine fish, 42×30 cm
Zoologisk Museum, CN 32
*Provenance:* Saint Croix, Virgin Islands, Kongelige Naturhistoriske Museum, 21, 11. 1842
*Literature:* Museum Wormianum p. 267.

1538

### Acipenser sp.

Stuffed sturgeon, 40×5 cm
Zoologisk Museum
*Literature:* Museum Wormianum p. 273-74.

1539

### Ostrarius cornutus (L.)

Stuffed coffer fish, 25×7 cm
Zoologisk Museum, CN 77
*Provenance:* Reunion, 1868.

1540

### Cetacea sp.

Vertebra of an undetermined whale, 98×78 cm
Zoologisk Museum.

1541

### Capra hicus (L.)

Cranium with horns of a tame goat, 58×55 cm
Zoologisk Museum
*Provenance:* Z.P.M.

1542

### Odobenus rosmarus (L.)

Cranium of a walrus, 52×38 cm
Zoologisk Museum, CN 481
*Literature:* Museum Wormianum p. 289-90 (ill.).

1543

### Ovies aries (L.)

Horn of a four-horned sheep (tame sheep), 37×38 cm
Zoologisk Museum, K 292

1544

### Monodon monoceros (L.)

Cranium with the tusk of a narwhal, 255×45 cm
Zoologisk Museum
*Literature:* Museum Wormianum p. 282 ff. (ill.)

1545

### Oryx algazel (Oken)

Cranium with horn of an oryx (mounted as a trophy), 90×15 cm
Zoologisk Museum, CN 1341
*Provenance:* Sahara, 1.11.1926
*Literature:* Museum Wormianum p. 340 (ill.).

1546

### Mammutus primigenius (Blumenbach)

Thighbone of a mammoth, 100×28 cm
Zoologisk Museum
*Provenance:* Flanders, 1643 Det kongelige Kunstkammer, 652/33 in 1737.

1547

### Alces alces (L.)

Cranium with two horns, one of which is double, 114×80 cm
Zoologisk Museum, CN 154
*Provenance:* Det kongelige Kunstkammer 658/13 in 1737.
*Literature:* Museum Wormianum p. 336-37.

1548

### Telypeutes tricinutus (L.)

Bony plates of a three-banded armadillo, 24×9 cm
Zoologisk Museum, CN 75
*Provenance:* Det kongelige Kunstkammer.
*Literature:* Museum Wormianum p. 335.

1549

### Rangifer tarandus (L.)

Cranium with antlers, 83×55 cm
Zoologisk Museum CN 1623
*Provenance:* Norway, 7.9.1935.
*Literature:* Museum Wormianum p. 337-38.

1550

### Maia squinado Herbst

Dried long-legged crab, 40×40 cm
Zoologisk Museum
*Literature:* Museum Wormianum p. 250.

1551

### Palinurus sp.

Dried spiny lobster on a wooden mount, 57×23 cm
Zoologisk Museum
*Provenance:* Consul Krebs, 5/1883.
*Literature:* Museum Wormianum p. 250 (ill.).

1552
### Limulus polyphemus (L.)
Dried king crab, 45×30 cm
Zoologisk Museum
*Provenance:* North America, Danmarks Akvarium, 1966.
*Literature:* Museum Wormianum, p. 249 (ill.).

1553
### Acropora cervicornis (Lmk,)
Madrepore, 62×45 cm
Zoologisk Museum, no. 40
*Provenance:* The West Indies/Ørsted, Kongelige Naturhistoriske Museum.
*Literature:* Museum Wormianum p. 230.

1554
### Acropora maniformis (Ltk.)
Madrepore, 42×15 cm
Zoologisk Museum, no. 12
*Provenance:* The West Indies/Riise.
*Literature:* Museum Wormianum p. 232.

1555
### Thalarctos maritimus (Phipps)
Stuffed polar bear cub, 65×35 cm
Zoologisk Museum, LN 473
*Provenance:* Nordisk Film, Paladsteatret, c. 1978.
*Literature:* Museum Wormianum p. 319.

1556
### Morus bassanus (L.)
Stuffed gannet, 85×25 cm
Zoologisk Museum, The Exhibit Collection

## Natural philosophy and medicine

After the Reformation the University of Copenhagen became all at once both a Lutheren seminary and an institution of higher education in the natural sciences. The requirements for admission were competence in Latin, which was further developed by the professors of Latin, Greek, Hebrew, physics and mathematics from the faculty of philosophy. This basic education was necessary in order to continue studies at the higher faculties: theology, medicine and law. For the professors the positions teaching in the preliminary subjects were primarily brief stepping stones. However, this did not keep them from dealing with current scientific problems, e.g. in physics (natural philosophy) during the weekly disputation exercises. Numerous of the annually printed short disputation exercises left by most of the professors illustrate this. Latin translations of the works of Aristotle were the basis for introductory education at all universities in every subject but theology. Every other year a common disputation exercise was held where the clever students could obtain their baccalaureate, whereas the master's degree required a few more years and greater maturity. Numerous students acquired the latter degree abroad, which was also the case with doctorates.

The two professors of medicine became the actual supporters of natural science development in the specialized subjects of anatomy, physiology, botany and zoology, whereas chemistry did not have the status of a university subject. The lectures in these subjects were recommended to prospective pastors; it was the medical faculty which in part created an international reputation for the university. *Caspar Bartholin* became professor of medicine in 1613, but in 1619 was ordered to write textbooks on philosophical subjects such as dialectics, physics and metaphysics. He based these writings on the teachings of the ancients about the four elements corresponding to the four bodily fluids (the cardinal humors). In 1611 he published an anatomy text, equally traditional in approach, which also came into use abroad. His son *Thomas Bartholin* published a revised edition in 1641 which included Harvey's new theory about the circulation of the blood from 1628. Not until 1642 was an anatomy auditorium built, but instruction via observation (autopsy) had by then long been in use, especially through the efforts of *Ole Worm,* who founded his famous museum for just that purpose.

Chemistry was still at a speculative stage. Inorganic matter was viewed as having life just did as organic matter. Since the Middle Ages miners had claimed that metals and precious stones grew, as the plants do in soil; apothecaries had gained some experience in laboratories, goldsmiths and enamel workers had experimented with dyes, but late in the 1600's the alchemists were still searching for the philosphers's stone, that which could change base metals to gold. *Paracelsus,* one of the most eccentric figures of the Renaissance, had suggested replacing the four elements with salt, sulphur and mercury; all products of nature contained healing powers. Mercury had been shown to be effective against venereal disease, and around 1600 the medical establishment was receptive to these new ideas. The Danish doctor *Peder Sørensen* had in his treatise from 1571. "Idea Medicinæ Philosophicæ", cleansed Paracelsisism of its most fantastical aberrations, and prepared the ground for iatrochemical theory, whose major exponent became Daniel Sennert at Wittenberg. *Ole Worm,* who had dabbled in chemistry in his youth, took a somewhat doubtful view of iatrochemical theory. In a university speech in 1619 he defended Aristotelianism against the secretive Rosecrucian movement, which was heavily steeped in superstition and mysticism. In this same year the requirement that only those with medical degrees were

1563

allowed to practice medicine was reiterated, and also that the medical faculty was to oversee the apothecaries.

The king followed his own lead. In 1611 he set up a "distillery" at Rosenborg Castle, lead by the Paracelsist *Peder Payngk.* It functioned more as an apothecary than as a scientific laboratory. When silver was discovered near Kongsberg in Norway, it also became a metallurgical testing station. The king himself laid out a medicinal herb garden at Rosenborg, but in 1600 he had also given the university a botanical garden.

*H. D. Schepelern*

1557

## Painting: Anatomical lesson of Dr. S. E. de Vrij

Thomas de Keyser, 1619
135×186 cm
Amsterdam Historisch Museum, A 7352
*Literature:* Blankert 1975/1979. Van Thiel 1983 128-195, spec. 169-171 177-178.

1557a

## Painting: The anatomical lesson of Dr. W. van der Meer

Pieter Michielz. van Miereveld, 1617
Canvas. 170×220 cm
Stedelijk Museum "Het Prinsenhof", Delft. Oude en Nieuwe Gasthuis B 112
Acquired 1984. Originally ordered by the surgical guild in Delft. 1860-1984 in the possession of The Old and New Hospital in Delft.
*Literature:* Houtzager 1979. De Stad Delft, cultuur en maatschjappij van 1572 tot 1667, Delft 1981, I. V. T. Spaander, R. A. Leeuwe ed.

1558

## De fire elementer (the four elements)

Four copper engravings by Hendrich Goltzius
28,5×17 cm
Den kgl. Kobberstiksamling 10,22-25
Allegorical depiction of Air (AER), a bird catcher; Water (AQVA) a fisherman; Earth (TERRA) a hunter, signed H. Goltzius inuent; Fire (IGNIS) a cook.
The doctrine of the four elements goes back to *Empedocles* (c. 495-435 B.C.). All visible natural objects are a mixture of these four. *Hippocrates* (5th to 4th cen, B.C.) viewed the biological processes as associated with the four corresponding fluids (blood, plegm, choler (yellow bile) and melancholy (black bile)), which in turn were responsible for the four temperaments; sanguine (blood = warm and humid = air); plegmatic (plegm = cold and humid = water); choleric (yellow bile = warm and dry = fire); melancholy (black bile = cold and dry = earth).
*Literature:* Bartsch 111, p. 100, 18-21.

1559

## Peter Diderichsen Payngk c. 1575-1645, royal court distiller

*Petri Theodorici Payngk collectio Formularum medico-chymicarum* (Peter Diderichsen Paygnk's collection of chemical-medical formulas). On the vellum cover PDP in stamped in gold; on page 1 the signature of Payngk's son, Ahasverus Payngk.
Manuscript in vellum binding with gilt edges. 682 pages Folio. Written in German. Numerous additions in Latin by the son, Dr. med. Ahasverus Payngk. P. 386 the opinions of Paracelsus on the philosphers' stone.
*Provenance:* After the death of the son in 1667 the book went to the king's library. A later entry in the catalogue in 1781 suggests that this already had occureed "under Schumacher" (later Griffenfeld).
*Literature:* Fjelstrup: 1911.

1560

## Peter Sørensen (Petrus Severinus)

*Idea Medicinæ Philosophicæ, [The philosphical base of medicine] (Fundamenta continens totius doctrinæ Paracelsicæ, Hippocrates & Galenicæ), Basel, 1571 4°*
Universitetsbiblioteket, 2. Department Pat. 17650
Bound into a late medieval theological parchment manuscript. The life of P. Sørensen, handwritten on the basis of H. P. Resen's funeral sermon in 1602; illegible signature. The author was the Royal physician to Frederik II after 1571, and continued to his death in 1602 as physician to Christian IV. His treatise influenced all of Europe in the direction of the use of chemical medical drugs as suggested by Paracelsus.
*Provenance:* Donated to the University library in 1730 by King Christian VI).
*Literature:* Translated by Hans Skov with an introduction by Dr. med. Eyvind Bastholm, (Acta Historica Scientiarum naturalium ete Medicinalium, edidit Bibliotheca Universitatis Hauniensis vol. 32, Copenhagen, 1979.

1561

## William Harvey

*De Motu Cordis Anatomica Exercitatio cum refutationibus Æmylii Parisani et Iacobi Primirosii, Leiden 1639*
(Anatomical exercises on the movement of the heart with a refutation of Emiglio Parigiano and James Primrose)
Universitetsbiblioteket, 2. Department Med. fys. 5550 4°
267 + 84pp. Vellum binding containing other anatomical works by several authors. Harvey's treatise, published in 1628, was opposed by a whole series of doctors (among them Ole Worm), who had misgivings about breaking with the thousand-year old doctrine on the body's four fluids.
*Literature:* Frank 1980.

1562

## Caspar Bartholin

*Institutiones Anatomicæ Novis Recentiorum opinionibus & observationibus, qvarum innumeræ hactenus editæ non sunt, figurisque auctæ. Ab auctoris Filio Thoma Bartholine, Leiden 1641*
(Textbook in anatomy enlarged with numerous new opinions and observations, as well as figures, not previously published, by the author's son Thomas Bartholin)
Universitetsbiblioteket, 2. Department Med.An. 8650 8°
A worn leather binding with gold edging bands 496 pp, + index. Title page engraving with portraits of Caspar Bartholin, Hippocrates, Galen and six other anatomists. Thomas Bartholin incorporated William Harvey's theory of the circulation of the blood in this first new edition of his father's widely used anatomy text.

1563

## Simon Paulli

*Flora Danica, Det er Dansk Vrtebog, København 1648, 4°*
Universitetsbiblioteket, 2. Department
Leather full binding, 20,5×15,5 cm, 393 pp. + index and illustration section with 384 plant illustrations in woodcuts done in Holland, depicting Danish plants, divided into 4 sections; winter plants (8), spring plant (136), summer plants (229) and autumn plants (11), corresponding to sections in the text, where each section is introduced with a seasonal allegory engraved in copper by Albert Haelwegh from an original by Karel van Mander. The title page engraving done by the same two artists. In the exhibited copy both the copper engravings and the plates of the plants are hand coloured.
Simon Paulli (1603-1680), was born in Rostock, and was called from there to a professorship in anatomy and botany. Flora Danica was prepared in Latin and translated to Danish by Niels H. Knopf.
*Literature:* Flora Danica I-III, facsimile edition ed. by Johan Lange and V. Møller-Christensen, Kbh. 1971-73; Skytte Christensen, 1973.

1564

## Caspar Bartholin

*Opuscula Quatuor singularia, Hafniæ 1628 8°*
Universitetsbiblioteket, 2. Department N. Hist. 5080
Bound in vellum 15,7×9,8 cm
The book contains four separately paged treatises
De Unicornu (on Unicorns) 48 pp
De lapide Nephritico cum pracipuis ad plerosque morbos Amuletis (on nephrite stones with special amulets for various illnesses) 30 pp
De Pygmæis (on pygmies) 29pp
De studio Medico Inchoando, Continuando et Absolvendo (On the beginning, continuation and completion of medical studies), 10 leaves. C. Bartholin was from 1624 a professor of theology, but he did not drop natural science and medicine completely, as this publication shows.
*Literature:* De studio Medico is translated by Niels W. Bruun, 1982, p. 78 11.

1565

*Apothecken Taxt, Kiøbenhavn 1619, 4°*
Universitetsbiblioteket, 2. Department Med.-taks. Danmark 8°
35 unnumbered pages. In 1619 a royal order decreed that only medical doctors were allowed to prescribe drugs for internal use and that they must be consulted by practising "apothecaries, barbers, chemists, occultists, herniotomists, quacksalvers and empirics". The medical faculty was to visit the two royal appointed apothecaries in Copenhagen twice a year. In the same year this extensive listing of a long series of natural and prepared medicinal drugs with their prices appeared. The herbal preparations play a completely dominating role.
*Literature:* Schæffer 1963.

1566

## Caspar Bartholin and Simon Paulli

*Künstliche Zerlegung des Menschlichen Leibes ... D. Caspari Bartholini, itzo durch Anordnung D. Simonis Paulli ... Allen Wundartzten zu nutz ins Deutsch übergesetzt, Kbh. 1648, 8°*
Universitetsbiblioteket, 2. Department Med.An. 8654
Vellum binding, 15,9×8,9 cm, 929 pp
Bound together with Simon Paulli's Latin program from the dedication of the anatomical auditorium 1644 (5 unnumbered leaves).
Poems and epigrams by Michael Kirstein. Latin and German indexes. Simon Paulli, whose name is inseparable from the founding of the anatomical auditorium at the university, played a greater role as a botanist than as an anatomist. His translation of Bartholin's anatomy shows his interest in the instruction of the ill-educated surgeons. The title page engraving shows the anatomy hall in Domus Anatomica.
*Literature:* Thomas Bartholin; Cista Medica Hafniensis, Hafniæ 1662, facs. ed. by Bruun and Loldrup, 1982, p. 185ff.

1567

## Christopher Heerforth

*Der Königlichen Provintzen Laalandt und Falster; Herbarium Vivum.* 2. Theil. Folio.
Botanisk Museum
Bound in red marbled paper. (The back of the binding has been lost, but it was most likely of vellum. Remains of linen ribbons for tying up). 195 leaves, edged with strips of marbled paper. Pressed plants glued in, one species per leaf. The plants are generally well preserved.
*Provenance:* In nature on Lolland and Falster, gathered by Apothecary Heerforth, donated by Frederik III, May 6, 1656.
*Literature:* Lind; 1917, p. 1-19.

1568

## Caspar Bartholin

*Enchiridion logicum ex Aristotele et opt. Eius Interpretum monumentis, Strassburg 1608, 8°*
Det kongelige Bibliotek 14-108
Worn full binding in leather with crown C4 13×9 cm, 449 pp. and index. Dedicated to the Crown Prince Christian.

1569

## Caspar Bartholin

*Enchiridion Metaphysicum ex ... Aristotelis optimorumqve eius interpretum monumentis adornatum ... Strassburg 1610 8°*
(Metaphysical handbook compiled from the works of Aristotle and those of his best interpreters)
Det kongelige Bibliotek 14-203
Vellum binding 13×8 cm, 40 pp

Dedicated to Bjørn Urup, Axel Urup and Jørgen Below in Strasbourg. Aristotles' Scholasticism had been the basis of all scientific discussion since the 1200-1300's, a condition which continued after the Reformation. Metaphysics, the discipline of basic concepts (existence-/non-existence, matter/form, singularity/plurality, good/evil, cause/effect, etc.) made up a part of all introductory subjects, especially logic, physics and mathematics, and many of the Copenhagen professors had made their debut with disputations in metaphysics. This was also the case with Caspar Bartholin, though it was his anatomy text that gave him international fame. Right up until his death in 1629 (by then a professor of theology), he continued to publish handbooks in physics and other introductory subjects. In 1619 a special professorship was established in metaphysics (eliminated in 1739), but it was never of great significance.

1570

## Jacob Fincke

*Disputationum Physicarum, Qvæ est de Primus Rerum Naturalium Principiis, In Academia Hafniensi publicè propositarum Prima, Præside Jacobo Finckio. Respondente Thoma Bartholino Casp. filio ad diem IV Julii Anno 1636*

Det kongelige Bibliotek 20-87 $4^0$

Recent cardboard binding 20×16 cm, 10 unnumbered leaves

"The first of the dissertations on physics, which is about the first principles of natural matter, [i.e. about the elements] publicly presented at the Copenhagen academy with Jacob Finck presiding and Thomas Bartholin, the son of Caspar, as the opponent, July 9, in the year 1636". Thomas Finck's son Jacob Finck (1592-1663) studied abroad for ten years and made his debut already in 1612 in Strasbourg with a dissertation on the elements. From 1623-35 he was professor of mathematics, and thereafter until his death, of physics. In his many short dissertations, authors other than Aristotle are rarely mentioned. At this first defense in physics, where the 20 year old Thomas Bartholin is the opponent, Petrus Ramus, Paracelsus and the Portuguese physicist Benedict Pereira of the 1500's are all mentioned.

# The University Library in the Church Loft

The hall above the Trinity Church, projected by Christian IV as accomodation for the University Library, was not finished in his time; the hall was not ready for use until after his death, and the solemn inauguration did not take place until 1657. The whole floor was kept free as the cupboards, which were placed along the walls, could hold all the books, the backs of which could be seen faintly through the wire lattice of the cupboard doors. In the 17th century the University Library was the virtual national library, as Christian IV had donated all the books belonging to his father and grandfather to the University. The original library was destroyed in the fire of 1728, but was soon reestablished, and gradually the free space was filled with books. A new building became a necessity, and in 1861 the library was moved to the building in Fiolstræde, which still contains part of the University Library of Copenhagen.

*Torben Nielsen og Harald Ilsøe*

1570a

## Manuscript from the medieval university library

Det kongelige Bibliotek, GKS 1813 4°

The contents of the old university library, founded in 1482, were destroyed in the fire of Copenhagen in 1728. Only a few manuscripts remain which with certainty can be traced to the library, among them an astronomical mixed manuscript which belonged to the library's patron Dr. Peder Albertsen c. 1500. On the inside cover it states that the book is donated to the university by Dr. Peder Albertsen; liber datus universitati per doctorem petrum alberti.

*Provenance:* University library prior to 1728

*Literature:* O. Pedersen 1982 p. 27-68.

1570b

## Catalogue from the University Library

*Catalogus Veteris Bibliotheca*

Handwritten catalogue of the old university library

Rigsarkivet. The Archive of the University of Copenhagen, 16.07.01

On the initiative of H. P. Resen, later well-known as the bishop of Zealand, a catalogue was compiled in 1602-03 of the books and manuscripts found in the University library. This collection became known as "Vetus bibliothecæ" (the old library) in order to separate it from new donations of books. [When the library was opened to the public in the 1650's, the catalogue was re-written and this copy sent to the archives, thus saving it from the flames in 1728].

*Literature:* H. Ilsøe 1980, p. 297-303

1570c

## Catalogue from the University Library

*Catalogus bibliothecæ Lymvicianæ*

A handwritten catalogue of the library of Anders Lemvig 1603

Rigsarkivet. The Archive of the University of Copenhagen, 16.07.01

A library catalogue preserved in the archives like the previous no. Professor Anders Lemvig was the first of a long series of benefactors who, in the course of the seventeenth century, brought the contents of the university library up to a considerable level. When Lemvig's book collection came to the library in 1603, according to the provisions of his will, it contained nearly 3,000 printed works and c. 175 manuscripts. The catalogue also contains a set of library rules which state that the professors are only allowed to borrow two books at a time and at the most for a fortnight.

1570d

## Claus Christoffersen Lyschander

*Adversaria in Christianum III et Fridericum II*
Manuscript from the old university library
Det kongelige Bibliotek, GKS 856 2°
The Danish historians' work papers, old manuscripts and documents, as well as transcriptions and historical surveys from c. 1550 and on, were gathered together in about 1600 at the university library, at the disposal of newer historians. From among these historical manuscripts is preserved a collection of excerpts for the history of Christian III and Frederik II made by the Royal historiographer Claus Lyschander. It was handed over to the library after his death in 1624, and because the manuscript had been borrowed by the historian Hans Gram in 1728, it was saved from the fire. The symbols on the right are the call numbers from the library.

1570e

## The gift book of the university library, started c. 1650

Rigsarkivet. The Archive of the University of Copenhagen. 16.04.01
In connection with the establishment of the new university library in the loft above Trinitatis Church at the beginning of the 1650's, the head librarian Thomas Bang started a gift book, beautifully bound in red velvet with engraved silver plates attached to the binding. On the front is the university coat of arms in the middle, above left the theological faculty, to the right the law faculty, lower left the medical faculty and to the right the philosophical faculty. In the book, two notices indicate gifts respectively from Christian IV's brother-in-law, James VI of Scotland and Christian IV himself. The latter large gift of 1605 was made up of both his father's and his grandfather's books in the Palace of Copenhagen. For reasons unknown, after recording these donations, the gift book was never used.
*Provenance:* The university library before 1728
*Literature:* The university's Liber Daticus from the XVII century, Konsistorium (ed.) 1935.

# Belles-lettres

The period of Christian IV has little to offer of what later generations view to be literature; that which at all assumes literary form is often characterized by an occasional or utilitarian purpose. Even so the period is not completely without significance in literary history; faltering but goal-oriented steps were made in the direction of creating a Danish literature with European characteristics.

The older domestic literary forms had not yet completely played out their roles. The first printed edition of Danish folk songs was published by Anders Sørensen Vedel in 1591, and the folk song style was still a living genre at the time; in Vedel's Hundredvisebog (One Hundred Songs) several of the songs were of his own composition. A plain, ordinary Danish style, also characterized Ranch's Fuglevise (Bird Songs) and the satirical poems of Skonning.

Another domestic Danish genre was Rimkrøniken (the rhyming chronicle), which became art under Lyschander's treatment, e.g. in his Den grønlandske Chronica (Chronicle of Greenland). In addition, the period of Christian IV had a lively tradition of school plays, and many a schoolmaster or pastor provided his disciples with dramatic texts that improved the students and amused the audience. These are commonly written in a natural, popular style; best known of them today is Ranch's "Karrig Niding", which has been played on Danish television, whereas the dramatic productions presented at court (e.g. Den store Bilager), for which men such as Lauremberg were responsible, point the way forward to the Baroque.

The Renaissance obtrudes itself in various ways, such as in the attempts to tame the intractable Danish language to behave according to the classical patterns. Aquillonius' tongue-twisting attempt to adjust Danish to the Latin principle of quantity was doomed to failure, and, with the support of the German Renaissance poet Opitz, both scholars and poets came to the conclusion that the syllabic accent had to be the natural principle of versification in Danish language poetry.

The greatest of the poetic efforts of the period of Christian IV is Anders Arrebo's grand epos on the creation, Hexaëmeron. Despite the age of the genre – from Danish soil as far back as 1200 had come Anders Sunesen's Hexaëmeron, known to us, though not to Arrebo – it was the French Renaissance poet du Bartas that Arrebo used as a model; and symptomatic of this strict Lutheran period, Christian poetry like that of the Huguenot du Bartas assumes a leading role.

Even poetry written in Latin achieved the distinction of having a Christian ribbon tied to its tail by Erik Pontoppidan in his Epigrammata sacra and Bucolica sacra.

An important contribution to the development of Danish as a literary language was translation of the Latin classics; the first work of significance was Peder Jensen Roskilde's translation of Vergil's Bucolica. The achievement of the century was Birgitte Thott's translation of Seneca; he is perhaps also the classical author closest to the Christian ethic. The secular also gained elbow room, not least through Søren Terkelsen's presentation of pastoral poetry. His discursive novel Astræa was not easily digested, but the songs, and especially the melodies – Terkelsen was not a great poet – long remained popular.

Few of the occasional poems of the period deserve mention; Arrebo's elegy on Queen Anna Cathrine achieved poetic quality. Peder Winstrup's poem on the finding of the first golden horn served a national-political mission.

*Torben Nielsen og Erik Petersen*

1571

## Svaning's manuscript

Det kongelige Bibliotek, NKS 815$^b$ 4°
The manuscript know as Svaning's consists of two originally independent manuscripts. Nor have they, as once thought, belonged to Svaning, but to his son-in-law, Anders Sørensen Vedel; as is also the case with the third of the four preserved folk song manuscripts that belonged to Vedel (Rentzell's), the manuscript was intended for use, thus distinguishing it from the other sources for folk songs from the period of Christian IV, the manuscripts of noble ladies.
*Provenance:* The manuscript belonged to the historian Hans Gram during the 18th century.
*Literature:* Sønderholm 1976, p. 321 ff.

1572

*It hundrede vduaalte Danske Viser ... Ribe 1591*
Universitetsbiblioteket, 1. Department N 700·8$^0$
Our first printed collection of folk songs (and Europe's) was produced by Anders Sørensen Vedel (1542-1616), canon at Ribe and Royal historiographer. The original is found in only four copies in Denmark, of which this is the only one that is complete.
*Provenance:* This copy was bought at the auction of the estate of Revenue Officer Peter Uldall in 1803 by Rasmus Nyerup and/or Knud Lyne Rahbek for use in theirs and Abrahamson's edition of folk songs 1810-14 and thereafter was added to the University Library.

1573

## Rentzell's manuscript

Det kongelige Bibliotek, GKS 2397 4°
Rentzell's manuscript is one of the four folk song manuscripts known to have been owned by Anders Sørensen Vedel. Valentin Rentzell is only known from a note at the beginning of the manuscript – who he was and what relationship he had to the manuscript are unknown. Anders Sørensen Vedel's handwriting is recognizable here and there in the manuscript.
*Literature:* Sønderholm; 1976, p. 309ff.

1574

## Kirsten Basses Danske Visebog, 1635

Det kongelige Bibliotek, NKS 485$^c$ 2°
The name of the creator and owner of this manuscript appears in the first letter of each line in a little verse under the inscription "Dagligt Mundheld" (Saying for the Day) on the page before the title page; KIRSTEN BASSE. On the title page appears the coat of arms of the Basses, and the initials of the owner; K(irsten) B(asse) N(iels') D(atter), Anno 1635. In addition to the folk songs, the manuscript contains a large selection of poems from the seventeenth century.
*Literature:* Sønderholm: 1976, p. 336 ff.

1575

## Hieronymus Justesen Ranch

*Fugle Vise / som viser huad for Fugle iblant Folck i Verden findis ... Kbn. 1630*
Det kongelige bibliotek 53-338 4°
This poem, which follows a tradition stemming from the animal rhymes of the Middle Ages, portrays human qualities in the guise of birds; it retained its popularity for many generations and was widely known and loved by the Danes.

1576

## Hans Hansen Skonning

*De wgudelige oc forvirrede Verdens Børns Klagemaal ... Aarhus 1648*
Det kongelige Bibliotek 54-31 4°
Skonning (1579-1661) was an energetic author, printer – and in periods, bellringer, in Århus. He gained a certain notoriety by his cantankerous, free style of language, but his old-fashioned satires are not without a popular pithiness of expression.

1577

## Jacob Jacobsen Wolf

*Jødiekrønike, tilsammenskreffuen aff den hellige Scrifft, oc Josepho, oc udi Rim korteligen befattit; Kbh. 1603*
Universitetsbiblioteket, 1. Department Th.bis 60235 8°
Jacob Jacobsen Wolf (1554-1635), professor of theology and Hebrew at the gymnasium in Odense, rewrote the Old Testament as an epic poem.

1578

## Claus Christoffersen Lyschander

*De Billers Iensis Sønners XVI Aaner*
Det kongelige Bibliotek, Thott 1095 2°
Lyschander(1558-1624) was attached to the Bille family throughout his life. He combined his talents as poet and historian in this rhymed chronicle from the end of the 1500's. A special feature of the poem is that it is the

women of the Bille family who relate the history of the family, and tell of the "foremothers" of both the paternal and maternal lines.
*Literature:* Lundgreen-Nielsen 1988.

1579

## Claus Christoffersen Lyschander

*Den grønlandske Chronica, Kbh. 1608*
Universitetsbiblioteket. 1. Department T 39983 8°
Lyschander had a lively mind and a marked feeling for the Danish language and for Danish history. He used the old Danish rhymed chronicle to good poetic purpose in his major poetic opus "Den grønlandske Chronica" (The Chronicle of Greenland), which was stimulated by Christian IV's active interest in Greenland. The Chronicle relates the history of Greenland from Erik the Red to Christian IV.
*Provenance:* This copy has belonged to Peder Syv.

1580

## Randershåndskriftet

Det kongelige Bibliotek, GKS 794 2°
The Randers manuscript is one of the most important sources for the old style Danish school plays. The manuscript is, in some way not yet entirely clear in all its details, related to the headmaster from Randers, Peder Thøgersen; it contains, among other details, a schedule for the repertoire of plays to be performed on a few days in May of 1607, and in addition some important information on the production forms of the drama. The manuscript also contains the texts of several school plays, a Danish version of "Comoedia de mundo et paupere" and several of Hieronymus Justesen Ranch's plays.

1581

## Hieronymus Justesen Ranch

*Kong Salomons Hylding; En ny lystig oc nyttig Comoedi ... Kbh. 1585*
Universitetsbiblioteket, 1. Department M 72330 4°
On the 16th of June, 1584, the future Christian IV was acclaimed heir to the throne at the Landsting in Viborg. Ranch (1539-1607), who was pastor at the Church of the Grey Friars in Viborg, wrote this Biblical drama for the occasion, and added a generous supply of allusions to the events of the day.

1582

## Hans Thomsen Stege

*Cleopatra, Eller en Historisk Tragoedia, om den sidste Dronning i Egypten ... Kbh. 1609*
Universitetsbiblioteket, 1. Department M 81392 8°
Odd coincidence would have it that a headmaster in Hobro, Hans Thomsen Stege (d. 1628 as the parish vicar at Fanefjord), should write an "Anthony and Cleopatra" at nearly the same time that Shakespeare wrote his. Stege's pupils performed his tragedy – the oldest in Danish literature – which had no relationship to Shakespeare's; it is by and large cut of the same cloth as the traditional school play.

1583

## Hans Lauremberg

*Zwo Comoedien / Darinnen fürgestellet I. Wie Aquilo / der Regent Mitternächtigen Länder / die Edle Princessin Orithyjam heimführet. II. Wie die Harpyiæ von zweyen Septentrionalischen Helden verjaget; und König Phinéus entlediget wird, Kbh. 1635*
Det kongelige Bibliotek 35-276 4°
Born in Rostock and professor of mathematics at Sorø, Hans Lauremberg (1590-1658) is best known as a poet as the author of Low German poems written in jest, but on the occasion of the wedding of the heir to the throne, Christian, in 1634, he played court poet and produced two plays in a pompous Renaissance style.

1584

## Bertel Knudsen Aquilonius

*Ad poeticam Danicam deductio, Kbh. 1641*
Universitetsbiblioteket, 1. Department H 250 8°
Bertel Knudsen Aquilonius (1588-1650) held the post of rural dean in Løderup in Skania at his death. He made a heroic attempt to transfer Latin metrics, which are founded on alternation between short and long syllables, directly to Danish, but this was only possible with such convoluted word order that the meaning was all but lost.

1585

## Peder Jensen Roskilde

*Prosodia Danicæ lingvæ*
Det kongelige Bibliotek, Add. 472 4°
Peder Jensen Roskilde (1575-1641?), translator of Vergil's Bucolica (cat. 1598), was the first to indicate the importance of the accent for Danish versification; his treatise was however not printed in the period, but influenced Hans Mikkelsen Ravn. (cat. 1586).
*Provenance:* Cambridge binding from the collection of Niels Foss.
*Literature:* The text was published in 1953 in Danske metrikere.

1586

## Hans Mikkelsen Ravn

*Ex rhythmologia Danica msc. epitome brevissima, Sorø 1649*
Universitetsbiblioteket, 1. Department H 3375 4°
Hans Mikkelsen Ravn (in Latin, Corvinus, c. 1610-63), whose major work is the musical theory study Heptachordum Danicum, created in this work on versification a theoretical basis for Danish poetry in the spirit of

*Anders Arrebo. Engraving after portrait in Vordingborg Church.*

the late Renaissance, influenced in part by Peder Jensen Roskilde (cat. 1585).

1587

## Søren Poulsen Judichær

*Synopsis prosodiæ Danicæ eller En kort Extract aff Riimkonsten, Kbh. 1650*

Universitetsbiblioteket, 1. Department H 3348 8°

Judichær (1599-1668), also known as Gotlænder from the island of his birth, was like H. M. Ravn close to Arrebo; as a metrician he is of no more significance than Ravn, but his little book was written in Danish, and thus its consequence. His long Prosodia Daniica was not published until 1671 by his widow.

1588

## Berthel Wichmand

*Nesbyholm, eller om Sindsens Rolighed, Sorø 1644*

Det kongelige Bibliotek, Hjelmstierne 1077 4°

Wichmand (1617-65) was aware that Danish metrics would have to be based on the realtionship between stressed and unstressed syllables. Wichmand's poem is a direct imitation of Martin Optiz's "Zlatna oder von der Ruhe des Gemüths" (1623). Nevertheless his Danish Alexandrines flow quite freely.

1589

## Anders Arrebo

*Hexaëmeron rhytmico-danicum. Det er: Verdens første Uges sex Dages præctige og mæctige Gierninger ... Kbh. 1661.*

Det kongelige Bibliotek, 53-187 4°

Anders Arrebo (1587-1637) is the great pioneer figure in Danish poetry. His rendering in Danish of du Bartas' "La semaine ou création du monde" (1579) is more than a mere translation; among others, the descriptions of Nature contain many passages which bear witness to an original poetic voice.

1590

## Anders Sunesen

*Hexaëmeron*

Det kongelige Bibliotek, E don.var. 155 4°

Poems on the six days of the Creation, Hexaëmeron, come from a tradition with deep European roots, which early bore fruit in Denmark. Anders Sunesen's great poem in Latin hexameters is from the period around 1200, i.e. roughly contemporary with Saxo's Gesta Danorum.

The only surviving manuscript of Sunesen's poem from the Middle Ages belonged to the Cathedral of Roskilde. Numerous scholars were interested in the poem during the time of Christian IV; among others, Huitfeldt, Ole Worm and Stephanius studied the work in the version of the Roskilde manuscript. Despite several attempts made during Christian IV's reign, a printed edition of the poem in its entirety was first published towards the close of the nineteenth century.

*Provenance:* The Cathedral of Roskilde

*Literature:* Ebbesen & Mortensen 1985.

1591

## Tycho Brahe

*Elegia de exilio suo. Halle 1613*

Det kongelige Bibliotek 42-243 4°

Tycho Brahe wrote his Latin "Elegy to Denmark" during his stay at Henrik Rantzau's castle in Holstein, "in the year of Our Lord 1597, the 20th of October, when I at Wandsbeck resumed my astronomical observations, which earlier in the year at the vernal equinox I had had to discontinue at Uraniaborg against my will; God, creator of Heaven and Earth, support me in my work". The poem, imbued with a tone of both bitterness and pride, circulated privately in handwritten copies before appearing in print in 1613, and was also seen by Christian IV while on a visit with Henrik Rantzau – the king read it without acknowledging any reaction to either the poem or its author.

1592
## Tycho Brahe

*Elegia de exilio suo*
Det kongelige Bibliotek, NKS 1990 4°
The Latin text in this manuscript follows the printed edition from Halle of 1613; the manuscript's significance lies in its additional information that the poem had been translated to Danish. After each Latin distich – a couplet made up of one hexameter and one pentamenter – appears the Danish translation, which metrically suits Danish speech:
"O Danemarck mit fædreland
huad er min skyld og brøde ..."
"Oh Denmark my fatherland
what is my fault and crime ..."

1593
## Caspar Bartholin

*Epigrammata Extemporanea, Kbh. 1621*
Universitetsbiblioteket, 1. Department Kl. 95738 8°
The polyhistor Caspar Bartholin also served, among his many posts, for a time as professor of Latin, or rhetoric, as it was known at the time. However, it is less due to this capacity than to the general exercise in poetic forms of expression which was an ordinary part of schooling that he published a collection of epigrams in 1641. The composition of poetry was more a question of the mastery of a formal style of idiom than inspiration.

1594
## Hans Lauremberg

*Satyra, 1636*
Universitetsbiblioteket, 1. Department Kl. 96988 8°
Lauremberg's Latin Satyra occupies a special position within the Latin literature of the period of Christian IV. Though not without its classical models – Juvenal and Persius serve as the classical patterns – his satire is pleasantly freed from the constraints that tradition placed on the genre. Lauremberg taught at the academy at Sorø; already there he must have confronted the perplexity of the classical humanist when faced with an upbringing which did not exclude other means than the bookish in the educational process. In accordance with this Lauremberg complained of the noble pupils' exercises in fencing: "so that the man whom you called your friend yesterday, tomorrow can fall in a duel". In particular the new French fashions and vices went against the grain with Lauremberg. His mode of expression is sharp and lacks that propensity to servility which otherwise mars much of the rest of the literature of the period.

1595
## Willich Westhoff

*Epigrammata, Kbh. 1637*
Universitetsbiblioteket, 1. Department Kl. 98324 8°
The epigram, with its brief and emphatic form, became one of the favorite poetic genres of the seventeenth century. Danish poets found inspiration both among the classical authors of antiquity and among their contemporaries, the Latin poets abroad. The Englishman John Owen, a master of the epigram, was one for the sources of Willich Westhoff's inspiration – who in turn stimulated other Danish epigramists. Westhoff had already by 1603 published his first collection of epigrams.

1596
## Willich Westhoff

*Emblemata ... Christiano IV ... dicata, Kbh. 1640*
Det kongelige Bibliotek 53-71 8°
An emblem consists of a motto, an allegorical illustration and verses which present the message of the motto and picture. Collections of *emblamata* were a favorite form of expression in the Renaissance – brief and illustrative, with a wealth of potential messages. Willich Westhoff dedicated this collection of emblems to king Christian IV. Among the themes are: "According to the example of David", "The king and queen bring clarity", and "the king, watchman of men".

1597
## Erik Pontoppidan

*Bucolica Sacra, Leiden 1643*
Universitetsbiblioteket, 1. Department Kl. 97732 8°
The classical – and heathen – literature exercised an exceedingly strong influence on literary taste throughout the period of Christian IV. But reading the classics had to be defended from a Christian point of view, so as not to lead souls astray.
Erik Pontoppidan published a collection of *Epigrammata Sacra* in Copenhagen in 1641; these sacred epigrams, modelled on the classic form still loved in this period, were structured according to the books of the Bible and had an inspirational Christian content. In 1643 he published in Leiden his *Bucolica Sacra,* sacred pastorals, which transport classical heathen themes, such as Vergil's, into a Christian world. A heathen genre is transformed into an instrument in the service of the Good Shepherd.

1598
## Peder Jensen Roskilde

*Bucolica, det er Vergilii Hyrdevers. Kbh. 1639*
Det kongelige Bibliotek 48-210 8°
Peder Jensen Roskilde's translation of the Roman poet Vergil's Bucolica belongs among the earliest translations

of the classics to Danish literature. The translator remarks about his work in his dedication to Christoffer and Axel Valkendorf, that he "has ... with the help of the Divine Spirit, which among other things also gives the gift of explaining tongues, and after the urging of good friends, set forth the same into Danish rhymes all in one stroke, as the very best way to reach the understanding of the simple, so that a pupil without troubling his schoolmaster or tutor can easily understand the Latin text".
The translation was not only a transfer from one language to another, but also from one metre to another; Vergil's Latin hexametres were transformed into Danish iambics by Peder Jensen Roskilde.

1599
## Birgitte Thott
*Lucii Annæi Senecæ Skriffter fordanskitt, Sorø 1558*
Universitetsbiblioteket, 1. Department Kl. 86824 2°
The noblewoman Birgitte Thott's translation of the Roman philosopher and statesman Seneca's writings in moral philosophy ranks among the greatest prose works of the seventeenth century, and is a classic within Danish literature in translation. Though published after the death of Christian IV, it is related to the period through Birgitte Thott's long preparation and thorough study. All of Europe experienced considerable interest in Seneca and his stoic philosophy at the time. – The work was printed by Jørgen Hantzsch in Sorø and also has monumental value as an example of the art of the book.

1600
## Søren Terkelsen
*Dend Hyrdinde Astrea / Ved H. Honor, af Urfe først Frantzøesk beskreffven. Lyckstad [= Glückstadt] 1645*
Universitetsbiblioteket. 1. Department Rom. 93200 4°
Neighbourly relations with literary circles in Hamburg made Terkelsen into an effective purveyor of the pastoral in prose and poetry. However the translation of the long novel was never completed.
*Provenance:* A glued-in label indicates ownership by Rasmus Bartholin.

1601
## Søren Terkelsen
*Astree Siunge-Choer Eller Allehaande artige og lystige ny Verdslige Viser / med deres Melodier, Lyckstad [= Glückstadt] 1648*
Det kongelige Bibliotek 53-135 8°
Søren Terkelsen (d. 1656 or 1657) was a customs officer in Glückstadt, the city Christian IV founded on the Elbe. Though his poetry was not of any originality, many of the melodies became great favorites, e.g. "Ak, Amaryllis".

1602
## Gabriel Voigtländer
*Allerhand Oden und Lieder, Sorø 1642*
Universitetsbiblioteket. 1. Department Mus. 37550 2°
The German musician Gabriel Voigtländer (c. 1596-1643) entered the service of Prince Christian in 1639 at Nykøbing Castle. His collection of songs is of high quality and long remained popular. Due to his early death only the first part was published.

1603
## Anders Arrebo
*En Sørgelig Ny Dict Om ... Dronning Annae Catharinae ... Saligste Fredfart af denne vsle Verden ... Kbh. 1612*
Det kongelige Bibliotek, Hjelmstierne 2340 4°
It was almost a matter of course that the 25 year old pastor of the palace congregation in Copenhagen would come forth with a memorial poem on Christian IV's queen. However in this case it is a true poet, and not merely a chance composer of occasional poems, wielding the pen.

1604
## Claus Christoffersen Lyschander
*Triumphus Calmarniensis, Den calmarske Triumph, Kbh. 1611*
Universitetsbiblioteket. 1. Department E 4202 4°
Christian IV's large scale onslaught on the Swedes did not produce the desired results, even though the final outcome of the war and the peace of Knærød gave Danmark certain advantages. The conquest of Kalmar strengthened Danish national feeling, and it was most appropriate that Lyschander sang its praises in the chronicle style of which he was the last practitioner.

1605
## Erik Pontoppidan
*Rosa Daniæ / Danmarcks Rose. Sorø 1643*
Det kongelige Bibliotek 45-245 2°
Poetry, both in Danish and Latin, was often used as a means of currying favour, but also to honor the dead. In 1643, the year after the death of Holger Rosenkrantz, Erik Pontoppidan published an elegy praising the deceased, which exploited the many possibilities for wordplay on the word "rose". The poem appeared in a duolanguage version, Latin and Danish.

1606
## Peder Winstrup
*Cornicen Danicus, seu Carmen de aureo ... cornu, Kbh. 1644*
Universitetsbiblioteketet. 1. Department Ø 7723 2°
Oehlenschläger is not the first Danish author to be inspired by the golden horns from Gallehus. Five years after the finding of the first golden horn, the Bishop of

*1612*

Lund, Peder Winstrup (1605-79), published a long poem in Latin in honor of the golden horn and the heir to the throne, Prince Christian; the year after it was translated into Danish (no. 1607).
*Provenance:* Dedication from the author to the provincial medical officer in Scania, Niels Foss; the copy most likely came to the library from his grandson, the well-known book collector of the same name.

1607

## Peder Winstrup

*Den danske Hornblæser / Det er en dict om ... H. Christians ... Guldhorn ... fundet ... 1639. U.st. 1644*
Universitetsbiblioteket, 1. Department Ø 7724 2°
Cat. 1606 translated by the rector in Malmø, Peder Hermansen (1610-66). In marginalia the reader has noted the anti-Swedish tendency of the work, which did not however hinder Winstrup in remaining in his bishopric after the Swedish conquest of Scania.

# The Law and the Courts
# Jurisprudence in Denmark

In the time of Christian IV there was not yet a fully uniform legal system in Denmark. The basis of the law was still the old so-called provincial laws for the three legal districts of Jutland (and Funen), Zealand and Skania. These provincial laws were written down in the early thirteenth century, but later other legistation was added, in particular under Christian III, Frederik II and also Christian IV. This newer legislation was in force within the whole country, and also in other areas there were tendencies towards legislative unformity. In 1590 the Jutish Law appeared in a modernized and linguistically adapted edition, and thus the Jutish Law began gradually to supplant the other provincial laws. In the highest court, the king's court, the Jutish Law was used as the expression of general legal principles.

An actual jurisprudence, which might be capable of yielding an independent contribution to the development of law, shows only the faintest of traces in this period. At the University of Copenhagen there was a faculty of law, but only one professor of law. The university was primarily a seminary for ministers of the church, and the law professor's task was to give these prospective theologians good moral examples from the law, primarily from Roman law, but to some extent also from Danish law. The exhibit shows a series of the disputations which formed the basis for the teaching of the law professors.

*Ditlev Tamm*

1608

## Jyske lov

*Das rette Judske Lowbock. København 1590*
Det kongelige Bibliotek 8-217 4°
The basis for Danish law in the time of Christian IV was still the old provincial laws from the 1200's. The most important of these, the Jutish Law, was published in 1590 in a modernized edition, which made the law much easier for the judges to understand.

1609

## Executioner's sword with sheath

Solingen c. 1620
Tøjhusmuseet nr. C. 197/42
Sword from the Gottorp armory. Straight blade with blunt point. On the blade a wheel and gallows.
*Provenance:* From the Rendsborg Armory, transferred from the Gottorp armory in 1854.

1610

## Norske lov

*Den Norske Low-bog. København 1604*
Det kongelige Bibliotek, 9-135 4°

*Literature:* Kong Christian Fjerdes Norske lowbog af 1604. Udgiven af Fr. Hollinger og Fr. Brandt; 1885.

1611

## Jyske lov

*Den rette Jüdske Lowbog. København 1642*
Det kongelige Bibliotek 8-217 4°
This edition of the Jutish Law printed in 1642, by the printer Jørgen Holst, was provided with a lovely engraved title page by Albert Haelwegh, which shows Christian IV presiding in the highest court of the land, the king's court.

1612

## Christian IVs reces. København 1643

Det kongelige Bibliotek 8-236 4°
To achieve clarity the most important of the laws were collected in the great recess of 1643, the largest collected Danish body of law since the provincial laws, and a forerunner for Christian V's Danish Law of 1683. The Recess was published in an stately edition with an engraving of the king, and a title page which demonstrates allegorically how piety and justice support the columns that bear the crown.

1613

## Anders Mikkelsen

*Verdslige Low og Skicke effter hvilcke Gud selff haffde befallit Israels Folck oc Menighed at styris oc Regeris. København 1605*
Det kongelige Bibliotek 4-3 4°
After the Reformation the Law of Moses played a significant role as a source of law. A life for a life became a fundamental principle in the judgement of cases of manslaughter, and the many prohibitions in the Bible against marriage between the closely related were also viewed as the law of God, to offend against which carried the death penalty. Penalties for witchcraft are another example. In 1605 pastor Anders Mikkelsen published this little work, in which he explains which sins in particular raise the wrath of God, and how these sins ought to be punished.

1614

## Leonhard Metzner

*Disputatio ex jure Naturali gentium et Civili Rerum Divisione, et acqvirendo Earum Dominio. København 1610*
Det kongelige Bibliotek 8-105 4°
Leonhard Metzner (1571-1629) was professor of law at the University of Copenhagen from 1605 to 1615. In a series of disputations he demonstrates how the function of jurisprudence was primarily to provide the theologians with examples of what was good and what was evil.

1615

## Leonhard Metzner

*Theses de Nuptiis decerptæ ex Jure Civili et Canonico. København 1608, and De Adulterio et Stupro København 1609*
Det kongelige Bibliotek 8-15 4° and 8-95 4°
In the back of a copy of Metzner's theses on marriage, a spectator has made a note of an exchange between the period's leading theologian, H.P. Resen, and Metzner. Resen reproached Metzner for only having included examples from Roman law and canon law in his theses on adultery. Resen thought that it would be instructive for the students also to hear about Danish examples.

1616

## Claus Plum

*Disputatio de Jure Connubiorum III 1627*
Det kongelige Bibliotek 8-109 4°
Since the reorganization of the university after the Reformation there had existed a small law faculty with just teacher. Until the early seventeenth century German legal scholars were called in to teach in law; in 1619 Claus Plum was named as the first Danish professor of law. Law was tailored to the needs of the theology students. A series of short disputations intended as the basis for exercises in disputation have been preserved. Exhibited here is such a disputation on marriage law from 1627 written by *Claus Plum.* Danish law was not made much of; the Roman law was the point of departure.
*Literature:* Popp Madsen og Reitzel Nielsen 1936, p. 47.

1617

## Christen Ostersen Veyle

*Glossarium juridico-danicum. København 1641*
Det kongelige Bibliotek 8-237 4°
In 1641 Christen Ostersen Vejle, councilman in Roskilde, published a so-called Glossarium juridico-danicum, as an aid to the use of the old laws. The book contained an explanation of the most important legal terms, and a table which showed which fines were to be assessed in different cases. The work was issued in three editions.

1618

## Jean Bodin

*Six livres de la république. Paris 1576*
Det kongelige Bibliotek Sfv I 359 2°
This work on the state by the Frenchman Jean Bodin (1530-96) is one of the major books in European political thought. Bodin considers the European types of states, and also discusses conditions in Denmark. The concept of sovereignty was of particular significance, and Bodin defined this as the highest, eternal power, raised above the law, the result of which was a series of rights repos-

GLOSSARIUM
JURIDICO-DANICUM
Det er
Alle Gamble-Danske Gloser
rette Forklaring som findis udi de Skonske, Sielandske oc Judske Lowbøger,
saa oc Kong. Recesser, Handfestninger,
Gaards oc Sørætter, Rigens oc Birke
retter, ohne Mandater oc Breffue.
Tienendis tillige:
Til it General Register offuer
ald huis forneffnde Lower oc Forordninger indeholder, letteligen effter en huers
fornødenhed at finde, alle som enten Active
eller Passive foraarsagis Retten at betiene,
til nytte oc gaffn sammenstreffuit,
Aff
CHRISTEN OSTERSEN, RAADMAND UDI ROSKILD.
Prentet udi Kiøbenhaffn, aff Melchior Martzan.
oc Forlagt aff Iochim Moltken Bogh.
M. DC. XLI.

*1617*

ing in the sovereign; the right to give laws, the right to pass judgement, to wage war, to collect taxes etc. This theory made itself felt in the Danish "Kongeloven" of 1665, which introduced absolute monarchy to Denmark.
*Provenance:* This first edition of 1576 belonged to Birgitte Thott.
*Literature:* Fabricius 1920.

1619

## Henning Arnisæus

*De Jure Regio, 1610*
Det kongelige Bibliotek
Henning Arnisæus (1570-1636) was born in Helmstedt in Germany. In 1619 he was called to Denmark to be court physician to Christian IV, who also used him as a reference for medical questions in the courts. Arnisæus achieved fame throughout Europe for his political thought. In 1610 he published the book *De jure regio,* which played a central role in introducing the thought of the French constitutionalist Jean Bodin in Northern Europe. Arnisæus here takes on the role of spokesman for absolute monarchy.
*Literature:* Fabricius: 1920, Dreitzel; 1970.

1620

## Henrik Ernst

*Catholica juris. København 1634*
Det kongelige Bibliotek 8-5 8°
There was instruction in law at the Academy at Sorø. A major figure there was the German jurist Henrik Ernst, who published a series of works on the law, among them *Catholica juris,* 1634, which contains a survey of the basic principles in the Roman law. Ernst came to Denmark in 1623 and stayed at Sorø after 1639, after accompanying Christian IV's son Valdemar Christian on a long trip abroad. As a pupil of Jean Bodin and Henning Arnisæus, Ernst was probably an early adherent of a stronger monarchy.
*Literature:* Fabricius; 1920 FS juridisk Eksamen, 1936, p. 48. Popp Madsen og Reitzel Nielsen; 1936, p. 48.

1621

## Hugo Grotius

*De Mare Liberum 1609*
Det kongelige Bibliotek 120-115
In 1603 a Dutch ship captured a Portuguese merchant ship in the straits of Malacca. As a contribution to the dispute that followed this episode the Dutchman Hugo Grotius wrote a book on prize law. One chapter in this book, published separately for the first time in 1609, became famous as the foundation for the doctrine of the freedom of the seas *(Mare liberum).* Grotius defended here the right of the Dutch to participate in the trade with Southeast Asia. Grotius later modified his viewpoint in his major work, De jure Belli et Pacis libri tres (1625).

1622

## Johan Isaksen Pontanus

*Discussionum historicarum libri duo, quibus quatenus & quodnam mare liberum vel non liberum clausumque accipiendum dispicitur expenditurque, Harderwijk 1637*
Det kongelige Bibliotek 8-41 8°
The Danish king claimed from time immemorial his sovereignty over the Baltic – *dominium maris Baltici* – and over the sea between Norway and Greenland – *dominium maris Septentrionalis.* These claims of sovereignty created political difficulties with other states which claimed rights to fishing or whaling in these waters, or even sovereignty itself. James I of England reasserted an old claim to "the British Seas", and in a famous work of 1635, *Mare Clausum,* the Englishman John Selden made a strong English claim on the North Sea all the way to the Jutish coast. Also the Norwegian Sea was claimed as English in this book. The Danish point of view was asserted against the English claims by the Royal historiographer Pontanus.
*Provenance:* The copy on exhibit belonged at one time to the law professor Peder Scavenius.
*Literature:* Rørdam 1897-98, p. 24 and 440-92. Dalgaard pp. 295-319.

1623

## Judgements on the gold chains from 1590

Herredagsdombog 1590-1595
Rigsarkivet
Christian IV attended court proceedings even as a boy. Among many important decisions from that period were two judgements in 1590, which lay down the so-called principle of restitution, according to which a person who lends or pawns something to another, can demand it returned, even though it has been handed on to a third party. This principle was laid down by the court in two decisions, where the cases concerned nobility who had loaned or pawned their gold chains.
*Literature:* Kolderup Rosenvinge p. 308-312, nr. 70. Danske Domme 1375-1662 V 1982 nr. 538, 639.

1624

## Christoffer Rosenkrantz's forged note of hand

Rigsarkivet
Dokumenter og akter vedk. div. retssager 1590-1614, nr. 35-52. Heri nr. 47; "Niels Krag til Aggerskrog, sekretær ... contra Christoffer Rosenkrantz til Kotbøl". K.K.R. dom. Københavns slot 1610, 17. marts (27 bilag vedlagt fra perioden 8. juni 1586 til 14. jan. 1610). Heri det falske gældsbrev, 1603, (Among papers re: court case between Krag and Rosenkrantz, the forged note of hand).
In Niels Slange's history of Christian IV an account is given of the king's great interest in the court system (p. 264-67). As an example the case against the nobleman Christoffer Rosenkrantz is related. Christoffer Rosenkrantz attempted to cheat his friend Christen Iuel's widow, Karen Strangesdatter, through the use of forged notes of hand. It was among others this account which lead the legal historian J. E. Larsen to declare that none had left a more honorable reputation with regard to participation in the administration of the courts than Denmark's immortal Christian IV. According to the account, the king exposed the fraud when he held the note up against the light to examine the seal and the genuiness of the signature, and accidentally noticed that the watermark was that of his own papermaker. However, the paper mill had first been established after the date on the debtor's note, and the king made sure that the paper mill had not earlier used that watermark. Troels-Lund compared Slange's thorough account about the fraud with the court records from 1610, which give the proceedings of the case, and discovered that the decision does say that Christoffer Rosenkrantz' note of hand was fraudulent. The original note, which is with the records, has, however, no such watermark as that dsescribed by Slange, and the court decision contains no mention of a watermark as a decisive piece of evidence against Rosenkrantz. There were sufficiently many other circumstances which told against Rosenkrantz, and he was sentenced on the 17th of March, 1610, to ignominy and punishment for fraud. Most probably another account of Christian IV as judge has been confused with the Rosenkrantz case. In the autobiography of the medical doctor Otto Sperling, written in the Blue Tower, there is an account of the king's excellent powers of judgement when he exposed a fraud by holding a note of hand up against the light in a case between two men from Christianshavn. He thus discovered that the paper was newer than the date on the note; "The handwriting is false, since the mark in the paper is John Ettersøn's mark ..., and in the year given on the note, I had not yet allowed the paper mill to be built", (cf. Dr. med. Otto Sperlings Selvbiografi, 1885, p. 87). But that probably is a cock and bull story as well. In the exhibit are documents from this case and others which illuminate Christian IV's activities as a judge.
*Literature:* Secher p. 283-87 and 301-09. Troels Lund 1872-73, p. 518-37.

1625

## Dr. med. Otto Sperlings Selvbiografi

Oversat i uddrag efter original håndskriftet ... af S. Birket-Smith (1885)
Det kongelige Bibliotek 9-76/92

1626

## Tingbog fra Ålborg Byting (Court records from Ålborg city court)

Landsarkivet for Nørrejylland NLA B 24-53
The country was divided into herreder, which served as court districts. The central institution in each was the court, where justice was administered. From the time of Christian IV a series of court record books are preserved, and they give an all around picture of the court life of the time. All types of cases are dealt with, from crimes like murder or witchcraft to quarrels between neighbours, impounding of cattle, boundary disputes and such.

1627

## Judgement on Bishop Anders Christensen Arrebo

*"Vidner Act og dom imod Anders Christensen Arebo superintendent over Trundhiembs Stifft, anno 1622*
Det kongelige Bibliotek NKS 1984 4°
In 1622 Christian IV was with the court in Norway, where among others the famous case against Bishop Anders Christensen Arrebo was decided. Arrebo lost his bishopric because of accusations of lax behaviour at a few wedding celebrations in the diocese.
*Literature:* Danske Domme 1375-1662, VII 1984, p. 184ff.

1628

## Punishment

Resolutioner om, hvad der skal gøres ved en del kvindelige fanger, som ere indsatte i Børne- og Tugthuset i København, (c. Oct. 1622).
The National Archive
Christian IV was intensely interested in the court system. Many of his letters show that he even outside the courts took a personal interest in cases, to see whether sentences already passed might be lowered.
*Provenance:* Turned over by the Ministry of the Navy.
*Literature:* EB I nr. 195.

# Superstition

Superstition permeated all of society; elves, trolls, and other creatures played a large role in everyday life.

Whereas the Catholic priest had often directly dealt with such affairs, now learned scholars moved into the vacuum which had arisen between the church and the people after the Reformation, and attempted to help or ward off these evils.

The belief in the devil was an important element in the theology of the time. If man did not fear the devil, he failed to fear God. It was exactly this belief in the powers of God, and especially the powers of the devil, over man and nature around him, which gave sustenance to the intense strength of superstition. Natural phenomena: comets, eclipses, freaks of nature, witchcraft and cases of possession by the devil, etc.; all these were viewed as divine warnings of coming events.

Christian IV most likely believed in the existence of witchcraft, but beyond that there is nothing to indicate that he was particularly interested in persecution of witches. His decree against witchcraft and its practitioners of 12.10.1617 did bring about a rise in witch trials, but above and beyond a few cases, Christian IV appears not to have had personal influence on the fact that witch trials reached their culmination during his reign.

*Gitte Kjær*

1629

## Niels Hemmingsen

*Admonitio de superstitionibus magicis vitandis. København 1575*
Det kongelige Bibliotek 14-250 8°
The most substantial of Danish theoretical works on witchcraft was Niels Hemmingsen's"; Admonitio de superstitionibus magicis vitandis" (Warning against magical superstition) from 1575. It appeared in a German edition in Wittenberg 1586 and in a Danish one translated by Rasmus Hanssøn Reravius; Niels Hemmingsen "En Vurdering ... hvad man skal dømme om den ... Bespottelse, som skeer met Troldom", 1618. (An evaluation ... of how to judge the blasphemy which occurs with witchcraft). Niels Hemmingsen was equally negatively disposed towards benign magic (white) as towards the harmful (black).

1630

## Niels Hemmingsen

*En Vnderuisning aff den hellige Skrifft huad mand dømme skal om den store oc grundige Guds Bespottelse / som skeer met Trolddom / Signelse / Maalelse / Manelse / oc anden Saadan Guds hellige Naffns oc Ords Vanbrug. København 1618.*
Det kongelige Bibliotek 14-250 8°

1631

## Niels Hemmingsen

*Om Ecteskab. København, no date*
Det kgl. Bibliotek 4-76 8°

1632

*Udschrifft af Kiøge Ting och Raadstue Belangende de Troldquinder som bleff henrettet och Brendt for Kiøge A, 1612-13.*
Det kongelige Bibliotek, NKS 1409k 4°

1633

## Draft for the order of October 12, 1617; "Om Troldfolk og deres Medvidere" (On Witches and their Accessories)

Rigsarkivet: Danske kancelli B 58
On October 12, 1617, a decree was issued on witches and their accessories which meant a turning point in the persection of witches in Denmark. A law was printed and made generally known to the public through the courts. Distinctions were made among magical healing, conjuring etc. which were punished by banishment, and the "true witches" who had made a pact with the Devil. The latter were given the death penalty. In the National Archives is a page proof of the law text, which shows that until the last minute there was uncertainty about the title of the order. The suggestion "Healing, Conjuring and Witchcraft and other Haunting" was dropped for the shorter "On Witches and their accessories", which more precisely denotes the new aspect of the law, i.e. that belief in the Devil was incorporated into the law. It was Christian IV's personal view of witchcraft that was expressed here.
*Literature:* Secher III 1891-94, no. 473, Jacobsen 1966, p. 172-73.

1634

## Christen Ostersen Vejle

*Glossarium Juridico-Danicum. Det er alle Gamle Danske glosers rette Forklaring som findis udi de Skonske, Sielandske oc Judske Lowbøger ... København 1652*
Det kongelige Bibliotek 8-238 4°

Councilman Christen Ostersen Vejle in Roskilde received in 1641 the privilege of printing and selling a Danish legal glossary, which appeared the same year (cf. no. 1660). A new augmented edition appeared in 1652 and a third edition in 1665.

1635

*Clavicula Salomonis*
Det kongelige Bibliotek, Thott 627 4°

1636

*Letter from Christian IV to Christen Friis Wolfenbüttel, 3rd April, 1726, in the king's own hand.*
Rigsarkivet
Christian IV wrote on April 3, 1626, to chancellor Christen Friis that the king had heard of some witches in Copenhagen and Elsinore, and he ordered the chancellor to warn all who were concerned with such cases to take their responsibilities seriously and not be persuaded to leniency through personal connections. It was for the best to cleanse the country of such skum, who had even attempted their black arts against the king's own person.
*Literature:* EB II no. 7.

1637

*Summons for Torben Gabrielsen of Krenkerup, ex-judge on Funen, to the Herredag (a higher court) 22nd of February, 1630*
Rigsarkivet
Christian IV had in 1629 removed judge Torben Gabrielsen Akelige, and now prosecuted him in court because he had not been willing to sentence an accused witch to burn at the stake.
*Literature:* Danske Magazin, 3. rk. V, 185, p. 173-245.

1638

## Cyprianus-Ms. Wittenborg 1607

Det kongelige Bibliotek, Thott 240 8°
The tradition of Cyprianus is manifold; as a rule a "Cyprianus" is compiled from many sources with a common purpose; to explain how to "make a pact with the Devil".
*Literature:* Published by L. Pio, 1892, Feilberg, 1891, pl. 97 ff.

1639

*Der Tübinger Reim-Faust von 1587/88 aus dem Prosa Volksbuch Historia von D. Johann Fausten (1587) in Reime gebracht von Johannes Feinang. Tübingen 1587-88.*
Det kongelige Bibliotek $117^{I}$-120
Shortly after the publication of the popular book on Johan Faust in the autumn of 1587, the printer Alexander Hoch made an agreement with Johannes Feinang to rewrite the story in rhymed verse. Their hope was to cash in on – or perhaps even surpass – the great sales success that Historia von D. Johan Fausten had been in Frankfurt.

1640

*Der Tübinger Reim-Faust von 1587/88 aus dem Prosa Volksbuch Historia van D. Johann Fausten (1587) in Reime gebracht von Johannes Feinang. Faksimjiledruck des einzigen vollständigen Exemplars in der Königlichen Bibliotek in Kopenhagen. Kirchheim/Denkendorf 1977*
Det kongelige Bibliotek hu-wa
The story of Johann Faust tells of a peasant son who becomes magister and later doctor of theology at Wittenberg. Later he disavowed his degrees and entered into a pact with the Devil.

1641

## Forbud mod spåkalendere 24.10.1633 (Prohibition against fortune-telling calendars 24.10.1633

Det kongelige Bibliotek 8-235 4°
*Literature:* Secher, IV, 1897, nr. 465.

1642

## Kong Salomons Nøgler, Heksetros tvivlere

Det kongelige Biblkotek $30^{3}$-173 4°

1643

*En ny Profetinde*
Trykt af Matz Vingaard 12. april 1581, (flyveblad)
Det kongelige Bibliotek 28-157 no. 571
Bound together with the German original; NEWE PROPHETIN VON SCHÖNEBECKE / in der Alten March / zwo Meilen von Stendel gelegen.
*Literature:* Stolpe I 1878, XIV no. 23 (genoptrykt 1977).

1644

*En Forskreckelig Oc sand Bescriffuelse om mange Troldfolck som ere forbrende for deris Misgerninger skyld, fra det Aar 1589 regendis ...*
Trykt af Laur. Benedicht 1591, (flyveblad)
Det kongelige Bibliotek, Hielmstjerne 14-304 4°
Gives an account of the witch trials in Trier, which between 1587-93 resulted in 368 people being burned at the stake. The description ends with the epitaph of Dumb Peter, a sorcerer who could transform himself into the guise of a vampire.
*Literature:* Stolpe I: 1878, XVIII no. 33 (reprinted 1977).

1644

sand bescriffuelse/ om mange Troldfolck:
som ere forbrende for deris Misgierninger skyld/
fra det Aar 1589. regnendis: Oc huad deris vd-
retning oc bekendelse haffuer været/ man-
gen til en tro at-
uarsel.

Desligeste om en Troldkarl ved naffn Stumme Peder/
huilcken som kunde giøre sig til en Varulff formedelst hans
Troldoms Konst. Oc huorledis hand er grummelige henrettet til
Døde/ vdi en By ved naffn Bøpper/ tre Mile fra Colne/
vdi det Aar 89. Oc huad ont hand haff-
uer bedreffuet.

Først tryckt vdi Colne/ met Caspar Schumans
aff Erfurt bekostning etc.
Oc nu vdi Kiøbenhaffn / aff Laurentz Benedicht/ 1591

1645

*"Sørgeligt Specktackel och Vndertegn Nu nyligen seet paa et nyfødt Pigebarn vdi Mørckøye liggendis i Sockelundsherret vdi Gladsaxe Sogn, til et ynckeligt Skuespeil for alle dem, som gienstridigen imod Guds alvorlig Trusel, holde hart ved deres ny Noder, høye Toppe oc forargelige Klædedragt. (Desuden Blods Tegn i Grested)*

Trykt hos Henrich Waldkirch 1625. (Flyveblad)

Det kongelige Bibliotek, Hjelmstjerne 1445 8°

The broadsheet was written by the then pastor of Gladsaxe, Hans Nielsen (Sæby). The event took place the 12th of August, 1625. It was the belief in God and, in particular, in the Devil which gave superstition its almost sinister stamp in the time of Christian IV. Much of the literature was in the form of broadsheets, often translated from German. Natural occurences were here described as God wreaking his anger on man, and as warnings from God for mankind to beware.

*Literature:* N. M. Petersen 1856, p. 195; Stolpe 1878, XLVI, p. 83, (repr. 1977).

1646

*Vnderlig oc ofuer-naturlig Fødsel, seet i Nagskou i Laaland, Aar 1628 dend 25 Augusti*
Kbhvn, Tr. Henrich Waldkirch, 1629. (Flyveblad)
Det kongelige Bibliotek, Hielmstierne 1646 8°
Three different accounts are given; of the birth on Lolland, the 2nd of Sept.; 1628, by the pastor in Nakskov, Anders Pedersen Perlesticker; of the blood sign on Funen, 7th of January, 1629, by the pastor at Vinding, Niels Povelsøn (Wellcius), and of the blood sign on Zealand, 20th of January, 1629, by the curate in Blidstrup, Johannes Mathiæ in a letter to the dean in Holbo herred Iens Iensen (Farum) in Helsinge, which Herr Oluf (Pastor in Blidstrup Oluf Jørgensen) had had him write on the written instructions of the dean.
*Literature:* Stolpe I 1878, XLVI, no. 94. (repr. 1977).

1647

*Extract Vdaff en Skrifft af Spandav, som Hederlige Herre M. Albertus Calerus Sognepræst der samme sted, skreff til en god Ven ... 19 Decembro, i det Aar 1594*
Trykt af Matz Viingaard 1595
Det kongelige Bibliotek, Thott 4157 8°
*Literature:* Stolpe I 1878, XXIII, no. 43. (repr. 1977).

1648

## Kristen Stephensen Årbog

Det kongelige Bibliotek, GKS 2355 4°
Pastor Kristen Stephensen of Ålborg carefully recorded the miracles of the time at the end of the sixteenth century.
*Literature:* Samlinger til Jydsk Historie og Topografi, V, 1874, p. 69-91

1649

*Benedichts spåbog: En Astronomische Beschriffuelse. København 1594*
Det kongelige Bibliotek, Hjelmstjerne 2549 8°
The title page suggests that the book explains several forms of fortune telling.
*Literature:* Brask 1984, p. 48611.

1650

## Tycho Brahe

Allernyeste og fuldstændigste Drømmebog. Odense 1902
Det kongelige Bibliotek 14-277 8°

# Faith and piety

The period of Christian IV saw the culmination of that Lutheran orthodoxy which rigidly insisted that only the teachings of Luther himself represented pure Protestant doctrine. The major representative of this line in Denmark, Bishop Hans Poulsen Resen, directed hard measures at divergent opinions with the king's support, and attacked with equal ferocity both Calvinist and Catholic tendencies. On the occasion of the one hundred year anniversary of Luther's breakthrough in 1617, Resen chose to celebrate the victory of orthodoxy with a treatise on the triumphant Luther. Neverthless, the learned theologian and Councilor of the Realm Holger Rosenkrantz developed his own understanding of Christianity, which brought him into conflict with the theologians and exposed him to the king's wrath in the course of the 1630's.

New translations of the Bible were produced that were more faithful to the text, and through new editions of the catechism the elementary doctrines of the faith were laid down, whereas a popular need for devotional literature was met by "spiritual handbooks" and inspirational collections of sermons by both Danish and German authors. Among the first were Bishops Jesper Brochmand and Jens Dinesen Jersin, among the latter, the Germans Philip Kegel and Johann Arndt. In addition it became a common custom to publish the funeral sermons preached on deceased members of the nobility, often by prominent preachers. In these books copper engravings were included which honoured the deceased, either portraits or heraldic devices of the family, or symbolic allegories illustrating the prevailing views on death.

*Ingrid Ilsøe*

1651

## Resen's Translation of the Bible

*Biblia, Paa Danske, Det er, Den gantscke Hellige Scriftis Bøgger, igennemseete effter Kong Christian IIII's Befalning. København 1607*
Det kongelige Bibliotek 1-27 8°
The first of the Bible editions which appeared in Christian IV's time was the edition of 1607, prepared by Hans Poulsen Resen, professor of theology and later Bishop of Zealand. Together with the book dealer Hans Aalborg and the minter Nicolaus Schwabe, Resen had obtained a royal privilege to print the Danish Bible in octave format. Resen's translation is the first into Danish from the original languages, in the sense that he revised the previous Danish Bible translations, and only respected their versions insofar as they were in accord with the original text. This loyalty to the text was achieved to some degree at the expense of readability.

1652

## Christian IV's Church Bible

*Biblia, Det er Den gantske Hellige Scrifft paa Danske igien offuerseet oc prentet effter ... K. Christian IVs Befaling. København 1633*

Det kongelige Bibliotek 1-27 2°

Christian IV's Church Bible is a revised reprinting of Frederik II's Bible from 1589, printed by the university printers Melchior Martzan and Salomon Sartor. The royal engraver, Simon de Pas, engraved the three large title page engravings and the portrait of the king, but the woodcut illustrations are the same as those found in Frederik II's Bible.

1653

## Christian IV's "Kvartbibel"

*Biblia, Paa Danske, Det er: Den gandske hellige Skriftis Bøgger, Paa ny igiennemseete, med fljd, efter den Ebræiske oc Grækiske Text ... Efter ... Kong Christian den IV. Befaling, København 1647.*

Det kongelige Bibliotek 1-28 4°

"Christian IVs Kvartbibel" (Christian IV's quarto Bible) is a reprint of Hans Poulsen Resen's Bible from 1607 revised by Hans Svane (1606-68), professor of theology and later bishop of Zealand. It is also known as the "Svanningske Bibel". It became the basis for Danish editions of the Bible for several centuries. It was printed by the two university printers, Melchior Martzan and Melchior Winckler, and provided with a portrait of Christian IV engraved by Albert Haelwegh, whereas the five title page engravings were done by H. A. Greys.

1654

## Hans Poulsen Resen

*Lutherus triumphans ... København u.å.*

Det kongelige Bibliotek, 2-213 8°

1617, the one hundred year anniversary of Luther's theses, was celebrated with a large-scale commemorative occasion, which was also used to give thanks for victory over Roman Catholic and crypto-Calvinist attacks on the pure Lutheran doctrines. Hans Poulsen Resen arranged that there will be held a commemoration of the Reformation every year on the 31st of October, both in the church and at the university – a tradition that was followed until 1906. As a guide for this celebration he published this work on the reformation and "the trumphant Luther".

1655

## Ole Worm

*Lapis Lydius Adami Contzii Numisma Romanum examinans*

Det kongelige Bibliotek, GKS 3119 II 4°

The anniversary of the Reformation in 1617 was not commemorated by the minting of medals as it was abroad. But in an addendum to the manuscript of the speech which Ole Worm held at the commemoration the next year, he included several suggestions for the design of such a medal. [E.g., on the front an opened Gospel and on the back a closed, to symbolize the Lutheran and the Roman Catholic Churches respectively, or on the front Christ the Good Shepherd and on the back, the Pope as the Babylonian Whore, killing the sheep. And all to be provided with suitable inscriptions].

1656

## Caspar Bartholin

*De studio theologico compendiaria ratione incoando et continuando. København 1628*

Det kongelige Bibliotek 1-3 8°

Caspar Bartholin (1585-1629), professor of medicine from 1613, became professor of theology in 1624. He then published a series of theological writings, among them this guide to the study of theology, in which he urged the young students to study the Holy Scriptures, first as children do, in their mother tongue, then in the original languages and finally in the commentaries.

1657

## Jesper Brochmand

*Universæ theologiæ systema. København 1633*

Det kongelige Bibliotek 3-49 4°

Jesper Brochman (1585-1652), a professor of theology and from 1639 successor to Hans Poulsen Resen as bishop of Zealand, was the foremost representative of Lutheran orthodoxy in Denmark. Among his extensive theological writings, his reputation in the world of theology is primarily based on this work. He provides here a complete statement of the whole Lutheran doctrine seen from the orthodox point of view; the work also gained a reputation in Germany, and was published both in Ulm and Lepzig in 1638.

1658

## Niels Mikkelsen Aalborg

*En kaart oc Nyttig Forklaring Offuer S. Johannis Obenbaring ... København 1611*

Det kongelige Bibliotek, Hielmstierne 100 4°

Pastor Niels Mikkelsen Aalborg (1562-1645) sent this explanation of the Revelations of St. John to censorship at the university, and the two professors Hans Poulsen Resen and Cort Aslaksen recommended it for publication without, however, having acquainted themselves with the contents. When published it offended no one. But in 1614 Aalborg fell out with Resen and was summoned before the governing body of the university because in his explanation of Revelations he had raised the possibility that pious heathens, who never had heard of Our Saviour, might attain salvation through the Grace of God. This doctrine was not in accord with the creed of

ΕΝΟΣ ΧΡΕΙΑ
CASPARVS ERASMVS BROCHMAND/S.S.THEOLOGIÆ DOCTOR/ET EIVSDEM IN ACADEMIA HAFNIENSI PROFESSOR REGIVS.
Brochmanni faciem, sacræ non munera mentis
Exprimit artificis ingeniosa manus.
Sed si picta suo mens sacra colore sit, in qua
Omnis inest virtus, jam mihi pictus erit.
Serenisſ. Daniæ Regis Sculptor Simon de Pas sculpsit.
MDCXXXII
Iacobus Matthias Aarhusius Eloq. Pr. P.

*1657*

the Danish Church. Though Aalborg was willing to recall his statement, which he claimed to have borrowed from the English theologian John Fox, he was removed from his living.

1659

## John Fox

*Eicasmi seu Meditationes in Apocalypsin S. Johannis ... Geneve 1596*

Det kongelige Bibliotek 84-250 8°

A note on the title page of the copy of John Foxe's commentary in Aalborg's hand shows that he bought it in Copenhagen in 1596. On the fly paper he wrote a quotation from Luther's Tischreden on the salvation of the wise heathens (especially Cicero) which indicates that even Luther had expressed himself similarly. The inscription is dated the 8th of June, 1614, the day he was examined by the university governing body.

1660

## Niels Mikkelsen Aalborg

*Sanct Johannis Aabenbaring. Kortelig oc eenfoldelig forklaret og nu Corrigeret ... København 1627*

Det kongelige Bibliotek, Hielmstierne 101 4°

After a few years Aalborg achieved a reconciliation with Resen, and in 1627 he published a second edtion of his commentary on Revelations, in which his earlier statement on the possibility of the salvation of heathens was expurgated.

1661

## Holger Rosenkrantz, called "the Learned" (1574-1642), Councilor of the Realm, theologian

Copper engraving by Simon de Pas 1644

Det kongelige Bibliotek, The Picture Collection 2°

The nobleman Holger Rosenkrantz was occupied with theological studies all his life, and exerted considerable influence on several theologians, among them Jesper Brochmand and Caspar Bartholin. He was also respected abroad. In his personal life he practised an active piety. The theology he developed was in many ways a reaction against the ruling orthodox Lutheranism. To Rosenkrantz the essential content of doctrine was piety, and in the issue of salvation he placed significance on the doing of good deeds. In the end this led to a break between him and the professors of theology.

*Literature:* Schepelern 1951, p. 45 no. 39

1662

## Holger Rosenkrantz

*Fürsten Spiegel, das is; Schrifften vnd Sendschreiben des ... Herrn Albrecht des Fünfften ... Aarhus 1636*

Det kongelige Bibliotek, 5-167 4°

This edition was the occasion for the final break between Rosenkrantz and the theological faculty. Here he put forth his doctrine of the double justification; the believer is justifed doubly, in part by faith, in part by the good deeds founded on faith, despite the inadequacies which as a consequence of sin are attached to such deeds.

1663

## Rosenkrantz tranlated by Birgitte Thott

*Försters Spegel ... 1636*

Det kongelige Bibliotek, Rostgaard 10 4°

A translation to Danish of "Fürsten-Spiegel" by Birgitte Thott (1610-62), a translator and learned lady of the nobilty. Dedication by her to Sophie Brahe, the wife of Holger Rosenkrantz, dated 24th of December, 1636.

1664

## Holger Rosenkrantz

*Præfatio og Apologiæ pars prima*
Det kongelige Bibliotek, GKS 125-26 2°
A defense written by Rosenkrantz in his quarrel with the theologians 1638-39. The manuscript has his dedication to Christian IV in his own hand, and is bound in blue velvet with Christian IV's crowned monogram.

1665

## Sophie Brahes regnskabsbog

Det kongelige Bibliotek, Add. 197 4°
In order to concentrate completely on his theological studies, Holger Rosenkrantz handed over the administration of his estate and house to his wife, Sophie Brahe. In 1637 expenditures for the poor came to 106 rigsdaler, 2 ort and 19 skilling, whereas the cost of their sons' education and travel abroad came to 2581 rigsdaler, 3 ort and 8 skilling.
*Literature:* Sophie Brahes regnskabsbog 1627-40, 1955.

1666

## Niels Heldvad

*Trifolium Theologicum, vdi hvilket ... er befattet oc comprehenderet den Papist-Jesviteske, Luther-Evangeliske oc Zwinglio-Calviniske Troe oc Lærdom. København 1628*
Det kongelige Bibliotek, Hielmstierne 619 8°
Pastor Niels Heldvad (1564-1634), who became the royal court astrologist and astronomer in 1616, gained many readers as a popular author. In this work he analyzes thoroughly the relationship of the Papists, Lutherans and Calvinists to each other, and distinguishes what beliefs they hold in common and what separates them.

1667

## Tidings of Jesuits

*Nye Tiender / Om tho Jesuwiter. København 1581*
Det kongelige Bibliotek, LN 1594 4°
This flyer is an early example of propaganda against the Jesuits, who represented both during Frederik II's and Christian IV's time the most aggressive agents of Roman Catholicism. The woodcut illustrates the account of a Jesuit who dressed up as a devil to frighten a woman away from the Lutheran faith.

1668

## Laurids Nielsen

*Confessio christiana, D.e. Den christelige Bekiendelse om Herrens Veig ... Brunsberg 1605*
Det kongelige Bibliotek 3-242 4°
The Norwegian born Jesuit Laurids Nielsen (1538-1622), often called Klosterlasse (Cloister Lasse), came to Denmark in 1606 from Germany in order to propagandize for the Catholic Church. He sent King Christian IV an apologetic on the Catholic faith written by himself, both in a Latin version and in this Danish translation. In a letter he also offered to help solve religous conflicts. However he was immediately deported by royal order and all copies of the work confiscated.

1669

## Forordning om tilhængere af den papistiske religion 19. juni 1613 [Decree on adherents to the Papist religion 19 June 1613]

Det kongelige Bibliotek 8-237 4°
This decree disinherited residents who were exposed as Catholics, forbad them from settling in Denmark, or entering into public service. This put an end to Catholic propaganda in Denmark.

1670

## The Church Ordinance

*Den rette Ordinants som paa Herre dagen i Ottense bleff offuerseet oc beseglet, Huorledis Kirckestienisten skal holdis vdi Danmarckis oc Norges Riger oc de Hertugdomme Slesuig/Holsten. København 1617*
Det kongelige Bibliotek 7-6 8°
The legal foundation for the church constitution was Christian III's Church Ordinance of 1537. In a copy of the edition of 1617, which was owned by the bishop of Ribe, Jens Dinesen Jersin (1588-1634), Christian IV has in his own handwriting altered a few words in the bishop's oath of the Church Ordinance before swearing in Jersin. On some white pages added to the binding Jersin has listed the ministers whom he ordained, and the oath of ordination which he used when he administered the oath to the ministers. Philipp Melanchton's instructio visitationes Saxonicæ, which was a guide for pastors, is also bound into this copy, in a Danish translation, København 1619.
*Literature:* Gjellerup: Biskop Jens Dinesen Jersin, 1868-70, p.67-68, 266-69.

1671

## Jacob Madsens visitatsbog

Landsarkivet for Fyn; Fyns Bispearkiv
The Church Ordinance required that the bishop was to inspect every single pastor and his congregation regularly through visitation of the individual parishes. Jacob Madsen Vejle (1538-1606), the bishop of the Diocese of Funen from 1587, has given a lively picture of conditions in the parishes in his visitation book, with characterizations of the pastors and information on the church buildings and their inventory. In most places he made a drawing of the church, but as a mirror image.
*Literature:* Den tredie fyenske evangeliske Biskops, Mes-

ter Jacob Madsens Visitatsbog, udg. af C. Crone, 1853, Den fyenske Biskop Mester Jacob Madsens Visitatsbog, ved A. R. Idum, 1929-32.

1672
## Martin Luther

*Enchiridion. En liden Catechismus / eller Christelig Lærdom; Gantske nyttelig for alle Sogneprester oc Predickere, Ocsaa for Børn oc vngt Folck. København 1586*
Det kongelige Bibliotek, LN 1093 8°
The foundation for teaching the congregation the Christian faith was Luther's short catechism, which appeared in numerous editions, some illustrated thoroughout with woodcuts.

1673
## Martin Luther

*Enchiridion. En Haandbog for menige Sogne-Præste oc Prædicantere. I gennem seet med Flijd effter Tydsken. København 1608*
Det kongelige Bibliotek 3-394 8°
In this edition of Luther's short catechism Resen has placed a verse on the verso of the title page, which was repeated for centuries in edition after edition:

Hør mig du Pawe ieg være vil
Din Pæstilentze mend ieg er til.
Naar ieg er død skalt du forgaa
Siger Luther, vaarer der paa.

[Listen, Pope, for all my days,
To you I'll be just as the plagues,
And at my death without a doubt
Luther tells me you to flout.]

1674
## On the Meaning of Perjury

*Huad en falsk Eed Aluorlig oc forfærlig betyder, effter som den hellige Scrifft vduiser ... U. st. 1605*
Det kongelige Bibliotek 8-233 4°
Through church attendence the congregation was made familiar with the law of God and the certain wrath of God if justice were not fully carried out. This brief work brings the same message and threatens loss of salvation for those who commit perjury. The three fingers used to take an oath are identified as the thumb, representing God the Father, the pointer finger, the son of God, and the third finger, the Holy Spirit. The text was included word for word in Christian V's Danish Law of 1683.

1675
## Hans Thomissøn

*Den ny Danske Psalmebog, København 1628*
Det kongelige Bibliotek 4-181 8°
Hans Thomissøn's salmebog (1st ed. 1569) remained the official hymnal. In the edition from 1628, which had been revised by Resen, only four new hymns were added, among them "Af højheden oprunden er", which is still in the hymnal (no. 87).

1676
## Spiritual Handbook

*En Aandelig Haandbog, Hourudi de fornemste Bøger aff Bibelen, Som Veyfarendis Folck mest bruger, findis. København 1639*
Det kongelige Bibliotek, Hielmstierne 1337 8°
During the period of orthodoxy, popular piety was nourished by an excessively abundant devotional literatue, which existed in proportions that suggest that literacy must have reached considerable levels, both among the nobility and the commoners. Alongside the official hymnal appeared new types along the lines of this work. The name of "handbook" indicates that this book could easily be carried along, and that it contained all that a Christian needed ready to hand; hymnal, catechism, prayer book, Biblical extracts and other devotional texts. The copper engraved double title page shows Tobias saying farewell to his parents on the right, and on the left, the Apostle Philip preaching before the Ethiopian tax master.

1677
## David's Psalter

*Dauid's Psalter met D: Mart: Lutheri Summarier, Helsingør 1610*
Det kongelige Bibliotek, 1-102 8°
It is characteristic of the devotional literature of the period to show a strong relationship to the Old Testament, especially the Psalms of David. This copy belonged to Queen Anna Cathrine. It is bound in burgundy coloured velvet with mountings and buckles of firegilt silver and tooled gold edges. In the middle of the binding the crowned monogram of the queen.

1678
## David's Psalter

*Den høye opliuste oc mectige Guds Mands Konning Davids Psalter. København 1632*
Det kongelige Bibliotek 1-103 2°
This edition of the Psalms of David was paid for by Ellen Marsvin (1572-1649), and was published by Niels Mikkelsen Aalborg. The text is printed with very large type faces out of consideration for the elderly and weak-

sighted. On the title page is a large woodcut vignette of King David playing the harp.

1679

## Jesper Brochmand

*Sabbati Sanctificatio, Det er: Gudelig Betenckning oc kort Forklaring offuer alle Evangelier oc Epistler ... Vinterparten. København 1635. Sommerparten. København 1638*
Det kongelige Bibliotek $6^{1}$-88 8°
Jesper Brochmand's other major work (cf. cat. 1657) was Huspostillen, as it was called in the later editions, which contained sermons on all the epistles and gospel readings for the whole of the ecclesiastical year. This was one of the most widely used devotional books and it appeared in numerous editions, the last in 1862. [The summer section of this copy belonged at one time to a learned lady of the nobility, Marie Below (1586-1651)].

1680

## Jens Dinesen Jersin

*Om Miracler, Tegn oc Obenbaringer oc deris Udleggelse. København 1631*
Det kongelige Bibliotek 5-103 8°
The bishop of Ribe, Jens Dinesen Jersin (1587-1634), wrote and published devotional books which were much appreciated both in Denmark and abroad. Actually they consisted of revised sermons like this one, which is aimed at the superstitions of the time. A peculiar inscription which had been discovered on a window pane in Ribe created a stir because people believed that it was an omen of evil things to come. Jersin seized the occasion to preach a sermon each day for a week against superstition.

1681

## Niels Heldvad

*Historiarum sacrarum Encolpodion. Det er, En Nye oc Nyttig Bog, om vor Herris Jesu Christi, Sampt hans hellige Apostlers, Confessorum oc Martyrers Liff oc Leffnets Historie ... København 1634*
Det kongelige Bibliotek 2-89 4°
Niels Heldvad (cf. cat. 1666) wrote many inspirational books. This "collection of sacred stories" contains the life of Jesus according to the gospels, the history of the Apostles, the history of the Danish Church, and accounts of the martyrs, divided into four books. Each book has a separate title page, at the bottom of which there is a portrait of the author in an oval medallion. (On the front of the binding is a stylized picture of Christian IV tooled in gold and on the back the crowned monogram of the king).

1682

## Philip Kegelius

*Zwölf geistliche Andachten. Magdeburg 1595*
Colour-plate IV
Det kongelige Bibliotek 92-337 8°
The domestic authors of devotional books could by no means satisfy demand, and foreign authors, mostly German, were popular, both in the original language and in Danish translations. Here is a German edition of the German devotional author Philip Kegelius' Twelve Spiritual Reflections. Even though a couple of Jesuitical works which had only undergone slight revision formed the basis of the book, it was so neutral from a confessional point of view that no one considered restricting its use. It appeared in Danish for the first time c. 1621, and was re-printed nine to ten times in the course of the seventeenth century. This copy is bound in a binding from c. 1595 which has a painted picture of Christian IV on the front cover and the Danish national coat of arms on the back.

1683

## Johann Arndt

*De Vero Christianismo, Lüneburg 1625*
Det kongelige Bibliotek 92-275 8°
The major work of the German theologian Johann Arndt (1555-1621), the inspirational book "Vier Bücher vom wahren Christentum", which appeared between 1605 and 1609, achieved widespread popularity and was translated into many languages, Danish among them. The first Latin edition has a copper-engraved title page with an unsigned portrait of Arndt and a picture which depicts the sending forth of the twelve apostles and above it the lamentation of Christ over the scribes and the pharisees; "The scribes and the Pharisees sit in Moses' seat". This copy belonged to Laurids Ulfeldt (1605-59).

1684

## Johann Valentin Andreae

*Reipublicae Christianopolitanae descriptio. Strasbourg 1619*
Det kongelige Bibliotek 92-218 8°
The German theologian Johann Valentain Andreae (1586-1654) was great admirer of Johann Arndt, to whom he dedicated this Christian utopia. Andreae's idea of the harmonious ideal society is illustrated by this copper engraving of a plan of a symmetrically laid-out imaginary city named Christianopolis.

1685

## J. J. Boissard

*Theatrum vitæ humanæ, Metz 1596*
Det kongelige Bibliotek $77^{2}$-154 4°
In the time of Christian IV death was more of an ever present reality than in our day. It was typical that this

*1690*

book of emblemata, which according to the title deals with the Theatre of Life, depicts in the copper engraving on the title page four stages of human life in which Death threatens by its presence. In 1602 the book belonged to Asmund Tygesen (d.c. 1645), vicar of Løvestad.

1686

## Homo disce mori

*Homo disce mori ... Hamburg 1593*
Det kongelige Bibliotek 144-267 8°
The copper engraving shows Cai Rantzau of Rantzau (1562-1591) on his deathbed surrounded by his family, servants and dogs. The man on the left is his father, the well-known viceregent in the duchies, Henrik Rantzau (d. 1598). The book belonged at one time to Jacob Høg of Trudsholm (d. 1610).

1687

## Jens Giødesen

*Raad oc Trøst ... Vdi ... Fru Christine Lungel[s] ... Nedsættelse oc Lijgfærd, som skede vdi Randers den 17. August Anno 1609. København u.å.*
Det kongelige Bibliotek 44-278 4°

It became common in the time of Christian IV for the sorrowing survivors to print the funeral sermons preached for the nobility. And it became fashionable to provide these books with illustrations, as has been done here with the coffin on the title page. Nor were allegories and/or coats of arms uncommon, the latter exhibited the good family of the deceased. Here the coats of arms of Christine Lunge's maternal and paternal lines peek out from under the shroud.

1688

## Hans Mikkelsen

*En Christelig Lijgprædicken ... Der ... Fru Anne Krabbe Mogenss datter, Hindis S[alig] Lijg bleff ... nedersat udi Sanct Knuds Kircke i Othense den 17. Octob. 1638 Aarhus 1642.*
Det kongelige Bibliotek 44-190 4°
The copper engraving facing the title page shows the heavy-handed symbols of Death; the human skull and the hourglass. Framing these symbols are the coats of arms of Anne Krabbe's forefathers, the paternal line on the left, the maternal on the right.

1689

## Thomas Cortsen Wegner

*Davids Aandelig Harpe eller Cither ... i en Lijgpredicken fremsat ... der ... S[alig] Axel Wrne til Rygaard ... Hans Lijgs sørgelige begengelse ... i S. Nicolai Kircke vdi Kiøbenhaffn skeede Aar 1627, København 1630*

Det kongelige Bibliotek 44-222 4°

A skull and cross bones in gold tooling was occasionally used as appropriate decoration on the bindings of funeral sermons. On the front and back covers of this binding have been stamped two medallions with an entwined monogram AWRS, presumably Salig Axel Wrne (til) Rygaard (Blessed Axel Wrne (of) Rygaard).

1690

## Jesper Brochmand

*Guds Børns Lengsel ... der ... Fru Birgitte Rud, Christen Skiels til Wallø, Hendis Adelige Lijgs Begengelse ... bleff huldet udi Helliggeistes Kircke i Kiøbenhaffn. København 1646*

Det kongelige Bibliotek 45-262 4°

The fold-out copper engraving by H. A. Greys depicts Birgitte Rud's reception in heaven. On the left Death with the scythe, on which appears the admonishing text; "Death brings separation and an end to all things". On the right are placed Birgitte Rud's mourning husband and children with a dog and a peacock on a terrace. The whole scene is provided with a few Biblical verses appropriate to the occasion. In the frame are Birgitte Rud's 32 ancestral coats of arms, paternal line on the left, maternal on the right.

1691

## Jesper Brochmand

*De sande oc salige Guds Børns wfeylbare Kiendemercker ... Der ... Fru Birgete Rosenspar. Salig Corfitz Ruds til Sandholdt, Hendis Adelige Lijgs Begængelse ... bleff huldet udi Helliggeistes Kircke i Kiøbenhafn. København 1647.*

Det kongelige Bibliotek 45-251 4°

H. A. Greys also engraved this large copper engraving for the funeral sermon on Birgitte Rosensparre. On the right is Birgitte Rosensparre, eyes raised towards the blessed, who according to the Revelations of St. John, ch. 7, worship God and the Lamb (Christ). On the left the surviving relatives in a manor garden, and framing the whole, the 32 ancestral paternal and maternal arms of Birgitte Rosensparre.

1692

## Laurids Jacobsen Hindsholm

*Førstelig Leffnetzs oc Døds Speyl ... Der ... Konning Christians den IV ... høysørgelig Ligbegengelse ... klagelig bleff holden udi vor Frue Kircke i Kiøbenhaffn den 18. Novemb. anno 1648. København 1649*

Det kongelige Bibliotek 35-271 4°

In his funeral sermon court chaplain Laurids Jacobsen Hindsholm gave an account of Christian IV's last hours, among other topics.

*Detail from*
*Caspar Bartholin and*
*Simon Paulli.*
*Cat. 1566*

Künstliche
Zerlegüng Menschlichen Leibes,
Des Hochgelährten vnd Weitberümbten
Herrn D. CASPARI BARTHOLINI;
itzo dürch Anordnüng
D. SIMONIS PAULLI.
*Med. Anat. ac Botan. P.P.*
In der Königlichen Academien
Kopenhagen,
mit fleisse
Allen Wündartzten zü nütz
ins Deütsche übergesetzet.
1648.

*Theatrum Anatomicum Regiæ Haffniensis Academiæ.*

*The Stock Exchange, Copenhagen. Built 1609-40.*

# Koldinghus

## *The Architecture of Christian IV*

Christian IV was the most ardent building-enthusiast of all the kings of Denmark. On his orders towns, castles and churches were constructed or altered, and his reputation is still kept alive today by Frederiksborg, Rosenborg, the Stock Exchange (Børsen) and the Round Tower – all buildings which are familiar to most Danes. Building-projects and works from the time of Christian IV still exist in abundance. For this exhibition we have selected a series of them which can serve to illustrate the King's own architecture, i.e. the architecture whose development he personally supervised, the architecture with which he had frequent contact, and which, in contemporary times and since, has been both the contextual frame and the image itself of Christian IV.

As is nearly always the case in Danish art, architecture in Christian IV's time was a combination of elements from many quarters. Trends in style were sought both from abroad and from older Danish architecture; architects and building-craftsmen brought new inspiration back from their travels, and the many architectural tracts of the time were used, directly or indirectly, as models. These different elements blended into one particular style, known by art historians as Gothic Renaissance or Dutch Renaissance, names which evoke some of the most evident style-features and reveal the complex nature of the architecture. The hybrid nature is itself characteristic. Christian IV surrounded himself with a quite particular architecture and elevated his status by this means to equal that of monarchs and princes of the highest level in Europe, conscious of international trends but at the same time deeply original.

### European Princely Culture

For a European prince at the close of the 16th century the strengthening of power was a central preoccupation. The 16th century had seen a series of strong royal rulers, first and foremost Charles V (1516-1556) over whose kingdoms the sun never set, and also Francois I of France (1515-1547), Philip II of Spain and the Netherlands (1556-1598), the English Kings and Elizabeth I (1558-1603) had brought their countries out of the feudal system's far-flung power-ramifications and strengthened the central power of the monarchy.

Of great importance for Northern Europe was the severance from Papal power which came about through the Reformation movements. Luther in particular strongly emphasized the position of the prince as the implement of God, the authority to whom all must submit, with unconditional obedience. The princes as a result emerged at a pinnacle of absolute power, spiritual as well as worldly.

Both the Catholic and the Protestant princes, in step with the growing centralization of power, built new frameworks around themselves. The 16th century became a time of blossoming for court ceremonial, for royal portraits and for palace architecture.

In architecture the influence of the Italian Renaissance spread. The 15th century had seen the creation of a new form-language, partly based on models from antiquity, incorporated into a humanistic world perspective. The architecture should be based on the simplest forms – circles, squares, cubes and forms derived from them – forms in complete balance, mirroring the universe's harmonic primary forms. A proportion-system built up from the simple rations 1:1. 1:2. 2:3 etc. ... along with symmetry and with a fixed axis-system, became absolutely essential requirements for 15th century Italian architecture.

When the rest of Europe in the course of the 16th century began to take an interest in Renaissance architecture, it was not a matter of adopting the system wholesale, however, but of incorporating a few elements of ornamentation into houses otherwise built in local style. Facades subdivided by columns or pilasters, or pillared portals and classical decoration turn up on bourgeois houses and castles whose layout is from the late Middle Ages (e.g. gable-houses). In medieval castles such as Fontainebleau near Paris attempts were made, via Renaissance details such as ceremonial staircases and triumphal gateways, to convert the house into a worthy royal residence. Both in the old and in the new structures the entrance axis is stressed; the route towards the prince takes on the character of a ceremonial triumph-procession. The symbolism which in the Italy of the 15th century lay in the very proportions of the corpus of buildings is now transferred to the details of decoration. The demand for symmetry grew steadily, through the 16th century, to become a significant factor in palace-structures. A culminating point was Philip II's Escorial near Madrid, completed in 1584.

This architecture's blend of medieval characteristics with Renaissance shapes and symbol-language became the framework for a ceremonial court life which similarly was a mixture of many different ingredients. Medieval royal tournaments, Renaissance triumphal processions on the model of classical antiquity, the Spanish court's rigid etiquette and black and white severe attire were blended with influences from England, where Elizabeth I set herself up as the Virgin Queen, half medieval saint, half Diana of antiquity.

The result was a princely ideology, common to all of Europe, which in the second half of the 16th century developed both in terms of politics and of art. The prince was elevated both through God's selection and by the power of his personal qualities. He was the "universal man" of the Renaissance, highly educated and wise, well-equipped with physical, intellectual and artistic talents and with high principles besides.

The prince's surroundings were a reflection of his qualities. Palaces grew in form and splendour; triumphal arches, battle-scenes and heroic exploits (those of the prince himself or of his ancestors), and astrological programmes were used to interpret the prince's knowledge of the ways of the world, his understanding of the ordering principle with which his own rule should comply.

In sumptuous pageantry, inspired by the triumphal processions of antiquity, royal power was displayed to the public, both as a demonstration of power on entry to occupied towns and as an element in festivities at coronations, weddings, etc. The court and its guests would participate in costume, dressed as allegorical figures, and there would be tournaments, masques, dancing and music combined in the particular genre of the court ballet. The performers would be the court itself, instructed by professional artists.

The whole of this courtly life was staged not merely as a diversion for the participants. It was a carefully worked out presentation of a political view of society: the prince's central place in the order of the world was confirmed, his power was displayed and hailed. It therefore became important to publicize court events, to recount them and to describe court life, and its architecture. The artist became a central person in the Renaissance courts. He was both producer and publicity agent. Portraits, medals and books spread the reputation of the prince, while the framework of court life – the architecture, the celebrations, the processions – were created by a circle of artists – painters, poets, musicians and pyrotechnists, often under the supervision of the master-builders. Court life developed in this context of participatory art, produced as a mixture of entertainment and political propaganda.

## A Danish princely court: Frederik II and Kronborg

In Denmark it was at the time of Frederik II's court that Renaissance culture flowered. His father, Christian III, had had the major tasks of reviving Denmark after the "War of the Counts" and of reorganizing the ruling of the country on a Lutheran basis; Frederik II then took over the responsibility for restoring Denmark's international standing. Through two wars, the Ditmarsch Expedition in 1559, and the Seven Years' War with Sweden, 1563-70, which were both considered Danish victories, Frederik II consolidated his position as the strongest Nordic power. The view of war as a knightly sport still played a role, as it had in the Middle Ages. The depiction of the King as "the conquering hero riding into Ditmarn with high hat and rosy cheek" and the conflict about the right to the coat of arms consisting of the three crowns, which became an issue in the Seven Years' War, both have roots in the conceptual world of feudalism.

Court life was arranged on the European pattern, with celebrations, plays, musical ensembles, but here older habits were also kept up – the holding of tournaments, and trumpet or canon salutes when the King of Denmark drank at a banquet.

Intellectually also Frederik II's court raised its international level. A generation of humanists met there. The interest in the past which in Italy was embodied in attempts to recreate antiquity was paralleled in Denmark by cultivation of the Danish Middle Ages. Saxo's History of Denmark had to be continued, ballads were collected and dances to them revived. In addition there was research in astronomy, astrology and theology. Leading personalities were Anders Sørensen Vedel, the historian, and Tycho Brahe, the astronomer, but Queen Sofie and the ladies of the nobility also took part in collecting and writing down texts. Some of the ballads which by tradition are assumed to be medieval were in fact evidently created by the noble ladies of this period.

Religion was coloured by the prevailing humanism. With Melanchton's theology as a departure-point humanity was interpreted as having been made in God's image, and therefore created with goodness and reason as outstanding qualities. The words of the Bible were explored as moral instructions, and were interpreted and debated. Significantly for art, the theologians declared the prohibition of pictorial images; narrative art was rejected as an element in the decoration of the Christian church. As at all times at court, during Frederik II's reign there was strong interest in architecture and art. At Kronborg a splendid framework was created for the life of the court.

Kronborg was a medieval castle, constructed as a defence for the important sea straits of Øresund and the power behind the collection of the Øresund toll. Frederik II converted the castle to a 4-wing Renaissance castle, completed in 1585. The fortress aspect was retained; the castle lies behind a rampart and moat-system, with bastions of the newest model, but the castle itself was adapted for royal representative purposes. It is still a symbol of power, but also a house which through its splendour bears witness to the King of Denmark's understanding of the European taste in princely surroundings.

While the medieval castles were closed in behind curtain walls and could only show their decoration on courtyard, facades and interiors, the Renaissance castle presented itself to the outer world. From the Sound can be seen the distinctively formed chapel gable, a watchman's gallery, richly decorated, which crowns the walls, and towers with spires rising over the castle's roof.

This outward-turned decoration sits high and forward so as to be seen over the ramparts, and is added to the outer walls which by their plain, strong construction show that they are part of the medieval castle's curtain-wall. Details are added to impress, in a form-language borrowed from the international fashion of the time, brought to Denmark by artists from the Netherlands. Among them were Hans van Steenwinckel the Elder (ca. 1550-1601), founding father of a line of artists who became very significant under Christian IV.

Typical decoration forms are the scrolls and cartouches, and on the chapel gable there are a series of details, pilasters, corniches and niches, built up as a 5-storey high ornamental facade. The design for an Italian Renaissance facade was adapted in the Netherlands to make a gable decoration, and came from there to Denmark, brought as a greeting to the ships that sailed past.

A number of building-features, the watchman's galleries and the high towers, which originally had defence functions, are traces left from the Middle Ages. They were converted to purely decorative elements. The use of decoration high up on the walls and gables is also a typically Gothic style-feature, continued at Kronborg in the high-placed decorations on the watchman's gallery and chapel gable.

Frederik II's master-builders created a style in which the mass of the building, its proportions and a series of particular characteristics, such as the towers, were an extension of Danish medieval architecture, whereas the form of the decorative details was taken from the new Renaissance style.

The blending of styles was also apparent in the entrance to the castle; the original entrance was through the rampart, and a underground S-shaped passage prevented those arriving from sighting the castle as a splendid entity. The primary impression was rather that of the menacing strength of the fortress. Only when one went on into the small courtyard between the rampart and the castle could one see both sides of the castle: the Dark Gate, a rustic fortress gate on the rampart side, and the Palace Gateway, a triumphal arch with Corinthian columns, which presented the visitor to the King, symbolized by the bay window to his room and his crowned monogram. The gateway's symbolism is typical Renaissance narrative, with emphasis on the significance of the entrance. This is the castle's most distinguished gateway, outward-turning and welcoming. In the courtyard of the castle there are a number of simpler variations of the triumphal arch motif; only the chapel doorway rises to the same standard as the Palace Gateway.

The castle's courtyard facades clearly show the signs of being the product of rebuilding. The original houses are incorporated in the structure and create irregular subdivisions which are highlighted by the use of different window-types. The staircase-turrets lead to the various wings and are characterized as functional towers in that they only reach roof-height and have low domes, whereas the tower over the entrance, linked to the prestige wing with the chapel and ballroom, is high and has a splendid spire. This tower was used by the King's trumpeters, who sounded toasting-fanfares from there during court banquets.

The interior of the castle was richly fitted out, particularly the ballroom, for which Frederik commissioned a series of tapestries woven under the direction of the artist Hans Kneiper from the Netherlands. Denmark's 100 kings, from King Dan to Christian, the Prince-Elect, could be seen there. A canopy belonged to the series, showing an allegory of the Ruler of the Three Rivers, Frederik II. This allegory was also used in the fountain in the courtyard.

In contrast to the castle's other areas the chapel was ascetic. A single white-washed room, with wooden galleries which were decorated with carved ornaments and sculpted figures. The altar-piece shows the Resurrected Christ between representations of the Crucifixion and the Serpent of Brass in the Wilderness, themes whose symbolic content dominates the dramatic narrative. Frederik II's theologians' ideals are reflected in this chapel, just as the court ceremonial is reflected in the rest of the castle.

Kronborg emerges as a mixture of Danish building- and decoration-traditions and foreign ornamentation details, and also as a mixture of fortress and palace – a typical transitional product between Gothic and Renaissance styles. This style became a departure-point for Christian IV's architecture, which copied it in many features; the whole conception of conscious royal prestige architecture took its departure-point from Kronborg.

This castle is the first Danish royal building which in its size and fittings really elevated itself over the level of the nobility. By this castle Frederik II enhanced his royal power. In his other building work he was more in line with the building-projects of the nobility, which prospered in the second half of the 16th century.

At Frederiksborg Castle, in about 1580, he built the Badstue (Bathhouse) – a miniature manor in shape and materials (red brick with sandstone decoration). The King was still treated by the Danish nobility as an equal, elected to direct the kingdom in practical matters. The King owned and managed a number of farms, just like any other rich lord. Frederik II's political desire for a stronger monarchy had a parallel in his will to surpass the nobility in the artistic realm: court life in Kronborg was arranged in a truly royal context. The 100 ancestors shown in the tapestry-series outbid the 32 noble forefathers which were the proof of true nobility, and Frederik II in 1576 forbade the erection of prestige burial-monuments; the monument he had commissioned for his father Christian III should not be over-shadowed by nobles. Frederik II's time thus laid down certain ideals and guidelines for royal ceremonial and royal surroundings.

## Christian IV's Architecture: the Basis and the Background

After Frederik II's death in 1588 the Regency government discouraged building operations and festive activities. A series of celebrations took place, however, when Princess Anna married James VI of Scotland (later James I of England), in 1589. The Regency government also commissioned a memorial for Frederik II.

With Christian IV's coronation, full royal glitter returned to court life. The coronation ceremony in 1596 presented him in the international arena with all the essential elements of a Renaissance celebration: Processions, tournaments, tilting at the ring, fireworks and theatre. At the same time it was stressed in the coronation ceremony that the power was transferred from the Council (Rigsråd) to the King, with the blessing of the Church; by means of the celebrations in Copenhagen, attended by many representatives of the Danish nobility and of foreign royalty, the King was also recognized by the people and by the other countries of Europe.

Immediately after his enthronement, Christian IV began to shape his own surroundings. During his youth he had experienced life at his father's court, and had followed the progress of the building-work at the castles. Now that he had the task of continuing the royal architectural projects, it was natural that he should take his father's achievements as a departure-point, but he was also able to look for inspiration to the buildings of the nobility. In the1590s some of the most modern architecture was erected by the Rantzau family in Holstein, proudly publicized by Henrik Rantzau.

The familiy's principal residence at Rantzau was rebuilt in 1591-94 as a 3-part construction following a main axis, with a fore-court on the lake-shore, and the main building as a parallel construction on an island, and then, further behind, another small island with a summer-house. The construction, which was depicted in the work of Lomeier in 1595, may have inspired the very similar plan for Frederiksborg, blended with features from the Rantzaus' Redingsdorf, published in 1590. The Rantzau family were closely related to the Oldenborg royal family. Henrik Rantzau had discussed architecture with Frederik II and also contributed to Christian IV's development into an architecturally talented sovereign. He wrote, for instance, in 1591 to the Prince about books which he had received from Rome describing Roman antiquities, cardinals' palaces and other pieces of architecture.

On Frederik II's death Henrik Rantzau erected a memorial pyramid in Holstein. This was also illustrated in the Rantzaus' family history. When Christian IV later proposed a pyramid in front of the Stock Exchange (Børsen) with the genealogical table of the Royal family, clearly the inspiration came from the Rantzau pyramid.

Henrik Rantzau, with his interest in the family, in architecture, and in ensuring perpetuation of remembrance through publication, was a typical Renaissance humanist, and an inspiring stimulus to the young King's interest in architecture.

An important source of inspiration for both King and nobility consisted of the many architectural tracts produced at the time. Following classical models (Vitruvius, 1st century A.D.) texts were written about all forms of architecture, towns, castles, fortresses, churches. While the 15th century Italian texts were to a large extent Utopian, covering the architecture of complete towns, the 16th century tracts more often consisted of directions for practical building-work. The tracts began to be more specialized, some dealing with fortified buildings (e.g. Dürer, 1528), some with castle-construction (Ducerceau, 1576) and others proposing models for the decoration of houses. Architectural books illustrating different types of colonnading became a widespread and sought-after commodity on the international market; among such books, for example, were several giving the different orders of columns, produced by Serlio, an Italian, which were published in many editions including, in 1608, a German version.

The influence of these tracts can also be seen in Danish architecture, in the houses of the nobility and in Frederik II's Kronborg, where the details are inspired by Serlio and the Dutchman Vredeman de Vries. Both of these, and the German Wendel Dietterlin as well, are copied in the details of Frederiksborg Castle.

Typical of the tracts from the second half of the 16th century and the beginning of the 17th century is the lack of connection between the decoration and the constructive system of the architecture. The coherent architecture of the Italian Renaissance became disrupted, and ornamentation became an independent element carrying symbolic meaning. The hierarchy of orders of columns, with Tuscan lowest and composite highest, was expanded with extravagant new forms, including national symbolism, as in the case of the French order of Philibert de l'Ormes. The orders were no longer only linked to columns; the idea was enlarged so that, e.g. in the work of Wendel Dietterlin (Architectura 1598) could be found fountains in different orders, and elsewhere there were gardens, fire-places and sepulchral tablets. The ornamental became an independent element, and many North-European tracts were essentially decoration-manuals, entirely devoted to the details of architecture. The master-builders chose from the tracts and decoration-manuals at will, and facades and surroundings were used as neutral background surfaces, while the significance of the house was conveyed by its decoration.

Christian IV and his master-builders shared this view of architecture as a composite, and eclectic, art. Danish architecture was a compound of numerous elements: Frederik II's building-style, the contemporary buildings of the nobility, and features from international tracts. Out of this blend of elements was created a style which reflects the contemporary European fashion, Mannerism, but seems in addition to possess a particular national quality. The King's solidarity with the country, the people and their history was emphasized through it.

## The Royal Setting: Castle Architecture

Christian IV's castles are in many ways still Gothic; the buildings are tall and narrow, with external stair-turrets, and the facades have irregularly-placed windows. At Frederiksborg Castle the wings are of varying depth. This may be directly inspired by Kronborg, like the use of Gothic-style windows in the Castle Chapel; the gateways to the King's and Queen's stair-turrets are also derivations from there. The irregularity in the whole construction, which at Kronborg was the result of alterations, at Frederiksborg was planned as a consciously old-fashioned style-feature. The retrospective connection was thus established; Christian IV was his father's natural successor, in the matter of castle architecture as in other respects. The political question concerning inherited monarchy here is given a commentary in artistic shape.

Another element taken over from Kronborg is the clear marking of the difference between the functional towers (staircase turrets) and towers for representative purposes. The towers intended to symbolize the power of the King are built up over roof-height and distinguished with tall spires. Christian IV introduced a new type of spire, the Dutch-style storeyed spire, which was used for the first time for the Blåtårn in 1596 and then almost became a trade-mark for castle architecture.

While towers and spires were a continuation of Gothic forms, out-of-fashion in the rest of Europe, other details – e.g. the shape of gables and gateways – were imported from abroad, either via the copying of tracts or by the purchase of completed art works. In this way the Marble Gallery for Frederiksborg Castle was bought in Amsterdam from Hendrick de Keyser, to whose workshops Christian IV sent many young artists, including several of Steenwinckel's sons. The retrograde elements in the

King's architecture did not stem from lack of knowledge, but were totally in keeping with the contemporary view of architecture: decoration was treated as an independant building-element, and "modern" details could therefore fit with a "Gothicized" house.

Even the course of construction of the architecture still had a Gothic stamp to it. It is characteristic of Christian IV's building-works that they were altered in the process of construction, with regard to both plan and decoration. The Gothic building-tradition in that respect contrasts with the Italian Renaissance principle according to which a house should be created as a coherent entity, to which alterations could only be detrimental. For Christian IV and his day it was natural that new fashions could be made features of architectural projects that had already been embarked on or had even been completed.

The erection of the Marble Gallery in the courtyard at Frederiksborg Castle demonstrates a new understanding of the terminal point of the entrance-axis, and the external, straight flights for stairs which were used at Rosenborg and at the Stock Exchange (Børsen) were similarly new features. They provide a more comfortable ascent than stair-turrets, and at the same time display the visitor in a prestigious context as he ascends to the ceremonial doorway, which in Rosenborg led to the royal banqueting-rooms, and in the Stock Exchange to the Merchants' main hall. A new understanding of architecture as a unity, an expression-through-facade, emerges here.

The main purpose of Christian IV's castles was ceremonial. Castle architecture was now entirely free of the enveloping fortress aspects which make Kronborg so sombre. Christian IV's castles were created with an eye to distant views and as rich an appearance as possible, in forms, materials and colours. The surroundings, exteriors and interiors were designed as coherent testimonies to the King's power, and as functioning ceremonial environments for court life, which still followed the 16th century pattern: music of a high international standard was cultivated, under the guidance of e.g. John Dowland and Heinrich Schutz, and conversation took place in Latin and other foreign languages. Christian IV for instance spoke Latin with the French Ambassador "as if they were speaking in their mother-tongue" (Ogier, 1634). Sports such as tilting at the ring and hunting were among the court's favourite occupations, and artistic taste was also a natural quality in a prince. Christian IV was not only keenly interested in architecture, but also collected paintings, and was the first Danish king to make full use of the possibilities of portrait-painting, both in private and in ceremonial contexts. The coronation ceremony in 1596 was depicted in illustrated books, and for the castles several series of pictures were commissioned with historical and ideological content.

The castle buildings provide the unifying framework which to the outside and to the inside reflect the functions of the royal ruler. The exterior of the castle echoes the form of the regalia: the spires parallel the sceptre (which in the language of those days was knows as the spire), the crown can be seen on the towers and spires (Koldinghus, Frederiksborg), and the monogram and coat of arms everywhere indicate the identity of the royal builder.

Christian IV was a Renaissance prince, for whom allegory and symbol were natural forms of expression. It was only at a later stage in his reign that representations of the King himself began to be incorporated into the architectural context, as a personification of power. The sculptor Francois Dieussart, who lived in Copenhagen in 1643-44, produced a bust of the King, possibly intended to be a decoration for a gateway, and Christian IV commissioned from him an equestrian statue, which however was never executed. It was a new royal ideology, Absolutism, and a new artistic form of expression, the Baroque, which Christian IV here introduced to Denmark, totally in step with the European trends at the time. During the whole period of his reign the King was active and developing, in art-politics as in other fields.

## Copenhagen Castle

The stronghold which Absalon built in 1167 for Copenhagen's defence was continually extended throughout the Middle Ages and the 16th century. Christian IV inherited a castle with an irregular ground-plan and wings of very differing character; a structure whose original defence-function had become obsolete. As the King's residence the Castle was to be part of the setting for the coronation festivities in 1596.

One of Christian IV's first architectural initiatives was the heightening of the old Blåtårn, the castle's original central tower. A spire was placed on the tower – a storeyed spire in Dutch style, with open and closed lanterns and three crowns at the top, symbolizing Christian IV's inheritance-claim to the three Nordic kingdoms. The original tower's physical force was thus re-interpreted as a symbolic assertion of the new King's strength, one which moreover was conspicuous in the profile of the town, which had previously been dominated by the Church-tower.

## Koldinghus

*Colour-plate IV*

Koldinghus is a medieval castle on the border between the Kingdom of Denmark and the Duchy of Slesvig – a defence-construction which Christian III had already converted into a civilian castle. Christian IV had the castle altered in the years 1598-1605 under the supervision of Hercules von Oberberg.

The great tower was erected as the buildings's dominant feature, square with a flat roof, from which four giant figures (Hannibal, Scipio, Hector and Hercules) watched over the realm, equipped with lances and shields showing the coats of arms of Slesvig, Denmark and Norway, and the three crowns, the coat of arms of Sweden or of the Union. The castle's original physical defensive function was re-interpreted as symbolic defence, its form inspired by older royal art: the form of the tower owes its inspiration to Kronborg's great guntowers, watched over by four lions; the Halbardiers have parallels in Christian III's and Frederik II's burial-monuments in Roskilde Cathedral, and were moreover used by Christian IV in ceremonial decorations for the coronation in 1596 and on the roof of Sparepenge at Frederiksborg Castle. These worthy watchmen for the Nordic King served to emphasize the prestige of Koldinghus as a border castle, constructed in a simple building-style, with its few ornamental details, e.g. the gateways, in a rough rustic style, a symbol of strength.

In the interior a number of elaborate rooms and a castle chapel were fitted out. The chapel was copied, on the King's orders, from the chapel at Hansborg, his uncle's castle in Haderslev. Both places followed the Lutheran ideal for royal chapels – a single space with a gallery around it where the prince's throne was placed. This pattern was repeated in Frederiksborg Castle Chapel.

## Frederiksborg Castle

*Colour-plate VI*

In 1560, through an exhange of property with Herluf Trolle, Frederik II became the owner of Hillerødsholm Manor. He rechristened it Frederiksborg and added to its structure; *inter alia* he had erected on the innermost of the site's three islands a number of stables and houses for the employees. These buildings still stand and line the access to the rest of Frederiksborg. Close to the Castle some smaller houses were built, including the Badstue *(Bathhouse),* c. 1580, and a house called *Sparepenge.* Only the Badstue has been preserved.

In 1599 Christian IV began building work on Frederiksborg in order to construct a stableyard north of the Castle lake. To this was linked a new Sparepenge planned as the terminal focus of the main axis across the two outer islands.

Sparepenge, demolished in 1720, was a two-storey cube-shaped house; on the balustrade of the flat roof stood four warriors. It was fitted out as the place for safe-keeping for Christian IV's distinguished personal riding equipment, armour and weapons. There was also an area for fencing practice. Sparepenge was naturally associated with the stable buildings, where the horses, bred to a standard appropriate for their royal owner, strong and of noble blood, could be inspected.

In 1602 all buildings on the two outer islands were torn down, and between then and 1620 the building of Christian IV's Frederiksborg took place. On the outermost island the main building was constructed – a three-wing structure with a low barrier-wall towards the middle island, on which two almost identical houses stood parallel on either side of the main axis of the construction. The middle island was closed off towards the innermost one by a barrier-wall in which was set the great Gate-Tower, one of the last parts of the castle to be constructed (1620). Christian IV's buildings lie symmetrically about an axis from the Gate-Tower to Sparepenge.

On the innermost of the castle's three islands, Frederik II's buildings were preserved, linked to the outermost island by a bridge which, because of a dislocation in the axis, is shaped like an S. On the middle island a building was erected in 1616, incorporating a mint and an audience room. The Audience House is linked to the north-west corner-tower of the main castle by a two-storey passage-way, the Privy Passage.

Through the whole of the castle's construction architectural motives were used as connecting elements. For example, Frederik II's low round corner-buildings are repeated on the main building of Christian IV's castle; on the latter they become angular and the sweep of the top of the roof is changed, but the basic shape is the same. These four low towers frame the middle island and thus emphasize the central point of the construction and function as a counterbalance to the forward-thrusting principal axis. The significance of the central point is further emphasized by the placing of the large Neptune Fountain, commissioned from the international court artist Adrian de Vries, and installed in about 1620.

At the same time the two towers on the main building form part of the harmony of the castle's many variations on the theme of towers. Both the stair-turrets in the castle courtyard and the external corner-towers of the north facade are of the same type, angular and with sweeping roof-lines, to which here is added a storeyed spire. In the houses on the middle island both the tower-

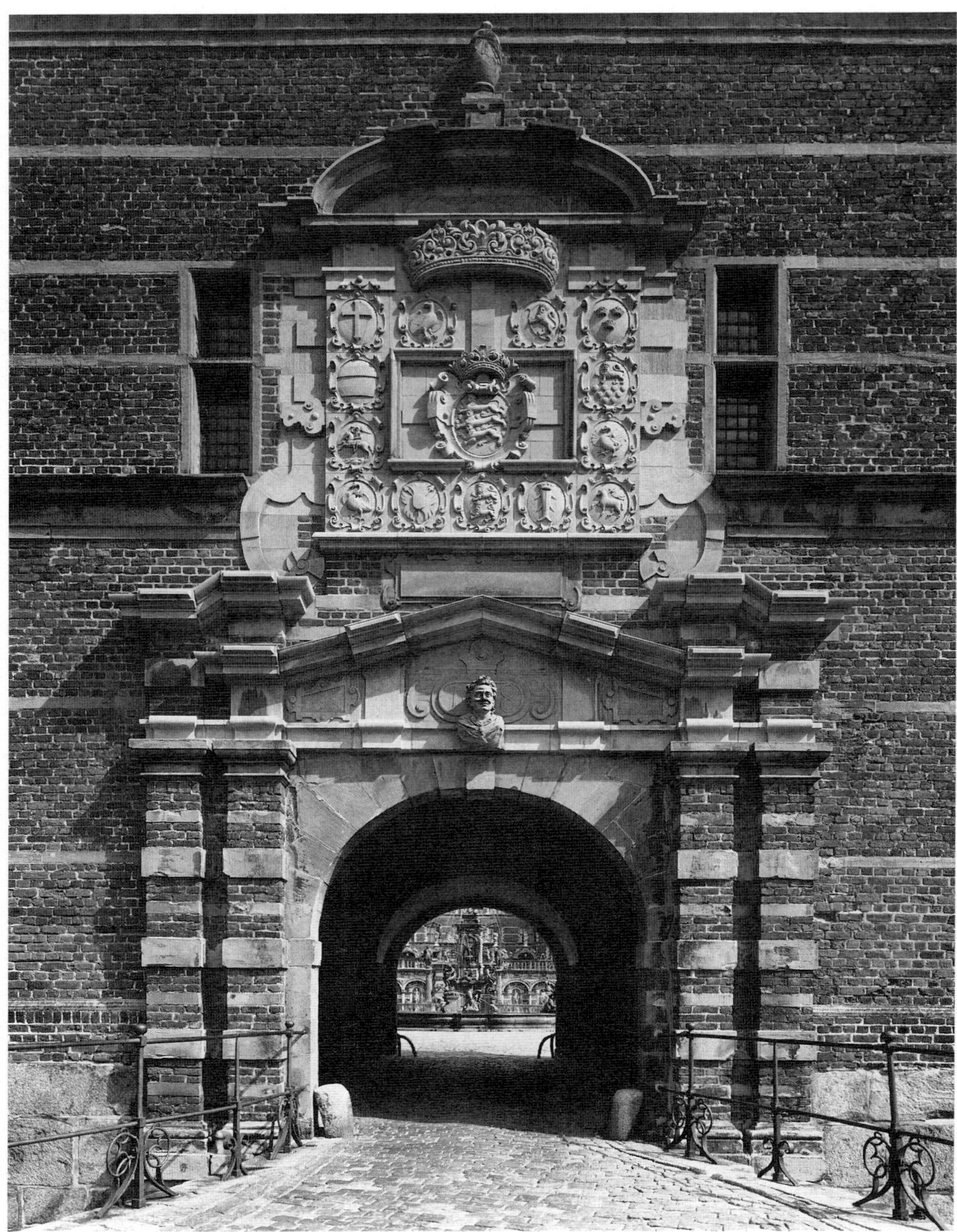

*Frederiksborg Castle. Barbican's north gate.*

shape and the sweeping gables of the main building are repeated. The castle's scale and splendid decoration are emphasized by this first courtyard, created with the same themes in a simpler form.

In the same way there originally was a connection between the terraced-wing, the transverse house on the castle's north facade and Sparepenge, all with flat roofs surrounded by balustrades.

Frederiksborg Castle is composed of a system of courtyards – the "stable street" on the first island, followed by the middle island's fountain courtyard and by the castle forecourt itself. In front of the Audience House lies the Carrousel Yard. One passes from courtyard to courtyard through a series of gateways, variations of the triumphal arch *motif,* the shapes becoming more and more ornate as one draws nearer the King's residence. The culminating point is reached in the Møntport at the Audience House and the great Marble Gallery which runs the length of the back wall of the castle courtyard. Both were designed as permanent ceremonial decorative pieces, the back cloth for the stage of the courtyard. Outdoor events were a central part of Renaissance court activities, and so the courtyards were also arranged as show-pieces.

The castle's outer decoration presents the King in varied contexts: as Mars, the God of War, he appears in the relief on the Møntport, which as a whole is designed to pay homage to him as protector of the Muses. The Neptune Fountain shows the King as lord of fertile and prosperous lands and waters, and through the gods of the planets in the Marble Gallery Christian IV recognized the significance of the orbits of the planets in organizing principles of the universe.

This symbolic decoration makes the castle courtyards a permanent homage to Christian IV and his wise rule.

The castle structure has a through-axis from the Porttårn (Barbican) to Sparepenge, but a number of details prevent the maintenance of symmetry. The main building's wings are of varying depth; in the castle courtyard the large tower at the west wing is dominant, without counterpart on the east wing, and indicates that the Chapel and the ballroom are the castle's most important ceremonial rooms. The Audience House likewise constitutes an asymmetric addition to the construction, produced as an independent element in terms of building material (sandstone in contrast to the rest of the castle's red brick) and also in terms of its simpler building-style. The Castle Chapel, as at Kronborg, has Gothic-style windows. It was more important to distinguish the consecrated space to the outside world than to carry through continuous uniform spacing of the facades. Small deviations from symmetry are visible everywhere, and this is typical of Christian IV's style, in which variation and surprise play an important role.

The main building of the castle contained in its north wing the royal living quarters, in its west wing the Chapel in the two lower storeys and the ballroom above, and in its east wing the kitchen below and living quarters above. All the inner rooms, except the Chapel, were destroyed in the fire of 1859.

The main rooms were equipped with great splendour, with carved wooden ceilings or plaster ceilings, with woven tapestries, many paintings, and furnishings in ebony and silver. Silver basins with running water and garderobes with flushing water provided comfort.

In the interiors also the power of the Kings showed itself in many different ways. The "Rose", the courtiers' room in the lower storey of the King's wing, was arranged as a stag-room, with many features referring to the hunt as a knightly sport, the privilege of the nobility and one of the courts' favourite entertainments.

The ground-plan of the Chapel follows the prototype of a Lutheran royal chapel – a rectangular space with a gallery running round it supported by pillars. Christian IV had used the same plan at Koldinghus, but here the space is larger and more splendidly decorated. A number of symbolic figures and inscription tablets here describe the King's role as God's representative on earth, an elevated and selected ruler with special rights and duties. The fittings of the Chapel are lavish, both in terms of the materials used and as regards their execution. Luther's recommendation of a simple style of church had to yield to Christian IV's desire for royal lustre.

Frederiksborg's ballroom housed among other items a series of tapestries showing Christian IV's coronation and his victories in the Kalmar War. The ceiling had representations of artes mecanicae (crafts), figures of the virtues and pictures of birds and animals. Here it is the King's participation in active pursuits, and his role as a victorious politician, that is shown to provide an appropriate context for celebrations with homage to the King as the focus. The King's strength is the guarantee of the kingdom's future; the crafts of both war and peace are secured by him.

In the Audience House (the interior of which was destroyed by fire in 1665), it was again, as in the Marble Gallery, the gods of the planets which formed the main decorative theme. Christian IV, as the agent of power, interpreted the orbits of destiny, as the planets reflected, according to the beliefs of the time. By using them as an ornamental *motif* he showed his will to rule in harmony with the divine order.

In Frederiksborg Castle we can thus see presented the whole royal scheme, the many roles of the sovereign, his elevated position and his political and religious responsibilities. Splendour in materials and construction provide at the same time a worthy setting for the King and his ceremonial image.

## Rosenborg

*Colour-plate XIX*

Rosenborg was constructed outside the walls of Copenhagen, as a country house in the garden which Christian IV had had laid out in 1606. Not until after the expansion of Copenhagen from 1627 onwards did Rosenborg and the Kongens Have (King's Garden) become part of the city. The original house was enlarged several times, and was only completed in 1634. In 1624 it was for the first time named "Rosenborg" by Christian IV.

The Castle is a single structure, long in relation to its shallow depth, and three storeys high, with bays and towers with storeyed spires. Both the ground-plan and the materials (red brick with sandstone decoration) link

*Kronborg seen from the east.*

Rosenborg to the manor-house architecture from the end of the 16th century and to Frederik II's Badstue at Frederiksborg Castle. The country house has here expanded to full size, ending up as a castle, stately enough for ceremonial purposes.

The location in the garden, on a miniature bastion with drawbridges, emphasizes the slight character of the castle, which still carries the stamp of a summer-house. Christian IV's arrangements of pipes which permitted music to be heard from unseen orchestras, and drawbridges which could be raised and lowered apparently without human intervention, underline the playful element of the house. The fragmented outer contours of the architecture, together with the closely-juxtaposed silhouettes of the spires, give the castle a make-believe effect which is not unreminiscent of the fairy-tale castles which the artist Inigo Jones drew as scenery for the English court masques. Queen Anne of England was Christian IV's sister, and there were close connections between Denmark and England; Christian IV visited England in 1606 and 1614.

Rosenborg, like a painted stage-set, is best seen from selected view-points, opposite the gables or the entrance facade. On the gable-ends the square form of the towers is repeated in the bays, and even the volute-patterned gable rears up ambitiously like the spires. Seen from the gable-end Rosenborg consists of three building-elements, which complement each other; the substantial forms of the towers give solidity to the high, slender gable. The picture of Christian IV on horseback in front of Rosenborg actually shows the castle gable, chosen as the most charming part. The entrance facade comprises the ascending form of the towers, the small, low staircase-turret, the two higher side-towers and, as its culmination, the great west-tower, which rises above the roof and gives depth to the whole composition.

The entrance to Rosenborg is situated in the long axis of the house. The gable-end is what is seen from the gate-house, and from there one is led forward into the entrance in the east facade. The Renaissance accent on the entrance-axis, directly opposite a main entrance in the centre of the long side of the house, is here completely repudiated in favour of a richly visual appreciation of the gables and towers of the building – an architectural conception of the house as a construction with several equally worthy facades. The garden, from where one could see the house from all sides while walking round, and also see its reflections in the waters of the moat, contributes to the building's picturesque effect.

Rosenborg has preserved its interior from the time of Christian IV. The ground floor houses the Vinterstue (Winter-room) with adjoining Skrivestue (Writing-room), set up in 1614-15. The Vinterstue has wood panels from floor to ceiling, with inset Flemish/Dutch paintings. These appear to be chosen for their decorative qualities; together with the wood-work, which has its natural, rather dark colouring, they give the room's walls a coherent character and a subdued but varied colour-scheme. The ceiling was originally plastered: the present painted ceiling is also from Christian IV's time but originally belonged to the room above the Skrivestue. With its violent figures in the foreshortening of perspective it disrupts the calm of the room.

The Skrivestue (Writing-room) is also decorated throughout with paintings, in an apparently haphazard mixture of motives – pastoral scenes, the four elements, portraits of women and of Christian IV's favourite dogs, and grotesques. On the door hangs a picture painted in 1625, depicting Christian IV's vision of the suffering of Christ. Beneath the picture can be seen an explanatory text, written by Christian IV himself. The decoration has throughout a strongly personal imprint; the Vinterstue and the Skrivestue are the King's private rooms, arranged without concern for ceremonial at a time when the castle was still thought of as a country residence.

In 1624 an extra storey was added to Rosenborg, to house a long hall which made the house usable for major social events. The interior was altered at the end of the 17th century, but sources describe a barrel-vaulted ceiling with paintings inset in frames of plaster and wood. The paintings portrayed the living conditions of the time, in series according to the stages of life, the liberal arts, the Roman gods and their influence, and scenes from antiquity and from the Bible. The whole interior can be seen as a royal mirror, a morality tale for the benefit of the young princes. The paintings which still exist seem to have a common object. The decoration of the room takes its inspiration from the major picture-series which were used e.g. in Roman palaces. It was the artists whose study-periods abroad had been financed by Christian IV who here painted under the influence of Italian Mannerism and early Baroque. The use of "trompe l'oeil" perspectives and the execution of a programme of themes from antiquity made this room a novelty in Christian IV's art; the country house was turned into a castle.

*Kronborg. Detail of the east wing.*

## Kronborg

In 1629 Kronborg burned down. For Christian IV it was of the greatest importance for the honour of the kingdom that the castle should be rebuilt. When the Rigsråd (Council) continually procrastinated, he proceeded to raise the Sound toll without their consent and went ahead with the work. Between 1631 and 1642 the rebuilding was achieved.

The exterior of the castle was reproduced largely in its old form, although individual details were changed: the tower was given higher, storeyed spires; the big dome on the gun-tower was not replaced; the watchman's gallery facing the castle courtyard was taken down, and a number of attic gables were broadened and raised.

The decorations, including those on the attic gables and the Chapel gable, were now given the strong, sweeping "Ohrmuschel"-style forms, but many sections were reconstructed using the original pattern as model. The exterior, even after rebuilding, was Frederik II's castle.

The interior was renovated in Christian IV's style, including the still-preserved ceiling paintings in the King's and Queen's apartments. In the Queen's Chamber can be seen the gods of the planets, painted by Morten Steenwinckel in Italian-influenced style; in the King's Chamber there is a series of paintings with motives from an ancient romance – Heliodurus's account of the love-story of an Ethiopian princess. This romance had been re-edited and was very popular at the time in Europe. The pictures, which Christian IV purchased in Holland, were the work of Gerrit van Honthorst, who also contributed to Christian IV's major undertaking of a pictorial series illustrating the history of Denmark.

The Danish history series was to be produced partly as paintings for Kronborg and partly as copper-plate engravings to be published in book form with a Latin text. The pictures were commissioned in Holland, and some of them were delivered, including several paintings by Honthorst (certain of them now at Kronborg, others in Sweden). The project was never completed, however. It was the honour of the country in Europe that Christian IV was trying to uphold by these means, both when he insisted on the rebuilding of Kronborg, the historic monument representing the Danish king greeting the ships on Øresund, and when he planned the publication of the history of Denmark. Denmark should be recognized internationally as a nation whose history could rival that of ancient Rome or of the Jewish people: an old but nonetheless vigorous realm.

## The social setting: churches and towns

The upholding of the honour of the realm, the process of making the sovereign's power visible through splendid surroundings and celebrations, was only one aspect of the King's duties. Another was the responsibility for the external relations and internal conditions of the country – a responsibility which in the 17th century fell to a growing extent on the King alone.

In Denmark the Lutheran Reformation took place in 1536. As a consequence the King became the head of the Church, the maker of Church laws, and was responsible for their observance. Spiritual content was determined by theologians, but the King's right to make appointments also gave him opportunities to direct the inner life of the Church. A strong theologian could, through the King, steer the Church and maintain it on a certain course. This happened under Christian IV when Hans Poulsen Resen built up a strongly Lutheran-orthodox Danish Church.

The actual words of the Bible, and belief in them as the revelation of the truth, became the foundation of the Church. All discussion and interpretation was rejected as heresy. The humanist colouring which the Church had taken on under Frederik II was wiped out, and a tightening of all Church affairs was the consequence.

The intention was to keep all the kingdom's inhabitants within the one faith – to collect them under an authority which according to Lutheran ideals required absolute obedience to the ruler appointed by God, i.e. the King. The many outbreaks of civil strife and disputes on religious grounds which Europe had witnessed in the 16th and 17th centuries (e.g. in France (the St. Bartholomew's Day massacre) and in the Netherlands) were awesome warnings of the danger of allowing Church unity to slacken. The danger came not simply from the Catholic desire to reconquer lost ground. To Christian IV it seemed that the different Calvinist tendencies presented the worst threat, *inter alia* because they increased the right of the people to appoint and dispose of authority. It became of the greatest importance to maintain Denmark in the pure Lutheran faith. The Church thus stiffened in the 17th century into an orthodoxy rigid with fear of new thoughts.

The physical setting for religious services naturally bore the marks of the theological content. Church-building after 1536 had been scarce. As yet no progress towards a Protestant architectural form had been made, but the focus instead was on redecoration of the old churches.

Under Christian IV, in connection with the construction of new towns and areas of towns, many new churches were built and others extended. These churches are very diverse, in plans, facades and interiors, but they have certain common features: they are large, vaulted and light, with large windows. Many of the church-plans show a tendency towards central construction. By the addition of large transepts the plans for Holmens Church and Skt. Petri Church approach the shape of a Greek cross; the church in Christianstad has short, broad transepts which open up the space in the cross-axis, and the never-completed St. Anna Rotunda had a central, 12-sided, plan.

The desire for an open, unified, space is a fundamentally Protestant concept. The first reformers rejected the sanctity of the churches and wanted a meeting-place for a congregation where all would be equal members. The function of the priest was that of teacher, and each individual was responsible for his own relationship with God. A central area, where the congregation could form a circle around the priest, where church ceremonies such as christenings and communions could take place in the centre, visible to all, became the ideal for a Protestant congregation. Many churches were built in the Protestant countries of Northern Europe, with different shapes, but with a central space as a common ideal. Particularly in Holland, where this central space was much used, the Calvinist service was built up around the Word, preaching, while communion lost its significance and was no longer seen as a holy ritual. The chancel then became superfluous, and the unity of space could be carried through. Dutch church interiors are light, and the prohibition of images persists; there are only sparing, symbolic decorations.

By means of the close artistic connections between Holland and Denmark under Frederik II and Christian IV the Dutch church-pattern came to be an inspiration for Danish churches.

The central area and the light-filled interior could be adopted directly, but the orthodox-Lutheran service demanded a different organisation of space. The pulput and altar are central elements of equal importance. This is emphasized by dividing the interior of the church into a preaching area and a communion area. In Holmens Church the pulpit is placed so that three of the transepts can be seen from it. This forms an area for preaching, while the fourth is arranged like a chancel, and only used for confession and communion, separated from the rest of the church by a screen. In the Trefoldighedskirke (Trinity Church) in Kristianstad the chancel is separated off by the placing of the pulpit in front of the chancel arch, in the main axis of the church. This arrangement was explicitly requested by Christian IV.

Because of this division of the space the chancel once more takes on the character of a sanctum, a segreated area, to which the congregation only had access on special occasions. It is orthodoxy's demand for respect of the rituals which here finds physical expression. The mystic side of Christianity once again becomes central. The role of the clergy again becomes holy, and at the same time the pastor became the servant of the King, with a duty to keep watch on the citizens' conduct of their lives. Ungodliness was punished; not only in the case of individual citizens, but also in that of the nation as a whole, stricken by God's retribution in the unfortunate years after 1625. Only stronger church discipline, penance and contrition, extra prayer-days and diligent church-attendance could placate God.

The King was the supreme leader of the Church and people, responsible for the state of the kingdom. Through church-discipline the piety of the people could be made visible; through church-building it could be demonstrated that the kingdom belonged to God. Churches were therefore constructed in larger and larger forms and sited as focal-points in the landscape. The culmination was the plan for St. Anna Rotunda. This church, whose diameter was over 60m., a huge wall-cylinder set on the outskirts of the new section of Copenhagen, was intended to be seen from a great distance, showing that this city was dedicated to God. The piety which should appease the wrath causing God to punish the country should be measured in self-sacrifice. In spite of the difficult times large amounts were donated to church building.

The plea which is made to God from the walls of the Round Tower (Rundetårn) is not a prayer for Christian IV personally, but a prayer whose fulfilment would secure the welfare of the whole kingdom: the true learning (doctrine) and the sword, which proctected the learning, are the basic prerequisites for creating and maintaining a happy and prosperous society.

Church and state, ruler and God, in Christian IV's time were indissolubly bound together. The congregation, gathered in the church, were all members of society; no-one could stand wholly outside society. The physical arrangement of the church, mirroring society, followed a ranking system where everyone had his fixed place, depending on occupation and fortune. The solidarity among the congregation hoped for by the fathers of the Reformation now dissolved into a multitude of closed pews and balconies. Wealthy citizens showed their position by gifts to the church; inscriptions and personal marks ensured eternal appreciation of the donor, and sepulchral tablets with portraits and memorial inscriptions were put up in large numbers, "In God's honour, for the adornment of the church, and in eternal remembrance of the giver". Church furnishings increased during Christian IV's time. The plain church-style which had been the ideal at the end of the 16th century was replaced by an increasingly elaborate decoration, in which narrative pictures again came to the forefront. According to orthodox thinking, this ornamentation, which developed particularly in the town churches, was a direct consequence of God's recognition of society, and at the same time the citizens, by adorning the House of God, were showing that they acknowledged Him and His power, and thus the whole structure of their society. The impressive House of God sealed the pact between God and the congregation.

The rigidly structured society, split into social layers and fixed under a single authority, represented by pastor, king and God, had to be kept secure. That was the expression of the Word of God. God had created society, as he had created the Universe and the order of the world. He was the greatest of all master-builders. The Bible moreover relates how God also gave the ground-rules of architecture to man: Noah's Ark was built according to his directions, the Temple in Jerusalem was created as a result of divine inspiration, and the New Jerusalem is an image of the ideal city.

The Christian God could thus be a model for the generation of architects who, marked by the strong religious qualities of the century of the Reformation, rejected the heathen architecture of antiquity as an artistic departure-point. Instead of adopting the neo-Platonistic ideal of beauty of the Italian Renaissance, it became architecture's task to interpret the guiding principles of the Christian world-picture.

The new architectural vision characterizes the Trintiy complex in Copenhagen. In these buildings, the Trinitatis kirke (Trinity Church), the Universitetsbibliotek (University Library) and Rundetårn (Round Tower), the order of the world was revealed through theology, research and astronomy. The architecture drew on medieval, Gothic and Romansque forms; without imitating any particular period, by incorporating older religious architectural elements it linked the construction to the traditions of learning and to the concept of God as the guiding principle, in architecture as elsewhere. The Round Tower, with its "snail-track" ramp, is a reinterpretation of the Tower of Wisdom, linked to the Tower of Babel, but now given a Christian context through its connection to the Church. The highest wisdom is reached by understanding of God's world-principle. It is this that in the "crowned heart" of Christian IV should govern his royal deeds and create in the Kingdom of Denmark an ideal state, a mirror of God himself.

The great divine order should permeate all elements of the kingdom. Orthodox Christendom strove to arrange life in society as if it were a great divine service, in which all worked at God's bidding. The frameworks of this society had to mirror the principle of order. It was in fact this ideal city that Christian IV was creating.

The many newly-created towns were elements in Christian IV's great work: to make the Danish kingdom into a model state. The building of towns was part of the creation of status for the Renaissance prince. The 15th century Italian architectural tracts had set out the basic types, the central structure with outward-radiating streets, or a square network. These town-plans were elaborated during the 16th century and reached Christian IV through the work in Germany and the Netherlands. In Christian IV's plans the functional aspects are important; fortification- and trading-possibilities were decisive in the placing of the towns, and the ultimate goal was to create towns whose ideal plans and functions created a setting for a correspondingly ideal life for their citizens.

The pastor in Kristianstad, P. J. Medelfar, compared the town to the Biblical town of Capernaum, and wrote that "it could be said of the authorities and the ordinary secular and ecclesiastical citizens in the same Kristianstad that each one was respected and honoured, so that there was a peaceful and desirable interchange among those of all stations found therein".

A church, a school and a vicarage were built, so that the inhabitants "should have grateful hearts towards God and the authorities", so it could be said of the town, as of Capernaum, "that it was the city of Christ and the Lord lived therein".

A series of ideal towns of this type were to be placed as strong and prosperous centres in different regions, representing the King's power and his efforts to create progress in his domains. That the towns were not seen merely as practical elements in contemporary trade and defence can be seen from their size – for instance the extension of Copenhagen and Christianshavn included areas, which were not built up until several hundred years had elapsed. This was an ideal vision, a picture of the future of the country in which the fully expanded towns would make the kingdom of Denmark into a divine state, where the inhabitants would live by God's order and thus create a firm foundation for a happily flourishing society.

## Trinity Church and the Round Tower (Copenhagen)

*Colour-plate XXXIX*

Christian IV ordered the construction of a three-part building complex for the use of the sciences: an observatory (the Round Tower), a church, and, at the top of the church building, a library, which until 1861 functioned as the University Library, and thus as a centre of learning for all Denmark. The whole complex was intended for the use of the University solely, so the church congregation consisted only of academics. Later on, however, the population of the Nyboder quarter was incorporated into the parish area, as the building of St. Anna Rotunda was abandoned. The original plan was to create a temple of wisdom where observations and the study of sources would complement each other and so show man's way to the understanding of the Universe, of the divine system itself. The unity of the whole complex was important. The astronomer, Longomontanus, proposed placing the observatory outside the town, to secure better conditions for viewing, but this was rejected by the King. In 1637 the foundation stone was laid, and the Round Tower was inaugurated in 1642; Trinity Church was consecrated in 1656. Trinity Church has a 3-sided chancel and is divided into 3 naves of equal height, separated by sturdy octagonal columns of the Tuscan order.

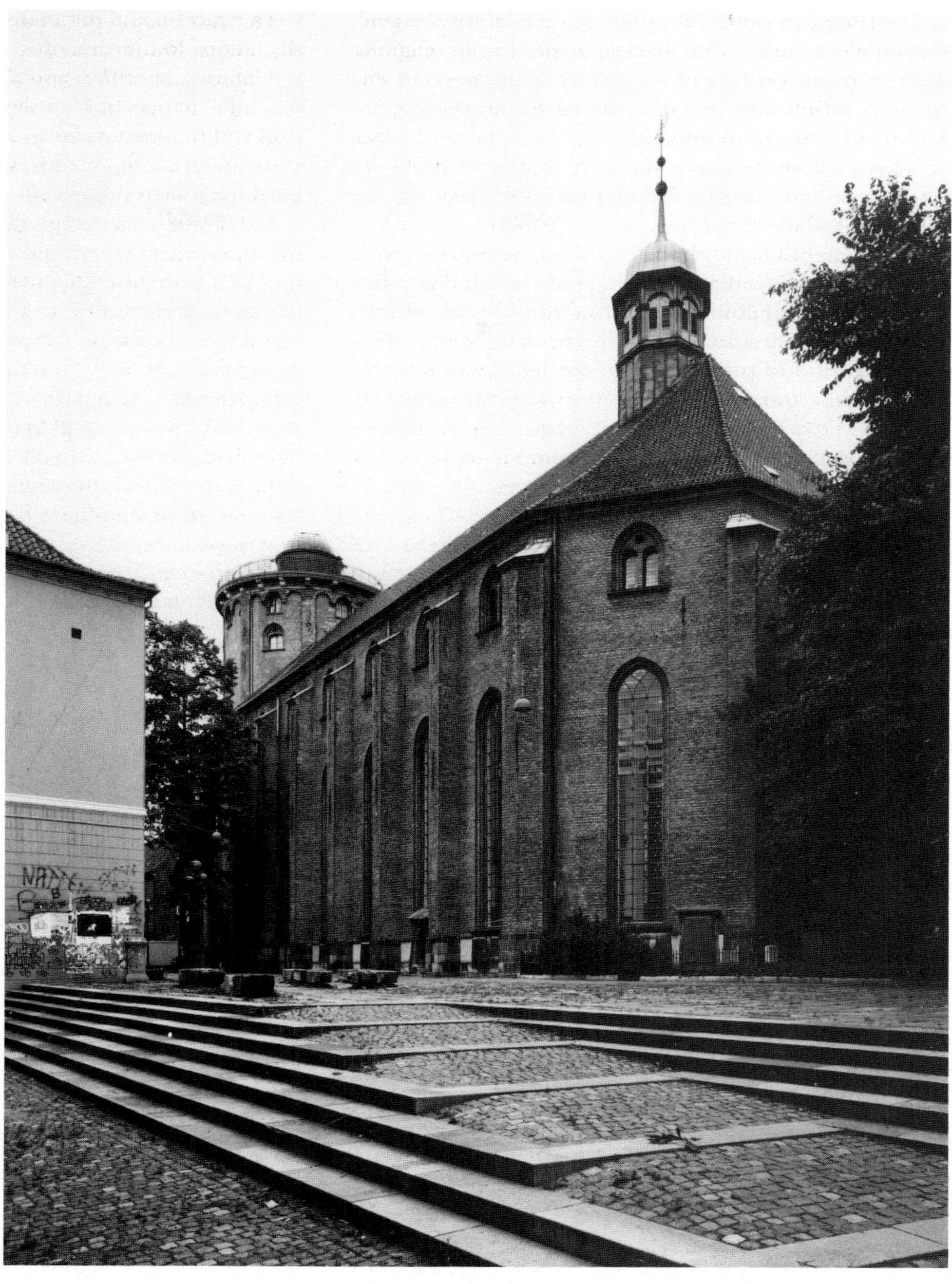


*Trinity Church and the Round Tower, Copenhagen.*

All three naves have star-vaulting. The columns divide the church into 7 sections; each has, on the outer walls, a tall, slim, pointed window. On the outside the division is marked with a number of buttresses which rise up to meet the walls between the originally square windows of the library above the church. The church bells hang on a ridge turret; the Round Tower was never meant to function as a church tower.

Many of these features are reminiscent of the late Gothic Danish church – the plan, the shapes of the windows and vaults – but the large and simple forms of architecture, and the consistent use of the holy number 7 are references to older sources: the earliest religious art, Solomon's Temple. The undecorated exterior and the light interior with the strong lines are images of the theology which Christian IV wanted to promote at the University: simple and strong.

Where a Gothic church would have had its tower we find the Round Tower: a cylinder with a flat roof, on the outside divided up by pilaster strips with a frieze of rounded arches at the top. This Romanesque design is united with the Gothic in the style of the windows: two tall, rounded windows combined within a pointed-arch frame with a circular oculus in the tympanum. This shape of window is known from contemporary descriptions of the Tower of Babel; the newel in the centre of the tower and the stepless "snail" ramp can be seen in depictions of the Tower of Wisdom. On the outer wall of the tower is a rebus designed by Christian IV himself. The meaning can be transcribed as follows: "The true faith (doctrinam) and justice (the sword) direct, O Lord, through the heart of the crowned Christian IV, 1642.

The Round Tower can be interpreted as a symbol of the renewed pact between God and Man. Wisdom had again reached the same heights as in the days of antiquity, but now without hubris. Here God is maintained as the basis for all research. Even the very form of the tower alludes to God himself. H. A. Greyss quotes on his engraving of the tower from 1646 the Book of Proverbs, 18, 10. "The name of the Lord is a strong tower: the righteous runneth into it, and it is safe". Here strength, wisdom and earnestness are united in the service of God and Christian IV.

## Holmens Church, Copenhagen

The building which became the nucleus of Holmens Church was originally a forge, associated with the shipbuilding at Holmen, the Royal Dockyard, built in 1562-63, under Frederik II. The gable of the forge, facing Copenhagen Castle, was given decorations in Italian Renaissance style, following models designed by Serlio. In 1619 the forge-building was extended and transformed into a church, but it was not until 1641-43 that the church was heightened and had two transepts added. In this way the final ground-plan of the church took on the approximate shape of a Greek cross, but it remained irregular because of the different phases of expansion. At the intersection of the arms of the cross a ridge turret was erected.

On the church's three new gables Christian IV used variations of his father's gable, adapting its pure high-Renaissance form to the heavier proportions of Mannerism and to its more sweeping lines.

The interior of the church had shallow barrel-vaulting, originally decorated with stucco-work, including, at the intersection of the cross, the coat of arms, and in the transepts Christian IV's signature, clusters of fruit and angels with musical instruments. Only a few panels from Christian IV's time, with allegorical figures of the virtues, have been preserved until today.

The church has many tall windows, with low arches like the earlier ones in the chancel gable. As in all Christian IV's churches, the interior was light. Later building-additions and restorations have altered the light-conditions; the windows in the chancel's three walls have partly been walled-over, so that it is only lit from one side-wall. Already in Christian IV's time balconies and closed pews had been installed in the church. They reduced the light in the three transepts for the congregation, but the light in the fourth, the chancel, could still stream in. This lighting effect emphasized the orthodox-Lutheran idea that the chancel should be a holy, segregated place, bathed in the clear light of the faith.

The whole of the west transept was arranged as the chancel, separated from the rest of the church by a screen, while the remaining three sections functioned as the preaching-church.

This was, in the Danish context, a new type of church which Christian IV here caused to shape: the central church, modest as to exterior, without tower or spire, and divided up functionally in a new consecration of the church space.

The interior houses many sepulchral tablets, partly from Christian IV's time; this was a typical tendency in the development of town churches in the 17th century. The altar-piece and pulpit are lavishly-carved works, made by Abel Schrøder in 1661-62. These works, although produced after Christian IV's period, are a result of the development of the church under Christian IV as a worthy setting for church services; the use of the dramatic pictorial narrative is a product of orthodox Lutheranism.

## Sankt Anna Rotunda, Copenhagen

As early as 1625 Christian IV planned to build a church in connection with the expansion of Copenhagen, for the use of the sailors in the Nyboder quarter of town. The work was not begun until 1640, and stopped again in 1643. The church was never completed. What had been erected was torn down in the 1660s. The church was situated on a bastion in the outskirts of town, just like the church in Kristianstad. From documents and excavations the plan of the church is known. It was 12-sided, 200ft. in diameter, with 24 external buttresses.

There were 22 tall windows in 11 of the 12 sides. On the last side there was a smaller abutting building.

There were 48 internal columns, arranged in 3 concentric circles, 24 in the outer ring and 12 in each of the inner ones. It was probably the intention to cover the area with a vaulted ceiling, and a contemporary source mentions an amphitheatrical arrangement of the room.

The single, central space typical of Lutheranism is here interpreted by Christian IV in a plan which was also used by those reformed congregations which he so deeply feared – e.g. the church in Willemstad, 1596, and the church in Hanau, 1622. The St. Anna Rotunda, however, was decisively set apart from both of those by its scale and also by its extravagant ground-plan. In its grandeur the church is reminiscent of the Roman Pantheon, which when it was in use as a church was called S. Maria Rotunda. St. Anna Rotunda even surpassed the Pantheon's diameter of 43 m. It was a church which was meant to bear out Christian IV's desired position as the champion of Lutheranism in Northern Europe, the victor over both Catholicism and Calvinism.

## Roskilde Cathedral

After the Reformation the diocese of Sealand was moved to Copenhagen, where Vor Frue Church (Our Lady's Church) acquired the status of principal church in Denmark. The cathedral in Roskilde, which had formed the centre of a rich diocese, now became an ordinary town church, and it did not become a cathedral again until 1922, as a result of the partitioning of the Sealand diocese.

The first king of the House of Oldenborg, Christian I, had donated and built a chapel in 1459 to the honour of the Three Magi. The chapel is built on the south side of the church, with a square ground-plan, and is in two storeys over a crypt. Christian I and his Queen were interred in the crypt. Above it is the actual chapel – a room with 4 vaults carried by a central column, originally with 2 relatively big windows with pointed arches in each of the 3 outer walls. On the top floor was a hall for the Order of Knights which Christian I had founded. Two arcades connect the chapel with the side-nave of the cathedral. The chapel's external facade is decorated with patterned masonry and a two-part gable with recesses and pinnacles.

Frederik II chose this chapel as burial-place for his father, Christian III. The House of Oldenborg did not have a particular burial-church; King Hans and Christian II were buried in Odense, Frederik I in Slesvig, and Christian III was originally buried in Odense. Inspired by the eager attempts of the nobility to convert the village churches (which after the Reformation had become the property of the nobility) into family mausoleums, Frederik II had his father's body moved to Roskilde, and ordered a splendid monument from Cornelis Floris in Antwerp. This was installed in the Chapel of the Three Magi in 1576, the same year that Frederik II forbade the erection by the nobility of free-standing burial-monuments. The royal house should raise itself above the nobility, and by choosing Roskilde Cathedral as a burial-church the House of Oldenborg achieved royal standing. This underlined the family's connection back to the Middle Ages, and by linking Christian I to Christian III the break in the succession around Christian II was under-played. Frederik II had created a beautiful starting-point for a grave-cult around the strong dynasty of the House of Oldenborg.

Christian IV's regency government continued this line with a burial-monument for Frederik II, made in 1594-98, also installed in the Chapel of the Three Magi. After this there was no futher room for royal graves in the chapel, and therefore Christian IV chose to construct a new chapel for himself. His Queen, Anne Cathrine, had died in 1612, and in 1614 the erection of a chapel on the north side of the church was begun.

The ground-plan of the chapel is clearly inspired by Christian I's chapel. It is a square room with a vaulted ceiling, here consisting of a big star-vault, and with windows with pointed arches in the 3 outer walls. Two arcades connect the chapel with the side-nave, where wrought-iron screens made by Caspar Fincke are situated. Beneath the chapel is the actual tomb.

The exterior of the chapel, like that of Christian I, has a decorated gable. Christian IV's chapel has only one storey, and the triangular shape of the gable is a unity, not in two parts like that of Christian I. The decoration of the actual gable, columns and niches is similar to that of Christian I's chapel. The same alternation between convex and concave shapes is evident. The emphasis on the vertical lines of the pinnacles on the gable of Christian I's chapel has a parallel in the free-standing figures on Christian IV's gable, just as the Gothic, patterned masonry with black-glazed bricks corresponds with the sandstone bands on Christian IV's chapel. The facade of Christian IV's chapel has a Mannerist decoration with columns on sturdy consoles and figures and frontons above the windows. The chapel revives Gothic forms; the line back to the beginning of the dynasty is emphasized, but at the same time completely contemporary decorative elements are incorporated: once again Christian IV has created a totally personal expression, a style which is both national and international.

In its interior the chapel was whitewashed, with the star-vaulting as the only decoration. It was meant to

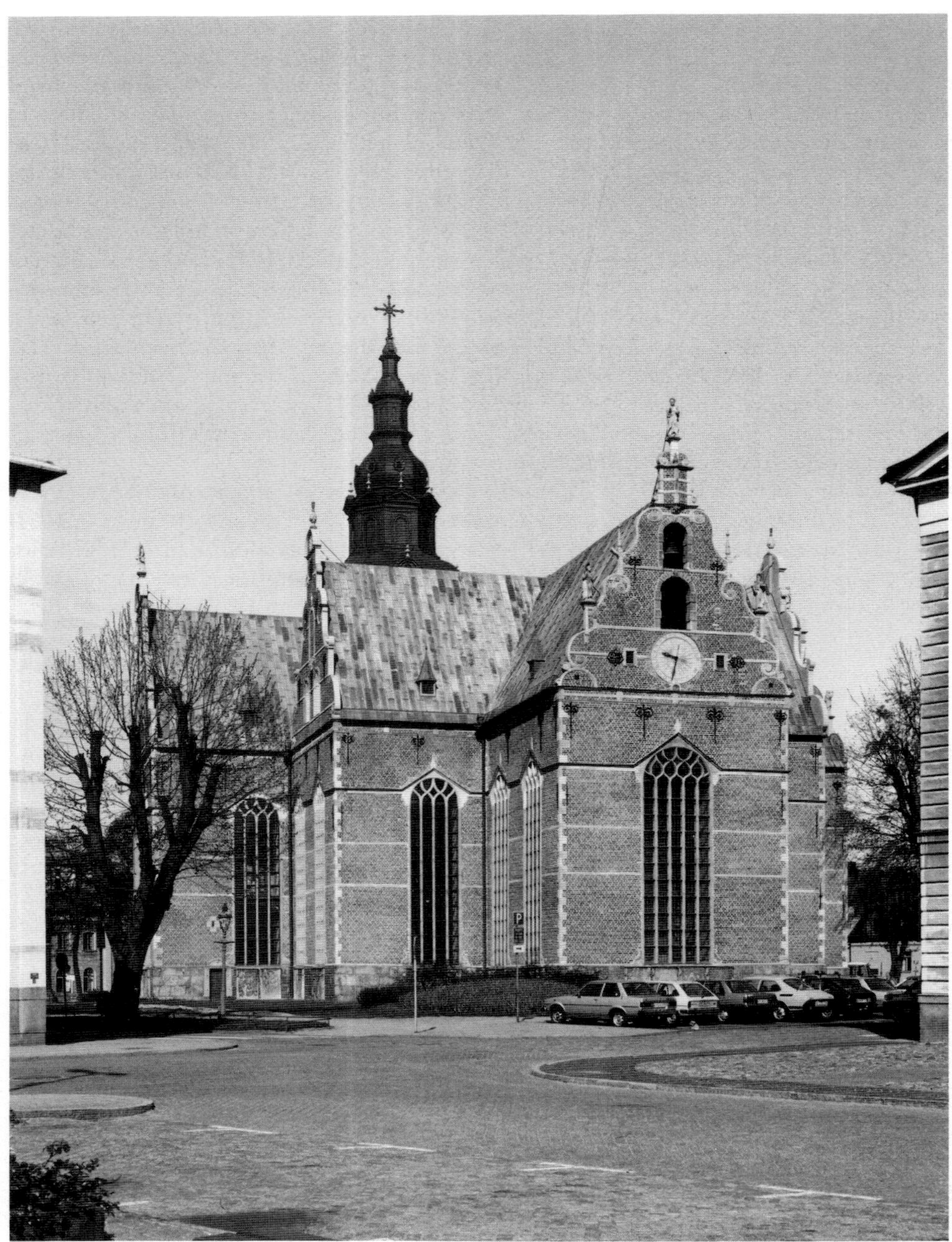

*Trinity Church, Kristianstad.*

house the grave-monument of Christian IV, but this was never installed. It was probably destroyed in a fire. Instead, today the coffins of Christian IV and his offspring stand lined up in the chapel, in strong contrast to the habits of the 17th century, according to which the coffins would have been placed in tombs.

The decoration of the chapel which was carried out in about 1850 altered the whole of its interior. The windows in the side walls, for instance, were walled up, so that the area became darker. The simple light-filled room, visible from the cathedral through the wrought-iron screen, would have been a fine framework for the memorial to Christian IV – a parallel to his other church interiors.

Christian IV equipped the cathedral with some of its furnishings; the pulpit was set up in about 1610, and opposite it, raised to the height of the gallery, an enclosed seat for the King was installed.

In 1635-36 Christian IV erected the 2 high spires on the west tower of the cathedral. The departure-point again was Gothic form, as in e.g. the spire on Vor Frue Church in Copenhagen. While the Gothic spire tapers gradually, Christian IV allowed the spires on Roskilde Cathedral to reveal the style of a later time; the flattened transition from tower to spire gives a daringly sweeping line, and the spire acquire a more slender but more dynamic profile than that of the Gothic spire.

A new west doorway, in triumphal arch style, with free-standing columns, was constructed at the same time (but moved to Holmens Church in Copenhagen in 1872). The whole of the cathedral's exterior appearance was thus improved and brought into harmony with the cathedral's new function as the burial-church of the royal house.

## The Trefoldighedskirke (Trinity Church), Kristianstad

A church was built in the newly founded town of Christianstad in Skåne. Work began on the building in 1617, and it was consecrated in 1628. It was placed in the outskirts of the town, on a bastion, close to one of the main squares of the town. The church is not placed according to the grid-pattern of the town-plan. Following medieval tradition it is oriented with the chancel to the east. It is thus at an angle to the square in front of it. Here the Nordic concept of architecture clashes with the ideal town plans of the Italian Renaissance, where all buildings followed the axis system.

Its situation makes the church the distinctive landmark of the town. It rose as an enormous building-mass above the low houses of the town. It is alone among Christian IV's town-churches in having a tower, which in the 17th century only had a low pyramid-shaped roof. It is not the tower but the building itself which catches the eye.

The church is seen at an angle from the streets of the town; it therefore does not have only one main facade, but is richly decorated on all sides. The ground-plan shows a long building with two short, broad transepts, with the tower in the west and the chancel in the east.

*Interior of Trinity Church, Kristianstad.*

The longitudinal axis is contradicted by the facades; each transept has a decorated volute gable flanked by two false gables in the length of the main building. This gives the impression of three parallel transepts. Portals in the west tower, as well as in the north and south gables, underline the impression of a central plan.

Internally, however, the longitudinal axis is stressed. 10 slender columns divide the church into three equally tall naves, all with star-vaulting. Since the nave is divided up into 6 sections, the columns are placed in the cross-axis, i.e. the axis through the transepts. Furthermore, there are two columns in the middle of the opening of the transepts towards the church. This eliminates any impression of unity of space in the cross-axis. The balconies in the transepts also underline the length of the building. The columns are so thin that the three naves are seen as one single space, directed towards the chancel. The original situation of the pulpit in the centre of the triumphal arch underlined the unity of the interior; all attention focused on the same point.

The plan of the church, its interior arrangement, the unity of the room and its light interior are inspired by Dutch churches. Among others Hendrich de Keyser had built such types, also with towers. Only the chancel reveals that the church is Lutheran, and the separation of chancel and congregation-area shows that orthodox theology lies behind the plan.

The interior of the church is simple: whitewashed and with pulpit and altar-piece restrained to black and white and designed in late Renaissance forms. The exterior is richly decorated with portals in early "Ohrmuschel" style and gables with volutes, scrolls and symbolic figures. Christian IV's monogram is incorporated into the decoration, together with the national coat of arms, figures of virtues, Christ, evangelists and apostles.

The contrast between exterior and interior, and that between the longitudinal plan and the stress given by the elevation to the cross-orientation, reflect the transitional phase of Danish art between Renaissance/Mannerism and early Baroque, but the church at the same time shows how Gothic features and Nordic characteristics influence both the totality and the detail.

## The Architecture as a speculum regale

Christian IV's life-long building activity, his endeavours to enhance, arrange and regulate both his close surroundings and the defence and trading situation of the realm can be seen as an attempt to assert the power of the monarch, but it was also done for the glory of God. As an active protagonist in the service of Christ, the King became a knight of Christ, a hero like those of antiquity, and one of the great figures of religion, seen in so many places in Christian IV's own architecture. His intervention in the Thirty Years' War can also be seen as a fight for the cause of religion. The equestrian portrait of the King which Karel van Mander painted in 1643 can be seen as a Protestant answer to Titian's representation of Charles V in the Battle of Mühlberg, where, as the warrior of Christ, he won victory for the Catholics. Christian IV was still meeting Renaissance expectations of the monarch, of courage and strength, of an active life in the service of the people.

The sinister austerity of religion, orthodoxy's demand for total submission, forms in Christian IV's time a strange contrast to the pomp and festivity of court life. The King's image of himself contained both humility, as in the painting of Christian IV placing his regalia in front of Christ, made for the prayer-chamber at Frederiksborg Castle, and the pride which is shown in the portraits. The architecture reflects the duality; in the splendour of the castles, in the arrangement of Roskilde Cathedral as the monument of the House of Oldenborg, in his endeavours to embellish Copenhagen, it is the splendid picture of the ruler that we are shown. In the churches and towns it is the picture of the King as intermediary for divine power, as servant for a higher cause, that is made evident.

A similar duality can be seen in the style of the architecture. The castles, the Stock Exchange, the chapel at Roskilde Cathedral, are richly decorated using the form-language of international Mannerism, while the Trinity complex and St. Anna Rotunda were built in a servere ascetic style, using simple forms and details inspired by older architecture, an "antique" style. To this can be added a functional architecture, e.g. the armoury complex, the Brewery House and the Nyboder quarter, where plans and facades are simple, but carried out with a sense of quality which gives the architecture its impressive nature.

The features which more recent times have seen as characteristic of the architecture of the Christian IV period are linked to the prestige architecture: the towers with storeyed spires, the volute gables, the red brick with sandstone decorations. An understanding of the wide compass of the royal architecture must also include other aspects. The idealism and severity are just as characteristic parts of Christian IV's architecture as the splendid and elaborate features.

Christian IV was a personality of the Renaissance: strong and many-faceted. The architecture shows the same qualities. Composed from juxtaposition of many sources of inspiration, it nevertheless is independent and personal, based on the King's own taste, and interpreting the national and religious views of the King and of his time. The architecture was meant to create the framework for the ideal state which the good monarch, Christian IV, God's representative, was to institute on earth.

*Mette Smed*

## Cities and fortresses

When Christian IV came to the throne in 1588, Denmark, with her more than 82 towns was the most urbanized country in Scandinavia. Most of the towns, however, were small and engaged in local trade only. The King, who like most of his contemporaries held that trade and navigation were the high road to prosperity, wanted an expansive trade policy. This conception is generally known as the Mercantile System. The mercantilist ideas of Christian IV are the basis of his urban policy.

To the Crown, a buoyant exchange of goods would mean an increase in customs receipts. This had been the case with the Sound Toll, which turned out to be a gold mine for Christian IV. The customs revenue on the shipping of timber from Norway was likewise rising. The possibility of an increasing income from customs dues was a major reason for the foundation of Glückstadt and Kristiansand.

The King's interest in the cities had a military aspect as well. Danish cities were usually open and unfortified, which exposed them to attacks in wartime. This turned out to be the case in two of the wars with Sweden. The Seven Years' War (1563-70) and The Kalmar War (1611-13). Among the towns, those of the border provinces of Halland and Blekinge were most severely exposed to Swedish attacks. Moreover, the conventional military defensive systems were now outdated. The additional fire-power and precision of the guns demanded new defensive strategies, as the high castle walls no longer afforded any protection. Frederik II, the father of Christian IV, had taken action in consequence to convert the medieval castles into fortresses. They were now surrounded by huge protruding ramparts, from the bastions of which an attacking or besieging enemy could be fired at. Kronborg and Varberg rank among the most distinguished examples of such fortresses.

Fortresses of this kind, however, gave no protection to the towns. This problem was solved by the so-called "fortified city", where town and fortress made a continuous whole. The fortified city as an idea originated from theorists of the Italian Renaissance, and it was put to a crucial test in the Dutch revolt against Spain in the years 1577-1608. The Dutch cities were provided with modern fortification and proved very difficult to capture. Christian IV observed this development closely and eventually introduced the fortified city into Denmark.

In Denmark-Norway this resulted in a radical process of change in urban development. "Cities", completely new, such as Christianshavn, Glückstadt, Kristianopel, Kristiansand, Kristianspris and Kristianstad, saw the light. Towns which had been damaged by war were removed to new and more strategic positions. This applied to Varberg, Kungälv and Olso, which on this occasion had its name changed to Kristiania. Other towns were dismantled. In Blekinge, Avaskær, Elleholm, and Lykå disappeared while Scania lost Trelleborg, Væ, and Åhus. All in all, it was a pronounced reorganization of the town structure of Denmark-Norway.

Internally, the towns changed with regard to the layout of the streets. The towns of Denmark and Norway had been founded during the Middle Ages. The streets were narrow and twisted and the squares were small. The towns were largely the result of natural development. They grew very slowly and the street-systems were of a more or less haphazard kind. The new cities were diametrically opposed to this. They were orderly and well planned. Before the city was built, a model of it was made, and the layout was studied carefully be the King, the engineer, and builder in charge. Not until then could the actual work begin. First the street-system was marked out. This project was generally attended by the King in person. After this the construction of the fortification of the city would begin.

The new cities reflected the Renaissance concept of the "ideal city". Its original form was derived from the "perfect", which according to Renaissance theorists could be found only in the pure geometrical forms. The circle was considered to be the most harmonious of the forms, and consequently the "ideal city" would be circular. Its centre would be a big open square in which all the main streets would meet. Anyone who took up a position in this centre could enjoy contemplating the splendid order which would meet his eye in all directions. The central square also served a rallying ground for the soldiers of the city. From this position they could be led to the ramparts fairly quickly along the radial streets. In Italian such a square is called Piazza d'armi, the "Arms" square.

None of the cities founded by Christian IV has the ideal circular shape. Christianshavn and Glückstadt come nearest to the ideal as their original form is the semicircle. The solutions most frequently chosen for the ground-plan were the rectangle and the square. They were chosen for cities such as Kristianstad in Scania and Kristiansand in Norway. Though it is obvious that the plan-arrangements differ, the inner construction nevertheless shows great similarity. The cities were all designed with a love of order and method. The street system is regular, often symmetrical. The streets link up in market squares, the ramparts are symmetrical and harmonious etc.

The original ground-plan of Kristianstad from 1620 is a good example of this. It is a thorough piece of engineering which explains how the city was parcelled out. The major building-lots are placed by the northern city square. It is here the magnificent Holy Trinity Church was built and a space was cleared for "His Royal Majesty's building" which was never built, however. The town hall was also built there. The northern square, in other words, was designed to express the divine order on which society was based with the church as the cornerstone. This principle was also underlined in the construction of the other parts of the city.

New towns had been founded before the time of Christian IV. His father, Frederik II, had founded Frederikstad in Norway in 1567. This task was accomplished in a manner very different from the foundations by Christian IV, as a comparison between Frederikstad and the cities of Christian IV clearly indicates. In the first place, Frederikstad was built at the request of the citizens. Secondly, the town did not have a regulated street system, and thirdly, it was unfortified. Only in the naming of the towns do father and son meet; both had towns called after them. It was the State's power and its desire to control and regulate society which had increased since the times of Frederik II.

Only a strong monarchy could create cities such as those created by Christian IV. It took planning and technical capability, and large sums of money. Accordingly, the pressure of taxation increased excessively under Christian IV.

The new cities were designed by professional engineers, or geometers, as they would call themselves. In the early years of Christian IV's reign the engineers came chiefly from the Netherlands, as the Dutch were the leading military engineers in Northern Europe. From c. 1630, they were increasingly replaced by Danes. In other words, the result of Christian IV's industrious building activity was that a Danish corps of engineers emerged with Axel Urup and Hans Jacobsen Schiørt as the most prominent figures.

The city plans of the geometers were submitted to the King for his approval, and the manuscript sources indicate that the King often raised objections. As a rule, the objections concerned practical problems, but occasionally whole plans were rejected, as in the case of Christianshavn. The criticisms that emerge from Christian IV's letters show him as an expert on fortification work. However, he can hardly be given the credit for having designed the cities himself as asserted by V. Wanscher. The engineers who were called in should be credited with that. But as the final decision was the King's and as he obviously took this problem seriously, Christian IV's influence on the foundation of the cities should not be underestimated. On the contrary, he probably made sure that the cities were as he wanted them.

## The New Cities Under Christian IV

Christian IV ruled Denmark-Norway for sixty years. Throughout his reign new cities were founded. The city foundations can be divided roughly into three periods: 1 (1588-1611), 2 (1613-25), and 3 (1625-1648).

The limits of the first period (1588-1611) are set by Christian IV's accession and the outbreak of the Kalmar War. This period is first and foremost a continuation of the fortification policy of the King's father, Frederik II. The period is remarkable for the foundation in 1599 of Kristianopel in Blekinge, the first fortified city in the North.

The second period (1613-1625) is the foundation period proper. In 1613 Denmark had concluded peace with Sweden and in 1625 Christian IV became engaged in the German War.

The result of the peace of Knærød in 1613 was that Denmark was assigned a million rix dollars, for indemnity. On the whole, the financial situation was exceptionally good in that period and building activity was given a great impetus. Such distinctive cities as Kristianstad, Glückstad, and Christianshavn were all founded in this period. Kristiania, originally a city of no great importance, was founded in 1624.

The third period (1629-1648) is likewise characterized by intense building activity. The period covers the years from the Peace of Lübeck in 1629, which secured Christian IV's emergence from the German War with body and soul intact up to the death of the King in February of 1648. The defense of Jutland was then the main problem after the peninsula had been occupied by imperial troops from 1627-1629. The plans for the new fortresses which have been handed down are less ambitious than earlier projects. This can be explained by the King's difficult financial position in the 1630s and 1640s. The plans to sacrifice the city of Kolding for the sake of a new fortified city on the north side of Kolding Fjord were abandoned, as a project of this size was now beyond the capacity of the State. The most important city foundation of the period is that of Kristiansand in Norway in 1641.

## Kristianopel

Fortified city in Blekinge, founded in 1599. Kristianopel foreshadows many of the new ideas which were later to become characteristic. With the foundation of Kristianopel, Christian IV interfered with the city-structure of Eastern Blekinge in a way which was unheard of for a King. The small towns of Avaskær, Elleholm, and Lykå were dismantled for the benefit of the new fortified city. The citizens were forced to move to Kristianopel if they wanted to keep their citizenship. The new powerful state, created by Christian IV, made such injustices against the local population legal, and Kristianopel was just the first example of this. Many more were to follow. New, too, was the idea of combining fortress and city and the straightened street system, inspired by the "ideal" city.

It is typical of Kristianopel, however, that it did not get much beyond the experimental stage. Making the citizens move to the new city proved to be very difficult. Still in 1606, markets were held in the former towns. Besides, the fortification which was placed round the city was out-of-date even from the start. Finally, the task of carrying through the orderly street system of the ideal city proved to be too difficult. The streets of Kristianopel are crooked and follow the nature of the ground.

## Kristianstad

Fortified city in Scania, founded in 1614. Kristianstad is situated in North-Eastern Scania on the fertile plain by the Helgeå River in the middle of the best agricultural areas of Scania. It caused great dismay when during the Kalmar War, Sweden devastated the plain and burned down the city of Væ. From a military point of view, the area needed to be protected, and instead of rebuilding Væ, it was decided to build a completely new fortified city. This was the beginning of Kristianstad. In 1617, the city of Åhus lost its municipal charter in order that Kristianstad could become the centre of local administration. A canal was built along the Helgeå River which made it possible to sail from the Baltic to Kristianstad. Kristianstad is constructed according to the pure geometrical form of the rectangle. Its principal axis runs betweeen the two city gates which are situated in the shorter sides of the rectangle. The axis crosses the two central market squares. By the northern square the axis is crossed by a canal which drains off the low-lying city. The inspiration is obviously Dutch. The city is surrounded by an almost symmetrical system of ramparts. One of the bastions, however, stands out from the rest by being larger and more flattened. This was in order to make room for the Trinity Church, as the subsoil at this particular spot is well suited to carry the load of a large and monumental building.

## Glückstadt

Fortified city in Holstein, founded in 1617. Glückstadt is situated by the Elbe at about 50 kilometres north-west of Hamburg. Glückstadt is the only city built by Christian IV which does not bear his name. The city was supposed to bring luck; it was the city of good fortune, which was to make a success of Christian IV's North-German policies, the object of which was to control the mouths of the Elbe and the Weser and to install his son Frederik in the office of Bishop of the diocese of Bremen. Glückstadt became the King's naval station by the Elbe. It also became a thorn in the flesh of Hamburg, who felt her free navigation in Elbe waters to be threatened, since Christian IV levied duties at Glückstadt as he did at Kronborg.

In Glückstadt the concept of the ideal city is expressed most pronouncedly. The fundamental form is the halfcircle. The centre of the halfcircle is a huge square, from which the streets extend in radial lines to the fortification, which in itself is rich in new ideas. The bastions extend futher from the ramparts than is customary, and in the moat are so-called "ravelins", which served to protect the entrenchment still futher; and finally there was a town gate. In the 1620s Glückstadt was the most advanced fortified city in Denmark.

## Kristiansand

City on the Norwegian coast overlooking the Skagerrak. Founded in 1641.

Norwegian exportation of timber increased rapidly in the early 17th century. Timber was mainly exported from small towns along the Norwegian side of the Skagerrak. As it was difficult for Christian IV to ensure that the duty, which was legally his, was collected, he wanted the overseas exportation of timber to be centralized in a new city which was to have a monopoly of timber trading. This city was granted a charter in 1641 and received the name of Kristiansand. Kristiansand was built as an open unfortified city. It was defended by the fortress of Christiansø, which was situated by the seaward approach to the city. In 1635 the construction of Christiansø began, the purpose of which was to protect the good natural harbour of the area, which had become a key base for the Danish navy. Kristiansand was designed by the Danish engineer Hans Jakobsen Schiørt. Christian IV had paid for Schiørt's training as an engineer at various European universities in the years 1631-38. Schiørt decided to give Kristiansand a square form with 7 long streets and 10 cross streets. In 1642 the ground-plan was submitted to Christian IV who was "graciously content". With regard to its ground area Kristiansand was the largest of the cities built by Christian IV. When fully developed it could accommodate 15,000-20,000 people. Kristiansand was to be the last of the cities founded by Christian IV.

## Copenhagen, the Metropolis of the Realm.

Copenhagen was the biggest and most important of the cities of Denmark. In 1588, when Christian IV acceded to the Throne, it was already the capital of Denmark. Foreigners, who were travelling in Denmark at the time, speak of the "metropolis of Copenhagen" and give more detailed descriptions of this city than of any other Danish city. The city attracted the attention of Christian IV to such a degree that it still bears his personal stamp. It seems appropriate therefore to single out Copenhagen for special mention.

Initially, it should be stressed that what is generally true of Christian IV's attitude to the cities is still more so where Copenhagen is concerned. The idea that the cities would flourish through trade and bring prosperity to the State is nowhere more obvious than in Copenhagen. In 1613-1625, the "years of prosperity" the King founded trading companies in Copenhagen that were granted monopolies on trading in far away parts of the world. Likewise Copenhagen was chosen when the King decided to establish an industry for preparing the silk which was brought home by the companies. Here Christian IV built the Stock Exhange, which was intended to serve as a meeting place for merchants from all over the world. Finally, the Copenhagen harbour was considerably enlarged by Christian IV.

Elsinore and Kronborg may well be regarded as "outpost" custom houses of Copenhagen. The Sound was the most important thoroughfare of the trade going between Western Europe and the Baltic area. Since the days of Erik of Pomerania, the kings of Denmark had the historic right to collect duty from this traffic. These revenues made the Sound area very important to the Crown, and they were decisive for the King's choice of Copenhagen as the seat of central administration.

Copenhagen also played an important military role. It was the home port of Denmark-Norway's trump card, the navy. Its presence there set power behind the toll collection at Kronborg, and it was the necessary basis for Christian IV's claim for sovereignty of the seas to the North Cape and the important Baltic. In the reign of Christian IV the number of naval ships almost trebled, and Bremerholm, the naval dockyard in Copenhagen, became one of the biggest working units of the city. Christian IV increased the navy's supply-capacity when, in 1598-1610, he constructed the big Navy Arsenal with the still existing Tøjhus (Royal Arsenal Museum). In order to protect the navy, it was necessary to enlarge the land-defences. To this end Christian IV set to work on a extensive modernization plan in 1606. The old city wall was replaced by ramparts and bastions and new and far more sumptuous city gates were added. To protect the city from attacks from the seaward side, Christian IV had defences built on the island of Amager, which had hitherto been unprotected. He thereby created Christianshavn, and this new addition to the city was connected with Copenhagen proper when Knippelsbro was built. These new additions of the city were completed in 1624.

The defences of the city were now considerably improved. However, Christian IV went one step further. To crown the achievement, Copenhagen was to have a citadel i.e. a fortress standing on high ground. This, however, led to plans for a large extension of the city on the north side. The ramparts which had just been completed followed the old borders of the city, and only the construction of Christianshavn had added new land to the area behind the ramparts. With the new plans, however, the scene was set for almost a trebling of the city acreage. The comprehensive and expensive plans met with opposition from the Council of the Realm and work did not begin in earnest until the 1640s. Christian IV did not live to see the extensions finished, but nevertheless the plans were carried out eventually. Copenhagen was thus saved from being locked within her own ramparts, a fate that befell many European capitals in the following century.

From a military and commercial point of view, Copenhagen developed along the lines of the other cities of the country, only the extent of the King's investments was much larger there. After all, Copenhagen was – as stated by foreign visitors – the metropolis of Denmark. There the King spent most of his time and from there laws and decrees were issued which were to be respected in all parts of the kingdom. There the Royal celebrations were held and there the King received foreign princes, ambassadors, bishops etc. Copenhagen had been the scene of Christian IV's coronation in 1596 and was likewise the scene of the Prince Elect's sumptuous wedding in 1634, known as "The Grand Wedding". In other words, Copenhagen was the scene of a variety of representative functions which made great demands in terms of splendour with which a celebration was held or a representative duty carried out which decided whether or not the event was a success. The period had its own term for this, "magnificence".

This attitude set special standards for the buildings and whole appearance of the city. It became essential that Copenhagen should have beautiful and distinguished-looking open spaces for promenading and festivities, and it was also essential that the King should have a stately residence. In 1588 Copenhagen could hardly live up to such modern standards, and the city that Christian IV took over had a somewhat old-fashioned character. For a young Prince of the Renaissance, who was full of enterprise and ambition, there was plenty of work to get down to.

As regards stylish open spaces there was first and foremost the Amagertorv. "Amagertorv is the most beautiful of the city squares and it is everywhere surrounded by beautiful houses", thus wrote the French secretary, Ogier, when in 1634 he accompanied his ambassador to the wedding in Copenhagen. According to an old custom, the King had a right to use the rooms in those of his citizens' houses that overlooked Amagertorv for his guests whenever the square was used for festivities such as tilting at the ring. Also, all houses which overlooked the square were subject to the proviso that they should be of a "good city type of building" which should be kept in good repair. The still-existing building of no. 6 Amagertorv is a good example of the rich architectural style which characterized the facades.

Gammeltorv, the other of the two squares, was quite small. Here, the rather unimpressive town hall was situated. This square was completely renovated by Christian IV. The town hall was rebuilt and given a magnificent new facade, and the square was enlarged by means of adding the still-existing Nytorv. The town hall was adorned with arcades, sandstone mouldings, and sweeping gables with volutes. The old well was removed at the same time and then transformed into a magnificent fountain where golden apples would dance in the water-jets on ceremonious occasions.

The period had a taste for gardens to promenade in. The new Rosenborg Castle, built by Christian IV, was surrounded by such a garden. Here the royal banquets would take place when the nobility was assembled for the "herredage" meetings in Copenhagen, and here the wedding guests were entertained at the "Grand Wedding". Some of the visitors from abroad were accustomed to gardens which were much more elaborately laid out. However, were one to compare the garden of Rosenborg with its predecessor, Frederik II's small garden near Bremerholm, the new garden would seem a great improvement.

The Stock Exchange, opposite Copenhagen Castle, was likewise suitable for promenading. The top floor was built as a long passage, surrounded on both sides by well-stocked stalls, where the latest goods from foreign countries were offered for sale. Ogier, the French secretary, gives the following description: "In the afternoon I walked in a building called the Stock Exchange, which is divided into two long passages. Here everything in the line of finery and millinery for both men and women is for sale. It is a new and magnificent building, where people of distinction go, women as well as men". He himself on one occasion met with Leonora Christine in the promenade of the Exchange. Compared with this, Copenhagen Castle was sadly lacking in dignity. The old overbuilt castle was not replaced by a new and up-to-date palace in Christian IV's days. The King contented himself with having the facade painted in preparation for the wedding festivities. It is likely, however, that plans were made for a new residence in the modern style in connection with the northern extension of the city, but the plans were never realized. Frederiksborg and Rosenborg, and later on the reconstruction of the burnt down Kronborg, probably swallowed up so much money that none was left for at new residence in Copenhagen.

The numerous renovations of the city which were carried out by Christian IV could not hide the fact, however, that the street system of Copenhagen was basically medieval. Amagertorv and Gammeltorv seemed to emerge as small open spaces from a labyrinth of narrow and crooked streets. In Copenhagen there was no basic order to be enjoyed. Amagertorv, after all, was nothing

*The Stock Exchange, Copenhagen.*

but a truncated triangle. The new ideals of harmony and order, however, could be studied at close quarters by crossing the Knippelsbro bridge. The marked-out street system of Christianshavn would then be within sight. This new part of the city was constructed as a semicircle in the same manner as Glückstadt. The centre was a regular square, and a navigable canal made it possible to transport goods fairly quickly. It was the King's desire that the order and regularity which characterized Christianshavn should be extended to the whole city of Copenhagen. The new ideas were also expressed in the plans for an extension of the city to the north. A preserved town plan from 1627 indicates the Kings's intentions. On the north is a huge fortress with three bastions looking like a king's crown. A chain of ramparts and bastions connect the fortress with Copenhagen which can be distinguished faintly on the far south behind the ramparts, built by Christian IV between 1606-1624. In other words, this new plan made a considerable part of the newly-finished and costly fortification of Copenhagen unnecessary. This, however, was no obstacle to the visionary Christian IV.

The new area fitted into a wide circle, the order of which was disturbed by the fortress to the north and Rosenborg to the south. Nevertheless, the plan is impressive. Calculations as to the size of the central square have shown that it was planned to have a diameter of almost 400 meters. This project for an extension of Copenhagen marks a climax in the theory of the ideal city in Denmark. With its imposing dimensions, St. Anna Rotunda, the church which was projected for the new city, was quite in tune with the grandiose town plan. This plan was never fully implemented, but parts of it were realized in the 1630s and the beginning of the 1640s. In this period, Christian IV built the Nyboder quarter in the new part of the city. The angled streets of Nyboder have often astonished the visitor. This is due to the fact that Nyboder was built according to the ideal plan from 1627 in which the streets were supposed to run polygonally. When the plan for the new city was later revised and it was decided to build a check-patterned street system, the result was that the small streets of Nyboder come to look rather odd.

## The Stock Exchange

Situated on the Slotsholmen in Copenhagen. The construction of the Stock Exchange began in 1619. Architects: Laurens Steenwinckel (died in 1619) and Hans Steenwinckel the Younger, Chief Architect to the King.

The Stock Exchange was the most magnificent of the lay buildings from the times of Christian IV. The still-preserved contract with the stone mason from 1619 mentions a "portal", window ornaments with "pediments", architraves and mouldings including "thermae" (i.e. columns with figures) which were to subdivide the facade. More ornaments were added to the building in 1623 when the King decided on attics for the roof, a monumental gable for the west wall, and a central spire where the later-so-famous dragon tails were to wind their way up.

The Stock Exchange was constructed on a plot in the Slotsholmen which had been filled in with earth. The excavation and the laying of the foundation were problematic and the house never had any cellars. The preserved building accounts state that the bricklaying started in 1620. In 1623 work had got as far as the level of the roof. In 1624 the roof was covered with lead and in the same year the west gable, adorned with Neptune, the ruler of the oceans was finished. With the construction of the tower in 1625, the Stock Exchange was practically complete. Minor works, however, were carried out up to about 1640, when the eastern gable was added. After the Torstensson War, it was necessary for Christian IV to pawn the Stock Exchange and this must indeed have been a bitter turn of events for the old King.

From an architectural point of view, posterity has been kind to the Exchange. Laurids de Thura considered it "glorious" though of Gothic proportions. He was especially pleased with the rich ornamentations. Recently, Harald Langberg has described the Stock Exchange as a building of an "unusual integrity" and as "a masterpiece of European standard". He refers to the steady rhythm given to the long facade by the positioning of windows, attic gables and store room doors.

*Lars Bisgaard*

1694

### Christian IV

Attributed to Karel van Mander
Oil on canvas. 223×149 cm
Gripsholm 1727
Repeat of Frederiksborg A 7298 (cat. 193)
*Provenance:* Presumed identical with a painting recued from the fire at Svartsjö 1667. To Gripsholm 1821 from the Royal Swedish Collection of Paintings.
*Literature:* Eller 1971 146 fg.

1695

### Christian IV

Alberg Haelwegh
Engraving. 59×45 cm
Den kgl. Kobberstiksamling
The King on horseback in front of Frederiksborg Castle. A civil version of the large equestrian portrait by Karel van Mander.
*Literature:* Styhr 3.

*The Stock Exchange. Detail of sandstone decoration.*

1696

## Specie 1603

Den kgl. Mønt- og Medaillesamling
On the obverse the enthroned King framed by columns.
*Literature:* Hede 1694 no. 49.

1697

## Stone Relief with the cut Monogram of Christian IV

Sandstone. 41×53 cm
Københavns Bymuseum 1936: 146
*Provenance:* Earth find from Østervoldgade 18-22, Copenhagen.

1698

## Tiles from c. 1605

Black glazed-ware tiles
Københavns Bymuseum, Rbfv. 450
Copy of a tile from an iron stove and fragment of a corner-tile, both of which are decorated with a representation of the young Christian IV. Christian IV had stoves which were adorned with this own portrait set up in all his castles.
*Provenance:* The unbroken tile was found at Koldinghus. The corner tile is an earth find from Copenhagen. Presents from the painter Svend Hammershøj.
*Literature:* Liebgott 1972 33ff.

1699

## Oluf van Steenwinckel (died 1659), Architect

Self-portrait?
Gouache. 15×13 cm
Frederiksborg A 903
Possibly a portrait of the artist held by a female figure. In the foreground the symbols of death: Hourglass, closed books, skull. Christian IV employed several members of the Steenwinckel-family as his architects. 1643-48 Oluf van Steenwinckel was working at Nyborg Castle, and for the Prince Elect at Nykøbing Castle. In 1644 he was active at the fortress of Malmø and in 1646 at the fortress of Nakskov. According to an 18th century inscription a self-portraitt by Steenwinckel.
*Literature:* DBL 3rd ed.

1700

## Christopher Suencke, (died 1644), "arkelimester"

Simon de Pas, 1635
Engraving. 24.5×18.5 cm
Det kgl. Bibliotek MP bd. 12 pl. 40 4°
Christopher Suencke was chief "arkelimester" and as such responsible for the fireworks at the Grand Wedding in 1634.

1701

## Axel Urup, 1601-71, chief engineer, Councillor of the Realm.

Albert Haelwegh 1657-58
Engraving. 32×21 cm
Den kgl. Kobberstiksamling
In the early 1630s he was engaged in the project of "Jyllandsby" (near Kolding). In 1631-38 he supervised the construction of Christianspris Fortress in the Duchy of Schleswig, of which he became the first governor. In 1646, together with the Lord High Constable, Anders Bille, he worked out a detailed fortification plan for Denmark. In 1647-56 he was in charge of the new fortification of Copenhagen. Probably engraved after Abraham Wuchters.
*Literature:* Sthyr 186. Lorenzen 1953.

1702

## Johan Sems (1572-1635), engineer

Engraving executed 1600. 10×10 cm
Det kgl. Bibliotek, Billedsaml.

1703

## Johan Sems

C. Sichem 1631
Engraving. 19×14.5 cm
Det kgl. Bibliotek, Billedsaml.
*Provenance:* Engraved after a lost painting by Martin Faber (1587-1648), painter and architect from Emden.
*Literature:* Lehmann-Haupt 1975 274-306.

1704

## Sabastiano Serlio

*Il primo libro d'Architectura di S. Serlio. Paris 1545*
Det kgl. Bibliotek 9-373 fol.

1705

## Hans Vredemann de Vries

*Architectura, oder Bauung der Antiquem aus dem Vitruvius 1581*
Det kgl. Bibliotek 9-399 fol.

1706

## Jacobus Androuet du Cerceau

*Livre d'Architecture. Paris 1582*
Det kgl. Bibliotek 9-466 fol.

*1718*

1707
## Windelmi Dieterlin
*Architectura, de V Colimnam 1593*
Det kgl. Bibliotek 9-400 fol.

1708
## Daniel Mayer
*Archterctura, oder Verzeichniss allerhand Eynfassungen an Thüren, Fenstern und Decken. Frankfurt a.M. 1609*
Statsbiblioteket, Århus.

1709
## Ludovico Guicciardino
*Omnium Belgii sive inferioris Germaniae regionum descripto. Amsterdam 1612*
Det kgl. Bibliotek, Kortsaml. 14333

1710
## Simon Stevin
*Sterchen Bouwingh. Amsterdam 1624*
Det kgl. Bibliotek 54-33-4

1711
## Hendrich de Keyser
*Architectura Moderna ofte Bouwinge van onsen. Amsterdam 1631*
Det kgl. Bibliotek 19-465 fol.

1712
## Simon Stevin
*Materia politcae Burgherliche Stoffen, Leyden 1649*
Det kgl. Bibliotek, Sfv. I 66-4°

1713

## Reinholdt Curicke

*Beschreibung der Stadt Danzig zusammengetragen 1645. Danzig 1688.*
Det kgl. Bibliotek 15-303 fol.

1714

## E. G. Ellerborch, 1640

The departure of the Prodigal Son
Oil on canvas. 191×238 cm
Statens Museum for Kunst, Stroe 454

1715

## E. G. Ellerbroch 1640

The return of the Prodigal Son
Oil on canvas. 193×253 cm
Statens Museum for Kunst, Stroe 445

1716

## Prospect of Kronborg Castle

Artist unknown, c. 1620
Oil on canvas. 78×135.5 cm
Helsingør Bymuseum HM 3642
Dutch and Danish warships before Kronborg Castle.

1717

## Kronborg Castle

Abraham Borth (1606-36). 1629
Engraving
Kungl. Bibl., Stockholm F 1700/2687
Kronborg Castle before the fire 1629.
*Provenance:* Illustration in A. Borth, Journal van de legatie gedaen inde iaren 1726 unn 1628.
*Literature:* Ilsøe 41.

1718

## The Bathhouse at Frederiksborg Castle

Artist unknown. Late 17th century
Paper, pen
Den kgl. Kobberstiksamling
Frederic II's "Bathhouse" in the Enclosure of Frederiksborg Castle was originally a small summer house (this accounts for the name "Jegersburg"), built in the Netherlands style. A long house with three small wings facing east and a stair turret facing west which opened out on a balcony attached to the roof from which there was a view. The Bathhouse served as model for Rosenborg.
*Literature:* Steenberg 1950 14ff.

1719

## Copenhagen Castle 1698

J. J. Bruun, c. 1740
Gouache. 14.7×23.1 cm
Rosenborg 19.111
The old Copenhagen Castle seen from Højbro. In the centre the medieval Blue Tower with its tripartite Renaissance spire erected by Christian IV. The three crowns represent the Danish claim to Sovreignty in the North.
*Provenance:* Possibly after a picture in Københavns Bymuseum (cat. 38).
*Literature:* Bencard 1986 no. 14.

1720

## Ground-Plan of Copenhagen Castle 1707

Paper. 56×49.8 cm
Det kgl. Bibliotek. Ny kgl. saml. 386° fol.
A survey of the first floor of the old Copenhagen Castle. The Blue Tower is visible in the upper section of the plan.
*Literature:* Gamrath 1975 54, 91, 145.

1721

## Koldinghus Castle from the west

Executed by Christian V c. 1660
Watercolour. 15×42.4 cm. Colour-Plate IV
Rosenborg 24.293
The sketch indicates the additions made by Christian IV to Koldinghus Castle: the Tower of the Heroes, the Great Hall, taking up the entire length of the west wing, and the Chapel with its Romanesquestyle windows beneath the Tower of the Heroes.
*Literature:* Norn 1986 70-100.

1722

## Map of Kolding and environs

Executed by Christian V c. 1660
Watercolour. 21×64.5 cm
Rosenborg 24.292

1723

## Equestrian Portrait showing the "Imperator"

Artist unknown. 1699 at the latest
Oil on canvas. 44.5×38.7 cm
Rosenborg 7.311
Equestrian portrait, showing the "Imperator" of the Haute Ecole. In the background Koldinghus Castle and stable yard as they looked between the Swedish Wars 1657-60 and Frederik IV's rebuilding in the Baroque style.

*1719*

1724
## Koldinghus Castle from the north east

J. J. Bruun c. 1740
Gouache. 14.7×23.2 cm
Rosenborg 11.5
Koldinghus Castle and stable yard c. 1690.
*Provenance:* Probably a copy of the above.

1725
## Head of Scipio

Attributed to Claus Lauridsen c. 1610
Sandstone. H. 40 cm
Museet på Koldinghus
Christian IV adorned the top of the Tower of the Heroes with sandstone statues of Hercules, Scipio, Hector, and Hannibal. The figure of Hercules is still there; of Scipio only the head remains, and the two last figures were destroyed in the castle fire of 1808.

1726
## Fragments in sandstone

Claus Lauridsen (attribution c.1605)
Sandstone
Museet på Koldinghus
A fool's head and the pedestal of a statue, both of which were originally placed at the top of the Tower of the Heroes at Koldinghus.

1727
## Frederiksborg Castle

Copy after cat. 1
Oil on canvas. 84×190 cm
Frederiksborg A 1872
This picture displays Frederik II's Frederiksborg Castle shortly before it was demolished by his son, Christian IV. Only the stable buildings on the southernmost islet and the Pantry Wing on the middle islet were spared.

1728

### Frederiksborg Castle

Karl Jensen (1851-1933). Copy after the original by Lazarus Baratta from c. 1652 af Gripsholm (cat. 4)
Oil on canvas. 205×208 cm
Frederiksborg A 2177
Frederiksborg Castle as it looked at the time of Christian IV. On the left the buildings of Frederik II on the southern islet. In front of the Chancellery Wing on the middle islet the clear-cut entrenchment is visible. On the right the Sparepenge with the stable yard.

1729

### Frederiksborg Castle at the time of Frederik II

J. J. Bruun C. 1740
Gouache. 15×23.2 cm
Rosenborg 19.108.

1730

### Frederiksborg Castle from the south

J. J. Bruun c. 1740
Gouache. 15×23.2 cm
Rosenborg 19.112

1731

### Frederiksborg Castle from the west

J. J. Bruun c. 1740
Gouache. 15×23.2 cm
Rosenborg 19.114

1732

### Frederiksborg Castle

J. J. Bruun c. 1740
Gouache. 15×23.2 cm
Rosenborg 19.115

1733

### Frederiksborg Castle from the south

Jacob Coning (1698-1724) 1706
Oil on canvas. 43.5×59 cm
Private collection

1734

### Frederiksborg Castle from the north

Jacob Coning 1706
Oil on canvas. 42.4×60.5 cm
Private collection
In the foreground to the left the gable of Sparepenge with corner-statues.

1735

### Frederiksborg Castle seen from Jægerbakken

Erik Dahlberg 1658
Blacklead pencil on prepared paper. 7×12 cm
Nationalmuseum, Stockholm inv. 233/1908.
*Provenance:* The notebook that Erik Dahlberg used to take with him when he was on active service.
*Literature:* Steenberg 1950 147.

1736

### Carl X Gustav's reception at Frederiksborg Castle and his departure

S. Pufendorf c. 1696
Engraving
Frederiksborg
Scene from the visit to Frederiksborg Castle on 26th February 1658 of the Swedish King Karl X Gustav together with Frederic III following the Peace at Roskilde. The depiction of Frederiksborg Castle on the scene below is reproduced after Dahlberg.

1737

### Karl X Gustav visiting the Danish King and Queen at Frederiksborg

S. Pufendorf 1696
Engraving
Frederiksborg
A representation of the banquet given in honour of the Swedish King Karl X Gustav in 1658 in the Angels' Hall at Frederiksborg Castle. On the left a fireplace and a staircase opening on to the Great Hall. The room is depicted laterally reversed.

1738

### Frederiksborg Castle 1646

Engraving. 33×25 cm
Det kgl. Bibliotek
From Johan Adam Berg, "Kurze und eigentliche Beschreibung", Copenhagen 1646.

1739

### Frederiksborg Castle, the inner courtyard

F. C. Lund 1858
Watercolour
Frederiksborg A 5009
The north-western corner of the inner castle courtyard before the fire in 1859, showing the Chapel Wing and a section of the Marble Gallery.
*Literature:* Stein 1972 35.

*1734. Cut in right side*

1740

## Christian IV's Oratory at Frederiksborg Castle before the fire in 1859

Heinrich Hansen 1859
Oil on canvas. 37×47 cm
Frederiksborg A 477
Christian IV's Frederiksborg is known to us mainly through sketches and paintings of the interiors executed by a number of artists before the fire in 1859. The sketches by Heinrich Hansen were used as a basis for the reconstruction of the Oratory, the Rose, and the Great Hall.

1741

## Mother Earth and Fertility. Wife of Saturn(?)

Geraert Lambertsz. 1619-21
Sandstone. H. 184 cm
Frederiksborg Castle
*Provenance:* From the arches above the Marble Gallery in the courtyard at Frederiksborg Castle.
*Literature:* Stein 1987 117 f.

1742

## Mars in his chariot

Hendrich de Keyser's studio 1619-21
Sandstone
Frederiksborg Castle

*1743*

*Provenance:* Relief in the Marble gallery at Frederiksborg Castle.
*Literature:* Stein 1987 111 ff.

1743

## Christian IV and an engineer in front of Rosenborg Castle c. 1640. Attributed to Karel van Mander

Oil on canvas. 63×78.7 cm
Rosenborg 7.108
The depiction of Rosenborg is not quite reliable. In about 1640, the two oriels on the gable had not yet been carried through to ground level.
*Provenance:* Bought from an art dealer in 1839.
*Literature:* Eller 1971 142 (reproduced p. 444). Bencard 1983 no. 1.

1744

## Rosenborg Castle seen from the Reform Church

Johan Herman Coning (attribution), 1734
Oil on panel. 30.1×46.5 cm
Rosenborg inv. 13.339
Rosenborg Castle seen from the east. The oriel on the south-gable is depicted hanging, which is correct. The terraced garden in the foreground was laid out in the beginning of the 18th century.
*Literature:* Bencard 1986 no. 20.

1745

## Model of Rosenborg Castle

N. Nielsen, Aalborg, c. 1750
Wood covered with mother-of-pearl and amber
Total length: 21.5 cm
Rosenborg 13.514
*Provenance:* Presented to Rosenborg in 1936.
*Literature:* Bencard 1986 no. 35.

1746

## The King's Garden at Rosenborg Castle

Otto Heider (died 1660) 1649
Det kgl. Bibliotek, Ny kgl. Saml. 371 c folio
Rosenborg Castle was built as a "villa" in a newly laid out ornamental garden with various small summerhouses and pavillions.

1747

## Holmens Church seen from the Stock Exchange

Johs. Rach (1721-93) and H. H. Eegberg (1723-84) 1748
Oil on canvas
Nationalmuseets 3. af. 369/1946
*Literature:* DK I, 4 41. Strømstad 1977.

1748

## Holmens Kirke seen from Holmens bro

Johs. Rach and H. H. E. E. Eegberg 1749
Oil on canvas
Nationalmuseets 3. af. 343/1946
*Literature:* Strømstad 1977.

1749

## The surveying of a portal 1635

Didrik Gercken 1743
Paper and pencil
Rigsarkivet. Partikulærkammeret. Bilag til bygningsregnskaber 1744 no. 12.

*1746*

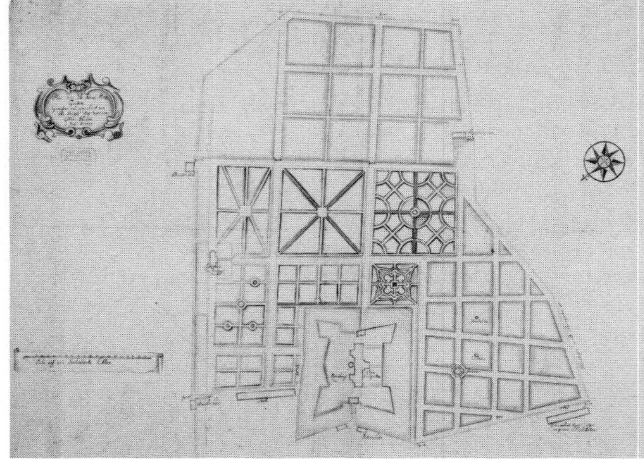

*1748*

The portal is the present west portal of Holmens Kirke in Copenhagen.
*Literature:* DK III, 2 1951 1421.

1750
## The transepts of the Holmens Church c. 1640

Artist unknown 1770
Paper and pen. 57.5×50 cm
Rigsarkivet TKS Søetaten DES C 168
*Literasture:* DK I 4 46.

1751
## The sepulchral Chapel of Christian IV at Roskilde Cathedral

I. Martin Petersen c. 1895
Watercolour
Nationalmuseet
A survey sketch of the north wall of the sepulchral chapel of Christian IV.
*Literature:* DK III, 3 1951 243.

1752.
## The Sepulchral Chapel of Christian IV at Roskilde Cathedral

H. G. F. Holm (1808-61). 1838
Watercolour
Nationalmuseet
*Literature:* DK III, 3 1951 155.

1753
## Prospect of the Round Tower and the Trefoldighedskirken

Johs. Rach and H. H. Eegberg 1749
Oil on canvas
Nationalmuseets 3. afd. 320/1946
*Literature:* DK I 4 258. Strømstad 1977

1754
## Prospect showing the fortress of Varberg c. 1610

Paper and pen. 11×19.5 cm
Rigsarkivet. Top. saml., papir Varberg slot No. 4 f.
Frederik II had already set to work on the fortification of Varberg. The enormous fortification work was continued by Christian IV, who had Varberg city moved so that it would be sheltered by the guns of the fortress.
*Literature:* Lorenzen 1937 225.

*1751*

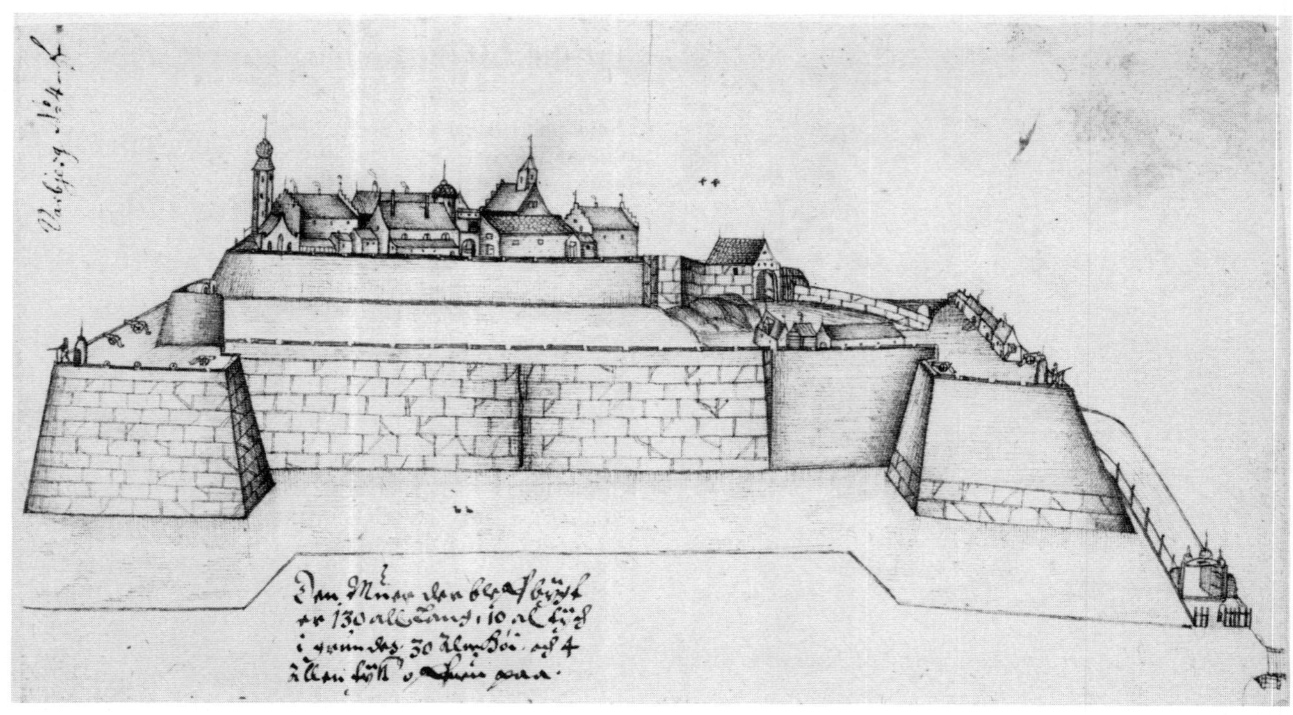

*1754*

1755

## Varberg. 1656

Engraving. 18×14 cm
Det kgl. Bibliotek, Billedsaml.
*Provenance:* Titelblad til Arent Berntsen: Danmarckis oc Norgis fructbar Herlighed 1650-56.

1756

## Plan of Varberg. 1645

Watercolour and pen. 98×80 cm
Kung. Krigsarkivet, Stockholm. Varberg no. 49
Survey of Varberg Fortress and environs. At the foot of the drawing are ramparts and bastions in sections. The survey must have been completed immediately after Varberg came under Swedish control.
*Provenance:* Kungl. Fortifikations Arkivet.
*Literature:* Lorenzen 1937 213.

1757

## Kristianopel. 1658

Engraving. 23×30 cm
Det kgl. Bibliotek. Kortsaml. 1113. 11661-0 1696/1
*Provenance:* From "De rebus a Carolo Guatavo gestis" by Samuel Pufendorf.

1758

## Groundplan of Kristianopel c. 1660

Paper. 40×84 cm
Det kgl. Bibliotek, Kortsaml.

1759

## Map of Kristianstad c. 1620

Paper and pen 41×52,5 cm
Det kgl. Bibliotek, Collection of Maps 1113, 111, 213-0-1620/1
The sketch shows the city's division into lots.
The ramparts are drawn in profile.
*Literature:* Lorenzen 1937 163. Andersson 1964 141ff.

1760

## Plan of Kristianstad from the time of its foundation after 1614

Watercolour and pen. 20×31.5 cm
Kungl. Krigsarkivet, Stockholm. Stads- og fästningsplaner. Kristianstad nr. 74.

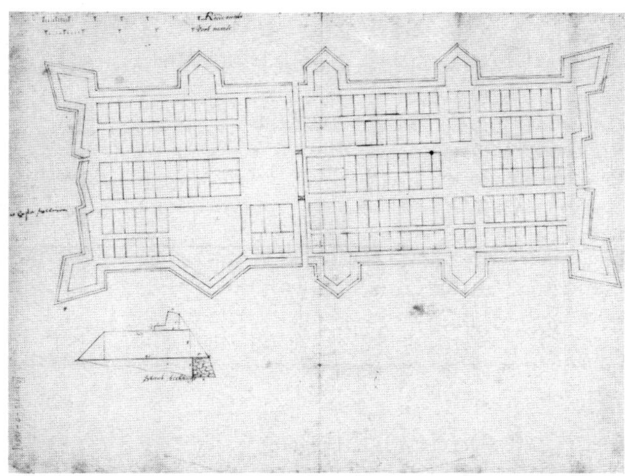

*1759*

1761

## Ground Plan of Kristianstad before 1658

Watercolour and pen. 53×55 cm
Kungl. Krigsarkivet, Stockholm / Kristianstad no. 75.
*Provenance:* Kungl. 1700-tals samlingarne. Kongl. Fortifikations-Arkivet.

1762

## Map of Kristianstad Showing the City when the tide is up in the River Helgeåen

Axel Magnus von Arbien, 1748
Paper, watercolour, and pen. 50×71 cm
Kungl. Krigsarkivet, Stockholm / Kristianstad no. 303
This map of the flooded areas of the Helgeåen shows Kristianstad as situated in a low-lying area.
*Provenance:* Kungl. 1600-tals samlingarne. Kongl. Fortifikations Arkivet no. III. E. E.2.

1763

## Karl X Gustav's entry into Kristianstad 1660

Erik Dahlberg (del.), N. Perelle f. (ecit) 1660-70
Engraving. 29×38 cm
Kungl. Bibliotek, Stockholm. Topographic plate Kristianstad B1
*Literature:* Pufendorf 1696 no. 78.

1764

## Speciedaler

Glückstadt, 1623
Den kgl. Mønt- og Medaillesamling
The reverse is adorned with the arms of Glückstadt, Fortune
*Literature:* Hede 1964 no. 156.

1765

## Map of Glückstadt

The 1620s
Paper and pen. 32×42 cm
Kungl. Krigsarkivet, Stockholm / Glückstadt no. 2
Glückstadt was founded 1617. It may originally have been planned as a hexagonal radiate city, but only half of the plan was carried out.
*Provenance:* Formerly in Axel Oxenstierna's collection of maps, the later Ridderstolp Collection.
*Literature:* Lorenzen 1937 333. Köhn 1974, 25.

1766

## Map of Glückstadt 1628

Paper, watercolour, pen
Kungl. Krigsarkivet, Stockholm / Glückstadt no. 1
The east part of Glückstadt is laid out as half a hexagonal with a central and a radial square. The city is divisioned by a dug-out canal with streets on either side, a Netherlands feature in the town-planning.
*Literature:* Köhn 1974, 25 ff.

1767

## Caspar Danckwerth

*Neues Landesbeschreibung der zwei Herzogthümer Schleswig und Holstein, Husum 1652*
Statsbiblioteket, Århus

1768

## Gui og Johannes Blaeu

*Novus Atlas, das ist Weltbeschreibung mit schönen neuen ... Landtafflen. Th. III. Amsterdam 1647-52*
Statsbiblioteket, Århus.

*1766*

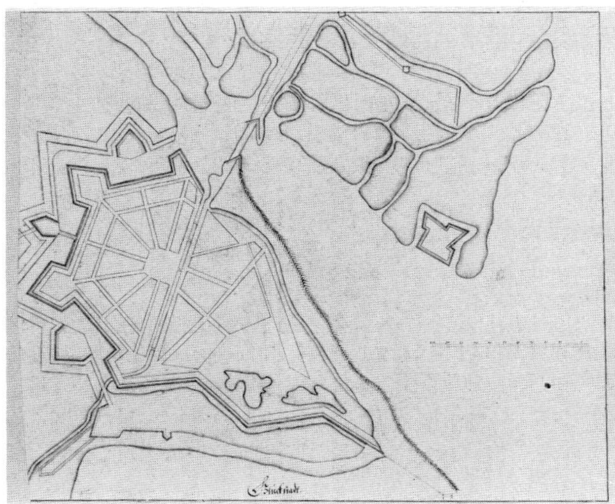

1769

## Prospect of Glückstadt

Johan Christian Leopold (1699-1755)
Engraving. 15×17 cm
Det kgl. Bibliotek, Billedsaml. Hertugdømmerne Glückstadt folio.

1770

## Map of Kristiania (Oslo) c. 1640

Watercolour and pen 29×30 cm
Kungl. Krigsarkivet, Stockholm / Kristiania no. 19
Contrary to the old Oslo, Christiania became a proper port.
*Provenance:* Kungl. 1700-tals samlingarna.
*Literature:* Lorenzen 1937 257.

1771

## Map of Kristiania

Isaac van Geelkerck, 1649. 70×89 cm
Universtitetsbiblioteket, Oslo / Map 2309
Appears to be a plan of adjustments for the fortress of Akershus and for the city-areas south and east of the fortress. The map is dated 24th April, 1649. Sketched after an original from 1646 in i.a. Det kgl. Bibliotek, Copenhagen
*Provenance:* Presented by The Royal Library, Copenhagen in 1853.

1772

## The King receiving the Oath of Allegiance at Akershus in 1648

Isaac van Geelkerck, 1648
Paper and pen. 40×63.5 cm
Det kgl. Bibliotek / Historiske blade 1601-57.

1773

## Prospect of Akershus Fortress

Jacob Coning 1699
Paper. 18.8 × 53. 8 cm
Den kgl. Kobberstiksamling. Td. 513

1774

## Double Specie

Kristiania, undated
Den kgl. Mønt- og Medaillesamling
On the reverse is a depiction of Akershus Fortress. The coin was struck in honour of the proclamation of Frederik III as hereditary King of Norway in 1661.
*Literature:* Hede 1964 no. 39.

1775

## Map of Gudsø Vig and Environs

Pieter Buysser (-1630 – 52,-), 1630
Paper and pen. 20×32.5 cm
Rigsarkivet. Krigsmin. afd. mappe no. 11
Project for at new fortified city, "The City of Jutland" at Emmernæs near Kolding Bay. According to the plan, Kolding was to be demolished and its inhabitants removed to the new city. The project was later implemented by the Little Belt with the foundation of Fredericia; Kolding, however, was not demolished.
*Literature:* Lorenzen 1937 127 and 1953 24 d.

1776

## Frederiksodde. 1655

Christof Heer, 1660-93
Paper. 41×31 cm
Det kgl. Bibliotek. Gl. kgl. Saml. 716 2°

1777

## Prospect of Christianspris

M. Merian, c. 1650
Engraving
Frederiksborg
A representation of the Christianspris Fortress seen from the south with ramparts and various barracks. The ramparts-system was not completed until 1642 and it is a matter of doubt whether the many buildings of the fortress were ever built.
*Provenance:* From Martinus Zeillerus, Sämptliche ... Topographiae XI Merian Topographia Germaniae. 1753.

1778

## Plan of Christianspris. 1643

Paper and pen. 35×41,5 cm
Kungl. Krigsarkivet, Stockholm / Kiel no. 5
Christianspris was built on the north side of the Kieler Bay (the Schleswig part) according to a plan made by the engineer Axel Urup in the years 1630-40. The fortress was dismantled after the Torstensson War (1643-45).
*Provenance:* From Fortifikationsakivet.
*Literature:* Lorenzen 1937 365 and 1953 40 ff.

1779

## Plan for the fortification of the Flekkerø. 1636

Paper and pen. 45×55 cm
Rigsarkivet. KTS D.Kanc. B 15
The map is inscribed with Christian IV's handwritten comments.
*Literature:* EB VII no. 54

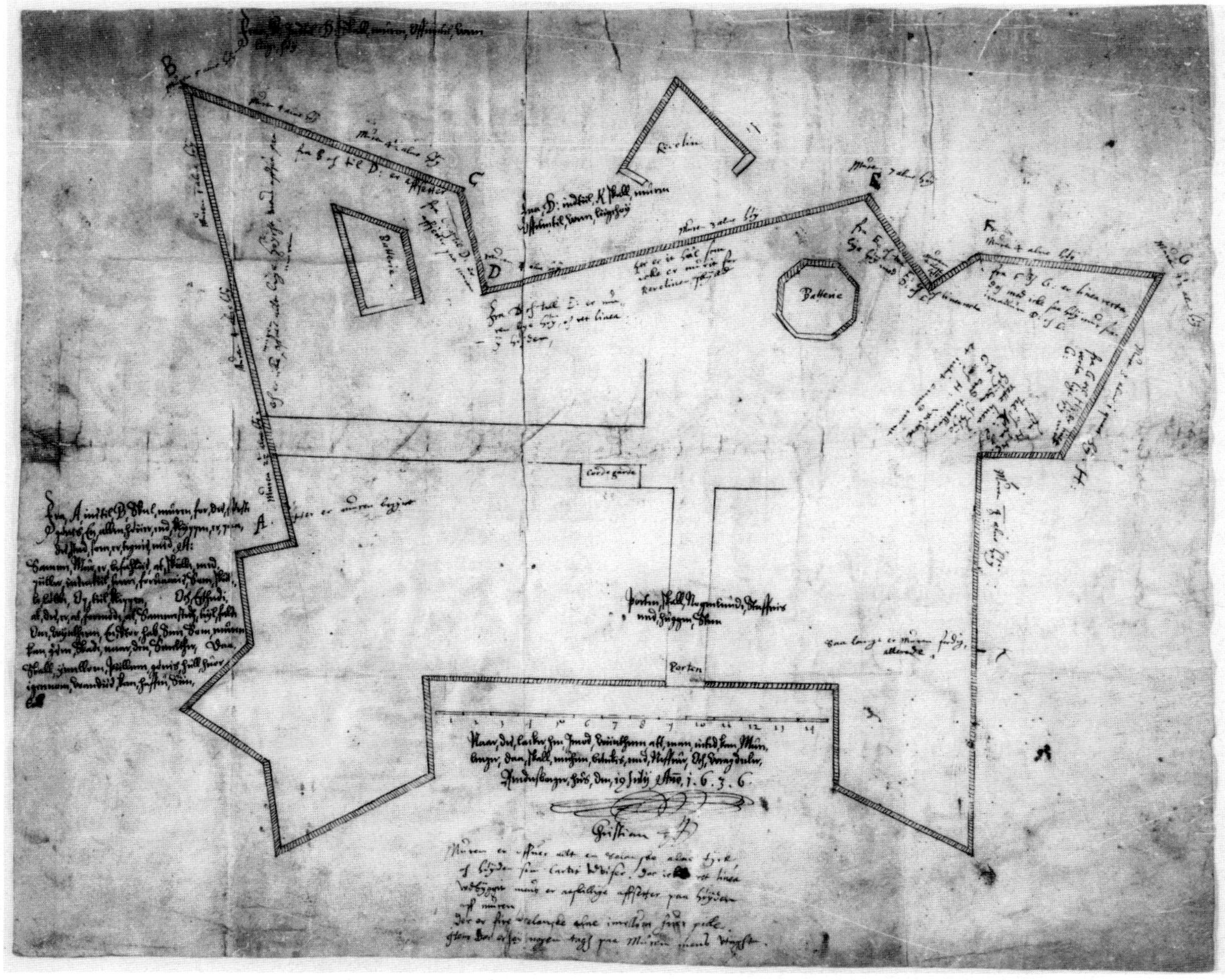

*1779*

1780
## Map of Kristiansand. 1662
Paper. 55.5×63 cm
Riksarkivet, Oslo DK 3

1781
## Kristiansand. 1665
Drawing. 42×42 cm
Det kgl. Bibliotek, Ny kgl. Saml. 712 fol.no. 43.

1782
## Gert Rantzau (1558-1627), Royal Governor of the Duchies
Engraved after a medal. 11×14.5 cm
Det kgl. Bibliotek, MP bd. 11 pl. 41 I 8.

1783
## Prospect of Copenhagen. 1587
Braun and Hogenberg, 1598
Statsbiblioteket, Århus
The city seen from the seaward side and from land, before Christian IV's extensive building activities began.

1784
## Nomina Sirenum
Copenhagen after 1590
Engraving
Statsbiblioteket, Århus.

1785

## Project for the Enlargement of Copenhagen

The early 17th century
Paper and pen
Rigsarkivet. Folioreg. 30
København 1,2,11
The only building in the old city that is indicated is the Church of Our Lady. The enlargement-project includes an exchange, built round a quadrangle, a square with a town hall, and the entrenchment of St. Anna Rotunda with a new Royal residence. The inspiration from the Netherlands is evident in the town plan.
*Literature:* Gamrath 1965 38-46

1786

## Project for Christianshavn

Johan Semp, 1617
Paper and pen. Illuminated
Det kgl. Bibliotek, Kortsamlingen
This first project for the city of Christianshavn shows the approximation to the "ideal city".
*Literature:* Lorenzen 1937 84. Gamrath 1968 14 ff.

1787

## Christianshavn, map of the building sites. 1636

Paper and pen. 30.5×40.5 cm
Det kgl. Bibliotek, Kortsamlingen
*Literature:* Gamrath 1968 40ff.

1788

## Project for "New Copenhagen". 1629

Paper and pen. 62×46 cm
Det kgl. Bibliotek / Gl. Kgl. Saml. fol. 350, tillæg no. 4
Project for a radial town plan for "New Copenhagen" with a central square.
*Literature:* Lorenzen 11937 98 f. Gamrath 1980 55, 72 ff

1789

## Map of Copenhagen and Christianshavn. 1648

Otto Heyder (died 1660)
Paper and pen. 59×75 cm
Forsvarets Bygningstjeneste. Ingeniørkorpsets hist. kortsamling
The drawing depicts Christianshavn, Slotsholmen, the fortification-lines of the old city, and New Copenhagen. The drawing also shows the planned entrenchment of St. Anne, which was later to be the citadel of Frederikshavn (usually called: Kastellet).

1790

## Prospect of Copenhagen

Allard, c. 1650
Engraving. 56×181 cm
Det kgl. Bibliotek, Billedsamlingen

1791

## Prospect of Amagertorv, Copenhagen. 1746

Engraving. 25×40 cm
Det kgl. Bibliotek, Billedsamlingen 1911 no. 11225
From Laurits de Thurah, Hafnia Hodierna, 1746-48

1792

## The Dutch fleet at the Copenhagen Roads. 1658

Willem I van de Velde (c. 1611-93)
Wash pencil-drawing, 3 sheets. 53.7×79.2, 53.7×62.5, and 53.7×67 cm
Den kgl. Kobberstiksamling. Største folio skuffe 18
Van de Velde came to Copenhagen in 1658 with the Dutch auxiliary fleet. The drawing depicts the harbour front with Rosenborg Castle and the uncompleted St. Annæ Rotunda i.a.

*1796*

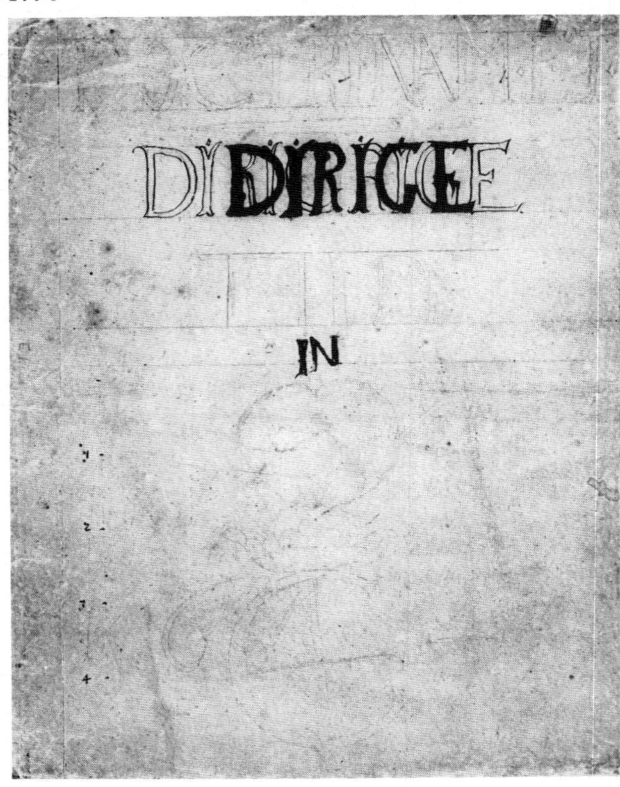

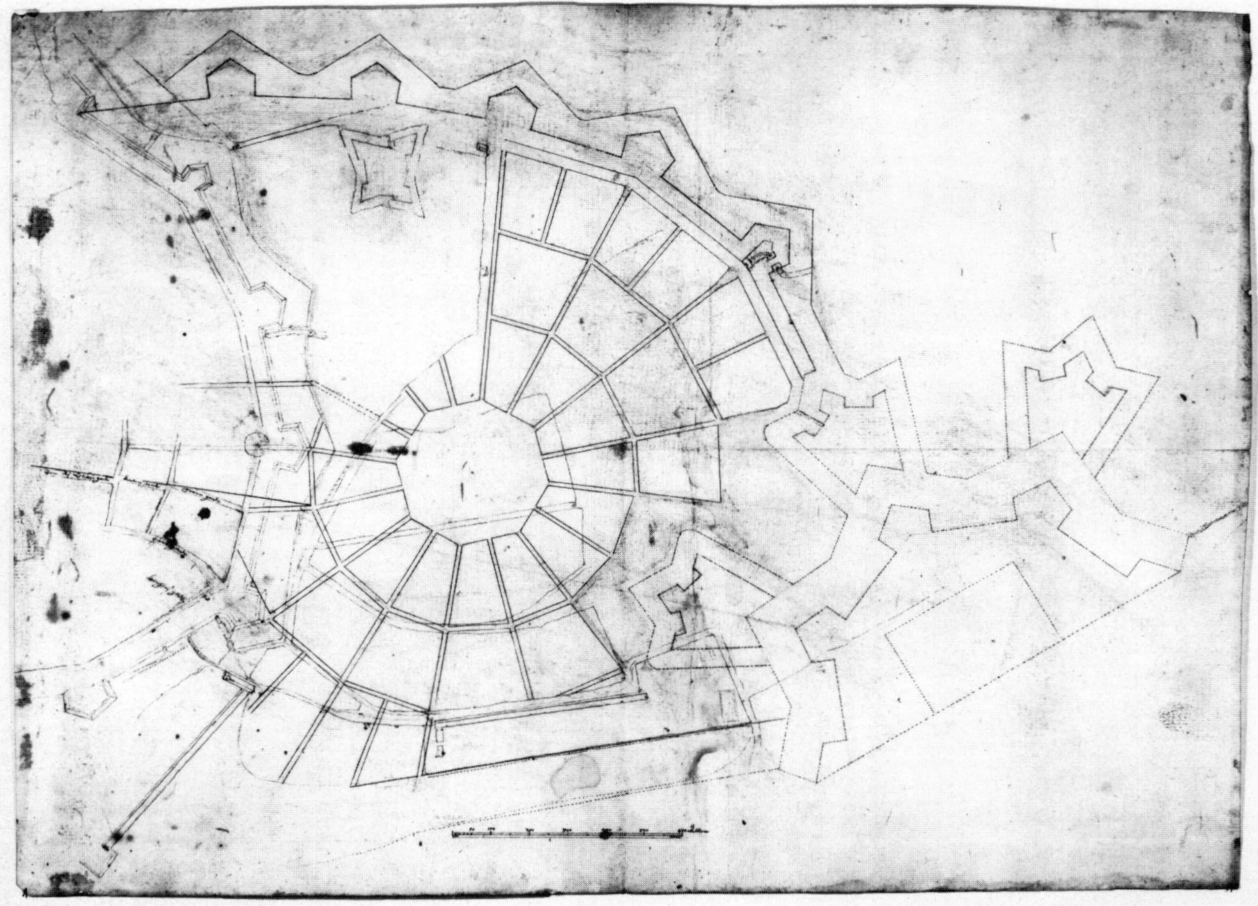

*1788*

1793

## The Symbol of Copenhagen

Laurids de Thurah (1706-59). The 1740s
Engraving 44.5×27 cm
Det kgl. Bibliotek, Billedsml. Folio Havnen
The symbol of Copenhagen was placed by the entrance to "Provianthavnen" by the Stock-Exchange. It appears in Dircksens engraving from 1611, though it is not possible to make out what it represents. The symbol was displayed in 1746 in "Den Danske Vitruvius" by Thurah, who describes it as Leda and the Swan. In 1977 Thurah's interpretation was questioned by Bramsen who suggested the Christian Caritas, around which the stork (Piety) or perhaps the pelican (the blood of Christ) is clinging. The symbol was demolished in 1798. There is nothing left of it.
*Provenance:* From Thurah, Den danske Vitruvius.
*Literature:* Bramsen 1977.

1794

## The shaft of a column from the Vesterport (West Gate of Copenhagen). 1627

Sandstone. H. 72 cm
Københavns Bymuseum, inv. 1945:128
Framed as a foot-mortar, in which a gun in vertical position has been placed. Of the gun only the breech-piece is preserved. Inscribed with the monogram C4.
*Provenance:* Vesterport was demolished in 1857.
*Literature:* Linde 137. Jensen 223f.

1795

## The Round Tower

Johan Andreas Greyss, 1646
Engraving. 27.1×17.2 cm
Københavns Bymuseum, inv. 1927:56

Kirchen Cermonien vnd Krönung des Jtzigen königs Christiani der vierden geschehen zu Koppenhagen den 29 Augusti Ao. 1596.

*1800*

1796

## Inscription on the Round Tower

Christian IV's own design
Paper and pen. 44×56.5 cm
Rigsarkivet. TKS Søetaten E1
*Literature:* Wanscher 1937 5.

1797

## The Royal Exchange

Engraving. 25×44 cm
Det kgl. Bibliotek, Billedsamlingen 1911 no. 11946
From Laurits de Thurah, Den Danske Vitruvius, 1746-48

1798

## The Gables of the Royal Exchange

Engraving. 26×44 cm
Det kgl. Bibliotek, Billedsamlingen 1911 no. 11949
From Laurits de Thurah, Den Danske Vitruvius, 1746

1799

## A Herma, originating from the sandstone ornamentation of the Royal Exchange

Sandstone. H. 150 cm
Københavns Bymuseum Rhfv. 933.

1800

## Triumphal Arch at Gammeltorv in Copenhagen on the Day of Christian IV's Coronation

Philip Uffenbach, 1596
Engraving. 20×27 cm
Det kgl. Bibliotek, Billedsaml. 1911 nr. 4250 Fol. Hist. blade 1570-1600
*Provenance:* From Augustinus Erich: Christian IVs kronings beskrivelse. 1596.
*Literature:* Krogh 1938 187-198.

1801

## Tilting at the Ring at the Coronation of Christian IV

Engraving 22×28 cm
Det kgl. Bibliotek, Billedsaml. 1911-4251.

1802

## The "Walkendorf-Book" 1581

Det kgl. Bibliotek. Ny kgl. Saml. 375 b fol.
The source of the so-called "Valkendorf-Book" of Copenhagen.

1803

## Jürgen Holst

Triumphus Nuptialis Danicus. Copenhagen 1648
Statsbiblioteket, Århus.

1804

## Atlas of Artillery and Fireworks c. 1650

Det kgl. Bibliotek, Gl. kgl. Saml. 352 fol.

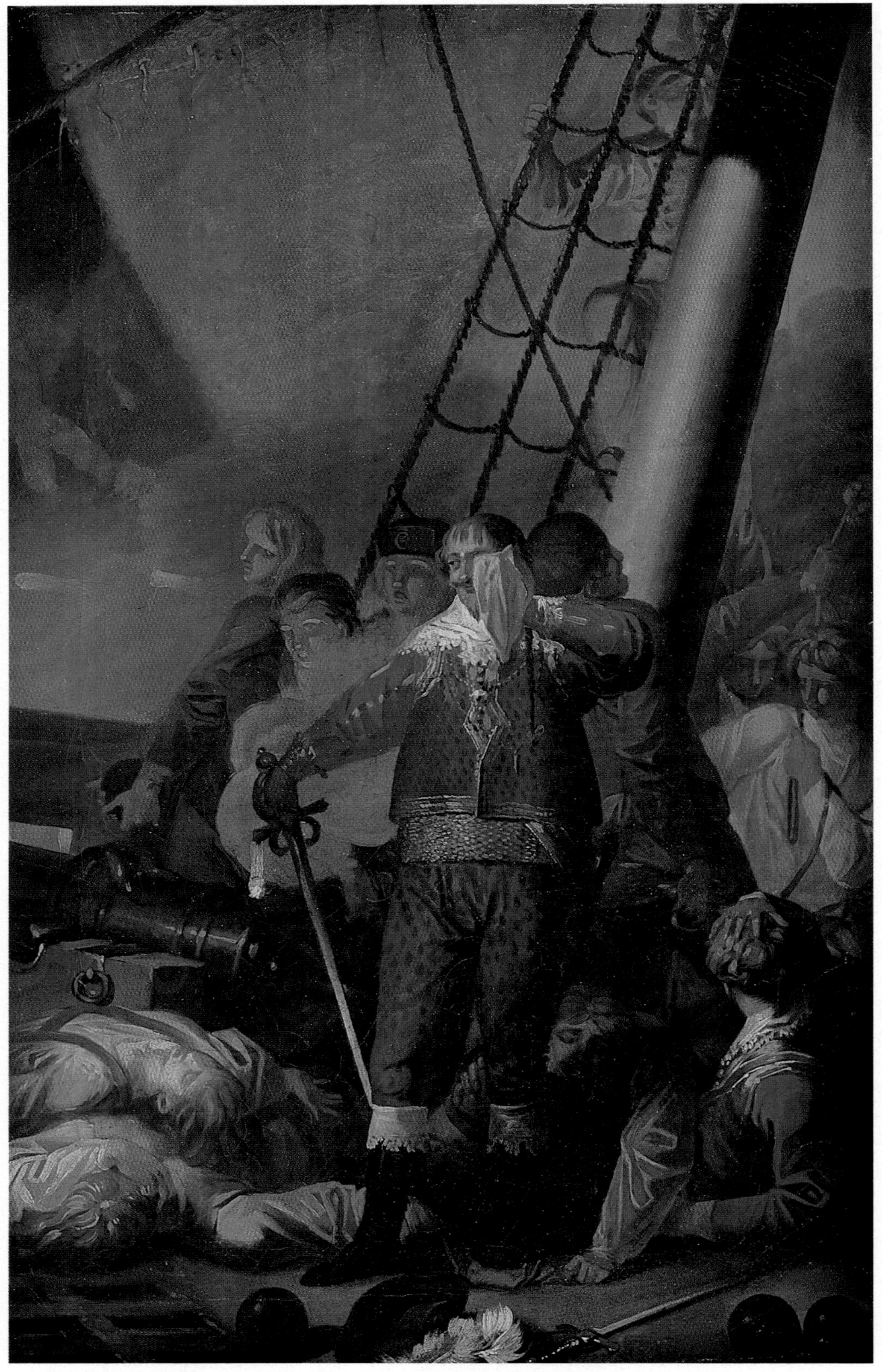

# Aarhus Kunstmuseum

## *Denmark's Christian · Christian IV: The Image for Posterity*

28.3-23.5.1988

### The Myth of the King

Christian IV has posthumously been the subject of more hero worship than any other Danish king. The creation of the myth of Christian IV as a popular king grew up in the beginning of the 18th century and had its roots in accounts of his deeds during the sea battle of Kolberger Heide in 1644.[1]

Christian IV was among the longest-reigning of the Danish kings, but his reign also covered the time when the reduction of the kingdom began. The kingdom he inherited was large and prosperous, and its power was relatively significant; the kingdom he left at his death was diminished and in political and economic chaos. The country's position of leadership in the Nordic region was lost, and the kingdom of Denmark-Norway had to suffer being outstripped by Sweden.

In spite of his generally unfortunate war exploits he still achieved a posthumous fame and a popular reputation greater than any other Danish king, perhaps because as a "private" individual he was one of the most colourful figures among the successive occupants of the throne – fond of drinking and womanizing, according to legend.

The writers of history bear part of the responsibility for this legend and its growth in the 18th and 19th centuries, just as controversy over it later came to a head first and foremost among circles of historians. As the royal servants of the absolute monarchy, historical writers in the 18th century and long into the 19th had to pay respect to the reputation of the Royal House ("gloria regis"). They therefore chose to describe individual episodes in history and tended to avoid evaluation of the course of historical events. Through abstaining from evaluating the period of Christian IV's rule as a whole and restricting themselves to describing single events, they allowed a positive total image of the King to grow up.

Writers, painters and sculptors helped create interest in Christian IV at the end of the 18th century at a time when the history of his reign had long before been described in history books, but because of the larger distribution of their works and the interest which they aroused they played an extensive part in the further development of the legend.

The depiction of Christian IV on the ship *Trefoldighed* is no doubt the best-known portrait of the King. Historians writing of Christian IV soon after the events of his reign had described the bravery and indomitable spirit displayed by the King when, after being hit by metal splinters from an exploding canon, he nevertheless stayed in command. In "Danmarks Riges Historie" from 1733, Ludvig Holberg declared the King "the big Hero". Niels Slange in "Den stormægtigste Konges Christian den Fierdes Historie" from 1749 stressed that the King's rapid repossession of his leadership role in spite of his wounds was extremely remarkable, taking into account the King's age – 67 years.[2] Ove Malling gave the episode the title "Bravery" in his book "Store og gode Handlinger af Danske, Norske og Holstenere" in 1777. When Johannes Ewald's ballad-opera "Fiskerne" was first performed in 1780 the Danish sea heroes were celebrated in a romance encapsulated in it. Because its language was so pictorially vivid, the verse about "Kong Christian", who "stood by the high mast amid smoke and fumes" was destined to become an important source of inspiration to later artists.

N. A. Abildgaard chose to depict Christian IV in a painting showing the King in action on board the *Trefoldighed,* when in 1782 he painted Christian IV for the series of Kings of the House of Oldenborg which was to decorate the Great Hall of Christiansborg. This painting was followed by a number of *Trefoldighed* paintings (cat. 1805-1809, 1819-1828). In all these paintings it is the heroic efforts of the King which are highlighted. The overall development of the war with Sweden and its results cannot be seen in the paintings. Only by reading modern history books can one learn of the actual defeat and the losses of land. The earlier historians and the painters are unanimous about maintaining the image of the conscientious old King with inexhaustible courage.

The majority of later paintings with Christian IV as the main subject were made during the period 1825-70. The paintings are characterised by being illustratory in nature and as a rule closely following the historians' texts. The work of Slange was much used by painters as a source of inspiration, probably because Slange recounts a number of episodes from Christian IV's life which could be used for genre-pieces and anecdotal presentations.

The painters preferred narrative to history for their subjects. There was consequently only a limited range of episodes from Christian IV's life which the painters considered suitable. As has been mentioned, the *Trefoldighed* motif was often used, especially in paintings of an official character, ordered in connection with decoration assignments. The other paintings of Christian IV occur both in the context of commissioned works and as paintings produced for private buyers. The preferred themes were "Niels Kaas hands over the keys of the realm to the young Christian IV"; "Christian IV pronounces judgement on Christoffer Rosencrantz"; "Christian IV visiting Tycho Brahe"; "Christian IV and Ole Vind", and different variations of the theme of "Christian IV supervising work on his buildings". In these subjects the virtues of the King which corresponded to the absolutist ideal of the monarch were highlighted: the unfailing diligence, the conscientious undertaking of the royal office, and the sense of justice. His constant appetite for participating and contributing, his courage and his pawky humour, were highlighted as characteristic of the King's mentality and were seen as a proof of the King's closeness to the people. The historical situations were depicted in the paintings as stories about people; the humanity of the King was given priority over a formal representation.

Many of these paintings appeared in the 1840s during a period when attempts to bring absolutism to an end and to introduce a bourgeois democratic system became increasingly intense. The enthusiasm for Christian IV must be seen in the light the national liberals' attempts to mobilize "the people" and, for instance via art, to educate them in political activity and national solidarity. The national liberal historians were interested in the individual human being and his fate, and worked outwards from ideas of the importance of the great active protagonist.[3] In his work "Haandbog i Fædrelandets Historie", first issued in 1840, C. F. Allen emphasized the characteristic features of Christian IV which were also dominant among the nationally-conscious and socially-aspiring bourgeoisie of the 19th century: the honest "Danishness" and courage, the competitive spirit, diligence, conscientiousness and straightforwardness – all of them good bourgeois virtues in 19th century society.

Christian IV could therefore stand as a symbol of all that was Danish, and as the ideal of the jovial leader-/father-figure, who through his just reign and because of his solidarity with his people could be the model for the kings of the 19th century as well as for the leaders of the incipient democracy.

The many presentations of the King paying salary to the workers employed in the royal building activities can thus be seen in relation to the idea of the unpretentious King, and to the predominant idea of the King's personal involvement in the construction of his many buildings. In the paintings the King is shown as one man among many; his figure is only highlighted by the fact that he is seated while the workers stand! (see cat. 1885-1887). Different legends are connected with the stone block on which most of the painters place the King in the wage-paying pictures. J. M. Thiele wrote in "Danmarks Folkesagn" from 1843 that the King used to sit on the carved boulder in Indelukket at Frederiksborg Castle when he paid wages to the building-craftsmen. Thiele mentioned also that Christian IV himself said that the stone was placed there "as an eternal memorial of the break with Kirsten Munk in 1628".[4] The painters chose to stick to the first explanation, probably because this version was better-suited to depiction of the King as popular and down-to-earth. The other explanation was probably too "daring" for a pictorial presentation in the middle of the 19th century, but on the other hand this story contributes to supporting the reputation of the King in his relationships with women.

The legend about the King's thirst also belonged to his image. It was first and foremost the carefully-kept diary of the Chancellery Secretary, Sivert Grubbe, which was instrumental in spreading the widely-held opinion that the King was a heavy drinker. There are many indications, however, that the King did not tend to drink exceptional quantities every day, but only on special occasions. Heavy drinking bouts were certainly common in the time of Christian IV. When it became traditional to focus on drinking-parties in tales of the King's exploits, the reason of course was that this was a particularly human trait in the King, and also very entertaining. Only one of the painters of later times, however, presented Christian IV at a drinking-party (cat. 1896).

The Christian IV portrayed by the historians, the poets and the painters stayed the same for a very long time. The historians of the late 19th century, now producing source-critical historical research, tried to show that the earlier image of the King was built more on legend than on reality. Increasingly as the historians developed source-critical methods the painters lost their interest in the King. The poetic and anecdotal elements which were previously included in history-writing, and which had been important for the artists' interpretations, were no longer accepted by the historians. The portrait of the brave monarch who heroically defended his domains against the aggression of the evil Swedish neighbour was now considered one-sided. This change of attitude must of course be seen in relation to Denmark's altered status after 1864, and the Scandinavian movement which fostered reconciliation with Sweden.

The highlighting of the King's positive sides, confirming his image as a popular figure, seems to have been a common feature of all later paintings. It could have been expected that the same scene would have been presented in a different way at different times, and that the changing attitude towards the King would have been reflected in the frequency of the different motives – or that certain motives would appear at certain times. The period during which later painters showed interest in Christian IV was relatively short, however, and was characterised by enthusiastic nationalism. So only very small variations in the perception of the King can be seen from one picture to the next.

The national liberal and moderate conservative historians could use Christian IV for their own ideological purposes, and the paintings of the King, with their illustratory character, matched the history-writing of the period.

After 1870 only a few historical paintings with Christian IV as the main figure were produced, and the historians' tales about the King were marked by consciousness of Denmark's situation after the loss of Schleswig. The national disasters of the 19th century were regarded as the culmination of the decline which started with Christian IV's anti-Nordic foreign policy.

Nevertheless, A. D. Jørgensen in his "Fyrretyve Fortællinger af Fædrelandets Historie", which was first issued in 1882, came to the conclusion that Christian IV had left himself a monument in the form of a fine reputation. "He was an honest Danish man, straightforward and bluff, strong in body and soul, a fearless sailor and brave warrior. What is more, he was a good master to his people, thrifty or generous according to time and situation, mild where it was possible to be so, and incorruptibly just in his verdicts".[5] A. D. Jørgensen wrote this book at the request of brewer J. C. Jacobsen (founder of the Carlsberg Brewery); it was intended as a popular history book which could be used in the cultural resistance movement in Schleswig. Brewer Jacobsen moreover paid for most of the reconstruction of Frederiksborg Castle after the fire in 1859, and for the installation of a national historical museum in the castle. In this way Jacobsen wanted to contribute to paying back the debt he felt he owed the nation because, as a politician, he had supported the national liberal politics which had led to the defeat of 1864. When he switched over, after the loss of Schleswig and Holstein, to a more conservative political line and wanted to influence the population in the direction of retreat from the 1849 constitution, he needed symbols which represented ideas rooted in absolutism. Here Frederiksborg Castle, with all its references to Christian IV, perfectly fitted his needs. Jacobsen's commissioning of historical paintings for the Frederiksborg Museum also reflected his conservative attitude. The events in the nation's history which Jacobsen wanted represented in paintings for the purpose of strengthening nationalistic consciousness all belonged to the period of Christian IV and before. (Cat. 1862, 1863, 1865).

The 19th century thus need the myth of Christian IV. The realities of his time were too reminiscent of the unsolved contemporary problems. In the 20th century only af few paintings with subjects from Christian IV's life and achievements have been made. Artists' interest in the King was greatest in the 1940s when national solidarity needed strengthening. The most famous play in which Christian IV appears, "Elverhøj" by Johan Ludvig Heiberg (written in 1828), was performed 2-16 times per season during the years 1938-46. The play was made into a film in 1939. But only a few new works of art with Christian IV as central figure have been produced – and mainly in connection with celebrations of anniversaries, etc. (Cat. 1911).

Christian IV's potential as a source of artistic material has been exhausted. Paintings of him from his own time or from the 19th century are now used for book illustrations or as material for derived works – e.g. Stig Brøgger used Wilhelm Marstrand's painting "Christian IV on the *Trefoldighed* as inspiration for one of the pictures in his series "Danmarksbillede i ni afsnit" from 1975 (cat. 1811).

## 19th century monuments to Christian IV

The decoration of Christian IV's chapel at Roskilde Cathedral occupied artists of the 19th century longer than any other official comission concerning Christian IV.

The chapel had stood, since its construction in 1614-18, with plain white walls; Lauritz de Thurah's project for a monument had never been realized (cat. 1812). It was Christian VIII who took the initiative for the decoration of the chapel, which was eventually realized during the 19th century. In 1840 he asked Bertel Thorvaldsen to make a statue which would be part of a monument outlined, in 1841, by Gustav Friederisch Hetsch (cat. 1813-1814). This monument was never made, probably because such a glorification of royalty could have caused offence in certain political circles during the 1840s, and after the abolition of absolutism (in 1849) it would have been unthinkable.

The wall and ceiling decorations of the chapel were carried out, but the work was not finished until 1866. The content of the decoration seems to have been fixed in accordance with Heinrich Eddelien's proposal of 1844, but several artists had been involved in the decorations before the work was completed with Wilhelm Marstrand's big wall paintings.

Marstrand presented the young Christian as the just judge (in the case against Christoffer Rosenkrantz) (cat. 1845-1854); the ageing King is presented as the victor on board his ship. The total impression of this painting is a mood of feasting and joy – acclaim for a king. Denmark's last absolute king, Christian VIII, thus arranged through his initiative in 1840 that Christian IV, the last non-absolute king of the country, was given an honourable memorial.

The 250th anniversary of the founding of Christiania (Oslo), in 1874, produced proposals for two monuments to Christian IV: a painting which was never realized, and a statue which was erected on the Stortorv in Oslo. Oscar II, the King of Sweden and Norway at the time, ordered from Adolf Tidemand a painting which was meant to depict the founding of Christiania. It was ordered to be hung in the planned new City Hall of Oslo. Tidemand made a series of composition sketches, a charcoal drawing and an oil-sketch (cat. 1855-1861). Tidemand died however in 1877, shortly after the enormous canvas, almost 5 × 9 m., had been prepared for the painting.

The public sculptures of Christian IV caused long discussions, both in 1870 when a royal statue was to be erected in Christiania, and in the 1890s, when plans were made for Copenhagen to have a Christian IV sculpture. In Norway Christian IV's role as the founder of the capital could be interpreted as a dictatorial measure, in that it involved the forceful removal of the old burned-out town. No less than two competitions consequently had to be held before the statue could be realized (cat. 1909-1910).

In the year 1900 the Danish state presented a Christian IV statue to the municipality of Copenhagen. Around this statue there was also controversy, but contrary to the case of the Oslo statue the debate in Denmark was more a matter of where the statue should be placed than of its form. In 1896, "Blæksprutten" (a satirical magazine entitled "The Octopus"), had in fact published a caricature with some proposals for a monument for "our famous sea hero, the founder of the Danish Stock Exchange and the builder of the Round Tower"; in 1897 the author of "Danske malede portrætter", E. F. S. Lund, wrote a number of newspaper articles about portraits which could be used as a model for a statue.[6] The newspaper polemics which followed mainly discussed the siting of the statue: Højbro Plads, Nytorv and Rosenborg Gardens were the places most often mentioned. Vilhelm Bissen made the statue, which in the year 1900 was unveiled at Nyboder, in memory of the construction by Christian IV of these houses as accomodation for the navy's permanent staff (c.f. the inscription on the statue's granite podium). The monarch here overlooks – holding onto a staff – one of his building projects, and one which moreover had the closest possible connection to the navy.

## "The most magnificent castle in the North"

North Sealand is inextricably linked to Christian IV's buildings: Frederiksborg Castle – where he was born, and which he later completely rebuilt; Kronborg, which he had restored and modernished after the fire of 1629, and where many of his children were born; and Rosenborg, the country castle which he had constructed in his rose-garden outside Copenhagen. In addition to these castles, Rundetårn, Tøjhuset, Børsen, Holmens Kirke and Regensen (the students' residence) can be mentioned.

The buildings in Copenhagen, with the exception of Rosenborg, have not been painted by later artists particularly on account of their royal originator. The buildings have formed the background and a framework for Copenhagen street-life in town-prospect genre pieces such as those by Eckersberg, H. G. F. Holm, Julius Friedländer and Martinus Rørbye.

Christian IV's castles and palaces have more often attracted painters – and poets – because of their historical value as memorials to the greatness of the past. Throughout the 18th century the castles were only occasionally used by the royal family, and the artists only painted them out of topographical interest. At the end of the 18th century, however, these prospect-paintings were given nationalistic overtones. In line with the historians' concept of Christian IV as a kind of hero-king, and the portrait-painters' growing interest in him, Christian IV's buildings also became themes for the artists' brushes.

Frederiksborg Castle, with its distinctive architecture and fine setting in the landscape, came to be regarded as a romantic relic of the past. The painters portrayed the castle as a majestic building, imbued with splendour and romance (cat. 1917, 1932). Poets and writers used the castle as a stage backcloth (cat. 1919, 1921) or wrote about it as if it had stepped out of a fairly-tale (cat. 1929, 1936).

The art historian Niels Laurids Høyen from 1831 onwards made a catalogue of the portrait collection in the castle, and often in speech and writing highlighted it as a suitable subject for painters. He regarded the castle as "the most beautiful castle northern Europe possesses",[7] and he encouraged several of the young painters of the 1830s to draw and paint the castle. Høyen's view was one of the main reasons why Christen Købke and Jørgen Roed worked so energetically with the castle as subject (cat. 1922-1933). Høyen's policy for art can be considered broadly as a parallel to the nation liberal policy. He wanted to strengthen national solidarity with the help of art; the Danes coul be reminded of their history through the use of selected art subjects. By examining and admiring Frederiksborg Castle the Danes could become more Danish. This attempt, led by Høyen, to influence attitudes, turned out give results; when Frederiksborg Castle was badly damaged by fire in 1859 many regarded it as a national disaster and as a symbol of the country's steady decline in status. The fire gave the castle renewed actuality as an artistic *motif*. Heinrich Hansen, who just before the fire had made a series of drawings and paintings of the castle exterior and particularly of its individual rooms, in the following years exhibited many paintings of the castle "as it was in Christian IV's time"; as the artistic director of the porcelain factory, Bing and Grøndahl, he became "the father of the Christian IV style".

Constantin Hansen also belonged to the circle of young artists who followed the advice and guidance of Høyen. In spite of this he thought that Kronborg offered more artistic potential than Frederiksborg. During the summer of 1834 he made studies of the castle and wrote to his friend Jørgen Roed about the many interesting artistic possibilities which the castle contained. A formalistic attitude can be traced in Constantin Hansen's letters: an aesthetic which later became dominant among the artists who painted the castle around the turn of the century (see cat. 1948, 1953, 1954). The architectural painters' interest in Christian IV's castles, lasting over a span of more than 150 years (1780-1940), stemmed from the fact that the buildings were regarded as part of the national cultural heritage and from romantic notions that the King had been his own architect – had even himself particpated in the actual building work.[8] This idea has had to be modified to some extent, but it was true that the King took a lively part in the planning and construction of his many buildings, not least in questions concerning the theoretical background of the building-plans, and corrections of the architects' drawings.

*Christian IV by V. Bissen, 1900. Nyboder.*

No other Danish king, after his death, received as much attention from artists as did Christian IV. Both he himself and his buildings were popular subjects for more that 200 years, especially during the period 1830-1870. His popularity seems to be growing again; in recent years several paintings with the King as central figure, or paintings of his castles, have been sold by auction in Denmark and abroad. Several were bought by private collectors in England and the U.S.A.

One can only guess at the reasons for this growing interest. Apart from the increasing general interest in Danish 19th century art, interest in Christian IV *motifs* is probably growing because they maintain the memory of the popular hero and good bourgeois virtues. The paintings furthermore provide opportunities to recall a time when all was still right with the world – at least when seen with hindsight and knowledge of what was to come! The pictures to a great extent pass over in silence the historical facts and contexts. If one wants to learn about those one has to read modern history books. The paintings of the 19th century show "Denmark's Christian" without depth or complexity, simply as the people's hero.

*Vilhelm Kyhn: Frederiksborg Castle seen from the Enclosure (Indelukket), 1844. Present owner unknown.*

*Notes and references*

1. For sources concerning the events at Kolberger Heide, see "Myte og realitet i danmarkshistorien" by Jørgen Mentz and Søren Mørch, 1975.
2. Ludvig Holberg: Dannemarks Riges Historie. 1733, vol. II, p. 856. Niels Slange: Den stormægtigste Konges Christian den Fierdes Historie. 1749, pp. 1242-1243.
3. For national liberal historiography see Leo Tandrup: På sporet af en progressiv historieskrivning. En kritisk analyse af C. F. Allens og A. D. Jørgensens syn på Christian IV, in: "Tradition og kritik. Festskrift til Svend Ellehøj den 8. september 1984.« 1984.
4. J. M. Thiele: Danmarks Folkesagn. 1843, vol. I, p. 58.
5. A. D. Jørgensen: Fyrretyve Fortællinger af Fædrelandets Historie. 1882. 1981 edition, p. 191.
6. Berlingske Tidende 24.4, 21.4, 3.5.1897.
7. N. L. Høyen: Frederiksborg Slot. 1831. In: Høyens Skrifter, by J. L. Ussing, 1871, vol. I, p. 226.
8. Vilhelm Wanscher: Christian IVs Bygninger. 1937.

*Nina Damsgaard*

# The official Christian IV paintings

## *Christian IV on board the Trefoldigheden*

1805

### Christian IV on board the *Trefoldigheden* during the Battle of Kolberger Heide in 1644. 1782

Nicolai Abraham Abildgaard. (Copenhagen 1743 – Copenhagen 1809). Not inscribed
Oil on canvas. 61×37 cm. Frontispiece p. 506
Statens Museum for Kunst inv. 1137 d
Study for a painting in the Great Hall at Christiansborg

Palace. The painting was destroyed in the palace fire of 1794. Some preparatory drawings of Christian IV, which have been attributed to Abildgaard, are in Roskilde Museum (inv. 5-56) and in the Nationalmuseum in Stockholm (inv. NMH 178/1961).
*Literature:* Swane 1926 42f. Bente Skovgaard fig. 15, 19. Bligaard 1978 cat. 28.

1806

## Christian IV on board the *Trefoldigheden* during the Battle of Kolberger Heide in 1644. 1828

Wilhelm Bendz (Odense 1804 – Vicenza 1832). Not inscribed
Oil on canvas. 229.0×202.5 cm
Statens Museum for Kunst inv. 3298
Executed for the "Parolsalen«, a room in Christiansborg Palace, after a study by Abildgaard from 1782 (cat. 1).
*Literature:* Madsen 1905 360. Bligaard 1978 43, 76.

1807

## Christian IV on board the *Trefoldigheden.* 1808

Andreas Flint (Copenhagen 1767 – Copenhagen 1824)
Aquatint with watercolour. 31.0×41.0 cm
Frederiksborg
Inscribed "Kong Christian den Fierde paa Skibet Trefoldigheden i Søeslaget ved Femern mod den svenske Flaade d. 1ste Julii i Aaret 1644. Skiønt bedækket med Saar og mistende sit højre Øje, vedblev den 68-aarige Helt Kommandoen og tilkæmpede sig en vigtig Sejr". "Hans Majestæt Kong Frederik den Siette allerunderdanigst tilegnet af A. Flint". "Malet af C. A. Lorentzen". "Stukket af A. Flint 1808". The painting by C. A. Lorentzen was last on sale in 1956 (Arne Bruun Rasmussen, Auctions 78, 96) and its present owner is unknown.
*Literature:* Bligaard 1978 no. 62.

1808

## Christian IV on board the *Trefoldigheden*

Niels Truslew (Løkken 1762 – Lyngby 1826). Inscribed "N. Truslew SC"
Aquatint with watercolour. 27.0×38.8 cm
Frederiksborg
Executed after a drawing by C. W. Eckersberg from 1803. In 1803 Eckersberg was working on the Christian IV *motif* for the first time (cat. 1809) and did not return to the subject until 1831, when he painted "Christian IV Visiting Tycho Brahe" (Hannover, fort. 438). In 1832 Eckersberg painted another version of the "Trefoldighed" *motif* (cat. 1809). In the first version of the events on board the warship, Eckersberg allows us to see a considerable part of the deck of the ship. The injured King has got to his feet and is pressing his handkerchief against his right eye. In Abildgaard's painting, Christian is depicted pressing the cloth to his left eye, though it was probably his right eye that was damaged.
*Literature:* Hannover 1898 no. 1. Bligaard 1978 no. 59.

1809

## Christian IV on board the *Trefoldigheden.* 1832

Christoffer Wilhelm Eckersberg (Blåkrog 1783 – Copenhagen 1853). Inscribed "E 1832"
Oil on canvas. 45.5×35.5 cm
Frederiksborg A 7210
Eckersberg started working on the subject in 1803 (pen, wash, 23.0×30.0 cm, Arne Bruun Rasmussen, Auction 175, 1965 no. 248) and he returned to it in 1832 when he painted it. This painting may well have taken inspiration from the rendering of Christian IV on board the Trefoldigheden which Bendz had painted in 1828 and which was a sketch by Abildgaard from 1782 (cat. 1805 and 1806). Contrary to the representation of Christian IV on Abildgaard's painting, the painting by Eckersberg de-

*Rosenborg by Constantin Hansen, 1850.*
*Present owner unknown.*

1807

picts the King about to give orders. The work of the various members of the crew is here described at length. A. Kittendorf (1820-1902) did a lithograph after this painting.
*Literature:* Hannover 1898 no. 467. Bligaard 1978 no. 78.

1810

## Christian IV on board the *Trefoldigheden* with the dead body of Eiler Ulfeldt

Rasmus Christiansen (Bjertrup 1863 – Copenhagen 1940)
Etching
Frederiksborg.

1810a

## Christian IV on board the *Trefoldigheden*

Constantin Hansen (Rome 1804 – Copenhagen 1880)
Pencil. 21.5×32.5 cm
Orlogsmuseet.

1811

## Christian IV on board the *Trefoldigheden*

Historical Painting. One in a Series of 9 "Denmark Pictures". 1975
Stig Brøgger. Born in Slagelse 1941
Serigraphy, tempera on canvas. 118×89 cm
Private collection
From a series of serigraphically reproduced double pictures representing principally the classics in the history of Danish Art. By inverting the historical *motifs* and placing them upside down in the same picture – just like a playing card – the artist obtains the effect of the lower part being visually emptied of its contents and the upper part drained of any historical pathos.

## *Sketches and studies for the decoration of Christian IV's Chapel in Roskilde Cathedral*

1812

### Study for a sepulchral monument to Christian IV

Laurids de Thurah (Århus 1706 – Copenhagen 1759)
Indian ink and wash. 43.0×44.0 cm
Nasjonalgalleriet, Oslo inv. B 15765
Christian IV's chapel in Roskilde Cathedral had stood since its construction in 1614-18 with white undecorated walls. The King himself had ordered a mausoleum, but before it was completed it was destroyed in a fire at the Arsenal. Christian VI revived the idea of a mausoleum erected to both Christian IV and Frederic III and commissioned Thurah to draw a project for a double mausoleum.
*Literature:* Weilbach 1924 84-85.

1813

### Preliminary study with the statue of Christian IV is placed on a pedestal in the Chapel in Roskilde Cathedral. About 1840

Gustav Friederich Hetsch (Stuttgart 1788 – Copenhagen 1864)
Pencil
Roskilde Cathedral archives inv. 1256
The first project for the location of the statue by Thorvaldsen. Hetsch has placed the statue in front of the window pier of the north wall with the coffins of Christian IV and Queen Anne Catherine on either side of the monument. See also cat. 1907-1908.

*1812*

*1822*

1814

## Study for a pedestal to support the statue of Christian IV in Roskilde Cathedral. 1840

Gustav Friederich Hetsch. Inscribed “13. Sept. 1840”
Watercolour
Roskilde Cathedral archives inv. 1255
The second project for the location of the monument.

1815

## Project for setting up the statue on a sarcophagus. 1841

Gustav Friederich Hetsch
Watercolour
Roskilde Cathedral archives inv. 1257
The drawing is inscribed “Andet Udkast 1841” and depicts Thorvaldsen’s statue placed on a sarcophagus into which the King’s coffin has been lowered. The artist suggests that the monument should be located by the window pier of the north wall.

1816

## Project for the monument and its location. 1841

Gustav Friederich Hetsch. Inscribed "Hetsch 1844"
Pencil
Roskilde Cathedral archives inv. 1258
The idea of the above project is developed further. On the back of the drawing is a later study for the monument.

1817

## Study for the monument to Christian IV. About 1841-1842

Gustav Friedrich Hetsch
Watercolour
Roskilde Cathedral archives inv. 1259
This study differs from cat. 13 as regards certain details.
*Literature:* DK III, 3 1521.

1818

## Studies for the glass paintings in the north windows. 1841 and 1842

Gustav Friederich Hetsch
Watercolour
Roskilde Cathedral archives inv. 1269 a-b
a: "Første Udkast 1841" for one of the north windows. Inscribed “Det approberede Udkast er afleveret til Bygningsdirectør”.
b: Studies for the two windows. These studies are different from each other and both differ from a. They are inscribed “Hetsch 1842”.

1819

## Project for the decoration of the walls of the Chapel. 1843

Gustav Friederich Hetsch
Pencil
Roskilde Cathedral archives inv. 1263
The north wall with the monument for Christian IV opposite the wall and a table inscribed with the King’s name and the year 1843. The east wall is adorned with wall paintings and on the south wall is “Frederik III på sin ligseng” painted by Ditmar.

1820

## Project for the decoration of Christian IV’s Chapel in Roskilde Cathedral. Plan of the floor. 1844

Gustav Friederich Hetsch
Pencil
Roskilde Cathedral archives inv. 1253

Plan of the floor including a project for the location of coffins and sarcophagi. Before the pilaster, separating the two windows in the north wall, the monument for Christian IV by Hetsch and Thorvaldsen has been sketched in outline.

1821

## Project for the decoration of Christian IV's Chapel in Roskilde Cathedral. Survey. 1844

Gustav Friederich Hetsch
Pencil
Roskilde Cathedral archives inv. 1254
In this study Hetsch has sketched out a project for placing Thorvaldsen's statue in front of the pilaster which separates the two north windows. He has placed the King's coffin in the middle of the floor surrounded by a lattice and by other royal coffins and sarcophagi placed along the walls. These objects have been added to the drawing afterwards, probably between 1854-1860. On the back of the drawing "Whitsunday, 1860", Hetsch sketched out the King's coffin surrounded by a lattice and he also drew a map of the starry vault. The latter is probably contemporaneous with the survey of the floor.

1822

## Project for decorating the north, east, and south walls with wall paintings and the windows of the north wall with glass paintings. 1844

Gustav Friedrich Hetsch. Inscribed "1844"
Watercolour
Roskilde Cathedral archives inv. 1260
Hetsch's project of painted panels illustrating episodes in the life of Christian IV was not carried out. According to Hetsch's project the panels were to illustrate "Christian IV on board the "Trefoldigheden", "Queen Sophie instructing the Young Prince Christian", "Christian IV at the North Cape", and "Christian IV the Architect".
*Literature:* DK III, 3 1505 H. Bligaard 1978 nos. 152-153.

1823

## The embellishment of the north-eastern corner of the Chapel. 1844

Gustav Friedrich Hetsch. Inscribed "Hetsch 1844"
Watercolour
Roskilde Cathedral archives inv. 1261
Perspective rendering of the north-eastern corner of the Chapel showing Thorvaldsen's statue on top of the sarcophagus between the windows of the north wall along with other sarcophagi on the floor, wall paintings, and glass paintings.

*1823*

1824

## The decoration of the northern part of the Chapel. 1844

Gustav Friederich Hetsch. Inscribed "H 1844"
Watercolour
Roskilde Cathedral archives inv. 1262
Perspective rendering of the Chapel as seen from the south facing north. The arrangement and the decorations are identical with those of cat. 1823.

1825

## Project for the decoration of the south wall. 1844

Gustav Friedrich Hetsch. Inscribed "Hetsch 1844"
Watercolour
Roskilde Cathedral archives inv. 1264 a-b

1826
## Project for the decoration of the east wall. 1844
Gustav Friedrich Hetsch. Inscribed "Hetsch 1844"
Watercolour
Roskilde Cathedral archives inv. 1265 a-b

1827
## Project for the decoration of the north wall. 1844
Gustav Friederich Hetsch. Inscribed "Hetsch 1844"
Watercolour
Roskilde Cathedral archives inv. 1266

1828

## Project for the decoration of the west wall. 1844

Gustav Friedrich Hetsch. Inscribed "Hetsch 1844"
Watercolour
Roskilde Cathedral archives inv. 1267

1829

## Plan of the starry vault. 1844

Gustav Friederich Hetsch. Inscribed "Hetsch 1844"
Pencil

1830

## The north-eastern corner of the Chapel. 1854

Gustav Friederich Hetsch. Inscribed "28. Sept. 1854 H"
Watercolour
Roskilde Cathedral archives inv. 1268
Once again the statue has been placed on a pedestal by the window pier of the north wall and the King's coffin in the middle of the floor surrounded by a lattice. The east window, which Heinrich Eddelien had got permission to darken in 1849 is now reopened and there are no glass paintings in the north windows as Hetsch had projected. The portrait medallions by Eddelien, which were painted in 1852 shortly before his death and completed by Hilker in 1854, are visible in the frieze in the uppermost part of the walls.

1831

## Study for the decoration of Christian IV's Chapel in Roskilde Cathedral. (1845)

Heinrich Eddelien (Greifswald 1802 – Stuer 1852)
Pen, black ink, brush, watercolour showing faint traces of pencil, gold bronze. 62.8×42.6 cm. Not inscribed
Den kgl. Kobberstiksamling Td. 640,2
In 1845, when Eddelien did his preliminary sketches for the decoration of the walls, he had taken on the subjects of the descriptive scenes from G. F. Hetsch (cat. 1819, 1822, 1825-28). Due to the death of Eddelien in 1852, however, only the vaults and the lunette sections were completed after his design. In the sketch is a project for a representation of Christian IV as a child. Above this are two friezes depicting episodes in the life of Christian IV: "Ove Gjedde, Admiral of the Realm, Presents the King with the Treaty for the Surrender of Tranquebar" and "Christian IV Meets Gustav Adolph". In the lunette section a representation "Faith, Hope and Charity".
*Literature:* Bligaard 1978 nos. 154-155.

1832

## Study for the decoration of Christian IV's Chapel in Roskilde Cathedral. (1845)

Heinrich Eddelien
Pen, black ink, brush, watercolour showing faint traces of pencil, gold bronze. 62.8×42.6 cm. Not inscribed
Den kgl. Kobberstiksamling Td. 640,3
Christian IV on board the Trefoldigheden and Christian IV at the North Cape. In the lunette section an allegory representing "Time, Victory, and History".
*Literature:* Bligaard 1978 nos. 154-155.

1833

## Study for the decoration of Christian IV's Chapel in Roskilde Cathedral. (1845)

Heinrich Eddelien
Pen, black ink, brush, watercolour showing faint traces of pencil, gold bronze. 62.8×42.6 cm. Not inscribed
Den kgl. Kobberstiksamling Td. 640,4
On the left: Christoffer Rosenkrantz on Trial and on the right Christian IV the Architect. In the lunette an allegory representing "Justice, Moderation, and Truth".
*Literature:* Bligaard 1978 nos. 154-155.

1834

## Study for the decoration of Christian IV's Chapel in Roskilde Cathedral. (1845)

Heinrich Eddelien
Pen, black ink, brush, watercolour showing faint traces of pencil, gold bronze. 62.8×42.6 cm. Not inscribed
Den kgl. Kobberstiksamling Td. 640,5
Eddelien intented Hetsch's sarcophagus with Thorvaldsen's statue to be placed by the north wall of the chapel (cat. 1907-08).
*Literature:* Bligaard 1978 nos. 154-155.

1834a

## Christian IV on board the *Trefoldigheden*

Constantin Hansen
Pencil on paper. 215×325 cm
Orlogsmuseet.

1835

## Christian IV on board the *Trefoldigheden*

Wilhelm Marstrand (Copenhagen 1810 – Copenhagen 1873)
Brown ink, pencil. 39.2×53.4 cm
Roskilde Museum inv. 1-58
This drawing and the following numbers of the catalogue are all studies for the large painting in Christian IV's

1838

Chapel in Roskilde Cathedral. When Marstrand took over the work on the wall paintings in the Chapel he also took over the subjects which had been sanctioned by Christian VIII about the middle of the 1840s. At that time the lunette of the vaults had already been decorated with allegories and Christian IV on board the Trefoldigheden and Rosenkrantz on Trial went well with the allegories of The Goddess of Victory and The Goddess of Justice.

1836

## Christian IV on board the *Trefoldigheden*

Wilhelm Marstrand
Watercolour and washed ink, mounted on canvas. 104.5×154.5 cm
Roskilde Museum inv. 12-71.

1837

## Christian IV on board the *Trefoldigheden*

Wilhelm Marstrand
Brown ink and pen on blue paper. 23.2×33.3 cm
Roskilde Museum inv. 1436-222.

1838

## Christian IV on board the *Trefoldigheden*

Wilhelm Marstrand
Pen and washed Indian ink on blue paper. 42.9×55.8 cm
Frederiksborg A 8197.

1839

## Christian IV on board the *Trefoldigheden*

Wilhelm Marstrand. Not inscribed
Pencil and pen. 18.4×27.3 cm
Den kgl. Kobberstiksamling Td 696,1
*Literature:* Bligaard 1978 no. 157.

1840

## Christian IV on board the *Trefoldigheden*

Wilhelm Marstrand. Not inscribed
Pencil, brush, and Indian ink. 37.5×51.0 cm
Den kgl. Kobberstiksamling Td. 696,8
*Literature:* Bligaard 1978 no. 158.

1841

## Christian IV on board the *Trefoldigheden*. 1861

Wilhelm Marstrand
Pen, watercolour. 25.5×34.7 cm. The frame has been mounted on to the picture
Den Hirschprungske Samling inv. 1618

This study was shown at the Charlottenborg Exhibition in 1861. The mounted-on frame was executed by Heinrich Hansen. After this study and cat. 1852 had been shown at the exhibition, Marstrand was commissioned in 1862 to execute large-sized paintings of the scenes in oil on plaster in Christian IV's Chapel in Roskilde Cathedral.
*Literature:* Bligaard 1978 no. 159.

1842

## Christian IV on board the *Trefoldigheden*

Wilhelm Marstrand. Not inscribed
Oil on canvas. 115×162 cm
Ny Carlsberg Glyptotek inv. 821 A
Study for the large paiting in Christian IV's Chapel in Roskilde Cathedral. A similar study is at Frederiksborg (A 7895).
*Literature:* K. Madsen 1905 384-396. Oppermann 1920 54-55. Bligaard 1978 no. 1650. Beretning fra Carlsbergfondet 1973-74 65.

1843

## Christian IV on board the *Trefoldigheden*

Wilhelm Marstrand
Pencil and watercolour on paper, mounted on canvas. 450×620 cm
Roskilde Cathedral
Cartoon for the painting in the Chapel at Roskilde. Apparently Marstrand used no kind of adjuncts such as a stippling system or squaring when he transferred his pictures to the walls. There is a strong presumption that he must have sketched out on the wall directly from the cartoon. The cartoons for this picture and for Rosenkrantz on Trial differ from each other in more than one respect.

1844

## Christian IV on board the *Trefoldigheden*

Joel Ballin (Vejle 1822 – Copenhagen 1885)
Steel engraving. 52.5×77.0 cm
Aarhus Kunstmuseum
Ballin's last work, which is based on Marstrand's painting in Roskilde Cathedral.

1845

## Christian IV passing judgement on Rosenkrantz

Wilhelm Marstrand
Pen, brown ink on top of pencil. 13.0×20.5 cm
Roskilde Museum inv. 258
This drawing and the following numbers in the catalogue are preliminary studies for the large painting in Christian IV's Chapel in Roskilde Cathedral. In this study Marstrand has chosen to place the throne in the middle, so that the scene is seen frontally and Rosenkrantz from the rear. Later on, he was to move the throne to the left part of the picture, which gave him more space for the floor. Thereby Rosenkrantz and the halberdiers were segregated still further from the other figures in the picture.

1846

## Christian IV passing judgment on Rosenkrantz

Wilhelm Marstrand
Pen, brown ink on paper. 24.0×21.0 cm
Roskilde Museum
Here Marstrand is comparing "goodness and justice" in the shape of the King with "wickedness and falseness" in the shape of Rosenkrantz.

1847

## Christian IV pronouncing sentence upon Rosenkrantz

Wilhelm Marstrand
Ink on top of pencil on blue paper. 12.3×11.5 cm
Roskilde Museum inv. 272-67.

1848

## Christian IV pronouncing sentence upon Rosenkrantz

Wilhelm Marstrand
Ink on top of pencil on blue paper. 11.0×18.0 cm
Roskilde Museum inv. 251-68.

1849

## Christian IV pronouncing sentence upon Rosenkrantz

Wilhelm Marstrand
Ink on blue paper. 13.5×11.0 cm
Roskilde Museum inv. 272-67.

1850

## Christian IV pronouncing sentence upon Rosenkrantz

Wilhelm Marstrand
Watercolour on top of pencil on blue paper. 19.5×32.0 cm
Roskilde Museum inv. 295-62.

1851

## Christian IV commanding the executioner to take off Rosenkrantz's Collar (of the Order of the Elephant)

Wilhelm Marstrand. Not inscribed
Pencil, pen, watercolour. 19.2×26.8 cm

*1852*
Den kgl. Kobberstiksamling Td. 696,3
*Literature:* Bligaard 1978 no. 162.

1852

## Christian IV pronouncing sentence upon Christopher Rosenkrantz. 1861

Wilhelm Marstrand
Pen, watercolour. 25.3×34.7 cm. Frame mounted on the picture
Den Hirschsprungske Samling inv. 1620
This project was exhibitied at Charlottenborg in 1861. The mounted-on frame was executed by Heinrich Hansen. See cat. 1841.
*Literature:* K. Madsen 1905 391. Bligaard 1978 no. 163.

1853

## Cartoon for Christopher Rosenkrantz on Trial

Wilhelm Marstrand
Pencil and watercolour on paper which has been mounted on canvas in two pieces: a: 200×630 cm; b.: 245×630 cm
Roskilde Cathedral
Cartoon for a wall painting in Christian IV's Chapel in Roskilde Cathedral (see cat. 1843). The main argument in favour of using the sentence-*motif* as well as the Trefoldigheds-*motif* for the decoration was that, in this way, two of the King's most characteristic personal qualities would be highlighted: his sense of justice and his courage. Nevertheless this decision led to a controversy in the press, where it was argued that the incident of Rosenkrantz's trial was hardly important enough to justify the prominent place the painting would be given in the Chapel.

1854

## Christian IV pronouncing sentence upon Christopher Rosenkrantz

Lithography. 27.3×40.0 cm
Frederiksborg
Executed after the painting by Marstrand in Christian IV's Chapel in Roskilde Cathedral.

## *Adolf Tidemand's painting for Oslo City Hall*

1855

### Study for an unfinished painting "Christian IV founding Christiania". 1875

Adolph Tidemand (Mandal 1814–Christiania 1876)
Pencil. 20.5×24.9 cm
Kobberstikksamlingen, Nasjonalgalleriet, Oslo inv. 4138
In 1874 King Oscar II commissioned Tidemand to paint a picture celebrating the 250th anniversary of Christiania. The painting was to be hung in "Repræsentantsalen" (Hall of Representatives) in Olso's new City Hall. However, Tidemand died before the picture was finished and the City Hall building was not completed either. A number of sketches and studies enable us to follow Tidemand's work on the subject and the composition. In this early composition-study, some of the figures have already reached their final form. The kneeling surveyor in the foreground and his assistant with the stick in the middle are maintained in the succeeding studies, while the King and his two companions are changed and moved several times.
*Literature:* Brenna 1980 51, 44.

1856

### Study for Christian IV founding Christiania. 1875

Adolph Tidemand
Pencil. 20.4×25.0 cm
Kobberstikksamlingen, Nasjonalgalleriet, Oslo inv.B 4137
The left part of the composition has reached its final stage with the officer and the deputation of citizens. The surveyours, the King, and the Mayor also remain the same in the succeeding sketches. The ditchers on the right and the man with the top hat behind the Mayor were later to disappear. Likewise, Akershus Castle has not yet reached its final form.
*Literature:* Brenna 1980 51, 45.

1857

### Study for Christian IV founding Christiania. 1875

Adolph Tidemand
Pencil. 47.7×40.9 cm
Kobberstikksamlingen, Nasjonalgalleriet, Oslo inv. 4531
Here, the King and his two attendants are drawn with great accuracy as are the two gentlemen standing next to the Mayor. The man in the flat hat, who has replaced the man in top hat, is Nils Glostrup, Mayor of Oslo.
*Literature:* Brenna 1980 52, 46.

1858

### Photography of a study in charcoal for Christian IV founding Christiania

Adolph Tidemand
Kobberstikksamlingen, Nasjonalgalleriet, Oslo
Tidemand did a charcoal sketch in full size, but this sketch remained in Düsseldorf where Tidemand used to stay for long periods. The charcoal sketch is belived to have been lost. All the details are explained on the drawing in order that Oscar II, by whom it had been commissioned, could sign his final approval. Contrary to the earlier sketches, some of the figures in the charcoal study have taken up positions like theatre actors posing for the photographer. Christian IV, for one, is no longer studying the town-plan but looking out of the picture towards the spectator.
*Literature:* Brenna 1980 53, 47.

1859

### Study in oil for Christian IV founding Christiania. 1875

Adolph Tidemand
Oil on canvas. 22.5×32.5 cm. Colour-plate XLII
Kobberstikksamlingen, Nasjonalgalleriet, Oslo inv. 799
This study follows the charcoal drawing closely. Originally, Akershus was sketched according to the drawing, but in 1876 it was painted over as Tidemand now had some new information on what the fortress looked like in the days of Christian IV.
*Literature:* Dietrichson 1878 123,209. Brenna 1980 55, 48.

1860

### Christian IV, based on an engraving by C. Fritzsch from 1735. 1875

Adolph Tidemand
Pencil. 20.5×14.9 cm
Kobberstikksamlingen, Nasjonalgalleriet, Oslo inv. B 4543
Compared with the engraving, Tidemand's copy is laterally reversed. The drawing is inscribed with various notes concerning colours: "Haar mørkebrunt", "Ansigtet brunligt Skjæg blond", "Hvid Krave". By the left sleeve: "Brunfigureret Plyds eller lignende", on trousers and jacket: "sort", on the bootlegs: "Mørk Læder", and on the topband lace of the boots: "Hvid". The inspiration for the inscriptions may well have come from the colours in Karel van Mander's portrait of the King at Amalienborg, which Tidemand saw during his stay in Copenhagen in the summer of 1875.
*Literature:* Brenna 1980 50, 43.

*1867*

1861

## Preliminary study of Christian IV for the painting of the foundation of Christiania

Adolph Tidemand
Pencil. 61.7×46.8 cm
Kobberstikksamlingen, Nasjonalgalleriet, Oslo inv. B 4533
Tidemand has used his copy of Fritzsch's engraving for this study. This drawing represents the final stage in the work preliminary to the painting. It is complete with a square grid in order to faciliate the transfer of the design to the cartoon for the large painting. The contemporary portrait of the King was not very important to Tidemand during the period when he had chosen to depict the King studying the plan for his new city. The sketched copy, however, becomes important when the artist, at the last moment, decides to give prominence to the King by making him look out towards the spectator.
*Literature:* Brenna 1980 50.

# *The large historical paintings in the Frederiksborg Museum*

1862

## The Priest, Ole Vind, repeating his sermon before Christian IV

Etching
Frederiksborg
Etched after a painting at Frederiksborg (A 27) by Carl Christian Andersen (1849-1906), which was ordered by the Museum Board in 1882. The subject has taken inspiration from the story of how Christian IV appointed Ole Vind, Court Chaplain, after a sermon, in which Ole Vind – according to the King's courtiers – had spoken slightingly of him. In the middle of the 1860s Marstrand painted various versions of this theme (in private collections) and the poet N. F. S. Grundtvig wrote a poem on the incident. There is a smaller version by C. C. Andersen (Arne Bruun Rasmussen, Auction 191, 1966 no. 85).

1862a

## Christian IV's Coronation Procession

Otto Bache (Roskilde 1838 – Copenhagen 1927)
Oil on canvas. 46×77 cm
Private collection
Preliminary study for the large painting from 1887 (Frederiksborg A 376).

1863

## Christian IV's Coronation Procession. 1859

Heinrich Hansen (Haderslev 1821 – Frederiksberg 1890)
Indian ink on transparent paper. 20.3×25.5 cm
Frederiksborg A 5012
Executed after a woven tapestry by Karel van Mander for Frederiksborg Castle. 1617-1619.
*Literature:* Dansk Kunsthistorie Vol. 2 1973 166.

1864

## Christian IV's Coronation Procession

Chr. Rosenberg (Copenhagen 1816 – Copenhagen 1883)
Pencil on paper. 15×21 cm
Frederiksborg A 3164
The Procession is seen passing through the streets of Copenhagen followed by rejoicing spectators. In the front rank a rider, then the King on horseback under a canopy carried by four members of the Council of the Realm. Then comes a large procession on horseback. Two women are strewing flowers before the procession.

1865

## Christian IV's Coronation Procession

Georg Paulli (Rocklitz 1838 – Frederiksberg 1928)
Xylography
Frederiksborg.

1866

## The Apotheosis of the Danish Navy. Study for an unifinished monumental painting

Otto Bache
Oil on canvas. 20.6×27.0 cm. Signed "Otto Bache"
Frederiksborg A 8205
Danish naval heroes throughout the ages are depicted

1864

together on the deck of a ship. In the foreground Christian IV in a red costume sitting in an armchair. Standing from left to right: Peter Willemoes, Olfert Fischer, Niels Juel, Iver Huitfeldt, Cord Adeler, Herluf Trolle, Peder Skram, Absalon, Otto Rud, C. V. Jessen, Tordenskjold, and Steen Bille. Victoria, Goddess of Victory, is carrying a rudder and the Danish national coat of arms. This study has taken inspiration from the poem "Ved Toldboden steg en Matros i Land" by Christian Winther. The poem ends "... får jeg lov at gå agter ud, til chefens kahyt den høje, der møder jeg Wessel, Juel og Rud og ham med det ene øje". In 1882, this study was shown to the Board of the Frederiksborg Museum. However, the Board turned down a proposal to have a large painting executed after the study, probably because it was the wish of the Museum Board that the Museum should mainly house representations of specific historical events. A charcoal drawing of the same subject is in "Søofficersforeningen" (the Society of Naval Officers).
*Literature:* Bligaard 1978 no. 171. Årsskrift fra Carlsbergfondet, Frederiksborgmuseet og Ny Carlsbergfondet 1984 77.

1867
## Christian IV as shipbuilder at the Royal Dockyard

August Jerndorff (Oldenburg 1846 – Copenhagen 1906)
Oil on canvas. 14×19 cm
Private collection
Study for an unfinished painting, ordered by the Frederiksborg Museum.

1868
## Christian IV in Coronation Robe

C. W. Eckersberg. Not inscribed
Pen, watercolour. 25.4×17.7 cm
Frederiksborg
Study for the painting in the "Solemnitetssal", a hall at the Sorø Academy. In 1827, when a new main building for Sorø Academy by Peder Malling was finished, the "Solemnitetssal" was adorned with full-length portraits of the five Danish kings who had been of special importance to the Academy. Eckersberg made sketches for the portraits which were then executed in large dimensions by some of his pupils. Albert Küchler did the final portrait of Christian IV for the Assembly Hall. This painting was shown at the Charlottenborg Exhibition in 1827 under the title "Portrait of King Christian IV" (Reitzel's Record).
*Literature:* Danmark no. 3 1944 85. Bligaard 1978 no. 77.

1869
## Study for the mosaic decoration of the tower base of the Royal Exchange. 1953

Boye Givskov (Born in Copenhagen 1912)
The mosaic was executed in Ravenna 1953-57
Private collection
*Literature:* Koloristerne 1957 no. 83.

*1868*

## *The popular hero Christian IV as warlord*

1871

### Christian IV leading his troops. A scene from the Kalmar War (1611-1613)

Christian Rosenberg (1816-1883)
Pencil on paper. 16×22 cm
Frederiksborg A 3170
The King is riding across a square where soldiers of the infantry are fighting. He is escorted by two officers on horseback. In the mid-foreground a dead soldier, on the right a soldier watching the others. In the left foreground a ruin and some shattered timber. Christian IV was disgusted at the ravaging and burning during the war, which he found to be undignified. He consequently forbade it, but with very little success, as plunder and spoils were the main rewards for the soldiers participating.

1872

### Christian Barnekow sacrificing his life to save Christian IV

Christian Rosenberg
Pencil on paper. 14.7×21.0 cm
Frederiksborg A 3172
When, after the Battle of Skellinge Hede in Halland in 1612, Christian IV had a fall with his horse, he was surprised by a superior Swedish army. Christian Barnekow, who was escorting the King, offered him the use of his horse saying, "Kongen min Hest, Fjenden mit Liv og Gud min Sjæl" (My horse to my King, my life to my enemy, my soul to God). Shortly after this, Barnekow was killed by the enemy. History, however, has been silent on this incident. It is Swedish tradition, written down in the 17th century at the earliest and not printed until about 1750 that has Barnekow sacrificing his own life to save his King. This story became a popular legend from the late 18th century. Rosenberg stresses the dramatic and dangerous by depicting the King's horse sinking deep into a swamp, while Barnekow with his rapier is pointing towards the hostile riders, who are seen in the background approaching at a gallop.
*Literature:* Bricka 1873 1-21.

1873

### Christian IV falling from his horse at Hameln

Christian Rosenberg
Pencil on paper. 14.7×21.0 cm
Frederiksborg A 3173
In 1625 Christian IV was severely injured in a fall from his horse during a tour of inspection to the ramparts of Hameln. In Rosenborg's drawing, the King is depicted lying unconscious beside his horse, surrounded by six men. Two of the men are trying to lift the King up while a third is attending to the horse.

1874

### Christian IV's vision during morning prayers at Rothenburg Castle. (1823)

Ditlev Blunck (Münstersdorf 1798 – Hamburg 1854). Not inscribed.
Oil on canvas. 124×100 cm. Colour-plate XLIII
Statens Museum for Kunst inv. 64
In 1626, prior to the decisive encounter with the troops of Commander Tilly on the plains of Lutter am Barenberg, Christian IV was haunted by nightmares and visions during which he kept seeing the tortured figure of Christ, bleeding in pain and blasphemed. The King was so wrapped up in his vision that he ordered a painting to be made of it. Several versions of this painting are known. One version, inscribed with the King's own manuscript account of the event, is at Rosenborg. In this

19th century interpretation of the event, Blunck has depicted the King at morning prayers just before leaving for the battlefield. The figure of Christ in Blunck's painting bears a strong resemblance to the depiction in the Rosenborg painting. The King is wearing the collar (of the Order of the Elephant) and ermine robe, which hardly fits the facts. The painting was acquired by the Royal Art Collection (Statens Museum for Kunst) immediately after it was finished.
*Literature:* Bligaard 1978 no. 93. Johannsen 1984 127-54.

1875

## Slaget vid Lutter. Könung Christians fara och rädding den 17. August 1626

(The Battle of Lutter am Barenberg 17th August 1626)
Carl Andreas Dahlström (Stockholm 1806 – Stockholm 1869)
Lithography. 21.3×32 cm
Frederiksborg
Dahlström, Swedish painter and lithographer, was commissioned by Karl XIV Johan to execute a number of pictures of scenes from the Thirty Years' War (1845-47, 2nd Edition 1851-52).

1876

## Christian IV on board a warship during the Battle of Hamburg 1630

Woodcut. 15.7×10.4 cm
Frederiksborg
Woodcut after a drawing by Rasmus Christiansen, executed by F. Hendrichsen.

1877

## Albert Eitzen, Mayor of Hamburg, sueing for peace with Christian IV on behalf of the citizens of Hamburg in 1630

Artist unknown
Litography. 15.7×10.4 cm
Frederiksborg.

1878

## Christian IV, Iver Vind, Eiler Ulfeldt, and Knud Ulfeldt on board a warship in 1630

Rasmus Christiansen
Woodcut. 13×12.8 cm
Frederiksborg.

1879

## Christian IV at the Battle of List

Wilhelm Heuer (Hamburg 1813 – Hamburg 1890)
Lithography. 22.8×16.6 cm
Frederiksborg
In January 1644 Swedish troops were forcing their way up through Jutland from the south. Danish troops, however, succeeded in preventing a Swedish invasion of Funen, and an attack on Sealand was likewise prevented.

*1873*

Christian IV decided to attack Sweden from the sea, where Swedish military power was not as strong, though it was aided by a Dutch auxiliary fleet. The King encountered the Dutch fleet in Listerdyb, the narrow strait between Sild and Rømø, on 16th May 1644. The strong Dutch fleet finally had to admit the defeat and sailed home.

1880

### Christian IV in the company of Iver Vind

Etching. 13.7×14.8 cm
Frederiksborg
After a drawing by Rasmus Christiansen.

1881

### Christian IV holding a Council of War on board a warship

Rasmus Christiansen
Etching. 14.8×14.3 cm
Frederiksborg
Christian IV together with the admirals Joachim Grabow and Pros Mund, the captains Staller and Claus Kaas, Jørgen Vind, Admiral of the Realm, and Corfitz Ulfeldt, Lord High Steward. The "Council of War" may well be an "artistic reconstruction" displaying how Rasmus Christiansen imagined such a council might have been conducted during the Battle of Kolberger Heide near Femern in 1644.

1882

### Christian IV visiting the Royal Dockyard

Woodcut. 13.3×10.8 cm
Frederiksborg
Executed by F. Hendrichsen after a drawing by Rasmus Christiansen.

## *Christian IV as architect*

1883

### Christian IV as architect

Wilhelm Marstrand (1810-1873)
Watercolour and pen. 18.8.×25.6 cm
Den Hirschsprungske Samling inv. 1619
Study for the decoration in Christian IV's Chapel in Roskilde Cathedral (see also cat. 1841, 1852). The architectural setting is by Heinrich Hansen.
*Literature:* Karl Madsen 1905 384.

1884

### Christian IV as architect

Wilhelm Marstrand
Pencil, brush, Indian ink. 37.2×51.5 cm
Den kgl. Kobberstiksamling
Study displaying an alternative project for a painting in Christian IV's Chapel in Roskilde Cathedral. Christian IV is presented with the plans for the Exchange in the Audience Hall at Rosenborg Castle. Among the paintings on the wall behind the King are representations of buildings by Christian IV: Frederiksborg Castle and the Round Tower.
*Literature:* Bligaard 1978 cat. 161.

1885

### Christian IV paying out wages to the builders at Frederiksborg Castle

Christian Rosenberg (1816-1883)
Pencil on paper. 14.9×21.2 cm
Frederiksborg A 3176
The King is sitting on the carved boulder in the Indelukket (Enclosure) near Frederiskborg Castle paying out wages to the builders. Behind the King a secretary is keeping accounts by means of a list. The workers are grouped around the King. In the foreground two noblemen; in the background the castle surrounded by scaffoldings. Rosenberg probably did this drawing after a painting he had already executed of the same subject and which is now in an American private collection. The subject was submitted for the Neuhausen competition in 1843, and Rosenberg's painting was executed and exhibited in that same year. In 1858, Edvard Lehmann exhibited a painting of the identical subject (in a private collection), and yet another depiction of the subject is known by an unnamed artist (see cat. 1886).
*Literature:* Bligaard 1978 no. 176. Rosenberg's picture: Winkel and Magnussen, Auction 168, 1935 no. 215. Arne Bruun Rasmussen, Auction no. 161, 1965, no. 162. Lehmann's picture: Winkel and Magnussen, Auction 144, 1933 no. 167.

1886

### Christian IV paying out wages to the builders at Frederiksborg Castle

Artist unknown
Oil on canvas. 32×30 cm
Private collection
In 1843 Rosenberg won the Neuhausen competition for a painting of the same *motif.* The painting was exhibited at Charlottenborg in the same year. In 1858 Edvard Lehmann painted another version which displays Christian IV sitting among the workers in Frederiksborg Slotshegn with the Castle as background. Unfortunately, it has not been possible to trace these paintings.

*1883*

1887

## Christian IV paying out the wages

August Schiøtt (Helsingør 1823 – Hellebæk 1895)
Pencil on paper. 25×34.5 cm
Frederiksborg A 3899
The King and the Queen are sitting under a canopy, while the King is paying out the wages. A secretary behind a desk is keeping accounts of the expenditure. On the back of the paper are two sketches of the King looking at an architectural drawing. The King is surrounded by his consort, a child, and a dog.

1888

## Christian IV laying the foundation stone for a building

August Schiøtt
Pencil on paper. 25.0×34.5 cm
Frederiksborg A 3900.

1889

## Christian IV supervising work on his buildings

August Schiøtt
Pencil on paper. 25.0×34.5 cm
Frederiksborg A 3898
Christian IV is sitting at a table holding an architectural drawing in his left hand while he is considering another plan, which is being presented to him. Behind the King are some men who are mentioned by name. Wilhelm Petersen (architect, 1830-1913); Klein (Vilhelm Klein, architect, 1835-1913); Collin (Edgar, journalist, theatrical historian, writer, 1836-1906); Petersen, actor (Peder Benjamin Theodor, 1851-1908).

1890

### Christian IV inspecting a shipbuilding industry

Christian Rosenberg (1816-1883)
Pencil on paper. 21.8×15.9 cm
Frederiksborg A 3177
Christian IV in conversation with a builder at the Royal Dockyard. In the background boats and ships being built. The King is holding an inch rule in his left hand, which indicates the King's personal role as superviser.

## *Christian IV as the righteous judge*

1891

### Christian IV discovers that Rosenkrantz's document is a forgery

Christian Rosenberg
Pencil on paper. 21.5×15.5 cm
Frederiksborg A 3168
In "Christian den Fjerdes Historie" by Niels Slange, there is an account of how the King unmasks Christoffer Rosenkrantz, who has tried to deceive the widow of Christen Juuel. This account inspired two pictorial *motifs:* The Unmasking, and The Judgment. In this drawing, Rosenberg has depicted the King standing at a window at Rosenborg holding the forged bond to the light in order to examine its watermarks. Rosenkrantz is seen in the background with his hands behind his back. Rosenberg also did a drawing of the King passing sentence on Rosenkrantz (cat. 1892), but the subject became especially popular after Marstrand's painting in Roskilde Cathedral (cat. 1845ff.).
*Literature:* Troels Lund 1873 518-537.

1892

### Christian IV passing sentence on Rosenkrantz

Christian Rosenberg
Pencil on paper. 14.6×19.5 cm
Frederiksborg A 3169
At the centre of the picture is Christian IV pointing at the forged document. In front of him Rosenkrantz, whose head is bent and Karen Strange Ottesdatter, whom Rosenkrantz tried to deceive, sitting with a handkerchief in her hand. Behind the King, four Councillors of the Realm at a table.

1893

### Christian IV passing sentence on the brothers Erik and Niels Friis in 1591

Christian Rosenberg
Pencil on paper. 16.0×21.5 cm
Frederiksborg A 3166
The young King standing before his chair under a

*1892*

1895

canopy at the end of the Council table. A representative of the Council is reading out a document. Two other noblemen are whispering to each other.

## *Christian IV gives away tokens of honour*

1894

### Christian IV presents Tyge Brahe with a Collar of Chivalry

Christian Rosenberg
Pencil on paper. 15.4×22.0 cm
Frederiksborg A 3165
This drawing is executed after the painting by Christian Fædder Høyer from 1815 (in the possession of the Handelskammeret, the Royal Exchange). The young Christian IV standing in a tiled hall escorted by four noblemen. He is presenting Tyge Brahe with a gold chain. Tyge Brahe is sitting on a square stone with his wife and one of his children while making some calculations. His wife is patting a Great Dane. Behind Tyge Brahe some pupils carrying folio editions and a bookcase.

1895

### Christian IV visiting Tycho Brahe. 1831

Christoffer Wilhelm Eckersberg (1783-1853)
Etching. 19.4×24.1 cm
Frederiksborg
In 1831, Eckersberg painted a representation of the young Christian IV on a visit to the astronomer Tycho Brahe at Uranienborg. The painting was acquired by Kunstforeningen in Copenhagen (Hannover no. 438). Shortly after this, he did another version of the subject (Hannover no. 441). The present owners of the pictures are unknown; one of them is in England. Eckersberg then did an etching of the subject which was printed by Kunstforeningen (Hannover no. 10 and 11, p. 416). Eckersberg also drew the subject on wood; the woodcut was executed by Andreas Flinch (Hannover no. 1, p. 426).

## *Christian IV in private*

1896

### Christian IV at a drinking-party at Sivert Grubbe's

Christian Rosenberg
Pencil on paper. 22.5×15.8 cm
Frederiksborg 3171
Probably a study for one of the illustrations in "Christian den Fjerde" by J. N. Høst, which was first published in 1839. The incident is mentioned in the diary of Sivert Grubbe, Chancellery Secretary, under 4th May 1598. In Rosenberg's drawing the young King is depicted in merry company – one of the "drinking companions" has already drunk himself literally under the table, and is being set on his feet again. Another is reaching for the bottle, and the King has got up and is raising his glass while holding on to the table. The drawing follows the diary-notes fairly closely. A representation of a king in this manner, however, would not have been possible before the 19th century, when the genre paintings began to pursue the private and the intimate as a theme.
*Literature:* Bligaard 1978 no. 174.

1896a

### Chancellor Niels Kaas on his deathbed gives Christian IV the key to the treasures of the Realm. 1824

Ditlev Conrad Blunck
Oil on canvas. 119.5×89 cm
Sammlung H-G Mody, Bad Schwartau

1897

### Christian IV falls in love with Karen Andersdatter at a wedding

Christian Rosenberg
Pencil on paper. 14.4×22.2 cm
Frederiksborg A 3167
Illustration for J. N. Høst's biography of Christian IV, in

*1897*

*1901*

which there is an account of the King's encounter with Karen at a wedding in 1613. Høst says that the King fell so deeply in love with her that after dancing with her "he took her back to the castle and made her stay with him". In Rosenberg's drawing the King is seen talking to Karen, while her fiancé and her parents can be seen behind them. In the background the wedding guests, some of whom are drinking at the tables while others are watching a dancing couple. Three musicians are playing on a platform.
*Literature:* Bligaard 1978 no. 175.

1898

## Christian IV ploughing on Samsø. 1845

Niels Simonsen (Copenhagen 1807 – Frederiksberg 1885). Inscribed "N. Simonsen 1845"
Oil on panel. 20.5×25.7 cm
Frederiksborg A 6561
The subject has been taken out of Danmarks Folkesagn by J. M. Thiele in which it is said that once when Christian IV "due to a heavy breeze landed west of Nordbye on the island of Samsøe, the vicar's farm hand was out ploughing. The King then took the plough out of his hand, furrowed for a while and then said to the farm hand: "Give my regards to your master and tell him that the King has ploughed for him" (Vol. I, 1843 p. 63).
*Literature:* Bligaard 1978 no. 173.

1899

## Christian IV plights the troth of the seven-year-old Leonora Christina to Corfitz Ulfeldt in 1628

Christian Rosenberg
Pencil on paper. 20.0×16.0 mm
Frederiksborg 3174
This betrothal scene might be classified as a "private" event, but has nevertheless a certain official quality. In 1833, Adam Müller exhibited a picture which showed another side of the King with his children, namely:

*1906*

Christian IV laying with one of his sons. Sophie, the Queen Dowager, is seen behind them. (Present owner unknown).

1900

## Interior of the winter parlour at Rosenborg showing Christian IV. 1874

Heinrich Hansen (1821-1890). Signed "HH 1874"
Oil on canvas. 37×40 cm
Private collection.

1901

## Christian IV's audience chamber at Rosenborg. 1854

Heinrich Hansen
Oil on canvas. 92.5×121.5 cm
Statens Museum for Kunst inv. 731.

1902

## Christian IV on his deathbed

Christian Rosenberg
Pencil on paper. 22.0×16.0 cm
Frederiksborg A 3175

The old King is lying in a four-poster bed. He is leaning on a servant while receiving Holy Communion ("som en god tærepenge og sikker lejde gennem dødens mørke dal") administered by his Court Chaplain, Mr. Laurids (Jacobsen Hindsholm). Corfitz Ulfeldt is leaning against the foot of the bed covering his eyes with his hand. Leonora Christina is kneeling down by a chair, her hands folded and her eyes looking upwards. The King died "at five o'clock sharp" on 28th February 1648.

1903

## A romance in Rosenborg Gardens

Anton Heinrich Harttung (Copenhagen 1831 – Frederiksberg 1902)
Coloured drawing. 25×20 cm
Teatermuseet
C. N. Rosenkilde as Peter and Mrs. Heiberg (Miss Pätges) as Christine in J. L. Heiberg's vaudeville from 1827. The plot, which was enacted in the Gardens of Rosenborg, was taken from a story by L. Kruse. The music was composed by C. E. F. Weyse, who incidentally lived in Kronprinsessegade, directly opposite the Gardens.
*Literature:* Teatret på Kongens Nytorv 1748-1948 By: Alf Henriques, Torben Krogh etc., 1948 87-88.

1904

## W. C. Holst (1807-98) as Christian IV in his own play *"Maigildet"*. 1829

Christian Bruun (Copenhagen 1794 – Copenhagen 1877)
Handcoloured engraving. 33.1×24.2 cm
Teatermuseet
In 1829 Holst's play "Maigildet", "a dramatic idyll with songs" was performed at the Royal Theatre. The scene was laid in a Zealand fishing hamlet in 1595 and Holst himself took the leading part as the young Christian IV.
*Literature:* Den danske Skueplads. Billeder fortæller Teatrets Historie fra 1722 til idag. 1943 33.

1905

## Dr. Ryge as Christian IV in *"Elverhøj"*. 1828

Christian Bruun
Engraving, tinted by hand. 28.3×21.3 cm
Teatermuseet
Dr. Ryge was the first actor to play the part of Christian IV in J. L. Heiberg's national pageant play, which was performed for the first time at the Royal Theatre in 1828. This engraving of the costume originates from "Danske Theater-Costumer tegnede og udgivne af Christian Bruun". Copenhagen 1828 (3rd Edition).

1906

## Christian IV and Agnete in *"Elverhøj"*. About 1835

Edvard Lehmann (Copenhagen 1815 – Copenhagen 1892). Signed: "El"
Pencil on paper. 26.3×20.0 cm
Teatermuseet
Stage picture dating from one of the early performances of "Elverhøj". Dr. J. C. Ryge as Christian IV and Johanne Luise Heiberg (Miss Pätges) in Act 4, Scene 5, in which Agnete has become aware that the man before her is the King of Denmark and falls on her knees. The character Christian IV had already been created at that time, when Dr. Ryge with the sturdy figure and the broad shoulders had played the part of the King in Nicolai Søtoft's play "Kongens Dom" from 1822. The grandiose figure of Christian IV in this stage picture resembles the interpretation of the King in some of the "Trefoldighed-pictures". Lehmann also worked on this *motif* in a watercolour (present owner unknown).

*1908*

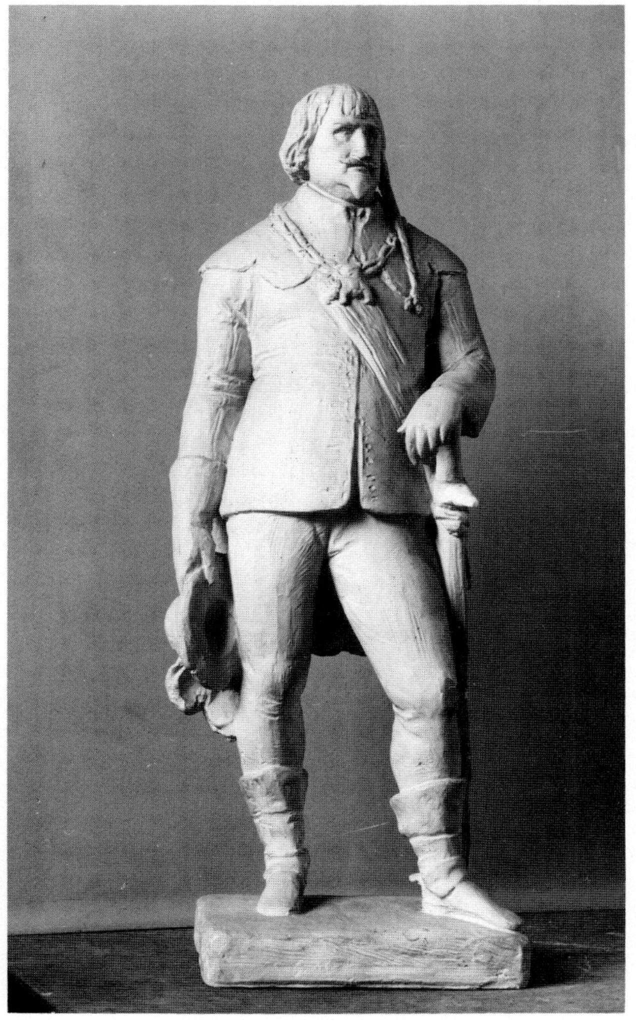

# *Statues representing Christian IV*

1907

## Study for a statue of Christian IV for the Chapel in Roskilde Cathedral

Bertel Thorvaldsen (Copenhagen c. 1770 – Copenhagen 1844). Not inscribed
Pencil on paper. 21.3×14.2 cm
Thorvaldsens Museum
Immediately after the interment of Frederic VI at Roskilde Cathedral, Christian VIII took the initiative for adorning Christian IV's Chapel. In 1840 Thorvaldsen was commissioned by the King to execute a statue for the Chapel. The statue of Christian IV as shown on Thorvaldsen's study is closely related to the royal hero on Abildgaard's painting from 1782 (cat. 1805). Like Abildgaard, Thorvaldsen depicts the King holding a handkerchief against his eye, thus emphasizing the heroic figure of the Battle of Kolberger Heide. In the final stage of his work, however, Thorvaldsen departed from this conception of the King, choosing instead to base his sculpture on the full-length portrait by Karel van Mander at Amalienborg (see cat. 5).
*Literature:* Repholtz 1911 48ff. Thiele IV 1856 109f, 138, 171, 179, 201. Bligaard 1978 no. 150.

1908

## Study for the statue of Christian IV in Roskilde Cathedral

Bertel Thorvaldsen
Plaster. H. 64 cm
Thorvaldsen's Samling på Nysø
On ordering the statue of Christian IV for Roskilde Cathedral, Christian VIII told Thorvaldsen that it had long been a wish of his to "honour that hero" (Repholtz p. 48). The heroic image which Christian IV acquired after the battle on board the *Trefoldigheden* was, however, only stressed in the first preliminary sketch. In the models for the statue, the subdued and "human" element in the King's character is more pronounced than the "heroic". The figure of the King is idealized, his bearing is relaxed, and the whole figure seems to be in equilibrium. The patriotic hero figure has had to give way to the impression of repose and harmony which is required of a statue on a sarcophagus.
*Literature:* Nyrop 1886 84ff. Repholtz 1911 48ff. Baronesse Stampes Erindringer. Publ. by Rigmor Stampe, 1912 62 ff.

*1910*

1910

## Christian IV. Study for a statue. 1875

Brynjulf Bergslien (Voss 1830 – Christiania 1898)
Bronze. H. 63.8 cm. Pedestal: 4×23×22 cm
Nasjonalgalleriet, Oslo inv. 592
In this model, Bergslien has chosen to perpetuate the same situation which inspired Tidemand in the painting for the City Hall – the moment when Christian IV founded Christiania. The King is pointing at the ground with his stick in a commanding gesture while giving orders that the new city should be placed there. The royal power and unyielding will is expressed through the whole figure which is characterized by concentration and balance. In a later project for the re-competition, Bergslien tried to avoid the presumptuous quality which characterized the first study. The result was that the King looked like a prudent elderly overweight gentleman. The study in bronze was cast in 1897 after the plaster-study for the competition. The plaster model was destroyed in the casting.

*Literature:* Thiis 1907 II 113. Revold 1953 II 341. Brenna 1980. Norges Kunsthistorie IV 1981 333.

1911

## Project for a monument to Christian IV. 1876

Vilhelm Dahlerup (Norup 1836 – Copenhagen 1907). Signed at the bottom right "VD 1876"
Pencil, watercolour. 39.2×64.7 cm
Samlingen af arkitekturtegninger. Kunstakademiet inv. A 11596 a.

1912

## Project for a monument to Christian IV on the gable of Holmens Church. 1896

Wilhelm Dahlerup. Not inscribed
Pencil. 61.4×50.9 cm
Samlingen af arkitekturtegninger. Kunstakademiet inv. 11596c.
In the light of the various projects for the location of a monument to Christian IV, Dahlerup suggested that the monument should be made in the shape of an epitaph which was to cover the entire end wall of the choir of Holmens Church. The epitaph was to be executed in accordance with the architectural style of Christian IV and to frame a statue of the King.
*Literature:* Illustreret Tidende 5. April 1896. National Tidende 17. April 1896.

1913

## Project for a monument to Christian IV on the gable of Holmens Church. 1896

Vilhelm Dahlerup. Signed at the bottom right "V Dahlerup 10/3 96"
Pencil, watercolour. 58.2×42.1 cm
Samlingen af arktiekturtegninger. Kunstakademiets Bibliotek inv. 11596b.

1914

## Model for an equestrian statue of Christian IV

Carl Johan Bonnesen (Aalborg 1868 – Copenhagen 1933)
Private collection.

1915

## Design for a monument to the young Christian IV

1925-34. Einar Utzon-Frank (Copenhagen 1888 – Copenhagen 1955)
Private collection
Design for an equestrian statue of Christian IV in the

heroic style. The monument, which was never realized, was projected to be placed in the drill ground in front of Rosenborg Castle. Model in bronze in a private collection, model in a private collection; sketched designs in a private collection.
*Literature:* Berlingske Tidende 18th February 1954. Billedhuggeren Ejnar Utzon-Frank i Tekst og Billeder 1945 (fig. 44 and 45. Bronze 1934) Ejnar Utzon-Frank. Skulpturer og tegninger. Skovgaard Museet 1984, no. 22 (bronze, 1934) and no. 218-220 (sketches).

1916

## Christian IV. 1957

William Fredericia. Born in 1909
Bronze. 15 cm
Private collection
Christian IV founded Christianshavn in 1618, and in 1639 he gave the town its coat of arms. On 14th January 1958, a mosaic sculpture of the King by Fredericia was unveiled to commemorate this event. For a number of years now, a small bronze sculpture – originally a model for the large one – has been given as a prize for the preservation of historical buildings in Christianshavn.

*1913*

# *Christian IV's castles in architectural painting. Frederiksborg Castle*

1917

## Frederiksborg Castle. 1786

Erik Pauelsen (Bygom 1749 – Copenhagen 1790). Inscribed "E: Paulsen. Pinx: 1786"
Oil on canvas. 44×63 cm
Statens Museum for Kunst inv. sp. 881.

1918

## From Frederiksborg Castle. Sketches from a Diary 1810-1816

C. W. Eckersberg (1783-1853)
Two sepia drawings, lead, and Indian ink. 8.2×18 cm
Det kongelige Bibliotek Add. 1138 4° 52v
*Literature:* Voss 1968 83f.

1919

## Frederiksborg Castle. 1814

Johan Christian Dahl (Bergen 1788 – Dresden 1857). Inscribed "Dahl 1814"
Oil on canvas. 53.3×89.0 cm
Statens Museum for Kunst inv. 1290
In his biographical work "Ungdomsvandringer i mit Fødeland", 1811, Molbech described how, during a visit to Hillerød "the glorious old Castle which grew up from the water like a cliff" all of a sudden became physically alive to him. "Large and massive it rises like a work made for eternity, a work by Denmark's great Christian" (p. 156). In several of his drawings and paintings of the Castle, J. C. Dahl succeded in perpetuating the dreamlike and romantic quality of the place, which Molbech had stressed.

1921

## Frederiksborg Castle at Sunset. 1828

A. J. Emil Wollf (Copenhagen 1807 – Copenhagen 1830)
Drawing
Den kongelige Kobberstiksamling
In the play "Tycho Brahes Spaadom" from 1819, by J. L. Heiberg a part of the plot takes place in the woods of Frederiksborg. Some of the characters are discussing "the beautiful Castle which is lighted by the last beams of the evening sun". Judging from the dialogue, however, the grandeur of the Castle depended on the fact that Christian IV himself had sketched the plans for the buildings and had personally supervised the construction. J. L. Heiberg, Skuespil I, 1896, p. 198f.

1922

## The Mint Bridge. 1832

Christen Købke (Copenhagen 1810 – Copenhagen 1848)
Pencil on paper. 24.3×19.5 cm
Den kongelige Kobberstiksamling Td. 668,9
*Literature:* Voss 1976 109. Nørregård-Nielsen 1980 24 ff.

1923

## Corner tower at Frederiksborg Castle. About 1833

Christen Købke
Pencil on paper. 14.3×10.0 cm
Den kongelige Kobberstiksamling
This pencil drawing is a study for the small oil painting representing the spires above the corner tower and the stair turret of the north-east corner of the north wing (cat. 1926). The sketch is probably one of the first that Købke ever did of the subject. The squaring indicates that the purpose has been to clarify the position of the towers in the picture to the right of centre.
*Literature:* Voss 1968 89. Same 1976 98.

1924

## Corner tower at Frederiksborg. About 1833

Christen Købke
Pencil, pen, Indian ink. 25.2×18.2 cm
Den kongelige Kobberstiksamling Td 669,1
In this version, Købke has moved the big tower somewhat further to the right compared to the pencil drawing (cat. 1923) which makes the tower look thinner and more elegant. This drawing is a study for the small painting in Davids Samling (see cat. 1926) and it has the same measurements as the painting.
*Literature:* Voss 1968 88ff. Same 1976 100. Nørregård-Nielsen 1980 30.

1925

## Frederiksborg Castle. View of the east wing (The Princess's Wing). About 1834

Christen Købke. Not inscribed
Lead, ink. 18.3×21.0 cm
Den kongelige Kobberstiksamling 675 b,2
This drawing is a study preliminary for a small painting which again was a study for the large painting for the dining room of baker Købke at Blegdammen (cat. 1926 og 1927).
*Literature:* Voss 1976 99. Nørregård-Nielsen 1983 201.

1926

## Frederiksborg. One of the small towers. About 1834

Christen Købke
Oil on canvas. 25.5×18.5 cm
Davids Samling inv. 20/1969
This painting served as a study for a larger version, which Købke painted in 1834 to be hung in his parents' dining room (see cat. 1927).
*Literature:* Krohn 1915 75. Hannover 1893 61. Voss 1968 87 f. C. L. Davids Samling, Dansk kunst og kunsthåndværk 1972. pl. 5.

1927

## One of the small towers at Frederiksborg Castle. The north-west corner tower. About 1833-35

Christen Købke. Not inscribed
Oil on canvas. 177×162 cm
Kunstindustrimuseet inv. 1325
Copy of the original painting which hung in baker Købke's dining room at Blegdammen in Copenhagen (no. 74 Blegdamsvej). In Købke's painting, the spire of the corner tower is rendered in the noble and slim shape of the original from the time of Christian IV, which had been destroyed in the fire of 1859. However, the painter has purposely overdimensioned the spire by painting the storks smaller than he had done formerly, when he did a small size painting of the subject.
*Literature:* Krohn no. 87. Hannover no. 76 70f. Voss 1968 87 f. Monrad 1984 19ff.

1928

## Frederiksborg Castle. The roof ridge with a view of the Castle Lake, the town, and woodland

Christen Købke
Oil on canvas. 177×171 cm
Kunstindustrimuseet inv. 1326
This painting originally hung at the end wall of the dining room in baker Købke's house at Blegdammen in Copenhagen.
*Literature:* Krohn no. 88. Hannover 76a 71-72.

1929

## Frederiksborg Castle in evening light as seen from Jægerbakken

Christen Købke
Oil on canvas. 71.8×103 cm
Private collection
An incomplete replica of a painting from 1835 in Den Hirschsprungske Samling (inv. 317). The idea of sub-

stantiating an elegiac atmosphere by means of an historical monument standing in majestic solitude, was adopted by Købke from German Romantiscism. In his paintings of the Castle in evening light, the monumental outline of the building and the red hue of the evening sky become almost unreal, and one is reminded of the Poem "Aftensang" which B.S. Ingemann wrote in 1838 about the castle "In the west" where the sun sets "behind banks of rosy clouds".

1930

## Frederiksborg Castle. View of the Mint Bridge. 1836

Christen Købke. Orignal inscription on the back of canvas "C Købke 2/1836"
Oil on canvas. 58×64 cm
Statens Museum for Kunst inv. 3148
When Købke had finished his picture of Frederiksborg Castle in evening light (cat. 125), he set to work on yet another representation of the Castle. As early as the summer of 1832, he had been sketching a view of Mint Bridge, but not until 1835 did he begin working on the subject in oil. In August, he wrote to his friend Jørgen Roed that he was setting to work on "the view I told you about", and a few days later he was able to write, "today I finished a colour-sketch of the view I had in mind once I had finished the Castle". Jørgen Roed incidentally aquired the sketch himself. (Statens Museum for Kunst, inv. 1493).
*Literature:* Krohn no. 100. Hannover no. 85 73. Voss 1976 109.

1931

## Frederiksborg Castle. View of the inner courtyard. About 1835

Christen Købke
Lead, pen 24.3×16.0 cm
Den kongelige Kobberstiksamling Td 675b, 3
*Literature:* Voss 1976 85f.

1932

## Frederiksborg Castle. View of the carrousel yard. 1834

Jørgen Roed (1808-1888)
Lead, Indian ink. 30.7×33.3 cm
Den kongelige Kobberstiksamling
*Literature:* Voss 1968 145 148.

1933

## Frederiksborg Castle. View of the carrousel yard. 1834-1835

Jørgen Roed. No signature or inscription
Oil on canvas. 32.6×35.1 cm
"Lunden", Museum of Art, Horsens inv. K 274
Study preliminary to the painting at Frederiksborg inv. A 369.
*Literature:* Voss 1968 145 f.

1934

## Frederiksborg Castle. View of the Audience House

Peter Christian Skovgaard (Ringsted 1817 – Copenhagen 1875)
Oil on canvas. 140×150 cm
Ordrupgaardsamlingen inv. 243
Executed for the Frederiksholms Kanal apartments of the stockbroker Hans Christian Aggersborg. Skovgaard's painting for the Aggersborg family reflects the same clarity, peacefulness, and monumentality as does the painting which Købke did for his parents' dining room at Blegdammen. The painting represents architecture in more than one sense, as the painter's eye for the effect of lines and structures in the composition is as much the subject of the painting as is the sunlit Castle with the green copper roofs. A similar but smaller version is at the Ny Carlsberg Glyptotek (inv. 3216). Skovgaard also executed a painting of a view of Højerup Church for the dining room, and his friend, Johan Thomas Lundbye, contributed with a painting of the "Gåsetårnet" at Vordingborg based on a watercolour by Skovgaard.
*Literature:* Bramsen 1938 20, no. 12.

1935

## View from Frederiksborg Castle. 1842

Peter Christian Skovgaard. Inscribed "Frederiksborg d. 14. April 1842"
Pen, wash, Indian ink. 24.7×40.5 cm
Aarhus Kunstmuseum inv. G 837.

1937

## Near Frederiksborg Castle. 1898

Christian Zacho (Grenå 1843 – Hellerup 1913)
Oil on canvas. 60×80 cm
Private collection
The historian A.D. Jørgensen belonged to the critical school of historians who began to write in the 1870s. He nevertheless pursues the national ideas of N.L. Høyen further when in his book "Fyrretyve Fortællinger" from 1882 he painted an idyllic picture of "the magnificent" Frederiksborg "by far the most beautiful building in the North, situated between hills and beech forests". Jørgen-

*1933*

sen ends his description by saying that the Castle "on a summer morning or a beautiful evening makes such an impression on the spectator that it is like a fairy tale come true" (the 1981 edition p. 185). Zacho's painting is likewise a continuation of the romantic idyl which originated with the painters of the early 19th century.

1939

## Frederiksborg Castle. The Privy Passage

Harald Holm (Fåborg 1866 – Genua 1920). Inscribed "Harald Holm"
Oil on canvas. 40.8×60.7 cm
Randers Kulturhistoriske Museum. De Buhl'ske Stuer. DBS 658.

1940

## From the old Frederiksborg Castle. 1896

Vilhelm Hammershøi (Copenhagen 1864 – Copenhagen 1916)
Oil on canvas. 45.7×32.2 cm
Private collection
Study for the right-hand section of a painting with the same title.
*Literature:* Bramsen 157. Ordrupgaard 1981 no. 44.

1941

### Frederiksborg. The Carrousel Yard and the Audience House. 1926

Svend Hammershøi (Copenhagen 1873 – Copenhagen 1948)
Oil on canvas. 85×67.3 cm
Sorø Kunstmuseum
*Literature:* Sorø Kunstmuseum Catalogue, plate 19.

## *Rosenborg*

1942

### Rosenborg Castle. 1842

Thorald Læssøe (Frederikshavn 1816 – Copenhagen 1878). Inscribed "Thorald Læssøe 1842"
Oil on canvas. 93.5×105.0 cm
Statens Museum for Kunst inv. 408
In one of his vaudevilles "Et Eventyr i Rosenborg Have", J. L. Heiberg laid the scene in the gardens in front of the Castle, and though the plot is actually about mistaken identity and love, Heiberg managed to include a homage to the Castle and its builder. Two of the young principal characters praise first one after another, later in a duet, King Christian and the Castle. Heiberg's characters are fascinated by the same things that attracted the historical painters, the architectural painters, and the poets who had concerned themselves with the subject of Frederiksborg: the King as a heroic figure; the garden as a monument of the past, and the Castle as a "castle of dreams", a "fairy palace" which "floats high up in the clouds". (J. H. Heiberg, Vaudeviller 2nd part, 1895 p. 108f.
*Literature:* Broby-Johansen 6th ed. 80 f.

1943

### Rosenborg

Heinrich Hansen (1821-1890)
Etching. 18.1×22.6 cm
Aarhus Kunstmuseum inv. G 4328.

1944

### Rosenborg Castle. 1915

Svend Hammershøi
Oil on canvas. 66×66 cm
Private collection.

## *Kronborg*

1945

### View of Kronborg Castle. 1825

Jens Peter Møller (Fåborg 1783 – Copenhagen 1854)
Oil on canvas. 50×40 cm
Helsingør Bymuseum
Kronborg may not be counted among the castles built by Christian IV in quite the same way as Frederiksborg and Rosenborg, although he had it rebuilt after it was destroyed by fire in 1629. The King showed such respect for the work of his father and the architect, Antonius van Opbergen, however, that he restored rather than rebuilt the Castle. To Christian IV, Kronborg was nevertheless always the symbol of the rights and the sovereignty of the King and the Danish Realm.

1946

### View of the sound at Kronborg. (Kronborg by moonlight). 1828

Johan Christian Dahl. Inscribed "J. Dahl 1828"
Oil on canvas. 34×48 cm
Nasjonalgalleriet, Oslo inv. 208
The romantic visions of Frederiksborg, which were so vivid among the modern painters, cannot be applied to the interest they took in Kronborg. The Castle has frequently been used as a point de vue in landscape paintings or the background for seascapes and marine paintings. There are, however, a number of pictures of the Castle by moonlight such as those by I. C. Dahl, and Swedish painters in particular found the Castle to be "interesting" in evening light.
*Literature:* Aubert 1893 152. Same 1920 425 f. Langgaard 1937 no. 324. I. C. Dahl, Kunstnere i Nasjonalgalleriet II 1957 33. I. C. Dahl og Danmark. Nasjonalgalleriet, Oslo og Statens Museum for Kunst 1973 no. 41.

1947

### Elsinore and Kronborg Castle. 1833

Thomas Fearnley (Frederikshald 1802 – Munich 1842)
Oil on canvas. 74.5×100.0 cm
Thorvaldsens Museum inv. B 193
View of Elsinore with Kronborg in the background. Fearnley painted two versions of the subject in two different seasons; both paintings were executed during his stay in Rome in 1833 where they were acquired by Thorvaldsen.
*Literature:* Willoch 1932 112. Stiftelsen Modums Blaafarveværk 1986 no. 33.

*1954*

1948

## Kronborg seen from the North. Preliminary study. 1834

Constantin Hansen
Oil on canvas. 28.5×42.5 cm
Statens Museum for Kunst inv. 6815
Painted in connection with a competition sponsored by the Kunstforeningen in Copenhagen in 1834. That summer, Constantin Hansen was continuously at work on the Castle *motif* and executed a number of sketches and studies in pencil and oil. His various experiments with composition and angles can be followed in his correspondance with his colleague, Jørgen Roed. This painting was finished at the beginning of October in Constantin Hansen's studio and was sent in to the Kunstforeningen where it won the prize.
*Literature:* Voss 1968 113-121. Danish Painting. The Golden Age. Katalog ved Kasper Monrad 1984 no. 26 134 f.

1949

## Kronborg Castle from the North

Constantin Hansen
Etching. 32.2×43.0 cm
Aarhus Kunstmuseum inv. G. 4333.

1950

## Kronborg Castle

Joachim Ferdinand Richardt (Brede 1819 – Oakland 1895)
Oil on canvas. 140×190 cm
Helsingør Bymuseum inv. 4073.

1951

## Kronborg Castle seen from the north bastion. 1848

Joachim Ferdinand Richardt. Inscribed "Ferdinand Richardt 1848"
Oil on canvas. 113.0×163.5 cm
Statens Museum for Kunst inv. 548d.

1952

## The coast north of Kronborg. 1859

Peter Christian Skovgaard
Oil on canvas. 31×48 cm
Private collection
Skovgaard has used Kronborg as a point de vue in this seascape, which is predominated by groups of dark trees, the light sea, and a typical Danish summer sky.
*Literature:* Kunst i privateje vol. II 314.

1953

## Kronborg Castle seen from the Commandant's Tower. 1897

Vilhelm Hammershøi
Oil on canvas. 84×86 cm
Private collection
"With this picture Hammershøi presents Kronborg Castle in a completely new and de-romanticized shape. When observed from the Commandant's Tower the light green roofs and the grey brown walls turn into a universe which, within its borders, contain a richness of energetic, clearly defined movements. All the individual parts of the picture communicate with one another: the deep view of the courtyard, for one thing, gives the roofs their upwards slope; the courtyard itself seems to tie the complete prospect to the ground, while the grey ocean with its long horizontal line is necessary if we are to see this totality as part of a greater whole. This picture music is admirable in its richness and consequence." (Poul Vad).
*Literature:* Michaelis/Bramsen 1918 no. 166. Ordrupgaard 1981 cat. 63. Poul Vad 1957 12 24.

1954

## Kronborg Castle from the south-west. (1904)

Albert Gottschalk (Stege 1866 – Copenhagen 1906). Not inscribed
Oil on canvas. 41×55 cm
Statens Museum for Kunst inv. 4606
In 1904, Gottschalk painted a number of pictures from Kronborg. The overall theme of this series was "the *motif* with the immense building and its towers which unite with the surrounding bastions and groups of trees, painted with different rhythms in the brushwork and the weight of the colouring" (Troels Andersen p. 89).
*Literature:* Troels Andersen 1977 no. 342. Broby Johansen 1983 87.

# Colour-plates

*Christian IV and Europe*

36

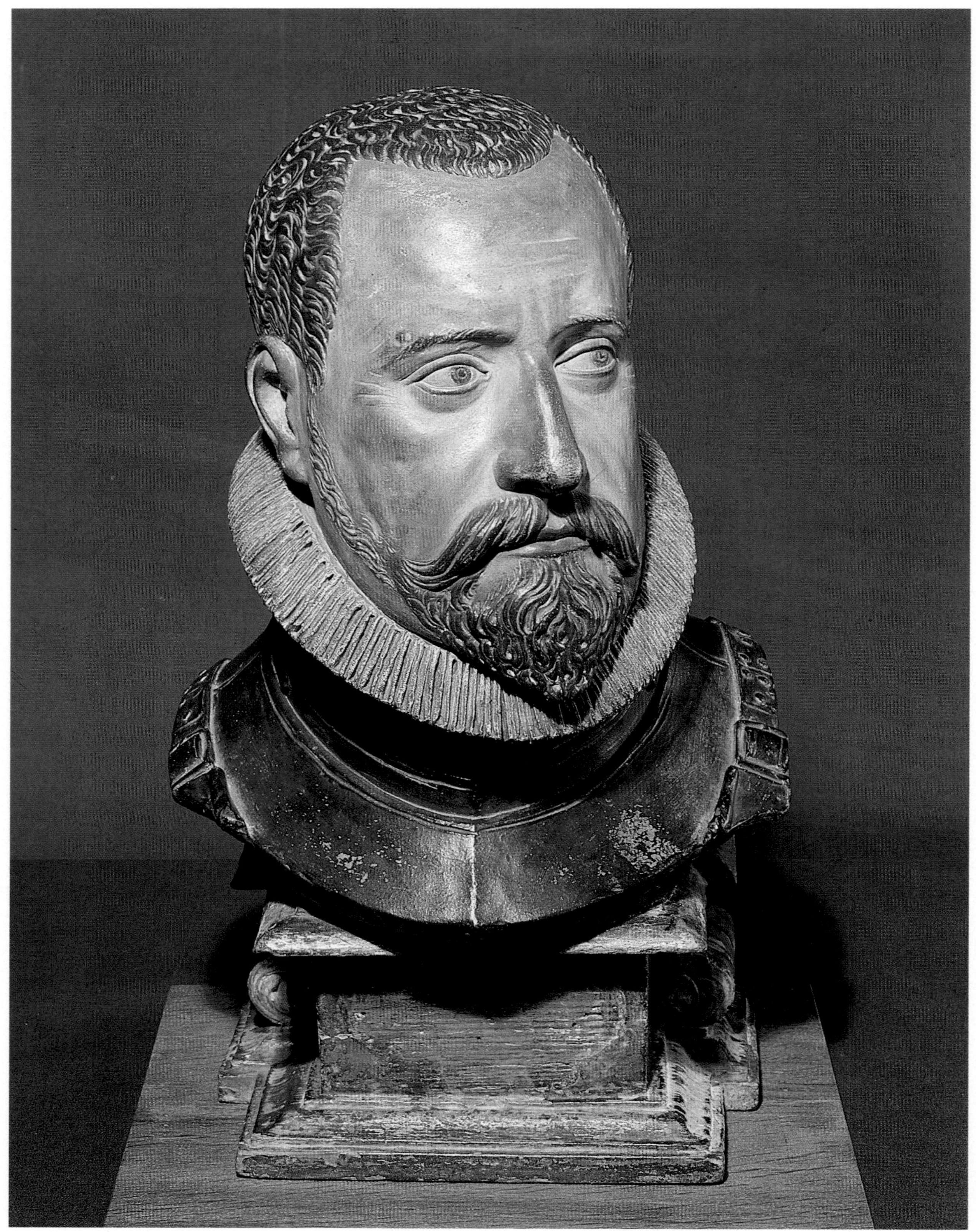

548 COLOUR-PLATE II

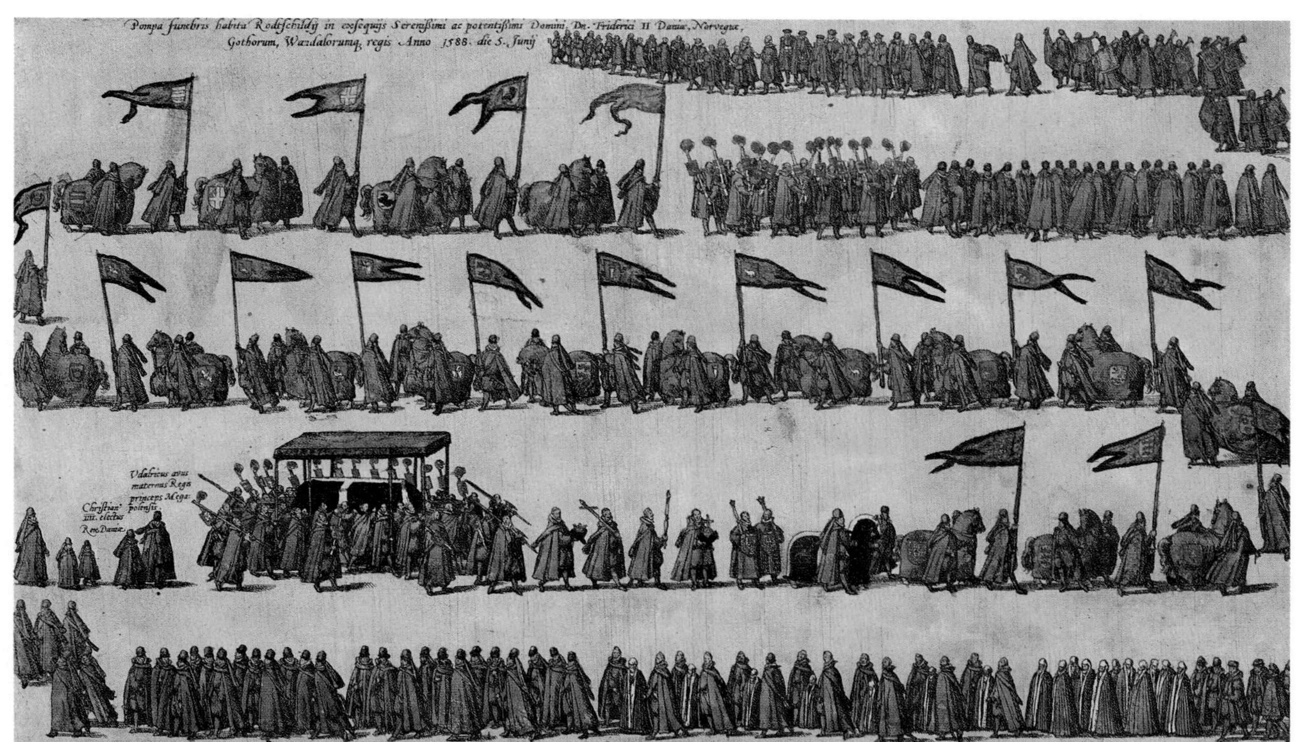
Pompa funebris habita Rodtschildij in exsequijs Serenißimi ac potentißimi Domini, Dn. Friderici II Daniæ, Norvegiæ,
Gothorum, Wandalorumq; regis Anno 1588. die 5. Junij
Vdalricus avus
maternus Regis
princeps Mega-
polensis.
Christian᾽
IIII. electus
Rex Daniæ.

*1486*

*1071*

1682

1721

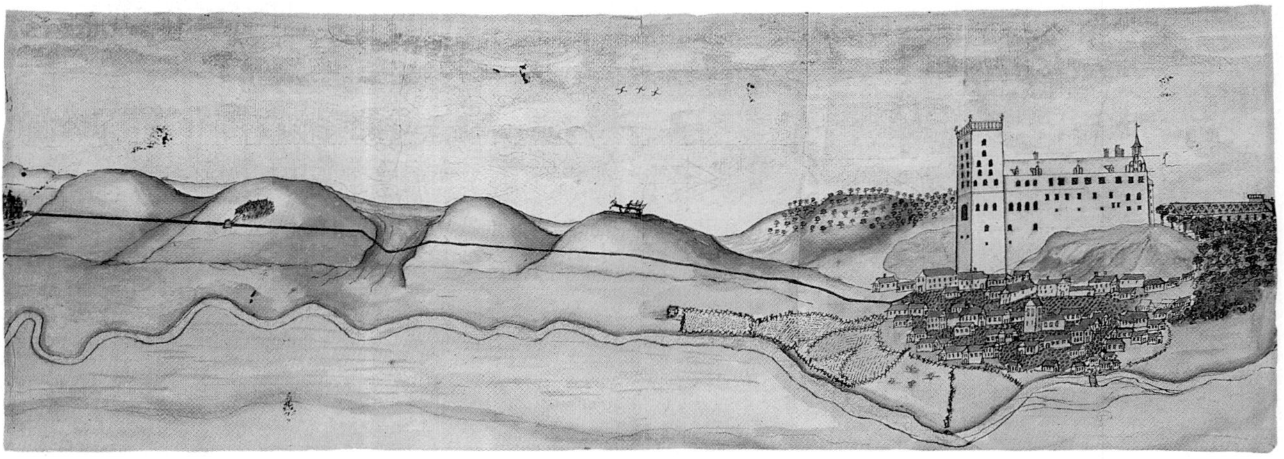

698

*Frederiksborg Castle. Built c.1600-1620*

*Frederiksborg Castle. The Altar. Silver and ebony. Acquired 1606 from Jacob Mores, Hamburg*

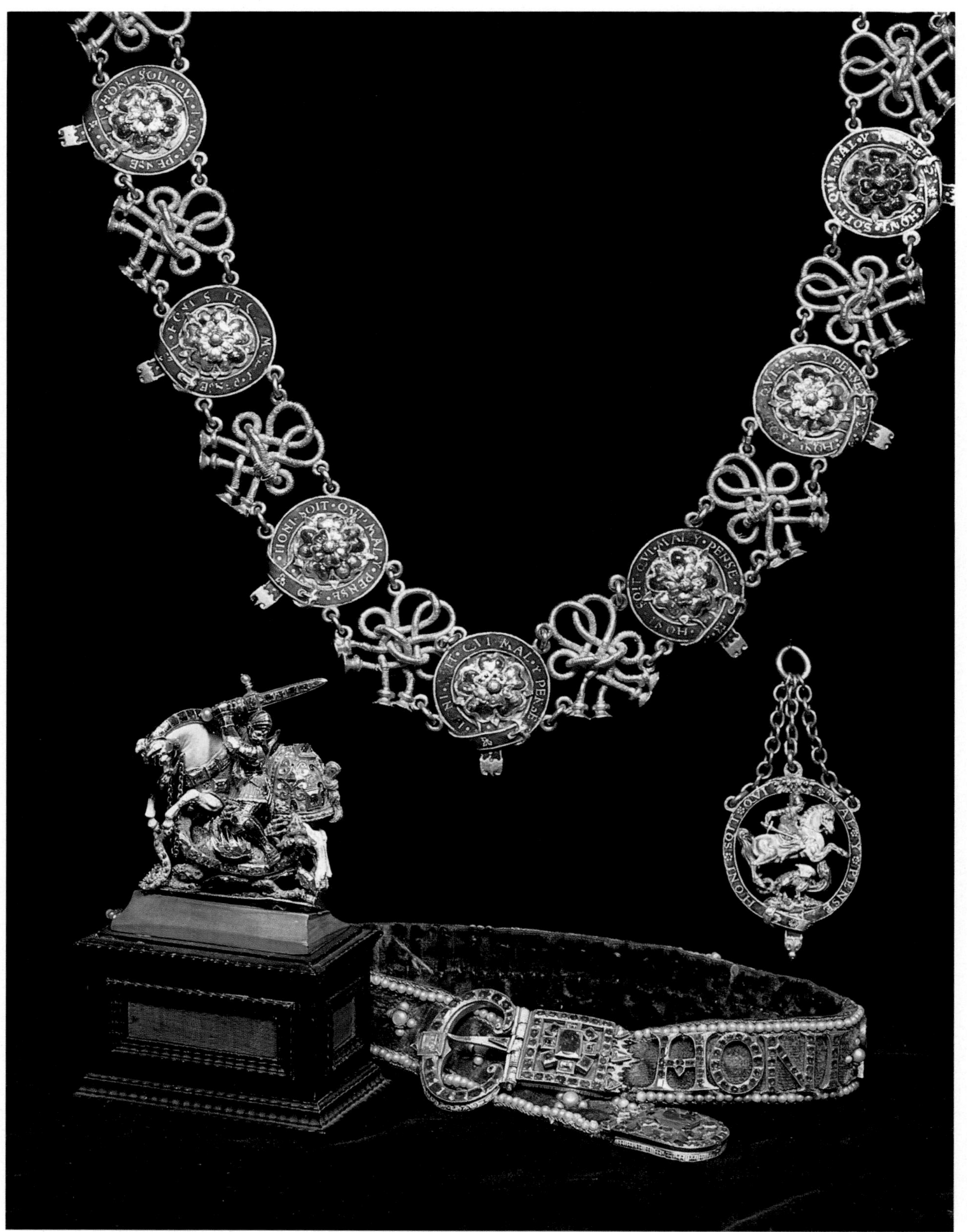

 COLOUR-PLATE VIII

565

566 567

569

94

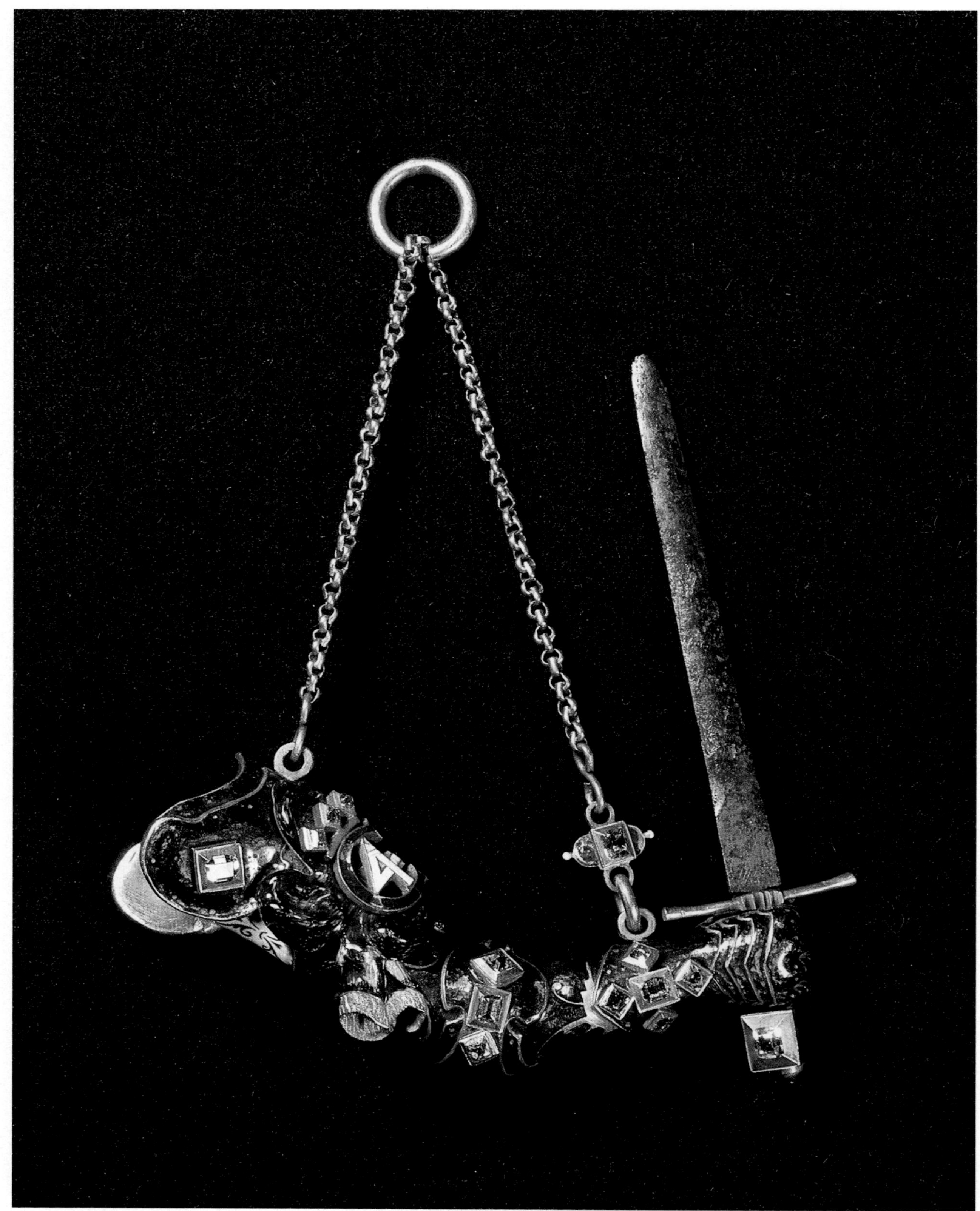

556 COLOUR-PLATE X

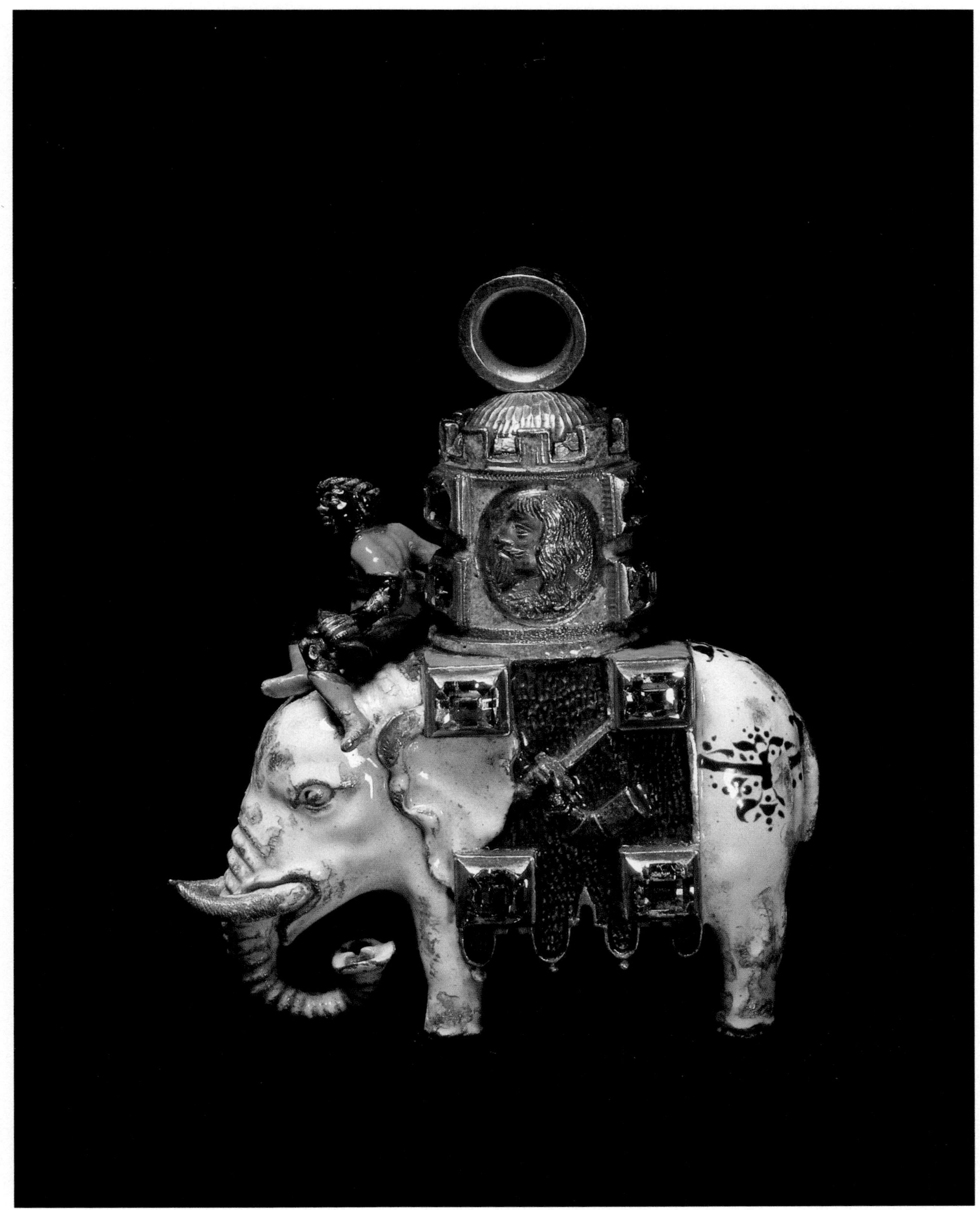

564

558 COLOUR-PLATE XII

1199

1290

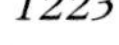

1223

1145

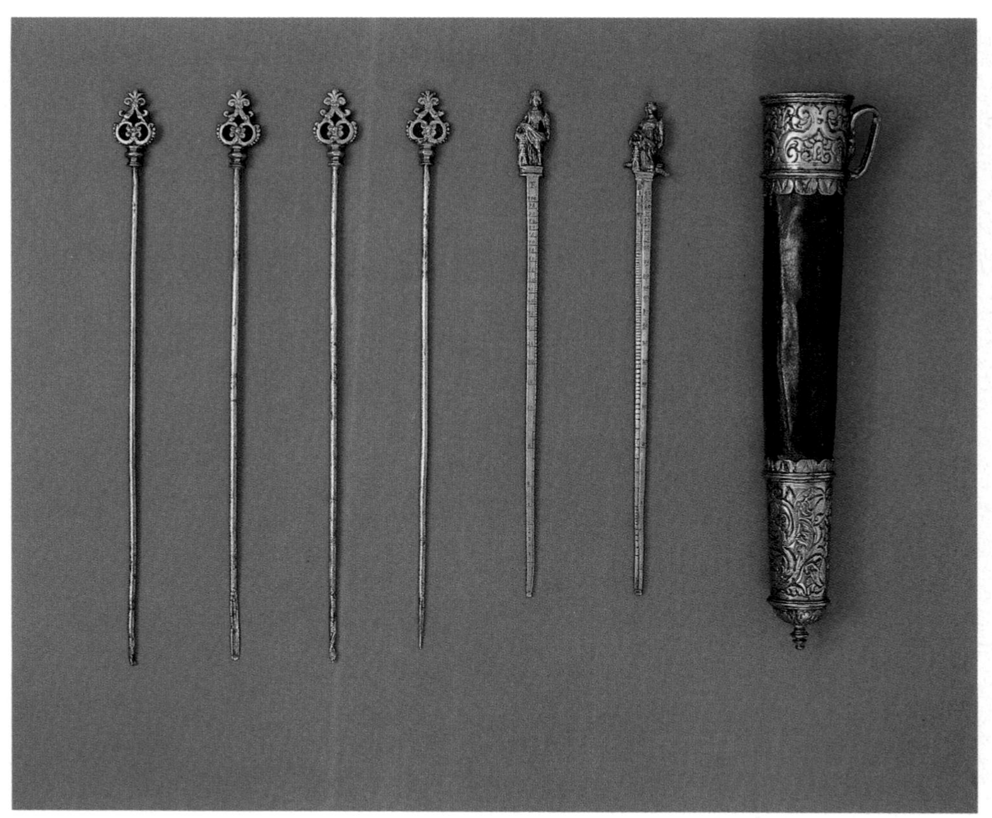

1438

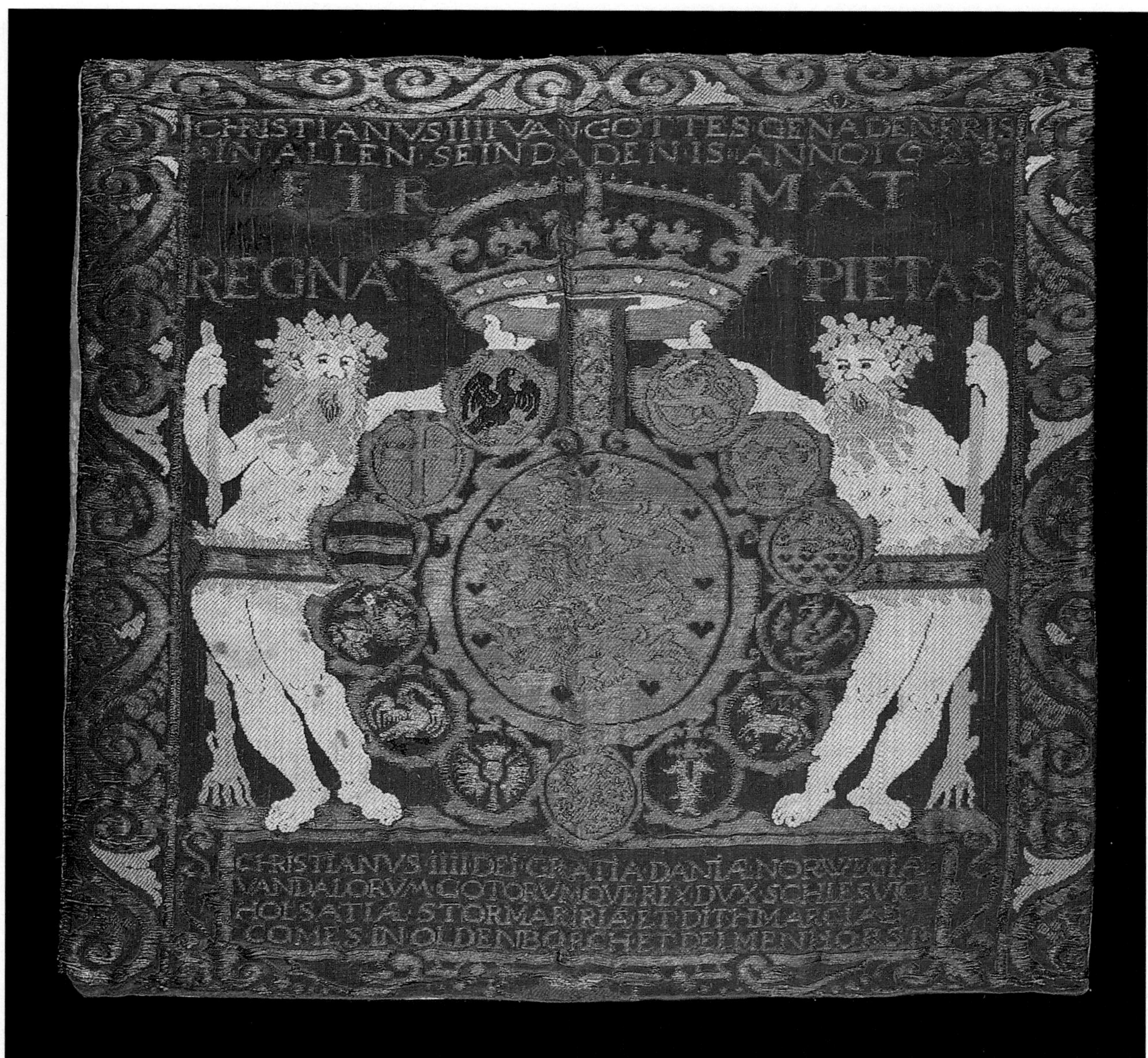


*733*

913 914 916b
911

980

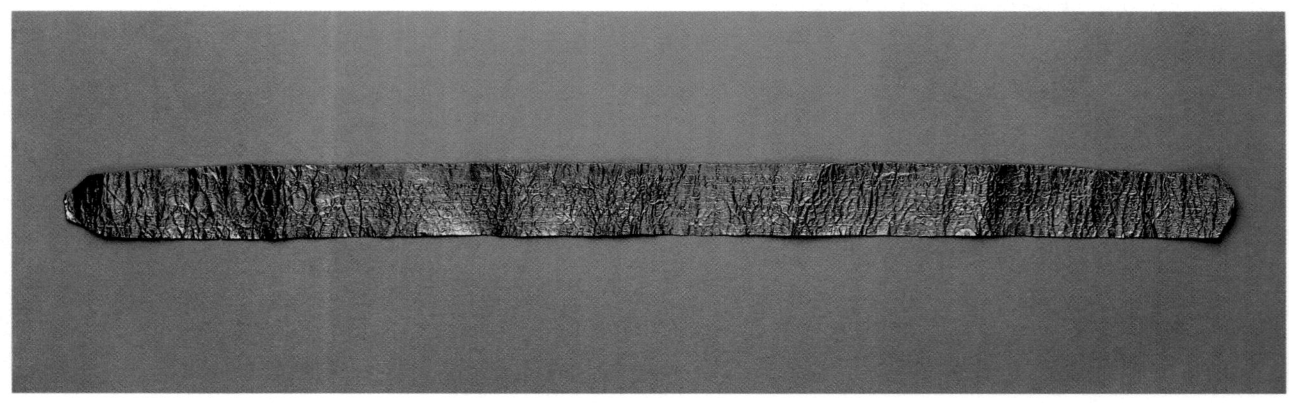

*798d 798c 798e*

*798b 798a*

*818*

721
585
642

632

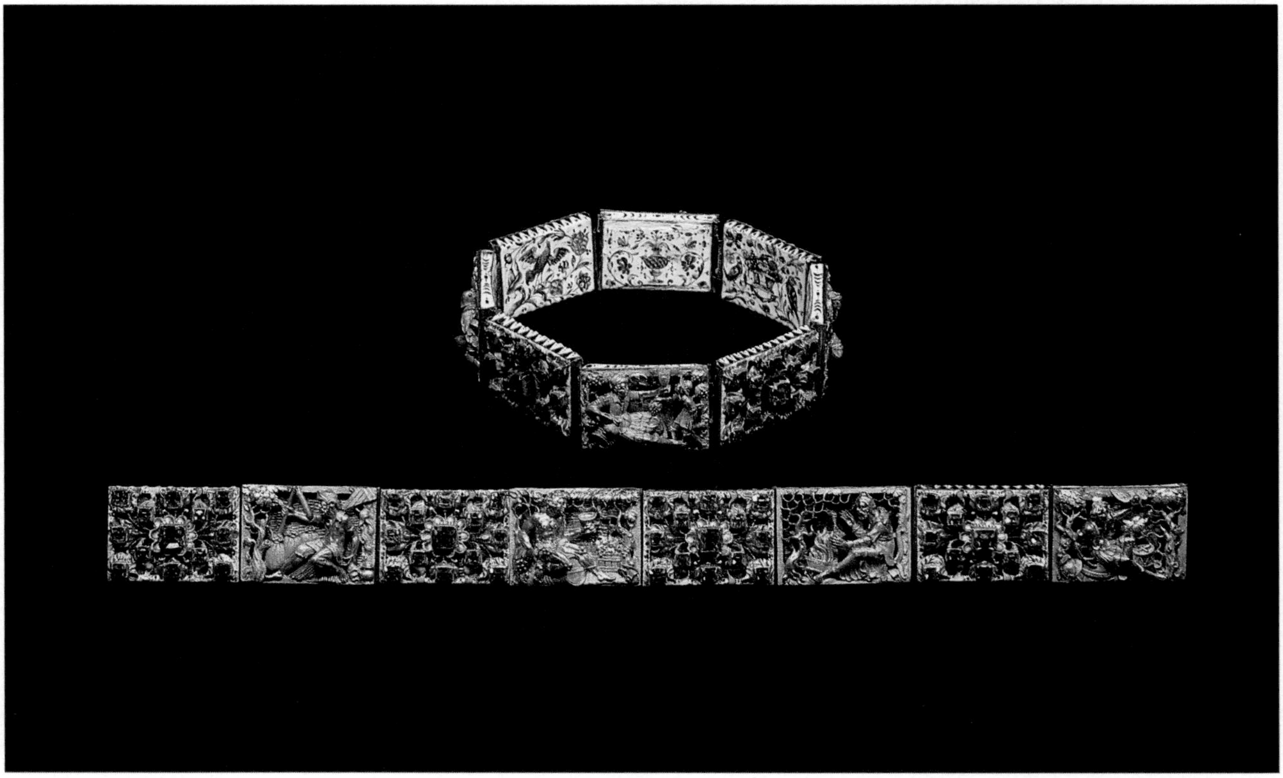

*Rosenborg Castle, Copenhagen. Built c. 1606-1624*

407

*322*

219

221

216

210

224

218

*1039*

*1081*

999

1069

1073

*1004*

*389*

521

578 COLOUR-PLATE XXXII

*113*

571a

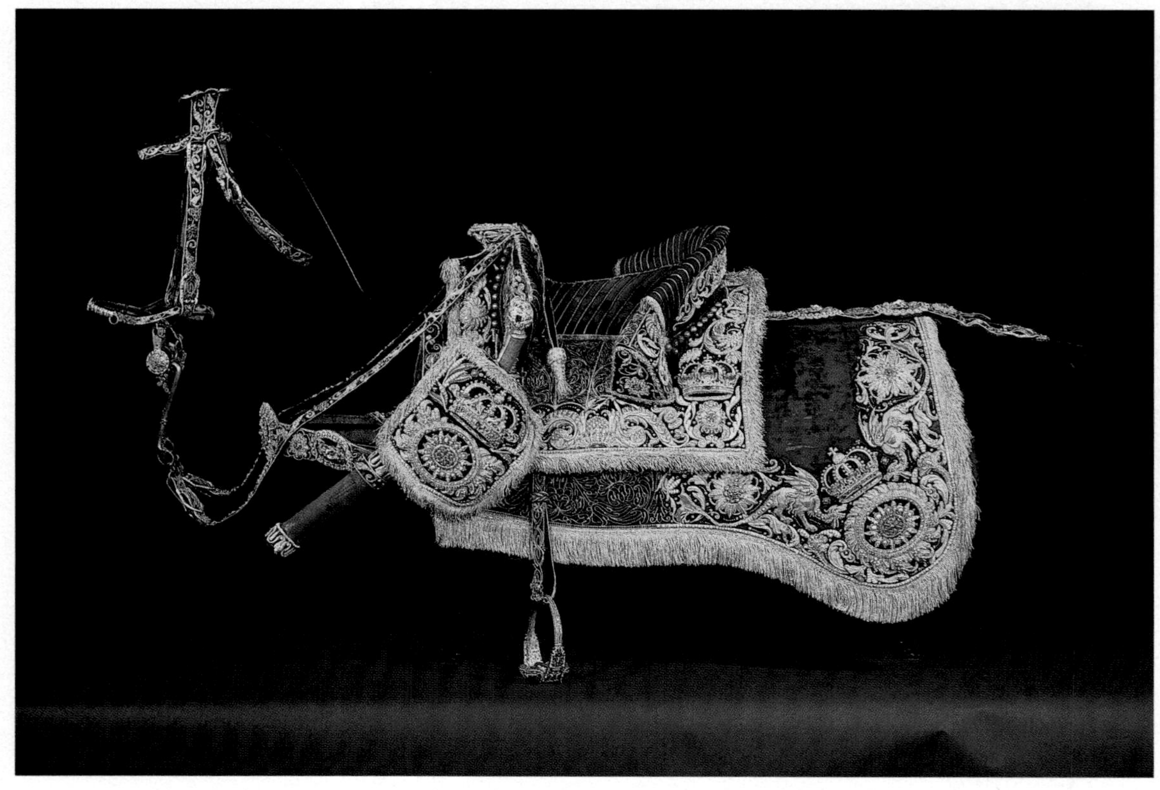

576

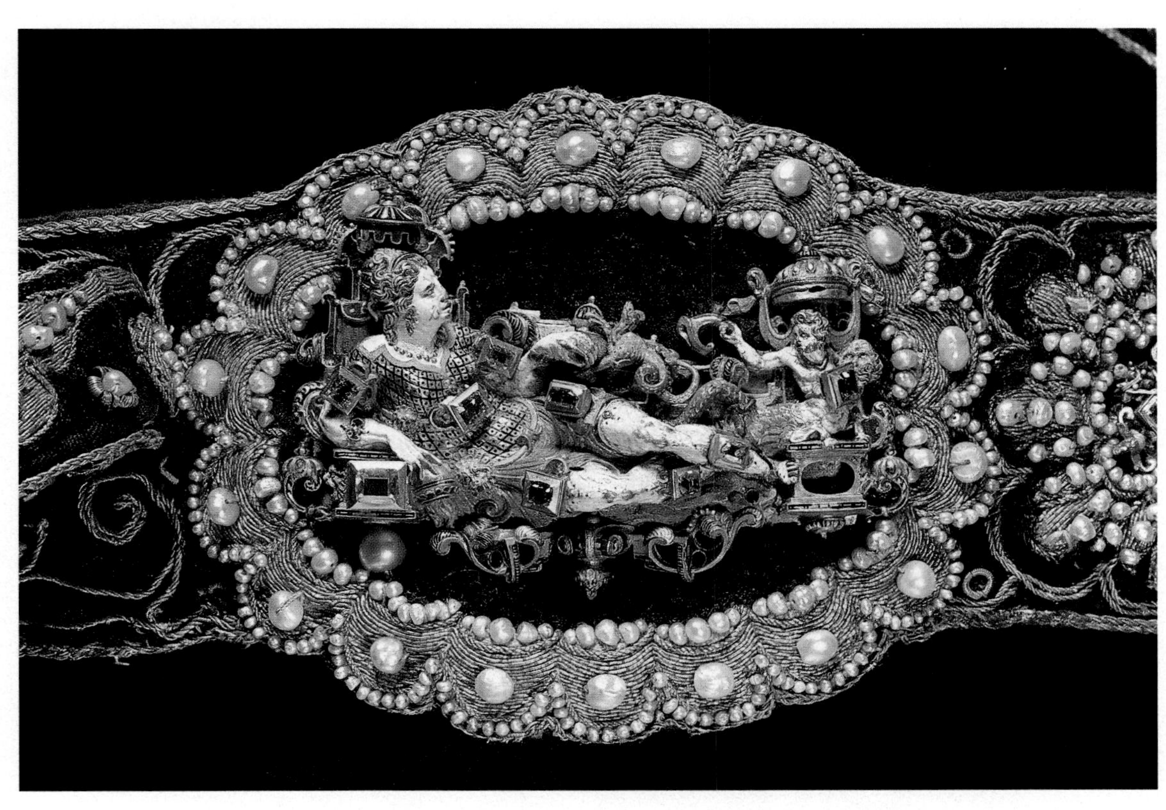

*Details 596*

 COLOUR-PLATE XXXVI

140

COLOUR-PLATE XXXVII 

*Whalers' Graves in Svalbard. 1630's (c.f. cat. 872)*

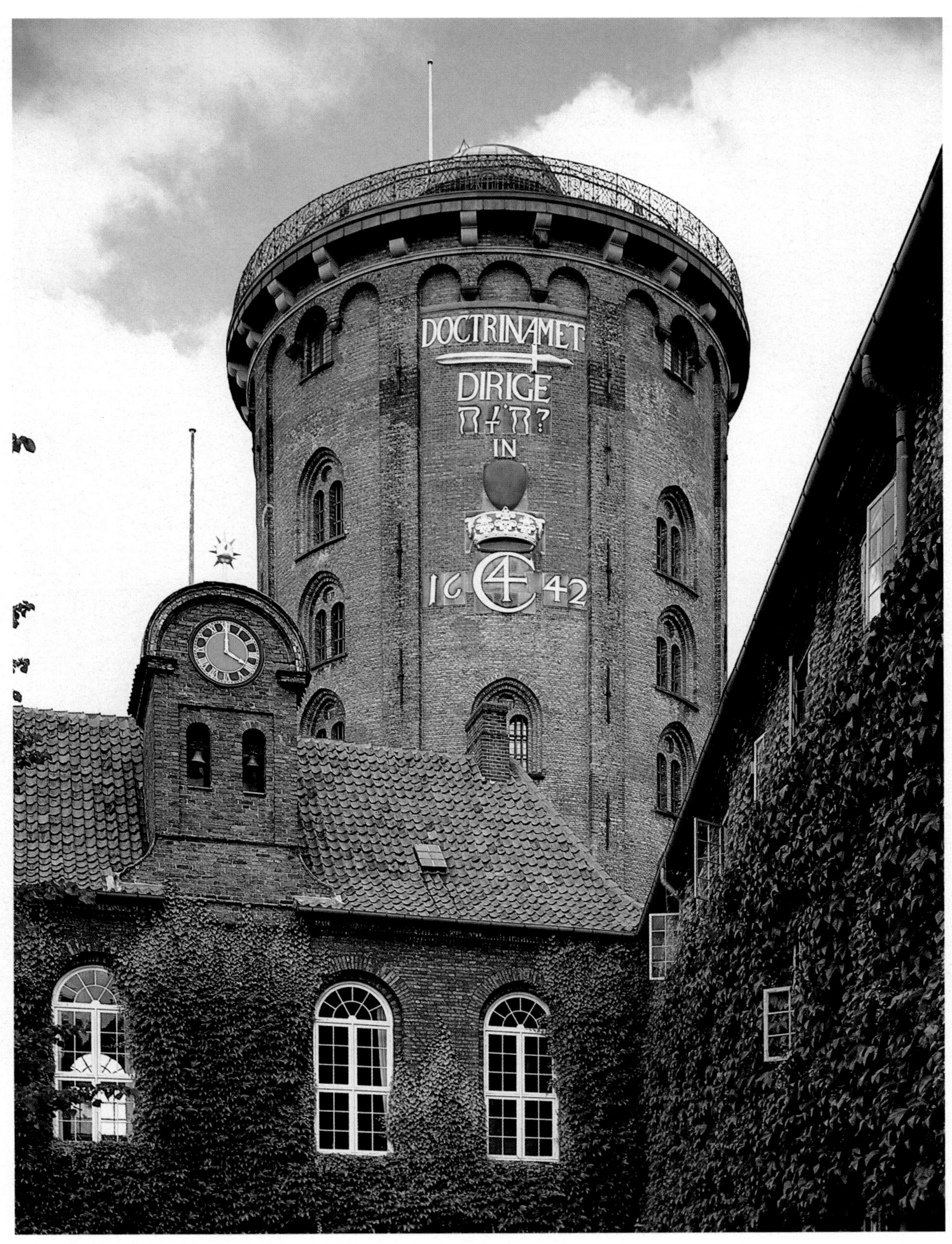


*Collegium Regium (Regensen), Copenhagen. Built 1618-1628. Later rebuilt.*
*Rundetårn (The Round Tower) from 1637-1642*

745

*199*

*69*

*F.C. Lund:*
*Christian IV pronounces judgment on Christoffer Rosenkrantz.*
*1855. 85×197 cm.*
*Private collection. United States.*

*1859*

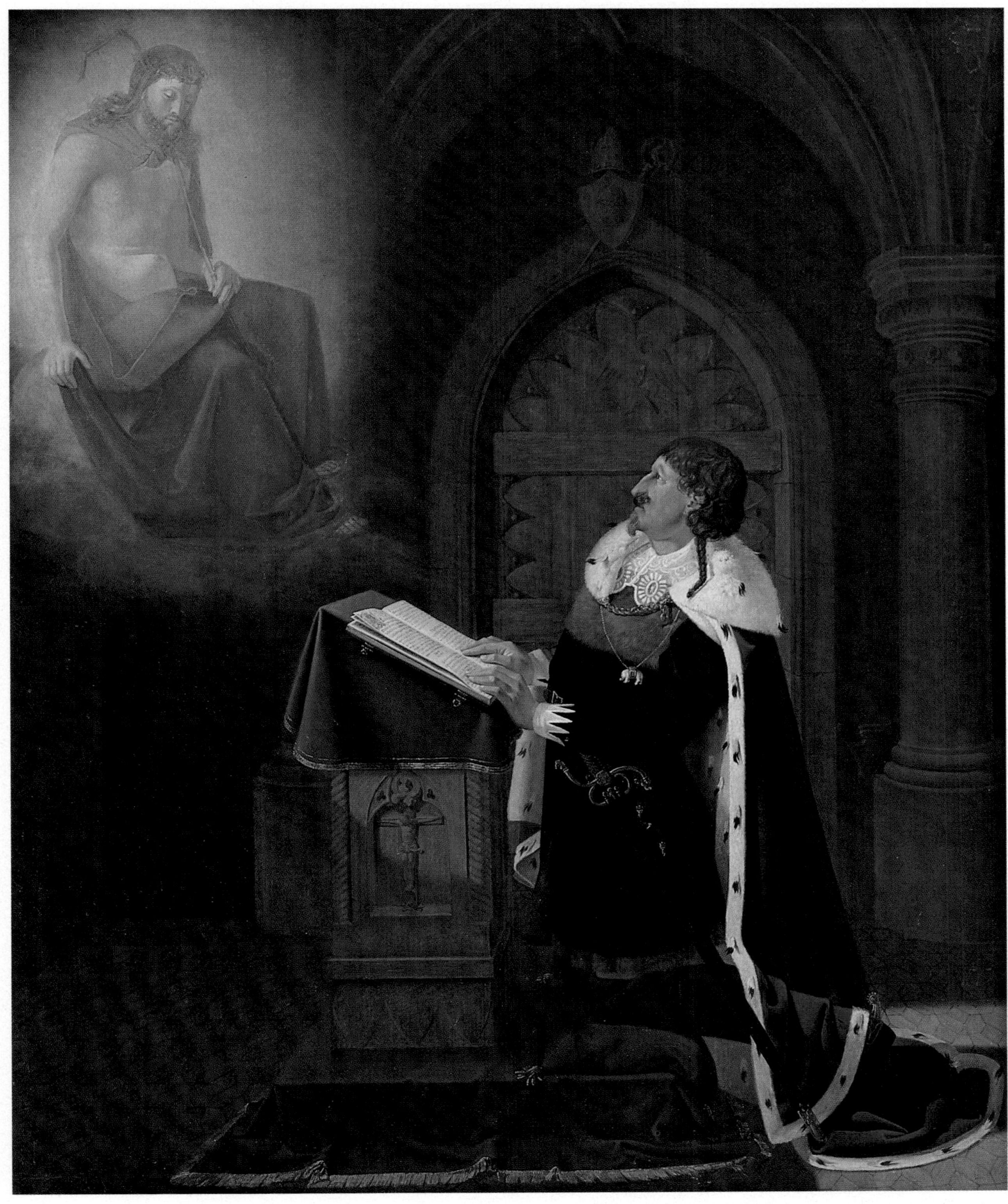

*1874*

# References


*Aarhus Kunstmuseum 1971:* »Verdensrum«. 3. Kunstmuseumsmåned. 3.-30. november 1971.
*Aarsberetninger fra Geheimearchivet.* København. *1872.*
*Abeler,* Jürgen: Meister der Uhrmacherkunst. Über 14000 Uhrmacher aus dem deutschen Sprachgebiet mit Lebens- oder Wirkungsdaten und dem Verzeichnis ihrer Werke. Wuppertal. *1977.*
*Acquisitions of the Art Museum. Princeton. 1983.*
*Acta Historia Scientiarum Naturalium et Medicalium,* edidit Bibliotheca Universitatis Hauniensis. Vol. 32: Petrus Severinus oversat af Hans Skov med kommentar af dr. med. Eyvind Bastholm. København. *1979.*
*Adils,* Jón J.: Den danske Monopolhandel paa Island 1602-1787. Bind 4. København. *1927.*
*Ahnlund,* Nils: Gustav Adolf den Store. 2. Oplag. Stockholm. *1932.*
*Ahnlund,* Nils: Axel Oxenstierna intill Gustav Adolfs död. Stockholm. *1940.*
*Albrethsen,* Svend E.: Dansk-norsk hvalfangst ved Svalbard i 1600-tallet. Nationalmuseets Arbejdsmark 1985. København. *1985.*
*Alm,* Josef: Eldhandvapen. Bind 1. Stockholm. *1933.*
*Alm,* Josef: Arméns Eldhandvapen förr och nu. Stockholm. *1953.*
*Alpers,* Svetlana: The Art of Describing. Chicago-London. *1983.*
*Alpers,* Svetlana: Kunst als Beschreibung. Köln. *1985.*
*Andersen,* J. O.: Holger Rosenkrantz den Lærde. København. *1896.*
*Andersen,* Jørgen: »Kærlighedens arter«. Kunstmuseets Årsskrift XXXVIII, 1951. København. *1952.* pp. 80-89.
*Andersen,* Troels: Albert Gottschalk. København. *1977.*
*Amos Andersons Kunst Galleri, Helsinki. 1971.*
*Andersson,* Torsten: De byggede staden. Staden vid Helgeå. En bok i anledning av Kristianstads 350års jubiläum. Red. A. Kroon, N. G. Hagander, T. Andersson. *1964. p. 41 ff.*
*Andresen,* Ludwig og *Stephan,* Walter: Beiträge zur Geschichte der Gottorfer Hof- und Staatsverwaltung von 1544-1659. Bind 1-2. Kiel. *1928.*
*Andrews,* Keith: Adam Elsheimer. II. Contento. Edinburgh. *1971.*
*Andrews,* Keith: Adam Elsheimer. Paintings-Drawing-Prints. Oxford. *1977.*
*Andrews,* Keith: Adam Elsheimer. Werkverzeichnis der Gemälde, Zeichnungen und Radierungen. München. *1985.*
*Andrup,* Otto m.fl.: Fortegnelse over to Hundrede af Baroniet Gaunøs Malerier af ældre Malere samt over dets Portrætsamling. København. *1914.*
*Andrup,* Otto: Et par hidtil ukendte Frederik III Portraiter. Kunstmuseets Aarsskrift IV, 1917. København. *1917.* pp. 67-75.
*Andrup,* Otto: Kunstnere ved den udvalgte Prins Christians Hof. Kunstmuseets Aarsskrift VI, 1920. København. *1920.* pp. 96a-110.
*Andrup,* Otto: Nyerhvervelser til Frederiksborgmuseet. Illustreret Tidende 64. Aarg. nr. 47. København. *1923.* pp. 957 f.
*Andrup,* Otto: Udvalg af Museets Erhvervelser 1913-1925. Det Nationalhistoriske Museum paa Frederiksborg. *1925.*
*Andrup,* Otto: Det Nationalhistoriske Museum paa Frederiksborg. Beretning om dets Virksomhed 1878-1928. *1928.*
*Andrup,* Otto: Noter vedrørende Karel van Manders Biografi I-II. Kunstmuseets Aarsskrift XIX, 1932. København. *1932.* pp. 104-140.
*Andrup,* Otto: Portrætter af Dronning Sofie. Lolland-Falsters Historiske Samfunds Aarbog *1933.* pp. 97-112.
*Andrup,* Otto: Noter vedrørende Karel van Manders Biografi III-V. Kunstmuseets Aarsskrift XXX-XXI, 1933-1934. København. *1934.* pp. 141-182.
*Andrup,* Otto: Noter vedrørende Karel van Manders Biografi VI. Kunstmuseets Aarsskrift XXIII, 1936. København. *1936.* pp. 101-122.
*Andrup,* Otto: Noter vedrørende Karel van Manders Biografi VII-VIII. Kunstmuseets Aarsskrift XXVI, 1939. København. *1939.* pp. 100-113.
*Arndt,* Karl: Unbekannte Zeichnungen von Pieter Bruegel d. Ä. Pantheon XXIV. München. *1966.* pp. 207-216.
*Arndt,* Karl: Pieter Bruegel d. Ä. und die Geschichte der Waldlandschaft. Jahrbuch der Berliner Museum XIV. *1972.* pp. 69-121.
*Arnold,* Janet: Lost from Her Majesties Back. London. *1980.*
*Arup,* Erik: Danmarks Historie 1-2. København. *1925-1932.*
*Askgaard,* Finn: Det oldenborgske rustkammer. Vaabenhistoriske Aarbøger X. København. *1959-1961.* pp. 237-305.
*Askgaard,* Finn: Det kongelige rustkammer i Rendsborg 1827. Vaabenhistoriske Aarbøger XI. København. *1962.* pp. 72-137.
*Askgaard,* Finn: Studier i Københavns Tøjhusregnskaber. Vaabenhistoriske Aarbøger XIa. København. *1962-1964.* pp. 187-250.
*Askgaard,* Finn: Våben fra Brobyværk 1648-51. Fynske Minder *1969.* Odense. 1970. pp. 20-42.
*Askgaard,* Finn: Med pike og musket. Vaabenhistoriske Aarbøger XVII. København. *1971.* pp. 7-71.
*Askgaard,* Finn: Kampen om Østersøen. Et Bidrag til nordisk søkrigshistorie på Carl X Gustafs tid 1654-1660. København. *1974.*
*Askgaard,* Finn: Prins Christian (V) en dansk våbenelsker. (Den udvalgte prins Christian). Vaabenhistoriske Aarbøger XXIV, *1978.* København. 1979. pp. 109-126.
*Atlantes Neerlandici II.* Gravenhage (Haag). *1969.*
*Attmann,* Arthur: The Russian and Polish Markets in International Trade 1500-1650. Meddelanden från Ekonomisk-historiska Institutionen vid Göteborgs Universitet 26. Göteborg. *1973.*
*Aubert,* Andreas: Professor Dahl. Kristiania. *1893.*
*Aubert,* Andreas: Maleren Johan Christian Dahl. Kristiania. *1920.*
*Auerbach,* Erna: Nicholas Hilliard. London. *1961.*
*Augsburg. Zeughaus. Rathaus 1980:* Welt im Umbruch. Augsburg zwischen Renaissance und Barock.
*Avery,* C. H. F.: Hendrich de Keyser as a Sculptor of small Bronzes, his Orpheus and Cerberus identified. Bulletin van het Rijksmuseum XXI. Haag. *1973.* pp. 3-24.
*Avery,* C. H. F.: Francois Dieussart (c. 1600-61), Portrait Sculptor to the Courts of Northern Europe. Victoria and Albert Yearbook 4. London. *1974.* pp. 63-99.
*Axel-Nilsson,* Jørgen: Hans Skovgaards och Anne Parsbergs pokal. Röhsska Konstslöjdmuseet Göteborg, Årstryck 1959. Göteborg. *1959.*
*Bachmann,* Erik: Ein Elfenbeinkruzifix von Georg Petel. Stifterjahrbuch VIII. *1964.* pp. 37-43.
*Baines,* Anthony: European and American Musical Instruments. London. *1966.*
*Baker,* C. H. Collins: Catalogue of Pictures at Hampton Court. Glasgow. *1929.*
*Bange,* E. F.: Die Bildwerke in Bronze und anderen Metallen, Arbeiten in Perlmutter und Wachs, geschnittene Steine. Die Bildwerke des deutschen Museums, Band II. Berlin-Leipzig. *1923.*
*Barfod,* Esther; Foltmann, Bo; Jensen, Lisbeth Ahlgren; Lyngberg-Larsen, Poul A.; Palsmar, Henrik og Røllum-Larsen, Claus: Musik i Danmark på Christian IV's tid, hæfte 7: Thomas Schattenberg: Jubilus S. Bernhardi. København. *1988.*
*Bartholin,* Thomas: De armillis veterum schedion. Hafniæ. *1647.*
*Bartholin,* Thomas: Cista Medica Hafniensis, Hafniæ 1662. Facsimileudgave ved Bruun og Loldrup. København. *1982.*
*Bartsch,* Adam: Le Peintre Graveur I-XXi. Vienne. *1802-1821.*
*Barudio,* Günther: Gustav Adolf der Grosse. Frankfurt am Main. *1982.*
*Barudio,* Günther: Der deutsche Krieg 1618 bis 1648. Frankfurt am Main. *1985.*
*Bauch,* Kurt: Der frühe Rembrandt und seine Zeit. Berlin. *1960.*
*Baudoin,* F.: Herinneringen ann. P. P. Rubens, nr. 29. Antwerpen. *1958.*

*Bauer,* Rotraud og *Haupt,* Herbert (ed.): Das Kunstkammerinventar Kaiser Rudolfs II 1607-1611. Jahrbuch der Kunsthistorischen Sammlungen in Wien, Band 72. Wien. *1976.*

*Bautier,* P.: Justus Suttermanns peintre des Médicis. Bruxelles-Paris. *1912.*

*Bayerische Staatsgemäldesammlungen. Städtische Kunstsammlungen Augsburg II. Deutsche Barockgallerie. Augsburg 1984:* Katalog der Gemälde. 2. Aufl.

*Bayerisches Nationalmuseum:* Georg Petel 1601-1634. *München 1964.*

*Bayerisches Nationalmuseum:* Die Welt als Uhr. *München 1980.*

*Beard,* C. R.: The Lion Jewel. The Connoisseur Vol. 101. London-Paris. *1938.* pp. 72-77.

*Becker,* P. W.: Samlinger til Danmarks Historie under Kong Frederik den Tredies Regiering af udenlandske Archiver. København. *1847.*

*Beckett,* Francis: Renaissancen og Kunstens Historie i Danmark. København. *1897.*

*Beckett,* Francis: Malerkunst fra Reformationen til Kristian IV. Kunstens Historie i Danmark. Red. af Karl Madsen. København. *1901-1907.* pp. 62 ff.

*Beckett,* Francis: Frederiksborg II. Slottets Historie. København. *1914.*

*Beckett,* Francis: Renæssancens Portrætmaleri. København. *1932.*

*Beckett,* Francis: The Painter Frantz Clein in Denmark. Det Kongelige Danske Videnskabernes Selskabs Skrifter, Historisk og filosofisk Afdeling, 7. række bind V: 2. København. *1936.*

*Beckett,* Francis: Kristian IV og Malerkunsten. København. *1937.*

*Bencard,* Mogens: Enhjørningen, narhvaler og gamle grønlændere. MIV, Museerne i Viborg Amt 13. Viborg. *1985.* pp. 114-125.

*Bencard,* Mogens og *Hein,* Jørgen: Three Cabinets on Stands from the Seventeenth Century. Journal of the Furniture History Society, vol. XXI. London. *1985.* pp. 137-156.

*Bencard,* Mogens: Kongens København, bybilleder 1640-1860. København. *1986.* (udstillingskatalog)

*Bender,* Elisabeth: Matthäus Gundelach. Leben und Werk. Frankfurt am Main. *1981.*

*Bendixen,* Kirsten: Sølvskatten fra Balle og Christian IV's møntpolitik. Aarbøger fra Nordisk Oldkyndighed og Hitorie 1973. København. *1974.* pp. 131-181.

*Bendixen,* Kirsten: Danmarks Mønt, 2. udgave. København. *1976.*

*Bengtsson,* Åke: Studies on the Rise of Realistic Landscape Painting in Holland 1600-1625. Figura III. Stockholm-Uppsala. *1962.*

*Berg,* Bjørn Ivar: Forførte gesellene Sandsvær-jenterne? Langs Lågen *1984,* nr. 1.

*Berg,* Johan Adam: Kurtze und eigentliche Beschreibung Des fürtrefflichen und weitberühmten Königlichen Hauses Friederichburg. Kopenhagen. *1646.*

*Berger,* Adolf: Inventar der Kunstsammlung des Erzherzogs Leopold Wilhelm von Österreich. Jahrbuch der Kunsthistorischen Sammlungen des Allerhöchsten Kaiserhauses I/2. Wien. *1883.* pp. LXXIX-CXCI.

*Bergsagel,* John: Anglo-Scandinavian Musical Relations before 1700. International Musicological Society, Report of the Eleventh Congress. Copenhagen. *1972.* Bind 1, pp. 263-271.

*Bergsagel,* John: Danish Musicians in England 1611-14. Dansk Årbog for Musikforskning VII, 1973-76. København. *1976.* pp. 9-20.

*Bergsagel,* John: Musik i Danmark på Christian IV's tid, hæfte 2: Instrumentalmusik. København. *1988.*

*Bergsagel,* John: Musik i Danmark på Christian IV's tid, hæfte 6: Messe og Lejlighedsmotetter. København. *1988.*

*Bergström,* Ingvar: Studier i holländskt stillebenmåleri under 1600-talet. Göteborg. *1947.*

*Bergström,* Ingvar: Dutch Still-Life Painting in the Seventeenth Century. New York. *1956.* (genoptrykt New York 1983).

*Bergström,* Ture: En undersøgelse af bibelregalet på Claudius' Samling. København (utrykt afhandling; i kopi på Musikhistorisk Museum og Carl Claudius' Samling). *1972.*

*Bergström,* Ture: At bygge en bibelregal. Orglet årg. 10, nr. 2. København. *1980.* pp. 5-10.

*Bering Liisberg* H. C.: Christian IV og Guldsmedene. København. *1919.*

*Berlin 1985:* Europa und die Kaiser von China. Berlin. *1985.*

*Berlingske Tidende 18.2.1954.*

*Berner Schilden Holsten,* H.: Falk Gøyes og Ide Ulfstands Gobelin. Fra Arkiv og Museum, 2. række bind I. *1925.* pp. 313 ff.

*Bernt,* Walter: Die niederländischen Maler und Zeichner des 17. Jahrhunderts (4. Aufl.), I-III. München. *1980.*

*Bie,* Cornelis de: Het Gulden Cabinet. Antwerpen. *1661.*

*Billedhuggeren Ejnar Utzon-Frank i Tekst og Billeder.* Red. af Kai Friis Møller. København. *1945.*

*Billinge,* Michael og *Shaljean,* Bonnie: The Dalway or Fitzgerald Harp (1621). Early Music, vol XV no. 2. London. *1987.* pp. 175-187.

*Birket-Smith,* K.: De Danskes Vej. København. *1929.*

*Birket-Smith,* S.: Leonora Christine Grevinde Ulfelds Historie. Del 1-2. København. *1879-1881.*

*Bjerg,* Hans Chr. og *Erichsen,* John: Danske orlogsskibe 1690-1860. København. *1980.*

*Bjurström,* Per: French Drawings. Sixteenth and Seventeenth Centuries. Stockholm. *1976.*

*Blade,* Timothy Trent: The Paintings of Dick van Delen. Dissertation 1976. Ann Arbor. *1987.*

*Blankert,* A.: Hendrick Avercamp 1585-1634 – Barent Avercamp 1612-1679 Frozen Silence. Amsterdam. *1982.*

*Bligaard,* Mette: Fædrelandshistoriske billeder. Udstillingskatalog. Det Nationalhistoriske Museum på Frederiksborg. Hillerød. *1978.*

*Block,* J. C.: Jeremias Falck, sein Leben und Werke. *1890.*

*Blom,* Carl: Bidrag til den danske Krigsmagts Hitorie I-III. København. *1868-1869.*

*Blomberg,* Aage Fasmer & *Andrup,* Otto: Fester hos Adelen. Danmark i Fest og Glæde I. København. *1935.* pp. 117-192.

*Blume,* Friedrich (udg.): Die Musik in Geschichte und Gegenwart. Allgemeine Enzyklopädie der Musik, Band 1-7. Kassel-Baden. *1949-1986* (2. udg.). Oxford. *1974.*

*Bodart,* Didier: Les peintres des Payes-Bas méridionaux et de la principauté de Liège à Rome au XVIIieme siècle I-II. Wetteren. *1970.*

*Bode,* Wilhelm: Studien zur Geschichte der holländischen Malerie. Braunschweig. *1883.*

*Boeck,* Wilhelm: Die Fürstenbüsten im Gotischen Hause zu Würlitz. Zeitschrift des deutschen Vereins für Kunstwissenschaft IV. *1937.* pp. 39-50.

*Boesen,* Gudmund og *Bøje,* C. A.: Gammelt dansk Sølv til Bordbrug. København. *1948.*

*Boesen,* Gudmund: De danske dronningers guldtoilette. København. *1956a.*

*Boesen,* Gudmund: Kam og Børste. Arv og Eje 1956. København. *1956b.* pp. 104-111.

*Boesen,* Gudmund: Nogle Guldsmedearbejder fra Nykøbing Slot. Lolland-Falsters Stiftsmuseums Årsberetning. Maribo. *1957.* pp. 21-27.

*Boesen,* Gudmund: Venetianske Glas på Rosenborg. København. *1960.*

*Boesen,* Gudmund: Noget om drikkeskik og drikkekar i Danmark. Arv og Eje. København. *1968.*

*Boesen,* Gudmund: Danmarks Riges Regalier. København. *1986.*

*Bol,* L. J.: Een Middelbrugse Bruegel-groep. VII-VIII. Adriaen Pietersz. van de Venne. Oud Holland LXXIII. Amsterdam. *1958.* pp. 59-79, 128-147.

*Bol,* J. L.: Die holländische Marinemalerei des 17. Jahrhunderts. Braunschweig. *1973.*

*Bol,* J. L.: The Bosschaert Dynasty. (Genoptrykt) Plymoth-London. *1980.*

*Bondesen,* Peter og *Kethnath,* Arthur: Gabriel Engels: David og Bathseba (1649). Meddelelser om Konservering, 2. række hæfte 2. Lyngby. *1973.* pp. 33-45.

*Boon,* K. G.: Netherlands Drawings of the Fifteenth and Sixteenth Centuries. Catalogues of the Dutch and Flemish Drawings in the Rijksmuseum, vol. II, I-II. Haag. *1978.*

*Boyer,* Martha: Japanese Export Lacquers from the Seventeenth Century in the National Museum of Denmark. København. *1959.*

*Sophie Brahes regnskabsbog 1627-40.* Udg. af Henning Paulsen. Aarhus. *1955.*

*Bramsen,* Bo: Gamle Danmarkskort. København. *1952.*

*Bramsen,* Henrik: Malerier af P. C. Skovgaard. Kunst i Danmark. København. *1938.*

*Bramsen,* Henrik: Det forsvundne Monument. København. *1977.*

*Brask,* Peter: Benedichts spå-bog. Dansk Litteraturhistorie 2: Lærdom og magi 1480-1620. København. *1984.* pp. 486-490.

*Braun,* Herman: Gerard und Willem van Honthorst. Dissertation. Göttingen. *1966.*

*Bredius,* A.: Catalogus van het Rÿks-Museum van Schilderÿen. Amsterdam. *1885.*

*Bredius,* A. og *Moes,* E. W.: De schildersfamilie Mytens II. Oud Holland, 25. Jahrgang. Amsterdam. *1907.*

*Bredius,* A.: Rembrandt. The Complete Edition of the Painting. Revised by H. Gerson. London. *1969.*

*Breen,* Adam von: Neuwe Nassauwische Waffenhandlung. Haag. *1618.*

*Brenna,* Arne: Christian 4: Statuen på Stortovet i Oslo og Adolph Tidemands arbejder til maleriet av Christianias grunnleggelse. Oslo. *1980.*

*Bricka,* C. F.: Har Chr. Barnekow frelst Christian IV's Liv i Træfningen på Skällinge Hede? Historisk Tidsskrift 4. række bind 3. København. *1872.* pp. 1-21.

*Brinckmann,* A. E.: Süddeutsche Bronzebildhauer des Frühbarocks. München. *1923.*

*British Museum:* British Heraldry. London. *1978.*

*British Museum:* Chinese Ivories from the Shans to the Qing. *1984.*

*Bro-Jørgensen,* J. O.: Svendborg købstads historie, bind 1. Svendborg. *1959.*

*Broby-Johansen,* R.: Med Broby i det gamle København indenfor voldene. København. *1986.*

*Broby-Johansen,* R.: Med Broby omkring Roskilde Fjord og i Nordsjælland. Lyngby. *1983.*

*Brock,* P.: Den oldenborgske Kongeslægt, især under Enevælden, belyst ved den Chronologiske Samling paa Rosenborg. København. *1870.*

*Brock,* P.: Egenhændige Arbejder udført af Medlemmer af det danske Kongehus. Tidsskrift for Kunstindustri. København. *1892.* pp. 103-115.

*Brockhagen,* Ernst: Deutsche und niederländische Malerei swischen Renaissance und Barock. Alte Pinakotek München. Katalog I (2. rev. udg.). München. *1963.*

*Brugge 1962:* La Toison d'Or.

*Bruhn,* Ada: Sværd og Kaarder i Roskilde Domkirke. Vaabenhistoriske Aarbøger VI. *1949-1951.* pp. 5-38.

*Bruhn,* Helge: Dannebrog og danske Faner gennem Tiderne. København. *1949.*

*Brun,* Georg og *Jaco,* Niels: Koldings gamle Lav. Byrådsbogen 1938-39 og 1939-40. Kolding. *1939-1940.*

*Bruun,* C.: Slaget ved Kolberger Heide d. 1. juli 1644 og de derefter følgende Begivenheder. København. *1879.*

*Bruyn,* J. *et al.*: A Corpus of Rembrandt Paintings. Stichting Foundation Rembrandt Research Project II. Dordrecht. *1986.*

*Brøndsted,* Johannes (red.): Vore gamle Tropekolonier. Bind 1: Ostindien. Guineakysten. København. *1952.*

*Buchwald,* Conrad: Adriaen de Gries. Leipzig.l *1899.*

*Bugge,* Anders & *Alsvik,* Henning (red.): Kongsberg kirke. Norges kirker, udg. af Riksantikvaren. Oslo. *1962.*

*Bugge,* Thomas: Beskrivelse over den Opmaalnings Maade, som er brugt ved de danske geografiske Karter, med tilføjet trigonometrisk Karte over Siæland og de der henhørende Triangler, beregnede Longituder og Latituder, samt astronomiske Observationer. København. *1779.*

*Burchard,* L.: Jasper van der Lanen: His Only Known Work? Burlington Magazine XC. London. *1948.* pp. 237-238.

*Burgers,* C. A.: Nogmaals Paschier Lammertijn. Oud Holland LXXX-3. Amsterdam. *1965.* pp. 139-168.

*Bøe,* Alf: Leonora Christina af Kongeportretterne i Kunstindustrimuseet i Oslo. Årsbok. Oslo. *1950-1958.* pp. 196-219.

*Bøggild-Andersen,* C. O.: Hannibal Sehested 1-2. København. *1946-1970.*

*Bøgh,* Knud: Thomas Brown og Gabriel Ackeleye. Fund og Forskning XVIII. København. *1971.* pp. 15-70.

*Bøje,* C. A.: Balsambøsser og Hovedvandsæg. København. *1950.*

Böttiger, John: Bronsarbeten af Adrian de Friis i Sverige särskildt i Drottningholm. Sthlm. *1884.*

*Böttiger,* John: Svenska statens samling av väfda tapeter I-III. Stockholm. *1895-1896.*

*Böttiger,* John: Tapisseries à figures des XVI et XVIIe siècles appartenant à des collections privées de la Suède. Stockholm. *1928.*

*Bøyesen,* Lars Rostrup: Abraham Wuchters i Sverige 1660-62. Kunstmuseets Aarsskrift XXVIII, 1941. København. *1941.* pp. 79-120.

*Bøyesen,* Lars Rostrup: Malerkunsten paa Christian IV's Tid. Danmark, 3. Aargang Hæfte 5. *1943.*

*C. L. Davids Samling:* Dansk kunst og kunsthåndværk. *København 1972.*

*Cat.Br.Dr.:* Catalogue of British Drawings. Volume One: XIV & XVIII Centuries. By Edward Croft-Murray & Paul Hulton. London. *1960.*

*Catalogue of Old Foreign Paintings.* Royal Museum of Fine Arts. Copenhagen 1951.

*Catalogus van de Schilderijen en Tekeningen.* Stedelijk Museum De Lakenhal. Leiden. *1983.*

*Cavalli-Björkman,* Görel (ed.): Målningar av Rubens i Nationalmuseum. Stockholm. *1977.* pp. 11-48.

*Cavallo,* S. Adolph: Tapestries of Europe and of Colonial Peru in the Museum of Fine Arts. Boston Mass. *1967.*

*Cederström,* Rudolf og *Malmborg,* Gösta: Den äldre Livrustkammaren 1654. Stockholm. *1930.*

*Centraal Museum Utrecht 1961:* Keutze uit tien jaar anwinsten 1951-1861.

*Centraal Museum Utrecht 1971:* Keutze uit 10 jaar aanwinsten 1961-1971.

*Centraal Museum Utrecht/Herzog Anton Ulrich-Museum Braunschweig 1986/87:* Holländische Malerei in neuem Licht.

*Charlottenborg, København 1860:* Fortegnelse over de ved det kongelige Akademie for de skjønne Kunster offentligt udstillede Kunstværker. København. 1860.

*Charlottenborg, København 1961:* 500 aars danske portrætter.

*Chiarini,* M. m.fl.: Sustermans sessant anni alla corte dei Medici. Firenze. *1983.*

*Christensen,* Aksel E.: Industriens Historie i Danmark. Udg. af Axel Nielsen. I: Tiden indtil c. 1730. København. *1943. (Genoptrykt 1979).*

*Christensen, C. & Nichols,* L. W.: »Cadmus, His Companions, and the Dragon«: a Newly discovered Painting by Hendrick Goltzius. Mercury. *1986.* pp. 3-19.

*Christensen, S. Flamand:* De Danske Kongers kronologiske Samling paa Rosenborg. Kongedragter fra 17. og 18. Aarhundrede I-II. København. *1940.*

*Christensen, William:* Lisbet Bryske og Beate Huitfeldt som personalhistoriske Forfattere. Personalhistorisk Tidsskrift 11. Række Bind 5. København. *1932.* pp. 1-20.

*Christiansborg Slot:* Under redaktion af Kristian Hvidt, Svend Ellehøj og Otto Norn. Bind 1-2. Udg. af Folketingets Præsidium. København. *1975.*

*Christiansen,* M. Skytte: Historien om Flora Danica. København. *1973.*

*Christiansen,* Tage E.: Det københavnske Guldsmedelaugs Bøsse. Historiske Meddelelser om København *1965.* pp. 7-24.

*Chudzikowsky,* Andrzej: Louis de Caulery et ses tableaux en Pologne. Bulletin de Musée Nationale de Varsovie VIII. *1967.* pp. 25-31.

*Cipriani,* N.: La Galleria Palatina Nel Palazzo Pitti A Firenze. Firenze. *1966.*

*Claudius & Skjerne 1931:* Carl Claudius' Samling af gamle Musikinstrumenter. Udg. af G. Skjerne. København. 1931.

*Clemmensen,* Tove & *Mackeprang,* Mogens B.: Kina og Danmark 1600-1950. Kinafart og Kinamode. Nationalmuseet. København. *1980.*

*Colding,* Torben Holck: Danish Miniaturist. København. *1948.*

*Colding,* Torben Holck og *Andersen,* Jørgen: An Elizabethan Love-Theme. Burlington Magazine XCII. London. *1950.* pp. 326-327.

*Colding,* Torben Holck: Aspects of Miniature Painting. Its Origin and Development. København. *1953.*

*Colding,* Torben Holck: Et jagtselskab. Carlsbergfondet. Frederiksborgmuseet. Ny Carlsbergfondet. Årsskrift. København. *1977.* pp. 108-111.

*Coninckx,* H.: David Vinkboons, peintre et son oeuvre et la famille de ce nom. Antwerpen. *1908.*

*Crocker Art Gallery, Sacramento California 1974:* The Pre-Rembrandtists.

*Cust, Lionel:* Marcus Gheeraerdts. Walpole Society III. Oxford. *1914.* pp. 9-45.

*Czobor,* Agnes: Zu Vinckboons. Darstellungen von Soldaterszenen. Oud Holland LXXVIII. Amsterdam. *1963.* pp. 151-153.

*DBL:* Dansk Biografisk Leksikon, 3. udgave. Red. Svend Cedergreen Bech København. *1979-1984.*

*DK:* Danmarks Kirker.
København I, 2 *1960-1965.*
Frederiksborg amt II, 1-4. *1964-1975.*
Københavns amt III, 3. *1951.*
Holbæk amt I, 3. *1987.*

*DMP:* Danske Malede Portrætter I-X, Udg. af E. F. S. Lund. København. *1895-1912.*

*DNT:* Danmarks-Norges Traktater 1523-1750. Udg. af L. Laursen. Bind II-IV (1561-1649). København. *1912-1917.*

*DT:* Danske tegninger fra Melchior Lorck til Fynboerne I-III. Udg. af Statens Museum for Kunst ved Peter Koch. København. *1945.*

*Daae,* Ludvig: Om Humanisten og Satirikeren Johan Lauremberg. Christiania. *1884.*

*Dahlerup m.fl.:* Ældre nordisk Architektur. *1872-1880.*

*Dal,* Erik og *Glahn,* Henrik: Niels Jesperssøns Graduale 1573. Facsimileudgave med efterskrift af Erik Abrahamsen (1935), Erik Dal og Henrik Glahn. København. *1986.*

*Dalgård,* Sune: Østersø, Vestersø, Nordsø. Dominium maris Baltici & maris Septentrionalis 1638. Historisk Tidsskrift XI række, 5. bind. København. *1956-1959.* pp. 295-319.

*Dalgård,* Sune: Dansk-norsk hvalfangst 1615-1660. En studie over Danmark-Norges stilling i europæisk merkantil ekspansion. København. *1962.*
*DANIA SONANS:* Udg. af Dansk Selskab for Musikforskning bd. I-VII. København. *1933-1986.*
*Danmark:* Redaktion Jørgen Banke, Sofus Franck, Thomas P. Hjejle, Erik Struckmann (senere m.fl.). 4. årg. *nr. 3.* København. *1944.*
*Danmark i Fest og Glæde:* Red. af Julius Clausen og Torben Krogh. København. 1935.
*Danmarks malerkunst fra middelalder til nutid:* red. Erik Zahle, 4. udg. *1956.*
*Dansk Boghaandværk gennem Tiderne 1482-1948.* København. *1949.*
*Danske Domme 1375-1662:* De private domssamlinger ved Erik Reitzel-Nielsen. *Bind 5:* 1590-1596. København. *1982. Bind 7:* 1609-1662. København. *1984.*
*Danske Magazin, 3. række, bind V. København 1857.* pp. 173-245: T. A. Becker: En Trolddomssag fra 1627-30.
*Den danske Skueplads.* København. *1943.*
*Danske Tegninger fra Melchior Lorck til Fynboerne* I-II. Udg. af Statens Museum for Kunst ved Peter Koch. København. *1945.*
*Davidsson,* Åke: Korrektur til ett danskt musiktryck år 1620. Nordisk tidskrift för bok- och biblioteksväsen, årg. 53. Uppsala. *1966.* pp. 97-103.
*Davies,* Alice J.: Allart van Everdingen. New York. *1978.*
*De Bosque,* Andre: Mythologie et Manierrisme 1570-1630. Peinture-Dessins. Antwerpen. *1985.*
*Degn,* O.: Rig og fattig i Ribe 1-2. Odense. *1981.*
*Degn,* O. og *Dübeck,* I.: Håndværkets Kulturhistorie bd. 2. København. *1983.*
*De Jonge,* C. H.: Paules Moreelse, Portreten en Genreschilder Te Utrecht 1578-1638. Assen. *1938.*
*Delbanco,* Gustav: Der Maler Abraham Bloemaert (1564-1651). Strasbourg 1928.
*Denucé,* J.: Inventare von Kunstsammlungen zu Antwerpen im 16. und 17. Jahrhundert. Antwerpen. *1932.*
*De studio Medico* inchoando, continuando et absolvendo consilium breve atque extemporaneum, Hafniæ 1628. Af Caspar Bartholin, oversat af Niels W. Bruun. København. *1982.*
*Dexel,* Thomas: Gebrauchsgerät Typen. München. *1981.*
*Dietrichson,* L.: Adolph Tidemand, hans Liv og hans Værker I-II. *1878-* 1879.
*Distelberger,* R.: Beobachtungen zu den Steinschneidewerkstetten der Miseroni in Mailand und Prag. Jahrbuch der Kunsthistorische Sammlungen. Band 74. Wien. *1978.* pp. 79-152.
*Dreitzel,* Horst: Protestantischer Aristoletismus und absoluter Staat. Die »Politica« d. Henning Arnisaeus. Wiesbaden. *1970.*
*Dreyer,* J. L. E.: Tycho Brahe. London. *1890 (1963).*
*Drost,* Willi: Barockmalerei in den germanischen Ländern. Handbuch der Kunstwissenschaft. Wildpark-Potsdam. *1926.*
*Dubon,* David: Tapestries from the Samuel H. Kress Collection at the Philadelphia Museum of Art. The History of Constantine the Great designed by Peter Paul Rubens and Pietro da Cortona. Aylesbury. *1964.*
*Duner,* U.: Halmstads Vapens Ursprung. Ale. Historisk tidskrift för Skåneland. Lund. *1965.*
*EB:* Kong Christian den Fjerdes egenhændige Breve 1589-1648. Ved C. F. Bricka og J. A. Fridericia. Bind I-VII *1878-91* samt supplementsbind VIII 1947 ved Johanne Skovgaard. Alle genoptrykt *1970.*
*Ebbesen,* S. og *Mogensen,* L. B.: Andrae Sunonis filii Hexaemeron. Corpus Philosophorum Danicorum Medii Aevi XI, 1. København. 1985.
*Egg,* E.: Caspar Grass und der Tiroler Bronzeguss der 17. Jahrhunderts. Veröffentlichungen des Museums Ferdinandeum in Innsbruck XL. 1960. Innsbruck. *1961.*
*Ehrencron-Müller,* H.: Forfatterlexicon for Danmark, Norge og Island indtil 1814 I-XII. København. 1924-1935.
*Eichler, F. og Kvis,* E.: Kameen in Kunsthistorischen Museum. Katalog. Publikationen an den Kunsthistorischen Sammlungen in Wien II. *1927.*
*Eitner,* Robert: Biographisch-Bibliographisches Quellen-Lexicon der Musiker und Musikgelehrten I-X. Leipzig. *1900-1904.*
*Eliassen,* P.: Kolding fra Middelalder til Nutid. *1910.*
*Eliassen,* P.: Bøddelens tang. Historiske Strejftog i Kolding og Omegn. Kolding. *1923.*
*Ellehøj,* Svend: Christian 4's tidsalder 1595-1660. Politikens Danmarks Historie, bd. 7. Red. J. Danstrup og H. Koch., København. *1964.*
*Ellehøj,* Svend: Anmeldelse af Povl Ellers Kongelige portrætmalere i Danmark 1630-82, København 1971. Historisk Tidsskrift 12. række bind VI, 1972-73. København. *1973.* pp. 591-605.
*Eller,* Povl: Frederiksborgs restaurering. Fra Frederiksborg Amt *1963.* Hillerød. 1964. pp. 107-154.
*Eller,* Povl: Ikonographische Erinnerungen an die Porträtsammlung in Schloos Husum. Nordelbingen 39. *1970.* pp. 108-126.
*Eller,* Povl: Kongelige portrætmalere i Danmark 1630-82. København. *1971.*
*Eller,* Povl: Hvad blev der af portrætterne på Hirschholm Slot? Hørsholm. *1972.*
*Eller,* Povl: Rigets mænd lader sig male 1500-1750. Dansk Kunsthistorie 2. København. *1973.*
*Elling,* Christian: Paraden. Kunst i enevældens Danmark. København. *1958.*
*Engberg,* Jens: Danske ceremonislagsværd. Vaabenhistoriske Aarbøger XI. København. *1962-1964.*
*Engelke,* Bernhard: Musik und Musiker am Gottorfer Hofe. 1. Band: Die Zeit der englischen Komödianten (1590-1627). Veröffentlichungen der Schleswig-Holsteinischen Universitätsgesellschaft 15,1. Breslau. *1930.*
*Erasmus,* Kurt: Roelant Savery, sein Leben und seine Werke. Halle a. S. *1908.*
*Erich,* August: Ausführliche und Wahrhaffte Beschreibung Des Durchlautigsten Fürsten Christian des Vierden Zu Dennemark etc. Königs zu Koppenhagen 29. Aug. 1596 geschehenen Krönung. Kph. *1597.*
*Erichsen,* John: Københavnske Motiver 1587-1807. Københavns Bymuseum 31. maj-31. juli 1974. København. *1974.*
*Erichsen,* John: Byen som motiv. Carlsbergfondet. Frederiksborgmuseet. Ny Carlsbergfondet. Årsskrift 1985. København. *1985.* pp. 130-134.
*Eriksen,* P.: Kanonhallen. Tøjhusmuseets Vejledninger. København. 1970.
*Erkelens,* A. M. L. E.: De wandtapijtkunst te Delft. Oud Delft 1. *1962.* pp. 53-102.
*Erslev,* Kristian: Aktstykker og Oplysninger til Rigsraadets og Stændermødernes Historie i Kristian IV's Tid. Bind I. København. *1883-1885.*
*Ertz,* Klaus: Jan Brueghel der Ältere. Köln. *1979.*
*Ertz,* Klaus: Joos de Momper der Jüngere (1564-1635). Feren. *1986.*
*Etnografiske genstande i Det Kongelige danske Kunstkammer 1650-1800.* Red. af Bente Dam-Mikkelsen og Torben Lundbæk. Udg. af Nationalmuseet. København. *1980.*
*Faaborg,* N. L.: Danske grafiske portrætter. Kongehuset. København *1980.*
*Fabricius,* Knud: Kongeloven. København. *1920. (Genoptrykt 1971).*
*Falck,* Gustav: Maleri- og Skulptursamlingens tilvækst fra Juli 1925 til 1929. Kunstmuseets Aarsskrift XIII-XV, *1926-1928.* København. *1929-1930.* pp. 176-196.
*Falke,* von: Aus dem Kamnitzer-Kreis. Pantheon 19. München. *1937.* pp. 13-17, 57-60.
*Fang,* A.: Vibeke Kruses Ørehæng. Fra Roskilde Museum XXI. Roskilde. *1960.* pp. 4-13.
*Feilberg,* F. F.: Cyprianus. Aarbog for dansk Kulturhistorie. København. *1891.* pp. 97-124.
*Feldbæk,* Ole & *Justesen,* Ove: Kolonierne i Asien og Afrika. Danmarks historie uden for Danmark. Red. af Svend Ellehøj og Kristof Glamann. København. *1980.*
*Ferrari,* Oreste & Scavizzi, Giuseppe: Luca Giordano I-II. Napoli. *1966.*
*Fett,* Harry: Gamle norske ovne. Norsk Folkemuseums Særudstilling nr. 3. Kristiania. *1905.*
*Feuchtmayr,* Karl og Schädler, Alfred et.al: Georg Petel 1601/02-1634. Berlin. *1973.*
*Finsten,* Jill: Isaac Oliver. Art at the Court of Elizabeth I and James I, bind I-II. New York. *1981.*
*Fischer,* Erik: Melchior Lorck. En dansk vagants levnedsløb i det 16. århundrede. Fund og Forskning 9. København. *1964.*
*Fitzgerald,* D.: English Chairs. Victoria and Albert Museum Picturebook. London. *1970.*
*Fjeldstrup,* August: Dr. Peter Payngk Kong Kristian IV's Hofkemiker. København. *1911.*
*Fjordside,* Per: No E 78: »Meget sjældent Stykke«. Meddelelser fra Musikhistorisk Museum og Carl Claudius' Samling III. København. *1986. pp. 6-16.*
*Fleischauer, W.: Der Edelsteinschneider Hans Kobenhaupt in Stuttgart und seine Werkstatt. Pantheon XXVIII, 14. München. 1970.* pp. 284-293.
*Fleischer,* Oskar: Führer durch die Sammlung alter Musik-Intrumente. Königliche Hochschule für Musik zu Berlin. *1892.*

*Floerke,* Hanns: Studien zur niederländischen Kunst und Kulturgeschichte. München-Leipzig. *1905.*
*Flora Danica I-III.* Facsimileudgave ved Johan Lange og V. Møller-Christensen. København. *1971-1973.*
*Fortegnelse over den Spenglerske Haandtegning- og Kobberstiksamling.* Manuskript i Den Kongelige Kobberstiksamling. København. *1812.*
*Frankfurt am Main 1987:* Die Bronzen der Fürstlichen Sammlungen Liechtenstein. Eine Ausstellung des Liebig-Hauses-Museum alter Plastik in der Schirn Kunsthalle.
*Frantzen,* Ole Louis: Nyt fra havets bund. Marinehistorisk tidsskrift, årg. 18, nr. 4, 1985. København. *1986.* pp. 11-15 (m.ill.).
*Franz,* Heinrich Gerhard: Niederländische Landschaftsmalerei im Zeitalter des Manierismus 1-2. Graz. *1969.*
*Fredriks,* J. W.: Dutch Silver. Haag. *1958.*
*Frederiksborghesten og det kongelige Frederiksborgske stutteri.* Udg. af Det Nationalhistoriske Museum på Frederiksborg. Hillerød. *1981.*
*Frederiksborgmuseet:* Udvalg af nyere erhvervelser. *1954-64.* Hillerød. 1964.
*Frederiksborg Slots Inventarium af 1650.* Udg. af Anton Petersen. Danske Samlinger, 2. bind. København. *1866-1867.* pp. 118-234.
*Frederiksborg Slotskirke.* Særtryk af Danmarks Kirker IV, Frederiksborg Amt bind 3. København. *1973.*
*Freise,* Kurt: Pieter Lastman. Leipzig. *1911.*
*Freytag,* Claudia: Neuentdeckte Werke des Francois du Quesnoy. Pantheon XXXIV. München. *1976.* pp. 199-239.
*Fridericia,* J. A.: Danmarks ydre politiske Historie 1629-60, bind 1-2. København. *1876-1881.*
*Fridericia,* J. A.: Adelsvældens sidste Dage (1648-60). København. *1894.*
*Friis,* F. R.: Samlinger til Dansk Bygnings- og Kunsthistorie. København. *1872-1878.*
*Friis,* F. R.: Bidrag til Dansk Kunsthistorie. København. *1890-1901.*
*Friis,* F. R.: Kulturhistoriske Studier, hæfte 1-2. København. *1904-1909.*
*Friis,* F. R.: Om nogle Jordglober og Himmelgglober i Det kgl. Bibliotek i København. Kulturhistoriske Studier 2. hæfte. København. *1909.* pp. 99-116.
*Friis,* Niels: Det danske Hoftrompeterkorps. København. *1947.*
*Frimmel,* Theodor von: Rundschau: Kopenhagen. Blätter für Gemäldekunde. Erster Band, Juni-Juli, heft 4. Wien. *1905.* pp. 69-70.
*Frimmel,* Theodor von: Der Monogramierte Sebastian Vrancx im Museo Nazionale zu Neapel. Blätter für Gemäldekunde. III Band, Sommer 1907, Heft 10. Wien. *1907.* pp. 193-195.
*Gad,* Finn: Grønlands historie, Bind 1, København. *1967.*
*Galster,* Georg: Danske og Norske Medailler og Jetons. København. *1936.*
*Gammelbo,* Poul: Cornelius Norbertus Gijsbrechts og Franciskus Gijsbrechts. Kunstmuseets Årsskrift XXXIX-XLII, 1952-55. København. *1956.* pp. 125-156.
*Gammelbo,* Poul: Some Paintings in Danish Collection: An Allegory from 1628 by Pieter Wtewael. Artes 2. København. *1966.* pp. 73-78.
*Gammelbo,* Poul: Nogle stillebenmalere fra Haarlem. En bog om kunst til Else Kai Sass. Herning. *1978.* pp. 207-219.
*Gamle danske Håndværk.* Red. af Georg Nellemann. København. *1971.*
*Gamrath,* Helge: Et udvidelsesprojekt til København fra begyndelsen af 1600-tallet? Historiske Meddelelser om København 1965. København. *1965.* pp. 38-45.
*Gamrath,* Helge: Christianshavns grundlæggelse og ældste bygningsmæssige udvikling. Historiske Meddelelser om København, *Årbog* 1968. pp. 7-118.
*Gamrath,* Helge: Residens- og hovedstad. Københavns Historie 2, 1600-1728. København. *1980.*
*Gamrath,* Helge og *Petersen, E. Ladewig:* Tiden 1559-1648. Gyldendals Danmarks historie bind 2.2 København. *1980.*
*Garde,* G.: Dansk billedvævning ca. 1500-1800. København. *1949.*
*Garde,* G.: Danske silkebroderede Lærredsduge fra 16. og 17. århundrede. Nationalmuseet. København. *1961.*
*Garde,* G.: Silkebroderede lærredsduge fra 16. og 17. århundrede i Nationalmuseet. Nationalmuseet. København. *1962.*
*Geissler,* Heinrich: Zeichnung in Deutschland. Deutsche Zeichner 1540-1640. Katalog Band 2 zur Ausstellung 1. Dezember 1979 bis 17. Februar 1980. Staatsgalerie Stuttgart. Graphische Sammlung. Stuttgart. *1980.*
*Germanisches National Museum, Nürnberg 1952.* Aufgang der Neuzeit. Deutsche Kunst und Kultur von Dürers Tod bis zum Dreissigjährigen Kriege 1530-1650.
*Germanisches National Museum, Nürnberg 1985.* Wenzel Jamnitzer.
*Gerson,* H.: Ausbreitung und Nachwirkung der holländischen Malerei des 17. Jahrhunderts. Haarlem. *1942.*
*Gerszi,* Terez: Bruegels Nachwirkung auf die niederländischen Landschaftsmaler um 1600. Oud Holland 90. Amsterdam. *1976.* pp. 201-229.
*Gerszi,* Terez: L'influence de Pieter Bruegel sur l'art du paysage de David Vinckboons et de Gillis d'Hondecoeter. Bulletin du Musée Hongroi nr. 53. *1979.* pp. 125-136.
*Gigas,* Emil: Grev Bernardino de Rebolledo, spansk Gesandt i Kjøbenhavn 1648-1659. København. *1883.*
*Gill,* Donald: The Orpharion and Bandora. The Galpin Society Journal 1960, no. XIII. London. *1960.* pp. 14-25.
*Gissel,* Svend (udg.): Jacob Ulfelds Jordebog på Ulfeldsholm, Selsø og Bavelse. København. *1964.*
*Gjellerup,* S. M.: Biskop Jens Dinesen Jersin. København. *1868-1870.*
*Glahn,* Henrik og *Sørensen,* Søren: The Clausholm Music Fragments. København. *1974.*
*Glahn,* Henrik: 20 Italienske madrigaler fra Melchior Borchgrevinck Giardino novo I-II, København 1605-06. Udg. af Musikvidenskabeligt Institut, Københavns Universitet. *1983.*
*Glahn,* Henrik: Musik i Danmark på Christian IV's tid. Hæfte 3: Klavermusik, København. *1988.* Hæfte 4: Mogens Pedersøns messe og motetter. København. *1988.* Hæfte 6: Messe og lejlighedsmotetter. København. *1988.*
*Glob,* P. V.: Ard og Plov i Nordens Oldtid. Jysk Arkæologisk Selskabs Skrifter bind. 1. *1951.*
*Goodman,* W. L.: The History of Woodworking Tools. London. *1964.*
*Goosens,* Korneel: David Vinckboons. Antwerpen-Haag. *1954.*
*Goosens,* Korneel: Nog meer over David Vinckboons. Jaarboe van het Koninklijk Museum voor Schone Kunsten te Antwerpen. Antwerpen. *1966.* pp. 59-106.
*Gosch,* C. C. A.: Danish arctic Expeditions 1605-1620. København. *1897.*
*Gottorf 1965:* Gottorfer Kultur im Jahrhundert des Universitätsgründung. Kulturgeschichtliche Denmäler und Zeugnisse des 17. Jahrhunderts aud der Sphäre der Herzöge von Schleswig-Holstein-Gottorf. Neue Schloss zu Kiel 31. Mai – 31. Juli 1965.
*Granberg,* Olof: Drottning Kristinas tafvelgalleri på Stockholms slott og i Rom, dess Uppkomst och dess öden ända til våra dagar. Stockholm. *1896.*
*Granberg,* Olof: Allart van Everdingen och hans »Norska« landskap. Stockholm. *1902.*
*Granberg,* Olof: Inventaire général des trésors d'art. Peintres & sculptures principalement de maitres etrangers (non-scandinaves) en Suède. Stockholm. *1911-1913.*
*Granberg,* Olof: Svenska konstsamlingarnas historia från Gustav Vasas tid till våra dagar (1525-1925). Bind I: Gustav Vasa – Kristina. Stockholm. *1929.*
*Grand Palais Paris 1974.* Valentin et les Caravagesques français.
*Grand Palais Paris 1977/78.* Le siècle de Rubens dans le collection publiques françaises.
*Grand Palais Paris 1984.* Le Tresor de Saint-Marc de Venice.
*Grandjean,* H. F.: De Kongelige Danske Ridderordener. København. *1903.*
*Grandjean,* Poul Bredo: Danske Købstæders Segl. København. *1937.*
*Grandjean,* Poul Bredo: Danske Haandværkerlavs Segl. København. *1950.*
*Grandjean,* Poul Bredo: Danske Kongelige Segl fra Frederik II's, Christian IV's og Frederik III's Tid 1559-1670. København. *1951.*
*Grandt-Nielsen,* Finn: Lav og lavsting i Odense. Odense 1969.
*Grandt-Nielsen,* Finn: Fynsk kirkesølv. Odense. *1980.*
*Gregersen,* H. V.: Niels Heldvad. Nicolaus Heluaderus. *1957.*
*Greindl,* Edith: Les peintres flamands de nature morte au XVIIe siècle. 2. udg. Sterrebeek. *1983.*
*Grinder-Hansen,* Poul: Klokker og kanoner. Skalk 1982:1. Højbjerg. *1982.* pp. 21-30.
*Grinder-Hansen,* Poul: Danske Klokkekonfiskationer i 16. og 17. århundrede. Arv og Eje 1983-84. *1985* pp. 213-228.
*Grose,* Eduard: Adam Olearius' Leben und Schriften. Aschersleben. *1867.*
*Grosse,* Rolph: Die holländische Landschaftskunst 1600-1650. Stuttgart. *1925.*
*Grossmann,* F.: Cornelis van Dalem Re-examined. Burlington Magazine XCVI. London. *1954.* pp. 42-51.

*Grossmann,* F.: Notes om some Dutch and Flemish Paintings at Rotterdam. Burlington Magazine XCVII. London. *1955.* pp. 335-338.
*Grove,* G. L.: Københavns Havn. København. *1908.*
*Gudewill,* Kurt: »Der Gesang der Venuskinder« von Heinrich Schütz. Bemerkungen zur Überlieferung und zu den Kopenhagener Hochzeitsfeierlichkeiten im Oktober 1634. Schütz Jahrbuch. Kiel. *1984.* pp. 72-92.
*Gudlaugsson,* S. J.: Aanvullingen omtrent Pieter Post's werkzaamhei als schilder. Oud Holland LXIX. Amsterdam. *1954.* pp. 59-71.
*Göbel,* Heinrich: Wandteppiche I: Die Niederlande. Leipzig. *1923.*
*H. N. v.: Rundschau. Pantheon VIII. München. 1931.* pp. 296-297.
*Haak,* B.: Das goldene Zeitalter der holländischen Malerei. Köln. *1984.*
*Haberditzl,* F. M.: Die Lehrer des Rubens. Jahrbuch der Kunsthistorischen Sammlungen des Allerhöchsten Kaisershauses XXVII. Wien. *1907-1909.* pp. 161-235.
*Hackenbroch,* Y.: Renaissance Jewellery. München. *1979.*
*Haenel,* Erich: Kostbare Waffen aus der Dresdner Rustkammer. Leipzig. *1923.*
*Hagen,* S. A. E.: Bemærkninger og Tilføjelser til Dr. Angul Hammerichs Skrift: Musiken ved Christian den Fjerdes Hof. Historisk Tidsskrift 6. række, bind IV. København. *1893.* pp. 3-27.
*Hahnloser,* H. R.: Corpus des Hartsteinschliffes. München. *1985.*
*Hainhofer:* Der Briefwechsel zwischen Philip Hainhofer und Herzog August d. J. von Braunschweig-Lüneburg. München. *1984.*
*Hairs,* M. L.: Les peintres flamands de fleur aux XVII^e siècle Bruxelles. *1955.*
*Hammerich,* Angul: Musiken ved Christian den Fjerdes Hof. København. *1892.*
*Hammerich,* Angul: Das Musikhistorische Museum Kopenhagen. København. *1911.*
*Hammerich,* Angul: Musical Relations between England and Denmark in the 17th Century. Sammelbände der Internationalen Musikgesellschaft. Leipzig. *1911-1912.* pp. 114-119.
*Hammerich,* Angul: Dansk Musikhistorie indtil ca. 1700. København. *1921.*
*Hammerich,* L. L.: Sproget. Holland-Danmark. Forbindelserne mellem de to Lande gennem Tiderne. Red. af K. Fabricius. København. *1945.* pp. 327-356.
*Hannover,* E.: Maleren Christen Købke. Studie i dansk Kunsthistorie. København. *1893.*
*Hannover,* E.: Maleren C. W. Eckersberg. Studie i dansk Kunsthistorie. København. *1898.*
*Hannover,* E.: Fortegnelse over den Hirschsprungske Samling af danske Kunstneres Arbejder. København. *1911.*
*Hansen, Thorkild & Seeberg,* Peter: Jens Munks Mindeekspedition 1964. København *1965.*
*Hansson,* Karl F.: Lundbiskoppen Peder Winstrup före 1658. Lund-København. *1950.*
*Hauber,* E. C.: Beschreibung des Stadt Kopenhagen und der königlichen Landschlösser. 2. oplag. København. *1777.*
*Hayward,* J. F.: Silver Furniture. Apollo, marts *1958.* London. pp. 71-74.
*Hede,* Holger: Danmarks og Norges mønter 1541-1814-1963. København. *1964.*
*Hede,* Holger: Danmarks og Norges mønter 1541-1814-1977. København. *1978.*
*Heiberg,* Steffen: De ti tønder guld. Historisk Tidsskrift, bind 76. København. *1976.* pp. 25-57.
*Heiberg,* Steffen: Et portræt af Gunde Rosenkrantz. Carlsbergfondet. Frederiksborgmuseet. Ny Carlsbergfondet. Årsskrift 1979. København. *1979.* pp. 76-80.
*Heiberg,* Steffen: Tyge Brahes portræt. Carlsbergfondet. Frederiksborgmuseet. Ny Carlsbergfondet. Årsskrift 1982. København. *1982.* pp. 96-102.
*Heiberg,* Steffen: Art and Politics. Christian IV's Dutch and Flemish Painters. Art in Denmark 1600-1650. Leids Kunsthistorisch Jaarboek *1983.* Delft. 1984. pp. 7-24.
*Heiberg,* Steffen: Samtidige portrætter af Frederik II. Tradition og Kritik. Festskrift Til Svend Ellehøj. København. *1984.* pp. 183-204.
*Heiberg,* Steffen: Engelske Christian IV portrætter. Carlsbergfondet. Frederiksborgmuseet. Ny Carlsbergfondet. Årsskrift 1986. København. *1986.* pp. 92-98.
*Heidelberg:* Die Renaissance in deutschen Südwesten. *1986.*
*Hein,* J.: Versteinertes Eis. Kunst und Antiquitäten I. *1985.* pp. 34-45.
*Held,* Julius S.: Malerier og Tegninger af Jacob Jordaens i Kunstmuseet. Kunstmuseets Aarsskrift XXVI. København. *1939.* pp. 1-43.
*Held,* Julius S.: The Oil Sketches of Peter Paul Rubens I-II. Princeton New Jersey. *1980.*
*Helk,* Vello: Stambøger fra det 16. århundrede i Det kongelige Bibliotek. Fund og Forskning XXI, 1974. København. *1974.* pp. 7-46.
*Helk,* Vello: Stambøger fra den første halvdel af 1600-tallet i Det kongelige Bibliotek. Fund og Forskning XXII, *1975-76.* København. 1976. pp. 39-88.
*Hellwig,* Friedemann: Sixt Rauwolf. Ausstellung der Stadt Augsburg. Welt im Umbruch II. Augsburg. *1980.* pp. 479 ff.
*Henningsen,* Henning: Kirkeskibe og kirkeskibsfester. København. *1950.*
*Henningsen,* Henning: »Christian IV's skibskompas«. Handels- og Søfartsmuseets Årbog 1980. Helsingør. *1980.*
*Herbst,* Hans: Der Landschaftsmaler IVDS. Weltkunst XXXII nr. 10. *1962.*
*Hermansen,* Victor: Måle og Vejeredskaber i Danske Museer. Nordisk Kultur XXX. København. *1936.* pp. 162-174.
*Hermansen,* Victor: Sparebøssen. Hillerød. *1943.*
*Hermansen,* Victor: Fra Kunstkammer til Antik-Cabinet. Antik-Cabinettet 1851. Udg. af Nationalmuseet. København. *1951.* pp. 9-56.
*Hermansen,* Victor: Den udvalgte prins Christian og rarieteterne. Kulturminder ny række bind 2. København. *1960.* pp. 16-44.
*Hernmarck,* C. G. M.: The Art of the European Silversmith 1430-1830, I-II. London. *1977.*
*Hertig,* Henrik: Marstrand-studier. Lolland-Falsters Stiftsmuseums Årsskrift. Maribo. *1976.* pp. 50-61.
*Hertz,* Peter: Den kongelige Malerisamlings Tilblivelse. Kunstmuseets Aarsskrift VIII-X, *1921-23.* København. *1924.* pp. 358-390.
Hertz, Peter: Malerisamlingens Tilvækst og Tilpasning gennem Tiderne. Kunstmuseets Aarsskrift XI-XII, *1924-25.* København. *1926.* pp. 290-352.
*Herzog Anton Ulrich-Museum Braunschweig Katalog 1969.* Verzeichnis der Gemälde.
*Herzog Anton Ulrich-Museum Braunschweig 1975.* Deutsche Kunst des Barock.
*Herzog Anton Ulrich-Museum Braunschweig Katalog 1976. Verzeichnis der Gemälde.*
*Herzog Anton Ulrich-Museum Braunschweig 1978.* Die Sprache der Bilder. Realität und Bedeutung in der niederländischen Malerie des 17. Jahrhunderts.
*Hibbard,* Howard: Caravaggio. London. *1983.*
*Hind,* Arthur M.: Engraving in England in the Sixteenth & Seventeenth Century I-II. Cambridge. *1952-1955.*
*Hirschmann,* O.: Hendrich Goltzius als Maler 1600-1617. Haag. *1916.*
*Hjelm,* Torben: Dansborg. Architectura 9. Arkitekturhistorisk Årsskrift. København. *1987.* pp. 89-120.
*Hoet,* Gerard: Catalogus of Naamlyst van Schilderyen I-II. Haag. *1752.*
*Hoet,* Gerard og *Terwesten,* Pieter: Catalogus of Namenlyst van Schilderyen III. Haag. *1770.*
*Hoff,* Arne: Ældre dansk bøssemageri især i 1600-tallet I-II. Udg. af Tøjhusmuseet. København. *1951.*
*Hoff,* Arne, *Schepelern,* H. D. og *Boesen,* G.: Royal Arms at Rosenborg I-II., København. *1956.*
*Hoff,* Arne: Feuerwaffen. Ein waffenhistorisches Handbuch I-II. Braunschweig. *1969.*
*Hoff,* Arne: Royal Danish Hunting Collection. The Connoisseur november 1977. London. *1977.* pp. 212-221.
*Holberg,* Ludvig: Dannemarks Riges Historie II. København. *1733.*
*Holland-Danmark.* Forbindelserne mellem de to Lande gennem Tiderne. Red. Knud Fabricius, L. L. Hammerich og Vilh. Lorenzen. Bind II. København. *1945.*
*Hollandsk Buket.* Jubilæumsudstilling på Kunstindustrimuseet 1. oktober-2. november *1969.*
*Hollstein,* F. W.: German Engravings, Etchings and Woodcuts c. 1400-1700, vol. 1-. Amsterdam. *1954-.*
*Hollstein,* F. W.: Dutch and Flemish Etchings, Engravings and Woodcuts vol. 1-. Amsterdam. *1949.*
*Holm,* Knud: »Et konstigt Jerngitterverck«. Nationalmuseets Arbejdsmark 1983. København. *1983.* pp. 47-61.
*Holst,* Karen: Music as Theme in Art and Life at the Court of Christian IV. Art in Denmark 1600-1650. Leids Kunsthistorisch Jaarboek 1983. Delft. *1984.* app. 137-156.
*Hoogewerff,* G. J.: Gerrit van Honthorst. Haag. *1924.*
*Hoogewerff,* G. J.: Jan van Bijlert. Schilder van Utrecht (1598-1671). Oud Holland LXXX. Amsterdam. *1965.* pp. 3-33.

*Hornby,* Joan: Etnografisk genstande i Det kongelige danske Kunstkammer 1650-1800. Red. af Bente Dam-Mikkelsen og Torben Lundbæk. Kina, pp. 155-220. Japan, pp. 221-253. Nationalmuseet. København. *1980.*

*Houbraken,* Arnold: De groote Schoubourgh der Nederlantsche konstschilders en schilderessen I-III. Amsterdam. *1718-1721.*

*Houtzager,* M. E. et al.: Röntgenonderzoek van de ouder Schilderijen in het Centraal Museum te Utrecht. Utrecht. *1967.*

*Hubala,* Erich: Peter Paul Rubens. Der Münchener Kruzifixus. Stuttgart. *1967.*

*Hubala,* Erich: Die Kunst des 17. Jahrhunderts. Propyläen Kunstgeschichte IX. Berlin. *1970.*

*Hulst,* R.-A. d': Jacob Jordaens en de Allegorie van de Vruchtbaarheid. Bulletin, Musées Royeaux des Beaux-Arts de Belgique I. Bruxelles. *1952.* pp. 17-31.

*Hulst,* R.-A. d': Jacob Jordaens. Schets van een chronologie zijner werken omstaaen voor 1618. Gentse Bijdragn tot de Kunstgeschiednis XIV. Antwerpen. *1953a* pp. 89-136.

Hulst, R.-A. d': Zeichnungen von Jacob Jordaen aus seiner Frühzeit, bis etwa 1618. Zeitschrift für Kunstgeschichte XVI. Berlin. *1953b.* pp. 208-221.

*Hulst,* R.-A. d': De tekeningen van Jacob Jordaens. Gent. *1956.*

*Hulst,* R.-A. d': Drie vroege schilderijen van Jacob Jordaens. Gentse Bijdragen tot de Kunstgeschiednis en de Oudheidkunde XX. Antwerpen. *1967.* pp. 71-86.

*Hulst,* R.-A. d': Jordaens Drawings. Bruxelles. *1974.*

*Hulst,* R.-A. d': Jacob Jordaens. London. *1982.*

*Hulst,* R.-A. d': Een paar toevoegingen aan het oeuvre van Pieter Crijnse Volmarijn. Essays in Northern European Art. Presented to Egbert Haverkamp-Begemann on his sixtieth Birthday (ed. Anne-Marie Logan). Doornspijk. *1983.* pp.3113-116.

*Hübertz,* J. R.: Aktstykker vedkommende Staden og Stiftet Aarhus, bind 1-2. København. *1845.*

*Hægstad,* A.: Tønders gamle rådhus-alen. Nordslesvigske Museer 11, 1984. Tønder. *1984.* pp. 25-29.

*Høyen,* N. L.: Frederiksborg Slots Beskrivelse. Dansk Ugeskrift nr. 5-11. *1831.*

*Høyen,* N. L.: Skrifter. Ved J. L. Ussing, Del 1-3. København. *1871* -1876.

*Høyen, N. L.:* Fortegnelse over den Moltkeske Malerisamling. Ved Karl Madsen. København. *1900.*

*Illustreret Tidende* bind 18, nr. 890, København 15. oktober *1876,* p. 31: Gustaf Adolf og Ebba Brahe.

*Illustreret Tidende,* bind 28, nr. 26, København 27. marts *1887:* Prof. Otto Baches Christian IV's Kroning. pp. 313-315.

*Illustreret Tidende* bind 36 nr. 5, København 4. november *1894,* pp. 73-74: Minder om Kirstine Munk og hendes Børn i Rosenborgsamlingen af P. Brock.

*Illustreret Tidende* bind 37 nr. 37, København 5. april *1896,* pp. 410 ff.: Christian IV's Monument og Christian IV's Kirke.

*Ilsøe,* Grethe: Arild Huitfeldts manuskripter til Christian 2.s og Christian 3.s historie. København. *1976.*

*Ilsøe,* Harald: Udlændinges Rejser i Danmark indtil år 1700. København. *1963.*

*Ilsøe,* Harald: Universitetets biblioteker til 1728. Københavns Universitet 1479-1979, bind IV. København. *1980.* pp. 289-364.

*Impey,* Oliver og *MacGregor,* Arthur (ed.): The Origins of Museums. Oxford. *1985.*

*Institut Neerlandais, Exposition, Paris 1970:* Saenredam 1597-1665. Peintre des Eglise.

*Isarlo,* George: Caravage et le caravaggisme europeen II. Catalogus. Aix-en-Provence. *1941.*

*Jacobsen,* J. C.: Danske Domme i Troldomssager i øverste Instans. København. *1966.*

*Jaefvert,* E.: Skomakarverktygets historia. Svensk Skotidning. *1932.*

*Jagd,* Palle Bolten: Danske forsvarsanlæg i 5000 år. Bind 1 af 3. København. *1984-1986.*

*Jahrbuch der Einbandkunst. Bind II. Leipzig. 1937.*

*Jantzen,* Hans: Das niederländische Architekturbild. Leipzig. *1910*/ Braunschweig. *1979.*

*Jensen,* Chr. Axel: Danmarks Snedkere og Billedsnidere i Tiden 1535-1660. København. *1911.*

*Jensen,* Chr. Axel: Hans Gudewerth eller Lorents Jørgensen? Fra Arkiv og Museum II, 1. København. *1925.* pp. 72-77.

*Jensen,* Chr. Axel: Roskildemesteren Brix Michgell Snedkers Skab i Nationalmuseet. Fra Nationalmuseets Arbejdsmark *1928.* pp. 49-60.

*Jensen,* Chr. Axel: Snitværker af Mester Hans Drejer. Fra Nationalmuseets Arbejdsmark *1931.* pp. 5-10.

*Jensen,* Chr. Axel: Maling og Staffering. Håndværkets Bog: Malerfaget. København. *1935.* pp. 385 ff.

*Jensen,* Chr. Axel: Københavns anden Vesterport. Historiske Meddelelser om København, 3. række bind II. København. *1936.* pp. 209-228.

*Jensen,* Frede P.: Bidrag til Frederik II's og Erik XIV's historie. København. *1978.*

*Jensen,* Frede P.: Danmarks konflikt med Sverige 1563-70. København. *1982.*

*Jensen,* J. S.: Hertug Hans den Yngre. København. *1971.*

*Jensen Roskilde,* Peder: Prosodia Danicæ Lingvæ. Udg. i Danske metrikere af Arthur Arnholtz, Erik Dal og Aage Kabell. København. *1953.*

*Jensen,* Uno Barner: Trankebarmønter ca. 1620-1845. København. *1978.*

*Jexlev,* Thelma, *Riismøller,* Peter & *Schlüter,* Mogens: Dansk glas i Renæssancetid 1550-1650. København. *1970.*

*Jexlev,* Thelma: Lensregnskaberne. En oversigt. København. *1976.*

*Johannesen,* Hugo: Regna Firmat Pietas. Hafnia. København. *1974.* pp. 67-140.

*Johannsen,* Hugo: Den ydmyge konge. Omkring et tabt maleri fra Christian IV's bedekammer i Frederiksborg slotskirke. Kirkens Bygning og Brug. Studier tilegnet Erna Møller. *1984a.* pp. 127-154.

*Johannsen,* Hugo: The Graphic Art of Hendrick Goltzius as Prototype for Danish Art during the Reign of Christian IV. Art in Denmark. Leids Kunsthistorisch Jaarboek 1983. Delft. *1984b.* pp. 85-110.

*Johansen,* K.: Nyopstillingen af Chr. IV's blodige klæ'r. Bulletin, Nordisk Konservatorforbund, danske afdeling, nr. 38. pp. 21-26. *1985.*

*Johnsson,* Bengt: Den danske skolemusiks historie indtil 1739. København. *1973.*

*Johnsson,* Bengt (udg.): Hans Mikkelsen Ravn. Heptachordum Danicum (1646) I-II. København. *1977.*

*Judson,* J. Richard: Gerrit van Honthorst. A Discussion of his Position in Dutch Art. Haag. *1959.*

*Just,* Ingrid: Hendrick van Balen d. Ä. Versuch einer Chronologie. Nederlands Kunsthistorisch Jaarboek XIV. Gravenhage (Haag). *1963.* pp. 83-128.

*Justesen,* Joan: Fra Kanton til Kunstkammeret. Træk af den danske kontakt med Kina i 1600- og 1700-årene. Det indianske Kammer. Red. af Torben Lundbæk & Henning Dehn-Nielsen. Nationalmuseet. København. *1979.* pp. 55-68.

*Jäfvert,* E.: Skomod och Skotilverkning från Medeltiden till våra dagar. Stockholm. *1938.*

*Jørgensen,* A. D.: Fyrretyve Fortællinger af Fædrelandets Historie. København. *1882.* (*1981*-udgave).

*Jørgensen,* Johan: Det københavnske patriciat og staten ved det 17. århundredes midte. København. *1957.*

*Jørgensen,* Johan: Rentemester Henrik Müller. København. *1966.*

*Jørgensen,* Poul Johs.: Dansk Retshistorie. København. *1940.* (2. udgave 1947).

*Kamenskaja,* T.: Unveröffentlichte Zeichnungen Abraham Bloemaerts in der Ermitage. Oud Holland LIV. Amsterdam. *1837.* pp. 145-163.

*Kancelliets Brevbøger* vedrørende Danmarks indre Forhold. Udg. af C. F. Bricka m.fl. København. *1885-.*

*Kannik,* Preben: Alverdens flag i Farver. København. *1956.*

*Katalog Boch-Rosenberg 1930.*

*Katalog over Den historiske Modelsamling 1896.*

*Katalog Nivaagaard 1908.*

*Katalog der Staatsgalerie Stuttgart.* Alte Meister. Stuttgart. *1962.*

*Katalog over ældre udenlandske Malerier fra Privateje* udtillede i Statens Museum for Kunst. København. *1946.*

*Kaufmann,* Thomas Dacosta: Empire Triumphant: Notes on an Imperial Allegory by Adriaen de Vries. Studies in the History of Art. Washington National Gallery of Art, nr. 8, Washington. *1978.* pp. 63-75.

*Kaufmann,* Thomas Dacosta: L'Ecole de Prague. La peinture à la cour de Rodolphe II. Paris. *1985.*

*Kejlbo,* Ib Rønne: Gyldendals reliefatlas. Af Poul Holmelund og Ib Kejlbo. København. *1968.*

*Kelch,* Jan (ed.): Holländische Genremalerei im 17. Jahrhundert. Symposium Berlin 1984. Berlin. *1987.*

*Keller,* Harald: Entstehung und Blütezeit des Freundschaftsbildes. Essays in the History of Art presented to Rudolf Wittkower (ed. Howard Hibbard & Milton J. Lewine). London. *1967.* pp. 161-173.

*Kelly,* F. M.: Shakespearean Dress Notes. Burlington Magazine XXICX. London. *1916.*

*Kelly,* F. M.: Mytens and his Portraits of Charles I. Burlington Magazine vol. XXXVII no. CIX, august 1920. London. *1920.*

*Keyes,* George S.: Landscape Drawings by Alexander Kerincx and Abraham Goovaerts. Master Drawings XVI. New York. *1978.* pp. 293-302.

*Keyes,* Georg S.: Esaias van den Velde 1587-1630. Doornspijk. *1984.*

*Klessmann,* Rüdiger: Die holländischen Gemälde, Kritisches Verzeichnis. Herzog Anton Ulrich-Museum, Braunschweig. *1983.*

*Klint,* Helge: Fæstningsbyggeriets århundrede i Danmark. Militært Tidsskrift årg. 104, marts *1975.* pp. 99-130.

*KLMN:* Kulturhistorisk Leksikon for Nordisk Middelalder I-XXII. København. 1956-1978.

*Knipping,* John B.: Iconography of the Counter Reformation in the Netherlands I-II. Niewkoop-Leiden. *1974.*

*Knutsson,* Johan: Tre pragtpokaler ur Skokloster samlingar. Skokloster Studier 15. Uppsala. *1983.*

*Koeman,* C.: Atlantes Neerlandici I-VI. Amsterdam. *1967-1985.*

*Koers,* N. H.: Werner van den Valckert: Familegroep als Caritas. Catharijenbrif nr. 15, september *1986.* pp. 5-7.

*Koester,* Olaf: Joos de Momper the Younger. Artes. Periodical of the Fine Arts II. København. *1966.* pp. 5-70.

*Kolderup-Rosenvinge,* J. L. A. (udg.): Udvalg af Gamle Danske Domme, afsagte paa Kongens Retterting og paa Landsting I-IV. København. *1842-1848.*

*Koloristerne, København 1957.*

*Kong Christian den Fjerdes Norske Lowbog af 1604.* Udg. af Fr. Hallager og Fr. Brandt. København. *1885.*

*Kongsted,* Ole: Heinrich Schütz og Danmark. Udstillingskatalog. Musikhistorisk Museum og Carl Claudius' Samling, 1985. København. *1985.*

*Kongsted,* Ole: Musik i Danmark på Christian IV's tid. Hæfte 5: kirkelig vokalmusik. København. *1988.*

*Kornerup,* Bjørn: Biskop Hans Poulsen Resen. Bind *I 1928.* Bind *II* ved Vello Helk *1968.*

*Kornerup,* Bjørn: Ribe Katedralskoles Historie. København. *1947.*

*Kort Udsigt over den Spenglerske Malerie Samling. København. 1809.*

*Krabbe,* Knud: Om Dværgebilleder i danske Kunstsamlinger samt nogle Undersøgelser over danske Hofdværge. Særtryk af Bibliotek for Læger. København. *1930.*

*Krabbe,* Niels og *Hatting,* Carsten: Musik i Danmark på Christian IV's tid. Hæfte 1: Verdslige viser. København. *1988.*

*Kraglund,* Jørgen: Den hvide kunst. Skalk 1981:3. Højbjerg. *1981.* pp. 18-26.

*Kriss,* E.: Meister und Meisterwerke der Steinschneidekunst I-II. Wien. *1929.*

*Kristen Stephensens Årbog:* Trykt i Samlinger til Jydsk Historie og Topografi V. *1874.*

*Kristensen, P. H*alkjær: Danske tinmærker. Udg. ved Holger Rasmussen. København. *1983.*

*Kristianstad 1977:* Christian IV och hans tid. Kristianstads Museum 9. september – 2. oktober 1977.

*Krogh,* Torben: Optogsbilleder fra Christian IV's Kroningsfest. Tilskueren 1938 nr. II. København. *1938.* pp. 187-198.

*Krogh,* Torben: Hofballetten under Chritian IV og Frederik II. København. *1939.*

*Krogh,* Torben: Ældre Dansk Teater. København. *1940.*

*Krogh,* Torben: Musik og Teater. København. *1955.*

*Krohn,* Mario: Maleren Christen Købkes Arbejder. København. *1915.*

*Kroman,* Erik: Danmarks middelalderlige annaler. København. *1980.*

*Kruse,* John: S:t Knutsgillet i Malmø. Stockholm. *1895.*

*Kuile,* O. ter: 500 Jaar Nederlandse Schilderkunt. Amsterdam. *1970.*

*Kuile,* O. ter: Daniel Mijtens »his Majesties Picture-Drawer«. Nederlands Kunsthistorisch Jaarboek 20. Bussum. *1969.* pp. 1-106.

*Kungliga Husgerådskammaren:* En värld i Miniatyr. Stockholm. *1982.*

*Kunst i Privateje.* Red. V. Winkel & Magnussen. I-III. København. *1944-1945.*

*Kunstens Historie i Danmark.* Red. Karl Madsen. København. *1901-1907.*

*Kunstforeningen, København, oktober 1896.*

*Kunst- og Industriudstillingen i Kjøbenhavn i Sommeren 1879.*

*Kunsthistorisches Museum. Wien 1976.* Porträtgalerie zur Geschichte Österreiches von 1400 bis 1800.

*Kunsthistorisches Museum. Wien 1978/79.* Giambologna 1529-1608. Ein Wendepunkt der europäischen Plastik.

*Kunstindustrimuseet, Kbh. 1950:* Kinas kunst i svensk aog dansk eje. Udstilling april 1950.

*Kunstindustrimuseet, Kbh. 1960:* Smykker i dansk eje. Udstilling 23. marts-18. april 1960. Red. Erik Lassen m.fl.

*Kunstindustrimuseet, København, 11. oktober-2. november 1969:* Hollandsk Buket.

*Kunstindustrimuseet, Kbh. 1980-81: Tønderske kniplinger. Udstilling november 1980 – januar 1981.*

*Kunstindustrimuseet, Kbh. 1983:* Alverdens broderier. Udstilling september – november 1983.

*Kunstindustrimuseet, Kbh. 1983-84:* Konkylien og Mennesket. Udstilling 25. november 1983-15. januar 1984. Red. Vibeke Woldbye og Bettina von Meyenburg.

*Kunstindustrimuseets Virksomhed.* Det danske Kunstindustrimuseums Virksomhed 1917. Ved Emil Hannover. *1917.*

*Kunstindustrimuseets Virksomhed.* Det danske Kunstindustrimuseums Virksomhed 1918. Ved Emil Hannover. *1918.*

*Kuznetsow,* J. I.: Nikolaus Knüpfer. Trudy gosudarttstvennogo Ermitaza VIII, Zaparno-europejskoe iskusstvo, 3. Leningrad. *1964a.* pp. 187-232.

*Kuznetsow,* J. I.: Het werkelijke onderwerp van de werken van A. Elsheimer en N. Knüpfer bekend onder de naam »Centento of de jacht naar het geluk«. Oud Holland LXXIX. Amsterdam. *1964b.* pp. 229-230.

*Kuznetsow,* J. I.: Nikolaus Knüpfer (1630?-1655). Oud Holland LXXXVIII. Amsterdam. *1974.* pp. 169-219.

*Kuznetsow,* J. I. og *Linnik,* I.: Dutch Painting in Soviet Museums. Leningrad. *1982.*

*Kyster,* Anker: Bookbindings in the Public Collections of Denmark. Vol. I: The Royal Library. København. *1938.*

*Københavns Bymuseum 31. maj-31. juli 1974:* Københavnske Motiver 1587-1807, ved John Eriksen.

*Köhn,* Gerhard: Die Bevölkerung der Residenz, Festung und Exulantenstadt Glückstadt von Gründung 1616 bis Endausbau 1652. Neumünster. *1976.*

*Landesgalerie, Hannover 1954:* Katalog der Gemälde alter Meister.

*Landström,* Björn: Regalskeppet Vasa från början till slutet. Stockholm. *1980.*

*Langberg,* Harald: Kronborg. Vejledning for slottets gæster. København. *1979.*

*Langberg,* Harald: Dansesalen på Kronborg. København. *1985.*

*Langgård,* Johan H.: J. C. Dahl's værk. Nasjonalgalleriet. Oslo. *1937.*

*Lange,* Hans Ostenfeldt: De hollandske Bogauktioner i deres første halve Aarhundrede. Uppsala. 1914. Særtryk af Bibliografiske Undersökningar 7. juni *1914.*

*Lange, Julius:* Kunstakademiets Afstøbningssamling. Renaissance-Skulptur. København. *1886.*

*Langeland-Mathiesen,* Aage: Det Kongelige Kjøbenhavnske Skydeselskab og Danske Broderselskab 1334-1934, bind 1-2. Københanv. *1934.*

*Langwill,* Lyndesay G.: An Index of Musical Wind-Instrument Makers. 6th Edition. Edinbourgh. *1980.*

*Larsen,* Jens Peter: Schütz und Dänemark. Sagittarius 2. Kassel. *1969.*

*Larsen,* Svend: Studier over det fynske Rådsaristokrati i det 17de Aarhundrede. Odense. *1965.*

*Larsson,* Lars Olof: Adrian de Vries 1545-1626. Wien. *1967.*

*Larsson,* Lars Olof: Bildhauerkunst und Plastik in Dänemark in der Regierungszeit Christians IV. Art in Denmark 1600-1650. Leids Kunsthistorisch Jaarboek II, *1983a.* Delft. 1984. pp. 25-36.

*Larsson,* Lars Olof: Die Brunnen auf Schloss Frederiksborg. Art in Denmark 1600-1650. Leids Kunsthistorisch Jaarboek II, *1983b.* Delft. 1984. pp. 69-84.

*Larsson,* Lars Olof: Katalog der Bronzen. Nationalmuseum Stockholm. Stockholm. *1984.* (Ms.).

*Lassen,* Erik: Dansk sølv. København. *1964.*

*Lassen,* G. F.: Bidrag til Børsens Historie ... København. *1858.*

*Lauridsen,* P.: Jens Munk Navigatio septentrionalis. København. *1883.*

*Lauridsen,* P.: Kartografen Johannes Mejer. Hitorisk Tidsskrift 6. række, bind. I. København. *1887-1888.* pp. 239-402.

*Lauritzen,* J.: Odense Smedelav igennem 400 Aar med en Efterslæt. Odense. *1896.*

*Leeuwenberg,* Jaap & *Halsema-Kubes,* Willy: Beeldhouwkunst in het Rijksmuseum. Catalogus. Amterdam. *1973.*

*Legêne,* Eva: The Rosenborg Recorders. The American Recorder Vol. XXV no. 2, May 1984. New York. *1984.* pp. 50-52.

*Legrand,* F.-C.: Les peintres flamands de genre au XVIIe siècle. Bruxelles. *1963.*
*Lehmann-Haupt:* H. C. van Sichem. A Family of Dutch Woodcutters. Godenberg Jahrbuch. *1975.*
*Leithe-Jasper,* M. & *Distelberger,* R.: The Treasury and the Collection of Sculpture and Decorative Arts. Kunsthistorische Museum. Wien. *1982.*
*Lerche,* Grith. The Ploughs of Medieval Denmark. Tool and Tillage, Vol. I:3. København. *1970.* pp. 131-149.
*Lesure,* François: Musik und Gesellschaft im Bild. Kasel-Basel-Paris-London-New York.' *1966.*
*Lichtenberg,* Hanne *Honnes de:* Adriaen de Vries' fontæne til Frederiksborg Slot. Konsthistorisk Tidskrift. Stockholm. XLIV. *1975.* pp. 15-22.
*Lichtenberg,* Hanne *Honnens de:* Frederik II's Frederiksborg. Art in Denmark 1600-1650. Leids Kunsthistorisch Jaarboek II, 1983. Delft. *1984.* pp. 37-53.
*Lichtenberg,* Hanne *Honnes de:* Johan Gregor van der Schardt. Sculptor and Architect. Hafnia 10. København. *1985.* pp. 147-164.
*Liebgott,* Niels-Knud: Kakler. Hovedtræk af kakkelovnens historie 1350-1650. Nationalmuseet. København. *1972.*
*Liebgott,* Niels-Knud: Kister og skabe. Nationalmuseet. København. *1975.*
*Liebgott,* Niels-Knud: Da klæde var en »mærkevare«. Nationalmuseets Arbejdsmark 1975. København. *1975* pp. 35-46.
*Liebgott,* Niels-Knud: Svenskekrigsfundet fra Hørløkke. Danefæ. Red. af P. V. Glob. Nr. 34. København. *1980.*
*Liedtke,* Walter A.: The new Church in Haarlem series: Saenredam's Style in Relation to Perspective. Simiolus Vol. 8, no. 3, *1975/76.* Amsterdam. 1976. pp. 145-166.
*Liedtke,* Walter A.: Faith in Perspective. The Dutch Church Interior. The Connoisseur, Vol. 193, no. 776, October 1976. London. *1976.* pp. 126-133.
*Liedtke,* Walter A.: Architectural Painting in Delft, Gerard Houckgeest, Hendrick van Vliet, Emanuel de Witte. Groningen. *1982.*
*Lieure,* Jules: Jacques Callot. Bind. 1-8. Paris. *1924-1929.* (Genoptrykt New York 1969).
*Liisberg,* H. C. Bering: Fra vore Museers Barndom. Kunstkammeret. Dets Stiftelse og ældste Historie. København. 1897.
*Liisberg,* H. C. Bering: Urmagere og Ure i Danmark. København. *1908.*
*Liisberg,* H. C. Bering: Hesten og Løven i Kongens Have og Christian IV's Buste paa Rosenborg. Historiske Meddelelser om København, 1. række, bind 6, København. *1917-1918.* pp. 561-582.
*Liisberg,* H. C. Bering: Efterslæt til »Christian IV's Buste paa Rosenborg«. Historiske Meddelelser om København, 1. række, bind 7. København. *1919-1920.* pp. 322-324.
*Liisberg,* H. C. Bering: De ældste danske Rigsregalier. Aarbøger for Nordisk Oldkyndighed og Historie, 3. række, bind 11, hæfte 3-4. København. *1921.* pp. 219-251.
*Liisberg,* H. C. Bering: »Hans Billedgyder« og Figurerne paa Kronborgfontainen m.m. Kunstmuseets Aarsskrift (Festskrift til Karl Madsen). København. *1921-1923.* pp. 121-138.
*Liisberg,* H. C. Bering: Peter Isacksen. Kunstmuseets Aarsskrift XI-XII, 1924-25. København. *1926.* pp. 195-228.
*Liisberg,* H. C. Bering: Christian den Fierde og Guldsmedene. København. *1929.*
*Lilienskiold,* J.: Rejsejournal 1668-1670. Udg. af Christian Sommerfeldt. Kristiania. *1916.*
*Lind,* H. D.: Kristian IV og hans Mænd paa Bremerholm. København. *1889.*
*Lind,* H. D.: Om Kong Christian den Fjerdes Orlogsflaade. Tidsskrift for Søvæsen. *1890.* pp. 315-343, 404-452.
*Lind,* H. D.: Underslæb paa Bremerholm under Korfits Ulfeldts Finansstyrelse. Historisk Tidsskrift 6. række, bind 5. København. *1894-1895.* pp. 367-410.
*Lind,* Jens: Apoteker C. Heerfordts Herbarier. Botanisk Tidsskrift 36. København. *1917.* pp. 1-19.
*Lindahl,* Fritze: Tandstikkere fra Christian IV's tid. Fra Nationalmuseets Arbejdsmark. København. *1962.*
*Lindahl,* Fritze: Guld fra Nordvestsjælland. Middelalder og renæssance. København. *1975.*
*Lindahl,* Fritze: Svenskekrigsfund fra Eltanggård. Danefæ. Red. af P. V. Glob. København. *1980.*
*Lindahl,* Fritze: Signeter til voks- og laksegl. Danefæ. Red. af P. V. Glob. Nr. 6. København. *1980.*
*Lindahl,* Fritze: En københavnerkande. Nationalmuseets Arbejdsmark *1982.* pp. 103-117.
*Linde,* Peter: Vor gamle Hovedstad. København. *1929.*
*Lindemann,* C. M. A. A.: Joachim Wtewael. Utrecht. *1929.*
*Linvald,* Axel: Mikkel Wibes Sølvbægre. Historiske Meddelelser om København 2. række, bind 3. København. *1927-1928.* pp. 1-9.
*Link,* E.: Die Landgräfliche Kunstkammer. Kassel. *u. å.*
*Livrustkammaren, Stockholm 1932:* Gustav II Adolf – 350 år efter Lützen.
*Lolland-Falsters Stiftsmuseum. Maribo 1940.* Udstiling af Malerier fra Godser i Stiftet. Katalog ved Leo Swane.
*Longhi,* R.: Ultimi studi sul Caravaggio e la sua cerchia. Proporzioni I. Firenze. *1943.* pp. 5-63.
*Longhi,* R.: Apropos de Valentin. La Revue des Arts VIII. Paris. *1958.* pp. 58-66.
*Lopez-Rey,* Jose: A Pseudo-Velazquez. The Picture of a Dwarf with a Dog. Gazette des Beaux-Arts 92e annee, VIe periode, tome XXXVII. Paris. *1950.*
*Lorenz,* Gottfried: Das Erzstift Bremen und der Administrator Friedrich während des Westfälischen Friedenskongres. Münster. *1969.*
*Lorenzen, Gustav:* Miniaturer. Kunstmuseets Aarsskrift XXVI, 1939. København. *1939.* pp. 114-123.
*Lorenzen, Vilh.:* Christian IV's Byanlæg (og andre bygningsarbejder). Selskabet for udgivelse af danske Mindesmærker. København. *1937.*
*Lorenzen, Vilh.:* Axel Urup. En dansk Ingeniør i det 17. aarhundrede. København. *1953.*
*Lossky,* Boris: La Benediction de la Paix, chef-d'oeuvre retrouve de Hendrick Martensz. Sorgh. La Revue des Arts VI. Paris. *1956.* pp. 15-20.
*Lowenthal,* Anne Walter: Some Paintings by Peter Wtewael (1596-1660). Burlington Magazine CXVI. London. *1947.* pp. 458-466.
*Lowenthal,* Anne Walter: The Paintings of Joachim Anthonisz. Wtewael (1566-1638). Dissertation 1975. Ann Arbor. *1982.*
*Lowenthal,* Anne Walter: Joachim Wtewael and Dutch Mannerisme. Groningen. *1986.*
*Lund, E. F. S.: Avisartikler i Berlingske Tidende 24/4* 1897, 21/4 1897, *3/5* 1897.
Lund, Troels: Om Dommen over Christoffer Rosenkrands. Historisk Tidsskrift 4. række, bind 3. København. *1872-1873.* pp. 518-537.
*Lund,* Troels: Historiske Skitser efter utrykte Kilder. København. *1876.*
*Lutteman,* Helena: Rubens i elfenben. Rubens i Sverige. Red. Görel Cavalli–Björkman, Stockholm. *1977.* pp. 131-140.
*Lütken,* Ingrid: Textil-analyser. Danskøya-projektet, Svalbard 1984. Brede. *1986.* (xerograferet rapport).
*Mackeprang,* M. & *Christensen,* S. Flamand: Kronborgtapeterne. København. *1950.*
*Mackeprang,* M.: Selvfundet fra Errindlev Præstegård. Fra Nationalmuseets Arbejdsmark *1930.* pp. 57-60.
*Madsen,* Emil: Om Artilleriet i de danske Hære i det 16. Aarhundrede. Historisk Tidsskrift 7. række, bind 2. København. *1899-1900.* pp. 135-176.
*Den fynske Biskop Mester Jacob Madsens Visitatsbog.* Oversat på Grundlag af A. Crones Udgave af A. R. Idum. Odense. *1929-1933.*
*Den tredie fyenske evangeliske Biskops. Mester Jacob Madsens Visitatsbog.* Udg. af A. Crone. Odense. *1853.*
*Madsen,* Karl: Hollandsk Malerkunst. København. 1891.
*Madsen,* Karl: Fortegnelse over Billeder af gammel Kunst udstillede i Kunstforeningen i København Oktober 1896. København. *1896a.*
*Madsen,* Karl: Kunst. Tilskueren, årg. 13. København. *1896b.* pp. 477-487.
*Madsen,* Karl: Kunst. En Udtilling af gammel Kunst i Kunstforeningen. Tilskueren, Februar 1897. København. 1897. pp. 117-134.
*Madsen,* Karl (red.): Kunstens Historie i Danmark. København. *1901-1907.*
*Madsen,* Karl: Fortegnelse over Den kgl. Malerisamlings Billeder af Ældre Malere. København. *1904.*
*Madsen,* Karl: Wilhelm Marstrand 1810-73. København. *1905.*
*Madsen,* Karl: Et og andet om Abraham Wuchters. Kunstmuseets Aarsskrift II. København. *1915.* pp. 166-187.
*Madsen,* Karl: Museets Forøgelse med flamske Malerier fra det 17. Aarhundrede. Kunstmuseets Aarsskrift XI-XII, 1924-25. København. *1926a.* pp. 53-74.
*Madsen,* Karl: Museets Tilvækst af ældre Malerkunst. Kunstmuseets Aarsskrift XI-XII, 1924-25. København. 1926b. pp. 117-155.
*Madsen,* Per: Ribe Raadhussamling. Mark og Montre. Fra sydvestjyske museer, 1983. Esbjerg. *1983.*
*C. Popp-Madsen og Erik Reitzel-Nielsen:* Festskrift i Anledning af Tohund-

rede Aars Dagen for Indførelsen af Juridisk Eksamen. København. *1936.*
*Malmborg,* Boo von: Samtida porträtt av Gustav II Adolf. Stockholm. *1944.*
*Malmborg,* Boo von: Drottningholm. En konstbok från Nationalmuseum. Stockholm. *1966.*
*Malmö Museums* Årsbog. *1977.*
*Mander,* Carel van: Het Schilder-Boeck. Haarlem. *1604.*
*Mander,* Carel van: Das Leben der niederländischen und deutschen Maler. Textabdruck nach der Ausgabe von 1617. Ed. Hannes Floerke. I-II. München-Leipzig. 1906.
Manners, Victoria: Dusart's Busts at Arundel Castle. The Connoisseur LXXXV-LXXXVI. London. *1930.* pp. 24-26.
*Mansuelli,* Guido: Galleria degli Uffizi. Le sculture I–II. Firenze. *1958-1961.*
*Martin, F.R.:* Dänische Silberschätze aus der Zeit Christian IV, aufbewahrt in der K. Schatzkammer zu Moskau. Stockholm. *1900.*
*Martin, W.:* De Hollandsche schilderkunst in de zeventiende eeuw. Amsterdam. *1935.*
*Matthiessen,* Hugo: Bøddel og Galgefugl. *1910.*
*Matthiessen,* Hugo: Byens Hægte. Festskrift til J. C. H. R. Steenstrup. *1915* pp. 100-120.
*Matthiessen,* Hugo: Tiggertegn. Fra Arkiv og Mueum, 2. serie, bind 1, 1916-25. København. *1925.*
*Maurice,* K.: Die deutsche Räderuhr. München. *1976.*
*McGowan,* Margaret M.: The Court Ballet of Louis XIII. London. *1987.*
*Meaume,* Edouard: Recherches sur La Vie et les Ouvrages de Jacques Callot I-II. Paris. *1860.*
*Meddelelser om Grønland,* hæfte 9. København. *1889.* pp. 41-42, tavle I: Resens Kaart fra 1605.
*Meer,* John Henry *Van der:* Beiträge zum Cembalo-Bau der Familie Ruckers. Jahrbuch des Staatlichen Instituts für Musikforschung. Preussischer Kulturbesitz. Berlin. *1971.*
*Meer,* John Henry *van der:* Verzeichnis der Europäischen Musikinstrumente, im Germanischen Nationalmuseum Nürnberg. Hörner und Trompeten, Membranophone, Idiophone. Wilhelmshaven. *1979.*
*Meer,* John Henry *Van der:* Musikinstrumente. München. *1983.*
*Meier,* Claudia Anette: Heinrich Ringerink und sein Kreis. Eine Flensburger Bildschnitzerwerkstatt um 1600. Schriften der Gesellschaft für Flensburger Stadtgeschichte E.V. Nr. 34. Flensburg. *1984.*
*Mejborg,* R.: Nogle Oplysninger om svenske og danske Faner, Flag og Felttegn i det 16de Aarhundrede. Antikvarisk Tidsskrift för Sverige. *1891.*
*Memoirer og Breve,* bind XX: Charles Ogier. Det store Bilager i Kjøbenhavn 1634. Udg. af Jul. Clausen og P. Fr. Rist. København. *1914.*
*Memoirer og Breve,* bind VII: Islænderen Jon Olafssons Oplevelse som Bøsseskytte under Christian IV. Udg. af Jul. Clausen og P. R. Rist. København. *1907.*
*Menger,* Reinhardt: Das Regal. Tutzing. *1973.*
*Mentz,* Jørgen & *Mørch,* Søren: Myte og realitet i Danmarkshistorien. *1975.*
*Menzhausen,* J.: The Green Vaults. Leipzig. *1970.*
*The Metropolitan Museum of Art. New York 1985/86:* Lichtenstein. The Princely Collections.
*Meyere,* J. A. L. de: Nieuwe gegevens over Gerard van Honthorst's beschilderd plafond uit 1622. Jaarboekje Oud-Utrecht, 1976 pp. 729, 1977 p. 17. Utrecht. 1976-*1977.*
*Meyere,* J. A. L de: Die Utrechter Malerschule, Caravaggisti des Nordens. Wallraf-Richartz-Museum. Köln. *1984.*
*Meyere,* J. A. L. de: Hendrick ter Brügghen en tijdgenoten (II). Nieuw Licht op de Gouden Eeuw. Antiek XXI, 9/I. Lochem. *197.* pp. 504-509.
*Meyerson,* Åke: Läderkanonen från Tidö i Livrustkammaren. Kungliga Livrustkammaren. Stockholm. *1938.*
*Meyerson,* Åke: Textilier. Wrangler, Brahe, Bielke. Stockholm. Særtryk af Livrustkammaren vol. 13. *1973.*
*Meyerson* Åke & *Rangström,* Lena: Wrangel's Armory. Stockholm. *1984.*
*Michaelis* & *Bramsen,* Alfred: Vilhelm Hammershøi. København. *1918.*
*Michel,* E.: Louis de Caulery au Musée d'Anvers. Revue Belge d'Archéologie et d'Histoire de l'art III. *1933.* pp. 224-229.
*Michelsen,* Peter: Danish Wheel Ploughs. København. *1959.*
*Middeldorf,* Ulrich: Ein Frühwerk von Georg Petel. Münchener Jahrbuch der bildenden Kunst XXIX. München. *1978.* pp. 49-64.
*Meidema,* Hessel (red.): Karel van Mander: Den Grondt der edel vry Schilder-Const, 1-2. Utrecht. *1973.*
*Millar, Oliver: The Painters and Charles I. Burlington Magazine CIV. London. 1962.* pp. 325-330.
*Millar,* Oliver: The Tudor, Stuart and early Georgian Pictures in the Collection of her Majesty the Queen I-II. London. *1963.*
*Mirimonde,* A. P. de: Le symbolisme musical chez Jérôme Bosch. Gazette des Beaux Artes 6: 77. *1971.* pp. 19-50.
*Misfeldt,* Willard E.: A Still Life by Pieter Claesz. Museum Monographs II. City Art Museum of St. Louis. Saint Louis. *1970.* pp. 118-131.
*Moen,* Kristian: Kongsberg Sølvverk 1623-1957. Oslo. *1967.*
*Molbech,* C.: Bidrag til Historien af det Gesandtskab, som Dronning Elisabeth 1582 sendte til Danmark for at bringe Kong Frederik II den engelske Hosebaandsorden. Nye Danske Magazin, bind 4, hæfte 4. København. *1823.* pp. 249-267.
*Molbech,* C.: Christine Munks egenhændige Bønnebog. Nordisk Tidsskrift for Historie, Litteratur og Kunst, bind 2. København. *1828.* pp. 587-592.
*Molbech,* C.: Om Corfits Ulfeldt som Landsforrædder, og om hans politiske Charakter og Handlinger. København. *1842.*
*Molbech,* C.: Historiske Bidrag til Kundskab om K. Christian den Fierdes Opdragelse og Ungdomsundervisning. Historisk Tidsskrift 2. række, bind 3. København. *1849-1850.* pp. 245-306.
*Molbech,* C.: Et Bidrag til Corfitz Ulfeldts Levnetshistorie. Historisk Tidsskrift, bind 4, hæfte 2. København. *1852.* pp. 1-98.
*Mollerup,* W.: Danmarks gamle Hovedstad. København. *1912.*
*Monrad,* Kasper: Købke på Blegdammen og ved Sortedamssøen. København. *1981.* (Udstillingskatalog)
*Morell,* Gerhard: Catalogue des Tableaux de Son Excellence Monsigneur Le Comte de Moltke, Comte de Bregentved. København. *1756.* (Ms).
*Morgan,* Fred: A Recorder for the Music of J. J. van Eyck. The American Recorder, Vol. XXV, no. 2, May 1984. New York. *1984.* pp. 47-49.
*Mosterio dos Jeronimos, Lissabon 1983* »Compriu–se O Mar. As Navegacoes Portuguesas e as suas Consequencias no Renaiscimento«. Mosterio dos Jeronimos, Lisboa maj-oktober 1983. XVII Exposicao Europeia di Arte.
*Musée des Beaux-Arts. Dijon 1983:* La peinture dans la peinture.
*Musée des Beaux-Arts, Gent 1954:* Roelant Savery 1576-1639.
*Musée du petite Palais, Paris 1970/71:* Le siécle de Rembrandt. Tableaux hollandais des collections publiques francaises.
*Musée de Picardie, Amiens 1983.*
*Museum of Art/Gemäldegalerie der Staatlichen Museen Preussischer Kulturbesitz/Royal Academy of Arts: Philadelphia-Berlin-London, 1984:* Masters of Seventeenth-Century Dutch Genre Painting.
*Museum Boymans-van-Beuningen. Rotterdam 1983:* Brood. De geschiedenis van het Brood en het brood-gebruik in Nederland.
*Museum Narodowe w Warszawie, Warszawa 1974:* Szutuka Baroku w Niemczek. Ze zbiorow. Herzog Anton Ulrich-Museum w Brunszwiku.
*Museum Regium:* Af Holger Jacobæus. Hafniæ *1696* og *1710* (udg. af Johannes Lauerentzen).
*Museum voor schone Kunsten, de Beyerd-Gent-Breda 1960/61:* Het Landshap in de Nederlanden 1550-1630.
*Museum Wormianum* seu historia rerum rariorum, tam naturalium, quam artificialium tam dometicarum, quam exoticarum, quæ Hafniæ Danorum in ædibus authoris servantur. Af Ole Worm. Amsterdam. *1655.*
*Mygdal,* E.: Af Dækketøjets Historie. Tidsskrift for Industri, bind 14. København. *1913.* pp. 157-186.
*Müller,* Hannelore: Das Maximillianmuseum. Städtische Kunstsammlungen Augsburg. München-Zürich. *1982.*
*Müller, Theodor* & *Schädler,* Alfred: Georg Petel 1602-1634. Bayerisches Nationalmuseum 3/6-27/9 1964. München. *1964.*
*Müller,* Wolfgang: Kunst in Schleswig-Holstein. *1960.*
*Müller-Hofstede,* J.: Zum Werke des Otto van Veen 1590-1600. Bulletin des Musees Royaux des Beaux-Arts VI. Bruxelles. *1957.* pp. 127-174.
*Müller-Hofstede,* J.: Zur Antwerpner Frühzeit von Peter Paul Rubens. Münchener Jahrbuch der bildenden Kunst XII. München. *1962.* pp. 179-215.
*Müller-Hofstede,* J.: Abraham Janssens. Zur Problematik des flamischen Caravaggismus. Jahrbuch der Berliner Museen XIII. Berlin. *1971.* pp. 208-303.
*Møller,* J. Glebe: Doctrina secundum pietatem. Holger Rosenkrantz den Lærdes teologi. København. *1966.*
*Møller,* Jens *Glebe:* Det teologiske Fakultet 1597-1732. Københavns Universitet 1479-1979, bind V. København. *1980.* pp. 93-212.

*Nasjonalgalleriet i Oslo og Statens Museum for Kunst i København. 1973:* J. C. Dahl og Danmark.
*The National Gallery, London 1976:* Art in Seventeenth Century Holland. A Loan Exhibtion.
*National Gallery of Art/ Detroit Institute of Art/ Rijksmuseum. Washington-Detroit-Amsterdam. 1980-81:* Gods, Saints & Heroes. Dutch Painting in the Age of Rembrandt.
*National Gallery of Art/ Los Angeles Country Museum of Art/ The Art Institute of Chicago, Washington-Los Angeles-Chicago 1986/87:* Renaissance Master Bronzes from the Collection of Kunsthistorisches Museum Vienna.
*The National Gallery of Canada:* Catalogue of Paintings and Sculpture. Vol. I: Older Schools. Ottawa. *1961.*
*National Maritime Museum 1982:* The Art of Van de Velde. London. 1982.
*National Tidende 17.4.1896.*
*Nationalmuseet 1953:* Fra Fruerstuen på Slotte og Herregårde. København. 1953.
*Nationalmuseets 2. afd. 1971:* Danmarks ældste urværker. Særudtilling 1971.
*Nationalmuseum Stockholm 1930: Ur Den kungliga Skattkammaren och Andre Samlinger.*
*Nationalmuseum Stockholm 1966:* Christina. Drottning av Sverige. 29. juni-16. oktober 1966.
*Nationalmuseum Stockholm 1985:* Bruegels tid. Nederländsk konst 1540-1620.
*Navigatio septentrionalis, Haffnia 1624.* Af Jens Munk.
*Neurdenburg,* E.: De zeventiende eeuwsche beeldhouwerkunst in de Nordelijke Nederlanden. Hendrick de Keyser, Artus Quellinus, Rombout Verhulst en tijdgenoten. Amsterdam. *1948.*
*Neverov,* O.: »His Majesty's Cabinet« and Peter I' Kunstkammer. The Origins of Museums. Edit. O. Impery & A. MacGregor. Oxford. *1985.* pp. 54-61.
*Nickel,* Ekkehart: Der Holzblasinstrumentenbau in der Freien Reichsstadt Nürnberg. München. *1971.*
*Nicolson,* B.: Hendrick Terbrugghen. Haag. *1958.*
*Nicolson,* B.: Notes on Adam de Coster. Burlington Magazine CIII. London. 1961. p. 185.
*Nicolson,* B.: Candlelight Pictures from the South Netherlands. Burlington Magazine CVIII. London. *1966.* pp. 253-254.
*Nicolson,* B.: Stomer Brought up-to-date. Burlington Magazine CXIX. London. *1977.* pp. 230-245.
*Nicolson,* B.: The International Caravaggesque Movement. Oxford. *1979.*
*Nielsen, Inger Hjort:* Danske tegninger: en oversigt med 181 illustrationer. Den Kongelige Kobberstiksamling. Statens Museum for Kunst. *1979.*
*Nielsen, Johannes:* Billeder af Folkeskolens historie. Bd. 1: 1536-1784. København. *1973.*
*Nielsen. K. S.:* Willum Hermansen. Sværdfeger og rustmester. Våbenhistorisk Aarbog. København. *1985.* pp. 87-93.
*Nielsen, Lundgreen,* Flemming & Petersen, Erik (udg.): C. C. Lyscanders digtning 1-2. København. *1988.*
*Nielsen,* O. (udg.): Københavns Diplomatarium I-VIII. København. *1872-1887.*
*Nordberg,* T. O.: Lebrun och Moeijaert i östra Ryd. *1918.*
*Nordiska Museet 1932:* Katalog över Gustav II Adolfsutställningen i Nordiska Museets hall. Stockholm. 1932. pp. 252.
*Norges Kunsthistorie* IV. red. af Knut Berg. Oslo. *1981.*
*Norn,* Otto: To grænseslotte. Frederik I's Gottorp og Christian IV's Koldinghus. Udg. af Historisk Samfund for Sønderjylland. Aabenraa. *1986.*
*Nyerup,* R.: Efterretninger om Kong Frederik den Tredie og de mærkværdigste i Danmark og Norge under hans Regjering indtrufne Begivenheder. København. *1817.*
*Nyrop,* C.: Strandmøllen. Aktstykker til Oplysning om den danske Papirfabrikation. København. *1878.*
*Nyrop,* C.: Meddelelser om dansk Guldsmedekunst. København. *1885.*
*Nyrop,* C.: Kristian IV's Statue ved Rosenborg (nu i Chr. IV's Kapel). Tidsskrift for Kunstindustri II. København. *1886.* pp. 84-90
*Nyrop,* C.: Fra Roskilde Smedelavs Lade. København. *1886.*
*Nyrop,* C.: Danske Haandværkerlavs Segl. Tidsskrift for Kunstindustri 2. række, bind 3. København. *1897* pp. 35-52, 117-131, 166-173, 195-212.
*Nystrøm,* Eiler: Jonas Charisius' Indkøb af Malerier og Musikinstrumenter i Nederlandene 1607-8. Danske Magazin, 5. række bind 6. København. *1909* pp. 225-236.
*Nørlund, N. E.: Danmarks Kortlægning. København. 1942.*
*Nørregård-Nielsen,* Hans Edvard: Magtens boliger. Af L. B. Jørgensen, H. Lund og H. E. Nørregård-Nielsen, Danmarks Arkitektur. København. *1980.*
*Nørregård-Nielsen,* Hans Edvard: Dansk Kunst 1-2. København. *1983.*
*Oberhuber,* Konrad Die stilistische Entwicklung im Werk Bartholomäus Sprangers. Dissertation. Wien. *1958.* (Ms.).
*Ogerii,* Caroli: Ephemerides sive iter Danicum, Svecicum, Polonicum. Paris. *1656.*
*Oldenbourg,* Rudolf: P. P. Rubens. Klassiker der Kunst, 4. udg. Stuttgart-Berlin. *1921.*
*Olrik,* Jørgen: Gammelt Tintøj. Tidsskrift for Industri. København. *1906.* pp. 53-77.
*Olrik,* Jørgen: Drikkehorn og Sølvtøj fra Middelalder og Renaissance. København. *1909.*
*Olrik,* Jørgen: Gamle Jærnovne fra Tiden 1550-1800. København. *1912.*
*Olsen,* Bernhard: Danske Lavssager. Tidsskrift for Kunstindustri, 4. årg. pp. 37-49, 5. årg. pp. 173-191. København. *1888-1889.*
*Olsen,* Gunnar: Dansk Ostindien 1616-1732. Vore danske tropekolonier I. Red. af J. Brøndsted. København. *1952.* pp. 3-142.
*Olsen,* Harald: Italian Paintings & Sculpture in Denmark. København. *1961.*
*Olsen,* Harald: Ældre udenlandsk skulptur I-II. Statens Museum for Kunst. København. *1980.*
*Olsen,* Johannes: Svendborg Bys historie. Svendborg. *1919.*
*Olsen,* Jørgen: Nyerhvervet Sølvtøj i Nationalmuseets Anden Afdeling. Fra Arkiv og Museum IV. København. *1909-1911.* pp. 455-473.
*Olsen,* Olaf: Christian IV's Tugt- og Børnehus. Historiske Meddelelser om København 4. række bd., hæfte 5-6. København. *1952.* pp. 257-356. Ny forøget udgave *1978.*
*Olsen,* Olaf: Danefæ idag. Nationalmuseets Arbejdsmark 1984. København. *1984.*
*Opel,* Julius Otto: Der niedersächsisch-dänische Krieg. Bind I 1872, bind II-III *1878-1894.* Magdeburg.
*Oppermann,* Carl Rud. Theodor: Wilhelm Marstrand. København. *1920.*
*Ordrupgaard, København 1981:* Vilhelm Hammershøj – en retrospektiv udstilling. Katalog ved Hanne Finsen og Inge V. Raaschou- Nielsen.
*Orgel,* Stephen & *Strong,* Roy: Inigo Jones. The Theatre of the Stuart Court. London. *1973.*
*Osten,* Gert von der: Katalog der Gemälde. Alte Meister in der Niedersächisischen Landesgalerie Hannover. Hannover. *1954.*
*Overton,* Friend Robert: Der Zink. Mains. *1981.*
*Pade,* Erling: Milevognen og andre ældre opmålingssystemer. København. *1976.*
*Palluchini,* Rodolfo & *Rossi,* Paolo: Tintoretto. Le opere sacre e profane I-II. Milano. *1982.*
*Palme,* Svend U.: Sverige och Danmark 1596-1611. Uppsala. *1942.*
*Paludan,* Charlotte & *Wieth-Knudsen,* Bodil: Damask og Drejl. Dækketøjest historie i Danmark. København. *1987.* (under udgivelse).
*Panofsky,* Erwin: Hommage to Fracastro in a Germano-Flemish Composition of about 1590. Nederlands Kunsthistorisch Jaarboek XII. Gravenhage (Haag). *1961* pp. 1-33.
*Panum,* Hortense: Christian IV's Gaillarde. Aarbog for Musik, 1923. København. *1924* pp. 41-51.
*Parker,* Geoffrey: Europe in Crisis 1598-1648. London. *1980.*
*Paulsen,* Jørgen: Samtidige portrætter af Leonora Christina. Lolland-Falsters Stifsmuseum. Årsskrift 1958. Maribo. *1958.* pp. 125.
*Paulsen,* Jørgen: Et lykketræf ved erhvervelsen af et par Frederiksborgbilleder. Carlsbergfondet. Frederiksborgmuseet. Ny Carlsbergfondet. Beretning *1974/75.* København. 1976. pp. 78-84.
*Pause,* J.: Silberreliefs aus der Husumer Schlosskapelle. Die Heimat 6/7, 88. Jahr. Neumünster. *1981.* pp. 177-186.
*Pauwels,* H: De Schilder Matthias Stomer. Gentse Bijdragen tot de Kunstgeschiednis XIV. Antwerpen. *1953.* pp. 139-192.
*Pedersen,* L.: Københavns Garverlavs Bog. København. *1935.*
*Pedersen,* Laurits: Helsingørske Haandværkerlav. *1910.*
*Pedersen,* Laurits: Helsingør i Sundtoldstiden, bind 2. *1929.*
*Pedersen,* Olaf: Som en brand ud af ilden. Bibliotek for Læger Årg. 174, suppl. 1. København. *1982* pp. 27-68.
*Peltzer,* R. A.: Der Hofmaler Hans von Aachen. Jahrbuch der Kunsthistorischen Sammlungen des allerhöchsten Kaiserhauses XXX. Wien. *1911-1912.* pp. 59-182.
*Peltzer,* R. A.: Hans Rottenhammer. Jahrbuch der Kunsthistorischen

Sammlungen des allerhöchsten Kaiserhauses XXXIII. Wien. *1916. pp. 293-365.*
*Petel, Georg, 1601/2-1634.* Af Karl Feuchtmayer, Alfred Schädler, Norbert Lieb og Theodor Müller. Deutscher Verein für Kunstwissenschaft. Berlin. *1973.*
*Petersen, A.* (red.): Frederiksborg Slots Inventarium af 1650. Danske Samlinger II. København. *1866-1867.*
*Petersen, C. S.:* Afhandlinger til dansk bog- og biblioteksshistorie. København. 1949.
*Petersen, E. Ladewig:* Veritas et honor regis. Odense. *1974.*
*Petersen, E. Ladewig:* Christian IV's pengeudlån til danske adelige. *1974.*
*Petersen, E. Ladewig:* Fra standssamfund til rangssamfund 1500-1700. Hverdag i Danmark fra istid til nutid. Forskning og samfund, årg. 6, 3, nr. 6. *1980* pp. 17-20.
*Petersen, E. Ladewig:* Fra standssamfund til rangssamfund 1500-1700. Dansk Social Historie 3. København. *1980.*
*Petersen, E. Ladewig:* Gustav II Adolf. En oversigt over nyere forskning. Historisk Tidsskrift bind 83. København. *1983.* pp. 195-206.
*Petersen, H.:* Om det oprindelige Monument til Christian den 4.s Capel. Særtryk af Tidsskrift for Kunstindustri. København. *1890.*
*Petersen, N. M.:* Bidrag til den danske Litteraturs Historie 1-5. København. *1853-1860.*
*Petit Palais:* Tresor des Rois de Danemark. Af H. D. Schepelern. Paris. *1978.*
*Philippovich,* Eugen von: Elfenbein. *1961.*
*Philioppovich,* Eugen von: Pulverflaschen mit eingebauter Uhr. Waffen- und Kostümkunde 2. *1962.* pp. 128-132.
*Pijl-Ketel,* C. L. van der: The ceramic Load of the Witte Leeuw. Rijksmuseum. Amsterdam. *1982.*
*Pio,* L.: Cyprianus. Efter et Manuskript paa Det store kgl. Bibliotek for første Gang i Trykken udgivet og forklaret af L. Pio. 2. udgave. København. *1892.*
*Plietzsch,* Eduard: Die Frankenthaler Maler. Leipzig. *1910.*
*Plietzsch,* Eduard: Holländische und flämische Maler des XVII Jahrhundert. Leipzig. *1960.*
*Pohlmann,* Ernst: Laute, Theorbe, Chitaronne. Die Instrumente, ihre Musik und Literatur von 1500 bis zur Gegenwart. Bremen. *1982.*
*Polisensky,* Josef: The Thirty Years War. London. *1970.*
*Pope,* A. V.: Survey of Persian Art. Vol. VI, 2. London. 1939. (genoptrykt *1973*)
*Pope-Hennessy,* John: Italian Sculpture in the Victoria and Albert Museum I-III. London. *1964.*
2000 Jaar Gewichten in de Nederlanden. De Tijdstroom Lochem. *Poperinge 1980.*
*Popper-Voskuil,* Naomi: Selfportraiture and Vanitas Still-life Painting in 17th-Century Holland in Reference to David Bailly's Vanitas Oeuvre. Pantheon XXXI. München. *1973.* pp. 58-74.
*Poulton,* Diana: John Dowland. London. *1972.*
*Prince,* Derek : Two Mariner's Astrolabes. The Journal of the Institute of Navigation. July *1956.*
*Prins Christian (V)'s breve.* Udg. ved J. O. Bro-Jørgensen & E. Marquard. Bind 1-2 (1626-1647). København. *1952-1956.*
*Prinz,* Wolfram: Das Motiv »Pallas Athena führt die Pictura in der Kreis der septen artes Liberales ein« und die sogenannte Cellini-Schale. Festschrift Wilhelm Meister zum 65. Geburtstag am 16. Maj 1974. Ed. Annaliese Ohm und Horst Reber. Hamburg. *1975.* pp. 165-173.
*Probst,* Niels M.: Slaget i Femern Bælt 13. oktober 1644: samtidige illustrationer af danske 1600-tals orlogskibe IV. Marinehistorisk Tidsskrift, 19. årg. nr. 2. København. *1986.* pp. 3-19.
*Pufendorf,* Samuel de: De Rebus a Carolo Gustavo Sveciæ Rege gestis Commentariorum Libri ... elegantissimis Tabulis æneis exornati triplici Indice. Noreiembergæ. *1696.*
*Puyvelde,* Leo van: Jordaens. Bruxelles. *1953.*
*Pyke,* E. J.: A Biographical Dictionary of Waxmodellers. Oxford. *1973.*
*Raadhusudstillingen af dansk Kunst 1901.* København. 1901.
*Rahbek, K. L. & Nyerup,* R.: Bidrag til den danske Digtekunsts Historie uddragne af Forelæsninger holdne over dette Æmne i Vintrene 1798-1800. Del 1-4. København. *1800-1808.*
*Ramdohr,* F. W. B. von: Studien zur Kenntniss der schönen Natur, der schönen Künste, der Sitten und der Staatsverfassung, aus einer Reise nach Dännemark. Erster Theil. Hannover. 1792.
*Rasbech,* Joh.: Frederiksborg Slots Beskrivelse. København. *1832.*
*Rasmussen,* Holger: Christian IV's syn. Fysnke Minder *1957-59.* Odense. 1960. pp. 60-75.
*Rasmussen,* Holger: Ret og straf i Danmark. Dansk Folkemuseums samling af retsantikviteter. Nationalmuseet. København. *1986.*
*Rawert,* Ole Jørgen: Verzeichniss einer Sammlung von Oelgemälden dem Herrn Konferenzrath und Geheim Kabinetskassirer Frederik Conrad Brugge, Ritter vom Dannebroge und Dannebrogsmanne gehörend. København. *1829.*
*Ravn,* V. C.: English Instrumentalists at the Danish Court in the Time of Shakespeare. Sammelbände der Internationalen Musikgesellschaft. Leipzig. *1911-1912.*
*Regiæ Nuptiæ,* eller kort: Beskriffuelse om prinsens Bryllup. København. *1637.*
*Regteren Altena,* I. Q. van: Het vroegste werk van Rubens. Mededelingen van de Koninklijke Academie voo Wettenschappen. Letteren en schone Kunsten van Belaië. Klasse der schone kunsten XXXIV, 2. Bruxelles. *1972.*
*Renckens,* B. J. A.: De Zeven werken van Barmhartigheid te Kassel. Niet Nicoles Knupfer, doch Maerten Stoop. Oud Hollandd LXV. Amsterdam. *1950.* pp. 74-78.
*Renger,* Konrad: Sine Cerere et Baccho friget Venus. Peter Paul Rubens. Werk und Nachruhm, herausgegeben vom Zentralinstitut für Kunstgeschichte und vom der Bayerischen Stattsgemäldesammlungen. München. *1981.* pp. 105-135.
*Repholtz,* Albert: Thorvaldsen og Nysø. København. *1911.*
*Reversau,* J.-P.: Musee de l'Arme. Paris. *1982.*
*Revold,* Reidar: Norges Billedkunst i det nittende og tyvende Århundrede. Bind 2. Oslo. *1953.*
*Reznicek,* E. K. J: Het begin van Goltzius Loopbaan als schilder. Oud Holland LXXV. Amsterdam. *1960.* pp. 30-49.
*Reznicek,* E. K. J.: Die Zeichnungen von Hendrick Goltzius I-II. Utrecht. *1961.*
*Reynolds,* Graham: English Portrait Miniatures. London. *1952.*
*Riismøller,* Peter: Fra Svendekro til Lavshus. *1940.*
*Riismøller,* Peter: Arkiv eller kontor. En studie i skuffer og skabe. Danske Museer II. *1951.* pp. 39-48.
*Rijksmuseum, Amsterdam 1955.* Le triomphe du manierisme europeen. De Michel-Ange au Greco.
*Rijksmuseum, Amsterdam 1976:* Tot Lering en Vermaak. Beteknissen van hollandske genrevorstellingen uit de zeventiende eeuw.
*Rijksmuseum Paleis Het Loo, Apeldoorn 19875-86.* amalie van Solms.
*Rimmer,* Joan: The Morphology of the Irish Harp. The Galpin Society Journal XVII. London. *1964.*
*Rimmer,* Joan: The Irish Harp. Irish Life and Culture XVI. Dublin. *1977.*
Robels, Hella: Frans Snyders Entwicklung als Stillebenmaler. Wallraf-Richartz-Jahrbuch XXXI. Köln. *1969.* pp. 3-94.
*Roberts,* Michael: Gustavus Adolphus. A. History of Sweden. 1611-1632. Bind I: 1611-1626, *1953* bind II, *1959.* London.
*Roberts,* Michael: Gustavus Adolphus and the Rise of Sweden. London. *1973.*
*Robinson,* M. S.: Van de Velde Drawings in the National Maritime Museum made by the Elder and the Younger van de Velde I-II. Cambridge. *1958-1974.*
*Rom og Danmark gennem Tiderne.* Red. Louis Bobe. Bind 1. *1935.*
*Rooses,* Max: L'Oeuvre de P. P. Rubens. Histoire et description de ses tableaux et dessins I-V. Antwerpen. *1886-1892.*
*Rooses,* Max: Rubens. Sa vie et ses ceuvres. Paris. *1903.*
*Rooses,* Max: Jordaens Leben und Werke. Stuttgart-Berlin-Leipzig. *1908.*
*Rosenberg,* M.: Der Goldschmiede Merkzeichen. Bind II: Frankfurt *1911.*, Bind III: Frankfurt-Berlin *1925.*
*Rosenborg, København 1948:* Christian IV 1648 – 28. februar 1948.
*Rosenborg, København 1970:* Fra danske dronningers smykkeskrin. Af Gudmund Boesen.
*Rosenborg, København 1986:* Sophie Amalie: den onde dronning? Af Jørgen Hein og Katia Johansen.
*Rosenkrantz, Hans: Rosenholm og Rosenkrantzerne. København. 1924.*
*Rottensen,* Birte & *Waaben,* Ebba: Danske vandmærker og papirmøller. Bind 1: Vandmærker. København. *1986.*
*Royal Museum of Fine Arts, Antwerp 1977:* P. P. Rubens. Paintings, Oilsketches, Drawings.
*Rubow,* Jørn: Pieter Stevens d. y. kaldet Stephani: Gedejagt i et klippelandskab. Kunstmuseets Årsskrift XLIII-L, 1956-63. København. *1963.* pp. 110-111, p. 153.
*Rubow,* Jørn: To flamske landskabsmalere. Kunstmuseets Årsskrift LI-LII, 1964-65. København. *1965* pp. 117-122.

*Rudloff,* Dieter: Die Porträtsammlung des Eutiner Schlosses. Nordelbingen 25. *1957.* pp. 164-193.
*Ruhnke,* Martin: Beiträge zu einer Geschichte der deutschen Hofmusikkollegien im 16. Jahrhundert. Berlin. *1963.*
*Rusconi,* A. J.: La Galleri Pitti. Rom. *1937.*
*Rygge,* E. Wiese: Et nordisk fyrsteportrett fra renessansen. Årsbok *1968-1969.* Kunstindustrimuseet. Olso. pp. 52-65.
*Rückert,* Rainer: Goldsschmiedearbeiten. Erwerbungen seit 1950. Jahrbuch der Hamburger Kunstsammlungen. Band 5. Hamburg. *1960.* pp. 151-232.
*Rønning,* Bjørn R.: Den kongelige Mynt 1628-1686-1806. Oslo. *1986.*
*Rørdam,* H. F.: Mester Anders Christensen Arrebos Levned og Skrifter. København. *1857.*
*Rørdam,* H. F.: Kjøbenhavns Universitets Historie fra 1539 til 1621. København. *1868-1877.*
*Rørdam,* H. F.: Historiske Samlinger og Studier vedr. danske Forhold og Personligheder. Bind 1-4. København. *1893-1901.*
*Sachs,* Curt: Sammlung alter Musikinstrumente bei der Staatlichen Hochschule für Musik zu Berlin. Beschreibender Katalog. Berlin. *1922.*
*Sadie,* Stanley (udg.): The New Grove Dictionary of Music and Musicians 1-20. London. *1980.*
*Sander,* L. C.: Berichtigung einiger Äusserungen über die Königliche Kunstkammer und einigen dahina gehörigen Kunstsachen, des Hon. Oberappelazionsrath von Ramsdorh aus seiner Reise nach Dänemark. Deutsches Magazin IV. København. *1792.*
*Sandrart,* Joachim von: Academie der Bau-, Bild- und Mahlerey-Künste von 1675. Leben der berühmten Maler, Bildhauer und Baumeister. Ed. A. R. Peltzer. München. *1925.*
*Sandvad,* Holger: Præsteindberetning fra Lemvig 1766. Hardsyssel Aarbog *1915.* pp. 135-139.
*Sass,* Else Kai: Anmeldelse af Povl Ellers Kongelige portrætmalere i Danmark 1630-82, Kbh. 1971. Historisk Tidsskrift 12. række, bind 6. København. *1972-1973.* pp. 575-591.
*Saxl,* F. & *Wittkower,* R.: British Art and the Mediterranean. Oxford. *1948.* (Genoptrykt 1969).
*Scharf,* G.: Catalogue of Pictures at Woburn Abbey. *1890.*
*Scheffler,* Wolfgang: Goldschmiede Niedersachsens I-II. Berlin. 1965.
*Schepelern,* H. D.: Simon de Pas og andre kobberstikkere omkring Christian IV. Kunstmuseets Årsskrift XXXVIII, *1951.* København. 1952. pp. 1-45.
*Schepelern,* H. D.: Ole Worms Philotheca eller stambog 1607-10. »Der junge Gelehrte« på rejse. Kulturminder ny række, bind 4. København. *1961.* pp. 19-54.
*Schepelern,* H. D.: Museum Wormianum. København. *1971.*
*Schepelern,* H. D.: Kongelige ordener. Hillerød. *1980.*
*Schiørring,* Niels: Det 16. og 17. århundredes verdslige danske visesang I-II. København. *1950.*
*Sciørring,* Niels: Musikkens historie i Danmark, bind 1. København. *1977.*
*Schiørring,* Ole: Tinstøbeforme fra 1600-årenes Ribe. Mark og Montre. Fra sydvestjyske museer *1979.* pp. 64-73.
*Schlee,* Ernst (red.): Gottorfer Kultur im Jahrhundert der Universitätsgründung. Kulturgeschichtliche Denkmäler und Zeugnisse des 17. Jahrhunderts aus der Sphäre des Herzöge von Schleswig-Holstein-Gottorf. Schloss Gottorf 31. Mai-31. Juli 1965. Schleswig. *1965.*
*Schlee,* Ernst: Die Bedeutung des Herzoghofes von Schleswig-Holstein-Gottorf für die Geschichte des Uhrenbaus. Gemessene Zeit, Uhren in der Kulturgeschichte Schleswig-Holsteins. Ausstellung zum 100 Jährigen Jubiläum 1875-1975 Schleswig-Holsteinisches Landesmuseum 29. Juni-19. Oktober *1975.* pp. 65-105.
*Schlegel,* J. H: Geschichte Christian des Vierten Königs in Dänemark von N. Slange: Kürtzer vorgetragen mit Anm. u. Zusätzen erweitert, und mit einer Einleitung versehen I-II. København-Leipzsig. 1757-*1771.*
*Schlegel,* J. H.: Samlung zur Dänischen Geschichte, Münzerkenntniss, Ökonomie und Sprache I. København. *1773.*
*Schlegel,* J. H. (udg.): Eigenhändige Anzeichnungen in König Christian IV Schreibkalender vom Jahre 1621. Sammlungen zur Dänischen Geschichte, Münzkenntniss, Oekonomie und Sprache II, 1. København. *1774-1776,* pp. 26-74.
*Schliemann,* E.: Die Goldschmiede Hamburgs I-II. Hamburg. *1985.*
*Schlosser,* J. von: Die Kunst- und Wunderkammer der Spätrenaissance. Leipzig. *1908.*
*Schlosser,* J. von: Werke der Kleinplastik in der Skulptursammlung des Allerhöchsten Kaiserhauses. Wien. *1910.*
*Schlosser,* J. von: Aus der Bildwerkstatt der Renaissance. Jahrbuch der Kunsthistorischen Sammlungen des Allerhöchsten Kaiserhauses XXXI. Wien. *1913-1914.* pp. 67-135.
*Schmidt,* Harry: Angaben über Gemälde in Gottorpischen Schlossinventaren. Separatdrück aus Band 43 der Zeitschrift der Gesellschaft für Schleswig-Holsteinische Geschichte. Kiel. *1913.*
*Schmidt,* Harry: Gottorfer Künstler I-II. Kiel. *1916-1917.*
*Schmidtchen,* V.: Bombarden, Befestigungen, Büchsenmeister von den ersten Mauerbrechern des Spätmittelalters zur Belagerungsartillerie der Renaissance. Eine Studie zur Entwicklung der Militärtechnik. Düsseldorf. *1977.*
*Schneider,* Arthur von: Caravaggio und die Niederländer. Marburg-Lahn. *1933.*
*Schröder,* Hans: Verzeichnis der Sammlung alter Musikinstrumente. Museum für Hamburgische Geschichte I. Hamburg. *1930.*
*Schädler,* Alfred: Georg Petel (1601/2-1634). Barockbildhauer in Augsburg. München-Zürich. *1985.*
*Schäfer,* Dietrich: Geschichte von Dänemark V. Vom Regierungsantritt Friederichs II (1559) zum Tote Christian IV (1648). A. H. C. Heeren o.a. (red.). Geschichte der europäischen Staaten 13. Gotha. *1902.*
*Schäfer,* Dietrich: Hanserecesse. Die Recesse und andere Akten der Hansetage III, Abt. 1-9 (1477-1530). Leipzig. 1181-*1913.*
*Schæffer,* Aage: Studier til dansk apotekervæsens historie. København. *1963.*
*The Scottish Arts Council Gallery, Edingburgh 1975:* A Kind of Gentle Painting. An Exhibition of Miniatures by the Elizabethan Court Artists Nicholas Hillard and Isaac Oliver.
*Secher,* V. A. (udg.): Samling af Kongens Rettertings Domme. Juridica placiti Regis Daniæ Justiarii 1595-1614. Bind I-II. København. *1881-1886.*
*Secher,* V. A. (udg.): Forordninger, Recesser og andre kongelige Breve, Danmarks Lovgivning vedkommende, 1558-1660. Corpus Constitutionum Daniæ I-VI. Bind III, 1596-1621, *1891-1894.* Bind IV, 1622-1638, *1897.* København.
*Segal,* Sam: The Flower Pieces of Roelandt Savery. Rudolph II and his Court. Leids Kunsthistorisch Jaarboek I 1982. Delft. *1983.* pp. 309-337.
*Segerman* E. & *Abbott,* D.: On the Palmer Orpharion. Fellowship of Makers and Restorers of Historical Musical Instruments, April 1976. pp. 48-56.
*Seiffert,* Max: Matthias Mercker. Ein ausgewanderter holländischer Musiker. Gedenkboek aangeboden aan Dr. D. F. Scheurkleer. S'Gravenhagen (Haag). *1925.* pp. 291-301.
*Seitz,* Heribert: Svärdet och värjan som armevapen. Stockholm. *1958.*
*Seitz,* Heribert: Blankwaff. Ein waffenhistorisches Handbuch. Braunschweig. *1965.*
*Seling,* H.: Die Kunst der Augsburger Goldschmiede 159-1868 I-II. München. *1980.*
*Shearman,* John: Raphael's Cartoons and the Tapestries for the Sixtine Chapel. Bristol. *1972.*
*Simpson, P. & Bell,* C. F.: Designs by Inigo Jones for Masques and Plays at Court. Walpole Society XII. Oxford. *1923-1924.*
*Sjöberg,* Niels: Gripsholm. Vasatiden. Stockholm. *1907.*
*Sjöhistoriska samfundet, Minneskrift.* Uppsala. *1944.*
*Skelton,* R. A. m.fl.: The Vinland Map and the Tartar Relation. New Haven-London. *1965.*
*Skjerne,* Godtfred (udg.): Carl Claudius' Samling af gamle Musikinstrumenter. København. *1931.*
*Skov,* Erik: Lolland-Falsterske prædikestole. Lolland-Falsters Stiftsbog *1979.* pp. 7-29.
*Skov,* Sigvard Preben: Anders Sørensen Vedels Ribebeskrivelse. Fra Ribe Amt 9. Ribe. *1937* pp. 98-109.
*Skovgaard,* Bente: Maleren Abildgaard. Kunst i Danmark. København. *1961.*
*Skovgaard,* Johanne: Georg Braun og Henrik Rantzau. Festskrift til Johannes Steenstrup. København. *1915.*
*Skovgaard Museet i Viborg, 1984.*
*Slange,* Niels (igjennemset og forbedret af Hans Gram): Den Stormægtigste Konge Christian den Fierdes konge til Danmark og Norge, de Venders og Gothers, Hertug til Slesvig, Holsten, Stormarn og Ditmersken, Greve til Oldenborg og Delmenhorst Historie I-II. København. *1749.*
*Slatkes,* Leonard J.: A Selfportrait Reidentified, an Oeuvre Reconstructed: Johannes van Swinderen (1594-1636). Essays in Northen European

Art Presented to E. Haverkamp-Begemann. Doornspijk. *1983.* pp. 245-248.
*Slomann,* V.: Ure af Steffen Brenner. Tilskueren, 1931 I. København. *1931.* pp. 178-189.
*Slomann,* V.: Selskabet Kunstindustrimuseets Venner 1911-1935. København. *1936.* pp. 88-93.
*Sluitjer,* Eric Jan: Niet Gysbert van der Kuyl uit Gouda, maar Gerad van Kuil uit Goorinchem (1604-1673). Oud Holland 91. Amsterdam. *1977.* pp. 166-194.
*Smith,* Otto: Christian IV's Tøjhus. København. *1926.*
*Smith,* Otto: Våbentrofæerne og Kamprelieferne på Frederik II's Gravmæle. Aarbog udg. af Historisk Samfund for Københavns Amt. *1927.* pp. 189-218.
*Smith,* Otto: Det kongelige partikulære Rustkammer I. Udg. af Tøjhusmuseet. København. *1938.*
*Sophienholm 1983.* Bevar for fremtiden. Af Stig Brøgger. Red. Steen Bjarnhof. Lyngby. *1983.*
*Sorø 28. maj-18. juni 1936:* Udstilling af soransk Kunst 1586-1936.
*Speth-Holterhoff,* S.: Un Cabinet d'Amateur au anversois du XVII siècle entre au Musee Royal d'Art Ancien de Bruxelles. Bulletin des Musées Royaux des Beaux-Arts IX. Bruxelles. *1960.* pp. 75-88.
*Sponsel,* J.-L.: Das Grüne Gewölbe zu Dresden I-III. Leipzig. *1925-1929.*
*St. Annen Museum/ Kulturgeschichtliches Museum/ Kunsthalle. Lübeck-Osnabrück-Bielefeld 1976:*
*Europäische Kleinplastik aus dem Herzog Anton Ulrich Museum Braunschweig.*
*Stampe,* Christine: Erindringer om Thorvaldsen. København. *1912.*
*Statens Museum for Kunst, København 1941:* Mit bedste Kunstværk.
*Statens Museum for Kunst, København 1946:* Katalog over ældre Malerier.
*Statens Museum for Kunst, København 1984:* Restaureringsbilleder. En udstilling om bevaring og undersøgelse af ældre kunst.
*Stechow,* Wolfgang: Drawings and Etchings by Jacques Foucquier. Gazette des Beaux-Arts XXXIV. Paris-New York. *1948.* pp. 419-439.
*Stechow,* Wolfgang: Heliodorus' Aethiopica in Art. Journal of the Warburg Institute XVI. London. 1953.
*Stechow,* Wolfgang: Dutch Landscape Painting in the Seventeenth Century. London. *1966.*
*Stedelijk Museum De Lakenhal, Leiden 1970:* Ijdelheid der Ijdelheiden. Vanitasvoorstellingen uit de zeventiende eeuw.
*Stedelijk Museum de Lakenhal. Leiden 1983:* Catalogus van de schilderijen en tekeningen.
*Steenberg,* Jan: Christian IV's Frederiksborg. Udgivet af Frederiksborg Amts Historiske Samfund. Hillerød. *1950.*
*Stein,* Meir: »Badning ved en orientalsk Havn«. København. *1970.*
*Stein,* Meir: Marmorgalleriet og Møntporten på Frederiksborg Slot i ikonologisk belysning. København. *1971.*
*Stein,* Meir: Christian IV's program for udsmykning af Rosenborgs riddersal 1618-1624. ICO-Iconographisk Post 2. Stockholm. *1982.*
*Stein,* Meir: Christian IV's Programme for the Decoration of the Great Hall at Rosenborg in Copenhagen. Art in Denmark 1600-1650. Leids Kunsthistorisch Jaarboek *1983.* Delft. 1984.
*Stein,* Meir: Christian IV – a »Renaissance Man«. Apollo Vol. 120, no. 274. London. *1984.*
*Stein,* Meir: Christian den Fjerdes Billedverden. København. *1987.*
*Steinberg,* Leo: Michelangelo's Florentine Pietà: The Missing Leg. The Art Bulletin 2. New York. *1968.* pp. 343-353.
*Steingräber,* E.: Alter Schmuck. München. *1957.*
*Steland-Stief,* Anne Charlotte: Jan Asselijn, nach 1610 bis 1652. Amsterdam, *1971.*
*Steneberg,* Karl Erik: Jacob van Doordt. Scandia. Tidsskrift för historisk forskning VII, 1934. Stockholm. *1934.*
*Steneberg,* Karl Erik: Kristinatidens måleri. Malmø. *1955.*
*Steneberg,* Karl Erik: David Beck i Danmark. Kunstmuseets Årsskrift XXXIV-XXXXII. København. *1956.* pp. 49-63.
*Sterling,* Charles: Cornelis van Dalem et Jan van Wechelen. Studies in the History of Art dedicated to William E. Suida. London. *1959.* pp. 277-288.
*Sthyr,* Jørgen: Nederlandske Landskabsmalerier i danske Samlinger. København. *1929.*
*Sthyr,* Jørgen: To hollandske Landskaber fra Begyndelsen af det 17. Aarhundrede. Kunstmuseets Aarsskrift XX-XXI. København. *1934. pp. 183-192.*
*Sthyr,* Jørgen: Kobberstikkeren Albert Haelwegh. Kunstmuseets Aarsskrift XXV. København. *1938.* pp. 5-69.
*Sthyr,* Jørgen: Kobberstikkeren Albert Haelwegh. København. *1965.*
*Sthyr,* Jørgen: Dansk Grafik I: 1500-1800 (1943). Værløse. *1970* (genoptrykt).
*Stiesdal,* Hans: Jacob Slange – en urmager på Christian IV's tid. Urmageren, Jan.-febr. 1951. København. *1951.*
*Stiesdal,* Hans: Et rejseur fra Christian IV's tid. Nationalmuseets Arbejdsmark *1987.* pp. 9-19.
*Stiftelsen Modums Blaafarveværk 24/5-30/9 1986.*
*Stolpe,* P. M.: Dagspressen i Danmark I-IV. Bind I. København. 1878. (Genoptrykt 1977).
*Stouenberg,* F.: Merkwürdigkeiten der Königlichen Schlosses Rosenburg. København. *1828.*
*Strohmer,* Erich V.: Bemerkungen zu den Werken des Adriaen de Vries. Nationalmusei Årsbok 1947-48. Uppsala. *1950.* pp. 93-138.
*Strong,* Roy: The English Icon. Elizbethan & Jacobean Portraiture. London. *1969a.*
*Strong,* Roy: Tudor and Jacobean Portraits Vol. I. National portrait Gallery Catalogue. London. *1969b.*
*Strong,* Roy: The English Renaissance Miniature. London. *1983.*
*Strunk,* A.: Samlinger til en beskrivende Catalog over Portraiter af Danske, Norske og Holstenere. Kongehuset. København. *1882.*
*Strömbom,* Sixten: Iconographica Gustavi Adolphi. Gustav II Adolf. Samtida porträtt. Stockholm. *1932.*
*Strømstad,* Poul: Danmarks ældste lavsvelkomst. Budstikken *1956.* pp. 25-33.
*Strømstad,* Poul: Fra Laugstiden. 2. udgave. Nationalmuseet. København. *1976.*
*Strømstad,* Poul: Holbergtidens København: skildret af malerne Rach og Egeberg. København. *1977.*
*Støckel,* J. F.: Håndskydevåbens Bedømmelse. Udgivet af Tøjhusmuseet. København. *1938.*
*Sullivan,* Scot A.: The Dutch Gamepiece. Totowa. *1984.*
*Sumowski,* Werner: Zeichnungen von Lastman und aus dem Lastman-Kreis. Giessener Beiträge zur Kunstgeschichte III. Giessen. *1975.* pp. 149-186.
*Sumowski,* Werner: Gemälde der Rembrandt Schüler III. Landau-Pfalz. *1986.*
*Supplement til Katalog for Gustav II Adolf Udtillingen 1932.* Katalog över Gustav II Adolfsutställningen i Nordiska Museets hall. Stockholm. 1932.
*Swane,* Leo: Nicolaj Abraham Abildgaard. Arkitektur og Dekoration. København. *1926.*
*Swane,* Leo: Malerisamlingens Erhvervelser af ældre Kunst. Kunstmuseets Aarskrift XVI-XVIII, 1929-31. København. *1931.* pp. 110-125.
*Swane,* Leo: Beretning om Samlingens Vækst. Kunstmuseets Aarsskrift XX-XXI, 1933-34. København. *1934.* pp. 71-97.
*Swane,* Leo: De senere års erhvervelser af malerkunst. Kunstmuseets Årsskrift XXXVII, 1950. København. *1951.* pp. 115-137.
*Svenska Flottans Historia.* Örlogsflottan i ord och bilder från dess grundläggning under Gustav Vasa til våra dagar. Bind I (1679). Malmå. *1942.*
*Sveriges Kyrkor.* Udg. af Riksantikvarieämbetet. Stockholm. *1917-.*
*Swillens,* P. T. A.: De Utrechtsche Schilders Dirk en Maerten Stoop II. Oud Holland LI. Amsterdam. *1934.* pp. 175-181.
*Sælebakken,* Per Halvor: Inskripsjoner i Knutefjell-området. Kongsberg. *1975.*
*Sønderholm,* Erik: Danmarks gamle folkeviser. Bind 12. København. *1976.*
*Sønderholm,* Erik: Søren Terkelsen. Astree Siunge-Choer. Kieler Studien zur deutschen Literaturgeschichte, herausgegeben von Erik Trunz. Bd. 12. Neumünster. *1976b.*
*Tagebuch Christian des Jüngeren, Fürst zu Anhalt.* Udg. af G. Krause. Leipzig. *1858.* pp. 90-103.
*Takacs,* Marianne H.: Un tableau de Sebastian Vrancx a la Galerie des Maîtres Anciens. Bulletin du Musée National des Beaux-Arts 18. Budapest. *1961.*
*Tandrup,* Leo: Mod triumf eller tragedie I-II. Århus. *1979.*
*Tandrup,* Leo: På sporet af en progressiv historieskrivning. En kritisk analyse af C. F. Allens og A. D. Jørgensens syn på Christian IV. Tradition og Kritik. Festskrift til Svend Ellehøj d. 8. september 1984. København. *1984.*
*The Tate Gallery 1969:* The Collections of the Tate Gallery. London. 1969.
*The Tate Gallery, London 1972-73:* The Age of Charles I. Painting in England 1620-1649.
*Teatret på Kongens Nytorv* 1748-1948. Af Alf Henriques m.fl. København. *1948.*

*Temler,* Chr. Fr.: Bibliotheca collecta, in ordinem redacta et secundum hunc ordinem descripta ab ipso. København. *1781.*
*Tervarent,* Guy de: L'Inconstance. Kunstmuseets Årsskrift XXXV-XXXVI, 1948-49. København. *1949.* pp. 224-225.
*Theuerkauff,* C.: Die Brandenburgisch-Preussische Kunstkammer. Eine Auswahl aus den alten Beständen. Berlin. *1981.*
*Thiel,* P. J. J. van: De aanbidding der koningen en ander vroeg werk van Hendrick ter Brugghen. Bulletin van het Rijksmuseum 19. Amsterdam. *1971.* pp. 91-116.
*Thiel,* P. J. J. van: All the Paintings of the Rijksmuseum in Amsterdam. A Completely Illustrated Catalogue. Amsterdam. *1976.*
*Thiel,* P. J. J. van: Werner Jacobsz. van den Valckert. Oud Holland 97. Amsterdam. *1983.* pp. 128-195.
*Thiel,* P. J. J. van: Cornelis Cornelisz. van Haarlem – his first ten Years as a Painter 1582-1592. Papers given at a Symposium in Nationalmuseum Stockholm, September 21.-22. 1984. Stockholm. *1984.*
*Thiele, J. M.: Danmarks Folkesagn I. København. 1843.*
*Thiele,* J. M.: Thorvaldsens Biographie. Bind IV: Thorvaldsen i Kjøbenhavn (1839-44). København. *1856.*
*Thiis,* Jens: Norske Malere og Billedhuggere I-III. Bergen. *1904-1907.*
*Thomas,* B.: Arms and Armour. Masterpieces ... London. *1963.*
*Thomsen,* Albert: Holbæk Købstads Historie. Holbæk. *1936-1937.*
*Thorlacius-Ussing,* Viggo: Arbejder af Fr. Dieussart, Fr. Duquesnoy og Barth. Eggers. Kunstmuseets Aarsskrift VIII-X, 1921-23. København. *1924.* pp. 305-321.
*Thornton,* P. & *Tomlin,* M.: Franz Cleyn at Ham House. *1980.*
*Thurah,* L. de: Den danske Vitruvius II. København. *1749.*
*Tidens Konsthistoria.* red. Nils Gösta Sandblad. 3. del. Stockholm. *1950.*
*Tietze-Conrat,* E.: Dwarfs and Jesters in Art. London. *1957.*
*Tokyo 1981:* Zaigui Nippon shiko. Kogei. Japanese Art: Selection from Western Collections. Applied Arts. Vol. 10. Tokyo. 1981.
*Toynbee, Margaret R.: A Portrait called »Henry Prince of Wales« by David Mytens. The Burlington Magazine LXXIV. London. 1939.* pp. 116-122.
*Toynbee,* Margaret R.: A Further Note on a Portrait called »Henry Prince of Wales« by David Mytens. The Burlington Magazine LXXXVI. London. *1940.* pp. 21-22.
*The Treasure Houses of Britain 1985.*
*Triumphus Nuptialis Danicus, København 1648.*
*Troels–Lund ed. 1969.* Troels-Lund: Dagligt liv i Norden i det sekstende århundrede 1-6. Udg. ved Erik Kjersgaard. København. 1968-1969.
*Tümpel,* Astrid: Claes Cornelisz. Moeyaert. Oud Holland 88. Amsterdam. *1974.* pp. 1-163, 245-290.
*Tøjhusmuseet, særudstilling 1947.*
*Tøjhusmuseet, særudstilling 1972.*
*Udstilling af Soransk Kunst 1586-1936. Sorø 28. maj-18. juni 1936.*
*Uldall,* Kai: Et Tilløb til dansk Fajancefremstilling i Renæssancetiden. Laurits Pottemager i Næstved. Fra Nationalmuseets Arbejdsmark *1934.* pp. 44-54.
*Universitetsbibliotekets Liber Daticus fra XVII Aarhundrede.* Udg. af Konsistorium. København. *1935.*
*Waagepetersen,* Chr.: Danske Møbler før 1848. København. *1980.*
*Vad,* Poul: Vilhelm Hammershøi. Kunst i Danmark. København. *1957.*
*Waddingham,* Malcolm R.: Another Look at Gysbert van der Kuyl. Paragone XI, nr. 125. Firenze. *1960.* pp. 45-51.
Wadsworth Atheneum Paintings: Catalogue I: The Netherlands and the German-speaking Countries. Hartford. *1978.*
*Valentiner,* Elisabeth: Karel van Mander als Maler. Strassburg. *1930.*
*Wallraf-Richartz-Museum/ Centraal Museum. Köln-Utrecht 1985-86:* Roelandt Savery in seiner Zeit 1576-1639.
*Vancouver Art Gallery, Vancouver 1986:* The Dutch World of Painting.
*Wanscher,* Vilhelm: Om Farvekompositioner hos de gamle Mestre. Kunstmuseets Aarsskrift II. København. *1915.* pp. 134-159.
*Wanscher,* Vilhelm: Rosenborgs Historie 1606-1634. København. *1930.*
*Wanscher,* Vilhelm: Christian 4's Bygninger. København. *1937.*
*Warburg,* Lise: Strikkeskeen: et glemt redsskab. Herning Museum. Herning. *1980.*
*Warburg,* Lise: Strik med begge ender. Cras 29. Silkeborg Kunstmuseum *1981.*
*Warburg,* Lise: De »nye« strikkeskeer. Cras 32. Silkeborg Kunstmuseum. *1982.,*
*Warburg,* Lise: Strik i de københavnske jordfund. Nordiskt Symposium om Textila Tekniker, Bohuslans Museum, Uddevalla 9.-12. september 1986. Uddevalla. *1987.*
*Wedgwood,* C. V.: The Thirty Years War. Harmondsworth. *1957.*
*Weilbull,* Curt: Gustav II Adolf. Scandia 6. Lund. *1933.*
*Weihrauch,* H. R.: Die Bildwerke in Bronze und in anderen Metallen. Bayerisches Nationalmuseum München, Katalog XIII/5. München. *1956.*
*Weihrauch,* H. R.: Europäische Bronzestatuetten. 15.-18. Jahrhundert. Braunschweig. *1967.*
*Weilbach,* Philip: Konst og Æsthetik. København. *1870.*
*Weilbach's* Kunstnerleksikon. Red. M. Bodelsen & P. Engelstoft. København. *1947-1949-1952.*
*Weinweich,* N. H.: Fortegnelse over den Bodendickske Malerisamling nu Hans Majestæt Kongen tilhørende. København. *1825.*
*Weisner,* Ulrich: Die Gemälde des Moyses van Uyttenbroeck. Oud Holland. Amsterdam. *1954.* pp. 189-228.
*Velde,* C. van de: Enkele biographische gegevens betreffende Louis de Caulery. Koninklijk Museum vor schone Kunsten Antwerpen Jaarboek 1966. Antwerpen. *1966.* pp. 221-214.
*West,* Hans: Raisonneret Catalog over Consul West's Samling af Malerier. København. *1807.*
*Westergaard,* P. B. C.: Danske Portrætter I-II. København. *1930-1933.*
*Westergaard-Petersen,* Christian: Melchior Schildt i Danmark. Dansk Årbog for musikforskning VII, 1973-1976. København. *1976.* pp. 237-246.
*Westfälisches Landesmuseum für Kunst und Kulturgeschichte/Staatliche Kunsthalle, Münster-Baden Baden 1979-80;* Stilleben in Europa.
*Wethey,* Harold E.: The Paintings of Titian, I-III. The Mythological and Historical Paintings. London. *1975.*
*Wheeler,* Joseph: Further Notes on the Classic Trumpet. The Galpin Society Journal XVIII. London. *1965.* pp. 14-22.
*Whinney,* Margareth & *Millar,* Oliver: English Art 1625-1714. Oxford. *1956.*
*Wibiral,* Fr.: L'iconographie d'Antonine van Dyck. London. *1877.*
*Vickers,* Michael: Rupert of the Rhine. A New Portrait by Dieussart and Bernini's Charles I. Apollo CVII. London. *1978.* pp. 161-169.
*Wichmann,* Heinrich: Leonaert Bramer. Sein Leben und seine Kunst. Leipzig. *1923.*
*Victoria & Albert Museum, London 1948:* Danish Art Treaures.
*Victoria & Albert Museum, London 1981:* Princely Magnificense. Court Jewels of the Renaissance, 1500-1630.
*Vikan,* Gary: Notes on Princeton Drawings 10: Abraham Bloemaert. Record of the Art Museum 33, 2. Princeton N. J. *1974.* pp. 2-17.
*Wilcke,* Julius: Christian IV's Møntpolitik 1588-1625. København. *1919.*
*Wilcke,* Julius: Møntvæsenet under Christian IV og Frederik III 1625-1670. København. *1924.*
*Wilenski,* R. H.: Flemish Painters 1430-1830 I-II. London *1960.*
*Williamson,* George C.: The History of Portrait Miniatures, Vol. 1. London. *1904.*
*Willoch,* Sigurd: Maleren Thomas Fernley. Oslo. *1932.*
*Winkler,* Friederich: Der unbekannte Sebastian Vrancx. Pantheon XXII, 1964. München. *1964.*
*Winther,* Carl: Hilliard & Elizabethan Miniatures. The Burlington Magazine LXXXIX. London. *1947.* pp. 175-183.
*Wit-Klinkhamer,* Th. M. Duyvene de: Een vermaarde Zilveres Becker. Nederlands Kunsthistorisch Jaarboek 17. Gravenhage (Haag). *1966.* pp. 79-103.
*Wittelsbach und Bayern:* 1980 II/1 & II/2. Udg. af Hubert Glasser. München. *1980.*
*Wittkower,* Rudolf: Gianlorenzo Bernini. The Sculpture of the Roman Baroque. 3.ed. Oxford. *1981.*
*Woeckel,* Gerhard: Meisterwerke aus Privatsammlungen im Bodenseegebiet. Zur Ausstellung im Künstlerhaus Bregenz, Palais Thurn und Taxis. Pantheon XXV. München. *1967.* pp. 468-469.
*Woldbye,* Vibeke: Omkring et par nautilpokaler med gammel dansk proveniens. Neptuns kabinet. Kulturen. Lund. *1985.* pp. 53-59.
*Woldbye,* Vibeke: Kronborg. En billedbog. København. *1986.*
*Volpe,* Carlo: Annotazione sulla mostra caravaggesca di Cleveland. Paragone, 263, arte, Gennaio. *1972.* pp. 50-76.
*Worm,* Ole: Monumenta Danica: Danicorum Monumentorum libri VI, e spissis antiquitatum tenebis et in Dania ac Norvegia extantibus ruderibus eruti. Hafnia. *1643.*
*Breve fra og til Ole Worm* 1607-1654. Oversat af H. D. Schepelern. Bind I-III. København. *1965-1968.*
*Voss,* Hermann: Handzeichnungen alter Meister im Leipziger Museum. Zeitschrift für bildende Kunst. Neue Folge, 24. Jahrgang. Leipzig. 1913.

*Voss,* Hermann: Die Malerei des Barock in Rom. Berlin. *1924.*
*Voss,* Knud: Guldalderens Malerkunst. København. *1968.*
*Voss,* Knud: Arkitekten Nicolai Eigtved 1701-1754. København. *1971.*
*Voss,* Knud: Guldaldermalerne og deres billeder på Statens Museum for Kunst. Lyngby. *1976.*
*Wrangler,* F. U.: Rikskansleren Axel Oxenstiernas resa till och i Frankrike 1635. Stockholm. *1914.*
*Vroom,* N. R. A.: A Modest Message as Intimated by the Painters of the »Monochrome Banketje«. Schiedam. *1980.*
*Wurfbain,* M. L.: Vanitas-Stilleben David Bailly (1584-1657). Openbar Kunstbezits 13. *1969.* pp. 7a-7b.
*Wörthmüller,* Willi: Die Nürnberger Trompeten und Posaunenmacher des 17. und 18. Jahrhunderts. Sonderdruck aus den Mitteilungen des Vereins für Geschichte der Stadt Nürnberg. Band 46. Nürnberg. *1955.*
*Wulf,* Inger: Krydderiernes verden. Det indianske Kammer. Red. af Torben Lundbæk & Henning Dehn-Nielsen. Nationalmuseet. København. *1979.* pp. 26-41.
*Wulf,* Inger & *Rishøj Pedersen,* Lise: Sydøstasien og Stillehavet. Etnografiske genstande i Det kongelige danske Kunstkammer 1650-1800. Red. af Bente Dam-Mikkelsen & Torben Lundbæk. Nationalmuseet. København. *1980.* pp. 135-154.
*Yde-Andersen,* David: To hodometre (vejmålere) fra renaissancen. Fra Nationalmuseets Arbejdsmark. København. *1952.* pp. 72-78.
*Young,* Philip: The Look of Music. Vancouver Museums and Planetarium Association. Vancouver. *1980.*
*Ysselsteyn,* G. T. van: Tapestry Waving in the Northern Netherlands. Leiden. *1936.*
*Ysselsteyn,* G. T. van: White Figured Linen Damask. Haag. *1962.*
*Zahle,* Erik: Billedkunst. C. L. David's Samling. Nogle Studier I. København. *1948.*
*Zimmermann,* Heinrich (ed.): Das Inventar der Prager Schatz- und Kunstkammer vom 6. Dezember 1621. Jahrbuch der Kunsthistorischen Sammlungen des Allerhöchsten Kaiserhauses XXV. *1905.* pp. XIII-LXXV.
*Zinner,* Ernst: Deutsche und Niederländische astronomische Instrumente des 11.-18. Jahrhunderts. *1956.*
*Zwollo,* An: Pieter Stevens. Ein vergessener Maler des Rudolfinischen Kreises. Jahrbuch der Kunsthistorischen Sammlungen in Wien 64. Wien. *1968.* pp. 119-180.
Årsskrift for Carlsbergfondet, Frederiksborgmuseet, Ny Carlsbergfondet. København. 1984. Beretning for året 1982-83. Modtaget i samlingerne: nr. 1: Den danske sømagts apoteose af Otto Bache. p. 77.

*Andrup,* O.: Leonora Christinas Krucifiks, Lolland Falsters Historiske Samfunds Aarbog, XL, 1952, Nykøbing F. *1952,* pp. 117-134.
*Boström,* J.-K.: David Bailley's stilleben, Kunsthistorisk Tidsskrift XVIII, 1949, Stockholm *1950,* pp. 99-110.
*Bruyn,* J.: David Bailley, »fort bon peintre en pourtraits et en vie coye«, Oud Holland, LXVI, 195, Amsterdam *1951,* pp. 148-164 and pp. 212-227.
*Galerie des Beaux-Arts, Bordeaux 1969:* L'art et la musique.
*Gammelbo,* Poul: Dutch Still-Life Painting from the 16th to the 18th Centuries in Danish Collections. Copenhagen *1960.*
*Jaffé,* Michael: Jacob Jordaens 1593-1678. The National Gallery of Canada/Ottawa *1968/1969.*
*Leithe-Jasper,* Manfred: Renaissance Master Bronzes from the Collection of the Kunsthistorisches Museum, Vienna. Washington *1986.*
*Philadelphia/London/Berlin. Philadelphia Museum of Art – Gemäldegalerie Berlin – Royal Academy of Arts 1984:* Masters of Seventeenth-Century Dutch Genre Painting.
*Sacramento, California. Crocker Art Gallery 1974:* The Pre-Rembrandtists.
*Utrecht/Braunschweig. Centraal Museum – Herzog Anton Ulrich-Museum. 1986-87:* Holländische Malerei in neuem Licht.
*Wadum,* Jørgen: Malerier på samlebånd. Nyt lys over Christian IV's vinterstue på Rosenborg Slot, Museumsmagasinet 39, *1987* 8ff.
*Wallraf Richartz-Museum, Köln 1984:* Die Utrechter Malerschule, Caravaggisti des Nordens.
*Washington/Detroit/Amsterdam. National Gallery of Art – Detroit Institute of Art – Rijksmuseum 1980-81:* Gods, Saints & Heroes. Dutch Painting in the Age of Rembrandt.
*Wurfbain,* M. L.: Vanitas-stilleven van David Bailly (1584-1657), Openbaar Kunstbezit 13, *1969,* pp. 7a-7b.

# Corrigenda

p. 28 right col. line 16 from bottom (cat. 39): Oil on canvas, read *Oil on panel*
p. 36 right col. line 23 top (cat. 84): Vibeke Kruse, read *Kirsten Munk*
p. 52 right col. line 23 bottom: Fredericia, read *Fridericia*
p. 63 right col. line 20 bottom (cat. 179): Oil on canvas, read *Oil on panel*
p. 81 left col. line 6 top (cat. 217): bethrothal, read *betrothal*
p. 91 left col. line 17 bottom (cat. 270): bethrothals, read *betrothals*
p. 101 left col. line 4 top (cat. 310): hearin, read *Hearing*
p. 101 left col. line 26 top (cat. 321): Sven's, read *Svend's*
p. 102 right col. line 2 bottom (cat. 315): Eller 197, read *Eller 1971 330*
p. 97 right col. line 16 bottom (cat. 295): some of which, read *two of which*
p. 97 right col. line 15 bottom (cat. 295): Timm, read *Timm (see cat. 323)*
p. 105 right col. line 10 top (cat. 325): Oil on canvas, read *Oil on panel*
p. 105 right col. line 22 bottom (cat. 326): Oil on canvas, read *Oil on panel*
p. 107 right col. line 5 top: Dutch school, read *Dutch School*
p. 108 right col. line 26 top (cat. 343): add *Signed F. Brentel 1635*
p. 109 right col. line 8 top (cat. 353): add *Signed F. Brentel 1635*
p. 123 right col. line 13 top (cat. 402): Small descant lude, read *Small descant lute*
p. 193 left col. line 11 top (cat. 692): delete Colour-plate XXII
p. 302 left col. line 26 from bottom: socalled, read *so-called*
p. 304 right col. line 17 from top: historical, read *history*
p. 305 right col. line 26 top (cat. 997): Turcks, read *Turks*
p. 315 left col. line 19 top (cat. 1018): Le siècle, read *Musée du Petit Palais*
p. 316 left col. line 2 bottom (cat. 1021): Millar 1972, read *The Tate Gallery, London 1972-73*
p. 323 left col. line 2 bottom (cat. 1046): Petit Palais, read *Musée du Petit Palais*
p. 329 right col. line 6 top (cat. 1067): *Prince,* read *Princeps*
p. 330 left col. line 22 bottom (cat. 1069): PAM 907, read *PAM 827*
p. 334 right col. line 21 top (cat. 1077): Petit Palais, read *Musée du Petit Palais*
p. 335 left col. line 24 bottom (cat. 1080): Augsburg, read *Bayerische Staatsgemäldesammlungen, cat. Augsburg*
p. 335 right col. line 12 bottom (cat. 1082): Saenredam, read *Institut Neerlandais, Paris*
p. 337 right col. line 5 bottom (cat. 1094): Moyeses, read *Moyses*
p. 347 right col. line 5 top (cat. 1124): 1965, read *1966*
p. 562 COLOUR-PLATE XVI: 980 read *890*
p. 571 COLOUR-PLATE XXV: The plate has been literally reversed
p. 574 COLOUR-PLATE XXVIII: The plate has been literally reversed
p. 592 left col. line 2 bottom: read *Cavalli-Björkman, Görel: Målninger av Rubens i Nationalmuseum, Rubens i Sverige (ed. Görel Cavalli-Björkman) Stockholm 1977, pp. 11-48*
p. 592 left col. line 36 bottom: Gries, read *Vries*
p. 596 right col. line 22 bottom: 1837, read *1937*
p. 596 left col. line 31 top: 3113, read *113*
p. 596 right col. line 36 top: Just, read *Jost*
p. 597 right col. line 23 top: 1630?, read *1603?*
p. 599 left col. line 19 bottom: Jaarboekje ... 1977, read *Jaarboek Oud-Utrecht, Utrecht 1976, pp. 7-29 and Maandblad Oud Utrecht L, 2 februari 1977, Utrecht 1977, p. 17*
p. 599 left col. line 14 bottom: 197., read *1987,*
p. 601 right col. line 16 top: Nicoles Knupfer, read *Nicolaus Knüpfer*
p. 604 left col. line 16 top: add after 1984: *pp. 73-84*

# Contributors to the catalogue and exhibitions organizers

Catalogue edited by Steffen Heiberg.
Editorial assistance: Bo Fritzbøger, Marie Hvidt, Paulette Møller, Søren Thorlacius-Ussing.

FREDERIKSBORG
*Catalogue:* Steffen Heiberg with assistance from Jytte Harboe.
*Exhibition:* Mette Bligaard, Povl Eller, Jytte Harboe, Steffen Heiberg.
*Architect:* Thorkil Ebert.

KRONBORG
*Catalogue and Exhibition:* Paintings and drawings: Charlotte Christensen with assistance from Jens Peter Munk. National historical paintings: H. D. Schepelern and Ulla Houkjær. Tapestries and Furniture: Vibeke Woldbye. Music: Mette Müller and Ole Kongsted. Theater: Lisbet Grandjean and Viben Bech.
*Exhibition:* Vibeke Woldbye, Charlotte Christensen, Mette Müller, Ole Kongsted, Lisbet Grandjean, Viben Bech and Maria Fabricius Hansen.
*Architect:* Ib Thoresen Lassen.

ROSENBORG
*Catalogue:* Jørgen Hein and Mogens Bencard with assistance from Katia Johansen, Preben Mellbye-Hansen, Anders Kold and Teresa Nielsen.
*Exhibition:* Mogens Bencard, Hans Hein, Jørgen Hein, Katia Johansen, Preben Mellbye-Hansen.
*Architect:* Ib Rasmussen.

NATIONALMUSEET
*Catalogue and exhibition:* Niels-Knud Liebgott, Henrik Larsen, Fritze Lindahl, Kirsten Bendixen, Bente Gundestrup, Kirsten Christiansen, Hans-Henrik Landert and Johan Jensen.
Further assistance: Svend Erik Albrethsen, Hanne Christensen, Birgit Als-Hansen, Gunvor Petersen, Hans Stiesdal, Lise Warburg and Ebba Waaben.
*Architect:* Niels Presskorn.

DEN KGL. KOBBERSTIKSAMLING
*Catalogue and exhibition:* Jan Garff and Eva de la Fuente-Pedersen.

STATENS MUSEUM FOR KUNST
*Catalogue:* Olaf Koester with assistance from Hanne Jönsson.
*Exhibition:* Olaf Koester.

TØJHUSMUSEET
*Catalogue and exhibition:* Finn Askgaard (Preface), Arne Orloff (firearms), Kay S. Nielsen (arms and armouries), Ole L. Frantzen (artilleri), Bjørn Nielsen (uniforms, flags), Lillian Westergaard (paintings, engravings).

RUNDETÅRN / TRINITATIS KIRKELOFT
*Catalogue:* Charlotte Christensen, Vivian Etting, Harald Ilsøe, Ingrid Ilsøe, Gitte Kjær, Peter Kristian Moesgaard, Torben Nielsen, Erik Petersen, H. D. Schepelern and Ditlev Tamm.
*Coordinator:* Jesper Düring Jørgensen.
*Reconstruction of Museum Wormianum:* Ib Thoresen Lassen.
*Display-layout:* Annelise Andersen.

KOLDINGHUS
*Catalogue and exhibition:* Poul Dedenroth-Schou, Mette Smed and Lars Bisgaard.
*Architect:* Mogens Brandt Poulsen. Models by Afdeling for Restaurering, Arkitektskolen, Århus

AARHUS KUNSTMUSEUM
*Catalogue and exhibition:* Nina Damsgaard.

*Photographers:* Svend Erik Albrethsen, Niels Elswing, Pierre Claude Galuzska, Jacob Gaasvig, Birgit Als Hansen, Erik Jul Det Kgl. Biblioteks atelier, Lennart Larsen, Aage Lund, Bent Næsbye, Hans Petersen, Kit Weiss, Ole Woldbye

The following institutions are thanked for lending photographs:
Boligministeriets Samlinger på Kronborg, Helsingør
Handels- og Søfartsmuseet på Kronborg, Helsingør
Helsingør Bymuseum

Det Nationalhistoriske Museum på Frederiksborg, Hillerød
Kunstmuseet »Lunden«, Horsens
Museet på Koldinghus, Kolding
De Danske Kongers Kronologiske Samling på Rosenborg, København
Den Hirschsprungske Samling, København
Det Kgl. Bibliotek, København
Den Kgl. Kobberstiksamling, København
Den Kgl. Mønt- og Medaillesamling, København
Kunstakademiets Bibliotek, København
Kunstindustrimuseet, København
Københavns Bymuseum
Musikhistorisk Museum og Carl Claudius' Samling, København
Nationalmuseet 2. afd., København
Nationalmuseet 3. afd., København
Rigsarkivet, København
Statens Museum for Kunst, København
Statsinventariekommissionen, København
Teatermuseet, København
Tøjhusmuseet, København
Thorvaldsens Samling på Nysø
Museet Møntergaarden, Odense
Roskilde Domkirkes Arkiv
Den antikvariske Samling, Ribe
Børge Nielsens Auktioner, Vejle
Aalborg Historiske Museum
Grünes Gewölbe, Dresden
Musée des Beaux-Arts et d'Archeologie de Rennes
Rijksmuseum, Amsterdam
Stedelijk Museum De Lakenhal, Leiden
Centraalmuseum, Utrecht
Kunstindustrimuseet, Oslo
Nasjonalgalleriet, Oslo
Lord Chamberlains Office, St. James' Palace, London
The British Museum, London
Victoria & Albert Museum, London
The Trustees of the Chatsworth Settlement
Courtauld Institute of Art
Malmö Museum
Skoklosters Slott, Bålsta
Drottningholms teatermuseum
Kungl. Husgerådskammaren, Stockholm
Kungl. Krigsarkivet, Stockholm
Statens Konstmuseer, Stockholm
The Art Museum, Princeton
Städtische Kunstsammlungen (Maximilianmuseum), Augsburg
Staatliche Museen Preussischer Kulturbesitz, Berlin
Herzog Anton Ulrich-Museum, Braunschweig
Niedersächsisches Landesmuseum, Landesgalerie, Hannover
Staatliche Kunstsammlungen, Kassel
Staatsgalerie Stuttgart, Stuttgart
Kunsthistorisches Museum, Sammlung für Plastik und Kunstgewerbe, Wien

The pattern on p. 259 (cat. 872h) was drawn by Gunnar Kramp

*English translation:*
Preface: Bente Gammeltoft
Frederiksborg: Joan F. Davidson and Lis Heiberg
Kronborg: Ann Caie, Charlotte Christensen, Lis Heiberg, Peter Thornton, Vibeke Woldbye, John Bergsagel
Rosenborg: Joan F. Davidson, Jennifer Draskau, Paulette Møller
Nationalmuseet: Joan F. Davidson and Virginia Laursen
Den Kgl. Kobberstiksamling: Joan F. Davidson
Statens Museum for Kunst: Hamish I. Barclay
Tøjhusmuseet: Joan F. Davidson, Lis Heiberg, Paulette Møller
Rundetårn/Trinitatis kirkeloft: Virginia Laursen
Koldinghus: Joan F. Davidson and Lis Heiberg
Aarhus Kunstmuseum: Joan F. Davidson and Lis Heiberg